ENCYCLOPEDIA OF INDUSTRIAL CHEMICAL ANALYSIS

VOLUME 13

Fluorine
to
Glycols

ENCYCLOPEDIA
OF INDUSTRIAL
CHEMICAL
ANALYSIS

Edited by Foster Dee Snell *and* Leslie S. Ettre

VOLUME 13

Fluorine

to

Glycols

Interscience Publishers
a division of John Wiley & Sons, Inc.
New York • London • Sydney • Toronto

CONTENTS

Volume 13

FLUORINE	1
FLUORINE COMPOUNDS, INORGANIC	6
FLUORO ACIDS, INORGANIC	37
FLUOROCARBONS	58
FLUOROCARBONS, POLYMERS	73
FORMALDEHYDE	100
FORMIC ACID	117
FOURIER TRANSFORM SPECTROSCOPY	139
FUMIGANTS	176
FUNGICIDES	198
FURAN AND FURAN DERIVATIVES	227
GALLIUM	251
GASES, NOBLE	286
GAS, NATURAL	310
GASOLINE	339
GELATIN	361
GERMANIUM	375
GLASS AND GLASS–CERAMICS	403
GLUES OF ANIMAL ORIGIN	487
GLYCEROL	494
GLYCOLS AND POLYHYDRIC ALCOHOLS	533

VOLUME 13

Editor-in-Chief
FOSTER DEE SNELL
Foster D. Snell, Inc.

Executive Editor
LESLIE S. ETTRE

Assistant to the Executive Editor
JOAN LUETHY BATTLE

Editorial Supervisor
GLORIA O. SCHETTY

Editorial Staff

Claire Wiener   Michalina Bickford   Kenneth N. Brown

Joseph M. Ricciardi

CONTRIBUTORS

D. K. Banerjee, *U. S. Industrial Chemicals Company, Division of National Distillers & Chemical Corp.,* Cincinnati, Ohio, Glycols and polyhydric alcohols

A. J. Barnard, Jr., *J. T. Baker Chemical Company,* Phillipsburg, N. J., Fluoro acids, inorganic; Formic acid

C. H. Barnstein, *National Formulary,* Washington, D.C., Gelatin

Joan L. Battle, *Encyclopedia of Industrial Chemical Analysis,* Fluorine; Fluorocarbons; Fluorocarbons, polymers

R. A. Bleidt, *Union Carbide Corporation,* South Charleston, West Va., Formaldehyde

G. A. Bozarth, *University of Missouri,* Columbia, Mo., Fumigants

Robert P. Bringer, *3M Company,* St. Paul, Minn., Fluorocarbons, polymers

C. C. Budke, *U. S. Industrial Chemicals Company, Division of National Distillers & Chemical Corp.,* Cincinnati, Ohio, Glycols and polyhydric alcohols

David L. Camin, *Sun Oil Company,* Marcus Hook, Pa., Gasoline

D. E. Campbell, *Corning Glass Works,* Corning, N.Y., Glass and glass–ceramics

John E. Going, *University of Wisconsin,* Milwaukee, Wis., Glycerol

E. F. Joy, *J. T. Baker Chemical Company,* Phillipsburg, N. J., Fluoro acids, inorganic

Carol Loeppky, *University of Missouri,* Columbia, Mo., Fungicides

M. J. D. Low, *New York University*, New York, N.Y., Fourier transform spectroscopy

Frederick A. Lowenheim, *Consultant*, Plainfield, N. J., Germanium

A. M. G. Macdonald, *University of Birmingham*, Birmingham, England, Fluorine; Fluorine compounds, inorganic

John W. Madden, *The Quaker Oats Company*, Barrington, Ill., Furan and furan derivatives

Hiroshi Onishi, *Japan Atomic Energy Research Institute*, Tokai-Mura, Ibaraki-ken, Japan, Gallium

C. L. Pearson, *Peter Cooper Corporation*, Gowanda, N. Y., Glues of animal origin

J. A. Ross, *University of Missouri*, Columbia, Mo., Fumigants

George E. Schmauch, *Air Products and Chemicals Inc.*, Allentown, Pa., Gases, noble

R. M. Speights, *Geochemical Systems, Inc.*, Orange, Calif., Formic acid

B. G. Tweedy, *University of Missouri*, Columbia, Mo., Fumigants; Fungicides

Ralph C. Vollmar, *Consultant*, Berkeley, Calif., Gas, natural

J. P. Williams, *Corning Glass Works*, Corning, N. Y., Glass and glass-ceramics

ABBREVIATIONS AND SYMBOLS

A	ampere(s)
Å	Angstrom unit(s)
AATCC	American Association of Textile Chemists and Colorists
ac	alternating current
Ac	acetate, acetyl (in formulas)
ACS	American Chemical Society
AIChE	American Institute of Chemical Engineers
AIP	American Institute of Physics
ANSI	American National Standards Institute, Inc.
AOAC	Association of Official Analytical (formerly Agricultural) Chemists
APHA	American Public Health Association
API	American Petroleum Institute
approx	approximately
ar-	aromatic (eg, ar-vinyl-aniline)
as-	asymmetric(al) (eg, as-trichlorobenzene)
ASA	American Standards Association (now American National Standards Institute, Inc., ANSI)
ASTM	American Society for Testing and Materials
atm	atmosphere(s)
at. no.	atomic number
at. wt	atomic weight
av	average
B	bel(s)
b	barn(s)

b (as in b_{11})	boiling (at 11 torr)
bbl	barrel(s)
Bé	Baumé
beV	billion electron volt(s)
Bhn	Brinell hardness number
bp	boiling point
BP	*British Pharmacopeia*
BS	British Standards
Btu	British thermal unit(s)
C	centigrade; Celsius; coulomb(s)
C-	denoting attachment to carbon (eg, *C*-acetyl-indoline)
cal	calorie(s); gram calorie(s)
calcd	calculated
cg	centigram(s)
cgs	centimeter-gram-second
Ci	curie(s)
CI	Colour Index
cm	centimeter(s)
cp	chemically pure
cP	centipoise(s)
cps	cycles per second
cSt	centistokes
cu	cubic
d	density
d-	*dextro-*, dextrorotatory
D-	denoting configurational relationship (related to *dextro*-glyceraldehyde)
D	Debye unit(s)
dB	decibel(s)
dc	direct current
dec	decomposes
dec pt	decomposition point
dl-, DL-	racemic
DOT	Dept. of Transportation (U.S.)
dp	dew point
DP	degree of polymerization

DS	degree of substitution	IP	*International Pharma-copeia*
DTA	differential thermal analysis	IR	infrared
dyn	dyne(s)	ISO	International Organization for Standardization
e	electron(s)		
ed.	edition(s); editor(s)		
emf	electromotive force	IU	international units
emu	electromagnetic unit(s)	IUPAC	International Union of Pure and Applied Chemistry
eq	equivalent(s)		
estd	estimated		
esu	electrostatic unit(s)	J	joule(s)
Et	ethyl (in formulas)	K	Kelvin
eV	electron volt(s)	kc	kilocycle(s)
exptl	experimental	kcal	kilogram-calorie(s)
F	Fahrenheit; farad(s)	keV	kiloelectron volt(s)
FCC	*Food Chemicals Codex*	kg	kilogram(s)
FDA	U.S. Food and Drug Administration	km	kilometer(s)
		kV	kilovolt(s)
fl oz	fluid ounce(s)	kW	kilowatt(s)
fob	free on board	kWh	kilowatt-hour(s)
fp	freezing point	l	liter(s)
ft	foot (feet)	*l-*	*levo-*, levorotatory
ft-lb	foot-pound(s)	L-	denoting configurational relationship (related to *levo-*glyceraldehyde)
g	gram(s)		
G	gauss		
gal	gallon(s)	lb	pound(s)
GC	gas chromatography	LD_{50}	dose lethal to 50% of the animals tested
gem-	geminal (attached to the same atom)		
		lm	lumen(s)
GLC	gas–liquid chromatography	ln	logarithm (natural)
		log (instead) of log_{10})	logarithm (common)
g-mol	gram molecular (as in g-mol wt)		
		m	meter(s)
g-mole	gram-mole(s)	*m-*	meta (eg, *m-*xylene)
hp	horsepower	*M*	molar
hr	hour(s)	mA	milliampere(s)
Hz	Hertz	mAh	milliampere-hour(s)
i-	inactive (eg, *i-*methionine)	max	maximum
		Mc	megacycle(s)
ibp	initial boiling point	MCA	Manufacturing Chemists' Association
ICC	Interstate Commerce Commission		
		Me	metal or methyl (in formulas)
ICT	International Critical Tables		
		meq	milliequivalent(s)
		MeV	million electron volt(s)
ID	inner diameter	mg	milligram(s)
in.	inch(es)	mil	0.001 inch
insol	insoluble	min	minute(s); minimum

ml	milliliter(s)	psia	pound(s) per square inch absolute
mm	millimeter(s)		
mμ	millimicron(s)	psig	pound(s) per square inch gage
mM	millimole(s)		
mo	month(s)	r	roentgen
mol wt	molecular weight	R	alkyl group
mp	melting point	R_f	retardation factor (chromatography)
mph	miles per hour		
MS	mass spectrometry, mass spectrometer; molar substitution	rh	relative humidity
		rpm	revolutions per minute
		rps	revolutions per second
n(as n_D^{20})	index of refraction (for 20°C and sodium D line)	S-	denoting attachment to sulfur (eg, S-methyl-cysteine)
n-	normal (eg, n-butyl)	sec	second(s)
N	normal as applied to concentration	sec-	secondary (eg, sec-butyl)
		sl sol	slightly soluble
N-	denoting attachment to nitrogen (eg, N-methylaniline)	sol	soluble
		soln	solution
		sp gr	specific gravity
NBS	National Bureau of Standards	sq	square
		St	stokes
ND	*New Drugs* (formerly *New and Nonofficial Drugs*) (American Medical Association)	STP	standard temperature and pressure (760 **torr** and 0°C)
		subl	sublimes
NF	*National Formulary* (American Pharmaceutical Association)	sym-	symmetrical (eg, sym-dichloroethylene)
		t-, $tert$-	tertiary (eg, t-butyl)
NMR	nuclear magnetic resonance	TAPPI	Technical Association of the Pulp and Paper Industry
no.	number	temp	temperature
o-	ortho (eg, o-xylene)	$tert$-, t-	tertiary (eg, $tert$-butyl)
O-	denoting attachment to oxygen (eg, O-acetyl-amine)	TLC	thin-layer chromatography
OD	outer diameter	torr	Toricelli (mm Hg)
Oe	oersted(s)	Twad	Twaddell
oz	ounce(s)	USASI	United States of America Standards Institute (now American National Standards Institute, Inc., ANSI)
p-	para (eg, p-xylene)		
P	poise(s)		
Ph	phenyl (in formulas)		
ppb	parts per billion $(1/10^9)$	USP	*(The) United States Pharmacopeia* (Mack Publishing Co., Easton, Pa.)
ppm	parts per million $(1/10^6)$		
pptd	precipitated		
psi	pound(s) per square inch	UV	ultraviolet

V	volt(s)	w/w	weight per weight
vic-	vicinal (attached to adjacent atoms)	X	halogen (in formulas)
		yd	yard(s)
vol	volume	yr	year(s)
vs	versus	μ	micron(s)
v sol	very soluble	μg	microgram(s)
v/v	volume per volume	μl	microliter(s)
W	watt(s)	μm	micrometer(s)
Wh	watt-hour(s)	μM	micromole
wt	weight	Ω	ohm(s)
w/v	weight per volume	Ω-cm	ohm-centimeter(s)

Prefixes Indicating Order of Magnitude

d	deci (10^{-1})	h	hecto (10^{2})
c	centi (10^{-2})	k	kilo (10^{3})
m	milli (10^{-3})	M	mega (10^{6})
μ	micro (10^{-6})	G	giga (10^{9})
n	nano (10^{-9})	T	tera (10^{12})
p	pico (10^{-12})		
f	femto (10^{-15})		
a	atto (10^{-18})		

GENERAL TECHNIQUES DISCUSSED IN PREVIOUS VOLUMES

Volume 1

ABSORPTION AND EMISSION SPECTROSCOPY, SURVEY
ACID–BASE TITRATIONS
ACTIVATION ANALYSIS
ADSORPTION CHROMATOGRAPHY
AIR POLLUTION AND ATMOSPHERIC ANALYSIS
AMPEROMETRIC TITRATIONS
AQUAMETRY
ATOMIC ABSORPTION SPECTROPHOTOMETRY
AZEOTROPY
BALANCES AND WEIGHING
BOILING POINT DETERMINATION
BUFFER SOLUTIONS
CALORIMETRY
CAPACITY AND DIELECTRIC CONSTANT
CHROMATOGRAPHIC METHODS
COLOR DESIGNATION AND SPECIFICATION
COLORIMETRIC METHODS OF ANALYSIS
COMPLEXATION IN AQUEOUS MEDIA
CONDUCTOMETRY AND OSCILLOMETRY
COULOMETRY AND COULOMETRIC TITRATIONS
COUNTERCURRENT DISTRIBUTION
CRITICAL–CONSTANT DETERMINATIONS
DENSITY AND SPECIFIC GRAVITY
DIFFERENTIAL REACTION RATE ANALYSIS
DIFFERENTIAL THERMAL ANALYSIS
DISTILLATION
ELECTRICAL METHODS OF ANALYSIS
ELECTRON DIFFRACTION
ELECTRON MICROSCOPY
ELECTRON PROBE MICROANALYSIS
EMISSION SPECTROSCOPY
EVALUATION OF ANALYTICAL DATA

Volume 2

FIELD EMISSION MICROSCOPY
FLAME PHOTOMETRY
FLAMMABILITY DETERMINATIONS
FLUOROMETRY AND PHOSPHORIMETRY
FREEZING POINT DETERMINATION
GAS ANALYSIS
GAS CHROMATOGRAPHY
GRAVIMETRIC METHODS OF ANALYSIS
HEAT OF FUSION
HEAT OF VAPORIZATION
INDICATORS
INFRARED SPECTROMETRY
INTERFERENCE MICROSCOPY
INTERFEROMETRY
ION EXCHANGE METHODS
IONIZATION CONSTANTS
LABORATORY DESIGN AND EQUIPMENT
LABORATORY SAFETY
LIGHT SCATTERING
LITERATURE OF ANALYTICAL CHEMISTRY
MAGNETIC SUSCEPTIBILITY
MASS SPECTROMETRY
MELTING POINT DETERMINATION
MICRO- AND SEMIMICROANALYSIS
MICROSCOPY
MICROWAVE SPECTROSCOPY
MOLECULAR WEIGHT DETERMINATION
NEAR-INFRARED SPECTROPHOTOMETRY
NEPHELOMETRY AND TURBIDIMETRY
NUCLEAR MAGNETIC AND ELECTRON PARA-MAGNETIC RESONANCE
OPTICAL ACTIVITY

Volume 3

PAPER CHROMATOGRAPHY
PARTICLE SIZE AND SURFACE AREA
PHASE EQUILIBRIA AND ITS ANALYTICAL
    APPLICATIONS
pH DETERMINATION
POLAROGRAPHY AND VOLTAMMETRY
POTENTIOMETRY AND POTENTIOMETRIC
    TITRATIONS
PRECIPITATION AND CRYSTALLIZATION
PRESSURE MEASUREMENT AND CONTROL
QUALITATIVE ANALYSIS, INORGANIC
QUALITATIVE ANALYSIS, ORGANIC
RADIOACTIVE ISOTOPE METHODS
RAMAN SPECTROSCOPY
RECORDERS
REDOX TITRATIONS
REFLECTANCE SPECTROPHOTOMETRY
REFRACTOMETRY
RHEOLOGICAL MEASUREMENTS, FLUID
SAMPLING AND SAMPLE PREPARATION
SEPARATION BY DIFFUSION
SEPARATION BY ELECTRICAL METHODS
SEPARATION BY EXTRACTION
SEPARATION BY MECHANICAL METHODS
SOLIDIFICATION POINT DETERMINATION
SOLUBILITY
SPECIFICATIONS, STANDARDS, AND STANDARD-
    SETTING ORGANIZATIONS
STANDARDIZATION OF SOLUTIONS
SUBLIMATION
SURFACE AND INTERFACIAL TENSION
    MEASUREMENTS
TEMPERATURE MEASUREMENT AND CONTROL
THERMAL METHODS OF ANALYSIS
THERMOGRAVIMETRIC ANALYSIS
THERMOMETRIC ANALYSIS
THERMOMETRIC TITRATIONS
THIN-LAYER CHROMATOGRAPHY
ULTRAVIOLET AND VISIBLE ABSORPTION
    SPECTROPHOTOMETRY
VACUUM ULTRAVIOLET SPECTROSCOPY
VISCOSITY
VOLUME MEASUREMENT: LIQUIDS
X-RAY METHODS OF ANALYSIS

Volume 6

BEAD AND FLAME TESTS

Volume 7

BIOASSAY

Volume 8

CARRIER GAS AND VACUUM FUSION METHODS

Volume 9

CENTRIFUGAL SEPARATION

F (continued)

FLUORINE

Fluorine, F, is a member of the halogen family of elements. It has an atomic number of 9, an atomic weight of 18.9984, and is the most electronegative element known. The electron configuration is $1s^2 2s^2 2p^5$. At room temperature it exists as a greenish-yellow diatomic gas, F_2, with a molecular weight of 37.9968. Fluorine gas has a characteristic sharp, penetrating odor which is detectable in concentrations as low as 20 ppb. Fluorine is not found free in nature, except very rarely as inclusions in certain rocks. Additional information on the chemistry and technology of fluorine and its compounds may be found in the general references (1–11).

Elemental fluorine was first isolated by Moissan in 1886 by electrolysis of a dilute solution of potassium fluoride in anhydrous hydrogen fluoride with the approximate formula $KF \cdot 12HF$ at $-23°C$ using platinum–iridium electrodes (12). Fluorine was not utilized to any great extent until the early 1940s with the requirements of the Manhattan Project for chemically stable fluids and polymers.

Elemental fluorine was used by the U.S. Atomic Energy Commission during World War II to separate uranium-235 from uranium-238 by the gaseous diffusion of uranium hexafluoride, UF_6. Uranium hexafluoride is also the basis of an enriched fuel for use in the nuclear electric power industry. Elemental fluorine has been used to manufacture sulfur hexafluoride, SF_6, a gaseous insulator for electric and electronic equipment. Fluorine, chlorine trifluoride, and oxygen difluoride have potential as rocket fuel oxidizers.

Properties

Fluorine is the most reactive member of the periodic table. It reacts with virtually all of the other elements and even some of the noble gases and with practically all organic and inorganic substances. Fluorides of xenon, radon, and krypton have been prepared by direct combination with elemental fluorine. Fluorine does not react with helium or nitrogen or fully fluorinated compounds. The potential of the normal fluorine electrode is -2.85 V versus the normal hydrogen electrode for the reaction:

$$2\,F^- \rightleftharpoons F_2 + 2e$$

Physical and thermodynamic properties of elemental fluorine are listed in Table 1. The only analytically important radioactive isotope is mass 18 fluorine, ^{18}F, which has a half life of 110 min. This isotope disintegrates by positron emission; the β^+ energy is 649 keV for 97% disintegration. The interatomic distance of fluorine, F_2, is 1.418 Å.

Fluorine gas and liquid fluorine are extremely corrosive and irritating to skin tissues. Inhalation causes severe irritation and at high concentrations lung congestion. The threshold limit value for fluorine published by the American Conference of Govern-

1

Table 1. Physical and Thermodynamic Properties of Elemental Fluorine

boiling point, °C	-188.2
melting point, °C	-218
density	
gas (air = 1), g/liter	1.695
liquid at -200°C, g/ml	1.14
liquid at boiling point, g/ml	1.108
solid, g/ml[a]	1.90
vapor pressure, log p in torr (T, in °C)	$9.175 - 442.72/T - 0.1315T$
transition temperature, solid, °C	-227.61
critical temperature, °C	-129
critical pressure, atm	55
refractive index, liquid at boiling point	1.2
surface tension, liquid, dyn/cm	
at -193.26°C	14.81
at -206.95°C	18.85
viscosity, cP	
liquid at -187.96°C	0.257
liquid at -203.96°C	0.414
vapor at 0°C, 760 torr	0.0218
heat of formation, kcal/g-mole	18.9
heat of transition, solid, cal/g-mole	173.90
heat of fusion, cal/g-mole	121.98
heat of vaporization, at boiling point, cal/g-mole	1561.3
standard entropy, cal/degree	
atomic fluorine	37.9
molecular fluorine	48.4
dielectric constant,	
at -189.95°C	1.517
at -215.76°C	1.567
thermal conductivity, gas, at 0°C and 760 torr,	
cal/(sec) (cm²) (°C/cm)	5.92×10^{-5}

[a] Mean estimated value.

mental Industrial Hygienists is 0.1 ppm in air for an 8-hr day, 40-hr week exposure Fluorine does not cause chronic toxicity. Fluorosis is the only chronic effect of fluorine assimilation; this condition, caused by increased fluorine content in the bone, occurs in man after exposure to large quantities of fluorine or fluoride over many years.

Occurrence and Methods of Manufacture

Fluorine is widely found combined in nature and composes approximately 0.065 wt % of the earth's crust. The most important industrial source of fluorine is the mineral fluorspar or fluorite, CaF_2, which contains about 49% fluorine. This mineral is widely distributed throughout the world; the chief deposits are in Illinois and Kentucky, in Derbyshire, England, and in southern Germany. The mineral cryolite, Na_3AlF_6, containing about 54% fluorine, is also industrially important; it is mined chiefly in Greenland and Iceland. Variable amounts of fluorine are also found in other minerals, such as fluorapatite or phosphate rock, $Ca_{10}F_2(PO_4)_6$; lepidolite, $(K,Li)_2Al_2(SiO_3)(F,OH)_2$; amblygonite, $LiAl(F,OH)PO_4$; topaz, $Al_2SiO_4(F,OH)_2$; and bastnaesite, $(Ce,La)_2F_6 \cdot (Ce,La)_2(CO_3)_3$. Fluoride occurs as a trace constituent in soils, waters, and plant and animal matter.

Fluorine is commercially prepared by the electrolysis of a molten mixture of about 1:4 potassium fluoride and hydrofluoric acid. The fluoride ion is anodically oxidized to elemental fluorine, and hydrogen is liberated at the cathode. High-purity anhydrous hydrofluoric acid, which is the principal raw material, is obtained by reacting fluorspar with sulfuric acid:

$$CaF_2 + H_2SO_4 \longrightarrow 2\,HF + CaSO_4$$

$$2\,HF \xrightarrow[KF]{electrolysis} F_2 + H_2$$

The major impurity in the commercial gas is hydrogen fluoride, varying from 5 to 11%, depending on the operating temperature and the melt composition. Absorption in sodium fluoride or refrigeration can reduce the hydrogen fluoride content to about 0.5%. Small amounts of carbon tetrafluoride are also present. In order to produce liquid fluorine, the combined hydrogen fluoride and carbon tetrafluoride impurities must be reduced to less than 0.2%. Typical commercial specifications for liquid fluorine, on a helium-free basis are:

fluorine	99.0 wt %, min
HF plus CF_4	0.3 wt %, max
O_2 plus N_2	1.0 wt %, max
total HF plus CF_4 and O_2 plus N_2	1.0 wt %, max

The extreme reactivity and toxicity of fluorine requires special materials for storage vessels and other equipment such as lines, fittings, valves, and gaskets. Nickel, Monel, aluminum, magnesium, copper, brass, stainless steel, and carbon steel are the metals and alloys commonly used with fluorine. Highly fluorinated polymers, such as polytetrafluoroethylene, are resistant to the gas under nominally static conditions. Any foreign matter present in the system could react violently with fluorine, causing a fire. Corrosion resistance of all materials in contact with fluorine can be insured by a pickling operation with gaseous fluorine to form a passive fluoride film on the metal surface.

Standard commercial instrumentation and control devices are used in fluorine systems. Bourdon-type gages or pressure transducers are used to measure pressure. Standard thermocouples are used to measure temperature. Gas flow rates are measured with orifices or rotameters and liquid flow with orifices or venturi meters. Packaging and shipment of fluorine gas is controlled by Interstate Commerce Commission regulations.

Methods of Analysis

A common method for the analysis of elemental fluorine or gases containing at least 50% fluorine consists of the following steps (13): The sample is passed through pelleted sodium fluoride in a pretreated nickel or copper tube to remove hydrogen by formation of the bifluoride, $NaHF_2$. The sample is then passed through anhydrous granular sodium chloride, which reacts with the fluorine to release an equivalent quantity of gaseous chlorine:

$$F_2 + 2\,NaCl \longrightarrow 2\,NaF + Cl_2$$

Chlorine can be absorbed in sodium hydroxide solution and the hypochlorite formed determined by iodometric titration. After removal of chlorine, oxygen in the gas stream can be absorbed in alkaline pyrogallol solution. Hydrogen fluoride is determined by dissolving the sodium fluoride pellets in water and titrating the hydrogen fluoride with standardized base to a phenolphthalein end point. If sodium bromide is used in place of sodium chloride, the bromine released can be measured spectrophotometrically by means of a flow cell.

Another procedure for the analysis of elemental fluorine involves removing hydrogen fluoride with potassium fluoride in a cooled copper trap and reacting the remaining gas with mercury to form solid mercury fluoride (14). The decrease in volume is a measure of the fluorine content. The residual gas can be analyzed for oxygen, carbon dioxide, and inert gases by usual Orsat techniques (see Vol. 2, pp. 139–145).

For analysis of gases containing less than 30% fluorine, the sample can be collected in an evacuated flask and the fluorine reacted with excess neutral potassium iodide solution. The liberated iodine is then titrated with sodium thiosulfate to the usual starch end point (1,15).

Low concentrations of fluorine and oxygen difluoride in air can be determined by passing the air sample over silica gel, which has been treated with a solution of potassium bromide and potassium carbonate and dried, and then the bromine formed is passed over silica gel treated with fluorescein and sodium hydroxide. A red color is formed which permits detection of as little as 0.34 μg of fluorine per liter of air (16). Similar concentrations of fluorine can also be determined by reaction with lithium chloride and measurement of the liberated chlorine by means of a silver–silver chloride–chlorine galvanic cell (17).

Gas Chromatography. Special gas chromatographic equipment has been designed and constructed for the analysis of corrosive gases such as fluorine (18–20). The components which contact the sample, sample inlet system, column tubing, connecting lines, as well as the surface of the thermal conductivity detector, are usually constructed of nickel, Monel, polytetrafluoroethylene, or stainless steel. Nickel or polytetrafluoroethylene-covered tungsten wire has been successfully used as a substitute for the usual tungsten wire filament of the thermal conductivity detector; the sensitivity, however, is reduced by a factor of three or four with the modified filament. A gas density balance has been successfully used as a detector in the analysis of corrosive gases, as the sample does not pass directly over the sensing elements. Electron capture detectors are extremely sensitive to chlorine atoms and somewhat sensitive to the other halogens, but it is absolutely necessary that corrosive gases do not contact the radioactive source.

An unusual form of radioactive detector using krypton-85 quinol clathrate has been used to determine 1–20 ppm of fluorine in air (21). On exposure to certain oxidants, the clathrate releases radioactive krypton, which is subsequently detected with a Geiger tube. Chlorine, bromine, chlorine dioxide, nitrogen dioxide, oxygen difluoride, nitryl fluoride, and nitryl chloride can also be determined. A device based on this principle for continuous monitoring of corrosive gases in air is the Tracerlab Toxic Gas Monitor (Tracerlab, Inc., Waltham, Mass.)

Fluorinated polymer oils such as Kel-F materials available from Kellogg Corp., Jersey City, N. J., or Hostaflon, available from Hoechst Chemical Company, London, England, are generally used as the stationary phase and support material. Lysyj and Newton (20) prepared an unusual substrate by plasticizing halogenated polymers with halogenated oils to yield a "monophase gel" which they used to separate fluorine, chlorine, and a number of reactive fluorides (see p. 64).

If fluorine, hydrogen fluoride, and other corrosive gases are first removed from the sample, residual nitrogen, oxygen, and inert gases can be determined by conventional gas chromatography with a molecular sieve 5A column at room or slightly elevated temperature using thermal conductivity detection (21).

Bibliography

GENERAL REFERENCES

1. P. J. Elving, C. A. Horton, and H. H. Willard, "Analytical Chemistry of Fluorine-Containing Compounds," in J. H. Simons, ed., *Fluorine Chemistry*, Vol. 2, Academic Press, Inc., New York, 1954, pp. 51–211.
2. C. A. Horton, "Fluorine," in I. M. Kolthoff and P. J. Elving, eds., *Treatise of Analytical Chemistry*, Vol. 7, Part 2, Interscience Publishers, a division of John Wiley & Sons, Inc., New York, 1962, pp. 207–334.
3. N. V. Sidgwick, *Chemical Elements and their Compounds*, Vol. 2, Clarendon Press, Oxford, 1950. pp. 1099–1138.
4. R. N. Haszeldine and A. G. Sharpe, *Fluorine and its Compounds*, Methuen, London, 1951.
5. A. G. Sharpe, "The Physical Inorganic Chemistry of The Halogens," in V. Gutmann, ed., *Halogen Chemistry*, Vol. 1, Academic Press, Inc., London, 1967 pp. 1–36.
6. J. H. Simons, ed., *Fluorine Chemistry*, Vols. 1–4, Academic Press, Inc., New York, 1950–1965.
7. M. Stacey and J. C. Tatlow, eds., *Advances in Fluorine Chemistry*, Vols. 1–6, Butterworths, London, 1960–1968.
8. V. Gutmann, ed., *Halogen Chemistry*, Vols. 1–3, Academic Press, Inc., New York, 1966–1969.
9. P. Tarrant ed., *Fluorine Chemistry Reviews*, Vols. 1–3, M. Dekker, New York, 1967–1969.
10. J. H. Simons, ed., *Fluorine Chemistry*, Vol. 4, Academic Press, Inc., New York, 1965.
11. H. R. Neumark and J. M. Siegmund, "Fluorine," in A. Standen, ed., *Kirk-Othmer Encyclopedia of Chemical Technology*, Vol. 9, 2nd ed., Interscience Publishers, a division of John Wiley & Sons, Inc., New York,.

SPECIFIC REFERENCES

12. H. Moissan, *Compt. Rend.* **102,** 1543–1544 (1886); **103,** 202–205, 256–258 (1886). *Gmelins Handbuch der Anorganischen Chemie*, System 5, 8th ed., Deutsche Chemische Gesellschaft, Verlag Chemie, Berlin, Germany, 1925, pp. 4–16.
13. Ref. 1, p. 59.
14. Ref. 1, p. 60.
15. *U.S. Atomic Energy Comm. Rept. TID-7015* (1957).
16. E. A. Peregud and B. S. Boikina, *Zhur. Anal. Khim.* **12,** 513 (1957); **14,** 141 (1959).
17. S. Kaye and M. Griggs, *Anal. Chem.* **40,** 2217 (1968).
18. J. F. Ellis, C. W. Forrest, and P. L. Allen, *Anal. Chim. Acta* **22,** 27 (1960).
19. G. Iveson and A. G. Hamlin, in R. P. W. Scott, ed., *Gas Chromatography 1960*, Butterworths, London, 1960, p. 333.
20. I. Lysyj and P. J. Newton, *Anal. Chem.* **35,** 90 (1963).
21. B. J. Gudzinowitz and W. R. Smith, *Anal. Chem.* **35,** 465 (1963).

A. M. G. MACDONALD
University of Birmingham, England
JOAN L. BATTLE
Encyclopedia of Industrial Chemical Analysis

FLUORINE COMPOUNDS, INORGANIC

Toxicity and safety precautions. 12
Analysis of inorganic fluorides. 14
    Identification. 14
    Separation. 15
    Determination of fluoride as a major constituent. 20
    Determination of fluoride as a minor or trace constituent. 24
    Specification tests. 33
Bibliography. 35

Fluorine is the most electronegative of the elements. Because of its great reactivity, fluorine forms compounds with virtually all other elements, including inert gases, such as xenon and krypton, and with most compounds that are not fully fluorinated. Many elements exhibit their highest oxidation states in the presence of fluoride, and many different complex molecules can be formed; the small size of the fluoride ion also facilitates complex formation.

Inorganic fluorides are used extensively in metallurgical processes, ceramics, electroplating, atomic energy, water treatment, and as rocket propellants and vermicides. Its best known use is as a trace constituent in drinking water; a concentration of 1 ppm has a beneficial effect on the incidence of dental caries. For additional information, consult the general references (1–4).

Hydrogen Fluoride and Hydrofluoric Acid. Anhydrous hydrogen fluoride, HF, is one of the most acidic substances and perhaps the strongest dehydrating agent known. It is a colorless gas or liquid. Some properties are listed in Table 1. It is very soluble in water with the evolution of much heat and fumes on contact with the atmosphere; it is only slightly soluble in hydrocarbons such as benzene or octane. Hydrogen fluoride exists as a monomer above about 88°C at atmospheric pressure. At lower temperatures, polymer consisting of two to six molecules exists probably in the form of a zigzag chain.

Table 1. Properties of Anhydrous Hydrogen Fluoride

formula weight	20.006
boiling point at 760 torr, °C	19.51
melting point, °C	83.37
density	
liquid at 25°C, g/ml	0.9576
vapor, saturated at 25°C, g/liter	3.553
vapor pressure at 25°C, psia	17.8
viscosity at 0°C, cP	0.26
surface tension at boiling point, dyn/cm	8.6
refractive index, $n_{5893Å}^{25}$	1.1574
critical temperature, °C	188
critical pressure, psia	941
critical density, g/ml	0.29

Hydrofluoric acid is an aqueous solution of hydrogen fluoride gas. It forms an azeotrope with water containing 38.2% HF and boiling at 112.2°C. Aqueous solutions of hydrogen fluoride behave as relatively weak acids; at 20–25°C, the dissociation constant for the reaction $HF \rightleftharpoons H^+ + F^-$ is $pK_1 = 3.10$ and for the reaction $HF + F^- \rightleftharpoons HF_2^-$, $pK_2 = 0.575$. The acid strength depends on the dilution, and solutions may contain H_3O^+, F^-, HF_2^-, $H_2F_3^-$, $H_3F_4^-$ and HF. It appears that hydrofluoric acid solutions contain both the strong acid HF_2H and the weak acid HF.

The major uses of hydrogen fluoride are in the manufacture of fluorinated organic compounds for aerosol propellants, foaming agents, cleaning fluids, and plastics and in the manufacture of aluminum fluoride and synthetic cryolite for aluminum production. Hydrogen fluoride is used as an alkylation catalyst in the petroleum industry, in pickling acids for stainless steel, for etching and polishing glass, and in the manufacture of fluorine, fluorides, fluoroborates, fluorosilicones, and dyes and pharmaceuticals.

Hydrogen fluoride is manufactured by the reaction of fluorspar (calcium fluoride) and concentrated sulfuric acid, and distillation of the gaseous product. It is commercially available as the liquid anhydrous material and as aqueous solutions containing 48 and 70% of the acid. Typical analysis of a technical grade liquid anhydrous hydrogen fluoride is given in Table 2 and specifications for reagent grade 48% hydrofluoric acid are given in Table 3.

Table 2. Typical Analysis of Anhydrous Hydrogen Fluoride

assay, %	99.95
hydrofluorosilicic acid, %	0.015
sulfite, %	0.003
sulfuric acid, %	0.005
water, %	0.02

Table 3. Commercial Specifications for Reagent Grade Hydrofluoric Acid

	ACS[a]	Rosin[b]
assay, % min	48.0–51.0	48
residue on evaporation, % max		0.002
residue on ignition, % max	0.0005	0.001
hydrofluorosilicic acid, % max	0.01	0.10
chloride, % max	0.0005	0.001
phosphate, % max	0.0001	0.0002
sulfate, % max		0.001
sulfite, % max		0.002
sulfate and sulfite, % max	0.0005	
arsenic, % max	0.000005	
copper, % max	0.00001	
heavy metals as Pb, % max	0.00005	0.0002
iron, % max	0.0001	0.0001

[a] Ref. 5a.
[b] Ref. 5b.

Ultrapure hydrogen fluoride can be prepared by passing hydrogen fluoride through a polytetrafluoroethylene filter and then freezing in a Kel-F tank with liquid nitrogen; when the cycle is repeated and the gas is introduced into conductivity water in a polytetrafluoroethylene bottle, the resulting 50% solution contains only 0.002 ppm of potassium and 0.00008 ppm of lead (5).

Other Fluoro Acids. Fluoroboric, fluorophosphoric, fluorosilicic, and fluorosulfuric acids are covered in the article on FLUORO ACIDS, INORGANIC, pp. 37–58.

Halogen Fluorides. Chlorine and bromine fluorides possess properties similar to elemental fluorine and are more convenient to handle and ship. Chlorine trifluoride,

Table 4. Properties of Halogen Fluorides

	Chlorine monofluoride, ClF	Chlorine trifluoride, ClF_3	Bromine trifluoride, BrF_3	Bromine pentafluoride, BrF_5	Iodine pentafluoride, IF_5	Iodine heptafluoride, IF_7
appearance	colorless gas; as liquid, slightly yellow	almost colorless gas at room temperature; as liquid, pale yellow; as solid, almost white	amber liquid	colorless liquid	liquid	colorless gas
boiling point, °C	−100.1	11.75	125.75	41.3	98	4
melting point, °C	−155.9	−83	8.8		9.6	5.5
freezing point, °C				−60.5		
sublimation point, °C			327			
critical temperature, °C	−14					
triple point, °C		−76.32	8.77			
density, g/ml						
liquid, at −108°C	1.67					
liquid, at −78°C						
liquid (T, in °C)		2.026	$3.623 - 0.002777T$			
liquid, at 0°C				2.57	3.19	
liquid, at 25°C				2.46	2.231	
liquid, at 15°C					3.75	
solid, at 0°C						
liquid, at 6°C						2.8
vapor pressure, torr log p (T, in °C)		$7.36711 - 1096.917/(T + 232.75)$	$7.74853 - 1685.8/(T + 220.57)$	$6.4545 + 0.001100T - 895/(T + 206)$	$8.6591 - 2159.0/T$[a]	$8.6604 - 1602.6/T$[a]
surface tension, at 0°C, dyn/cm		26.6				

[a] T, in °K.

ClF_3, is extremely reactive and useful as a fluorinating agent. Chlorine trifluoride, bromine trifluoride, BrF_3, and bromine pentafluoride, BrF_5, are powerful oxidizers; they are useful in the manufacture of uranium hexafluoride and are of interest as propellants for rockets and missiles. Properties of halogen fluorides are listed in Table 4.

Halogen fluorides are generally prepared by direct combination of the elements in the desired proportion at definite temperatures. Chlorine trifluoride is prepared by passing chlorine and fluorine through a nickel or Monel tube at 290°C. Chlorine monofluoride, ClF, is prepared by mixing chlorine and chlorine trifluoride. Bromine tri- and pentafluoride are prepared by mixing bromine and fluorine in the appropriate ratio in a nickel or copper tube; the trifluoride is formed at 80°C and the pentafluoride at 200°C. Iodine pentafluoride, IF_5, is prepared by passing fluorine over iodine crystals. The heptafluoride, IF_7, is prepared by passing fluorine gas through liquid iodine pentafluoride at 90°C and then heating the vapors to 270°C.

Perchloryl fluoride, ClO_3F, is a colorless, readily liquefied gas with a characteristic sweet odor. It is a very stable compound with low reactivity. Anhydrous material does not attack glass or most metals at ordinary temperatures. Properties are listed in Table 5. Perchloryl fluoride is slightly soluble in a wide variety of polar and nonpolar solvents. Liquid perchloryl fluoride is a typical nonpolar solvent; it dissolves most inorganic and organic salts. Perchloryl fluoride has been used mainly in blends with halogen fluorides as storable liquid oxidizers for rocket engines. It is used as a highly specific fluorinating agent for steroid drugs and to introduce the chlorate group onto aromatic rings.

Nitrogen Fluorides. Nitrogen trifluoride, NF_3, is a colorless gas with a moldy odor. It liquefies at −129.01°C at 760 torr and solidifies at −206.79°C. It is a strong oxidizing agent but relatively inert at ordinary temperatures. It is insoluble in water. Nitrogen trifluoride is prepared by electrolysis of molten ammonium bifluoride or by direct combination of the elements by an electrical discharge. It has potential use in rocket fuel oxidants.

Tetrafluorohydrazine, N_2F_4, is a colorless gas with a musty odor. It liquefies at −73°C at 760 torr and freezes at −163°C. Tetrafluorohydrazine is prepared by reacting nitrogen trifluoride with metals such as copper, at elevated temperatures.

Table 5. Properties of Perchloryl Fluoride, ClO_3F

boiling point, °C	−46.67
melting point, °C	−147.7
density, g/ml	
solid at −190°C	2.19
liquid at melting point	2.003
liquid at 25°C	1.412
vapor at 25°C	0.065
vapor pressure, psia	
at −80°C	2.25
at 0°C	84.01
at 25°C	176.0
at 54.44°C (130°F)	355.0
viscosity, at boiling point, cP	0.145
surface tension at boiling point, dyn/cm	20.7
critical temperature, °C	95.9
critical pressure, psia	779
critical density, g/ml	0.637

Other nitrogen and fluorine compounds are known and are of research interest such as *cis-* and *trans-*difluoroazine, N_2F_2; azine fluoride, N_3F; nitrosyl fluoride, NOF; and nitryl fluoride, NO_2F.

Oxygen Fluorides. Oxygen difluoride or fluorine monoxide, OF_2, is a colorless gas which condenses to a pale yellow liquid and is the only relatively stable oxygen fluoride. Properties are listed in Table 6. It is a powerful oxidizing agent, but is somewhat less reactive than elemental fluorine, and is more easily handled. It does not attack glass at low temperatures and reacts slowly with water. Oxygen difluoride is prepared by passing fluorine into 2% aqueous sodium hydroxide solution; the gaseous product is fractionated at $-145°C$. Oxygen difluoride is of use as an ingredient of high-energy rocket propellant systems.

Table 6. Properties of Oxygen Fluorides

	Oxygen difluoride, OF_2	Dioxygen difluoride, O_2F_2	Trioxygen difluoride O_3F_2
boiling point, °C	-145.3	-57 extrapolated	-60 extrapolated
melting point, °C	-223.8	-163.5	
freezing point, °C			-190
density of liquid, g/ml (T, in °K)			$2.357 - 0.00676T$
-153 to $-145°C$	$2.190 - 0.00523T$		
-156 to $-87°C$		$2.074 - 0.00291T$	
vapor pressure, log p in torr (T, in °K)			
-195 to $-145°C$	$7.2242 - 555.42/T$		
below $-100°C$		$7.515 - 1000/T$	
-194 to $-159°C$			$6.1343 - 675.57/T$
critical temperature, °C	-58.0		
critical pressure, atm	48.9		
critical density, g/ml	0.553		

Dioxygen difluoride, O_2F_2, is an amber-colored solid. Properties are listed in Table 6. It is relatively unstable and decomposes to the gaseous elements above $-78°C$. It is an extremely powerful oxidizing and fluorinating agent. Dioxygen difluoride is prepared by passing a 1:1 mixture of oxygen and fluorine through a high-voltage electric discharge tube cooled by liquid nitrogen.

Trioxygen difluoride, O_3F_2, is a dark red liquid which solidifies at $-190°C$ but readily decomposes above this temperature to dioxygen difluoride and oxygen. Properties are listed in Table 6. Trioxygen difluoride is also prepared by an electric discharge process using a 3:2 mixture of oxygen and fluorine. The compound has potential use in rocket propulsion systems.

Tetraoxygen difluoride, O_4F_2, is the least stable oxygen fluoride. It is a reddish brown solid at $-196°C$ and is probably one of the most powerful oxidizers known. It is prepared by an electric discharge method using a 2:1 mixture of oxygen and fluorine. It decomposes above $-183°C$ to trioxygen difluoride and oxygen.

Sulfur Fluorides. Sulfur hexafluoride, SF_6, is a colorless, odorless, and tasteless gas. It is one of the most stable gases known, has high dielectric strength, is not flammable, and is completely nontoxic. Properties are listed in Table 7. Sulfur hexafluoride is prepared by burning lump sulfur with gaseous fluorine.

Table 7. Properties of Sulfur Fluorides

	Sulfur hexafluoride, SF$_6$	Sulfur tetrafluoride, SF$_4$	Disulfur decafluoride, S$_2$F$_{10}$	Disulfur difluoride, S$_2$F$_2$
boiling point, °C		−40.4	29	−10.6
melting point, °C	−50.8 (at 2.21 atm)	−121	−92	−165
density of liquid at 0°C, g/ml	1.540		2.08	
vapor pressure, log p in atm (T, in °K)				
−50.8 to +48.6°C	$4.3571 - 889.85/T$			
surface tension, dyn/cm				
at bp		19.85		
at 0°C			13.9	
at −50°C	11.63			
at −20°C	8.02			
critical temperature, °C	45.64	90.9		
critical pressure, atm	37.193			
critical density, g/ml	0.725			

Sulfur tetrafluoride, SF$_4$, is a toxic colorless gas with an odor resembling sulfur dioxide. Properties are listed in Table 7. It is highly reactive and fumes in moist air. Sulfur tetrafluoride can be prepared by burning sulfur or carbon disulfide in fluorine or by reacting sulfur dichloride with sodium fluoride suspended in acetonitrile at 70–80°C. The compound is used to replace carbonyl oxygen with fluorine.

Table 8. Properties of Some Fluoride Salts

Compound	Formula weight	Boiling point, °C	Melting point, °C	Density, g/ml	Solubility in water °C	Solubility in water g/100 ml
NaF	42.0	1705	1010	2.558 (at 41°C)	18	4.22
Na$_3$AlF$_6$	209.96		1000		25	0.061
KF	58.1	1505	846		18	92.3
LiF	25.94	1676	842	2.601	25	0.151
RbF	104.47	1410	775	3.557	18	75.06
CsF	151.90	125J	682	4.115	18	76.3
CaF$_2$	78.08	2500	1360	3.18	25	0.0016
MgF$_2$	62.32	2260	1225	∼3	25	0.013
SrF$_2$	125.63	2460	∼1350	4.24	25	0.039
BaF$_2$	175.36	2260	1287	4.893	25	0.121
MnF$_2$	92.93		856	3.98	25	0.186
CoF$_2$	96.93	1400	∼1200	4.46	20	1.36
ZnF$_2$	103.37	∼1500	872	4.95	18	1.60
CdF$_2$	150.40	1758	1100	6.64	20	4.0
AlF$_3$	83.97	1291	1040	3.07	25	0.559
PbF$_2$	245.21	1292	822	8.24	25	0.066
FeF$_3$	112.84		>1000	3.52	25	0.091
BiF$_3$	266.0		727	5.32 (at 20°C)		
CeF$_3$	197.13	2300	1460	6.16		
ThF$_4$	308.03	>1680	>900	6.32		
ThF$_4$.4H$_2$O	380.09				25	0.245
NaBF$_4$	109.82		384 dec	2.47	26.5	109
KBF$_4$	125.92		529		20	0.44

Disulfur decafluoride or sulfur pentafluoride, S_2F_{10}, is a toxic, colorless, volatile liquid. Physical properties are listed in Table 7. The compound is not commercially produced.

Disulfur difluoride or sulfur monofluoride, S_2F_2, is a colorless gas with an odor resembling sulfur monochloride. Boiling and melting points are listed in Table 7.

Metal Fluorides. Individual metal fluoride salts are covered in the compound section under the particular element; for example, those sections which have already been published include aluminum fluoride and sodium fluoroaluminate, Vol. 5, pp. 177–180; antimony trifluoride and pentafluoride, Vol. 6, pp. 48–50; beryllium fluoride and fluoroberyllates, Vol. 7, pp. 122–123; bismuth trifluoride and pentafluoride, Vol. 7, pp. 197–199; boron trifluoride, fluoroboric acid, and fluoroborates, Vol. 7, pp. 335–339; cadmium fluoride, Vol. 8, p. 42; calcium fluoride, Vol. 8, pp. 88–91; and cobalt fluorides and fluorosilicates, Vol. 10, pp. 337–338.

Properties of some fluoride salts are listed in Table 8. The stabilities of fluoride complexes decrease in the following order: Zr^{4+}, $Hf^{4+} > Th^{4+} > La^{3+} > Nb^{5+} > Ta^{5+} > Al^{3+} > Sn^{4+} > Be^{2+} > Fe^{3+} > B^{3+} > Ga^{3+} > Tl^{3+} > In^{3+}$, Ge^{4+}, Si^{4+}.

Fluorspar, calcium fluoride, CaF_2, is the most important fluoride-bearing mineral (see p. 2). Metal fluorides are usually prepared by reacting the metal hydroxide or carbonate with hydrofluoric acid. Commercial specifications for reagent grades of ammonium, potassium, and sodium fluoride are given in Table 9 (5c). Sodium fluoride is used as a standard in fluoride analysis.

Table 9. Commercial Specifications for Reagent Grade Ammonium, Potassium, and Sodium Fluorides

	Ammonium fluoride	Potassium fluoride	Sodium fluoride
assay, % min	98	98.5	98.5
water insoluble matter, % max		0.02	0.02
loss on drying, % max			0.30
residue on ignition, % max	0.020		
acid fluoride, as NH_4HF_2, % max	0.5		
free acid, as HF, % max		0.05	0.05
free alkali, as K_2CO_3, % max		0.15	
as Na_2CO_3			0.10
chloride, % max	0.002	0.010	0.005
nitrate, % max	0.002		
fluorosilicate, % max			
as H_2SiF_6	0.3		
as K_2SiF_6		0.10	
as Na_2SiF_6			0.10
sulfate, % max	0.020	0.020	0.030
sulfite, % max		0.005	0.005
heavy metals, as Pb, % max	0.001	0.002	0.003
iron, % max	0.003	0.001	0.002
sodium, % max		about 0.002	

Toxicity and Safety Precautions

Fluorine, hydrogen fluoride, the interhalogen compounds, and other fluorine-containing gases are extremely reactive and toxic. Sulfur hexafluoride is a peculiar exception; it is tolerable in concentrations up to about 1000 ppm. Suggested threshold limits for other fluorine-containing gases are as follows: 3 ppm for hydrogen fluoride; 1 ppm for boron trifluoride; 0.1 ppm for chlorine trifluoride; and 0.025 ppm for disulfur decafluoride. Fluoride as dusts or fumes should not be present above 2.5 ppm. Selenium hexafluoride, tellurium hexafluoride, sulfur tetrafluoride, and oxygen difluoride are even more toxic, and are intolerable in any measurable concentration. Oxygen difluoride is particularly insidious because it can be inhaled without discomfort at lethal concentrations. On the other hand, 3 ppm of hydrogen fluoride may cause discomfort in breathing, and concentrations of 30–50 ppm will not be voluntarily accepted. References 6–8 should be consulted for additional information on the toxicity of fluorine compounds.

The toxicity of inorganic fluorine compounds depends on the facility with which the compounds can be broken down to the fluoride ion. For example, fluoroborate can pass through the body unchanged whereas fluorosilicate is highly toxic, and insoluble compounds such as fluorspar and cryolite are, in their untreated condition, virtually nontoxic. Accordingly, in exposure tests it is customary not to determine the total atmospheric fluoride content, but to carry out urine analysis; excretion of 20 mg of fluoride or more per day indicates a dangerous situation leading to chronic fluorosis.

Acute fluoride poisoning is normally accidental or suicidal in intent. The indubitably lethal dosage of sodium fluoride appears to be about 5 g but smaller quantities may cause death. Since sodium fluoride is used as an insecticide and rodent killer, its accidental misuse has caused mass poisoning. Certain cloth rust removers containing hydrofluoric acid and ammonium fluoride have also been the cause of acute accidental or intentional poisoning. The symptoms of acute fluoride poisoning are vomiting, abdominal pains, diarrhea, followed by convulsions, cardiorespiratory difficulties, and death after an interval of some hours to several days. In such cases, immediate diagnosis may be assisted by the fact that the vomitus will etch glass. Milk and dilute lime water provide useful emergency treatment, and gastric lavage, preferably with milk, is suitable if it can be applied promptly. The recognized treatment is intravenous injection of 10% calcium gluconate solution which should be administered continuously even after the patient appears to have recovered. This should be accompanied by intravenous glucose administration and blood transfusions. Similar treatment is advisable in cases of accidental inhalations of high concentrations of fluoride-containing gases or dusts, which are commoner industrial hazards. Large doses of steroids to prevent pulmonary emphysema, and bronchial evacuation with inhalants (eg, epinephrine) are also indicated. Chronic fluoride poisoning arises from continuous ingestion of fluoride-containing compounds and is most commonly found among cryolite workers. Crippling fluorosis appears gradually as a continuous osteosclerotic change leading to the "poker back" symptom.

Sodium fluoroacetate, which is used as a rat killer, varies remarkably in its toxicity for different species, dogs being particularly susceptible, whereas frogs and toads are relatively immune. In this case, the toxicity does not depend on the ease of dissociation of fluoride ions but on enzyme inhibition. Monoacetin appears to be the only practical remedy supported by barbiturates to control convulsions; failing this, about 250 ml of a 1:1 mixture of ethanol and vinegar administered orally may avail.

Acid burns from hydrofluoric acid or acid fluoride solutions may not be immediately felt but can become exceedingly painful after a few hours. Extensive acid burns are usually fatal owing to pulmonary edema since they normally involve also excessive inhalation of fluoride. Immediate thorough washing with water is essential whether the burn is large or small; in fact, even if a slight contact with concentrated hydrofluoric acid is only suspected, copious washing with water may prevent later pain. Industrial hygiene practice should include availability of drenching showers. After washing, borax–boric acid solutions or a magnesium oxide paste can be applied, but the most important treatment is intravenous and intracutaneous injection of calcium gluconate solution in the case of extensive burns. For small burns, application of a paste containing 20 parts of magnesium oxide, 100 parts of magnesium sulfate, 2 parts of gum arabic, 100 parts of glycerol, and 130 parts of water is beneficial.

Analysis of Inorganic Fluorides

The analytical chemistry of fluorine and fluorides is difficult, largely due to its great reactivity and lack of clearcut reactions. The two outstanding landmarks in the early history of fluoride analysis are the gravimetric calcium fluoride method of Berzelius (11) and the fluorosilicic acid distillation–thorium(IV) titration method of Willard and Winter (12). These methods are now rarely used. The introduction of the lanthanum fluoride electrode in 1966 (13) has made possible the automation of many fluoride analyses.

Laboratory Precautions. Great care is essential in handling fluorine, hydrogen fluoride, or other fluorine-containing gases. Hydrofluoric acid and hydrogen fluoride will vigorously attack glass or silica to form volatile silicon tetrafluoride. In the great majority of analytical reactions, fluorosilicic acid will behave like a fluoride solution since it is readily hydrolyzed; therefore, precautions should normally be aimed at preventing losses by volatilization from solutions, rather than at preventing formation of fluorosilicic acid. However, if borosilicate glassware is used, fluoride may be lost by interaction with boron and/or aluminum in the glass, even in alkaline solutions. Fluoride solutions should be stored in plastic vessels, and wherever possible plastic apparatus, such as beakers, flasks, and pipets, should be used for handling these solutions. Scratched plastic should not be employed, since in certain operations losses can be caused, possibly by adsorption to dirt in the scratches. If fluoride is to be separated as fluorosilicic acid by distillation, any preliminary evaporation of the solution should be done in the flask from which the distillation is to be carried out, otherwise fluoride losses will occur (9). In general, it is advisable to carry out any necessary evaporations in platinum vessels. Analytical procedures involving acidic fluoride solutions, and especially evaporations, must be carried out in well-ventilated hoods. When strong hydrofluoric acid solutions are used, stout plastic gloves must be worn.

For spectral studies of gases, calcium fluoride or sapphire windows can be used. A diamond window cell has been described for spectral studies of molten fluorides (10).

IDENTIFICATION

Spectrographic techniques have been used for the detection of fluoride; dc arc, ac spark, hollow-cathode discharge, and flame emission have been used (14). Most methods are based on the band head of calcium fluoride at 5291 Å. When a hollow-cathode discharge is used, 5 µg of fluoride can be detected by the line at 7128 Å (15).

X-ray diffraction patterns are valuable in the identification of individual crystalline compounds in solid mixtures.

Etching and Hanging Drop Tests. When most inorganic fluorides are heated with concentrated sulfuric acid, volatile hydrogen fluoride is liberated and will etch glass. In the presence of silica or glass, hydrogen fluoride forms silicon tetrafluoride, which hydrolyzes in water to gelatinous silica and hexafluorosilicic acid.

$$CaF_2 + H_2SO_4 \longrightarrow CaSO_4 + 2\,HF$$

$$SiO_2 + 4\,HF \longrightarrow 2\,H_2O + SiF_4$$

$$3\,SiF_4 + 3\,H_2O \longrightarrow 2\,H_2SiF_6 + SiO_2.H_2O$$

Elements such as aluminum and boron, which form strong fluoride complexes, reduce the sensitivity of the test.

The etching test is carried out by heating the sample with sulfuric acid in a platinum, plastic, or lead vessel and observing the exposed surface of a polished glass plate cover that has been partially covered with a thin layer of paraffin. A simple procedure for the hanging drop test follows.

Procedure

Place a few mg of the sample in a depression punched in a small lead plate and mix well with a little powdered silica or sodium silicate. Add a few drops of concentrated sulfuric acid and cover with a sheet of thin clear plastic which has a drop of water hanging immediately above the depression. After 1–2 min, turbidity develops in the hanging drop if fluoride is present. The same test without the addition of silica indicates the presence of fluorosilicate.

Fluorescence Test. Fluorescent complexes of metals such as aluminum or magnesium are decomposed in the presence of traces of fluoride. The following method introduced by Feigl (16) is based on the quenching of the fluorescence of metal-8-quinolinolate complexes by fluoride ion.

Procedure

Place 1 drop of test solution and 3 drops of concentrated sulfuric acid in a microcrucible and cover with a piece of qualitative filter paper (this contains sufficient metal ion impurity for metal addition to be unnecessary) with an overlap of about 2 cm. Heat at 50–60°C for 5 min and then wet the paper with 1–2 drops of 0.05% (w/v) 8-quinolinol solution in chloroform. Fluoride is indicated when the exposed area shows only slight fluorescence under ultraviolet light compared to the unexposed surrounding circle. The limit of detection is 0.05 μg of fluoride or 0.5 μg in the presence of boron and the dilution limit is $1:10^6$.

SEPARATION

Fluoride can be separated by volatilization of silicon tetrafluoride from concentrated sulfuric acid medium or by distillation as hexafluorosilicic acid. The latter method is preferred. Separation by pyrolysis was introduced in the Manhattan Project but has been less widely adopted, although it has many advantages.

Anion exchange resins allow separation of fluoride from other anions, such as sulfate and phosphate, which often interfere in the final determination. Cation exchange can be useful in removing bulk salts before a determination of fluoride, but such methods need great care in application because of the tendency of fluoride to form positively as well as negatively charged complexes.

Diffusion methods find many applications in clinical and biochemical work; Teflon diffusion cells have been described (17) and it has been shown (18) that high-vacuum silicone grease facilitates the diffusion of fluoride. Such methods are, however, rather outside the industrial field.

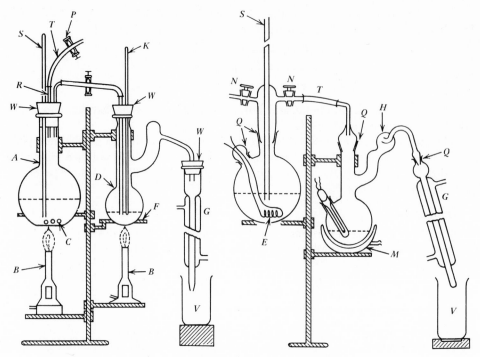

Fig. 1. Apparatus for volatilization of fluoride.

A. Steam generator flask, 1000-ml or 2000-ml Florence type.
B. Bunsen burner.
C. Boiling chips, or porous pumice.
D. Distilling flask, modified Claisen type.
E. Nichrome heating coil, platinum wire through glass.
F. Hard asbestos plate with 2 in. diameter hole.
G. Condenser, Liebig-type heat-resistant glass, 300 mm water jacket.
H. Trap for entrained liquid in vapor.
K. Thermometer, calibrated for bulb immersion only, 0–150°C.
L. Mercury temperature-sensing unit for thermoregulator, adjusted to make and break
        contact at 135 ± 2°C.
M. Fiberglas insulated electric heating mantle, for maximum temperature of 175°C.
N. Stopcocks.
P. Pinchclamps, adjustable type.
Q. Standard taper glass joints.
R. Steam-release tube.
S. Safety pressure-release tube.
T. Rubber tubing.
V. Plastic receiver, 100–500 ml beaker or cylinder.
W. Rubber stoppers.

Distillation as Hexafluorosilicic Acid. The method introduced in 1933 by
Willard and Winter (12) involves steam distillation from perchloric or sulfuric acid at
135°C in the presence of glass beads or quartz powder. Many modifications of apparatus and distillation conditions have been proposed (19). For samples that do not
contain much fluoride-retaining material, such as aluminum, boron, zirconium, or
gelatinous silica, quantitative recovery of fluoride can be achieved in 75–100 ml of
distillate, but retentive materials may make it necessary to distill as much as 500 ml.

Distillation has been recommended from sulfuric acid at temperatures varying from 120 to 180°C, from perchloric acid at temperatures of 120–140°C, and from phosphoric acid at 135–175°C. The higher the temperature of the steam distillation, the better designed must the apparatus be to prevent carryover of undesirable ions, but the less interference there is from fluoride-retaining materials. Soluble silver salts are useful in retaining other halides and phosphates, but barium salts for the retention of sulfate must be used cautiously, because barium fluorosilicate is very insoluble.

The method described below is based on the recommendations of Horton (19) and is adequate for most purposes. It is worth noting that Grimaldi et al. (20) and some later workers preferred to distill from a 10:1 mixture of perchloric acid and phosphoric acid at 140°C; the presence of phosphoric acid helps to avoid the retarding effect of iron, aluminum, and gelatinous silica. The distillation apparatus is shown in Figure 1 (21). A 250-ml Claisen-type flask is used as the distillation flask, and should be made of silica or low-boron glass. The steam generator is a 1- or 2-liter Florence flask, and steam generation is controlled by a pinchclamp or stopcock between the two flasks. Porous pumice or boiling rings should be placed in the steam generator to reduce bumping.

Procedure

If the sample contains organic matter or highly refractory substances, it should be pretreated before the distillation. For example, with chopped vegetation samples, mix a dried 1–5 g sample with about 12% of the sample weight of fluoride-free calcium oxide or purified magnesium oxide (22) in a platinum dish, add sufficient water to cover, and mix well. After ensuring that the solution is alkaline, evaporate the water and char under infrared light, assisting the charring process with gradual heating on a hot plate. Then ignite the ash at 600° in a muffle furnace for 2 hr or until the ash is white. Transfer the ash to a nickel crucible, add 5 g of sodium hydroxide, and fuse at 600° for 10 min. Dissolve this melt in the minimum amount of water and transfer to the distillation flask, using the acid to ensure quantitative transfer.

For rocks and refractory ores, prior fusion is usually essential. Many fusion mixtures have been recommended. The following procedure is that of Grimaldi et al. (20). Fuse a 1-g sample in a nickel or platinum crucible with 6 g of sodium carbonate and 1.2 g of pure zinc oxide; if a platinum crucible is used, the fusion must be made under oxidizing conditions. Add 30 ml of water to the cooled crucible in a 100-ml beaker and soften the melt by heating the covered beaker on a steam bath. Remove the crucible and rinse it thoroughly with about 20 ml of water. Boil the solution gently, stirring well to break up any lumps. After a few minutes of boiling, allow to cool and then filter the solution into the distillation flask. Wash the residue by decantation with a little hot aqueous 2% sodium carbonate solution, then transfer it to the filter and wash further. The final volume of the solution should be about 70 ml.

The conditions for rock analysis involve further distillation after addition of 20 ml of 70% perchloric acid and 2 ml of 85% perchloric acid. Place about 650 ml of water in the steam generator and add one pellet of sodium hydroxide and 1 ml of phenolphthalein indicator solution; the water must be alkaline during steam generation. Add a few glass or quartz beads to the distillation flask and place the sample or sample solution in the flask, adjusting the volume to 30–60 ml with water. Connect up the apparatus as far as possible and place a 250-ml or 500-ml plastic measuring cylinder under the outlet of the condenser. Then rinse the sample vessel with 50 ml of 70–72% perchloric acid containing 1 ml of 50% silver perchlorate solution, quickly transfer this to the distillation flask, and insert the flask stopper. Heat the solution in the flask to 135°C, and only then release steam into the flask from the generator. Maintain a temperature of 135°C and a volume of about 50 ml in the distillation flask by adjusting the rates of heating and steam generation. Swirl the flask occasionally to avoid large deposits of fluoride-retentive gelatinous silica. Collect 100 ml of distillate for straightforward samples or up to 500 ml of distillate for samples containing high concentrations of fluoride-retentive substances. The distillation is usually carried out at a rate of 4–5 ml/min.

It is vital to carry out blank determinations under the conditions used. Blanks can vary very widely if the same still is used successively for samples containing different fluoride contents. It is advisable to keep different stills for different fluoride levels

Pyrohydrolytic Separation. A great deal of work was done on pyrohydrolytic separation of fluoride during the Manhattan Project, but a published method did not become available until 1954, when Warf, Cline, and Tevebaugh (23) described a procedure in which various metal fluorides were pyrohydrolyzed at 1000°C in steam in a platinum tube. Fluoride could be removed quantitatively from heavy metal fluorides and magnesium fluoride, but alkali and alkaline earth fluorides required the addition of uranium oxide, U_3O_8, as an accelerator.

Because of cost and maintenance problems with platinum tubes, later workers have preferred other materials for the pyrolysis tubes; nickel and nickel–stainless steel apparatus have been designed, but most investigators, following the example of Powell and Menis (24), have used silica tubes. Powell and Menis (24) showed that moist oxygen could beneficially replace steam, allowing quantitative recovery of fluoride from materials such as aluminum, neptunium, thorium, or zirconium fluorides at a temperature of 800–900°C with tungsten trioxide as accelerator. At these temperatures, silica tubes are quite satisfactory, and there is then no danger of retention of fluoride by metal in the cool zones of the apparatus. Tungsten trioxide appears to be quite satisfactory as an accelerator, though Newman (25) suggested vanadium pentoxide, which melts at about 670°C, and so acts as a flux. Vanadium pentoxide was successfully used in analysis of silicate rocks, micas, and fluorspar at temperatures of about 750°C (ie, below the distillation temperature of vanadium pentoxide) in a moist air stream.

Some analysts have encountered difficulties in the application of pyrohydrolytic techniques, and the method does not seem to be widely applied, although reported recoveries are generally superior to those obtained by the Willard–Winter distillation process. Its lack of popularity is rather surprising, since it obviates the need of preliminary fusions, and demands less art than the distillation method. Newman (25), commenting on this aspect, states that successful pyrohydrolysis depends on three factors: (1) very thorough and intimate grinding of the sample and accelerator in an agate mortar; (2) avoidance of fog formation, which leads to fluoride losses, and can be prevented by ensuring that the tube leading to the absorber is not too cold; (3) avoidance of water condensation on the cooler parts of the pyrolysis tube, by means of gentle heating where necessary with a gas flame.

The method given in detail below is based on the recommendations of Powell and Menis (24). Similar procedures have been applied to silica–alumina catalysts at 760°C (26), iron ores, flue dusts, phosphate rocks and glass at 1000°C (27), and silicate rocks (28). The time required for quantitative recovery of fluoride varies from 10 to 40 min,

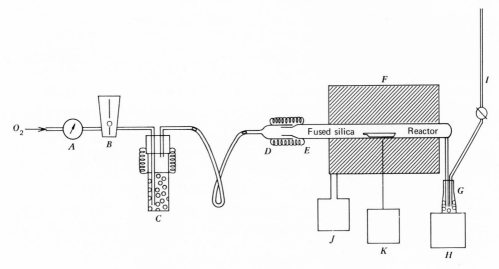

Fig. 2. Micro and macro pyrolytic apparatus

A. Gas regulator.
B. Flowmeter.
C. Water tower.
D. Fused silica joint.
E. Pyrolytic reactor tube, fused silica.
F. Split type furnace, 12 in.; 1¼ bore.

G. Receiving flask.
H. Magnetic stirrer.
I. Goose-neck buret.
J. Variable transformer.
K. Thermocouple and pyrometer.

depending on the temperature, the accelerator, and the sample material. Fluorspar and lanthanum fluoride cling tenaciously to their fluoride, wheras zirconium fluoride is more reactive.

A schematic diagram of the apparatus is shown in Figure 2. The oxygen from a cylinder is passed through a water tower or bubbler to saturate it with moisture and then to the pyrolysis system. The fused silica tube is about 60 cm long with an external diameter of 3–3.5 cm and is connected to the gas flow via a 29/42 standard taper joint, which is lubricated with graphite powder. The delivery tube, also of pure silica, is 25 cm long with an external diameter of 1 cm. It is worth noting that some workers (25) prefer to place a water condenser around the outlet tube. A split-type combustion furnace controlled by a Variac transformer is used. The sample boats used can be of platinum, Alundum, or silica, and should be about 9 cm long, 1.5 cm wide, and 0.75–1 cm high.

Procedure

Set up the apparatus as shown, and adjust the flow rate to 2–3 liters/min. Adjust the furnace temperature to about 825°C. Place a suitable volume of 0.002 N sodium hydroxide solution (or other concentration depending on the amount of fluoride to be retained) in a plastic measuring flask as receiver and place the flask over the delivery tube so that the tip is immersed to a depth of several cm. Add phenolphthalein indicator solution to the receiver solution and ensure that this solution remains alkaline at all times during the pyrohydrolysis.

For the preparation of solid samples grind 0.1–2 g of sample depending on the fluoride content, very finely with 3 g of finely powdered pure tungsten trioxide in a mortar, and transfer the mixture quantitatively to a suitable sample boat.

For the preparation of liquid samples, transfer about 2 ml to the sample boat and make it just alkaline to phenolphthalein with 2 N sodium hydroxide solution. Evaporate to dryness under infrared heating, making sure that the sample remains alkaline. Add 3 g of tungsten trioxide to the residue and pack down well.

Insert the sample boat into the center of the furnace and immediately replace the joint, fixing it with springs. Continue the pyrohydrolysis for 15–60 min depending on the type of sample. Samples of unknown type should be checked initially by varying the time of pyrohydrolysis.

Other halogens and sulfur or nitrogen oxides will be evolved with fluoride and therefore interfere. Simple fluorides can be determined by back-titration of the excess alkali. Phosphates and silicates are held in the boat and do not interfere.

DETERMINATION OF FLUORIDE AS A MAJOR CONSTITUENT

The classical method for large amounts of fluoride is gravimetric determination as calcium fluoride (11). Lead chlorofluoride is now preferred for gravimetric determination because of the ease of handling the precipitate. Since 1966, the single-crystal lanthanum fluoride electrode has practically supplanted most other techniques of fluoride analysis.

Potentiometric Methods with Fluoride-Selective Electrode. The single-crystal lanthanum fluoride electrode introduced by Frant and Ross in 1966 (13) provided for the first time not only reliable direct potentiometric measurements of fluoride activity but also a convenient means of detecting the end points of potentiometric titrations of fluoride with metal ion solutions. The methods based on the use of this electrode are generally so superior to earlier methods that they are worth including in detail despite their relative novelty.

The design of the electrode is shown in Figure 3. The sensor is a single crystal of lanthanum fluoride which has been doped with 0.5–1% europium(II) and glued into a plastic body (13,29). The electrode is filled with a reference solution, which is usually 0.001 M sodium fluoride in 0.1 M potassium chloride, and can be replaced if necessary.

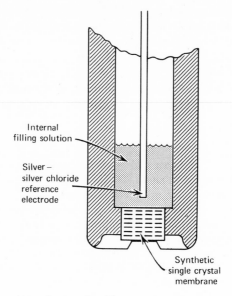

Internal
filling solution

Silver –
silver chloride
reference
electrode

Synthetic
single crystal
membrane

Fig. 3. Lanthanum fluoride crystal membrane electrode.

A silver–silver chloride electrode dips into this solution to provide contact. The electrode is relatively costly but is serviceable for at least 2 yr of constant routine use. This electrode is marketed by Orion Research Inc., Cambridge, Mass. (Model 94–09). A similar electrode, which appears to be no different in its properties from the Orion electrode, is available from Beckman Instruments Inc., Fullerton, Calif., and other instrument firms may also have electrodes available. So far as is known, only the single-crystal electrodes possess the remarkable sensitivity and selectivity described by Frant and Ross (13), and no other preparation of lanthanum fluoride behaves so well. The electrode has a fairly high resistance and so must be used with a high-input impedance potentiometer. An expanded-scale pH meter can be used, but suitable special "ion meters" are available from several firms, and these are particularly useful in direct measurements. A silver–silver chloride or saturated calomel electrode can be used as the reference electrode. Care may be needed in the measurement of solutions of high ionic strength to avoid changes in liquid junction potential at the reference electrode. Many of the reported difficulties with the sensing electrode can be traced to erratic reference electrodes (30).

The electrode responds linearly to the activity of the fluoride ion, a_{F^-}, according to the Nernst equation:

$$E = K - \frac{2.3\,RT}{F} \log a_{F^-}$$

where R, T, F have their usual meanings and the constant K depends on the particular electrode used. It must be noted that the electrode responds to the fluoride activity in the solution and not to the total fluoride concentration. The response is linear to fluoride activity (about 59 mV/pF) over the range 0.5–10^{-5} M fluoride and a usable response is obtained down to 10^{-6} M in pure solutions. The response time is generally similar to that of a glass electrode, except at concentrations below 10^{-5} M, when several minutes may be necessary to reach equilibrium.

The electrode is remarkably free from interferences, the only serious interference being hydroxyl ion at concentrations greater than ten times the amount of fluoride.

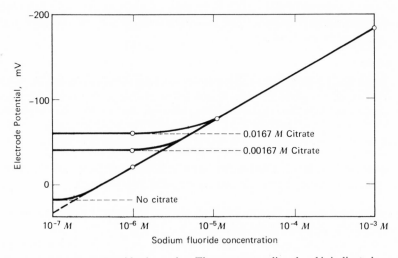

Fig. 4. Effect of citrate on a fluoride electrode. The constant sodium level is indicated on each curve.

However, the electrode constant value can be shifted by high concentrations of different electrolytes, and it is, therefore, essential always to standardize the electrode under conditions closely approximating those of application when direct potentiometric measurements are made. This problem can be largely avoided, and the interferences of various ions which form stable complexes with fluoride (eg, aluminum, iron) can be overcome by means of the total ionic strength adjustment buffer (TISAB) (31); this buffer is about M in sodium chloride and sodium acetate and about 0.0015 M in sodium citrate. The effect of citrate on the electrode itself is shown in Figure 4 (29). When an alkaline buffer solution containing citrate and tartrate is used with 10^{-4} M fluoride, potential shifts of only 1–2 mV are caused by 0.1 M NaCl, or by 0.01 M MgSO$_4$, Fe$_2$(SO$_4$)$_3$, H$_3$BO$_3$, H$_2$SiO$_3$, or TiOSO$_4$ (in 0.1 M Na$_2$SO$_4$) but large errors are caused by 0.01 M aluminum, beryllium, or zirconium salts (32). Compounds such as glucose, urea, and hydrogen peroxide in 0.1 M concentrations caused slight errors of ± 1 mV (32). Slight negative potential shifts on introduction of another ion can often be explained by fluoride impurities in the substance added, whereas positive shifts are normally caused by fluoride complex formation. Up to M sodium or potassium chloride concentrations have no effect when corrections are made for fluoride impurities (33). Fluorosilicate behaves in exactly the same way as fluoride ion (33). The electrode shows a Nernstian response to fluoride in 1, 5, or 10 M phosphoric acid (34) but the potentials shift positively as the acidity increases, although the effect of M acid is very slight; 10 M phosphoric acid removes the interferences of aluminum(III), iron-(III), uranyl, and thorium(IV) (34), but it is not recommended that the electrode be used constantly under such conditions.

Direct Measurement. For direct measurements, temperature control is important, though the electrode can be used at any temperature in the range of -5–100°C (37). Most workers prefer room temperature and control to ± 0.5°C. Air-driven magnetic stirring (eg, from G. F. Smith, Chemical Co., Columbus, Ohio) avoids the possibility of changing temperatures from conventional magnetic stirrers.

The majority of applications of direct potentiometric measurement with the fluoride electrode up to 1970 have been to determinations of fluoride as a minor or trace constituent. Such applications are dealt with in the article on FLUOROCARBONS. The ease of the direct measurements is, however, making their application to fluoride as a major constituent more frequent. The following method (35) for fluoride in mineral samples is given as an example.

Procedure

Fuse a finely ground 0.01–0.05 g sample with 1.2 g of sodium hydroxide gently in a silver crucible in the usual way. Dissolve the melt in a large plastic beaker containing 800 ml of water by magnetic stirring, and rinse out the crucible. Adjust the pH to 7.0–8.0 with hydrochloric acid; care is needed to avoid local excess of acid during the addition. Transfer the solution to a 1-liter volumetric flask and dilute to volume with water. Measure the fluoride activity directly in this solution. Prepare standard fluoride solutions bracketing the unknown solution which contain the same amount of sodium hydroxide and are adjusted to pH 7.0–8.0.

The results obtained by this method are within 5% relative of the true value for samples such as Na$_3$AlF$_6$ and Na$_5$Al$_3$F$_{14}$.

A somewhat similar procedure involving fusion of 0.5 g samples with 6 g of flux, and addition of a buffer containing 0.5 M potassium chloride, 0.5 M potassium acetate, and M sodium citrate has been applied to Hall electrolyte and aluminum fluoride samples (36).

Titration Methods. Potentiometric titrations are at present a more reliable method of determining higher amounts of fluoride, though if facilities exist for computer calculations there is probably little difference between the variances of the direct and titration methods. Lingane (37,38) has made intensive studies of the potentiometric titration of fluoride with metal ion solutions, using the fluoride electrode to detect the end point. The following procedure, which is very suitable for use with automatic titrators, is based on Lingane's recommendations.

The best titration curves are obtained in unbuffered solutions containing 50–70% ethanol at about pH 5. Amounts varying from 1 to 100 mg of fluoride in volumes of 50–100 ml provide excellent titration curves when the concentration of lanthanum nitrate titrant is 0.005–0.1 M. The point of maximal slope should not be taken as the end point of the titration; it is better to establish the equivalence point potential in titrations of standard fluoride solutions, though the error involved is not large when lanthanum(III) is used as the titrant. Dyrssen et al. (39) have shown that mixed complexes are formed when fluoride is titrated with thorium(IV) or lanthanum(III) in acetate-buffered media, and that Gran plots can yield highly accurate estimates of the equivalence points when titrations are done in unbuffered media.

No detailed interference studies have been made for these titrations. Ions such as phosphate which precipitate lanthanum(III) interfere, but comparatively high concentrations of other halides, nitrate, and perchlorate and at least moderate concentrations of sulfate can be tolerated. Cations which form fluoride complexes will, of course, interfere, and a preliminary separation of fluoride in metallurgical or geochemical analyses is probably necessary. The method should be very suitable as a completion to a pyrohydrolytic separation.

Procedure

Place the sample containing 1–100 mg of fluoride in about 20–100 ml of solution in a polyethylene beaker; the initial solution should not be less than 1 mM in fluoride (40). Adjust the pH of the solution to 4.5–5 and add an equal volume of ethanol. Insert the electrode pair and stir magnetically while titrating the solution with aqueous 0.005–0.05 M lanthanum nitrate solution depending on the amount of fluoride present. Standardize the lanthanum(III) solution against pure sodium fluoride under the same conditions. If an automatic titrator is used with an automatic cut-out, it is important to maintain the same geometric configuration of electrodes and a constant stirring rate.

Electrodes which are used in titrations may deteriorate more rapidly than those which are used in direct potentiometric measurements, because of accumulation of precipitate on the crystal surface. Any deposits can be removed by gentle rubbing with fine jeweler's rouge or other fine abrasive paste, such as toothpaste (34,39).

Gravimetric Determination as Lead Chlorofluoride. Although gravimetric methods rarely now find application in routine analyses, they still find occasional use for standardization or referee purposes. The lead chlorofluoride method given here (41) is simple, requires little art, and is at least as accurate and precise as other gravimetric and titrimetric procedures for the determination of fluoride at the range used. The relative error will not exceed 1% in routine use, and with careful work should not exceed 0.3%. Interferences include moderate amounts of ammonium, bromide, iodide, and borate ions. Cations which form strong fluoride complexes and anions which form insoluble lead salts, such as phosphate, sulfide, sulfate, or arsenate interfere. The procedure given is not suitable for less than 10 mg of fluoride, owing to the solubility of the precipitate ($\sim$32 mg/100 g of water), but could readily be modified for large amounts of fluoride by increasing the volume of added reagent.

Procedure

Prepare a lead chloronitrate solution by dissolving 10.5 g of pure lead chloride and 13 g of pure lead nitrate in 1 liter of water by boiling. Cool and filter if necessary. Any slight precipitate which appears on prolonged storage can be ignored; heavy precipitates are redissolved by heating.

The sample solution should contain 10–30 mg of fluoride in a volume of 50–80 ml. Neutralize the solution to methyl red indicator with $2 N$ sodium hydroxide solution or nitric acid and heat almost to boiling. Add 1 ml of 3:7 acetic acid followed by 50 ml of hot lead chloronitrate solution. Stir constantly until precipitation starts, then reheat just to boiling and allow to cool overnight. Filter on a fine-porosity sintered glass crucible, transferring the precipitate with a saturated solution of lead chlorofluoride. Wash the precipitate with two 10-ml portions of the saturated solution and two 10-ml portions of acetone. Dry at 110–150° for 30 min and weigh after cooling for 30 min in a desiccator.

DETERMINATION OF FLUORIDE AS A MINOR OR TRACE CONSTITUENT

Potentiometric methods based on the fluoride selective electrode and colorimetric methods are used almost exclusively to determine small amounts of fluoride. An atomic absorption method using the depressing effect of fluoride on the magnesium absorption at 2852 Å has been proposed (42). Radiometric methods have been reviewed by Foreman (43). X-ray fluorescence has also been studied (44).

Direct Potentiometric Methods. The general characteristics of the fluoride-selective electrode have been discussed, p. 20. This electrode has found its greatest use in analyses for fluoride as a minor or trace constituent. In trace analyses, the most precise results are obtained by measuring bracketing standards in the same series of measurements as the sample solutions, unless regression analysis is used. Some applications of this method are given in detail below.

Other industrial applications of direct potentiometry have been made to chromium plating baths (45), animal feeds (46), beverages (47), and fluoridated toothpastes (48). The fluoride electrode is not affected by intense γ-radiation and has been used in the direct analysis of zirconium decladding solutions and uranium feed solutions in nuclear fuel reprocessing (49). Fish protein concentrates require a preliminary separation of fluoride by distillation before the electrode measurement (50). Modifications of the fluoride electrode for μl samples (51) and to provide a microelectrode (52) have also been described. Light (53) has outlined some of the considerations involved in designing continuous monitoring equipment based on this and similar electrodes. Various means of improving the precision of the potential measurements have been described. Durst was able to achieve a relative standard deviation of about 0.5% over the range 10^{-3}–$2 \times 10^{-6}\ M$ fluoride by means of linear null point potentiometry (54), and about the same deviation at the 10^{-3}–$10^{-4}\ M$ fluoride level by "analyte addition" potentiometry (55).

Fluoride in Potable Waters. In this procedure (31), which has a precision of $\pm 5\%$ at the 1-ppm level, citrate serves to complex any aluminum or iron(III) ions present in the waters.   The method has been checked against a zirconium–SPADNS (2-(4-sulfo-phenylazo)-1,8-dihydroxynaphthalene-3,6-disulfenic acid) procedure (31) and against various colorimetric methods, including the alizarin fluorine blue method (56), and found preferable.   A continuous monitoring system based on the method has been described (57), and the electrode procedure has been evaluated by Harwood (58).

Procedure

Prepare a total ionic strength adjustment buffer (TISAB) by dissolving 57 g of glacial acetic acid, 58 g of sodium chloride, and 0.3 g of sodium citrate in 500 ml of redistilled water, titrating to pH 5–5.5 with 5 N sodium hydroxide solution and diluting to 1 liter with water.

To 10 ml of the water sample, add 10 ml of TISAB, stir well and measure the potential after 3 min.   Read the fluoride concentration from a calibration graph prepared by adding known amounts of fluoride to unfluorinated waters and treating in the same way; the graph should be linear down to 0.2 ppm of fluoride.

If required, better precision $(+1\%)$ can be obtained by means of potentiometric titration (59).   The fluoride is first concentrated by ion exchange on 50/100 mesh Dowex 1-X4 resin, pretreated with 40 ml of N hydrochloric acid, and washed with water until the effluent has a pH of 7.   A 1-liter water sample is passed through a 100 mm × 10 mm column at a flow rate of 1 ml/min.   The fluoride is eluted with 45 ml of 0.1 M potassium chloride solution, the first 5 ml being discarded.   The solution is adjusted to pH 2, 40 ml of ethanol is added, and the solution is titrated with 0.005 M thorium nitrate solution; the fluoride electrode is used as an indicating electrode with an automatic titrator, and the correct equivalence point potential is established from titration of standard fluoride solutions.   The standard deviation on this method is 0.013 mg/liter compared with 0.047 mg/liter for direct potentiometry.

Fluoride in Natural and Seawaters.   The major problem in application of the direct potentiometric method to seawaters is their high and variable salinity.   Though nothing seems to have been published (up to 1970) on this type of analysis for industrial effluents, similar difficulties would probably be found.   Warner (60) has shown that if the electrode is standardized against water of the same salinity, relative errors of only $\pm 5\%$ are attainable at the 1.4 ppm level in Atlantic waters.   Anfält and Jagner (61) have discussed the problems of releasing fluoride from its complexes with magnesium and calcium ions without damage to the electrode, and have recommended a standard addition procedure, in which an automatic titrator is used.

Procedure

Weigh about 150 g of seawater into a polyethylene beaker and add 0.5–0.75 ml of 0.1 N hydrochloric acid.   For normal seawaters, which contain about 2.4 mM of bicarbonate at 35% salinity, this acid addition brings the pH to about 6.6, and buffering is then provided by the carbonate–bicarbonate system.   Record the potential with the fluoride electrode and add increments of 0.05 ml of 0.01 M sodium fluoride solution at 15–20 sec intervals until 2 ml has been added.

If v_0 is the volume in ml of the water sample of fluoride concentration, xM, and v ml increments of yM sodium fluoride solution are added, then when

$$F_1 = (v_0 + v)\ 10\ \exp EF/RT$$

is plotted against v ml, the extrapolated straight line intersects the v-axis at $v = v_{eq}$ where $v_{eq} = v_0 x/y$.   The total fluoride concentration in the sample can then be calculated. If a computer is available, the F_1 plot can be corrected for dilution of the magnesium and calcium complexes during the titration by means of the following equation:

$$F_2 = F_1 \left(1 + \frac{1.07 \, v_0 \, S}{35(v_0 + v)} \right)$$

where S is the salinity, and the value 1.07 is derived from the stability constants of the complexes (61). The program calculates a value of F_2 for each titration point from the data obtained for potential readings and titrant addition, and the best fit is then calculated. A mean deviation of 0.6% is claimed at levels of about 1 ppm.

Similar but manual plots have been used by Liberti and Mascini (62), who examined 10^{-2}–10^{-5} M fluoride solutions in M sodium nitrate media, adding increments up to a total of 10 ml of M nitrate solution containing a concentration of fluoride which was 10–100 times the unknown concentration. This procedure gave lower errors than the TISAB procedure. Interferences were indicated by curving of the plot. The procedure was also applied to samples after addition of an equal volume of buffer 2 M in sodium nitrate, 0.5 N in acetic acid, 0.5 M in sodium acetate, and 0.1 M in sodium citrate.

Fluoride in Urine. The determination of fluoride in urine of workers exposed to fluorine compounds is an essential feature of industrial safety, since levels above about 5 mg/liter require surveillance. Two simple methods have been described in the literature (63,64), the more recent of which (64) is given here. This procedure was found to give results in excellent agreement with the far more tedious distillation–colorimetric method on a series of samples containing 0.3–13.5 ppm of fluoride, the high level coming from aluminum workers. The urea content causes only a negligible error.

Procedure

Prepare a TISUB analogously to the TISAB buffer (p. 25) but using 57.8 g of sodium nitrate instead of sodium chloride, and adjusting the pH to 5.25.

For the calibration curve, pipet 50-ml portions of TISUB into 100-ml volumetric flasks and add 1–10 ml portions of standard sodium fluoride solution containing 0.1 mg fluorine/ml; if high fluoride concentrations are expected, use a solution containing 1 mg fluorine/ml. Dilute the solutions to volume with a simulated urine solution containing 11.6 g of sodium chloride, 2 g of ammonium dihydrogen phosphate, and 1 ml of concentrated sulfuric acid per liter. Measure the potential of these solutions and plot mV readings against pF.

Collect urine samples in polyethylene bottles and add 0.2 g of EDTA for each 100 ml; refrigerate until ready for analysis. Mix 5.0 ml of urine sample and 5.0 ml of TISUB, and measure the electrode potential after equilibrium has been reached, which may require 15–20 min for extremely dilute solutions. Determine the fluoride concentration from the calibration curve.

Fluoride in Stack Gases and Air. Fluoride in gaseous or particulate form can readily be determined after sorption on formate-impregnated filters (65). For normal air samples, sampling is done by passing air at 4 ft³ min through a specially designed sequential sampler for 4 hr. The collection medium is cellulose acetate paper soaked in a 1:1 aqueous ethanol solution containing 10% sodium formate, and air-dried. The exposed filter is shaken for 1 hr with 20 ml of 0.1 M sodium citrate solution and the electrode potential is then measured. For stack gases, a cyclone, Whatman filter, and Greenburg-Smith impingers were used to collect fluoride after conversion to hexafluorosilicic acid with a hot glass probe. A 10-ml portion of the composite solution is mixed with an equal volume of 0.2 M sodium citrate solution, and the electrode potential measured. For these analyses, calibration curves were prepared for the range of 0.1–1000 μg fluorine/ml, from sodium fluoride solutions with the same concentration of buffer.

Hydrofluoric Acid in Fuming Nitric Acid. Hydrofluoric acid in concentrations of 0.4–0.8 wt % is often added to fuming nitric acid to inhibit its attack on metal containers. Large samples are difficult to neutralize for titration methods, and direct potentiometry provides results of sufficient accuracy (66).

Procedure

Dilute 1 g of the inhibited acid to 100 ml with a 0.1 N acetic acid–0.1 M sodium acetate buffer. Mix and further dilute a 5-ml aliquot of this solution to 100 ml with the acetate buffer. Measure the electrode potential. Calibrate against mixtures of standard fluoride solution and the buffer solution.

Fluoride in Tungsten. The usual separation of fluoride from tungsten can be avoided if the electrode method is used (67).

Procedure

Cover 0.25–1.5 g of tungsten sample with 0.6 g of sodium nitrate and 1.2 g of sodium hydroxide in a platinum crucible. Heat initially at 200°C and increase the temperature slowly over 30 min to 550°C; then heat at 550°C for 5–10 min. Cool and dissolve the melt with water. Transfer the solution to a 50-ml volumetric flask, neutralize to bromocresol purple indicator with concentrated hydrochloric acid, cool, and dilute to about 45 ml with water. Adjust the pH to 6.0–6.2 with hydrochloric acid or sodium hydroxide using a combination glass electrode and dilute to volume with water. Solid platinum oxide and tungstic acid can be ignored, but a sleeve-type reference electrode is advisable to avoid clogging with solids. Measure the potential after it reaches equilibrium.

Prepare a calibration graph covering the range 2–100 μg of fluoride by fusing 1-g samples of fluoride-free tungsten as above and adding standard fluoride solution to the resulting solution of the melt. The standard deviation is ±2 μg at the 95% confidence level.

Fluoride in Phosphate Rocks. Singer and Armstrong (68) described a method for fluoride in ashed bone, which simply involved dissolution in 0.25 N hydrochloric acid, adjustment to pH 4.7, and direct measurement. When a similar method is used for phosphate rocks, alumina contents above 1% cause low recoveries of fluoride. This can be avoided by using a concentrated citrate buffer (69). The procedure given is suitable for rocks containing 1–4% fluoride, 30–40% phosphate, iron, and up to 6% alumina; the relative error is about 4%.

Procedure

Dissolve a 50-mg rock sample in 1 ml of 5 N hydrochloric acid, dilute to 100 ml in a volumetric flask and transfer to a polyethylene beaker. Mix 10 ml of the solution with 10 ml of a citrate buffer prepared by dissolving 294 g of sodium citrate dihydrate in water, adjusting to pH 6 with 5 N hydrochloric acid, and diluting to 1 liter. Measure the electrode potential as soon as it attains equilibrium. With such a high concentration of citrate, it is important not to leave the electrode immersed for longer than necessary; rinse it very thoroughly after use. Prepare a calibration graph for the range 2.5–20 ppm fluoride using the same buffer solution.

Colorimetric Methods. Most of the colorimetric methods for fluoride are based on the bleaching of complexes between metal ions such as zirconium, thorium, titanium, aluminum, and iron(III), and organic dyes. These methods tend to be very sensitive to variations in experimental conditions. The first direct color reaction of the fluoride ion was reported by Belcher, Leonard, and West (70) in 1959; cerium(III) was found to form a red complex with alizarin complexone, which turned blue on addition of fluoride ions. This reaction, preferably with lanthanum(III) instead of cerium, has since been very widely applied. In the decade of 1960–1970, analytical opinion seems to have hardened in favor of either this procedure or the zirconium–eriochrome cyanine R method of Megregian (71) as the spectrophotometric method of choice.

ALIZARIN FLUORINE BLUE METHOD. Cerium(III), lanthanum(III), and a few other rare earth metals form a red complex with alizarin complexone, 1,2-dihydroxy-anthraquinon-3-ylmethylamine-N,N-diacetic acid, which becomes blue on addition of fluoride ions. Initially, cerium(III) was used (70) and it was shown (72) that a 1:1:1 metal–F$^-$–ligand complex is formed, although the exact structure has not been fully elucidated. In later work, lanthanum(III) has become preferred to cerium(III) (73,74). There is no significant difference in the sensitivities with these two metal ions, though other rare earths give a less sensitive, or no reaction for fluoride (73,74). The popularity of lanthanum(III) is accounted for by the fact that there are fewer problems with reagent stability.

High concentrations of chloride, bromide, and nitrate cause only salt effects, and amounts of sulfate and silicate about 200–1000 times that of fluoride have no effect. Phosphorus, as phosphate, interferes in amounts about half that of fluoride, but less tolerance is shown for phosphite. Arsenic, as arsenate, can be present in up to three-fold concentrations (75). The tolerance of the method for interfering ions can be increased by increasing the ratio of metal to reagent to 2:1 (76). Separations of large amounts of sulfate as the barium salt are suspect because of the insolubility of barium fluorosilicate (73). Metals which form strong fluoride complexes interfere. Copper, cobalt, and mercury can be masked with cyanide and nickel or lead with 2,3-dimercaptopropanol (74). Aluminum(III) (73,74), iron(III), chromium, and vanadium (74) can be extracted with 8-hydroxyquinoline in chloroform. However, if high concentrations of various metals are present, a preliminary separation of fluoride itself is advisable.

Two convenient ranges of application are available, linear calibration graphs being obtained in the ranges 0–30 μg of fluoride by the procedure given below for rocks and minerals, and 0–300 μg of fluoride if the reagents are prepared ten-fold stronger (74,75). The optimal pH for the more sensitive range is 4.2–4.3, but a pH of 5.2 is necessary for the higher range to avoid reagent precipitation. The lower range is normally preferred because the lower pH gives a greater freedom from interferences.

Improved sensitivity can be achieved by addition of organic solvents; acetone (73–76), acetonitrile (76), dimethylformamide (77), and dimethyl sulfoxide (78) have been proposed. Acetone is probably best for routine purposes. Another means of improving sensitivity is to extract the blue complex into tribenzylamine–pentanol–2-butanol (79), 10% n-propylamine in 1-butanol (80), or hydroxylamine hydrochloride in 3-butanol (81).

Several commercial preparations of mixed lanthanum(III), alizarin complexone, and buffer are available; there is often a slight loss of sensitivity with these preparations which are designed for use with 2-propanol media, but in many analytical situations, this may be useful.

The wavelength of maximum absorbance has been reported variously as from 615 to 630 nm, probably owing to errors in calibration of the wavelength adjustment controls. The absorbance peak is quite rounded so that the setting is not critical.

The method has been applied to many different substances. It has been used after pyrohydrolysis for analyses of various metal fluorides (76) and plutonium materials (80), and for deposit gauge samples (82). Many materials of biological interest, such as bone, blood, teeth, and vegetation have been analyzed (4), and the method can follow on separation processes varying from microdiffusion to distillation. Preservative-treated woods can be analyzed by leaching the wood with sodium hydroxide solution and a drop of hydrogen peroxide at 130°C, followed by colorimetric determination of the neutralized extract (83). In lime–silica–sulfate–fluoride systems, sulfate can be titrated oscillometrically after an ion exchange process, and fluoride determined colorimetrically in the titrated solution (84). Applications to fluoride in ores, air, and water are described below to illustrate the method.

Fluoride in Rocks and Minerals. The alizarin fluorine blue method can be used for the analysis of phosphate rocks after an ion exchange separation (85). Silicate rocks, such as biotites and micas, containing 0.2–3% fluoride, can be analyzed by the following simple method (86); interfering elements are separated in the preliminary dissolution process. The method gives the same results as those obtained by distillation procedures.

Procedure

Mix 1 g of powdered rock sample with 6 g of anhydrous sodium carbonate in a platinum crucible, cover and fuse over a Meker burner for 20 min. Digest the cake obtained in 100 ml of hot water, filter through Whatman No. 41 paper and wash the residue well with hot water. Add 2 g of powdered ammonium carbonate to the filtrate in a 250-ml beaker, digest on a steam bath for 30 min, allow to cool, add 1 g of ammonium carbonate and leave for 12 hr. Filter through Whatman No. 41 paper, washing well with a dilute ammonium carbonate solution, into a 1-liter flask. Make the filtrate just acid to methyl orange indicator with 1:1 hydrochloric acid, stirring vigorously to remove carbon dioxide. Dilute to 500 ml in a volumetric flask. Determine the fluoride in a suitable aliquot of the solution by the following method (74,75) or by a method with a commercial reagent preparation.

Prepare 0.0005 M alizarin complexone solution as follows. Dissolve 0.1926 g of alizarin complexone in water by adding a minimal amount of freshly prepared 2 N sodium hydroxide solution. Dilute to about 750 ml with water, add 50–100 mg of sodium acetate and then add 2 N hydrochloric or acetic acid until the solution turns red (about pH 5). Add 50 ml of acetone, mix well and dilute to 1 liter with water. This solution is stable for at least 1 month when stored in amber glass. Prepare a pH 4.3 buffer containing 105 g of sodium acetate trihydrate and 100 ml of glacial acetic acid, diluted to 1 liter with water and the pH adjusted if necessary.

Transfer portions of sample and standard sodium fluoride solution containing 5 μg F/ml covering the range of 5–40 μg of fluoride to 100-ml volumetric flasks and add some water. Add 10 ml of 0.0005 M alizarin complexone solution, 2 ml of pH 4.3 buffer, and 10 ml of 0.0005 M lanthanum nitrate solution. Mix well, add 25 ml of acetone, and dilute to volume with water. After 60 min, measure the absorbance at 620 nm against a reagent blank in 4-cm cells. The calibration graph should be linear to at least 30 μg.

Fluoride in Air. The alizarin fluorine blue method is also useful in air-pollution analysis, and has been applied after collection of fluoride in filters impregnated with

20% potassium hydroxide solution containing 10% triethanolamine (87), silver filters coated with sodium carbonate (88), filters impregnated with sodium hydroxide (89), or water-filled scrubbers (90). Particulates usually require preliminary separation, eg, microdiffusion (90). However, the normal types of separation can be avoided if the sampled air is simply bubbled through a scrubber containing concentrated sulfuric acid at 70°C; this serves to separate fluoride from aluminum, iron, calcium, zinc, and copper, which would interfere in the colorimetric method, yet allows quantitative recovery of fluoride in the following water bubbler even at gaseous fluoride concentrations of 10 ppm (90). The procedure given below (90) is suitable for fluoride in air down to the ppb level. The final apparent pH of the measured solution is 4.1–4.2, which yields an improved sensitivity compared to the previous method, and calibration graphs are linear over the range 0–0.5 μg F/ml in the measured solutions. Sulfamic acid is added to the scrubbers to prevent the interference of nitrogen dioxide. Provided that the specified order of reagent addition is followed, color development is complete in 5 min, and the color is stable for at least 4 days. The standard deviation of the method is about 1% at the 95% confidence limit.

Procedure

Prepare 0.001 M alizarin fluorine blue solution by dissolving 0.385 g of the dye in a minimum amount of 2 N sodium hydroxide solution and diluting to 1 liter with buffer solution containing 34 ml of anhydrous acetic acid and 18.8 g of anhydrous sodium acetate per liter.

Prepare 0.002 M lanthanum buffer solution as follows: weigh 0.866 g of lanthanum nitrate hexahydrate, add 222 ml of glacial acetic acid and 89 ml of 10 N hydrochloric acid, and dilute to 1 liter with water.

Use three 30-ml fritted glass scrubbers (Mine Safety Appliance Company) in series. Place 10 ml of concentrated sulfuric acid in the first, and maintain at 70°C. Place 10 ml of water containing 50 mg of sulfamic acid in each of the other two. Sample air through the bubblers at flow rates up to 8 liters/min depending on the expected fluoride content. Rinse the contents of the water scrubbers into a 100-ml volumetric flask and add 10 ml of alizarin fluorine blue solution, 10 ml of lanthanum-buffer solution, and 25 ml of acetone. Dilute to volume and measure the absorbance at 618 nm in 1-cm cells after 5 min.

Prepare a calibration graph with standard sodium fluoride solution to cover the range 0–0.5 μg F/ml in the final measured solution.

A method for the production of standard hydrogen fluoride atmospheres (91) may be of interest in connection with the analysis of air.

Fluoride in Potable and Natural Waters. Yamamura et al. (76) applied the cerium-(III) method to potable fluoridated waters and this procedure has been pronounced (93) an improvement on the zirconium–eriochrome cyanine R method because no preliminary water treatment is required, although the electrode method (p. 20) is superior to both (56). The standard deviation of the two color methods was found to be similar at about 2% (92). The only interferences in waters are aluminum above 20 ppm, and iron(III) and copper above 2000 ppm. The precision of the method is about ±1%.

An automatic method has been developed with the Technicon Auto-Analyzer shown in Figure 5 (93). Glass or polyethylene tubing is used for connections, where possible, because of the effect of acetone. Acidflex tubing must be renewed daily if

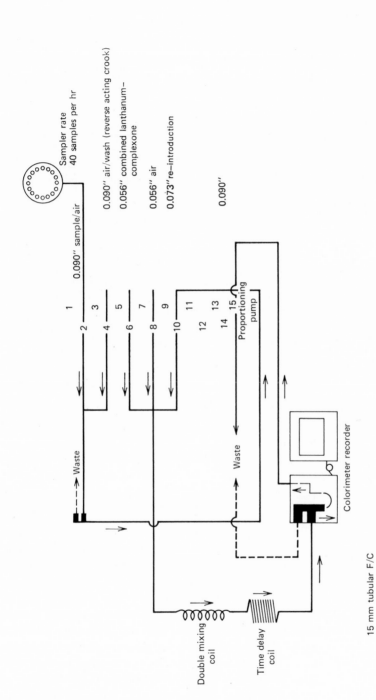

Fig. 5. Auto-Analyzer flow diagram for determination of fluoride. Values in inches refer to tubing diameters.

used for pumping the reagent. A displacement bottle is preferable for dispensing the reagent.

Procedure

For seawaters, dissolve 0.24 g of alizarin fluorine blue in a mixture of 0.5 ml of concentrated ammonium hydroxide and 15 ml of 6.7% ammonium acetate solution. Filter through qualitative paper into a 1-liter flask containing 41 g of anhydrous sodium carbonate and 30 ml of glacial acetic acid in 300 ml of water. Slowly add 500 ml of acetone. Then add 0.2 g of spectrographic grade lanthanum oxide dissolved by warming in 12.5 ml of 2 N hydrochloric acid. Dilute to volume with water. This solution is stable for 1 week. For fresh waters, use 70 ml of acetic acid instead of 30 ml.

Prepare a standard sodium fluoride containing 1 mg F/ml with addition of 1 ml of 0.1 N NaOH/liter. Prepare daily a solution containing 1.0 μg F/ml by suitable dilution.

Pump the samples through a debubbler to remove air introduced through the reverse acting crook and then reintroduce the samples through 0.056 in. tubing segmented with air. After mixing with reagent in the mixing coil, allow the reaction to proceed to completion for 15 min in a half-time delay coil. Then remove the segmenting air in a debubbler and pass the solution through a 1.5 cm flow cell for measurement in a phototube colorimeter at 625 nm. Place a neutral density filter (density 0.2) in the compensating beam of the colorimeter to allow for the intense red color of the reagent. The effluent pH should be in the range of 4.45–4.85.

At the start of each series of nonsaline water samples, chlorinity <12%, stabilize the system on water plus reagents, and set the instrument to read transmittance. Calibrate against fluoride solution containing 0.1 μg F/ml. The manifold shown in Figure 5 gives linear response up to 1.6 μg F/ml. For routine analyses of higher concentrations, the bore of the sample pumping tube should be reduced, and the water pumping rate should be increased correspondingly.

With saline waters of a chlorinity of 12–20%, stabilize the system on 0.1 N acetic acid, and calibrate either against a solution containing 0.1 μg F/ml in 0.1 N acetic acid, or against artificial seawater alone and spiked with 0.1 μg F/ml. If the 0.1 N acetic acid solution is used for calibration, a correction factor of 1.02 is necessary because of the salt error.

A manual method has been used to analyze natural waters including seawaters (73). The single lanthanum–alizarin complexone solution is analogous to that for the automatic method.

Procedure

Place a 15-ml sample of water, filtered if necessary, in a 25-ml volumetric flask, and add 0.5 ml of 6 N acetic acid or (0.4–0.2x) ml of acetic acid depending on the chlorinity, x, of the water. Add 8.0 ml of the composite reagent solution, dilute to volume, and mix well. Measure the absorbance of the solution after 30 min in 1-cm cells at 620 nm against a reagent blank. Calibrate the method against sodium fluoride for the range 0.5–2 ppm in the initial sample. If the chlorinity exceeds 15%, a correction factor of 1.04 is necessary.

ZIRCONIUM–ERIOCHROME CYANINE R METHOD. Of the very numerous colorimetric methods based on bleaching by fluoride of metal–dye complexes, the Megregian method (71) has been very widely applied and the least affected by minor modifications. The method given below is suitable for use after isolation of fluoride such as by distillation.

Procedure

Weigh zirconyl chloride or zirconyl nitrate to give 0.075 g of zirconium. Add 700 ml of concentrated hydrochloric acid, dilute to 1 liter with water, and cool to room temperature before use. To 50 ml of sample solution containing 5-60 μg of fluoride, add 5 ml of zirconium solution and 5 ml of aqueous 0.18% eriochrome cyanine R solution and mix well. Determine the absorbance of the solution at 525–530 nm versus a reference solution containing 10 ml of the dye solution, 100 ml of water, and 7 ml of concentrated hydrochloric acid diluted to 10 ml with water. The temperatures of the calibration and sample solutions should not differ by more than 2°C. The interference of up to 5 ppm aluminum can be avoided by letting the color reach equilibrium for a period of 2 hr. In the absence of interferences, color equilibrium is established immediately.

SPECIFICATION TESTS

Analysis of individual metal fluorides is discussed in the article on the particular metal. The tests for sodium fluoride given here are typical and in general can be applied to other metal fluorides.

Sodium Fluoride. Sodium fluoride is available in many grades, and is the most important standard in fluoride analysis. Since the minimum assay for the purest material available commercially is only 98.5%, tests for impurities are essential. The tests outlined below are those given in reagent grade specifications, and can be modified for less stringent requirements.

Procedures

WATER-INSOLUBLE MATTER. Dissolve 5 g of sample in 100 ml of water in a platinum vessel by digesting on a steam bath for 1 hr. Filter off undissolved material on a platinum Gooch crucible, wash with hot water, dry at 105°C and weigh.

LOSS ON DRYING. Dry a 2-g sample to constant weight at 150°C.

FREE ACID OR ALKALI. Dissolve 2 g of sample in a platinum vessel in 40 ml of water and add 10 ml of aqueous saturated potassium nitrate solution. Cool to 0°C. Add 0.2 ml of phenolphthalein indicator solution and titrate with 0.1 N sodium hydroxide solution until a pink color persists for 15 sec, or with 0.1 N hydrochloric acid until the pink color is discharged, depending on the initial color of the indicator. Reserve the solution for determination of silicofluoride.

CHLORIDE. Dissolve 0.4 g of sample in 20 ml of water and add 1 ml of 1:9 nitric acid, 0.2 g of boric acid, and 1 ml of 0.1 N silver nitrate solution. The turbidity should not exceed that of a blank containing the specification limit of chloride.

FLUOROSILICATE. Use the titrated solution from the free acid test. Boil it and titrate hot with 0.1 N sodium hydroxide solution to a permanent pink color.

SULFATE. Evaporate 1 g of sample in a platinum dish with 10 ml of 1:4 hydrochloric acid on a steam bath and repeat the treatment four times. Dissolve the residue in water, filter, dilute the filtrate to 50 ml, and to 10 ml add 1 ml of 0.5 N hydrochloric acid and 1 ml of 10% barium chloride solution. The turbidity should not exceed that of a blank solution containing the specification limit of sulfate.

SULFITE. Dissolve 6 g of sample in 150 ml of water, add 2 ml of 1:9 hydrochloric acid and 2 ml of 0.5% starch solution, and titrate with 0.1 N iodine solution.

HEAVY METALS. Dissolve 1.5 g of sample in 40 ml of hot water, filter, and dilute to 60 ml. Take a 10-ml aliquot, add 0.03 mg of lead(II), equivalent to a specification limit of 0.002 ml, dilute to 50 ml, and add 1 ml of 1 N acetic acid. To the remaining 40 ml add 1 ml of N acetic acid and dilute to 50 ml. To each add 10 ml of saturated aqueous hydrogen sulfide solution. The sample should be paler than the standard solution.

IRON. Boil 1 g of sample in a platinum dish with 20 ml of water and 2 ml of 1:9 hydrochloric acid for 5 min. Cool, transfer to a separatory funnel, add 50 mg of ammonium persulfate and 15 ml of reagent prepared by dissolving 10 g of potassium thiocyanate in 10 ml of water, adding 90 ml of *n*-butanol and shaking until clear. Shake well and leave to separate. Prepare a blank similarly containing the specification limit of iron(III).

Hydrofluoric Acid. Aqueous solutions of hydrogen fluoride can be visually titrated with standardized alkali using phenolphthalein as indicator. Glass electrodes should not be used in potentiometric titrations in the presence of fluoride, but the quinhydrone or antimony electrode is suitable for use with a saturated calomel electrode (95). Various metallic impurities in hydrofluoric acid are best determined spectrographically by conversion to their sulfates, evaporation, and arcing at a graphite electrode (96).

The following procedures are for specifications for reagent grade 48–51% hydrofluoric acid.

Procedures

EVAPORATION AND IGNITION RESIDUES. Evaporate 45 ml of sample in a platinum dish on a steam bath, dry at 105°C for 1 hr, and weigh. Then add 3 drops of concentrated sulfuric acid, ignite to bright redness for 5 min and reweigh.

HYDROFLUOROSILICIC ACID. Weigh 2 g of sample into a platinum vessel containing 7 ml of water and cool to 0°C. In another platinum vessel mix 10 ml of saturated aqueous potassium nitrate solution and a little less than the amount of N sodium hydroxide solution required to neutralize the sample. Add phenolphthalein indicator and cool to 0°C. Add the sample quantitatively, and titrate with N sodium hydroxide solution until the pink color persists for 15 sec. Now heat the solution to boiling and titrate further. The second titer after boiling is equivalent to the hydrofluorosilicic acid content.

PHOSPHATE. Mix 9 ml of sample in a platinum vessel with 10 mg of sodium carbonate and evaporate to dryness. Dissolve the residue in 2 ml of 1:3 sulfuric acid and 20 ml of warm water, add 1 ml of 5% ammonium molybdate in 0.5 N sulfuric acid and 1 ml of aqueous 0.5% *p*-methylaminophenol sulfate solution containing 20% sodium hydrogen sulfite. Heat for 10 min at 60°C. The blue color should not exceed that of a blank containing the specification limit of phosphate.

SULFATE. To 9 ml of sample in a platinum vessel add 10 mg of sodium carbonate and evaporate to dryness on a steam bath. Heat the residue with 0.5 ml of N hydrochloric acid and 5 ml of water, filter, wash with water, and dilute to 10 ml. Add 1 ml of 10% barium chloride solution. The turbidity should not exceed that of a blank containing the specification limit of sulfate.

SULFITE. To 10 ml of sample add 40 ml of oxygen-free water and 0.05 ml of 0.1 N iodine solution. The solution should be definitely yellow.

HEAVY METALS. Mix 30 ml of water, 10 ml of saturated hydrogen sulfide water, and 5 ml of sample, in that order, and neutralize with concentrated ammonium hydroxide, using litmus paper. On addition of 1 ml of N hydrochloric acid solution, no brown color should form.

IRON. Transfer 9 ml of sample to a platinum vessel, add 10 mg of sodium carbonate, and evaporate to dryness. Dissolve the residue in 2 ml of concentrated hydrochloric acid and 10 ml of water and complete the test as described for sodium fluoride.

Bibliography

GENERAL REFERENCES

1. "Fluorine Compounds, Inorganic," in A. Standen, ed., *Kirk-Othmer Encyclopedia of Chemical Technology*, Vol. 9, 2nd ed., Interscience Publishers, a division of John Wiley & Sons, Inc., New York, 1966, pp. 527–686.
2. C. A. Horton in C. N. Reilley, ed., *Advances in Analytical Chemistry and Instrumentation*, Vol. 1, Interscience Publishers, a division of John Wiley & Sons, Inc., New York, 1962, pp. 151–197.
3. A. M. G. MacDonald in C. L. Wilson and D. W. Wilson, eds., *Comprehensive Analytical Chemistry*, Vol. 1C, Elsevier, Amsterdam, 1962, pp. 319–340.
4. A. M. G. MacDonald in F. A. Smith, ed., *Handbuch der experimentelle Pharmakologie*, Vol. 20, Part 2, Springer Verlag, Berlin, 1970, pp. 1–43.

SPECIFIC REFERENCES

5. M. Tatsumoto, *Anal. Chem.* **41**, 2088 (1969).
5a. *Reagent Chemicals*, 4th ed., American Chemical Society, Washington, D.C., 1968, pp. 287–289.
5b. J. Rosin, *Reagent Chemicals and Standards*, 5th ed., D. Van Nostrand Company, Inc., Princeton, N.J., 1967, pp. 226–227.
5c. *Ibid.*, pp. 40, 41, 379–381, 460–462.
6. R. Y. Eagers, *Toxic Properties of Inorganic Fluorine Compounds*, Elsevier Publishing Company, Amsterdam, 1969.
7. H. C. Hodge, F. A. Smith and P. S. Chen, in J. H. Simon, ed., *Fluorine Chemistry*, Vol. 3, Academic Press, Inc., New York, 1963.
8. J. W. Clayton in P. Tarrant ed., *Fluorine Chemistry Reviews*, Vol. 1, Marcel Dekker, Inc., New York, 1967.
9. R. C. Specht, *Anal. Chem.* **28**, 1015 (1956).
10. L. M. Toth, J. P. Young, and G. P. Smith, *Anal. Chem.* **41**, 683 (1969).
11. J. J. Berzelius, *Schweigg's J.* **16**, 423 (1816); *Ann. Chim. Phys.* (2), **3**, 26 (1816).
12. H. H. Willard and O. B. Winter, *Ind. Eng. Chem., Anal. Ed.* **5**, 7 (1933).
13. M. S. Frant and J. W. Ross, *Science* **154**, 1553, (1966).
14. Ref. 2, p. 281.
15. F. T. Birks, *Spectrochim. Acta* **6**, 169 (1954).
16. F. Feigl, *Spot Tests in Inorganic Analysis*, 5th ed., Elsevier Publ. Co., Amsterdam, 1958, p. 275.
17. N. W. Alcock, *Anal. Chem.* **40**, 1396 (1968).
18. J. Tušl, *Anal. Chem.* **41**, 352 (1969).
19. Ref. 14, pp. 238–242, 299–302.
20. F. S. Grimaldi, B. Ingram and F. Cuttitta, *Anal. Chem.* **27**, 918 (1955).
21. Ref. 14, p. 240.
22. O. D. Smith and T. D. Parks, *Anal. Chem.* **27**, 998 (1955).
23. J. C. Warf, W. D. Cline and R. D. Tevebaugh, *Anal. Chem.* **26**, 342 (1954).
24. R. H. Powell and O. Menis, *Anal. Chem.* **30**, 1546 (1958).
25. A. C. D. Newman, *Analyst (London)* **93**, 827 (1968).
26. L. W. Gamble, W. E. Price, and W. J. Jones, *Anal. Chem.* **32**, 189 (1960).
27. M. J. Nardozzi and L. L. Lewis, *Anal. Chem.* **33**, 1261 (1961).
28. H. Bennett and W. G. Hawley, *Trans. Brit. Ceram. Soc.* **62**, 397 (1963).
29. J. W. Ross, "Ion-Selective Electrodes," in R. A. Durst, ed., *Special Publication 314*, U.S. Govt. Printing Office, Washington, D.C., 1969.
30. J. W. Ross, personal communication, 1969.
31. M. S. Frant and J. W. Ross, *Anal. Chem.* **40**, 1169 (1968).
32. R. Bock and S. Strecker, *Z. Anal. Chem.* **235**, 322 (1968).
33. R. E. Mesmer, *Anal. Chem.* **40**, 443 (1968).
34. E. W. Baumann, *Anal. Chim. Acta* **42**, 127 (1968).
35. J. C. Van Loon, *Anal. Letters* **1**, 393 (1968).
36. R. T. Oliver and A. G. Clayton, *Anal. Chim. Acta* **51**, 409 (1970).
37. J. J. Lingane, *Anal. Chem.* **39**, 881 (1967).
38. J. J. Lingane, *Anal. Chem.* **40**, 935 (1968).
39. D. Dyrssen, T. Anfalt, and D. Jagner, *Anal. Chim. Acta* **43**, 487 (1968); T. Anfalt and D. Jagner, *Anal. Chim. Acta* **48**, 475 (1969); **50**, 23 (1970).

40. T. Eriksson and G. Johansson, *Anal. Chim. Acta* **52**, 465 (1970).
41. R. Belcher and A. M. G. Macdonald, *Mikrochim. Acta* **1957**, 510.
42. A. M. Bond and T. A. O'Donnell, *Anal. Chem.* **40**, 560 (1968).
43. J. K. Foreman, *Analyst (London)* **94**, 425 (1969).
44. C. L. Luke, *Anal. Chim. Acta* **43**, 245 (1968).
45. M. S. Frant, *Plating* **54**, 702 (1967).
46. L. Torma and B. E. Ginther, *J. Assoc. Off. Agric. Chem.* **51**, 1177 (1968).
47. W. P. Ferren and N. A. Shane, *J. Food Sci.* **34**, 317 (1969).
48. N. A. Shane and D. Miele, *J. Pharm. Sci.* **57**, 1260 (1968).
49. H. H. P. Moeken, H. Eschrich, and G. Willeborts, *Anal. Chim. Acta* **45**, 233 (1969).
50. P. J. Ke, L. W. Regier, and H. E. Power, *Anal. Chem.* **41**, 1081 (1969).
51. R. A. Durst and J. K. Taylor, *Anal. Chem.* **39**, 1483 (1967).
52. R. A. Durst, *Anal. Chem.* **41**, 2089 (1969).
53. T. S. Light, Ref. 29, p. 349.
54. R. A. Durst, *Anal. Chem.* **40**, 931 (1968).
55. R. A. Durst, *Mikrochim. Acta* **1969**, 611.
56. N. T. Crosby, A. L. Dennis, and J. G. Stevens, *Analyst (London)* **93**, 643 (1968).
57. R. H. Babcock and K. A. Johnson, *J. Am. Water Works Assoc.* **60**, 953 (1968).
58. J. E. Harwood, *Water Research* **3**, 273 (1969).
59. T. S. Light, R. F. Mannion, and K. S. Fletcher 3rd, *Talanta* **16**, 1441 (1969).
60. T. B. Warner, *Anal. Chem.* **41**, 527 (1969); *Science* **165**, 178 (1969).
61. T. Anfalt and D. Jagner, *Anal. Chim. Acta.* **53**, 13 (1971).
62. A. Liberti and M. Mascini, *Anal. Chem.* **41**, 676 (1969).
63. L. Linger, W. D. Armstrong, and J. J. Vogel, *J. Lab. Clin. Med.* **74**, 354 (1969).
64. J. D. Neefus, J. Cholak, and B. E. Saltzman, *Am. Ind. Hyg. Assoc. J.* **31**, 96 (1970).
65. L. A. Elfers and C. E. Decker, *Anal. Chem.* **40**, 1658 (1968).
66. E. F. Croomes and R. C. McNutt, *Analyst (London)* **93**, 729 (1968).
67. B. A. Raby and W. E. Sunderland, *Anal. Chem.* **39**, 1304 (1967).
68. L. Singer and W. D. Armstrong, *Anal. Chem.* **40**, 613 (1968).
69. C. R. Edmond, *Anal. Chem.* **41**, 1327 (1969).
70. R. Belcher, M. A. Leonard, and T. S. West, *Talanta* **2**, 92 (1959); *J. Chem. Soc.* **1959**, 3577.
71. S. Megregian, *Anal. Chem.* **26**, 1161 (1954).
72. M. A. Leonard and T. S. West, *J. Chem. Soc.* **1960**, 4477 (1960).
73. R. Greenhalgh and J. P. Riley, *Anal. Chim. Acta.* **25**, 179 (1961).
74. R. Belcher and T. S. West, *Talanta* **8**, 853, 863 (1961).
75. M. Fernandopulle and A. M. G. Macdonald, *Microchem. J.* **11**, 41 (1966).
76. S. S. Yamamura, M. A. Wade and J. H. Sikes, *Anal. Chem.* **34**, 1308 (1962).
77. G. F. Brunzie and R. T. Pflaum, *Proc. Iowa Acad. Sci.* **69**, 186 (1963).
78. L. Molle and H. Hanocq, *Anal. Chim. Acta* **40**, 13 (1968).
79. C. A. Johnson and M. A. Leonard, *J. Pharm. Pharmacol.* **13**, 164T (1961).
80. A. G. Davies and J. K. Foreman, *Proc. S. A. C. Conf. 1965*, Heffer, Cambridge, 1966, p. 167.
81. R. J. Hall, *Analyst (London)* **88**, 76 (1963).
82. P. G. Jeffery and D. Williams, *Analyst (London)* **86**, 590 (1961).
83. A. I. Williams, *Analyst (London)* **94**, 300 (1969).
84. M. J. Bowley, *Analyst (London)* **94**, 787 (1969)
85. H. N. S. Shafer, *Anal. Chem.* **35**, 53 (1963).
86. A. Hall and J. N. Walsh, *Anal. Chim. Acta* **45**, 341 (1969).
87. C. Huygen, *Anal. Chim. Acta,* **29**, 448 (1963).
88. M. Buck and H. Stratmann, *Brennstoff-Chem.*, **46**, 231 (1965).
89. B. S. Marshall and R. Wood, *Analyst (London)*, **94**, 493 (1969).
90. P. W. West, G. R. Lyles and J. L. Miller, *Environmental Sci. Tech.* **4**, 487 (1970).
91. B. S. Marshall and R. Wood, *Analyst (London)* **93**, 821 (1968).
92. O. Backer Dirks and F. H. Cox, *Caries Res.* **1**, 295 (1967).
93. K. M. Chan and J. P. Riley, *Anal. Chim. Acta* **35**, 365 (1966).
94. T. U. Oldfield and E. P. Bridge, *Analyst (London)* **85**, 97 (1960).
95. L. J. Warren, *Anal. Chim. Acta* **53**, (1971) 199.

A. M. G. MACDONALD
University of Birmingham, England

FLUORO ACIDS, INORGANIC

Fluoroboric acid 37
Fluorophosphoric acids. 42
Fluorosilicic acid. 47
Fluorosulfuric acid. 50
Bibliography. 57

During the 20th century, various fluoro acids that are analogs of oxy acids have become commercially available. Some fluoro acids with boron, phosphorus, silicon, and sulfur as the central atom are now offered in tonnage quantities. These more important fluoro acids are listed in Table 1 together with the formula of the corresponding oxy acid. Only one chloro analog of these fluoro acids is of commercial importance; see CHLOROSULFONIC ACID, Vol. 9, pp. 528–534.

Table 1. Some Important Fluoro Acids

Central atom	Formula	Assigned names	Formula of corresponding oxy acid
B	HBF_4	fluoroboric acid fluoboric acid tetrafluoroboric acid	HBO_2
P	$FPO(OH)_2$	monofluorophosphoric acid mono-FP acid	H_3PO_4
P	$F_2PO(OH)$	difluorophosphoric acid di-FP acid	H_3PO_4
P	HPF_6	hexafluorophosphoric acid	HPO_3
Si	H_2SiF_6	fluorosilicic acid fluosilicic acid hexafluorosilicic acid silicofluoric acid hydrofluosilicic acid hydrofluorosilicic acid	H_2SiO_3
S	$FSO_2(OH)$	fluorosulfuric acid fluosulfonic acid fluorosulfonic acid	H_2SO_4

These fluoro acids warrant separate treatment because the establishment of their composition involves special methods. Additionally, these products have specialized uses and require special handling because of their hydrolysis to hydrofluoric acid and their corrosive acidic nature.

FLUOROBORIC ACID

Fluoroboric acid (fluoboric acid, tetrafluoroboric acid, HBF_4) is available only as its aqueous solution since the anhydrous acid has not been isolated. Solutions of the acid may be prepared by the reaction of boron trifluoride with water; commercially, the acid is prepared by the exothermic reaction of boric acid with concentrated hydrofluoric acid.

Fluoboric acid in recent years has received increasing attention in the cleaning and etching of metal surfaces before electroplating. This acid dissolves both metal oxides and silicates. It serves to strip solder and metal plating from the matrix metals.

An electropolishing process for aluminum employs a 2.5% solution of this acid as the electrolyte and the metal serving as the anode. Fluoboric acid is used as an alkylation and polymerization catalyst. Inorganic fluoborate salts are obtained by neutralization of the acid with the hydroxide or carbonate of the relevant cation.

For more information on the industrial aspects of fluoboric acid and its salts, and on the problems associated with its analysis, see References 1–4.

Properties

Fluoboric acid in concentrated solution attacks glass. Dilute solutions can be stored in glass without appreciable attack, but polyethylene containers are more suitable. Plastic- and rubber-lined equipment are appropriate for the containment of the acid. Certain high-nickel, high-chromium ferrous alloys show resistance to fluoboric acid and can be used, along with impregnated carbon, for pumps and heat exchangers. The commercial product is offered in polyethylene-lined containers.

Both Ryss (3) and Sharpe (4) have reviewed the literature on the properties, structure, and reactions of fluoboric acid and its salts.

Some of the more important physical and thermodynamic properties of fluoboric acid are given in Table 2. The density of 43% fluoroboric acid has been measured by Garrett et al. (5) over the range −70 to 25°C. The density is linear with temperature and can be expressed by the following equation:

$$\text{Density} = 1.346 - 0.000905(T - 273.16)$$

where T is in °K.

Table 2.   Properties of Fluoboric Acid

formula weight	87.813
boiling point, 760 torr, °C	about 100
density, 20°C, g/ml	
42% solution	1.32
48% solution	1.38
78% solution	1.77
specific conductivity, 43% solution, 25°C, $\Omega^{-1}\text{cm}^{-1}$	0.64
freezing point, 48% solution, °C	< -78
heat of formation 25°C, aqueous solution, kcal/mole	−365.
refractive index, n_D^{20}, 20% solution	1.3284
color	colorless
odor	pungent

In aqueous solution, the tetrafluoborate ion undergoes stepwise hydrolysis to BF_3OH^-, $BF_2(OH)_2^-$, $BF(OH)_3^-$, and H_3BO_3, with the concurrent production of hydrofluoric acid. In a 5.41 M ($\sim$37%) solution of fluoboric acid, the extent of hydrolysis to the monohydroxytrifluoroborate ion is only 5.5% and additional hydrolysis to the dihydroxy and trihydroxy ions is negligible (3,6).

Commercial Grades and Specifications

Fluoboric acid is offered with a nominal strength of 48% and with a typical free boric acid content of 3%. Formerly a 42% solution was offered. However, the greater strength became available in the 1950s with the introduction of 70% hydrofluoric acid. Shipments must carry the Department of Transportation (DOT) corrosive liquid white label for acids.

Methods of Analysis

ASSAY METHODS

Acidimetric Methods. To determine the amount of fluoboric acid present in the commercial product, the sample is hydrolyzed under reflux in the presence of calcium chloride, and the strong acid content is titrated to the methyl orange end point with sodium hydroxide, added in part during the hydrolysis. The total acidity is expressed as fluoboric acid (7). The process is described by the following reaction:

$$HBF_4 + 2\,CaCl_2 + 4\,NaOH \rightarrow 2\,CaF_2 + H_3BO_3 + 4\,NaCl + H_2O$$

Mannitol or other polyol is then added and the boric acid present is determined by a titration with sodium hydroxide to the phenolphthalein end point. The boric acid content, thus determined, may be expressed as fluoboric acid.

In this simple scheme, the presence of acids other than fluoboric acid, such as boric acid or hydrofluoric acid in the original sample, is neglected. As a consequence, the lower of the two fluoboric contents obtained by the two titrations is reported as the fluoboric acid content. If the second percentage is larger than the first, as is usual for the commercial product, the difference in the two percentages, suitably expressed, is taken as % free boric acid. If the second percentage is smaller than the first, the difference, suitably expressed, is taken as % free hydrofluoric acid.

Procedure

Weigh a suitable sample, for example, 2 g, into a platinum thimble or a vial of polyethylene, polypropylene, or poly(tetrafluoroethylene), and transfer with water rinses to a 500-ml conical flask fitted with a standard-taper ground-glass joint. Add 25 g of solid calcium chloride, a few drops of a methyl orange indicator solution, 3–5 drops of 1-octanol as an antifoaming agent, and several boiling chips. Attach the flask to a vertically positioned Liebig condenser and heat the solution to boiling. From a buret mounted above the condenser, add N sodium hydroxide solution slowly, so that the methyl orange just exhibits its acid color. If the solution is accidentally made alkaline and if on additional reflux it does not become acidic, add a measured volume of standard N sulfuric acid and apply a correction for the base neutralized by the sulfuric acid. After the last addition of the base, reflux for an additional 15 min. Cool the flask and contents with the condenser in place by immersion in a water bath. Remove the condenser after washing down its tube with water. Complete the titration of the flask contents to the methyl orange end point with the N sodium hydroxide solution.

To the resulting mixture, add about 35 g of mannitol (as a saturated aqueous solution, preneutralized to the phenolphthalein end point, if necessary) and a few drops of a phenolphthalein indicator solution. Titrate with N sodium hydroxide to an end point persisting for at least 30 sec.

Express the results of the two titrations as follows:

$$\% \text{ total acidity (hot), as } HBF_4 = \frac{(V_1)(N)(2.1953)}{w}$$

$$\% \text{ total } H_3BO_3, \text{ as } HBF_4 = \frac{(V_2)(N)(8.781)}{w}$$

where V_1 and V_2 = volumes of the sodium hydroxide solution required for the first and second titrations, respectively, in ml

N = normality of the sodium hydroxide solution

w = sample weight, in g

Report the lower value of these two percentages as the fluoboric acid content. If the second percentage is the larger, as is usual, express the difference as free boric acid:

$$\% \text{ free boric acid} = (\% \text{ total } H_3BO_3, \text{ as } HBF_4 - \% \text{ total acidity, as } HBF_4)(0.7042)$$

If the first percentage is the larger, express the difference as free hydrofluoric acid:

$$\% \text{ free hydrofluoric acid} = (\% \text{ total acidity, as } HBF_4 - \% \text{ total } H_3BO_3, \text{ as } HBF_4)(0.9113)$$

Calculate the total % boron from the results of the second titration as shown below:

$$\% \text{ total boron} = (\% \text{ total } H_3BO_3, \text{ as } HBF_4)(0.12311)$$

A more complicated scheme for the establishment of the composition of fluoboric acid in solutions has also been developed (8). In this method, the fluosilicic acid and sulfuric acid contents are separately determined, and a correction is applied to the fluoboric acid content determined essentially by the procedure described above.

Procedure

Carry out the procedure as given above and calculate % total acidity, expressed as HBF_4 and the % total H_3BO_3 expressed as HBF_4. Then determine the % sulfuric acid and % fluosilicic acid from a separate original sample, as follows:

SULFURIC ACID. Evaporate a suitable sample, eg, 10 g, in a platinum dish on a steam bath until white fumes cease, ie, for about 2 hr. Add 10 ml of water, evaporate, and repeat the addition of water and the evaporation until the vapors do not have the pungent odor of fluoboric acid. Add 25 ml of water and some phenolphthalein indicator solution, and titrate with 0.5 N sodium hydroxide solution.

$$\% \text{ sulfuric acid} = \frac{(V_3)(N)(4.904)}{w}$$

where V_3 = volume of sodium hydroxide solution required for the titration, in ml

N = normality of the sodium hydroxide solution

w = sample weight, in g

FLUOSILICIC ACID. Weigh a suitable sample, for example, 3 g, transfer it to a 150-ml beaker with 25 ml of water, add 1 g of solid potassium nitrate, and stir until the latter is dissolved. Add 30 ml of ethanol or 2-propanol, stir, and allow the mixture to stand for 1 hr. Filter the resulting precipitate, consisting of potassium fluoborate and potassium fluosilicate employing either paper or a sintered-glass filter crucible. Wash the precipitate with portions of 1:1 water–ethanol or 2-propanol, containing 2% potassium nitrate and made alkaline to the color of phenolphthalein, until further washings are free of acidity. That point is attained when 1 drop of 0.1 N sodium hydroxide solution to a portion of the washing yields a pink color with phenolphthalein. Place the paper or filter crucible in the *original* beaker, add 100 ml of water, and heat to 40°C (not above 50°C) until the precipitate dissolves, indicating that the fluosilicic acid is hydrolyzed. Add some phenolphthalein and titrate promptly with 0.5 N sodium hydroxide until a faint pink persists for 15 sec.

$$\% \text{ fluosilicic acid } = \frac{(V_4)(N)(3.602)}{w}$$

where V_4 = volume of sodium hydroxide solution required for the titration, in ml

N = normality of sodium hydroxide solution

w = sample weight, in g

Calculate the actual % fluoboric acid and free boric acid as follows:

$$\% \text{ actual fluoboric acid } = A - (B)(0.4477) - (C)(0.9141)$$

$$\% \text{ actual free boric acid } = (D - \% \text{ actual fluoboric acid})(0.7042)$$

where A = total acidity (hot), expressed as HBF_4

B = % sulfuric acid

C = % fluosilicic acid

D = % total boric acid, expressed as HBF_4

These last two calculations are for the usual commercial product, which contains free boric acid; where free hydrofluoric acid is present, analogous equations may be devised.

The determination of sulfuric acid fails if the fluoboric acid has been placed in contact with glass for protracted periods of time, since metal salts would be present in the residue obtained in the evaporation step. In such a case, the % "total solids" may be determined by drying the final residue in an oven at 105°C and weighing.

The procedure given for the determination of fluosilicic acid is reported to give slightly high results (8).

Nitron Method. Fluoboric acid may also be determined in the presence of its hydrolysis products by the addition of nitron ($C_{20}H_{16}N_4$, 1,4-diphenyl-3,5-(phenyl-imino)-Δ^2-1,2,4-triazoline). The slightly soluble nitron fluoborate will precipitate and its amount can either be determined gravimetrically (9,10) or it may be dissolved in acetone and the fluoboric acid content determined by titration with alkali hydroxide (6).

Procedure

Transfer a weighed amount of the sample into an excess of an ice-cold solution of nitron acetate. Separate the precipitated nitron fluoborate, $C_{20}H_{16}N_4$.HBF_4, by either centrifugation or filtration and wash the precipitate with ice-cold water, previously saturated with nitron fluoborate. Dissolve the washed precipitate in acetone and dilute with 4 vol of water. Add 1 vol of chloroform. Titrate the fluoboric acid with standard sodium hydroxide solution to the phenolphthalein end point with vigorous stirring. During the course of the titration the water insoluble nitron progressively dissolves in the chloroform phase.

Other Methods. The use of cetyltrimethylammonium chloride as a precipitant for fluoroboric acid has been recommended (12). The crystalline precipitate, $C_{19}H_{42}N.BF_4$, is reported to have less than one tenth the solubility of nitron fluoborate. After separation of the precipitate by filtration, the excess of the cetyltrimethyl-ammonium ion is precipitated by addition of potassium ferrocyanide, and the excess of that anion is titrated with permanganate.

The introduction of an electrode selective for the tetrafluoroborate ion (Orion Research Inc., Model 92-05) offers possibilities for the potentiometric determination of fluoboric acid. Using tetraphenylarsonium chloride as the titrant to form insoluble tetraphenylarsonium fluoborate, a potentiometric titration has been effected with good accuracy at 2°C (12). Another approach involving conductometric titrations and the determination of the fluosilicic acid content photometrically as silicomolybdenum blue has been reported (13).

Where determination of the hydrolysis products of the fluoborate ion (BF_3OH^-, etc) is of interest, the analytical methods employed by Wamser (6) should be considered.

DETERMINATION OF IMPURITIES

The determination of the sulfuric acid and fluosilicic acid contents and either the free boric acid or the free hydrofluoric acid content of fluoboric acid have been described above as part of the determination of the fluoboric acid content of solutions.

Metallic impurities in fluoboric acid can be determined by the procedures commonly employed for the determination of such impurities in sulfuric acid, after their conversion to sulfates by fuming with sulfuric acid. Spectrographic methods are also applicable after this treatment or after aerial neutralization of fluoboric acid via diffusion of ammonia into the solution (14). Where fluoboric acid is used as an electrolyte, an EDTA titration of the lead content is appropriate (15). The procedure is given below.

Procedure

Dilute 10 ml of the filtered fluoboric acid electrolyte with 100 ml of water, add 5 drops of a 30% hydrogen peroxide solution, 25 ml of a 4% sodium fluoride solution, and 50 ml of water, then boil for 15 min. Cool the solution to room temperature, add an excess of a 0.1 M solution of disodium ethylenedinitrilotetraacetate, and some eriochrome black T; 0.2 g of a 1:99 ground mixture of the dye with sodium chloride is recommended. Add ammonical buffer mixture consisting of 54 g of ammonium chloride and 150 ml of aqueous ammonia dissolved and diluted to 1 liter with metal-free water until the solution turns blue and then add 5 ml of the buffer in excess. Back-titrate the excess of EDTA with standard 0.04 M zinc sulfate solution. Determine the equivalence of the EDTA solution with the zinc sulfate solution under the condition of the titration.

Total fluoride can be determined gravimetrically by the Ryss method (16). The neutralized sample is boiled with an excess of calcium chloride. Total conversion of the fluoride to filterable calcium fluoride occurs if the liberated hydrogen ion is slowly neutralized by the addition of appropriate amounts of potassium chlorate and potassium iodide and a small amount of potassium vanadate as a catalyst. The calcium fluoride is separated by filtration, washed with hot water, dried, and weighed.

FLUOROPHOSPHORIC ACIDS

Three fluorophosphoric acids ("FP" acids) are now available in the United States on a commercial basis. Monofluorophosphoric acid (mono-FP-acid, H_2FPO_3, or $FP(:O)(OH)_2$), and difluorophosphoric acid (di-FP-acid, HF_2PO_2, or $F_2P(:O)(OH)$) are offered as anhydrous liquids. Hexafluorophosphoric acid (hexa-FP-acid, HPF_6) is offered as an aqueous solution containing about 65% in HPF_6 and some of its hydrolysis products corresponding to 11% HPF_6.

Both the mono- and di-FP acids are used as catalysts for isomerization and polymerization. The mono-FP acid may be used to catalyze the alkylation of aromatics and the acylation of thiophene, and the di-FP acid can serve as a catalyst for the production of enol acetates from ketones and carbonyl compounds. The reaction of di-FP acid with an alcohol yields the ester of the mono-FP acid. In the processing of spent nuclear fuels containing zirconium, the di-FP acid can be applied to form soluble uranium salts in the presence of complexing agents. Reinforced coatings for the high-temperature protection of metals prepared from zirconium oxide, ammonium phosphate, and the mono-FP acid may have aerospace applications. Cements for oil wells based on aluminum oxide, phosphoric acid, and fluorophosphoric acid have been described.

The hexafluoro acid serves as a catalyst. In the separation of sulfur compounds from hydrocarbons or other mixtures, this acid is valuable as it forms solid addition compounds with divalent sulfur. The acid forms crystalline salts with some sterols, allowing their separation from mixtures. Solutions of the hexa-FP acid may be used in the electropolishing of stainless steel and brass. For more information on the fluorophosphoric acids, White's review should be consulted (17).

Handling and Storage. Fluorophosphoric acids should be handled with care. Mono-FP acid can be in contact with the skin for several minutes without producing a burn. Liquid di-FP acid in contact with the skin can cause burns unless promptly removed and the exposed area treated. The emergency treatment parallels that for hydrofluoric acid and requires application of a slurry of magnesia. Typical hydrofluoric acid burns are not observed with hexafluorophosphoric acid solution, but inhalation of the fumes should be avoided. Laboratory amounts of the three products are shipped in polyethylene bottles of up to 1-gal capacity and larger quantities in polyethylene drums up to 55 gal. Shipments must carry the DOT corrosive liquid white label for acids.

The anhydrous di-FP acid and the concentrated hexafluorophosphoric acid can be stored in aluminum. The anhydrous mono-FP acid may also be handled and stored in aluminum at or slightly above room temperature if no excess of phosphoric acid is present. Dilute aqueous solutions of these acids dissolve aluminum. Magnesium is also suitable for these acids and will tolerate dilute aqueous solutions of the hexa-FP acids. Stainless steel can be used to store aqueous solutions of the three acids and for short contact times to store concentrated or anhydrous acids. Contact with stainless steel for some days may lead to discoloration of the product due to dissolution of the alloying elements.

In the industrial application of dilute solutions of these acids, lead or lead-lined equipment is often used. Hastelloy (Union Carbide Co) lined equipment is also quite suitably resistant.

In laboratory experiments, borosilicate glassware can be used with the mono-FP acid and also with the di-FP acid in the absence of moisture and below about 50°C. Polyethylene and fluorocarbon vessels and bottles are also serviceable.

Properties

Monofluorophosphoric Acid. The mono-FP acid is a colorless, nonvolatile, viscous liquid with little odor. On cooling it becomes glassy and has no definite melting point. In vacuum, it is stable up to at least 185°C. It has a specific gravity (25°/4°C) of 1.818. This acid is completely soluble in water and behaves as a diprotic acid. On titration of a 0.05 N solution with base, "breaks" occur in the titration curve at pH 3.5 and 8.5. The slow hydrolysis of the mono-FP acid at low pH gives orthophosphoric acid, H_3PO_4, and hydrofluoric acid.

Difluorophosphoric Acid. Difluorophosphoric acid is a mobile, clear, colorless liquid that fumes in air. This acid melts at $-96.5 \pm 1°C$ and boils at 116°C. The vapor pressure in the 50–90°C region is given by the following equation:

$$\log P = 7.322 - (1732.2/T)$$

where P is in torr and T in °K. The latent heat of vaporization is 7925 cal/g-mole. A fresh solution in water behaves as a monoprotic acid and on titration with base a "break" is found in the titration curve at about pH 7.3.

Hexafluorophosphoric Acid. Hexafluorophosphoric acid is not obtainable in a pure state. The anhydrous acid obtained at reduced temperatures dissociates at room temperature to hydrofluoric acid and phosphorus pentafluoride. The "FP Acid No. 3" of commerce is an aqueous solution having the approximate composition of 65% HPF_6, 6% HF, 8% HPO_2F_2, H_2PO_3F, and H_3PO_4, and 21% water. This acid is a clear, colorless liquid that fumes. On dilution with water, the product hydrolyzes slowly to the di-FP and mono-FP acids, and finally to orthophosphoric acid and hydrofluoric acid. A crystalline hexahydrate with a mp of 31°C has been obtained by cooling the hexafluorophosphoric acid and water in appropriate ratio.

Commercial Grades and Specifications

Commercial specifications and typical compositions for the fluophosphoric acids are given in Table 3.

Table 3. Typical Compositions of Commercial Fluorophosphoric Acids

	Monofluoro-phosphoric acid, commercial grade, wt %	Difluoro-phosphoric acid, anhydrous grade, wt %	Hexafluoro-phosphoric acid, concentrated grade, wt %
total fluorine	18.0–19.5	37.0 min	58–62
total phosphorus	30–32	29.6 min	
H_2FPO_3	60[a]	3.5[b]	
HF_2PO_2	15–20[a]	96.5[a]	
HPF_6	≤1[a]		63 min
H_3PO_4	15–20[a]		
HF			6[a]
color	colorless	slight	colorless

[a] Not a specification but a typical value.
[b] Determined by NMR spectroscopy.

Methods of Manufacture

The production of the monofluorophosphoric acid involves an exothermic reaction between 69% hydrofluoric acid and phosphorus pentoxide. The product contains 15–20% each of orthophosphoric acid and difluorophosphoric acid and it cannot be distilled. Aluminum reactors can be used if the mixing is adequate, heat is dissipated, and the temperature is kept at a low level.

The production of difluorophosphoric acid involves the reaction of anhydrous phosphorus pentoxide and hydrofluoric acid in a 1:3 molar ratio to yield an equimolar mixture of monofluoro- and difluorophosphoric acids. The difluoro acid is distilled from the mixture under reduced pressure. Silver, aluminum, and stainless steel equipment can be used for the reaction and distillation.

Commercial concentrated hexafluorophosphoric acid is prepared by the reaction of phosphorus pentoxide and hydrofluoric acid in a 1:12 molar ratio in a closed system constructed of either aluminum or silver.

Methods of Analysis

The methods for the analysis of the three commercial fluorophosphoric acids have been developed at the Special Chemicals Department, Ozark-Mahoning Company, Tulsa, Oklahoma. The following discussion is based on information obtained from that company.

Elemental Analysis

Total Fluorine. For each of the three acids, the total fluoride content is determined by a conventional Willard-Winter distillation from sulfuric acid (see pp. 16–18) and titration of fluoride ion in the distillate with thorium nitrate to the Alizarin Red S end point. For the mono-FP acid, for example, a 1.25–1.30 g sample is diluted with water to 100 ml and a 20-ml aliquot taken for the distillation. A 50-ml aliquot of the first 250 ml of the distillate is adjusted with acid and base just to the discharge of the pink color of Alizarin Red S, and a titration with 0.025 M thorium nitrate solution performed to a permanent pink color. The titration is repeated on the next 100–150 ml of the distillate.

Total Phosphorus. The mono-FP and di-FP acids are decomposed to phosphoric acid by heating with nitric acid, and then the total phosphorus content is determined. Ammonium phosphomolybdate is precipitated, the filtered precipitate is dissolved in sodium hydroxide, and the excess of base back-titrated with hydrochloric acid (see Phosphorus).

For the determination of total phosphorus in hexafluorophosphoric acid, alkaline fusion with potassium hydroxide is necessary, since the use of nitric acid, as in the case of the mono- and di-FP acids, results in some loss of phosphorus. The fusion mixture is dissolved in water, treated with a slight excess of nitric acid, boiled, and then the method summarized above is followed.

Composition Analysis

Monofluorosphosphoric Acid. For the first check of purity, the total fluorine content is determined; the value should fall in the range of 18.0–19.5 wt %. The H_2FPO_3 content is determined by precipitation of silver monofluorophosphate, $Ag_2(PO_3F)$, from a solution in 75% ethanol which is neutral to phenol red, and cooled to ice temperature. The precipitate is isolated by centrifugation and subjected to the Willard-Winter distillation mentioned above. The fluoride content of the distillate is determined by titration with thorium nitrate and the % H_2FPO_3 is calculated:

$$\% \ H_2FPO_3 = (\% \ F)(5.26)$$

Hydrogen fluoride, if present, does not interfere, since silver fluoride is soluble in the ethanol–water medium. Any di-FP acid initially present will contribute some monofluorophosphate due to hydrolysis occurring during the sample preparation. An empirical correction can be applied by the following equation:

$$\text{wt \% } H_2FPO_3(\text{corrected}) = (\% \text{ F})(5.26) - (\% \text{ HF}_2PO_2)(0.77)$$

Any orthophosphate present is contained in the precipitate and therefore is included in the mono-FP acid reported.

The HPF_6 content (usually less than 1%) is determined by precipitation of the insoluble nitron hexafluorophosphate salt from a solution made acidic to methyl red with acetic acid and weighing. In order to prevent the interference of difluorophosphate, which also forms an insoluble nitron salt, the sample solution is made alkaline with sodium hydroxide and heated almost to boiling for 1 hr, thereby hydrolyzing completely the difluorophosphate anion. The HPF_6 content can be calculated in the following way:

$$\% \text{ HPF}_6 = \frac{(A)(31.85)(2.5)}{w}$$

where A = weight of nitron precipitate, in g
w = sample weight, in g

The HF_2PO_2 content is determined by the combined precipitation of PF_6^- and $PO_2F_2^{2-}$ as their nitron salts. The gravimetric result is corrected for the HPF_6 determined separately in the following way:

$$\% \text{ HF}_2PO_2 = \frac{(B)(24.61)}{w} - (\% \text{ HPF}_6)(0.904)$$

where B = weight of the combined nitron precipitate, in g
w = sample weight, in g

Phosphoric acid is determined in the mono-FP product by precipitation of silver orthophosphate at pH 5.8-6.5 and determination of the excess of silver ion in the filtrate by titration with thiocyanate solution using iron(III) as indicator.

From the results obtained for H_2FPO_3, HF_2PO_2, HPF_6, and H_3PO_4, the phosphorus balance is calculated and compared with the result of the determination of total phosphorus. If the latter is somewhat higher, the difference is expressed as HPO_3. Similarly, the fluorine balance is calculated and compared with the result of the total fluorine determination. If the latter is higher, the difference is expressed as free hydrofluoric acid.

Difluorophosphoric Acid. The determination of the individual components present is carried out according to the methods discussed above for the monofluorophosphoric acid.

Hexafluorophosphoric Acid. For the hexa-FP acid, the HPF_6 content can be determined by the gravimetric nitron procedure. However, a gravimetric procedure based on the formation of the insoluble tetraphenylarsonium hexafluorophosphate salt, $(C_6H_5)_4AsPF_6$, is preferred. The reaction with tetraphenylarsonium chloride is effected under alkaline conditions. The interference of difluorophosphate is avoided by boiling the alkaline sample solution. The method consistently gives results 102% of theory; consequently, a correction is applied:

$$\% \ PF_6^- = \frac{(A)(0.2744)(98)}{w}$$

$$\% \ HPF_6 = 1.0069(\% \ PF_6^-)$$

where A = weight of precipitate, in g
$\quad w$ = sample weight, in g

It is assumed that the principal hydrolysis equilibrium is expressed by the following equation:

$$HPF_6 + 2 \ H_2O \rightleftharpoons HF_2PO_2 + 4 \ HF$$

Based on this assumption, the amount of HF_2PO_2 is calculated from the difference in the phosphorus content obtained from the total phosphorus determination and corresponding to the determined amount of HPF_6:

$$\% \ HF_2PO_2 = \frac{\% \ P - (\% \ HPF_6)(0.202)}{0.308}$$

The amount of free hydrofluoric acid is calculated from the fluoride balance of HPF_6 plus HF_2PO_2 as compared to the result of the total fluorine determination:

$$\% \ HF = \frac{\% \ F - (\% \ HPF_6)(0.781) - (\% \ HF_2PO_2)(0.373)}{0.95}$$

The water content of commercial hexafluorophosphoric acid is calculated as the difference:

$$\% \ water = 100 - (\% \ HPF_6 + \% \ HF_2PO_2 + \% \ HF)$$

FLUOROSILICIC ACID

Fluorosilicic acid (fluosilicic acid, hexafluorosilicic acid, silicofluoric acid, hydrofluosilicic acid, or hydrofluorosilicic acid; H_2SiF_6) is known only as its aqueous solution and is commonly offered as a 30% solution, having a specific gravity of 1.27. Contrary to statements that have appeared in the literature, the acid does not exist in the vapor state.

The aqueous solution is clear and colorless. It decomposes on boiling, forming the volatile silicon tetrafluoride and hydrogen fluoride. Enrichment of hydrogen fluoride in the solution occurs as the boiling continues.

The aqueous solution of the acid can be obtained by the passage of silicon tetrafluoride into water. Colloidal silica is formed as a by-product and may be present in the solution. Much of the commercial product results from the hydrolysis of silicon tetrachloride in the waste gas scrubbers of phosphate fertilizer plants (18).

The aqueous solution can be concentrated to 61% by distillation under reduced pressure at room temperature.

High-purity acid is obtained by dissolving silica (quartz sand) in hydrofluoric acid and allowing the reaction to proceed to completion with an excess of silica present.

The hazards encountered in the handling of fluosilicic acid are similar to those of hydrofluoric acid and care should be taken to avoid skin contact with the acid or its salts and to avoid ingestion.

Properties

The properties and solution equilibria of fluosilicic acid and its salts have been critically reviewed by Ryss (19). Selected physical and thermodynamic properties of aqueous fluosilicic acid are listed in Table 4 (19–21). The relationship between composition and specific gravity of aqueous solutions is given in Table 5 (22,23).

Table 4. Properties of Aqueous Fluosilicic Acid Solution

formula weight	144.092
boiling point, 30.2% soln, 720 torr, °C	108.5
heat of formation	
from elements, aqueous solution, kcal/mole	−374
from SiF_4 and HF, aqueous solution, kcal/mole	−34
from SiF_4 and water to SiO_2(aq) and H_2SiF_6(aq), kcal/mole	−545.4
	−556.2
refractive index, n_D^{20}, 61% solution	1.3465
color	colorless to light green

Table 5. Composition and Specific Gravity of Aqueous Fluosilicic Acid Solutions

H_2SiF_6, wt %	Sp gr, 17.5/17.5°C	H_2SiF_6, wt %	Sp gr, 17.5/17.5°C
2	1.0161	20	1.1748
4	1.0324	22	1.1941
6	1.0491	24	1.2136
8	1.0661	26	1.2335
10	1.0834	28	1.2537
12	1.1011	30	1.2742
14	1.1190	32	1.2951
16	1.1373	34	1.3162
18	1.1559	60.79	1.4634[a]

[a] 25/25°C.

Commercial Grades and Specifications

Commercial grades of fluosilicic acid in the past have ranged from 30 to 35% fluosilicic acid. More recently, lower concentrations, nominally 25% and 23%, have been shipped in drums and tank cars. Typical composition of the 30% acid is the following:

fluosilicic acid	30.0 wt %
free silicon dioxide	0.25 wt %
sulfuric acid	0.2 wt %

Shipments of fluosilicic acid require the DOT corrosive liquid white label for acids.

Methods of Analysis

Assay Methods

The determination of fluosilicic acid in the commercial products is conventionally based on acid–base titrations (23). In ice-cold solution, on addition of potassium nitrate and ethanol, potassium fluosilicate is precipitated. The hydrogen ion present in the solution can then be titrated with standard base. The result corresponds to the total acidity of the sample expressed as fluosilicic acid:

$$H_2SiF_6 + 2 KNO_3 + 2 NaOH \rightarrow K_2SiF_6 + 2 NaNO_3 + 2 H_2O$$

Subsequently, the resulting solution is heated and further titrated with sodium hydroxide. The result corresponds to the fluosilicic acid content of the sample, as follows:

$$K_2SiF_6 + 4\,NaOH \rightarrow SiO_2 + 4\,NaF + 2\,KF + 2\,H_2O$$

If no other acids are present, it is apparent from the two equations that the amount of base required for the second titration should be twice that required in the first titration. Consequently, any departure from this relation corresponds to other acids present, which are usually expressed as hydrofluoric acid. The procedure is given below.

Procedures

Add an appropriate amount of the sample, for example, 3 g, to 25 ml of ice-cold water in a 150-ml beaker. Add 1 g of solid potassium nitrate, stir, and then add 30 ml of ice-cold ethanol. Cool the mixture in an ice-water bath, add a few drops of phenolphthalein indicator solution, and titrate rapidly with N sodium hydroxide. Heat the resulting solution to 80°C and continue the titration with N sodium hydroxide.

$$\% \text{ total acidity, as } H_2SiF_6 = \frac{(V_1)(N)(7.2046)}{w}$$

$$\% \ H_2SiF_6 = \frac{(V_2)(N)(3.6023)}{w}$$

$$\% \text{ other acids, as } HF = (\% \text{ total acidity, as } H_2SiF_6 - \% \ H_2SiF_6)(0.278)$$

where V_1 = volume of sodium hydroxide solution, required in the first titration, in ml

V_2 = volume of sodium hydroxide solution, required in the second titration, in ml

N = normality of the sodium hydroxide solution

w = sample weight, in g

A negative correction corresponding to 0.6% fluosilicic acid has been recommended (23) for the consumption of sodium hydroxide by silicic acid. Where free silica is present in the sample in significant amounts, it may be estimated by performing the initial titration step with and without the addition of neutral fluoride. For fluosilicic acid high in silica, a special assay procedure has been reported (24).

Where other acids are absent or present in minute amounts, notably in the reagent grade product, the first titration may be omitted and a less exacting approach be adopted, namely, a rough titration at room temperature, heating, and completion of the titration (25). This simplified procedure is given below.

Procedure

Place a suitable sample of fluosilicic acid, for example, 3 g, in a 150-ml beaker, add some phenolphthalein indicator solution, and titrate at room temperature with N sodium hydroxide solution. Then heat to 80°C and continue the titration to a permanent pink. Calculate total acidity from the total volume of sodium hydroxide solution needed for the titration and express it as fluosilicic acid:

$$\% \ H_2SiF_6 = \frac{(V)(N)(2.4015)}{w}$$

where V = volume of sodium hydroxide solution needed for the titration, in ml

N = normality of the sodium hydroxide solution

w = sample weight, in g

A more recent study (26) suggests that even under ice-cold conditions and with ethanol present, potassium fluosilicate undergoes some hydrolysis so that the consumption of base is high in the first procedure. For this reason, the substitution of barium nitrate for potassium nitrate was recommended in the titration in ice-cold solution because the molar solubility of barium fluosilicate is significantly smaller. However, the subsequent titration fails because the hydrolysis of the fluosilicate ion is then incomplete. Therefore, application of the barium salt method to commercial fluosilicic acid would require titration of a second sample with heating similar to the simplified approach of the second procedure.

Determination of Fluosilicic Acid as a Minor Impurity

Fluosilicic acid in lower concentrations as found, eg, in commercial hydrofluoric acid, is preferably determined by the spectrophotometric α-silicomolybdic acid method after masking the excess of fluoride with aluminum (27) or by the heteropoly blue method after low-temperature evaporation of hydrofluoric acid and complexing of the residual fluoride with boric acid (28).

Determination of Impurities

The residue after evaporation is determined conventionally by evaporation in a platinum dish with addition of a few drops of sulfuric acid.

Most impurities in commercial fluosilicic acid can be determined after the evaporation of the product with the addition of sodium carbonate. Sulfate is determined turbidimetrically, and iron by the conventional thiocyanate photometric or visual comparison procedure. Heavy metals are determined by sulfide precipitation from an acetate-buffered medium. Chloride is determined directly in the acid by a turbidimetric silver chloride procedure. Arsenic can be determined in fluosilicic acid by using the photometric approach of Vašák and Šedivic involving volatilization of arsine and its reaction with silver diethyldithiocarbamate (29). For details of the methods, see the articles dealing with the respective compounds.

FLUOROSULFURIC ACID

Fluorosulfuric acid, $HFSO_3$ or FSO_2OH, earlier commonly termed fluosulfonic or fluorosulfonic acid, is a clear, nearly colorless, mobile liquid that fumes strongly in contact with moist air and reacts vigorously with liquid water. The acid may be considered the half fluoride of sulfuric acid and under the IUPAC 1957 nomenclature rules has the preferred systematic name of fluorosulfuric acid. Thorpe and Kirman (30) identified and characterized this acid in 1892. In the United States, the acid became available commercially in the early 1940s.

Fluorosulfuric acid can be prepared by the interaction of equimolar amounts of sulfur trioxide and hydrogen fluoride. The reaction can be carried out directly with cooled anhydrous reactants or preferably in fluorosulfuric acid as the solvent. The product can be purified by distillation; however, it is difficult to remove traces of sulfur trioxide completely. The conventional product is free of an excess of hydrogen fluoride and even at its boiling point does not attack glass apparatus.

Fluorosulfuric acid finds use as a catalyst and reagent in various organic reactions including alkylation, acylation, polymerization, isomerization, sulfonation, and the production of organic fluorosulfates. The industrial uses of fluorosulfuric acid have been summarized by Eibeck (31) and in the trade literature (32). The lower viscosity and freezing point of fluorosulfuric acid give it advantages over sulfuric acid as a strongly acidic reaction medium.

Fluorosulfuric acid is an excellent fluoridating reagent and reacts readily, often at room temperature, with many oxides or oxyacids (33,34). The products are usually oxyfluorides, but may be fully fluoridated compounds. Potassium permanganate yields permanganyl fluoride, MnO_3F, whereas potassium perchlorate above $50°C$ gives perchloryl fluoride, ClO_3F. Potassium chromate and dichromate both react to give chromyl fluoride, CrO_2F_2. Boric acid and arsenic(III) oxide react to give the fully fluorinated products boron trifluoride and arsenic trifluoride, respectively.

Fluorosulfuric acid is a super acid of low freezing point. It has been utilized in the nuclear magnetic resonance study (34) of the protonation of weak bases. Paul and co-workers have investigated its use as a titrant in nonaqueous acid–base titrimetry conducted in acetic acid or alcoholic media (35,36). The use of both potentiometric indication and acid–base indicators is possible. Bases that have been determined include butylamine, picoline, piperidine, and morpholine.

Fluorosulfuric acid is classified as a corrosive liquid and for shipping must carry the DOT white label for acids. For information on the handling of large quantities of this acid, safety data sheets (37) and a manufacturer's bulletin (32) should be consulted.

All laboratory and analytical work with fluorosulfuric acid should be performed in a hood and with a face shield and rubber gloves and an apron should be worn. A safety shower should be available in the immediate vicinity. Small containers of the acid should be well-cooled before opening and care taken to relieve any gas pressure developed. Fluorosulfuric acid reacts violently with water and under no condition should water be brought into a closed container that contains or did contain this acid. If water is excluded, fluorosulfuric acid can be stored in glass, otherwise polymeric fluorocarbon or platinum apparatus should be employed. Precautions and first-aid measures relevant to concentrated sulfuric acid, oleum, and hydrofluoric acid are applicable. In the event of injury, a fluorosulfuric acid burn should be treated as a hydrofluoric acid burn. Where fluorosulfuric acid is spilled indoors, it can be absorbed by an inert material such as sand, vermiculite, or powdered clay. The spent absorbent should be buried or be washed with water out of doors.

Properties

Some of the properties of fluorosulfuric acid are listed in Table 6 (30,34,38,39). This acid is soluble in acetic acid, ethyl acetate, nitrobenzene, and ethyl ether, but insoluble in carbon disulfide, carbon tetrachloride, chloroform, and tetrachloroethane. Many compounds, both inorganic and organic, dissolve in fluorosulfuric acid. The solvent properties of this acid and acid–base behavior in it have been studied and reviewed by Gillespie (34).

The infrared and nuclear magnetic resonance spectra of fluorosulfuric acid have been studied (40). Fluorosulfuric acid is thermally stable and does not decompose below $900°C$. In the vapor phase, dissociation into hydrogen fluoride and sulfur trioxide may occur. Fluorosulfuric acid reacts vigorously and exothermally with water, but the hydrolysis reactions seem somewhat complex. Fluorosulfuric acid is one of the

Table 6. Properties of Fluorosulfuric Acid

formula weight	100.07
boiling point, °C	
at 760 torr	162.7
at 120 torr	110
at 19 torr	77
freezing point, °C	-88.98
density, g/ml	
at 15.6°C	1.743
at 18°C	1.740
at 25°C	1.726
vapor pressure at 25°C, torr	2.5
specific conductivity at 25°C, $\Omega^{-1}cm^{-1}$	1.085×10^{-4}
heat of formation ΔH_f (from SO_3 and anhydrous HF), kcal/g-mole	18.4
viscosity, cP	
at 0°C	3
at 25°C	1.56
at 100°C	0.95
color	nearly colorless
odor	sharp

strongest of the simple protonic acids. The conductivity of the anhydrous product is due to the ions resulting from the autoprotolysis as described by the following equation:

$$FSO_3H + FSO_3H \rightleftarrows FSO_3H_2^+ + FSO_3^-$$

The equilibrium concentration of each ion is about 2×10^{-4} molal.

Finely divided hydrated silica reacts vigorously with fluorosulfuric acid to give silicon tetrafluoride, but glass is not attacked in the absence of moisture. When free of hydrofluoric acid, fluorosulfuric acid does not attack glass even at its boiling point, 162.7°C.

Commercial Grades and Specifications

Fluorosulfuric acid is offered commercially as a 98.5% technical grade. The product contains typically about 1% sulfuric acid, 0.5% free sulfur trioxide, and 0.1% sulfur dioxide; it can also be supplied with an excess of hydrogen fluoride on a custom basis. The product is offered in tank wagons, tank cars, nonreturnable steel drums, and glass bottles, placed inside a metal can for breakage protection.

Methods of Analysis

Assay Methods

Conductometric Titration. The commercial product can be assayed by the conductometric titration of the free sulfur trioxide with water and measurement of the specific conductivity at the point corresponding to the conversion of all of the free sulfur trioxide to sulfuric acid (41). This conductivity value is related to the sulfuric acid content of the product. Where free hydrogen fluoride is present in the product, a known amount of pure sulfur trioxide is added initially. The fluorosulfuric acid content is calculated by difference. For the determination, a three-neck flask of special design is used (see Fig. 1) in which a thermometer is so positioned that it provides clearance for the magnetic stirring bar. A Koch automatic microburet of 1-ml capacity

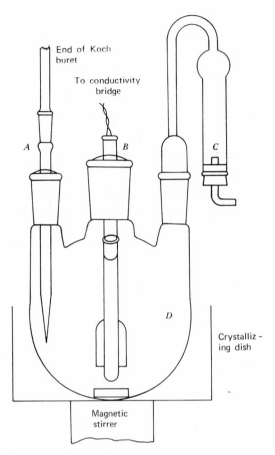

Fig. 1. Conductometric titration assembly for the determination of fluorosulfuric acid. *A*. Capillary tip of a 1-ml automatic Koch microburet. *B*. Conductivity cell. *C*. Drier tube. *D*. Three-neck flask.

with a 7/25 standard taper outlet is necessary, with a special capillary tip having a complimentary joint and also carrying a 24/40 standard taper joint so that it fits one neck of the flask. The conductivity cell with bright platinum electrodes with a cell constant of about 1 is installed in the other neck of the flask. It is connected to a conductivity meter or Wheatstone bridge for the range of 50–2000 Ω. A drying tube is inserted in the third neck of the flask.

Procedure

Fill the drying tube of the conductometric titration assembly with activated alumina or calcium sulfate and hold in place with plugs of glass wool. Place the magnetic stirring bar in the flask and insert the drying tube and the conductivity cell into the necks, as illustrated.

Place the thoroughly dry titration assembly, with the neck for the buret closed with a 24/40 standard taper glass stopper, on a trip balance and determine the tare weight. Fill the flask somewhat more than half full of sample (500–600 ml), restopper, and reweigh to determine the sample weight.

Fill the Koch buret reservoir with water and attach the microburet tip. Fill the tip with water from the buret making sure that no air bubbles are retained and that no water clings to the outside of the tip.

Insert the tip of the microburet into the third neck of the flask and place the assembly in a crystallizing dish on a magnetic stirrer. Fill the dish about half full with carbon tetrachloride at 26–28°C. Clamp the flask in position and connect the conductivity cell leads to the conductivity meter. Add a few drops of mercury to the thermometer well and insert the thermometer. Start the stirrer and continue mixing until the thermometer reading becomes constant in the range 26–30°C. Warm or cool the carbon tetrachloride bath, as necessary, to bring the sample temperature within this range. Stopper the flask and determine the resistance of the sample.

Titrate the sample with increments of 0.01–0.05 ml of water from the buret, mixing the sample well after each addition, stopping the stirrer, and reading the resistance. Keep the temperature of the sample between 26 and 30°C throughout the titration. Unless the sulfur trioxide content is unusually high, the temperature does not change appreciably during the titration.

Plot the resistance readings against the volume of water added on two cycle by two cycle log-log paper. Draw straight lines through the points and extend them to their intersection. Take this intersection as the end point. Calculate % free sulfur dioxide.

$$\% \text{ free SO}_3 = \frac{(A)(4.44)(100)}{w}$$

where A = the volume of water added corresponding to the end point, in ml

w = sample weight, in g

Table 7. Relationship between Specific Conductivity and Amount of Sulfuric Acid Present in Fluorosulfuric Acid at 28°C[a]

Specific conductivity, $\Omega^{-1}\text{cm}^{-1}$	H_2SO_4, wt %	Specific conductivity, $\Omega^{-1}\text{cm}^{-1}$	H_2SO_4, wt %	Specific conductivity, $\Omega^{-1}\text{cm}^{-1}$	H_2SO_4, wt %
0.00100	0.20	0.00250	2.46	0.00400	6.08
0.00110	0.28	0.00260	2.67	0.00410	6.35
0.00120	0.37	0.00270	2.89	0.00420	6.63
0.00130	0.47	0.00280	3.11	0.00430	6.92
0.00140	0.58	0.00290	3.33	0.00440	7.21
0.00150	0.71	0.00300	3.56	0.00450	7.50
0.00160	0.84	0.00310	3.80	0.00460	7.81
0.00170	0.99	0.00320	4.03	0.00470	8.12
0.00180	1.15	0.00330	4.28	0.00480	8.43
0.00190	1.31	0.00340	4.52	0.00490	8.76
0.00200	1.49	0.00350	4.77	0.00500	9.09
0.00210	1.67	0.00360	5.02	0.00510	9.44
0.00220	1.86	0.00370	5.28	0.00520	9.79
0.00230	2.05	0.00380	5.54	0.00530	10.16
0.00240	2.25	0.00390	5.81	0.00540	10.54

[a] Equal-argument data calculated via computer fitting of a 4th degree equation to the experimental conductivity data of Allied Chemical Corp. (32). The equation derived is

$$\% \text{ H}_2SO_4 = 0.017479x^4 - 0.23384x^3 + 1.366263x^2 - 1.43078x + 0.48870$$

where $x = 1000$(specific conductivity, in $\Omega^{-1}\text{cm}^{-1}$).

Draw a third line parallel to the resistance axis from the end point to its intersection with the rounded central portion of the titration curve. Assume the resistance value of this intersection as the true resistance of the sample at the end point. Calculate the specific conductance from the relationship:

$$C = K/R$$

where C = specific conductance, in $\Omega^{-1}\text{cm}^{-1}$
    K = cell constant determined separately (see below), in cm^{-1}
    R = the true resistance of the sample at the end point, in Ω

Calculate % sulfuric acid originally present in the sample from the following equation:

$$\text{wt \% } H_2SO_4 \text{ originally present} = S - \frac{(A)(5.44)(100)}{w}$$

where S = % sulfuric acid obtained from Table 7

If the nonvolatile content of the sample is significant, determine it separately (see p. 57).

Calculate the % fluorosulfuric acid from the following equation:

$$\text{wt \% } HFSO_3 = 100.0 - (\% \ X + \% \ Y + \% \ Z)$$

where $\% \ X$ = amount of nonvolatiles present, in wt %
    $\% \ Y$ = amount of sulfuric acid originally present, in wt %
    $\% \ Z$ = amount of free sulfur trioxide, in wt %

DETERMINATION OF THE CELL CONSTANT. Thoroughly rinse the three-neck flask and two 24/40 standard taper glass stoppers with water, dry in an oven and cool to room temperature. Fill the flask with a 0.1000 F potassium chloride solution, insert the conductivity cell into the flask, and stopper the two necks. Read the resistance and the temperature and calculate the cell constant from the following equation:

$$K = Cr$$

where K = cell constant
    r = measured resistance of the potassium chloride solution
    C = specific conductivity of the potassium chloride solution obtained from Table 8

In the procedure, the assumption is made that sulfur trioxide is in excess in the sample. This may be tested by adding 1 g of flowers of sulfur to a 50-ml portion of the fluorosulfuric acid sample under evaluation. Reaction of sulfur trioxide and sulfur leads to the compound S_2O_3, a blue-green solid, which dissolves in the medium resulting in a blue color. Therefore, the appearance of a blue color indicates the presence of an excess of sulfur trioxide. The absence of this color indicates the possible presence of free hydrofluoric acid. In this case, the sample containing the sulfur should be titrated with pure sulfur trioxide until a definite blue color appears. The volume required for a sample of 500–600 ml should be calculated and during the determination, after establishing the weight of the sample, the volume of pure sulfur trioxide estimated to be in excess of the free hydrofluoric acid present should be added by using a 5-ml buret inserted into the three-neck flask in the neck reserved for the microburet. The

Table 8. Specific Conductivity of 0.1000 F Potassium Chloride Solutions

Temperature, °C	Specific conductivity, $\Omega^{-1}cm^{-1}$
22	0.01215
23	0.01239
24	0.01264
25	0.01288
26	0.01313
27	0.01337
28	0.01362
29	0.01387
30	0.01412
31	0.01437
32	0.01462
33	0.01488

buret tip must be beneath the surface of the liquid. When the addition is accomplished, this buret should be replaced by the microburet and the determination carried out as given above in the procedure. In this case, the % free hydrofluoric acid present in the sample is calculated from the following equation:

$$\text{free HF, wt \%} = \frac{(1.93\ B - 4.44\ A)(0.25)(100)}{w}$$

where A = volume of water added as specified in the procedure, in ml
$\qquad B$ = volume of sulfur trioxide added to the sample, in ml
$\qquad w$ = sample weight, in g

Then, in the equation for the calculation of the % fluorosulfuric acid, % z becomes the net % of free hydrofluoric acid.

Fluosilicic acid, if present, will be reported as fluorosulfuric acid. It should be mentioned that according to the Allied Chemical Corporation, where this method was developed, no difficulty was encountered with the conductimetric titration or conductivity measurement with samples that had corroded glassware.

Indirect Method. The composition of fluorosulfuric acid samples may also be evaluated by the determination of total sulfate and total fluoride and calculation of % $HFSO_3$ from these results.

For the determination of sulfate, a weighed sample can be treated with water and allowed to react. Hydrochloric acid and barium chloride are then added, and the resulting barium sulfate precipitate is separated and weighed. Since some barium fluoride is carried down, the weighed precipitate is fumed with sulfuric acid, thereby converting barium fluoride to barium sulfate. Reweighing of resulting material allows a correction to be applied (42).

A more expeditious approach is to heat a sample, diluted with water, to 133°C, using a heating jacket containing boiling chlorobenzene to maintain constant temperature. A stream of air passing through the system removes fluorine as hydrogen fluoride, and the sulfate remaining in the solution can be determined by a conventional barium sulfate gravimetric procedure (43).

Total fluoride can be determined by addition of perchloric acid to a diluted sample, followed by the application of a conventional Willard and Winter steam distillation and determination of the amount of fluoride in the distillate (43).

DETERMINATION OF IMPURITIES

Nonvolatile Matter. The amount of nonvolatile matter present can be determined in the conventional way by evaporation and ignition of the residue.

Sulfur Dioxide. Sulfur dioxide can be determined by the conventional iodometric titration to the starch end point. As an alternative, polarography can also be considered (44). About 2.5 parts of the product are diluted with 100 parts of redistilled water to about 2.5% $HFSO_3$ and the polarographic wave established, using a dropping mercury electrode (glass capillary, 2–5 sec drop time) and the saturated calomel electrode as reference. The salt bridge consists of an agar gel containing a saturated sodium fluoride solution. The diffusion current of the sulfite wave ($E_{1/2}$ of about -0.4 V vs SCE) is measured.

Bibliography

1. H. S. Halbedel, "Fluoboric Acid and the Fluoborates," in A. Standen, ed., *Kirk-Othmer Encyclopedia of Chemical Technology*, Vol. 9, 2nd ed., Interscience Publishers, a division of John Wiley & Sons, Inc., New York, 1966, pp. 562–572.
2. E. F. Joy and A. J. Barnard, "Commercial Acids and Bases," in F. J. Welcher, ed., *Standard Methods of Chemical Analysis*, Vol. 2A, 6th ed., D. Van Nostrand Co., Inc., Princeton, N.J., 1963, pp. 534–626.
3. I. G. Ryss, "The Chemistry of Fluorine and Its Inorganic Compounds," State Publishing House for Scientific Technical and Chemical Literature Moscow, 1956; Engl. translation, F. Haimson, Oak Ridge, *U.S. Atomic Energy Commission Translation Series*, AEC-tr-3927 (Pt. 2), 505–525 (1960).
4. D. W. A. Sharpe, in M. Stacey, J. C. Tatlow, and A. G. Sharp, eds., *Advances in Fluorine Chemistry*, Vol. 1, Butterworths Scientific Publications, London, 1960, pp. 68–128.
5. A. B. Garrett, J. Welsh, S. Woodruff, R. Cooper, and J. J. Heiks, *J. Phys. Colloid Chem.* **53**, 505–518 (1949).
6. C. A. Wamser, *J. Am. Chem. Soc.* **70**, 1209–1125 (1948); **73**, 409–416 (1951).
7. I. G. Ryss, *J. Gen. Chem. U.S.S.R.* **16**, 531–536 (1946); *Chem. Abstr.* **41**, 1170 (1947).
8. H. Flisik, C. F. Swinehart, and A. R. Bumblish, Harshaw Chem. Co.; H. S. Booth and D. R. Martin, *Boron Trifluoride and Its Derivatives*, John Wiley & Sons, Inc., New York, 1949, pp. 230–238.
9. W. Lange, *Ber. Deut. Chem. Ges.* **59**, 2107–2113 (1927).
10. C. A. Lucchesi and D. D. DeFord, *Anal. Chem.* **29**, 1169–71 (1957).
11. H. J. Schaack and W. Wagner, *Z. Anal. Chem.* **146**, 326–338 (1955).
12. M. J. Smith and S. E. Manahan, *Anal. Chim. Acta* **48**, 315–319 (1969).
13. M. T. Berkovich and I. M. Novoselova, *Tr. Ural'sk Nauchn. Issled. Khim. Inst.* **11**, 62–69 (1964); *Chem. Abstr.* **63**, 15562 (1965).
14. E. M. Murt and T. J. Manns, *Chemist-Analyst* **50**, 13 (1961).
15. I. M. Yurist and P. G. Shaklova, *Zavodsk. Lab.* **26**, 1354–1355 (1960); *Chem. Abstr.* **55**, 17366 (1961).
16. I. G. Ryss, *Zavodsk. Lab.* **12**, 651–655 (1946); *Chem. Abstr.* **41**, 5052 (1947).
17. W. E. White and C. Pupp, "Fluorophosphoric Acids" under "Fluorine Compounds, Inorganic," in A. Standen, ed., *Kirk-Othmer Encyclopedia of Chemical Technology*, Vol. 9, 2nd ed., Interscience Publishers, a division of John Wiley & Sons, Inc., New York, 1966, pp. 636–649.
18. A. C. Byrns, "Fluosilicic Acid," in "Fluorine Compounds, Inorganic," in Ref. 17, pp. 654–661.
19. I. G. Ryss, "Fluosilicic Acid and Its Salts," in Ref. 3, Part 1, pp. 370–474.
20. H. v. Wartenburg, *Z. Anorg. Allgem. Chem.* **151**, 326 (1926).
21. W. A. Roth and H. Troitzsch, *Z. Anorg. Allgem. Chem.* **260**, 337–344 (1949).
22. F. Stolba, *J. Prakt. Chem.* **90**, 193–200 (1863).

23. C. A. Jacobson, *J. Phys. Chem.* **27**, 577–580, 761–770 (1923); **28**, 506–509 (1924).
24. S. M. Thomsen, *Anal. Chem.* **23**, 973–975 (1951); *J. Am. Chem. Soc.* **74**, 1690–1693 (1952).
25. E. F. Kern and T. R. Jones, *Trans. Am. Electrochem. Soc.* **57**, 273–279 (1930).
26. A. A. Blumberg, J. San Filippo, Jr., and P. E. Siska, *Chemist-Analyst* **55**, 45–46 (1966).
27. P. R. Graff and F. J. Langmyhr, *Anal. Chim. Acta* **21**, 429–431 (1959).
28. Committee E 15, American Society for Testing and Materials, tentative method in preparation.
29. J. Meyer, *Z. Anal. Chem.* **229**, 409–413 (1967).
30. T. E. Thorpe and W. Kirman, *J. Chem. Soc.* (*London*) **61**, 921–924 (1892).
31. R. E. Eibeck, "Fluorosulfuric Acid," in Ref. 17, pp. 676–681.
32. *Fluosulfonic Acid, Technical Bulletin TA 30711,* General Chemical Division, Allied Chemical Corp., New York.
33. A. Engelbrecht, *Angew. Chem. Intern. Ed. Engl.* **4**, 641–645 (1965); A. Engelbrecht and A. V. Grosse, *J. Am. Chem. Soc.* **76**, 2042–2045 (1954); A. Engelbrecht, A. Aignesberger, and E. Hayek, *Monatsh.* **86**, 437–470, 735–740 (1955).
34. R. J. Gillespie, *Accounts Chem. Res.* **1** (7), 202–209 (1968).
35. R. C. Paul, S. K. Vasisht, K. C. Malhotra, and S. S. Pahil, *Anal. Chem.* **34**, 820–826 (1962).
36. R. C. Paul and S. S. Pahil, *Anal. Chim. Acta* **30**, 466–472 (1964).
37. *Sulfuric Acid, Chemical Data Sheet SD20* and *Hydrofluoric Acid, Chemical Data Sheet SD25,* Manufacturing Chemists Assoc., Inc., Washington, D.C., 1963 and 1957.
38. J. Barr, R. J. Gillespie, and R. G. Thompson, *Inorg. Chem.* **3**, 1149–1156 (1964); R. J. Gillespie, J. B. Milne, and R. C. Thompson, *Inorg. Chem.* **5**, 468–473 (1966).
39. *Gmelins Handbuch der Anorganischen Chemie,* 8th Aufl., System No. 9, "Schwefel," Part B, Section 3, 1963, pp. 1737–1747.
40. R. J. Gillespie and E. A. Robinson, *Can. J. Chem.* **40**, 644–657, 675–685 (1962).
41. *Provisional Procedures FS-1-P,* General Chemical Division, Allied Chemical Corp., New York, Dec. 1954.
42. J. Meyer and G. Schramm, *Z. Anorg. Allgem. Chem.* **206**, 24–30 (1932).
43. A. A. Woolf, *J. Chem. Soc.* (*London*) **1954**, 2480–2483; **1955**, 433–443.
44. H. P. Raaen, *Anal. Chim. Acta* **44**, 205–210 (1969).

E. F. Joy
A. J. Barnard, Jr.
J. T. Baker Chemical Company

FLUOROCARBONS

The organic fluorochemicals industry was founded as a result of the search for new refrigerants which are nonflammable and have properties such as low toxicity, chemical stability, and good thermodynamic properties. The refrigerant and air-conditioning industry still consume a large portion of fluorocarbon production, mainly as the chlorofluorocarbons dichlorodifluoromethane, chlorodifluoromethane, trichlorofluoromethane, chlorotrifluoromethane, chloropentafluoroethane, 1,2-dichlorotetrafluoroethane, and 1,1,2-trichlorotrifluoroethane. Industrial production today still consists mainly of chlorofluorocarbons with minor amounts of fluorocarbons, fluorohydrocarbons, and other fluorochemicals.

The largest commercial application of chlorofluorocarbons is in aerosols as propellants. The principal compounds used as propellants are dichlorodifluoromethane, trichlorofluoromethane, 1,2-dichlorotetrafluoroethane, and chloropentafluoroethane, and many formulations require a mixture of two compounds to obtain the correct pressure. See also AEROSOLS, Vol. 4, pp. 452–461 and COSMETICS, Vol. 11, pp. 95–98. Chlorofluorocarbons such as trichlorofluoromethane and dichlorodifluoromethane are also used as blowing agents to increase the thermal insulation properties of urethan foams. 1,2-Dichlorotetrafluoroethane is used in foaming polyethylene. Chlorofluoromethanes are used as solvents and for degreasing. Commercial homo and copolymers are produced from chlorotrifluoroethylene.

The commercial production of fluorocarbons is limited to a few compounds because of the high cost of raw materials and manufacture. Carbon tetrafluoride is used in low-temperature refrigeration. Hexafluoroethane and octafluoropropane have some use as refrigerants and dielectric gases. Octafluorocyclobutane is used as an aerosol propellant for foods and as a refrigerant where high stability is required. Vinyl fluoride, vinylidene fluoride, tetrafluoroethylene, and hexafluoropropylene are used in the manufacture of inert and stable polymers. Organic fluorine compounds are also used as pharmaceuticals, anesthetics, insecticides, fungicides, dyes, dielectrics, and as petroleum catalysts. Additional information on the chemistry and technology of fluorinated hydrocarbons may be found in the general references (1–9).

To avoid using complicated chemical names, Du Pont developed a numbering system for its fluorocarbon refrigerants. The first digit on the right is the number of *fluorine* atoms; the next digit to the left is the number of *hydrogen* atoms plus 1; the third digit to the left is the number of *carbon* atoms minus 1 but is not used when equal to zero; the fourth digit to the left is the number of double bonds. If all of the carbon bonds are not occupied by fluorine or hydrogen atoms, the remainder are attached to chlorine. If bromine atoms are present, the same number is used as if they were chlorine atoms, but followed by the letter B and the number of bromine atoms. Cyclic compounds are indicated by the letter C preceding the number. For compounds containing three or more carbon atoms, the method of indicating various isomers becomes cumbersome. The numbering system was originally part of the Freon trademark, but it was donated to the industry by Du Pont while retaining possession of its trademark Freon.

Other trademarks for these compounds include Genetron (Allied Chemical Corp.), Isotron (Pennsalt Chemicals Corp.), Ucon (Union Carbide Corp.), and Kaiser (Kaiser Chemicals). Numerous other designations are used in other countries (1).

Properties

The carbon–fluorine bond is characterized by a high bond energy, short bond length, low polarization, and small radius. These characteristics impart both chemical and thermal stability to highly fluorinated hydrocarbons. Another property arising from fluorine substitution is weak intermolecular forces in liquid fluorocarbons. This is reflected in low boiling points, low surface tension, decreased solubility, and low heats of vaporization. Fluorocarbons generally have much higher liquid densities than the corresponding hydrocarbons. Completely fluorinated alkanes are essentially nontoxic. With unsaturated compounds, the toxicity increases with the fluorine content. Fluorocarbons are typical nonpolar liquids and are good solvents for other nonpolar materials and poor solvents for highly polar compounds. The properties of chlorofluorocarbons are similar to those of the fluorocarbons, high density, low boiling point, low viscosity, low surface tension, good stability, and low toxicity. The major commercial fluorocarbons and chlorofluorocarbons are completely nonflammable. Some physical properties of these compounds are listed in Table 1.

Fluorocarbons react with molten alkali metals but are not affected by acids or oxidizing agents. Higher molecular weight fluorocarbons show less thermal stability but decomposition is appreciable only above 400°C. Partially fluorinated compounds are less stable depending on the fluorine-to-hydrogen ratio. Chlorofluorocarbons do

Table 1. Physical Properties of Fluorocarbons and Chlorofluorocarbons

Compound	Formula	Refrigerant number	Boiling point, °C	Melting point, °C	Density of liquid, g/ml (at °C)	Refractive index, n_D (at °C)	Critical temperature, °C	Critical pressure, atm	Critical volume, ml/g
methyl fluoride	CH_3F	41	−78.5	−142	0.843 (−60)				
difluoromethane	CH_2F_2	32	−51.7	−136	1.100 (20)				
trifluoromethane	CHF_3	23	−82.0	−155	0.670 (25)	1.215 (−73)	25.9	47.7	1.904
carbon tetrafluoride	CF_4	14	−128.0	−184	1.317 (−80)	1.151 (−73)	−45.7	37.0	1.598
fluoroethane	CH_3CH_2F	161	−37.1	−143	0.818 (−37)	1.3033 (−37)			
1,1-difluoroethane	CH_3CHF_2	152a	−24.7	−117	0.966 (19)	1.3011 (−72)			
1,1,1-trifluoroethane	CH_3CF_3	143a	−47.6	−111	0.942 (30)				
1,1,2-tetrafluoroethane	CH_2FCF_3	134	−26.5	−101					
pentafluoroethane	CHF_2CF_3	125	−48.5	−103		1.5012 (19)			
hexafluoroethane	CF_3CF_3	116	−78.2	−101	1.587 (−73)	1.206 (−73)	19.7	29.4	1.648
vinyl fluoride	$CH_2=CHF$	1141	−72.0	−160	0.675 (10)		54.7	51.7	3.125
vinylidene fluoride	$CH_2=CF_2$	1132a	−85.7		0.750 (10)		29.7	44.0	2.415
trifluoroethylene	$CHF=CF_2$	1123	−61	−78	1.265 (27)	1.3011 (−72)			
tetrafluoroethylene	$CF_2=CF_2$	1114	−76.3	−142.5	1.519 (−76)		33.3		
octafluoropropane	$CF_3CF_2CF_3$	218	−36.7	−183	1.350 (20)		71.9	26.45	1.592
decafluorobutane	$CF_3(CF_2)_2CF_3$		−2.2	−128	1.543 (20)		113.3	23	1.59
octafluorocyclobutane	C_4F_8, cyclic	C-318	−5.9	−41	1.524 (20)	1.217 (25)	115.3	27.5	1.611

			bp, °C	fp, °C					
dodecafluoropentane	CF$_3$(CF$_2$)$_3$CF$_3$		29.2	−126	1.620 (20)	1.2514 (22)			1.904
tetradecafluorohexane	CF$_3$(CF$_2$)$_4$CF$_3$		58	<−74	1.68 (25)				1.917
hexadecafluoroheptane	CF$_3$(CF$_2$)$_5$CF$_3$		82.5	−51	1.733 (20)	1.262 (20)	19		1.729
chlorofluoromethane	CH$_2$ClF	31	−9.1	−133	1.271 (20)				
chlorodifluoromethane	CHClF$_2$	22	−40.8	−160	1.194 (25)	1.256 (25)	96.0	49.1	1.792
dichlorofluoromethane	CHCl$_2$F	21	8.9	−135	1.366 (25)	1.354 (25)	178.5	51.0	1.804
chlorotrifluoromethane	CClF$_3$	13	−81.4	−181	1.298 (−30)	1.199 (−73)	28.9	38.2	
dichlorodifluoromethane	CCl$_2$F$_2$	12	−29.8	−158	1.311 (25)	1.287 (25)	112.0	40.6	
trichlorofluoromethane	CCl$_3$F	11	23.8	−111	1.476 (25)	1.374 (25)	198.0	43.2	
2,1,1,1-chlorotrifluoroethane	CH$_2$ClCF$_3$	133a	6.1	−101	1.389 (0)	1.3090 (0)			
1,2,1,1,1-dichlorodifluoroethane	CH$_2$ClCClF$_2$	132b	46.8	−101	1.416 (20)	1.3619 (20)			
1,1,1,2,2-chlorotetrafluoroethane	CHF$_2$CClF$_2$	124a	−10.2	−117	1.379 (20)				
1,2,1,1,2-dichlorotrifluoroethane	CHClFCClF$_2$	123a	28.2		1.498 (10)	1.327 (20)			
chloropentafluoroethane	CClF$_2$CF$_3$	115	−38.7	−106	1.291 (25)	1.214 (25)	80.0	30.8	1.679
1,1-dichlorotetrafluoroethane	CCl$_2$FCF$_3$	114a	3.1	−60	1.478 (21)		145.6	32.5	1.717
1,2-dichlorotetrafluoroethane	CClF$_2$CClF$_2$	114	3.8	−94	1.456 (25)	1.288 (25)	145.7	32.2	1.736
1,1,2-trichlorotrifluoroethane	CCl$_3$CF$_3$	113a	45.7	14	1.579 (20)	1.361 (20)			
1,1,2-trichlorotrifluoroethane	CCl$_2$FCClF$_2$	113	47.6	−35	1.565 (25)	1.354 (25)	214.1	33.7	
1,1,1,2-tetrachlorodifluoroethane	CCl$_3$CClF$_2$	112a	91.5	40.6	1.649 (20)				
1,1,2,2-tetrachlorodifluoroethane	CCl$_2$FCCl$_2$F	112	92.8	26	1.634 (30)	1.413 (25)	278	34	1.810
1,1,1,2,2-pentachlorofluoroethane	CCl$_3$CCl$_2$F	111	137	100	1.74 (25)				

not react with most metals below 200°C or with acids or oxidizing agents. Chlorofluorocarbons exhibit some chemical reactivity; most compounds can be decomposed with molten alkali metals but react very slowly with alkali in the presence of water. Chlorofluorocarbons are not quite as thermally stable as the fluorocarbons.

Methods of Manufacture

Fluorocarbons are prepared by substitution of hydrogen in an organic molecule by elemental fluorine or reaction with silver, cobalt, or lead fluoride, or by exchange of chlorine, bromine, or iodine by fluoride in the form of the antimony, sodium, or potassium salt. Reaction with a high-valence metal fluoride such as cobalt trifluoride can produce fluorohydrocarbons containing one to more than twenty carbon atoms from the corresponding hydrocarbons. Fluorohydrocarbons have also been commercially prepared by electrolysis of solutions of alcohols, acids, or amines in anhydrous hydrogen fluoride. Fluorinated ethylenes are prepared by the pyrolysis of a saturated compound.

Chlorofluorocarbons are commercially manufactured by successive substitution of chlorine by fluorine using hydrogen fluoride. Chlorofluorocarbons with more than two carbon atoms are also prepared by replacement of chlorine with fluorine using various inorganic fluorides.

Commercial specifications for some of the more important chlorofluorocarbons are given in Table 2 (10) and Table 3 (11).

Table 2. Commercial Specifications for Trichlorotrifluoroethane[a]

appearance	clear, colorless liquid
boiling point at 760 torr, °C	47.6
assay, % min	99.9
other chlorofluorocarbons, % max	0.1
residue, soluble plus insoluble, ppm, max	1
water, ppm, max	10
acid number, mg of KOH/g of sample, max	0.003
chloride, ppm, max	0.1
particulate matter, max	
25–100 μm	100/100 ml
>100 μm	10/100 ml

[a] Freon Precision Cleaning Agent.

Methods of Analysis

Gas Chromatography

Organic fluorine compounds are not as corrosive as the inorganic gases and therefore do not require specialized chromatographic equipment unless they are in mixtures with corrosive components; see Vol. 13, p. 4. Conventional stationary phases can be used with Celite or firebrick support materials. Electron capture detection is commonly used. Chlorofluoromethanes are, however, soluble in the Apiezon and silicone high-vacuum greases and a special stopcock grease consisting of 7:14:36 mannitol–dextrin–glucose is recommended (12).

Pollard and Hardy (13) use a column of activated charcoal and partition columns with liquid phases dibutyl phthalate, dinonyl phthalate, and silicone oil 702 on Celite 545 to separate a number of halogen-substituted methanes. The retention data are listed in Table 4.

Table 3. Commercial Specifications for Freon Chlorofluorocarbon Refrigerants

	Freon 11 trichloro-fluoro-methane	Freon 12 dichloro-difluoro-methane	Freon 22 chloro-difluoro-methane	Freon 113 1,1,2-trichloro-trifluoro-ethane	Freon 114 1,2-dichlorotetra-fluoroethane	Freon 502 azeotrope, 48.8% chlorodifluoromethane and 51.2% chloro-pentafluoroethane
boiling point, at 760 torr, °F	74.8	−21.6	−41.4	117.6	38.4	−49.8
boiling range, °F, max	0.5	0.5	0.5	0.5	0.5	0.5
high-boiling impurities, vol %, max	0.01	0.01	0.01	0.01	0.01	0.01
water, ppm by wt, max	10	10	10	10	10	10
nonabsorbable gases in vapor phase, vol %, max	1.5	1.5	1.5	1.5	1.5	1.5
chloride ion	none	none	none	none	none	none

Table 4. Retention Volumes of Halogen-Substituted Methanes

| | Corrected retention volumes, ml[a] | | | |
| | liquid phases | | | |
Compound	dibutyl phthalate at 20°C	dinonyl phthalate at 24.5°C	silicone oil 702 at 40.1°C	activated charcoal at 137°C
trifluoromethane	2.5	1.8	0.45	7.6
chlorotrifluoromethane	0.6	0.6	0.54	17.3
chlorodifluoromethane	21.6	17.3	5.57	53.0
dichlorodifluoromethane	8.3	9.5	6.10	152
dichlorofluoromethane	88.0	131.5	41.0	453
trichlorofluoromethane	171	80.5	47.0	1160
chloroform		27.3	22.0	57.5

[a] 1 ft column length.

Lysyj and Newton (14) prepared a special type of column packing by dissolving No. 13–21 halocarbon oil in a suspension of trichloroethylene and Kel-F moulding powder No. 300, 30/50 mesh, refluxing for 15 min, then evaporating the solvent in air. The resulting material contained a "monophase gel" on solid particles and permitted the separation of fluorine, chlorine, and a number of reactive fluorides. The operating conditions are as follows:

column	10 ft × ¼ in. OD, Monel metal, packed
column temperature	26°C
carrier gas and flow rate	helium, 33 ml/min
detector	thermal conductivity
retention times	
silicon tetrafluoride	2.8 min
carbon tetrafluoride	4.5 min
nitrogen trifluoride	4.6 min
hydrogen fluoride	7.0 min
sulfur hexafluoride	12.5 min
chlorotrifluoromethane	14.0 min
fluorine	15.5 min
bromotrifluoromethane	31.5 min
chlorine trifluoride	46.5 min
chlorine	50.0 min
dichlorodifluoromethane	56.0 min
chlorotrifluoroethylene	67.5 min
dibromodifluoromethane	430.0 min
dichlorofluoromethane	448.0 min

For the routine analysis of a large number of Freon fluorocarbon mixtures, 3 m × ⅛ in. OD columns packed with (1) 30 wt % DC-200 methyl silicone oil on 60/80 mesh Chromosorb P, (2) 80/100 mesh Porapak Q microporous beads, or (3) molecular sieve 13X are used (15). Helium is the carrier gas with a flow rate on the order of 30–50 ml/min. In all cases, gas chromatographs containing a flame ionization detector are used. The quantitative response of the detector is determined by analyzing known mixtures and these factors are then applied to the analysis of the unknown samples.

Table 5. Retention Data for Freon Mixtures

Components of mixture	Column temperature, °C	Helium flow rate, ml/min	Retention time, sec
Freon-12			92
Freon-114	40	30	135
Freon-11			370
Freon-12			86
vinyl chloride	50	30	158
Freon-11			280
Freon-12			67
Freon-11	110	30	121
nitromethane			192
Freon-11	70	30	217
Freon-113			300
Freon-113	100	50	95
Freon-112			225
Freon-11	175	30	70
α-methylstyrene			385

Standards are usually mixed by weight in pressurized cylinders. Either gas or liquid sampling valves can be used depending on the nature of the sample. Special considerations are necessary for mixtures of components with widely differing volatility. Cylinders containing standards or samples are connected directly to the sampling valve. If the mixture might be partially condensed in the cylinder, sampling is done with the cylinder inverted.

The DC-200 partition column is used for a wide variety of Freon mixtures at temperatures ranging from 40 to 175°C. A few examples are found in Table 5.

The Porapak column is used for the following mixtures: Freon-12 and Freon-22 at 120°C; Freon-12, Freon-114, and isobutane at 95°C; Freon-12, Freon-114, and vinyl chloride at 110°C; Freon-14 and Freon-23 at 40°C; Freon-22 and propane at 100°C; and Freon C-318 and Freon-115 at 85°C. The molecular sieve column is used for binary mixtures containing nitrogen or nitrous oxide. A typical example is the analysis of a Freon-116 and nitrous oxide mixture under the following conditions:

column temperature	150°C
carrier gas and flow rate	helium, 40 ml/min
sample volume	0.168 ml, gas
retention times	
Freon-116	112 sec
nitrous oxide	137 sec

Propellant composition of aerosol products is determined by dissolving the aerosol in a less volatile solvent and analyzing by gas chromatography using the following conditions:

column	6 m × ¼ in. OD, packed
column packing	20 wt % di-2-ethylhexyl sebacate on 60/80 mesh Chromosorb P
column temperature	50–100°C
carrier gas and flow rate	helium, 40–60 ml/min

Frequencies of infrared absorptions of carbon–halogen bonds in organic materials are strongly affected by interactions with neighboring groups. The interactions are greatest with fluorine substitution. A single fluorine atom usually causes moderate absorption in the 1100–1000 cm^{-1} region. The frequency rises with additional fluorine substitution and two peaks occur with very intense absorption in the frequency range of 1400–1000 cm^{-1}. The spectra of fully fluorinated hydrocarbons are very complex with a series of very intense bands in the 1350–1100 cm^{-1} region, most of which are probably associated with carbon–fluorine stretching vibrations (16).

DETERMINATION OF FLUORINE CONTENT

The commercial fluorocarbon refrigerants and aerosol propellants are not usually analyzed for fluorine content. Samples containing organically bound fluorine are difficult to decompose because of the stability of the carbon–fluorine bond. The difficulty in decomposition increases with the degree of fluorination for both aliphatic and aromatic compounds. The most satisfactory decomposition methods involve combustion in oxygen using either a flask technique or a conventional combustion tube and reduction by fusion with sodium or potassium metal (17). The first adequate method for organic fluorine involved fusion with alkali metal in a sealed bomb (18). The oxygen flask decomposition method (19,20) is widely applicable and suitable even for volatile and stable highly fluorinated compounds. The sample is enclosed in a suitable container which is fixed in a platinum gauze hinge or basket holder and burned in pure oxygen in a conical flask(see Vol. 2, p. 557 and Vol. 9, pp. 416–417). Fluorocarbons can also be combusted in hydrogen or a mixture of hydrogen and oxygen. The Wickbold method (21) involves decomposing fluorinated compounds by vaporizing them in a stream of oxygen, mixing with hydrogen, and igniting at a nozzle; the method is applicable to highly volatile, very stable, and organometallic compounds and can be used for both major and minor fluorine contents. Parr bomb fusion with sodium peroxide can sometimes be applied to monofluorinated compounds.

These methods yield fluorine in the ionic form which can then be determined by the methods given for inorganic fluoride in Vol. 13, pp. 14–20. The same caution regarding attack of silica by fluoride applies.

Fusion methods other than alkali metal fusion and wet combustion methods are not advisable because they introduce large amounts of electrolyte into the final sample solution and are not applicable to high fluorine contents. Hydrolysis methods are not usually applicable because of the stability of the carbon–fluorine bond. Compounds which have a carbonyl linkage adjacent to the fluorine atom can be hydrolyzed by heating with strong sulfuric acid or potassium hydroxide solution (22).

SPECIFICATION TESTS

Some commercial specification tests for fluorocarbons are discussed here. Methods which are specific for fluorocarbons used as aerosols are given in Vol. 4, pp. 457–461 and Vol. 11, pp. 96–98.

Boiling Point and Boiling Range. The boiling point of liquid fluorocarbons may be determined by refluxing 250 ml of sample in a 500-ml round-bottom flask equipped with a water-cooled condenser and a calibrated thermometer. The boiling point varies with the atmospheric pressure. The boiling range of these compounds is usually taken as the boiling temperature after each successive 5 ml of a 100-ml sample has evaporated until 15 ml remain.

Water. Fluorocarbons used as refrigerants, propellants, and dielectrics are currently available with water contents less than 10 ppm. Highly sensitive methods are required at this level; these include infrared spectroscopy, gas chromatography, Karl Fischer titration, electrical monitors, as well as the classical phosphorus pentoxide absorption. Care is required in sampling extremely dry fluorocarbons to avoid contaminant moisture. Connecting lines should be purged with the sample before the sample collection is made.

Gravimetric Determination. The phosphorus pentoxide absorption method is generally accepted as a reference procedure for the calibration of other methods. A

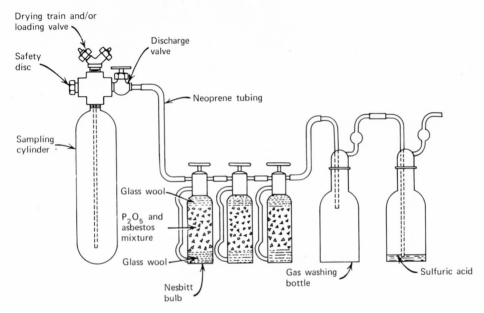

Fig. 1. Apparatus for determination of water in liquid Freon refrigerants.

mixture of phosphorus pentoxide and asbestos or other supporting material is contained in three tared bulbs. The sample is collected and weighed in a sampling cylinder, vaporized by warming if necessary and passed through the absorption bulbs. A typical apparatus assembly is shown in Figure 1 (11). The bulbs are always weighed full of dry air. The gain in weight of the first bulb corrected for the average gain or loss in weight of the second and third bulbs gives the weight of water in the sample. Oil present in the sample is an interference.

Karl Fischer Titration. Refinements in the Karl Fischer technique permit determination of 1–20 ppm of water. Several automatic titrators are now available to enable precise end point detection with very dilute titrants (less than 0.2 mg of water/ml of reagent). The titrant is prepared by diluting commercial Karl Fischer reagent and is standardized against sodium tartrate dihydrate. Low-boiling fluorocarbon samples are best collected in predried pressure vessel cylinders. The entire sample containing 0.3–6 mg of water is transferred to the titration flask by allowing it to distill through a fritted glass gas sparger. Because of its sensitivity and precision, the Karl Fischer titration is the preferred reference method for the calibration of other methods. See also Vol. 1, pp. 142–147.

Infrared Spectroscopy. Infrared spectroscopy is often used to determine the composition of propellant and refrigerant blends, and water can be determined at the same time by the absorption at 2.67 μm. Impurities such as oils interfere. This method is seldom used to determine water alone. See Vol. 1, pp. 155–156.

Gas Chromatography. Without a preliminary concentration step, gas chromatography lacks the sensitivity to be applicable to the low water contents in fluorocarbon refrigerants, propellants, and dielectrics. Water in fluorocarbon and other solvents has been determined by gas chromatography using the following conditions (23):

column	6 ft × ¼ in. OD, packed
column packing	50/80 mesh Porapak Q polyaromatic beads, washed with the following solvents in order: methanol, water, 1:4 hydrochloric acid, water, methanol, acetone
temperature	
of injection port	200°C
of column	115°C for 7 min, then programmed at 60°/min to 200°C, and held there for complete elution
of detector	250°C
carrier gas and flow rate	helium, 50 ml/min
detector	thermal conductivity
sample size	100 μl
internal standard	methanol

Electrical Methods. Electrolysis provides a very sensitive method for determining moisture. The Electrolytic Moisture Analyzer (24–25) operates by absorption of water from gases or vaporized liquids by a phosphorus pentoxide film and electrolysis by a direct current voltage applied across two platinum electrodes in contact with the film. The resulting electrolysis current is related to the water content by Faraday's law. Oil or other nonvolatile liquids interfere and must be removed prior to the test. The instrument is available from Manufacturer's Engineering and Equipment Corp., Warrington, Pa.; Beckman Instruments Inc., Fullerton, Calif., and Consolidated Electrodynamics Corp., Pasadena, Calif. The method has a sensitivity of less than 0.3 ppm.

The Du Pont Moisture Analyzer (model 510, E. I. du Pont de Nemours & Co., Inc., Wilmington, Del.) utilizes two quartz crystal oscillators, each coated with a thin film of hygroscopic material and operating at a normal frequency of 9 Mc. Change in the weight of the crystal caused by moisture absorption varies the oscillating frequency. The difference in frequency between the two crystals is electronically related to the water content in ppm (v/v). The sample must be completely in the vapor state before absorption. The instrument is applicable to a range of 0–25,000 ppm of water.

Acidity. The total acidity of fluorocarbons which are liquid at room temperature is determined by nonaqueous titration with potassium hydroxide in isopropyl alcohol using phenolphthalein as indicator.

Procedure

Prepare 0.01 N potassium hydroxide solution in isopropyl alcohol as follows: Add approximately 1 g of potassium hydroxide to approximately 1 liter of anhydrous isopropyl alcohol in a 2-liter Erlenmeyer flask. Boil gently for 5–10 min, stirring to prevent the solids from forming a cake on the bottom. Add 2 g of barium hydroxide and boil again gently for 5–10 min. Cool to room temperature. Allow to stand for several hours and filter the supernatant liquid through a fine sintered glass or porcelain filtering funnel. Avoid unnecessary exposure to carbon dioxide. Store the solution out of contact with cork or rubber and protect it with a guard tube of Ascarite. Standardize against potassium acid phthalate. Use a 10-ml buret with a Teflon polytetrafluoroethylene stopcock and a micro-platinum tip.

Add 20 ml of isopropyl alcohol to a 250-ml Erlenmeyer flask, add 3 drops of 0.5% phenolphthalein indicator solution in isopropyl alcohol and titrate to the pink end point with standardized 0.01 N potassium hydroxide solution in isopropyl alcohol. Stopper the flask until the sample is added to minimize carbon dioxide contamination. Weigh 20 ml of fluorocarbon sample, add it to the pretitrated solvent, and titrate to the same end point which should persist for 15 sec.

$$\text{Acid number, in mg of KOH/g of sample} = \frac{(V)(N)(56.1)}{w}$$

where V = volume of potassium hydroxide solution, in ml
N = normality of potassium hydroxide solution
w = sample weight, in g

Free acid impurities in fluorocarbons can be extracted with water of known low conductivity and determined by the increase in the conductivity of the water (26). Ionizable acids such as hydrochloric acid, sulfur dioxide, and carbon dioxide are extracted and measured as well as other water-soluble ionizable material. This method is capable of accurate determination in the ppb concentration range.

Procedure

Calibrate a 300-ml polyethylene bottle and mark on the outside to indicate 20, 120, and 220 ml. Add deionized fluorocarbon to the 20-ml mark. Cap the bottle, shake for several minutes, and discard the fluorocarbon. Place another 20 ml of deionized fluorocarbon in the bottle and add deionized water to the 120-ml mark. Cap the bottle, shake for 2 min, and measure the conductivity of the water phase. The conductivity should be less than 0.5 $(\mu\Omega)^{-1}$; this value is used as the blank. Weigh the bottle containing water and the deionized fluorocarbon. Add fluorocarbon sample to the 220-ml mark and reweigh to obtain the sample weight. Cap the bottle, shake for 2 min, and measure the conductivity of the aqueous layer. Calibrate the method with known concentrations of hydrochloric acid; 1 $(\mu\Omega)^{-1}$ conductivity is equivalent to 52.4 ppb of hydrochloric acid using a Serfass Model RCM-15B1 conductivity bridge and a dip-type Model Cel-A01 conductivity cell (both available from Industrial Instruments, Inc., Cedar Grove, N. J.).

Halides. A qualitative test for halide involves treating the sample with a methanolic solution of silver nitrate; if halide is present, insoluble silver halide will form and produce turbidity. For liquid samples, a ratio of 1 : 1 methanol–fluorocarbon should be maintained since excess fluorocarbon will interfere.

Ionizable chloride in fluorocarbons is determined by titration with mercuric acetate solution using *sym*-diphenylcarbazone as the indicator.

Procedure

Prepare 0.01 N mercuric acetate solution by dissolving 1.6 g of mercuric acetate in water, adding 5 ml of glacial acetic acid, and diluting to 1 liter. Use a 1.0-ml Gilmont microburet and standardize the mercuric acetate solution against a standard sodium chloride solution with a chloride ion concentration of 0.001 mg/ml.

For volatile fluorocarbons, collect and weigh the sample in a 7 cu. in. cylinder, and bubble it through a train of two scrubbers each containing 50 ml of water. Reweigh the sample cylinder and combine the water from the scrubbers in a 250-ml Erlenmeyer flask. For liquid fluorocarbons, extract 100 ml of sample with several portions of water and combine the water extracts in a 250-ml Erlenmeyer flask. Add 5 drops of 0.5% methanolic *sym*-diphenylcarbazone indicator solution and titrate with the mercuric acetate solution to the purple-pink end point. Also run a blank determination.

Iron in the sample masks the end point and must be removed prior to analysis. Iron can be precipitated as the hydroxide with excess sodium hydroxide and filtered.

Nonabsorbable Gases in the Vapor Phase. Nonabsorbable or noncondensable gases consisting primarily of oxygen, nitrogen, and carbon monoxide are determined by dissolving a known volume of fluorocarbon vapor in tetrachloroethylene and measuring the residual gas volume (27). It is applicable to the vapor phase of fluorocarbons which are soluble in tetrachloroethylene but insoluble in water.

Procedure

The apparatus is shown in Figure 2. The absorption vessel is available from Lab Glass Inc., Vineland, N. J. (Cat. No. LG-11119). The leveling bulb is 250-ml capacity.

Add a mixture of 1 part of Siliclad silicone concentrate, available from Scientific Glass Company, Bloomfield, N. J., and 100 parts of water to the clean absorption vessel. Swirl to completely coat the inner surfaces. Let stand for 5 min and then discard the solution. Rinse the vessel with water, dry at 100°C for 10 min, and cool.

Add 20 ml of water to the vessel and fill with tetrachloroethylene previously saturated with air and water. Also add sufficient water to the leveling bulb to give a water seal. Make certain the sample vessel is filled to the top of the stopcock stem with water. Repeat the silicone treatment when water forms droplets on the walls of the vessel rather than a thin film. Purge the connecting lines with sample to remove residual air. Adjust the valve on the fluorocarbon cylinder to give a slow, barely detectable flow. Attach the sample line to the stem of the sample vessel and open the stopcock allowing the sample vapor to flow by displacement into the sample vessel. Adjust the volume of sample to exactly 100 ml by keeping the sample vessel slightly lower than the leveling bulb and quickly turn the stopcock to vent the excess sample vapors. Tilt the vessel as shown in Figure 2b to remove all the water which separated the tetrachloroethylene from the sample vapor; do not allow any of the gas to move into the lower chamber during this operation. Allow the tetrachloroethylene to flow into the upper chamber and gently agitate to aid in the absorption of the fluorocarbon. When 80–90% of the sample has been absorbed, agitate the vessel vigorously for 15 sec. Return the vessel to an upright position, allowing the water to flow back into the buret section. Adjust the water in the vessel and the bulb to the same level and read on the calibrated column the volume of residual gas.

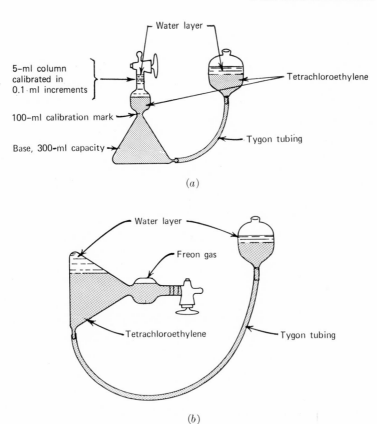

Fig. 2. (*a*) Apparatus for determination of nonabsorbable gases in fluorocarbon vapor. (*b*) Position of the apparatus during absorption of fluorocarbon in tetrachloroethylene.

Determine a blank value by measuring the nonabsorbable gas in a vaporized portion of the liquid phase of the same fluorocarbon. The blank represents the amount of air displaced from the air-saturated tetrachloroethylene. Approximately, thirty-five analyses can be performed with each charge of tetrachloroethylene.

Fluorocarbon samples which cannot be analyzed for nonabsorbable gases by tetrachloroethylene absorption can be analyzed by gas chromatography (28) using the following conditions:

column	4 m $\times$ $\frac{1}{4}$ in. OD, packed
column packing	30/60 mesh molecular sieve 13X
column temperature	40°C
carrier gas and flow rate	helium, 110 ml/min
detector	thermal conductivity
sample size	5 ml vapor

The oxygen content of the vapor phase of fluorocarbon aerosol products can be determined with the same molecular sieve column but with a column temperature of 70°C and helium carrier gas at a flow rate of 50 ml/min (29). The aerosol can is punctured and attached directly to the gas sampling valve.

Air in the vapor phase of aerosols has also been determined using the following conditions (30):

column	4 m × ¼ in. OD, packed
column packing	20 wt % di-2-ethylhexyl sebacate on 60/80 mesh Chromosorb W
column temperature	70°C
carrier gas and flow rate	helium, 50 ml/min

Bibliography

GENERAL REFERENCES

1. R. C. Downing, "Fluorinated Hydrocarbons," in A. Standen, ed., *Kirk-Othmer Encyclopedia of Chemical Technology*, Vol. 9, 2nd ed., Interscience Publishers, a division of John Wiley & Sons, Inc., New York, pp. 739–751.
2. J. H. Simons, ed., *Fluorine Chemistry*, Vol. 1, Academic Press Inc., New York, 1950.
3. J. H. Simons and T. J. Brice, "Fluorocarbon Chemistry," in J. H. Simons, ed., *Fluorine Chemistry*, Vol. 2, Academic Press Inc., New York, 1954.
4. A. M. Lovelace, W. Postelnek, and D. A. Rausch, *Aliphatic Fluorine Compounds, ACS Monograph No. 138*, Reinhold Publishing Corp., New York, 1958.
5. F. L. M. Pattison, *Toxic Aliphatic Fluorine Compounds*, Elsevier Publishing Co., London, 1959.
6. J. M. Hamilton, Jr., "The Organic Fluorochemicals Industry," in M. Stacey, J. C. Tatlow, and A. G. Sharpe, eds., *Advances in Fluorine Chemistry*, Vol. 3, Butterworth, Inc., Washington, D.C., 1963.
7. M. Hudlicky, *Chemistry of Organic Fluorine Compounds*, The Macmillan Company, New York 1962.
8. D. Osteroth, *Chemie und Technologie aliphatischer fluororganischer Verbindungen*, Ferdinand Enke Verlag, Stuttgart, 1964.
9. R. N. Haszeldine and A. G. Sharpe, *Fluorine and Its Compounds*, John Wiley & Sons, Inc., New York, 1951.

SPECIFIC REFERENCES

10. *Quality Specifications and Methods of Analysis for Freon Precision Cleaning Agent*, Technical Bulletin FST-2, E. I. du Pont de Nemours & Co., Inc.
11. *Quality Specifications and Methods of Analysis for the Freon Fluorocarbon Refrigerants*, Freon Product Information Bulletin B-8, E. I. du Pont de Nemours & Co., Inc., Wilmington, Del., 1969.
12. *Federal Specification, Freon Gas Compressed, BB-F-671a*, July 3, 1952.
13. F. H. Pollard and C. J. Hardy, D. H. Desty, ed., in *Vapour Phase Chromatography*, London, Butterworths, 1957, p. 115.
14. I. Lysyj and P. J. Newton, *Anal. Chem.* **35**, 90 (1963).
15. L. J. Pijanowski, *Freon Solutions. Determination of Composition by Gas Chromatography*, E. I. du Pont de Nemours & Co., Inc., Orchem Method 6-30-6B, March 20, 1967.
16. L. J. Bellamy, *The Infrared Spectra of Complex Molecules*, 2nd ed., John Wiley & Sons, Inc., New York, 1958, pp. 328–330.
17. A. M. G. MacDonald, "Analysis of Organic Compounds Containing Fluorine," in C. L. Wilson and D. W. Wilson, eds., *Comprehensive Analytical Chemistry*, Vol. 1B, Elsevier, Amsterdam, 1960, pp. 551–561.
18. P. J. Elving and W. B. Ligett, *Ind. Eng. Chem., Anal. Ed.* **14**, 449 (1942).
19. W. Schöniger, *Mikrochim. Acta* **1956,** 869.
20. A. M. G. MacDonald, "The Oxygen Flask Method," in C. N. Reilley, ed., *Advances in Analytical Chemistry and Instrumentation*, Vol. 4, Interscience Publishers, a division of John Wiley & Sons, Inc., New York, 1965, pp. 75–116.
21. R. Wickbold, *Angew. Chem.* **66**, 173 (1954).
22. C. A. Horton, "Fluorine," in I. M. Kolthoff, P. J. Elving, and E. B. Sandell, eds., *Treatise on Analytical Chemistry*, Part 2, Vol. 7, Interscience Publishers, a division of John Wiley & Sons, Inc., New York, 1961, p. 237.

23. J. M. Hogan, R. A. Engel, and H. F. Stevenson, *Anal. Chem.* **42**, 249 (1970).

24. E. S. Taylor, *Refrig. Eng.* **64**, 41 (July 1956).

25. F. A. Keidel, U.S. Patent 2,830,945 (1958); *Anal. Chem.* **31**, 2043 (1959).

26. H. C. Black, *The Determination of Trace Amounts of Ionizable Contaminants in Fluorosolvents by Aqueous Conductivity*, Freon Solvent Bulletin FST-2A, E. I. du Pont de Nemours & Co., Inc., Deepwater, N.J. *Paper, Fourth Annual Tech. Meet. of the Am. Assoc. for Contamination, Miami Beach, Fla., May 25–28, 1965.*

27. *Determination of Nonabsorbable Gas in Freon Fluorocarbon Products; Modification of Perchloroethylene Absorption Method Using Water Rather Than Mercury*, Freon Technical Bulletin B-38, E. I. du Pont de Nemours & Co., Inc.

28. *Gas Chromatographic Determination of Nonabsorbable Gases in the Vapor Phase of Freon Products*, Orchem Method 6-30-7A, E. I. du Pont de Nemours & Co., Inc., April 15, 1968.

29. *Determination of Oxygen Content in Vapor Phase of Aerosol Products by Gas Chromatography*, Freon Products Laboratory Report, E. I. du Pont de Nemours & Co., Inc., April 18, 1966.

30. *Determination of Air in Vapor Phase of Aerosol Products by Gas Chromatography*, Freon Products Laboratory Report, E. I. du Pont de Nemours & Co., Inc., April 18, 1966.

JOAN L. BATTLE
Encyclopedia of Industrial Chemical Analysis
with the cooperation of
E. I. du Pont de Nemours & Co., Inc.

FLUOROCARBONS, POLYMERS

Tetrafluoroethylene polymers	73
Polytetrafluoroethylene	73
Tetrafluoroethylene–hexafluoropropylene copolymer	89
Bibliography	92
Other fluorine-containing polymers	93
Bibliography	99

TETRAFLUOROETHYLENE POLYMERS

POLYTETRAFLUOROETHYLENE

Polytetrafluoroethylene is a fully fluorinated polymer with the chemical formula $(-CF_2CF_2-)_n$; it contains 76 wt % of fluorine. The polymer was discovered in 1938 by R. J. Plunkett of E. I. du Pont de Nemours & Co., Inc. (1). Polytetrafluoroethylene possesses a unique combination of useful chemical and physical properties. It possesses unusual toughness at temperatures as low as $-273°C$, has an unusually high virgin crystalline melting point of $342°C$, an extremely high melt viscosity of 10^{11} P at $380°C$, and outstanding thermal stability. It offers useful properties over a $550°C$ temperature range. The polymer is insoluble in all common solvents and is highly resistant to chemical attack. It has an outstanding combination of electrical properties; dielectric strength is high and dielectric constant and dissipation factors both extremely low and constant over a wide temperature range. Other important characteristics of this unique polymer are its nonadhesive and low frictional properties and its excellent weatherability. Although the unusual properties of polytetrafluoroethylene make it suitable for a wide range of critical applications, some of these same properties necessitate that special methods be used for processing and analysis. The polymer is neither a "true" thermoplastic nor thermoset resin. Additional information on the

Table 1. Properties of Polytetrafluoroethylene

apparent density, at 23°C and 50% rh, g/liter	175–950
specific gravity, 23/4°C	2.13–2.20
particle size, at 23°C and 50% rh, μm	175–725
water absorption, sample thickness ⅛ in., 24 hr at 23°C	
% increase in weight	0.01
dimensional change, in./in.	0.00
flammability, at 23°C and 50% rh	self-extinguishing
specific heat, Btu/(lb)(°F)	
at 20°C (68°F)	0.23
at 100°C (212°F)	0.25
at 260°C (500°F)	0.28
thermal conductivity, Btu/(hr)(°F/in.)(ft²) [a]	
at −129°C (−200°F)–182°C (360°F)	1.7
at −253°C (−423°F)	0.9
coefficient of thermal expansion, in./(in.)(°F)	
>23°C (73°F)	5.5×10^{-5}
<23°C (73°F)	4.7×10^{-5}
thermal instability index, at 23°C and 50% rh	<50
resistance to weathering, outdoor Florida	no change in >10 yr
hardness	
durometer, at 23°C (73°F)	55–70
Rockwell, at 23°C (73°F)	R58
impact strength, notch Izod, (ft)(lb)/in.	
at −57°C (−70°F)	2.0
at 23°C (73°C)	3.5
at 77°C (170°C)	6.0
compressive strength, psi	
at −250°C (−420°F)	32,500
at −195°C (−320°F)	21,000
at 23°C (73°F)	17,000
at 55°C (131°F)	13,000
at 100°C (212°F)	7500
elongation, ultimate, at 23°C (73°F), %	200–400
flexural modulus, psi	
at −250°C (−420°F)	750,000
at −195°C (−320°F)	720,000
at −101°C (−150°F)	470,000
at 23°C (73°F)	90,000
at 55°C (131°F)	58,000
at 100°C (212°F)	28,000
tensile strength, ultimate, at 23°C (73°F), psi	2500–5000
tensile strength, yield, psi	
at −250°C (−420°F)	19,000
at −195°C (−320°F)	16,000
at −129°C (−200°F)	11,500
at −73°C (−100°F)	7700
at −55°C (−68°F)	3800
at 0°C (32°F)	1800
at 23°C (73°F)	1300
at 70°C (158°F)	800
at 121°C (250°F)	500
tensile impact, at 23°C, (ft)(lb)/in.²	320

Table 1 (*continued*)

tensile elongation, %	
at −250°C (−420°F)	2
at −195°C (−320°F)	6
at −129°C (−200°F)	90
at −73°C (−100°F)	160
at 23°C (73°F)	275
tensile modulus, psi	
at −250°C (−420°F)	600,000
at −195°C (−320°F)	500,000
at −129°C (−200°F)	370,000
at −73°C (−100°F)	260,000
at 23°C (73°F)	50,000
at 100°C (212°F)	10,000
dielectric constant, at 23°C and 60 Hz	2.1
at 23°C and 10^6 Hz	2.1
at 23°C and 10^9 Hz	2.1
dissipation factor, at 23°C and 60 Hz	<0.0001
at 23°C and 10^6 Hz	<0.0001
at 23°C and 10^9 Hz	0.0004
dielectric strength, short time, V/mil	
at 10 mils	2000
at 60 mils	600
at 125 mils	480
surface resistivity, Ω	
at 23°C, dry	$>10^{16}$
at 23°C and 50% rh	3.5×10^{13}
at 23°C and 100% rh	3.6×10^{12}
volume resistivity, Ω-cm	
at 23°C, dry	10^{19}
at 23°C and 50% rh	$>10^{18}$
at 23°C and 100% rh	10^{15}
arc resistance, sec	$>300^b$

[a] Measured by Cenco-Fitch apparatus.
[b] Never tracks.

chemistry and technology of polytetrafluoroethylene may be found in References 2 and 3.

Polytetrafluoroethylene is now commonly produced under a variety of trademarks: Algoflon (Montecatini), Fluon (I.C.I.), Fluoroplast (USSR), Halon (Allied Chemical), Hostaflon (Hoechst), Polyflon (Daikin Kogyo), Soreflon (Ugine Kuhlmann), Teflon (Du Pont), Teflon (Mitsui Fluorochemicals Co.), Tetran (Pennwalt). World consumption of polytetrafluoroethylene is in excess of 10,000,000 lb/yr. Major uses are in electronics as wire coatings, chemical processing as gasket and packing material, and mechanical engineering. It is used for flexible braided hose and coatings on frying pans and other cooking utensils. Polytetrafluoroethylene-impregnated metal bearings need no lubrication in light-duty applications. In the form of an aqueous dispersion, it is used for impregnation of porous surfaces, coating, casting film, and spinning fibers.

Properties

The primary valence forces binding carbon and fluorine provide one of the strongest of chemical bonds. The carbon-to-carbon bond is also very strong. The strength of these carbon–carbon and carbon–fluorine bonds contributes significantly to many of the unique properties of polytetrafluoroethylene. Typical properties are listed in Table 1 (4,5). The polymer is stable at very high temperatures. It has excellent weathering resistance and is resistant to oxidation and ultraviolet light, but is adversely affected by high-energy, ionizing radiation (6). In the absence of oxygen, this effect of radiation is diminished 10–100 times. Due to a symmetrical, nonpolar nature, the polymer has excellent dielectric properties. Over the range of 60–10^9 Hz, dielectric constant and dissipation factor remain fairly constant, and are only slightly altered at elevated temperatures. On exposure to an arc, the polymer does not "track" or form a conductive path due to carbonization.

There is no known solvent that will dissolve or swell polytetrafluoroethylene at temperatures below 300°C. This chemical resistance is attributed to (1) fluorine atoms tightly bonded to the carbon chain, (2) carbon chain protected completely by the fluorine atom sheath, and (3) the weak attraction of perfluorocarbons for other molecules. The excellent resistance of the polymer to chemical attack is well known. Even at elevated temperatures, fuming sulfuric and nitric acids, aqua regia, hydrofluoric acid, strong alkaline solutions, and hydrogen peroxide have no effect on the polymer (7). Only molten alkali metals, sodium in liquid ammonia, chlorine trifluoride, and fluorine at elevated temperatures and pressures have an effect (8).

Toxic hazards of the polymer have in many cases been misinterpreted or exaggerated (9). Feeding tests of animals have produced no observable detrimental effects when sintered polytetrafluoroethylene is ingested (10). The same research has indicated that the polymer at processing temperature can affect laboratory animals if the quantity of resin is great enough and exposure is long enough. Large quantities of the polymer have been processed safely over the years. Although there is no record of workers being adversely affected from heated polymer, fumes are increasingly toxic in heavy concentrations, as are fumes of many common polymers, elastomers, and paint solvents. Proper ventilation should be used at all times when heating polytetrafluoroethylene above its melt point (11).

Methods of Manufacture

Fluorspar and sulfuric acid are reacted to form hydrogen fluoride, which is treated in turn, with chloroform to give the chemical intermediate chlorodifluoromethane:

$$CaF_2 + H_2SO_4 \rightarrow 2\,HF + CaSO_4$$
fluorspar

$$2\,HF + CHCl_3 \rightarrow CHClF_2 + 2\,HCl$$
chlorodifluoro-
methane

Pyrolysis at high temperatures converts chlorodifluoromethane to gaseous tetrafluoroethylene monomer:

$$2\,CHClF_2 \rightarrow CF_2CF_2 + 2\,HCl$$
tetrafluoroethylene
monomer

Finally, polymerization under heat and pressure in the presence of a suitable initiator transforms the monomer into the long, straight-chain, closely packed molecules of polytetrafluoroethylene:

$$n \begin{bmatrix} \text{F} & \text{F} \\ | & | \\ \text{C} = \text{C} \\ | & | \\ \text{F} & \text{F} \end{bmatrix} \rightarrow \begin{bmatrix} & \text{F} & \text{F} & \text{F} & \text{F} & \text{F} & \text{F} \\ & | & | & | & | & | & | \\ \text{\tiny{www}}-\text{C}-\text{C}-\text{C}-\text{C}-\text{C}-\text{C}-\text{\tiny{www}} \\ & | & | & | & | & | & | \\ & \text{F} & \text{F} & \text{F} & \text{F} & \text{F} & \text{F} \end{bmatrix}_x$$

polytetrafluoroethylene

Number-average molecular weights have been estimated to have a range of 400,000–10,000,000 based on radioactivity measurements on polymers prepared with a bisulfite initiation system containing radioactive sulfur.

Polytetrafluoroethylene is produced as granular resins or fine powder resins. Granular resins have median particle sizes ranging from 30 μm for fine cut materials to 600 μm for coarser ground resins. The specific surface area of granular resins measures approximately 2–4 m²/g. This specific surface area is at least a 1000-fold greater than the observed outer surface of the particles, thus confirming the spongy, porous nature of the particles. Apparent densities of granular resins range from 200 to 800 g/liter. The second form of polymer, often referred to as fine powder, is obtained by coagulation of aqueous dispersion. This polymer consists of agglomerates with average particle diameters of 450 μm made up of primary particles ranging in size from 0.05 to 0.5 μm. Specific surface areas of these fine powders are on the order of 10–12 m²/g and the apparent density is 475 g/liter. Aqueous dispersions are formed as an interim step in the manufacturing process. They are milky white colloidal liquids containing up to 60 wt % polymer. The dispersion resins are generally of lower molecular weight than granular resins and the average particle diameter is 0.2 μm (12).

Because of the very high melt viscosity, conventional techniques for processing polymers, such as injection molding or melt extrusion, are not applicable to polytetrafluoroethylene. Processing generally involves three steps: (1) the dry polymer is compressed, with or without a lubricant, at pressures of 1500–5000 psi to drive out air, (2) the material is heated above the melting point to sinter the particles, and (3) the polymer is then cooled at a controlled rate to give the desired degree of crystallinity. This procedure is quite similar to that used in processing ceramics and powdered metals. Permeability, stiffness, flex life, and tensile properties are controlled by the processing conditions. The molecular weight can be lowered by degradation during the sintering step. Varying the rate at which the polymer is cooled from the melt causes a wide variation in the degree of crystallinity.

Films, coatings, and spinning fibers are manufactured using the aqueous dispersion. For less heat-resistant materials, such as mat structures and woven fabrics, a useful degree of chemical resistance and antistick properties can be achieved by dipping and drying without sintering. For thermally stable materials, sintered coatings are prepared. In this process, woven fabrics of glass or asbestos are passed continuously through a dip tank containing the dispersion. The impregnated fabric is passed through a series of circulating air ovens for drying and baking to remove the wetting agent, and sintering. For spinning fibers, the dispersion is mixed with a matrix-forming material and then forced through a spinneret into a coagulating bath.

To improve properties of cold flow and compressive creep and to improve resistance to wear, polytetrafluoroethylene is filled with a variety of inorganic materials,

Table 2. Commercial Specifications for Polytetrafluoroethylene

Type I Granular powder for general purpose molding and extrusion

	Class 1	Class 2	Class 3	Class 4	Class 5	Class 6
melting point, °C	327 ± 10	327 ± 10	327 ± 10	327 ± 10	327 ± 10	327 ± 10
specific gravity	2.13–2.18	2.13–2.18	2.13–2.18	2.13–2.18	2.13–2.18	2.13–2.18
apparent density, g/liter	500 ± 50	625 ± 50	500 ± 50	550 ± 50	625 ± 50	625 ± 50
average particle diameter, μm	575 ± 150	550 ± 75	350 ± 50	325 ± 75	275 ± 100	375 ± 75
water content, % max	0.03	0.03	0.03	0.03	0.03	0.03
thermal instability index, max	50	50	50	50	50	50
tensile strength, min, kg/cm²	141	141	178	141	141	141
psi	2000	2000	2500	2000	2000	2000
elongation, % min	140	140	200	140	140	140

Type III Powder for extrusion purposes

	Class 1	Class 2	Class 3
melting point, °C	327 ± 10	327 ± 10	327 ± 10
specific gravity	2.19–2.24	2.15–2.20	2.17–2.23
apparent density, g/liter	475 ± 100		
average particle diameter, μm	500 ± 150	500 ± 150	425 ± 150
water content, % max	0.04	0.04	0.04
thermal instability index, max	50	50	50
tensile strength, min, kg/cm²	190	211	211
psi	2700	3000	3000
elongation, % min	400	200	200

Type IV   Granular powder of ultra-fine particle size

	Class 1	Class 2	Class 3	Class 4	Class 5	Class 6	Class 7	Class 8
melting point, °C	327 ± 10	327 ± 10	327 ± 10	327 ± 10	327 ± 10	327 ± 10	327 ± 10	327 ± 10
specific gravity	2.13–2.19	2.13–2.19	2.13–2.19	2.13–2.19	2.13–2.19	2.13–2.19	2.13–2.19	2.13–2.19
apparent density, g/liter	250 ± 75	300 ± 50	325 ± 75	475 ± 75	575 ± 50	625 ± 75	720 ± 75	875 ± 75
average particle diameter, μm					650 ± 75			
retention on No. 230 (62 μm) screen, % max	12	12	12	8				
water content, % max	0.04	0.04	0.04	0.04	0.04	0.04	0.04	0.04
thermal instability index, max	50	50	50	50	50	50	50	50
tensile strength, min, kg/cm^2	282	282	282	282	282	282	261	282
psi	4000	4000	4000	4000	4000	4000	3700	4000
elongation, % min	300	300	300	300	300	300	250	300

such as glass fiber, graphite, bronze, and molybdenum disulfide. Glass fiber is the most used filler for polytetrafluoroethylene since glass has the least effect on chemical and electrical properties and yet adds significantly to the mechanical properties. Graphite-filled polytetrafluoroethylene is used where the low friction properties of graphite reduce starting friction and initial wear. Bronze-filled compounds have higher hardness, lower wear, higher compressive strength, lower creep and cold flow, higher thermal conductivity, and better dimensional stability than either glass- or graphite-filled polytetrafluoroethylene. However, bronze-filled compounds are neither suitable for applications that involve corrosive environments nor for electrical applications. Molybdenum disulfide, usually used in conjunction with other fillers, adds considerably to stiffness, hardness, and wear resistance; at the same time it reduces starting friction and does not affect the electrical and chemical properties of the polymer.

Commercial Grades and Specifications

Commercial specifications for various grades of polytetrafluoroethylene, as published by the American Society for Testing and Materials (13), are listed in Table 2.

Analysis of Polytetrafluoroethylene

CHARACTERIZATION BY INFRARED SPECTROSCOPY

A typical infrared absorption spectrum of a thin film of polytetrafluoroethylene is shown in Figure 1. The band at 4.23 μm, due to overtones of C—F stretching in the 8–9 μm region, is useful analytically in correcting for thickness and density of the test specimen. The C—F bending modes are near 18 μm. The bands in the 12–14 μm region arise only in the amorphous portion of the resin and are useful for determining inherent density. A calibration curve of the ratio of the intensity of the band at 12.80 μm to that at 4.23 μm versus inherent polymer density is shown in Figure 2. The difference between this inherent polymer density and the actual density measured by displacement in water is a measure of the voids content. Crystallinity as wt % is determined by the relationship

$$\% \text{ crystallinity} = 762.25 - (1524.5/\text{inherent polymer density})$$

or using the graph shown in Figure 3, which is based on x-ray diffraction measurements.

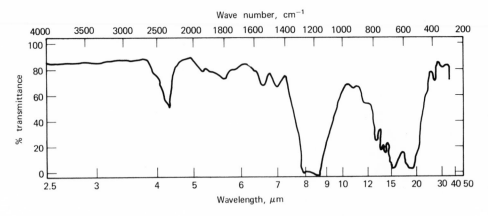

Fig. 1. Infrared spectrum of polytetrafluoroethylene, 0.005 cm film thickness.

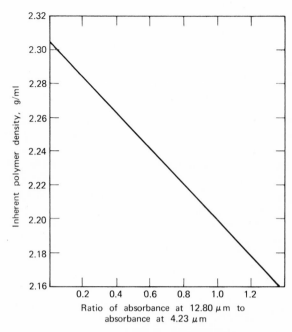

Fig. 2. Typical calibration curve for determining inherent polymer density from infrared measurements.

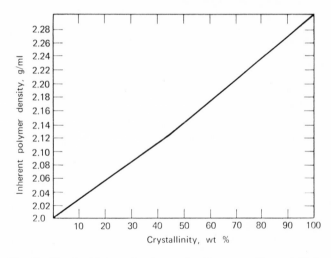

Fig. 3. Graph of inherent polymer density versus % crystallinity.

ASSAY METHODS

Tetrafluoroethylene polymers are not usually analyzed for fluorine or carbon content. Infrared spectroscopy and differential thermal analysis can provide sufficient assay information.

Pyrolysis. Polytetrafluoroethylene decomposes to volatile products when heated to 600°C. In the absence of oxygen, inorganic fillers, if present, are not affected. The following method for pyrolysis in a nitrogen atmosphere determines the polymer content by weight difference and the residue is the filler, which can be subjected to further analysis.

Procedure

Assemble the apparatus shown in Figure 4. Use a $8 \times 2 \times 1$ cm platinum boat and a 11.5×2 cm platinum tubular sleeve. Adjust the nitrogen flow rate to 1.6 liters/min. Weigh the platinum boat and sleeve assembly. Remove the boat from the sleeve and add 2.5 g of sample. Insert the boat into the sleeve so that sleeve protrudes approximately 2 cm over the boat at each end and reweigh the assembly to obtain the sample weight. Remove the stopper from the nitrogen inlet side of the quartz tube and place the boat assembly at a point midway between the ends of the furnace. Place the end of the thermocouple so that it extends into the sleeve and contacts the boat. Replace the stopper, turn on the power to the furnace, and adjust the furnace so that the temperature is raised uniformly to 450°C in a period of 2 hr. Raise the temperature uniformly to 600°C during the next hour, then hold at 600°C for 4 hr. Switch off the power, open the furnace, and allow the temperature to drop below 250°C. Remove the stopper at the nitrogen inlet side of the quartz tube and slide the boat assembly to the open end of the tube. Transfer the assembly to the desiccator, allow to cool to room temperature, and weigh.

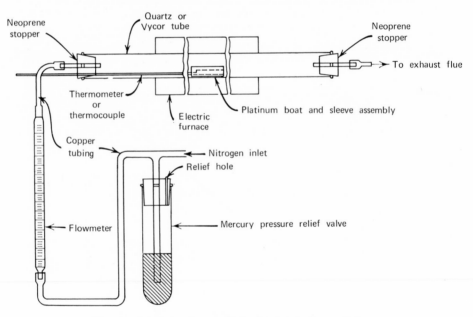

Fig. 4. Apparatus for pyrolysis of polytetrafluoroethylene.

Solids Content of Aqueous Dispersions. The solids content of dispersions is normally determined by the following gravimetric method, which also provides the wetting agent content.

Procedure

Weigh an aluminum weighing dish. Add 5 g of the dispersion and reweigh to obtain the sample weight. Place the dish in a circulating air oven at 100–105°C for 90 ± 5 min. Remove the dish from the oven, cool in a desiccator, and reweigh to determine total solids. Transfer the dish to a circulating air oven at 380°C for $10 \pm$

1 min. Remove the dish from the oven and place directly underneath the oven to cool approximately 5 min. Place the dish in a desiccator for 10 min and reweigh. The loss in weight represents the wetting agent content.

A hydrometer technique is useful for determining solids content during processing, such as coating where the concentration is continually changing. Specific gravities are within the range of 1.18–1.31, and % solids are determined from the chart shown in Table 3.

Table 3. Conversion of Hydrometer Specific Gravity to % Solids for Aqueous Tetrafluoroethylene Polymer Dispersion

Specific gravity, 25/25°C	% solids	Specific gravity, 25/25°C	% solids	Specific gravity, 25/25°C	% solids
1.192	28.9	1.233	33.8	1.274	38.4
1.193	29.0	1.234	33.9	1.275	38.5
1.194	29.2	1.235	34.0	1.276	38.6
1.195	29.3	1.236	34.1	1.277	38.7
1.196	29.4	1.237	34.3	1.278	38.8
1.197	29.5	1.238	34.4	1.279	38.9
1.198	29.7	1.239	34.5	1.280	39.1
1.199	29.8	1.240	34.6	1.281	39.2
1.200	29.9	1.241	34.7	1.282	39.3
1.201	30.0	1.242	34.8	1.283	39.4
1.202	30.1	1.243	34.9	1.284	39.5
1.203	30.2	1.244	35.1	1.285	39.6
1.204	30.4	1.245	35.2	1.286	39.7
1.205	30.5	1.246	35.3	1.287	39.8
1.206	30.6	1.247	35.4	1.288	39.9
1.207	30.7	1.248	35.6	1.289	40.0
1.208	30.8	1.249	35.7	1.290	40.1
1.209	31.0	1.250	35.8	1.291	40.2
1.210	31.1	1.251	35.9	1.292	40.3
1.211	31.2	1.252	36.0	1.293	40.4
1.212	31.3	1.253	36.2	1.294	40.5
1.213	31.4	1.254	36.3	1.295	40.7
1.214	31.5	1.255	36.4	1.296	40.8
1.215	31.6	1.256	36.5	1.297	40.9
1.216	31.8	1.257	36.6	1.298	41.0
1.217	31.9	1.258	36.7	1.299	41.1
1.218	32.0	1.259	36.8	1.300	41.2
1.219	32.2	1.260	37.0		
1.220	32.3	1.261	37.1		
1.221	32.4	1.262	37.2		
1.222	32.5	1.263	37.3		
1.223	32.6	1.264	37.4		
1.224	32.7	1.265	37.5		
1.225	32.9	1.266	37.6		
1.226	33.0	1.267	37.7		
1.227	33.1	1.268	37.8		
1.228	33.2	1.269	37.9		
1.229	33.4	1.270	38.0		
1.230	33.5	1.271	38.1		
1.231	33.6	1.272	38.2		
1.232	33.7	1.273	38.3		

Preparation of a Molded Specimen. Several of the following specification tests require a molded specimen rather than the powder form. ASTM D 1457 (13) recommends the following procedure.

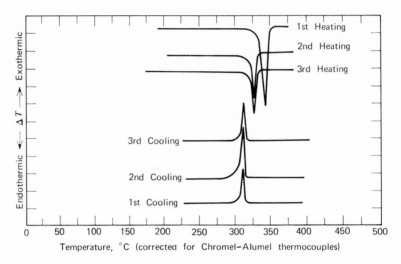

Fig. 5. Differential thermal analysis scan of polytetrafluoroethylene.

Procedure

Place a flat aluminum disc into a 3 in. diameter die mold. Screen 14.5 g of sample through a No. 10 screen into the mold. Draw a straight-edge across the top of the mold cavity to level the powder and place a second aluminum disc on the powder. Insert the mold in a suitable hydraulic press and apply pressure, approximately at a rate of 500 lb/sec, to a total pressure of 5000 psi. Hold this pressure on the disc for 3 min. Remove the disc from the die and measure its thickness. Sinter by placing it in an air oven at 380°C for 30 min. Reduce the temperature at a rate of $1.2 \pm 0.5°C/min$ to 300°C and then cool in air to room temperature. Again measure the thickness of the chip. Trim to a finished diameter of 6.6 cm. Observe and count black specks, which are an indication of contamination due to carbonized organic material.

In molding, polytetrafluoroethylene resins show anisotropic behavior. The growth or shrinkage of the specimen depends on the preform pressure, sintering time, and cooling rate. In general, molded specimens expand in thickness and shrink in diameter with sintering.

Melting Point. Melting point data are valuable for polymer identification. The melting point of previously unmelted polytetrafluoroethylene can be more than 10°C higher than reported values of 327°C, depending on resin type and analysis conditions. Differential thermal analysis has shown conclusively that the first melting of virgin polymer is an irreversible process; see Figure 5. On remelting, the polymer melts reversibly at a lower value, such as the widely accepted value temperature of 327°C. This melting behavior is analogous to that of linear polyethylene, in which an extended polymer chain structure melts irreversibly and, on cooling, forms a folded chain structure by crystallization. Molten polytetrafluoroethylene has such a high melt viscosity, 10^{10}–10^{11} P, that the melt is quite form stable.

The melting point of polytetrafluoroethylene may also be determined by the following modified Fisher-Johns method (13).

Procedure

Use a Fisher-Johns melting point apparatus with a 2-in. immersion thermometer calibrated in the range of 200–400°C and an aluminum shield $3\!/_{16}$ in. thick with an OD of $1\frac{1}{2}$ in. and having a tapered center hole $5\!/_{16}$ in. at the top and $7\!/_{16}$ in. at the bottom.

Shave a piece of molded sample approximately 0.25–0.37 mm thick, 1.25–1.88 mm wide, and 12.7–19.0 mm long. Place the shaving between two $3\!/_{4}$ in. diameter cover glasses. Put this assembly into the well of the Fisher-Johns melting point apparatus, and cover the entire assembly with a 1 in. diameter of cover glass. Position the aluminum shield over the sample assembly with the large end of the center hole towards the bottom. Set the transformer to give the maximum voltage, so that the temperature will rise at the rate of approximately 25°C/min. When the temperature reaches 310°C, decrease the voltage so that the rate of temperature rise is approximately 1°C/min. After the temperature reaches 310°C, observe the specimen at 1 min intervals. The temperature at which the shaving changes from milky white to gray translucent at the outer edge is taken as the melting point. Cool the sample and repeat the measurement. Two successive readings should agree within 3°C.

Specific Gravity. Specific gravity or density is an indication of crystallinity, molecular weight, and the presence of voids in these polymers. Since crystallization decreases with increasing molecular weight, samples prepared from high molecular weight polymers and cooled from the melt at a constant, slow rate have lower standard specific gravities than those prepared from low molecular weight polymers cooled at the same rate.

Specific gravity can be determined by the pycnometer method, using water as the displacement liquid (14); 2 drops of wetting agent should be added to the water, in order to reduce the surface tension and insure complete wetting of the sample disc. The density-gradient technique (15), which is described below, is commonly used in quality control. It provides, in particular, an indication of excessive void content.

Procedure

Mix 485 ml of 1,2-dibromoethane and 120 ml of bromoform for the more dense phase, and use 605 ml of 1,3-dibromopropane for the less dense phase. Place the liquids in a water bath at 23 ± 1°C for 30 min. Use a water-jacketed gradient tube, 38 mm ID by 44 in. in length, and assemble the apparatus as shown in Figure 6. Prime the tube which leads to the gradient tube with the more dense liquid and close the stopcock. The delivery end of this tube should have a capillary tip for flow control and should extend approximately 3 in. into and toward the side of the density tube. Prime the tube between the two beakers with the less dense liquid and close the stopcock. Use a high-speed magnetic stirrer in the second beaker as shown, and adjust the speed of stirring such that the surface of the liquid does not fluctuate greatly. Start the delivery of the liquid to the gradient tube by opening the two stopcocks simultaneously. Adjust the flow of liquid into the gradient tube to a very slow rate, permitting the liquid to flow down the side of the tube. Fill the tube to the desired level; preparation of a suitable gradient tube will require 60–90 min or longer.

Use ten floats, calibrated to ±0.0002 g/ml at 23 ± 0.1°C, with densities ranging from 2.115 to 2.555 g/ml. Starting with the most dense, drop the floats one at a time into the prepared gradient tube. Allow to stand at least 2 hr, and preferably overnight, to reach equilibrium. Remove any bubbles adhering to the floats by tapping the side of the tube. Read the position of the calibrated floats and plot the position versus density. The curve should be smooth and essentially linear, if the tube has been prepared properly. Recalibrate the float positions at frequent intervals.

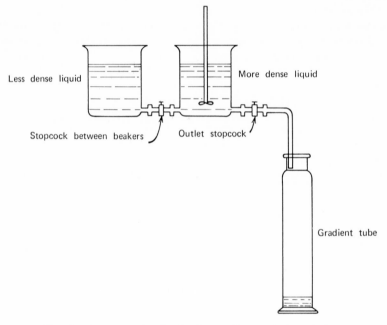

Less dense liquid

More dense liquid

Stopcock between beakers

Outlet stopcock

Gradient tube

Fig. 6. Apparatus for the density gradient technique (115).

Determine the density of samples using molded specimens less than 5 mm square, allowing them to sink to an equilibrium position, and reading the density from the calibration curve. The tube may be cleaned by removing old samples with a wire screen basket attached to a long wire. If care is used, this process will not destroy the gradient. However, recalibrate the tube following this cleaning procedure.

Apparent Density. Polytetrafluoroethylene resin particles have feather-like characteristics, and pack very readily under small amounts of compression, so standard methods for determination of bulk density are not applicable. Screening of the sample under standard conditions is required for valid results (13).

Procedure

Condition not more than 1 lb of powder sample at 23 ± 2°C for 4 hr prior to the test. Screen 500 ml of sample for 10 min on an automatic screener, using U.S. Standard sieves No. 20, 30, 40, 50, and 60. Recombine the fractions in a cylindrical container and tumble end over end for 3–4 min. Tare a 250-ml volumetric cup.

Use a feeder with a No. 8 wire screen placed over approximately the top two thirds of the trough, and a funnel mounted permanently in the feeder outlet. Adjust so that the distance of free fall from the feeder outlet to the top rim of the cup is 2.54 ± 0.32 cm ($1 \pm \frac{1}{8}$ in.). Place the sample on the feeder screen and vibrate all of the powder through the screen twice. Adjust the feeder control so that the cup is filled in 20–30 sec. Fill the cup so that the polymer forms a mound and overflows. Let the powder settle for about 15 sec without agitation, and then gently push the cup beneath a leveling device. Weigh the filled cup. Calculate the apparent density as the weight, in g, of 1000 ml of polymer.

Eliminating the initial screening and recombination step provides a more representative end-use test.

Particle Size. The following wet-sieve method utilizes perchloroethylene to facilitate fractionation, and is applicable to powders having an average particle diameter between 150 and 1000 μm (13).

Procedure

For types I and III powders, use U.S. Standard sieves No. 18, 20, 25, 35, 40, 50, and 325. For type II powder, use No. 40, 50, 60, 70, 80, 100, and 325. Assemble the sieves in a trough and adjust the flow rate of perchloroethylene to 6 ± 0.5 liters/min. Weigh 50 ± 0.1 g of polymer sample, place it on the top sieve, and spray with perchloroethylene for 1 ± 0.2 min. Remove the top sieve and place it in a hood to air dry for 30 min or longer, or dry in an oven at 90°C for 15 min. Repeat the spraying of each sieve in order. Weigh the material retained by each sieve; discard the material retained by the No. 325 sieve. Plot cumulative % polymer on each sieve versus the average opening size corresponding to each mesh number in μm. The average particle size is the point on the plot corresponding to the cumulative 50%.

For ultra-fine powder resins, such as type IV, a modification of this method is employed using only two sieves (13).

Procedure

Assemble a No. 20 and a No. 230 sieve in a trough and adjust the flow rate of perchloroethylene to 6 ± 0.5 liters/min. Weigh 5 ± 0.01 g of polymer sample and place on the top sieve. Spray with perchloroethylene for exactly 1 min. Remove the No. 20 sieve and discard the contents. Spray the No. 230 sieve for exactly 6 min and wash the retained material to one side during the last minute. Dry the sieve in an oven at 80–120°C for 20 min or until the odor of solvent disappears. Remove the material retained on the sieve and weigh. Report as % polymer retained by No. 230 sieve.

The Sub-Sieve Sizer available from Fisher Scientific Company (16) measures the air permeability of a bed of sample which depends on the porosity of the bed and the pressure drop across it. The method is applicable to powders having an average diameter between 1 and 50 μm and actually measures surface area accessible to flow rather than actual average particle size.

The micromerograph available from Sharples Corp. Philadelphia, Pa. (17) is based on air sedimentation of particles in the range of 1–250 μm according to Stokes law. The powder sample is dispersed in the top of a sedimentation column, the particles fall down the column onto the pan of a recording balance, the larger diameter particles falling faster, and the cumulative weight is recorded as a function of time.

The average particle size of polytetrafluoroethylene aqueous dispersions can be determined by visible absorbance of a diluted solution at 546 nm and comparison with standard curves.

Specific Surface Area. The specific surface area of polytetrafluoroethylene resins is measured by nitrogen adsorption. It employs an apparatus based on gas chromatographic principles, such as the Perkin-Elmer–Shell Model 212-D Sorptometer. Nitrogen is adsorbed by the sample at liquid nitrogen temperature from a gas stream of nitrogen and helium and is later eluted upon warming the sample. The nitrogen adsorbed and later liberated (desorption) is measured by thermal conductivity. See Vol. 8, pp. 221–223.

Water Content. Polytetrafluoroethylene does not absorb moisture; the moisture can be present only as adsorbed surface moisture and/or droplets. The following gravimetric method is recommended by ASTM (13).

Procedure

  Wash an aluminum weighing dish and cover with water, rinse with acetone, dry thoroughly in an oven at 50–80°C, and store in a desiccator until ready for use. Obtain the tare weight of the dish plus lid. Place 35–40 g of resin powder in it and reweigh. Dry to constant weight in a vacuum oven, at 660 torr and 150°C. Remove the dish from the oven, cover, allow to cool in the desiccator for at least 30 min, and reweigh.

The water content of polytetrafluoroethylene can also be determined by Karl Fischer titration after absorption of the water in methanol.

Procedure

  Weigh 35 ± 1 g of sample powder into a glass-stoppered flask containing 50 ml of pretitrated methanol. Shake to mix with a swirling motion for a few minutes. Titrate with standardized Karl Fischer reagent to a visual or electrometric end point. See Vol. 1, pp. 142–147.

The most accurate method for determination of surface moisture of powder samples utilizes a moisture analyzer comparable to the Consolidated Electrodynamics moisture analyzer supplied by Bell and Howell. The sample is placed in a small aluminum boat, put into an oven, and heated, driving off the moisture which is adsorbed by phosphorus pentoxide. The adsorbed water is electrolyzed to hydrogen and oxygen and the current required for this electrolysis is continuously integrated and provides a read-out directly in μg of water.

Thermal Instability. The thermal instability index is an indication of the decrease in molecular weight with heating (13). Sample discs are molded as described on p. 84, sintered at 380°C for either 30 min or 2 hr, and cooled at the specified rate.

$$\text{Thermal instability index} = (s_b - s_a)\ 1000$$

where s_a is the specific gravity of the sample heated for 30 min and s_b is the specific gravity of the sample heated for 2 hr.

Color. Most tetrafluoroethylene molded parts are used in the natural white state, and the determination of color is sometimes required as a quality control test. The yellowness of a molded plaque can be determined by measuring the absorbance at 480 nm and comparing the results with standards. The yellowness index can also be determined by ASTM D 1925 (18).

TETRAFLUOROETHYLENE–HEXAFLUOROPROPYLENE COPOLYMER

Tetrafluoroethylene–hexafluoropropylene copolymer is a thermoplastic which retains nearly all the desirable properties of polytetrafluoroethylene and possesses melt viscosities low enough for conventional processing such as extrusion, injection molding, blow molding, and vacuum forming. The copolymer has outstandingly good mechanical and electrical properties, excellent thermal stability, and chemical inertness. From -250 to $+200°C$, molded parts retain their mechanical toughness and strength. There are thermoplastics which are mechanically stronger at room temperature but almost all of these materials are degraded or are very weak compared to the copolymer at temperatures over 150°C. The copolymer is capable of continuous service at temperatures up to 200°C, limited at this temperature by a lack of stiffness.

The major end use of the copolymer is found in electric applications, consuming 70% of the resin produced. Chemical applications account for 20% of the resin consumed; principal uses are found in heat exchangers, lined pipes, and fittings. The copolymer finds application in labware, such as beakers and bottles, in spaghetti tubing, and overbraided hose. Mechanical applications are limited principally to seals and anti-stick applications. In the form of an aqueous dispersion, the copolymer is used in coated glass fabrics, wire insulating tapes, and adhesive coating for bonding bearings of polytetrafluoroethylene to metallic and nonmetallic components for anti-friction or antistick coatings for metals. The various forms of tetrafluoroethylene–hexafluoropropylene copolymer are manufactured only by Du Pont with the registered trademark of Teflon FEP-Fluorocarbon Resins.

Properties

Tetrafluoroethylene–hexafluoropropylene copolymer, like polytetrafluoroethylene, is highly resistant to chemical attack. Under certain conditions, it will react with fluorine and powerful fluorinating agents, such as oxygen difluoride, OF_2, or chlorine trifluoride. Molten sodium hydroxide and molten alkali metals will attack the copolymer as will certain activated alkali metal complexes. Measurable increases in weight, on the order of 0.5 to 2%, are recorded for a limited number of solvents, primarily highly halogenated solvents, such as carbon tetrachloride. Typical properties are listed in Table 4. The copolymer has outstanding electrical properties; over a very wide range of temperature and frequencies, not only are the dielectric constant and dissipation factor extremely low, but also remain relatively unchanged with temperature.

The precautions necessary for the copolymer are the same as those used in handling polytetrafluoroethylene. The unheated resin is essentially inert. Animal tests have indicated that the resin does not produce skin irritation and may be taken in foods without ill effect. For temperatures below the suggested maximum operating temperature of 200°C (392°F), the rate of decomposition is so minute that no special precautions are necessary. However, at processing temperatures of 270–400°C (464–752°F), adequate ventilation should be provided (11).

Methods of Manufacture

The preferred method for making the copolymer is copolymerization of tetrafluoroethylene and hexafluoropropylene in aqueous media under conditions similar to those used for the homopolymer. The dispersion can be processed by essentially the

Table 4. Properties of Tetrafluoroethylene–Hexafluoropropylene Copolymer

specific gravity, 23/4°C	2.14–2.17
melt viscosity, P	3×10^4–1×10^5
water absorption, sample thickness ⅛ in., 24 hr at 23°C	
% increase in weight	<0.01
dimensional change, in./in.	0.00
melting point, °C	254–271 (490–520°F)
flammability, at 23°C and 50% rh	self-extinguishing
specific heat, Btu/(lb)(°F)	
at 20°C (68°F)	0.26
at 260°C (500°F)	0.31
thermal conductivity, Btu/(hr)(°F/in.)(ft²) [a]	
at −129°C (−200°F)–182°C (360°F)	1.4
at −253°C (−423°F)	0.8
coefficient of thermal expansion, in./(in.)(°F)	
>23°C (73°F)	5.2×10^{-5}
<23°C (73°F)	3.2×10^{-5}
thermal instability index, at 23°C and 50% rh	<50
heat deflection temperature, °C	
at 66 psi	70
at 264 psi	52
resistance to weathering, outdoor Florida	
accelerated, high ultraviolet, 100 ppm ozone	no change in 8000 hr
hardness	
durometer, at 23°C (73°F)	59
Rockwell, at 23°C (73°F)	R25
impact strength, notch Izod, (ft)(lb)/in.	
at −54°C (−65°F)	2.9
at 23°C (73°F)	no break
elongation, ultimate, at 23°C (73°F), %	325
flexural modulus, psi	
at 23°C (73°F)	95,000
at 100°C (212°F)	16,000
tensile strength, average, psi, at 23°C (73°F)	3200
tensile strength, yield, psi	
at −250°C (−420°F)	24,000
at −195°C (−320°F)	19,000
at −129°C (−200°F)	14,000
at −73°C (−100°F)	9,000
at −55°C (−68°F)	4,000
at 0°C (32°F)	3,000
at 23°C (73°F)	1,800
at 70°C (158°F)	1,000
at 121°C (250°F)	500
dielectric constant	
at 23°C and 60 Hz	2.1
at 23°C and 10^6 Hz	2.1
at 23°C and 10^9 Hz	2.1
dissipation factor	
at 23°C and 60 Hz	<0.0001
at 23°C and 10^6 Hz	0.00025
at 23°C and 10^9 Hz	0.0004
at 23°C and 10^{10} Hz	0.0007
dielectric strength, short time, V/mil	
at 1 mil	4000
at 10 mils	2100
surface resistivity, at 23°C, Ω	>10^{16}
volume resistivity, at 23°C and 50% rh, Ω-cm	>10^{18}
arc resistance, sec	>165[b]

[a] Measured by Cenco-Fitch apparatus.
[b] Melts, does not track.

same techniques as used with polytetrafluoroethylene dispersion, such as impregnation of glass or asbestos cloth, yarn, or braid, and the dip or spray coating of smooth surfaces. Critical coating thicknesses, the maximum coating thickness that can be applied in a single pass without cracking, are generally thinner for copolymer dispersions than for polytetrafluoroethylene dispersions, being about half or 0.5 mil (0.013 mm). For most impregnations and surface coatings, the dispersion is diluted with water to a viscosity of 8 cP. Like polytetrafluoroethylene dispersions, the heat-treating cycle required to form a homogeneous coating involves removal of water, removal of wetting agent, and fusion.

Commercial Grades and Specifications

The copolymer is commercially available as injection-molding, extrusion grade resins, and a special resin with superior stress-crack resistance. The extrusion grade has a melt viscosity approximately three times that of the injection-molding resin. The special grade resin with increased stress-crack resistance is used primarily in severe chemical service, and has a higher molecular weight than either of the other two resins and a melt viscosity about six times greater than that of the extrusion grade material. Typical commercial specifications are given in Table 5 (19). The copolymer

Table 5. Commercial Specifications for Tetrafluoroethylene–Hexafluoropropylene Copolymer

melting point, °C	270 ± 20
specific gravity, 23/23°C	2.14–2.17
melt flow rate, g/10 min	4–12
tensile strength at 23°C, min	
kg/cm²	175.7
psi	2500
elongation at 23°C, % min	275

dispersion is commercially available as a 55 wt %, aqueous-based, hydrophobic, negatively charged colloid, containing approximately 6% of a mixture of volatile, nonionic and anionic dispersing agents. The average particle size of the copolymer dispersion is about 0.10–0.25 μm.

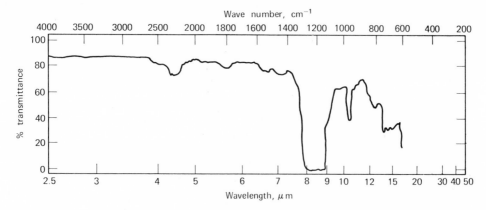

Fig. 7. Infrared spectrum of tetrafluoroethylene–hexafluoropropylene copolymer.

Analysis of Tetrafluoroethylene–Hexafluoropropylene Copolymer

The methods for analyzing the copolymer are similar to those described for the homopolymer on pp. 80–88. A typical infrared spectrum is shown in Figure 7 and a differential thermal analysis scan in Figure 8.

Molded specimens are prepared using a "picture frame"-type of compression molding (19). The sample is heated to $340 \pm 5°C$ and compressed at 88 ± 6 kg/cm^2 (1215 ± 83 psi) for 1–1.5 min. While still under pressure, the assembly is cooled at a rate of $10 \pm 1°C$/min to $150 \pm 10°C$. The pressure is then released, and the molded sample is allowed to reach room temperature.

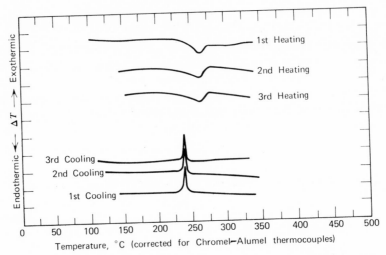

Fig. 8. Differential thermal analysis scan of tetrafluoroethylene–hexafluoropropylene copolymer.

Melt Flow. The flow behavior of molten polymers is useful as a quality control test, and is related to molecular weight. The melt flow rate of tetrafluoroethylene–hexafluoropropylene copolymer is determined at 373°C. The apparatus is an extrusion plastometer described in ASTM D 1238 (20) modified by the use of a corrosion-resistant alloy for the barrel lining, orifice, and piston tip. The sample weight required is 5.0 ± 0.5 g and the total load on the piston is 5000 g. Five successive extruded portions are collected at 30 sec intervals and weighed. See also Vol. 12, pp. 373–375. The change in the melt flow rate with time at the elevated temperature is useful as a control test for polymer stability.

Bibliography

1. U.S. Pat. 2,230,654 (Feb. 4, 1941), R. J. Plunkett (to Kinetic Chemicals, Inc.).
2. D. I. McCane, "Tetrafluoroethylene Polymers," in N. M. Bikales, ed., *Encyclopedia of Polymer Science and Technology*, Vol. 13, Interscience Publishers, a division of John Wiley & Sons, Inc., New York, 1970, pp. 623–670.
3. S. Sherratt, "Polytetrafluoroethylene" under "Fluorine Compounds, Organic," in A. Standen, ed., *Kirk-Othmer Encyclopedia of Chemical Technology*, Vol. 9, 2nd ed., Interscience Publishers, a division of John Wiley & Sons, Inc., New York, 1966, pp. 805–831.
4. *"Teflon" Fluorocarbon Resins, Mechanical Design Data*, Plastics Dept., E. I. du Pont de Nemours, & Co., Inc., Wilmington, Del., 1965.

5. Technical Service Note, *Physical Properties of Polytetrafluoroethylene, F-12,* 2nd ed., Imperial Chemicals Industries, Ltd., Jan. 1968.
6. K. Matsumae, M. Watanabe, A. Nishioka, and T. Ichimiya, *J. Polymer Sci.* **28,** 653–655 (1958).
7. M. M. Renfrew and T. E. Lewis, *Ind. Eng. Chem.* **38,** 870–877 (1946).
8. C. A. Sperati and H. W. Starkweather, *Fortschr. Hochpolymer. Forsch.* **2,** 465–495 (1961).
9. C. E. Lewis and G. R. Kerby, *J. Am. Med. Assoc.* **191,** 103–106 (1965).
10. J. A. Zapp, *Arch. Environ. Health* **4,** (3), 335–346 (1962).
11. *Handling and Use of "Teflon" Fluorocarbon Resins at High Temperatures,* E. I. du Pont de Nemours & Co., Inc., Wilmington, Del., 1961.
12. J. F. Lontz and W. B. Happoldt, Jr., *Ind. Eng. Chem.* **44,** 1800–1805 (1952).
13. *ASTM D 1457-69, Specifications for Tetrafluoroethylene Resin Molding and Extrusion Materials,* American Society for Testing and Materials, Philadelphia, Pa., 1969.
14. *ASTM D 792-66, Tests for Specific Gravity and Density of Plastics by Displacement,* American Society for Testing and Materials, Philadelphia, Pa., 1969.
15. *ASTM D 1505-68, Test for Density of Plastics by the Density-Gradient Technique,* American Society for Testing and Materials, Philadelphia, Pa., 1969.
16. E. L. Gooden and C. M. Smith, *Ind. Eng. Chem., Anal. Ed.* **12,** 479–482 (1940).
17. F. S. Eadie and R. E. Payne, *Iron Age,* **174,** 99 (1954).
18. *ASTM D 1925-63T, Test for Yellowness Index of Plastics,* American Society for Testing and Materials, Philadelphia, Pa., 1969.
19. *ASTM D 2116-66, Specifications for FEP-Fluorocarbon Molding and Extrusion Materials,* American Society for Testing and Materials, Philadelphia, Pa., 1969.
20. *ASTM D 1238-65T, Measuring Flow Rates of Thermoplastics by Extrusion Plastometer,* American Society for Testing and Materials, Philadelphia, Pa., 1969.

JOHN A. BLAIR

E. I. du Pont de Nemours & Co., Inc.

OTHER FLUORINE-CONTAINING POLYMERS

Polychlorotrifluoroethylene. Polychlorotrifluoroethylene plastic is a hard, intermediate-strength material, which possesses excellent chemical resistance, and good electrical and physical properties (21,22). It is only slightly less chemically inert than polytetrafluoroethylene. Useful physical properties of polychlorotrifluoroethylene include thermal stability, chemical and biological inertness, strength and toughness, nonflammability, toughness at cryogenic temperatures, optical clarity, good electrical properties, weatherability, and low permeability. Typical properties are listed in Table 6. The melting point of polychlorotrifluoroethylene is 420°F and it is stable to over 500°F, giving off only minute amounts of halogen acids; rapid polymer degradation takes place above 570°F.

Chlorotrifluoroethylene is commercially polymerized to plastic materials by bulk, suspension, or emulsion techniques. Several grades are manufactured which vary according to molecular weight. High molecular weight polymers are sold as plastic molding powders, dispersions, and films; lower molecular weights as oils, greases, and waxes. Thermal history during fabrication determines the degree of crystallinity of the plastics. Highly amorphous forms are clear, tough, and ductile, whereas highly crystalline plastics are opaque, brittle, and nonyielding. Commercial specifications for molding plastics are given in Table 7 (23). The polymer can be fabricated by the techniques commonly used for thermoplastic materials, extrusion, injection, compression and transfer molding.

The major uses of polychlorotrifluoroethylene plastics are chemical process equipment; electrical wire insulation and components; cryogenic seals, gaskets, valve seats, and liners; instrument, window, and outdoor protective covering; chemically

Table 6. Typical Properties of Polychlorotrifluoroethylene Plastic

	Amorphous	Crystalline
zero strength time, sec	250	250
specific gravity	2.105	2.131
refractive index, at 77°F	1.43	
specific heat, Btu/(lb)(°F)		0.2
thermal conductivity, Btu/(hr)(°F/in.)(ft^2)	1.78	1.83
hardness at 77°F		
Shore D	76	79
Rockwell S	80	85
impact strength, notch Izod, at 77°F, (ft)(lb)/in.	5.0	3.0
flexural strength at 77°F, psi	7,800	10,700
flexural modulus at 77°F, psi	190,000	254,000
tensile strength at 77°F, psi	5,600	5,400
tensile elongation at 77°F, %	190	125
tensile modulus at 77°F, psi	153,000	185,000
dielectric constant at 77°F		
at 10^2 Hz	2.59	2.63
at 10^5 Hz	2.34	2.40
dissipation factor at 77°F		
at 10^2 Hz	0.0215	0.0617
at 10^5 Hz	0.0144	0.0143

resistant and electrical insulation coatings; flexible printed circuitry; and long-term protective packaging against saltwater and industrial atmospheres. The oils and waxes are used as sealants, inert liquids, and gyroscope fluids, and the greases are used in corrosive and oxidative environments.

Chlorotrifluoroethylene–Vinylidene Fluoride Copolymer. Copolymers of chlorotrifluoroethylene and vinylidene fluoride are elastomers with excellent resistance to oils and solvents and high resistance to chemicals. The presence of the CH_2 group in the polymer chain introduces flexibility and furnishes a point for crosslinking. The elastomers may be cured with either amines or peroxides. Useful physical properties include high tensile strength, good extensibility, tear strength, and resistance to aging up to 400°F. The copolymer elastomers are used as weatherproof and corrosion-resistant coatings, gaskets, O-rings, tubing, hose, protective clothing, diaphragms, and propellant binders.

Poly(vinyl Fluoride). Poly(vinyl fluoride) is characterized by resistance to weathering, outstanding chemical resistance and toughness, and high dielectric strength and dielectric constant (24). It is commercially available as a thin, flexible film; Tedlar is the tradename of E. I. du Pont de Nemours & Co., Inc.

Table 7. Commercial Specifications for Polychlorotrifluoroethylene

	Grade 1	Grade 2	Grade 3	Grade 4	Grade 5
zero strength time, sec	115–175	176–300	301–750	751–2500	>2500
specific gravity, 23/23°C, min	2.10	2.10	2.10	2.10	2.10
solution viscosity, cSt	0.64–0.82	0.83–1.05	1.06–1.44		
flow index, mg/min	35.1–92.0	12.1–35.0	2.4–12.0		
deformation under load, at 1000 psi, 24 hr, 70°C, % max	10	10	10	10	10

Poly(vinylidene Fluoride). Poly(vinylidene fluoride) is a partially fluorinated polymer, containing over 59% fluorine, with the chemical formula $(-CH_2-CF_2-)_n$ (24a). It is a tough linear polymer with a crystalline melting point of 170°C and a glass transition temperature of −40°C. Poly(vinylidene fluoride) exhibits high mechanical strength and high impact strength as compared to polytetrafluoroethylene and polychlorotrifluoroethylene. It is resistant to elastic deformation under load, abrasion, and repeated flexure. It possesses excellent chemical resistance and inertness to water, oxidation, and weathering. Kynar is the trade name of Pennsalt Chemical Corporation. It can be fabricated on conventional thermoplastic processing equipment. Uses include wire and cable insulation, chemical process equipment, and corrosion-resistant coatings for pipe and fittings.

Vinylidene Fluoride–Hexafluoropropylene Copolymer. Copolymers of vinylidene fluoride and hexafluoropropylene are elastomers with excellent high-temperature properties. Fluorel is a tradename of the 3M Company; typical commercial specifications are given in Table 8.

Table 8. Commercial Specifications for Two Types of Fluorel Elastomers[a]

	FC-2160	KF-2143
viscosity		
at 212°F, in Mooney units, ML-4		65
at 250°F, in Mooney units, ML-10	25–35	
volatiles, % max		0.7
cured compound[b]		
compression set, after 24 hr at 400°F, % max	10	
hardness, Shore A_2	70–80	
tensile strength, psi, min	1,600	
tensile elongation, % min	140	

[a] Courtesy of 3M Company, St. Paul, Minn.

[b] 100 Parts FC-2160, 30 parts Thermax MT carbon black, 100 parts Maglite D magnesium oxide, 2 parts calcium hydroxide, and 1 part 3M Brand curing agent HC-5, press cured for 20 min at 335°F, and post cured for 1 hr at 250°F, 1 hr at 300°F, 1 hr at 350°F, 1 hr at 400°F, and 20 hr at 500°F.

Methods of Analysis

The analysis of these polymers is similar to that described for polytetrafluoroethylene on pp. 80–88. See also ELASTOMERS, Vol. 12, pp. 81–161, and ETHYLENE AND PROPYLENE POLYMERS, Vol. 12, pp. 341–394. Some specification tests for these polymers are given below.

Zero Strength Time. The zero strength time test is a specification requirement for polychlorotrifluoroethylene plastic (23). It measures the time for a weighted specimen to break after it is heated to 260°C. The results can be correlated with molecular weight.

Procedure

Weigh 100 g of sample and place in a 3-in. positive-pressure compression mold. Apply about 50 psi pressure and heat the mold to 100°C. Then apply maximum pressure and maintain for 5 min. Immediately remove the preform from the mold, place on a 0.40 in. chrome-plated metal plate, and cover with a second plate. Place appropriate spacers to provide a 0.062 in. thick sheet between the plates and place the assembly in a press with the platens at a temperature of 260 ± 5°C. The plates should touch the spacer stops within 3 min. Then apply full pressure for an additional 3 min. Immediately remove the plates and sample and quench in cold water at 15°C. Strip the sample sheet from the plates. It is not necessary to make a preform when using a pelletized form of the plastic.

The apparatus consists of a cylindrical brass thermostat, 5 in. in length and 4 in. in diameter, containing two smooth straight holes, 0.75 in. in diameter, for the test specimens. The holes are parallel to the axis of the cylinder, and are coated with a high-temperature black paint. There are also two additional holes, one to hold a 76-mm immersion thermometer and the other to hold a bimetallic thermo-regulator.

Cut two strips of molded sample 2.0 in. long, 0.187 in. wide, 0.062 in. thick. Notch the sides of the strip along the 2-in. length at the center line so that the width at the notches is 0.047 in. and the sides of the notch form a 90° angle. Insert one end of each notched strip into the specimen holder and clip a 7.5 g weight on the other end. Place the assembly into the furnace maintained at 250°C and start the timer. Record the time, in sec, as each specimen breaks.

Volatiles. The following test for volatiles content is applicable to fluorocarbon elastomers, emulsifiers, and resins.

Procedure

Weigh 10 g of sample and place in a tared aluminum weighing dish. Place the dish in a forced air oven at 300 ± 10°F for 4 hr. Remove the dish from the oven, place in a desiccator to cool, and weigh. The loss in weight is taken as volatiles content.

Mooney Viscosity. The shearing disc viscometer measures the viscosity of rubber and other elastomers (25). The sample preparation in the following method is recommended for fluorocarbon elastomers.

Procedure

Use a Thropp roll mill or equivalent. Turn on cold water to the mill. Tighten the rollers as much as possible and start the mill. Pass about 100 g of sample through the mill until the material is clear. Widen the roller setting to "1" and continue to pass the material through the mill. Widen the roller setting to "2" and then to "3," which should give the appropriate thickness of test specimens of about ¼ in. Allow the milled material to stand about 15 min to reach room temperature. Cut two round specimens, each weighing 25 ± 1 g.

The shearing disc viscometer is shown in Figure 9 (25). It is a motor-driven disc device for measuring the effect of temperature and time on the viscosity of elastomeric materials. The platens are equipped with a heating device capable of maintaining the die cavity at the specified test temperature. The test can be applied using either a large rotor 1.500 in. in diameter and 0.218 in. in thickness or a small rotor 1.200 in. in diameter with the same thickness. The rotor is operated at a speed of 2 rpm. A dial indicator or recorder measures the viscosity in Mooney units.

Assemble the apparatus with the large rotor in place and bring the temperature of the die cavity to 212 or 250°F as required by the product specifications. Adjust the torque indicator to zero while the viscometer is running, unloaded, at the operating pressure. Remove the hot rotor from the cavity, quickly insert the stem through the center of one of the test specimens, and replace in the viscometer. Place the second test specimen on the center of the rotor and immediately close the dies. Record the time from the instant the dies are closed. Allow a 1-min warm-up

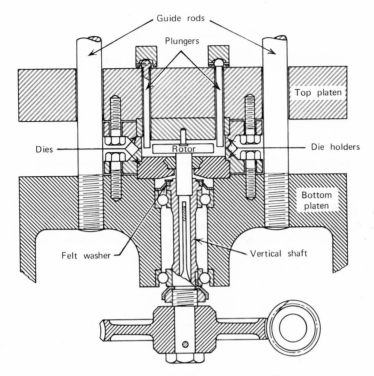

Fig. 9. Shearing disc viscometer (25).

time, and a 4-min running time. Occasionally a 10-min running time may be specified. Take several readings during the specified running time and plot a curve of viscosity, in Mooney units (M), versus time, in min. Report the result with the test conditions including temperature, rotor size (large, L, or small, S), and running time.

Physical Tests for Cured Elastomers. Compression set, hardness, and tensile properties of the compounded and cured elastomer are frequently required for commercial specifications. The following method is described for Fluorel elastomer FC-2160 (3M Company) but may be adapted to other fluorocarbon elastomers.

Procedure

SAMPLE PREPARATION. Use a Thropp roll mill or equivalent. Place a sheet of polyethylene, polyester film, paper, or a glass dish under the rollers and turn on the cold water to the mill. Tighten the rollers as much as possible and start the mill. Pass a weighed 200-g sample through the mill and allow it to band on a roller. Widen the roller setting to give a low bank of rubber on the mill, about the size of a pencil. As the sample is being milled, add a weighed mixture of the following dry materials: 60 g of Thermax MT carbon black, 20 g of Maglite D magnesium oxide, 4 g of calcium hydroxide, and 2 g of curing agent HC-5 (3M Company). Sprinkle the dry mixture at the bank and allow it to be milled in. Catch any loose material and sprinkle it back on the rollers. Cut back and forth each way six to eight times, allowing all the rubber to band back on the roller each time. Then cut the sheet again and remove from the mill as the rollers are turning. Tighten the rollers as much as possible and mill the sample four to six times without allowing it to band on

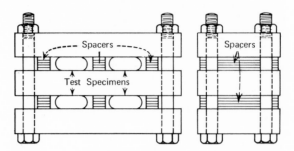

Fig. 10. Device for compression set test under constant deflection.

the roller. Widen the rollers six times, one setting each, and each time mill the sample four to six times without allowing the sample to band on the roller. The number "6" setting should produce a sheet of the desired thickness for the compression set plugs. Using an inside bevel punch with $1\frac{1}{8}$ in. diameter and a cold press, cut four plugs from the milled sheet. Each plug should weigh 10–11 g.

Roll up the balance of the milled sample and pass it through the mill two or three times with the rollers as tight as possible. Widen the rollers one setting at a time to the number "3" setting, each time milling the sample two or three times without allowing it to band on the roller. This should produce a sheet of the desired thickness for the hardness and tensile tests. Cut two 3 in. × 3 in. square pieces weighing about 50 g.

COMPRESSION SET. Use a $4\frac{1}{2} \times 4\frac{1}{2}$ in. square by $\frac{1}{16}$ in. four cavity compression set mold. Apply a light coating of release agent to the mold, place it in a hydraulic press with protective plates heated to 335°F, and preheat for 15 min. Remove the mold from the press and quickly place two prepared plugs in each of two diagonal cavities. Return the mold to the heated hydraulic press and quickly apply 50 tons pressure. Press cure for 20 min at 350°F. Remove the mold from the press and immediately remove the test specimens from the mold without quenching or cooling. Place the test specimens on aluminum foil or a chrome plate that has been coated with a release agent and step cure in a forced air oven as follows: 1 hr at 250°F; 1 hr at 300°F; 1 hr at 400°F; and 20 hr at 500°F. Remove the cured specimens from the oven and allow to cool for at least 30 min. Measure the "initial" thickness of each specimen at the center.

Place the cured test specimens between the plates of a compression device such as shown in Figure 10 (26) using 0.375 in. spacers. Compress the plates in a cold press or vise until the spacers are held tightly and then tighten the four nuts. Remove the assembly from the press and place in a forced air oven at 400 ± 5°F for 22 hr. Remove from the oven and immediately replace the compression device in the cold press. Quickly apply pressure, loosen the nuts, and remove the compressed specimens. Allow the specimens to cool for at least 30 min and then measure the final thickness.

$$\% \text{ compression set} = \frac{(t_i - t_f)(100)}{(t_i - t_s)}$$

where t_i, t_f, and t_s are the initial and final thicknesses of the specimen and the thickness of the spacer bar, respectively.

HARDNESS. Apply a light coating of release agent to a single cavity mold, place the mold in a hydraulic press with protective plates heated to 335°F, and preheat the mold for 15 min. Remove the mold and quickly place both previously prepared 3 in. square pieces in the cavity. Return the mold to the heated hydraulic press and apply 50 tons pressure as quickly as possible. Press cure for 20 min at 335°F. Remove the mold from the press and immediately remove the pressed sheets from the mold without quenching or cooling. Allow the sheets to stand for 15–20 min to reach room temperature. Place the sheets one on top of the other and determine the hardness of the double thickness of "pre-cured" sample with a Shore A durometer using a 5-sec time interval for the readings (27).

Place the pressed sheets on aluminum foil or a chrome plate that has been coated with a release agent and step cure in a forced air oven as follows: 1 hr at 250°F; 1 hr at 300°F; 1 hr at 400°F; and 20 hr at 500°F. Remove the cured specimens from the oven and allow to cool for 15–20 min. Again determine the hardness of a double thickness; this is the "initial" hardness. Also record the hardness at 24, 48, and 72 hr after the "initial" time.

After determining the initial hardness, cut three dumbbells from each cured pressed sheet. Place three of the dumbbells on aluminum foil or a chrome plate that has been coated with a release agent and place in a forced air oven at 575 ± 5°F to "heatage" for 16 hr ± 15 min. Remove from the oven and allow to cool for 15–20 min. Again determine the hardness.

TENSILE STRENGTH AND ELONGATION. Measure the thickness and width of each dumbbell at its center and determine the area of the cross section. Using white ink, mark off a 1-in. segment as near the center as possible. Determine tensile strength, elongation, and 100% modulus on an Instron Tester Model TM using the following conditions:

jaw separation	2 in.
jaw and chart speed	20 in./min
total pounds across the chart	50 lb

Elongation, in %, is recorded at the break point. The 100% modulus, in psi, is the load at 100% elongation divided by the area of the cross section. Tensile strength, in psi, is the load at the breaking point divided by the area of the cross section.

Bibliography

21. R. P. Bringer, "Polychlorotrifluoroethylene," under "Fluorine Compounds, Organic," in A. Standen, ed., *Kirk-Othmer Encyclopedia of Chemical Technology*, Vol. 9, 2nd ed., Interscience Publishers, a division of John Wiley & Sons, Inc., New York, 1966, pp. 832–833.

22. R. P. Bringer, "Chlorotrifluoroethylene Polymers," under "Fluorine-Containing Polymers," in N. M. Bikales, ed., *Encyclopedia of Polymer Science and Technology*, Vol. 7, Interscience Publishers, a division of John Wiley & Sons, Inc., New York, 1967, pp. 204–219.

23. *ASTM D 1430-69, Specifications for Polychlorotrifluoroethylene Molding Plastics*, American Society for Testing and Materials, Philadelphia, Pa., 1969.

24. L. E. Wolinski, "Poly(vinyl fluoride)", under "Fluorine Compounds, Organic," in A. Standen, ed., *Kirk-Othmer Encyclopedia of Chemical Technology*, Vol. 9, 2nd ed., Interscience Publishers, a division of John Wiley & Sons, Inc., New York, 1966, pp. 835–840.

24a. W. S. Barnhart and N. T. Hall, "Poly(vinylidene fluoride)" under "Fluorine Compounds, Organic," in A. Standen, ed., *Kirk-Othmer Encyclopedia of Chemical Technology*, Vol. 9, 2nd ed., Interscience Publishers, a division of John Wiley & Sons, New York, 1966, pp. 840–847.

25. *ASTM D 1646-68, Test for Viscosity and Curing Characteristics of Rubber by the Shearing Disc Viscometer*, American Society for Testing and Materials, Philadelphia, Pa., 1969.

26. *ASTM D 395-69, Tests for Compression Set of Vulcanized Rubber*, American Society for Testing and Materials, Philadelphia, Pa., 1969.

27. *ASTM D 2240-68, Test for Indentation Hardness of Rubber and Plastics by Means of a Durometer*, American Society for Testing and Materials, Philadelphia, Pa., 1969.

JOAN L. BATTLE
Encyclopedia of Industrial Chemical Analysis
with the cooperation of
ROBERT P. BRINGER
3M Company

FLUOROXENE.   See ANESTHETICS, Vol. 5, pp. 355–421.

FLUOTHANE (HALOTHANE).   See ANESTHETICS, Vol. 5, pp. 355–421.

FORMALDEHYDE

Although the basis for understanding the chemical nature of aldehydes was established in 1835 with Liebig's research on acetaldehyde, it was not until 1868, after the discovery of such aldehydes as propionaldehyde and butyraldehyde, that August Wilhelm von Hofmann successfully prepared formaldehyde by passing a mixture of methanol vapors and air over a heated platinum spiral.

Actually, formaldehyde was first prepared by Alexander M. Butlerov in 1859 as a product of an attempted synthesis of methylene glycol.   Butlerov failed to isolate the unstable glycol but did publish an accurate description of formaldehyde solution, formaldehyde gas, and formaldehyde polymer with an account of chemical reactions, including the formation of hexamethylenetetramine from the reaction of formaldehyde with ammonia.   He did not characterize the methylene oxide polymer (from the reaction of methylene iodide and silver oxalate or silver oxide) as a formaldehyde polymer, but he was aware that it behaved like the unknown "formyl aldehyde."

Formaldehyde is of value principally because of its properties: its high order of chemical reactivity, its colorless nature, its stability, and the purity of its commercial forms.   From an application standpoint, the significance of these properties is brought out by its utilization as a resinifying agent, synthetic agent, hardening agent, stiffening agent, tanning agent, disinfectant, bactericide, and preservative.   In organic synthesis, it is used to link together similar or dissimilar molecules and radicals by means of methylene linkages.   Major volume applications include the production of phenolic resins, urea–formaldehyde resins, melamine–formaldehyde resins, ethylene glycol, and pentaerythritol.   Recent research has led to the commercialization of high molecular weight homopolymers, the new and rapidly growing polyacetal resins (du Pont's Delrin, Celanese's "Celcon, and Imperial Chemicals' Alkon), which are tough thermoplastic resins with good mechanical and chemical properties and reasonable thermal stability.   For more information on formaldehyde, the general references (1–4) should be consulted.   See also CARBONYL COMPOUNDS, Vol. 8, pp. 331–367.

Properties

Pure, dry formaldehyde is a colorless gas which condenses on chilling to give a liquid which boils at $-19°C$ and freezes to a crystalline solid at $-118°C$ (5).   Formaldehyde, in both liquid and gas forms, polymerizes rapidly at both ordinary and low temperatures and is sold or shipped only in solution or in the polymerized state. The aqueous solutions of formaldehyde have a high degree of stability even though they are extremely reactive chemically. When monomeric formaldehyde is required, it is best prepared from the commercial solutions or polymer at the point of use. Properties of monomeric formaldehyde gas are listed in Table 1.

Table 1. Properties of Monomeric Formaldehyde Gas

boiling point, °C	−19	(5)
freezing point, °C	−118	(5)
molecular weight	30.03	
heat of combustion, kcal/g	4.47	(7)
heat capacity at 25°C, cal/(mol)(°C)	8.461	(8)
entropy at 25°C, cal/(mol)(°C)	52.26 ± 0.1	(8)
heat of formation at 25°C, kcal/mol	−27.7 ± 1.5	(8)
free energy at 25°C, kcal/mol	−26.27	(8)
explosive limits in air, vol %	7–72	(9)

Since all other aldehydes of the aliphatic series contain an alkyl group in place of one of the hydrogen atoms of formaldehyde, this aldehyde cannot be regarded as a typical one. Accordingly, it differs from its homologs in some of its reactions (6). Three of these are the basis of assay methods of formaldehyde: (a) Fehling's solution plus formaldehyde precipitates cuprous oxide. (b) Formaldehyde and ammoniacal silver nitrate yield metallic silver, which will form a silver mirror if the glass walls of the container are very clean. (c) Hydrogen peroxide oxidizes formaldehyde quantitatively to formic acid.

In addition, the following reactions are somewhat unique for formaldehyde: (a) It is the only aldehyde that yields a primary alcohol when the product of its reaction with a Grignard reagent is hydrolyzed. (b) With an excess of dilute ammonia solution, formaldehyde solution yields, after standing and evaporation at 100°C, hexamethylenetetramine, a white solid with a sweet taste, which sublimes at 263°C without melting and with partial decomposition. (c) When an aqueous solution containing formaldehyde and sodium hydroxide stands or is warmed, simultaneous oxidation and reduction of the aldehyde occur (Cannizzaro reaction), yielding an alcohol and a formate salt.

Solubility. Anhydrous formaldehyde gas is only moderately soluble in nonpolar solvents, such as ethyl ether, chloroform, or toluene, at room temperature. Dissolution in such solvents at low temperatures produces a concentrated solution, but heating leads to polymerization and vaporization of the solute. However, concentrated solutions of formaldehyde in polar solvents, such as methanol and water, are readily obtained at room temperature. At ordinary temperatures, solutions containing over 30 wt % of formaldehyde become cloudy on standing and polymers precipitate. Solution clarity with increasing formaldehyde concentration can be maintained by the addition of methanol as a stabilizer. Formaldehyde is sold commercially primarily as an aqueous solution with 1–15 wt % of methanol added. Concentrated solutions containing up to 55% formaldehyde in about 30 wt % methanol with very little water are also available.

Formaldehyde in aqueous solutions is present principally in the form of the mono-hydrate, methylene glycol:

$$\underset{H}{\overset{H}{\diagdown}}C=O + H-O-H \;\rightleftharpoons\; HO-\underset{H}{\overset{H}{C}}-OH$$

However, a series of low molecular weight polymeric hydrates or polyoxymethylene glycols, $HO-(CH_2O)_n-H$, is also present. With increasing quantities of formaldehyde, the percentage of methylene glycol decreases and the percentage of higher polymers of methylene glycol increases. For example, in solutions containing 35 wt % of equivalent formaldehyde at 35°C, approximately 30 wt % is present as methylene glycol and 70 wt % as polyoxymethylene glycols with chain lengths up to and exceeding ten carbon atoms (10). The amount of monomeric formaldehyde in solution is very small: a 30 wt % aqueous solution at 60°C contains less than 0.03 % free formaldehyde (11).

The addition of methanol to formaldehyde solutions probably results in an equilibrium reaction between methylene glycol and methanol to give the methyl hemiformal and water:

$$HO-\underset{H}{\overset{H}{C}}-OH + CH_3OH \;\rightleftharpoons\; HO-\underset{H}{\overset{H}{C}}-OCH_3 + H_2O$$

The tendency of the hemiformal molecule to polymerize is reduced because of the absence of one hydroxyl end group. Accordingly, a 37% formaldehyde solution with 1% methanol is relatively stable at 40.5°C, whereas the minimum temperature without the methanol would be 67–71°C. Also, with 7% methanol, the same solution is stable at temperatures as low as 21°C (10).

Distillation. The equilibrium reactions of formaldehyde in aqueous or alcoholic solutions described previously result in mixtures which do not follow the usual distillation behavior. When higher distillation pressures are used, thus increasing solution temperatures, the equilibrium reaction is shifted in the direction of formaldehyde vapor with an increase in formaldehyde volatility. Vacuum distillation lowers solution temperatures and reduces formaldehyde volatility. Accordingly, then, either water or formaldehyde–water azeotrope may be distilled overhead depending upon the distillation pressure.

Polymerization. Pure, dry formaldehyde gas, at temperatures up to 100°C, shows no visible polymerization and obeys the ideal gas law (12). However, a trace of water will cause rapid polymerization.

Formaldehyde can react with itself, water, or methanol to form various homopolymers. Although the term "formaldehyde polymers" normally refers to the polyoxymethylenes, $(-CH_2-O-CH_2-O-CH_2-O-)_n$, other polymers which are linked through the carbon atom are also known:

$$-\underset{OH}{\overset{H}{C}}-\underset{OH}{\overset{H}{C}}-\underset{OH}{\overset{H}{C}}-\underset{OH}{\overset{H}{C}}-\underset{OH}{\overset{H}{C}}-$$

These are known as the polyhydroxyaldehydes, and hexose sugars are apparently the highest members of the group.

The polyoxymethylenes are the more important of these types and exist in both linear and cyclic forms. The lowest molecular weight members of this group, the glycols, are very soluble in water and release monomeric formaldehyde readily. The glycols exist chiefly in solution and are extremely difficult to isolate; concentration of such solutions results in higher molecular weight paraformaldehyde; dehydration at temperatures above 100°C with either catalysts or dehydrating agents only leads to still higher molecular weight polymers. The formaldehyde content of these polymers is in the range of 77–99.9 wt %, with the balance being mainly water. The high molecular weight polyoxymethylenes, the polyacetal resins, contain more than 500 formaldehyde units.

From the polyoxymethylenes, two, paraformaldehyde and trioxane, are of considerable commercial importance.

Paraformaldehyde is a white or colorless solid with a formaldehyde content of 90–99%. It is the specific name used for the low molecular weight polyoxymethylene polymers (13):

$$\text{HO---(---}\overset{\displaystyle H}{\underset{\displaystyle H}{\text{C}}}\text{---O---})_n\text{---H} \qquad \text{where } n = 8\text{--}100$$

Paraformaldehyde is commercially available in powder, granular, or flake forms. It has the characteristic pungent odor of formaldehyde, and melts in the range 120–170°C, with the melting range being an index of the degree of polymerization.

At normal temperatures, paraformaldehyde decomposes to monomeric formaldehyde slowly; the depolymerization is accelerated at temperatures above 130–150°C. It is flammable, with a flash point of about 93°C (open cup); however, it is not considered a hazardous material by the Department of Transportation (14).

The preparation of paraformaldehyde is usually carried out from concentrated (80–90%) formaldehyde solutions obtained by vacuum distillation at pressures of 25–200 torr. Separation of paraformaldehyde is obtained on cooling the concentrated solutions.

A typical formaldehyde solution is obtained when paraformaldehyde is dissolved in water. An equilibrium composition of methylene glycol and polyoxymethylenes is obtained, which is a function of the amount of equivalent formaldehyde in solution. Temperature, pH, and molecular size greatly influence the rate of solution.

Trioxane or α-trioxymethylene, the cyclic trimer of formaldehyde, has the following structure:

$$\begin{array}{c} \text{H}_2 \\ \text{C} \\ \diagup \quad \diagdown \\ \text{O} \qquad\quad \text{O} \\ | \qquad\qquad | \\ \text{H}_2\text{C} \qquad \text{CH}_2 \\ \diagdown \quad \diagup \\ \text{O} \end{array}$$

It is a colorless crystalline material, melting at 62–64°C, boiling without decomposition at 115°C, and forming an azeotrope with water which contains 70 wt % trioxane and boils at 91.3°C. Its flash point is about 45°C (open cup). It burns easily with a colorless blue flame. Concentrations of trioxane of 3.57–28.7% in air are explosive (15).

Trioxane is soluble in water, alcohols, ketones, organic acids, esters, ethers, phenols, and chlorinated hydrocarbons, but is only slightly soluble in pentanes and lower paraffin fractions. Trioxane hydrolyzes in aqueous solution in the presence of a strong acid to a solution of low molecular weight polyoxymethylenes; it is inert under neutral or alkaline conditions, and yields negative results when analyzed by the normal procedures for formaldehyde, such as the sodium sulfite or alkaline peroxide methods.

The depolymerization of trioxane to formaldehyde readily takes place under anhydrous conditions in the presence of such strong acids as sulfuric, hydrochloric, and phosphoric. The monomeric formaldehyde thus produced is extremely reactive and combines easily with materials capable of reacting with formaldehyde. Otherwise, the monomer polymerizes to a high molecular weight polyoxymethylene.

Trioxane is generally produced by heating paraformaldehyde or concentrated formaldehyde solutions with small quantities of a strong acid.

Tetraoxane, the cyclic tetramer of formaldehyde, melts at 112°C and boils about 170°C. The eight-membered ring is believed to be more stable than the six-membered trioxane ring. Tetraoxane currently has little or no commercial use (16).

Toxicity. Formaldehyde gas has a pungent odor and is extremely irritating to the mucous membranes of the eyes, nose, and throat at concentrations as low as 20 ppm (17). The toxic properties of paraformaldehyde are essentially the same as of formaldehyde and the polymeric vapors of trioxane are not irritating and possess a pleasant, chloroform-like odor.

Methods of Manufacture

Two processes are significant for the commercial production of formaldehyde (3): the methanol process and the hydrocarbon process. The former represents the major production route, accounting for over 90% of the world production (18), although increasing quantities are being made by the hydrocarbon process.

Essentially pure formaldehyde, with some methanol and traces of formic acid, is obtained from the methanol process, which consists of passing a mixture of methanol vapors and air over a stationary catalyst at approximately atmospheric pressure and absorbing the product gases in water. Catalysts used are silver, copper, or an iron–molybdenum oxide, and the methanol content of the product is dependent on the catalyst system selected. Raw materials employed are chemically pure, synthetic methanol, air, and water.

The second commercial process is based on the partial oxidation of a hydrocarbon gas, usually natural gas, propane, or butane, under pressure. This is followed by rapid cooling, condensation, and absorption of the products in water, yielding a crude solution which is then processed to separate formaldehyde from the other reaction products, such as alcohols, aldehydes, and acids. Propane and butane are preferred to methane or ethane because of the lower oxidation temperatures permitted. Higher hydrocarbons yield increasingly complex by-products. Typical products manufactured by the oxidation of propane and butane include, in addition to formaldehyde, acetaldehyde, acetone, propionaldehyde, methanol, n-propanol, isopropanol, and butanols. Use of the hydrocarbon process has decreased over the past 20–30 years because of low yields and difficulties encountered in separating formaldehyde from other oxidation products of low exploitability.

The preferred material for formaldehyde processing is stainless steel. Aluminum may be used for scrubbers and formaldehyde storage. Other materials recommended for storage of formaldehyde are 18-8 stainless steel, glass, stoneware, acid-resistant enamels, and rubber. Resistant storage tanks may be fabricated by the use of phenolic-resin coatings and asphalt-based paints. Iron, copper, nickel, and zinc alloys should be avoided.

Commercial Grades and Specifications

Formaldehyde monomer is available commercially only in solutions stabilized with methanol. In most cases, these are aqueous solutions with methanol contents ranging from 1 to 15 wt %. The ACS grade material (19) falls into the high methanol content category, whereas the *U.S. Pharmacopeia* specification (20) requires "not less than 37% formaldehyde" and methanol "added to prevent polymerization." The trade name Formalin is sometimes used in referring to formaldehyde solutions. This is a carryover from Europe, where this term was used for the standard 37 wt % formaldehyde solutions. Commercial grades (21,22) are distinguished, in general, by the terms "inhibited" and "uninhibited" which, again, refer to high and low methanol contents. Another commercial grade (23) contains approximately 55 wt % formaldehyde and only about 10% water, with the remainder being methanol. Selection of the proper grade is dependent upon the intended use. A summary of the various specifications is given in Table 2; the USP and ACS specifications are identical except that the former has no color requirement.

Table 2. Specifications of Formaldehyde Solutions

	ACS and USP (19.24)	37.2% Uninhibited solution (21)	37.2% Inhibited solution (22)	Methyl formcel 55% (23)
formaldehyde, wt %	36.0–38.0	37.0–37.4	37.0–37.4	55 ± 0.5
methanol, wt %	10–15	1.0 max	10.0–11.0	10.0–11.0
water, wt %				10.0–11.0
residue after ignition, wt %, max	0.005			
acidity (as HCOOH), wt %, max	0.03	0.03	0.03	0.04
chlorine, wt %, max	0.0005			
sulfate, wt %, max	0.002			
heavy metals (as Pb), wt %, max	0.0005			
iron, ppm, max	5	0.5	0.5	0.5
copper, ppm, max		1	1	
specific gravity, 25/15.6°C		1.1076–1.1112	1.0837–1.0873	
pH, at 25°C		3.0–5.0	3.0–5.0	
odor		pungent	pungent	
color, APHA, max	10[a]	20	20	10

[a] USP specifications list no color requirement.

Methods of Analysis

SEPARATION

Formaldehyde solutions suitable for analytical testing can usually be obtained from such products as textiles and paper, which have been treated with formaldehyde or urea–formaldehyde condensates, polyvinyl formals, protein products which have been hardened or insolubilized by formaldehyde treatment, and formaldehyde-tanned leather. Formaldehyde is usually present in these materials combined with hydroxy compounds in the form of formals or methylene ethers, or as methylene derivatives of amino or amido compounds. The material to be studied is heated with a 10–20% solution of a strong mineral acid. Sulfuric acid is preferred because of its nonvolatility. The acid-treated material is then distilled or steam-distilled with the condenser outlet placed well below a little water in the receiver so that released formaldehyde will be dissolved. Formaldehyde can be quantitatively distilled from such aqueous solutions at concentrations less than approximately 10%; formaldehyde will usually be present in the first 10–60% of the distillate.

Gas chromatography is another means of separating formaldehyde from other components in a mixture. For details, see p. 113.

IDENTIFICATION

Colorimetric Spot Tests

There are many unique colorimetric spot tests for the identification of formaldehyde. They are summarized in Table 3; the three most important tests are discussed below.

Table 3. Color Spot Tests for Formaldehyde

Reagent	Color	Sensitivity	Interferences	References
modified Schiff reagent	blue-violet	<1 ppm	acrolein, glyoxalic acid	(25)
chromotropic acid	violet	3 ppm	glyceraldehyde, furfural	(26)
acetylacetone + ammonium acetate + acetic acid	yellow	[a]	large amounts of acetaldehyde	(27)
potassium ferricyanide + phenylhydrazine hydrochloride + sodium hydroxide	red	<15 μg	aliphatic aldehydes	(28)
phenylhydrazine	red	1 μg	none specified	(29)
ammoniacal silver nitrate (Tollen's reagent)	black precipitate	2 ppm	none specified	(30)
2,7-dihydroxynaphthalene	violet	0.5–2.0 μg/ml	acrolein	(31)
morphine hydrochloride + sulfuric acid	violet ring at liquid junction	<5%	none specified	(32)
2-hydroxycarbazole + sulfuric acid	dark blue	0.004 μg	pyruvaldehyde	(33)

[a] Not given.

Schiff Test. An extremely simple and highly sensitive (1 part formaldehyde in 10,000 parts acetaldehyde) colorimetric procedure is based on the production of a specific blue-violet color when formaldehyde reacts in the presence of strong acids with Schiff's fuchsin–bisulfite reagent (34). Acetaldehyde and higher aliphatic aldehydes do not interfere, but acrolein or glyoxalic acid may interfere. Modified Schiff's reagent (35) may be stored for up to 2 yr without loss of effectiveness. Acetaldehyde present in concentrations of approximately 2% sometimes gives a purple red color, but this color fades rapidly in 10 min, whereas the characteristic formaldehyde color does not fade in 6–12 hr (36). For details see CARBONYL COMPOUNDS, Vol. 8, p. 344.

Chromotropic Acid Test. Another highly specific color test involves the use of chromotropic acid, 1,8-naphthalenediol-3,6-disulfonic acid, and strong sulfuric acid (28,29). The violet color which develops is sensitive for the detection of formaldehyde at concentrations as low as 3 ppm. Most other aldehydes do not interfere with this test, but glyceraldehyde yields a yellow color with a green fluorescence and furfural yields a yellow-brown color. Acrolein gives a negative test with this reagent. The chromotropic acid test is sensitive to any substances which yield formaldehyde upon hydrolysis in concentrated sulfuric acid (39). For details, see CARBONYL COMPOUNDS, Vol. 8, pp. 344–345.

Hantzsch Test. This test is based on the Hantzsch reaction (40), the reaction of formaldehyde with acetylacetone and an ammonium salt to give diacetyldihydrolutidine. The reaction is carried out under mild conditions and may be used for the identification and determination of formaldehyde in living material. This procedure is useful in systems in which the sulfuric acid in the chromotropic acid technique reacts with the matrix material resulting either in a color or the liberation of formaldehyde. The yellow lutidine derivative is measured spectrophotometrically at 412 mm. The time required for optimum color development varies with temperature. The test is not satisfactory in the presence of large amounts of acetaldehyde, but little interference is noted when approximately equimolar quantities of formaldehyde and acetaldehyde are present in a sample.

Derivatives

For small quantities of formaldehyde, characteristic derivatives are useful for identification. The more significant derivatives of formaldehyde are listed in Table 4 (41).

Table 4. Formaldehyde Derivatives (41)

Reagent	Conditions	Product	Melting point	References
methone or dimedon (dimethyldihydro-resorcinol, 5,5-dimethylcyclo-hexanedione)	add few drops of 5–10% solution of reagent in ethanol to sample which has been made slightly acidic with acetic acid	methylene bis-methone (precipitate)	189°C (recrystalized from methanol and water)	(45)
p-nitrophenyl-hydrazine hydrochloride	mildly acid ethanol solution containing formaldehyde	formaldehyde–p-nitrophenyl-hydrazone (precipitate)	181–182°C (recrystalized from ethanol)	(46)
2,4-dinitrophenyl-hydrazine hydro-chloride	mildly acid aqueous ethanol solution containing formal-dehyde	formaldehyde-2,4-dinitrophenyl-hydrazone (precipitate)	166–167°C (recrystalized from ethanol)	(47)
β-naphthol	treat few drops of for-maldehyde-containing solution with 33% alcohol, reagent, and a little hydrochloric acid	methylene dinaphthol (precipitates as small white needles on gently boiling mixture)	turns brown at 180°C; melts with decomposition to a brownish-red liquid at 189–192°C	(48)

Spectroscopy

The carbonyl group in formaldehyde absorbs infrared radiation in characteristic regions (42), and this absorption may be used as a sensitive measure with appropriate calibration. However, one of these regions (1740–1720 cm^{-1}) is characteristic of many carbonyl group absorptions and would be the sum total of all compounds containing carbonyl groups. The other region (2900–2700 cm^{-1}) is due to the C-H stretching frequency of the aldehyde group and, because of the strong influence of the carbonyl oxygen, is virtually independent of the rest of the molecule. For details, see CARBONYL COMPOUNDS, Vol. 8, pp. 345–347.

Ross (43) reports the infrared spectra of the 2,4-dinitrophenylhydrazone derivatives of formaldehyde and other aldehydes. The spectra may be useful for identification even when the melting points of the derivatives are quite close.

Nuclear magnetic resonance spectroscopy is useful for detection when the component is present in greater than trace concentration.

A significant mass peak appearing at 30 mass units (m/e) in the mass spectrum of a sample, when analyzed on an analytical mass spectrometer at 70 eV ionizing current, can usually be associated with formaldehyde. However, extreme caution should be exercised, and the contribution of fragment mass peaks from other possible organic compounds in the sample being analyzed to the m/e 30 peak must be determined accurately from good calibration mass patterns. Most amines contribute significantly to the m/e 30 peak. The presence of formaldehyde should be verified by appropriate major mass fragment intensities at m/e equals 29 and 28 (44).

Gas Chromatography

After separation, the identity of the formaldehyde peak may be established by matching the retention time of the suspected peak with that of a known sample of formaldehyde or by using tabulated retention data. A more reliable technique is to trap the respective fraction as it elutes from the gas chromatograph and verify its identity by infrared or mass spectrometry. Caution must also be used in this technique; formaldehyde should be trapped in a solvent which will prevent polymerization.

ASSAY METHODS

For the determination of formaldehyde, present as a major component, several chemical methods are applicable. An assessment of these methods has been carried out by Büchi (49) and by Reynolds and Irwin (50). The latter study is concerned with impure formaldehyde solutions while Büchi studied the analysis of commercial solutions of formaldehyde. Büchi concluded that, when considering the merits based on accuracy, simplicity, reliability, and economy with respect to time and apparatus, only the sodium sulfite, alkaline peroxide, iodometric, ammonium chloride, and mercurimetric methods were valid for serious consideration. According to him the sodium sulfite method was quite dependable, and the most satisfactory for the analysis of commercial formaldehyde solutions.

Sodium Sulfite Method. When formaldehyde reacts with sodium sulfite to form the formaldehyde–bisulfite addition product, sodium hydroxide is liberated quantitatively according to the following equation:

$$CH_2O + Na_2SO_3 + H_2O \longrightarrow NaOH + CH_2(NaSO_3)OH$$

The amount of base produced is determined titrimetrically (51).

Procedure

Prepare a sodium sulfite solution by dissolving 125 g of anhydrous sodium sulfite or 250 g of hydrated sodium sulfite in water and dilute to 1 liter. Transfer 100 ml of the sodium sulfite solution to a 500-ml Erlenmeyer flask, add 1.8–2.2 g of sample, and swirl the mixture to effect complete solution. Add 3–5 drops of 0.1% ethanolic thymolphthalein indicator solution and titrate with 0.5 N sulfuric acid to the first colorless end point. Carry out a blank determination, and run duplicates of both sample and blank determinations.

$$\text{Formaldehyde, wt \%} = \frac{(A - B)(N)(MW)(100)}{(w)(1000)}$$

where A = volume of sulfuric acid solution required for sample titration, in ml
B = volume of sulfuric acid solution required for blank titration, in ml
N = normality of the sulfuric acid solution
MW = g-mol wt of formaldehyde (30.03)
w = sample weight, in g

Alkaline Peroxide Method. Formaldehyde is oxidized with hydrogen peroxide in the presence of excess base according to the following equation:

$$2\,HCHO + 2\,NaOH + H_2O_2 \longrightarrow 2\,HCOONa + 2\,H_2O + H_2$$

The excess of base is determined by titration with standard acid (19). Acetone (less than 7 wt %) and acetaldehyde (less than 0.5 wt %) do not interfere (49).

Procedure

Accurately weigh about 10 ml of water into a stoppered 250-ml Erlenmeyer flask, add 3 ml of sample from a pipet, holding the tip of the pipet just above the surface of the water, and weigh again. Add 50 ml of N sodium hydroxide solution and then, immediately but slowly through a small funnel, add 50 ml of neutral hydrogen peroxide solution, prepared by neutralizing 10 ml of 30% hydrogen peroxide solution to bromothymol blue indicator solution with N sodium hydroxide solution and diluting to 100 ml. Leave the funnel in the neck of the flask and heat the mixture cautiously on the steam bath for 15 min, shaking cautiously with a general rotary motion. Cool the flask and contents to room temperature with cold water and rinse the funnel and walls of the flask with water. Add 2–5 drops of bromothymol blue indicator solution and titrate the excess sodium hydroxide with N sulfuric acid to a bluish-green end point. Carry out a blank determination.

$$\text{Formaldehyde, wt \%} = \frac{(A - B)(N)(MW)(100)}{(w)(1000)}$$

where A = volume of sulfuric acid solution required for sample titration, in ml
B = volume of sulfuric acid solution required for blank titration, in ml
N = normality of sulfuric acid solution
MW = g-mol wt of formaldehyde (30.03)
w = sample weight, in g

Iodometric Method. The reaction of formaldehyde with hypoiodite reagent serves as a method of determination, according to the following equation (52):

$$HCHO + NaOI + NaOH \longrightarrow HCOONa + NaI + H_2O$$

Many other aldehydes and ketones also react with the iodine reagent, and the method described is basically useful only with known systems. The recovery of formaldehyde is approximately 98.5% (53). The interference of methanol, a known constituent in commercial formaldehyde solutions, has been disputed (54,55). This iodometric method, sometimes referred to as the Romijn procedure, is particularly useful for the determination of small concentrations of formaldehyde in aqueous solutions.

Procedure

Measure a sample containing up to 0.16 g of formaldehyde into an iodine flask and dilute with water to about 100 ml. Introduce 30 ml of 3 N sodium or potassium hydroxide solution and then 75 ml of 0.2 N sodium hypoiodite solution. Stopper the flask and allow the mixture to stand at room temperature for 30 min. Add approximately 95 ml of N sulfuric acid and titrate the liberated iodine immediately with 0.1 N sodium thiosulfate solution, using starch indicator. Carry out at least one blank determination with each set of samples.

$$\text{Formaldehyde, wt \%} = \frac{(A - B)(N)(MW)(100)}{(w)(2)(100)}$$

where A = volume of sodium thiosulfate solution required for sample titration, in ml

B = volume of sodium thiosulfate solution required for blank titration, in ml

N = normality of sodium thiosulfate solution

MW = g-mol wt of formaldehyde (30.03)

w = sample weight, in g

Potassium Cyanide Method. Another volumetric procedure for the determination of formaldehyde involves the use of potassium cyanide. The determination is based on the following equation (56):

$$\text{HCHO} + \text{KCN} \longrightarrow \text{CH}_2(\text{OK})\text{CN}$$

Unreacted cyanide is converted to silver cyanide by the addition of a measured amount of standard silver nitrate solution, and excess silver nitrate is determined by titration with thiocyanate. The method, originally proposed by Romijn, has been modified by Mutschin (57) and Weinberger (58).

Procedure

Weigh the sample containing approximately 0.15–0.25 g of dissolved formaldehyde into a glass-stoppered Erlenmeyer flask to which has been previously added 100 ml of 0.1 N potassium cyanide solution. Shake the mixture for a short time and wash it into a 200 ml-volumetric flask containing exactly 40 ml of 0.1 N silver nitrate and about 10 ml of 1:9 nitric acid. Fill the flask to the mark, shake thoroughly, and filter the contents. Determine the unreacted silver in 100 ml of the filtrate by titrating with 0.1 N potassium thiocyanate solution, using ferric alum as an indicator.

$$\text{Formaldehyde, wt \%} = \frac{[100 - (40 - 20A)](N)(MW)(100)}{(w)(1000)}$$

where A = volume of thiocyanate solution required for titration, in ml

N = normality of the thiocyanate solution

MW = g-mol wt of formaldehyde (30.03)

w = sample weight, in g

Hydroxylamine Method.   The hydroxylamine method is widely used for the determination of carbonyl compounds and is useful with formaldehyde, particularly in the presence of alkali-sensitive products and impurities, such as phenol, cresol, and resinous materials.   Both hydroxylamine and its hydrochloride or sulfate salt are used in three major variations of the method:

1. Formaldehyde is allowed to react with hydroxylamine, which is a strong base, and the excess reagent is back titrated.

2. Formaldehyde is allowed to react with hydroxylamine hydrochloride or sulfate, and the mineral acid liberated in the reaction is titrated.

3. The water formed in either of these reactions is determined by the Karl Fischer method.

The first variation, which involves the preparation of free hydroxylamine by complete or partial neutralization of the acid of a hydroxylamine salt, has the disadvantage of the instability of the free hydroxylamine, requiring frequent preparations of the reagent.   In the second variation, titration using indicators cannot be used because of the highly buffered system, and potentiometric titration is necessary, although some modifications, involving the addition of pyridine to the system, permit visual titration with bromophenol blue as the indicator.   The third variation would not appear too useful for commercial formaldehyde solutions, which contain a large amount of water initially.   For the procedures for these variations, see CARBONYL COMPOUNDS, Vol. 8, pp. 356–358.

Ammonium Chloride Method.   Formaldehyde is converted to hexamethylene-tetramine by the reaction with ammonia:

$$6\ HCHO + 4\ NH_3 \longrightarrow (CH_2)_6N_4 + 6\ H_2O$$

This reaction is the basis for a quantitative determination, with the excess ammonia being determined by steam distillation or by titration (59).   Büchi modified the technique for the use of neutralized ammonium chloride, with ammonia determined by titration with standard acid to the bromothymol blue end point.   Ethanol and acetone have no significant effect on the analysis, but acetaldehyde in concentrations higher than 0.5% leads to high values (49).   Büchi reports that results by this method, in general, are about 0.1% low.

Procedure

Weigh a 6-g sample of the approximately 37% formaldehyde solution into a 100-ml volumetric flask and dilute to volume.   Add 25 ml of this solution to an Erlenmeyer flask, together with 3 drops of a 0.1% bromothymol blue indicator, and neutralize with N sodium hydroxide solution until the indicator color changes to blue.   Add 1.5 g of neutral ammonium chloride and 25 ml of N sodium hydroxide solution rapidly, close the flask tightly by using vaseline to insure a perfect seal, and allow the reaction mixture to stand for 1.5 hr.   Titrate the excess ammonia with N hydrochloric acid until the color changes to green.   Carry out a blank determination.

$$\text{Formaldehyde, wt } \% = \frac{(B - A)(N)(180.2)(100)}{(w)(1000)}$$

where A = volume of hydrochloric acid required for sample titration, in ml
B = volume of hydrochloric acid solution required for blank titration, in ml
N = normality of hydrochloric acid
w = sample weight, in g

Mercurimetric Method. The reaction of Nessler's reagent (alkaline potassium mercury iodide) with formaldehyde precipitates mercury as follows:

$$K_2HgI_4 + HCHO + 3\,NaOH \longrightarrow Hg + HCOONa + 2\,KI + 2\,NaI + 2\,H_2O$$

The precipitated mercury is determined iodometrically. Principal interfering substances are organic hydroperoxides and acetaldehyde in concentrations as low as 0.5%. Acetone and methyl and ethyl alcohols have no appreciable effect (60).

Procedure

Weigh a 1.75 g sample of 37% formaldehyde solution, or its equivalent, into a 500-ml volumetric flask and dilute to volume. Pipet 25 ml of this solution to a 200-ml glass-stoppered Erlenmeyer flask, containing a solution of 1 g of mercuric chloride and 2.5 ml of potassium iodide in 35 ml of water plus 20 ml of 2 N sodium hydroxide solution. Shake the mixture vigorously for 5 min, then acidify it with 25 ml of 2 N acetic acid. Immediately add by pipet 25 ml of 0.1 N iodine solution and agitate the mixture until the precipitate is completely dissolved. Backtitrate the excess iodine with 0.1 N sodium thiosulfate solution, using starch solution as the indicator. Carry out a blank determination.

$$\text{Formaldehyde, wt \%} = \frac{(B - A)(N)(MW)(100)}{(w)(2)(1000)}$$

where B = volume of sodium thiosulfate solution required for blank titration, in ml

A = volume of sodium thiosulfate solution required for sample titration, in ml

N = normality of the sodium thiosulfate solution

MW = g-mol wt of formaldehyde (30.03)

w = sample weight, in g

DETERMINATION IN MIXTURES

The color spot tests listed in Table 3 can be used for the quantitative determination of formaldehyde in mixtures if the proper calibration is carried out to yield a quantitative value from the absorbance intensity. Care should be exercised in considering the known interferences with each individual technique. Two of the color tests deserve special mention. The chromotropic acid test is rugged and yields results for formaldehyde from all components which will break down on hydrolysis with strong sulfuric acid to give formaldehyde. The acetylacetone (2,4-pentanedione) test is carried out under much milder conditions and yields only "free" formaldehyde. These two tests, used together, serve as a useful measure for "free" and "total" or "combined" formaldehyde in mixtures.

The colored 2,4-dinitrophenylhydrazone, prepared by reaction with 2,4-dinitrophenylhydrazine, has a characteristic absorption maximum at 331 nm, which may be used for quantitative determination of formaldehyde. Other carbonyl compounds also form colored derivatives (61), but most of these have maxima at slightly different wavelengths. For details, see CARBONYL COMPOUNDS, Vol. 8, p. 342.

Polarography. Small amounts of formaldehyde may be determined polarographically with a dropping mercury electrode. As with the usual polarogram, the current–voltage curve obtained is proportional to the formaldehyde concentration.

Higher aldehydes are reduced at higher voltages than formaldehyde and do not interfere. Determinations made in this manner should be carried out on samples which do not contain materials whose half-wave potentials are in the region of -1.4 to -1.8 V. Formaldehyde is reduced at -1.63 V versus normal calomel electrode in potassium chloride–potassium hydroxide solution (62), and can be determined at concentration ranges as low as 0.07 ppm in aqueous solution with an estimated accuracy of 10% (63).

Gas Chromatography. Bombaugh and Bull (64) have reported a gas chromatographic method which yields quantitative information on mixtures containing formaldehyde. The procedure produced symmetrical peaks for formaldehyde, water, and both methanol and butanol. For the determination, 5 m $\times$ ¼ in. columns containing 10 wt % Ethofat 60/25 (Armour Industrial Chemical Co.), a polyoxyethylene monostearate with an average of 15 ethylene oxide units as the liquid phase on a solid support, was used. Among the solid supports studied, Columpak T (Fisher Scientific Company) produced the sharpest peaks for all components, and columns prepared from these materials required no preloading or conditioning for reproducible results. Satisfactory separations were obtained at a column temperature between 110 and 125°C, with formaldehyde eluting in less than 17 min. The order of elution from the Ethofat column was methyl formate, methanol, water, formaldehyde, and butanol. In the presence of other aldehydes, formaldehyde was eluted after acetaldehyde, methanol, and butyraldehyde. Samples containing as little as 0.007% water were analyzed. From a study of several liquid phases, it was concluded that the unique long retention time of formaldehyde by this technique was through the formation of an unstable hemiacetal with the liquid phase material containing primary hydroxyl groups.

The retention position of formaldehyde was extensively altered by the use of porous polymer materials (65), such as Porapak (Waters Associates, Inc.), as column packing. A 6 ft $\times$ 3/16 in. column of Porapak N at 100°C, with a flow rate of 55 ml/min, separated formaldehyde, water, and methanol in less than 8 min; formaldehyde was eluted first (66). Onuska, et al. (67), reported the separation of formaldehyde, water, and acetic acid, in that order, with Porapak N at 120°C. Constant elution times and unchanged column performance existed throughout a period of use of 1 yr. Similar separations are reported for Porapak R and T, but not for Porapak Q and S or PAR-1 and PAR-2 (polyaromatic resins produced by Hewlett-Packard) (68). Chromosorb 105 (Johns-Manville), another microporous polymer, effectively separated water and methanol from formaldehyde, in that order, in a little over 6 min (69). Little or no tailing of the formaldehyde peak was incurred in any of the above techniques, all of which were obtained with thermal conductivity detection.

Davis and Hillman (70) have applied gas chromatography to improve the selectivity of sensitive color tests for formaldehyde.

The response of the hydrogen flame ionization to formaldehyde is minimal. This is probably associated with the oxidation state of formaldehyde, which is just one stage removed from formic acid. Formic acid, similar to water, has no response on this detector. Harrison (71) overcame this difficulty by reducing small amounts of formaldehyde to methanol with sodium borohydride in sodium hydroxide and determining the resultant methanol with a column of Carbowax 1500 polyoxyethylene glycol (Union Carbide Corp.) on Chromosorb W at 60°C. Methanol and methyl formate interfered with this determination. Harrison was able to determine as little as 10 ppm formaldehyde, free from interference, by placing a reactor tube containing powdered potassium borohydride between the separation column (Citroflex

A8 and phosphoric acid on Chromosorb G, and operated at 60°C) and the flame ionization detector.

A major difficulty in quantitative work by gas chromatography is the proper calibration for the materials of interest. Formaldehyde offers a unique problem in this respect because of the polymerizing tendency of the high-purity monomeric gas. One approach for obtaining 99.24% formaldehyde for gas chromatographic calibration is to heat paraformaldehyde in a glass generator to 160–175°C. The evolved gas is swept into a heated gas sampling valve loop by a 15–25 ml/min flow of inert gas. From the sampling loop, it is injected directly into the gas chromatographic column. As a given generator charge is depleted, it is necessary to raise the temperature to maintain the degradation rate; impurities increase as the temperature increases. The 37% aqueous solutions, as well as the 55% alcoholic solutions, are also possible calibration sources. Caution must be observed, however, with due consideration being given to the state of formaldehyde in the various solvents.

DETERMINATION OF IMPURITIES

In general, most of the specification tests for the determination of impurities in commercial formaldehyde solutions are not specific for formaldehyde, but are tests also applicable to other carbonyl compounds.

Procedures

ACIDITY. See CARBONYL COMPOUNDS, Vol. 8, p. 358.

CHLORINE. See CARBONYL COMPOUNDS, Vol. 8, p. 362.

IRON (19,21). Dilute a 2-ml sample to 15 ml. Add 6 ml of a 10 wt % hydroxylamine hydrochloride solution and 4 ml of a phenanthroline solution prepared by dissolving 0.1 g of 1,10-phenanthroline monohydrate in 100 ml of water which contains 0.1 ml of a 10% hydrochloric acid. Adjust the pH to approximately 5 with ammonium hydroxide. Any color should not exceed that produced by 0.01 mg of iron (Fe) in an equal volume of solution containing the quantities of reagents used in the test. Compare 1 hr after adding the reagents to the sample and standard solutions.

HEAVY METALS. See CARBONYL COMPOUNDS, Vol. 8, p. 363.

SULFATE. See CARBONYL COMPOUNDS, Vol. 8, p. 363.

COPPER (21). Prepare a standard copper solution in the following way. Dissolve 0.393 g of copper sulfate pentahydrate, $CuSO_4.5H_2O$, in 500 ml of water containing 5 ml of concentrated sulfuric acid. Dilute to 1 liter in a volumetric flask with water and mix well. Transfer 100 ml of this solution to a 1-liter volumetric flask containing approximately 500 ml of water and 5 ml of concentrated sulfuric acid, dilute to volume with water, and mix well. The copper concentration of this solution is 0.01 mg/ml.

Prepare a sodium diethyldithiocarbamate solution by dissolving 1.000 g of the powder (Eastman No. 2546 or equivalent) in water and dilute to 1000 ml. Store the solution in a glass-stoppered amber-glass bottle.

Into one of two 50-ml tall-form Nessler tubes introduce 10 g of sample. Introduce 10 ml of water into the second tube and reserve for the blank control determination. By means of a suitable graduate cylinder, add 10 ml of concentrated ammonium hydroxide and 10 ml of the sodium diethyldithiocarbamate solution to each of the Nessler tubes. Dilute the contents of each tube to 50 ml with water, stopper with clean rubber stoppers, and mix the contents. From a microburet, add the standard copper solution dropwise to the blank control tube until, after mixing, the color matches that of the sample tube.

The volume of standard copper solution, in ml, required to produce the matching color in the blank control tube is equivalent to the copper concentration of the sample, expressed in ppm.

RESIDUE AFTER IGNITION (19). Evaporate 20 g of the sample to dryness in a tared dish on a steam bath, add 0.05 ml of concentrated sulfuric acid to the residue, and ignite gently to volatilize the excess sulfuric acid. Ignite at $800 \pm 25°C$ for 15 min. Determine the residue by reweighing the dish and express as wt % of the original sample.

Methanol. In commercial formaldehyde solutions, methanol is used as stabilizer. If the expected methanol concentration range is known, the methanol concentration is calculated from the determined formaldehyde content and specific gravity by means of the following equation:

$$\text{Methanol, wt \%} = \frac{A + BF - (G - C)}{D}$$

where
F = formaldehyde content, in wt %
G = specific gravity at $20/20°C$
$A, B, C,$ and D = constants selected according to the expected methanol concentration range, from the following table:

Expected methanol concentration range, wt %	A	B	C	D
0–2	1.0017	0.003	0.0015	0.00253
6–8	1.0015	0.003	0.0016	0.00250
10–15	1.0210	0.0025	0.0017	0.00257

Bibliography

GENERAL REFERENCES

1. J. F. Walker, *Formaldehyde*, American Chemical Society Monograph Series No. 159, 3rd ed., Reinhold Publishing Corp., New York, 1964.
2. G. E. Haddeland, *Formaldehyde*, Stanford Research Institute, Menlo Park, Calif., Feb., 1967.
3. J. F. Walker, "Formaldehyde," in A. Standen ed., *Kirk-Othmer Encyclopedia of Chemical Technology*, Vol. 10, 2nd ed., Interscience Publishers, a division of John Wiley & Sons, Inc., New York, 1966, pp. 77–99.
4. J. Mitchell, Jr., "Determination of Carbonyl Compounds," in J. Mitchell, Jr., I. M. Kolthoff, E. S. Proskauer, and A. Weissberger, eds., *Organic Analysis*, Vol. 1, Interscience Publishers, Inc., New York, 1953, pp. 243–307.

SPECIFIC REFERENCES

5. R. Spence and W. Wild, *J. Chem. Soc.* **1935**, 506–509 (1935).
6. D. J. Cram and G. S. Hammond, *Organic Chemistry*, McGraw-Hill Book Co., Inc., New York, 1959.
7. H. V. Wartenberg and B. Lerner-Steinberg, *Z. Angew. Chem.* **38**, 591–592 (1925); *Chem. Abstr.* **19**, 3202 (1916).
8. *JANAF (Joint Army-Navy-Air Force) Thermochemical Tables*, Dow Chemical Co., Thermal Laboratory, Midland, Mich., 1965.
9. Ref. 1, p. 39.
10. Ref. 2, p. 38.
11. Ref. 1, p. 61.

12. M. Trautz and E. Ufer, *J. Prakt. Chem.* **113**, 105–136 (1926); *Chem. Abstr.* **20**, 2816 (1917).
13. Ref. 2, p. 45.
14. Ref. 2, p. 46.
15. Ref. 1, p. 192.
16. Ref. 2, p. 51.
17. H. W. Haggard, *J. Ind. Hygiene* **5**, 390 (1923).
18. Ref. 2, p. 3.
19. *Reagent Chemicals*, 4th ed., American Chemical Society Publications, Washington, D. C., 1968, pp. 261–262.
20. *The Pharmacopeia of the United States of America* (*The United States Pharmacopeia*), 17th rev. ed., New York, 1965, p. 260.
21. *Formaldehyde, 37.2% Solution (Uninhibited)*, Specification No. 1-4A-1b, Chemicals and Plastics Division, Union Carbide, Sept. 21, 1967.
22. *Formaldehyde, 37.2% Solution (Inhibited)—Winter Grade*, Specification No. 1-4A1-1.2a, Chemicals and Plastics Division, Union Carbide, Sept. 21, 1967.
23. *Methyl Formcel 55%*, Sales Specification, CCC-19-1, Celanese Chemical Company, Dec. 23, 1968.
24. Ref. 20, p. 984.
25. G. N. Umbreit, "Carbonyl Compounds," in THIS ENCYCLOPEDIA, Vol. 8, p. 344.
26. Ref. 25, pp. 344–345.
27. Ref. 1, p. 472.
28. M. Tanenbaum and C. E. Bricker, *Anal. Chem.* **23**, 354–357 (1951).
29. R. Mari, M. Feve, and M. Dzierzinski, *Bull. Soc. Chim. France* **1961**, 1395–1399; *Chem. Abstr.* **56**, 934h (1953).
30. O. Heim, *Ind. Eng. Chem., Anal. Ed.* **10**, 431 (1938).
31. P. W. West and B. Sen, *Z. Anal. Chem.* **153**, 177–183 (1956); *Chem. Abstr.* **51**, 7949i (1948).
32. L. E. Hinkel, *Analyst* **33**, 417–419 (1908); *Chem. Abstr.* **3**, 353 (1900).
33. E. Sawicki, T. W. Stanley, H. Johnson, and F. P. Fox, *Microchim. Acta* **1962**, 741–745 (1962); *Chem. Abstr.* **57**, 6591h (1954).
34. C. L. Hoffpauir, G. W. Buckaloo, and J. D. Guthrie, *Ind. Eng. Chem., Anal. Ed.* **15**, 605 (1943).
35. F. R. Georgia and R. Morales, *Ind. Eng. Chem.* **18**, 305 (1926).
36. P. Heerman, *Textilber.* 101–121 (1922); *Chem. Abstr.* **16**, 2406 (1913).
37. E. Eegriwe, *Z. Anal. Chem.* **110**, 22 (1937); *Chem. Abstr.* **31**, 8442 (1928).
38. M. J. Boyd and M. A. Logan, *J. Biol. Chem.* **146**, 279 (1942).
39. C. E. Bricker and H. R. Johnson, *Ind. Eng. Chem., Anal. Ed.* **17**, 400 (1945).
40. T. Nash, *Biochem. J.* (*London*) **55**, 416–421 (1953).
41. R. L. Shriner, R. C. Fuson, and D. Y. Curtin, *The Systematic Identification of Organic Compounds*, 4th ed., John Wiley & Sons, Inc., New York, 1960.
42. N. B. Colthup, *J. Optical Soc. Am.* **40**, 397–400 (1950).
43. J. H. Ross, *Anal. Chem.* **25**, 1288–1303 (1953).
44. H. M. Kelley, *Anal. Chem.* **23**, 1081–1085 (1951).
45. E. C. Horning and M. G. Horning, *J. Org. Chem.* **11**, 95 (1946).
46. E. Zerner, *Monatsh.* **34**, 957–961 (1913); *Chem. Abstr.* **7**, 3465.
47. N. R. Campbell, *Analyst* **61**, 392 (1936); **30**, 5534 (1927).
48. R. Fosse, P. de Graeve, and P. E. Thomas, *Compt. Rend.* **200**, 1450–1454 (1935); *Chem. Abstr.* **29**, 7869 (1926).
49. J. Büchi, *Pharm. Acta, Helv.* **6**, 1–54 (1931).
50. J. G. Reynolds and M. Irwin, *Chem. Ind.* (*London*) **1948**, 419–424, 1948.
51. *ASTM Method D 2194-65, Concentration of Formaldehyde Solutions*, American Society for Testing and Materials, Philadelphia, Pa., 1965.
52. Ref. 4, p. 267.
53. W. H. Hatcher and W. H. Mueller, *Trans. Roy. Soc. Can.* [3] **23**, 35–44 (1929); *Chem. Abstr.* **24**, 570.
54. L. F. Goodwin, *J. Am. Chem. Soc.* **42**, 39–45 (1920).
55. S. Dal Nogare, T. O. Norris, and J. Mitchell, Jr., *Anal. Chem.* **23**, 1373–1378 (1951).
56. Ref. 4, p. 273.
57. A. Mutschin, *Z. Anal. Chem.* **99**, 335 (1934).
58. W. Weinberger, *Ind. Eng. Chem., Anal. Ed.* **3**, 357 (1931).

59. B. H. Smith, *J. Am. Chem. Soc.* **25**, 1028–1035 (1903).
60. R. Gros, *J. Pharm. Chim.* **26**, 415–425 (1922); *Chem. Abstr.* **17**, 1402 (1914).
61. F. H. Lohman, *Anal. Chem.* **30**, 972–974 (1958).
62. M. J. Boyd and K. Bambach, *Ind. Eng. Chem., Anal. Ed.* **15**, 314–315 (1943).
63. Ref. 4, p. 295.
64. K. J. Bombaugh and W. C. Bull, *Anal. Chem.* **34**, 1237–1241 (1962).
65. O. L. Hollis, *Anal. Chem.* **38**, 309 (1966).
66. *Chromatography Notes*, 1 (1), 6 (Jan.–Feb. 1970), Waters Associates, Inc., Framingham, Mass.
67. F. Onuska, J. Janak, S. Duras, and M. Krchmarova, *J. Chromatog.* **40**, 209–212 (1969).
68. S. F. Spencer, *Facts and Methods*, **8** (2), 5–7 (1966).
69. *Chromatographic News* **May 1970**, 3 (Chemical Research Services, Inc., Addison, Ill.).
70. J. E. Davis and D. E. Hillman, *Talanta* **16**, 421–423 (1969).
71. S. Harrison, *Analyst* **92**, 773–778 (1967).

R. A. Bleidt
Union Carbide Corporation

FORMAMIDE.   See Carboxylic acids, derivatives, Vol. 8, pp. 557–612.

FORMIC ACID

Properties.. 118
Methods of manufacture... 121
Commercial grades and specifications........................... 122
Methods of analysis... 124
Formic acid esters... 131
Methods of analysis... 132
Formic acid salts.. 134
Methods of analysis... 135
Bibliography.. 137

Formic acid, methanoic acid, HCOOH, is a colorless, fuming liquid, having a characteristic pungent odor, irritating to the eyes, nose, and throat, and able to burn and blister the skin.

Formic acid derives its name from the red ant, *Formica rufa*, in which it occurs as the free acid. The acid and its salts occur in many plants, in stinging nettles, in fluids of biological origin, and as a product of the bacterial fermentation of carbohydrates and polyhydric alcohols. Brunfels early in the 16th century observed that the vapor from ant hills reddened vegetable colorings. Etmüller about 1684 reported that the distillation of ants produced an "acid spirit" that corroded iron. But the discovery of formic acid is best ascribed to S. Fisher. In a letter to the *Philosophical Transactions* of January 13, 1671, J. Ray gave an account of some experiments performed and communicated to him by Fisher (who died in 1665). Fisher distilled ants with water and found in the aqueous distillate an acid resembling the "spirit of vinegar." He prepared the lead and iron salts. On distillation of the lead salt, formic acid was recovered. In contrast the lead salt of vinegar, lead acetate, on distillation produced an inflammable oil, water, and no acid. Marggraf in 1749 apparently first isolated formic acid in essentially pure form. The chemical individuality of the acid was firmly established by Suersen by 1805. For details on the chemistry, technology, and applications of formic acid and its derivatives, the general references (1–8) should be consulted.

Properties

Table 1 summarizes some of the more important properties of pure formic acid; solubility data are given in Table 2 while Table 3 lists the densities of aqueous formic acid solutions. The vapor–liquid diagram of formic acid is presented in Figure 1 (7).

Table 1. Properties of Formic Acid

formula weight	46.0259
boiling point, °C	
10 torr	3.8
300 torr	71.9
760 torr	100.6
$\Delta bp/\Delta p$, 750–770, °C/torr	0.044
vapor pressure, torr	
20°C	33.1
30°C	52.2
entropy at 25°C, cal/°C	
gas, monomer	−60.00
liquid	−30.82
flash point, Tag open cup, °F	138
freezing point, °C	8.4
volume increase on melting, ml/mole	5.94
heat capacity, cal/deg-mole	23.57
heat of combustion, kcal/g-mole	63.0
heat of fusion, cal/g	65.87
heat of vaporization, at 25°C, 760 torr, cal/g-mole	4782
ionization constant at 25°C	
K_a	1.77×10^{-4}
pK_a	3.752
refractive index, n_D^{20}	1.3714
$\Delta n/\Delta t$, 20–40°C	0.00042
specific gravity, 20/20°C	1.2225
Δ sp gr/Δt, 10–40°C	0.00124
specific heat, at 20°C, cal/g-°C	0.526
specific magnetic susceptibility, at 20°C	$−0.428 \times 10^{-6}$
standard free energy of formation, kcal/mole	
gas, monomer	−86.67
liquid	−97.8
surface tension, at 20°C, dyn/cm	37.0
odor	pungent
color	none

Table 2. Solubility of Formic Acid

Solvent	g/100 g of solvent, at 25°C
benzene	14.4
bromoform	2.45
carbon disulfide	1.28
carbon tetrachloride	3.43
ethanol	complete
ethyl ether	complete
glycerin	complete
toluene	11.9
water	complete
xylene	8.74

Table 3. Density of Aqueous Solutions of Formic Acid at 20°C

Density, g/ml	Formic acid content		
	wt %	g/liter	molarity
1.0000	1	10.009	0.2175
1.0115	5	50.575	1.0988
1.0246	10	102.46	2.2261
1.0371	15	155.56	3.3800
1.0488	20	209.76	4.5574
1.0609	25	265.23	5.7626
1.0729	30	321.87	6.9932
1.0847	35	379.65	8.2486
1.0965	40	438.60	9.5294
1.1085	45	498.83	10.8380
1.1206	50	560.30	12.1736
1.1318	55	622.49	13.5248
1.1424	60	685.44	14.8925
1.1541	65	750.17	16.2989
1.1655	70	815.85	17.7259
1.1769	75	882.67	19.1779
1.1857	80	948.56	20.6093
1.1953	85	1016.0	22.0745
1.2044	90	1084.0	23.5520
1.2140	95	1153.3	25.0576
1.2212	100	1221.2	26.5329

Formic acid forms an azeotrope with water. The composition of the azeotrope at 760 torr is 77.6% formic acid and 22.4% water and its boiling point is 107.6°C.

The absorption of formic acid in the ultraviolet shows a maximum at 205 nm (log ϵ = 1.65) (9). Liquid formic acid shows the following infrared absorption bands (s = strong, m = medium, w = weak, sh = shoulder): $\sim$3151 (s), $\sim$2999 (s), 2768

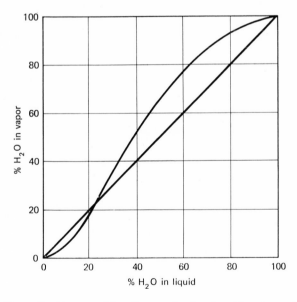

Fig. 1. Vapor–liquid composition diagram for formic acid–water system (12).

(m), 2751 (m), 2361 (w), ~1724 (s), 1391 (sh), 1362 (s), 1195 (s), 1067 (w), 1019 (w), 875 (w), and 669 (w) cm^{-1} (10).

Formic acid finds many industrial applications where its acid strength, reducing action, and reactivity give it special advantages. The major commercial use of formic acid and its salts lies in the textile and leather industries, where it finds use as an acidulent and as a dye exhausting agent for cotton, viscose rayon, wool, silk, and the newer synthetic fabrics. With chrome mordant dyeing the reducing properties of formic acid function to convert hexavalent chromium to trivalent chromium. Formic acid is also used in treating textiles with aminoplast resins for crease-proofing, shrink-proofing, and enhancement of wash-wear characteristics.

In leather tanning, formic acid is employed as an easily controlled deliming agent, as a leveling agent for dyestuffs, and a pickling agent with preservative properties. Formic acid is a coagulant for rubber latex and is often preferred over acetic acid. Formic acid is used in formulations for stripping enameled wire before soldering.

Formic acid forms both salts and esters of commercial interest. Sodium formate is utilized in the tanning of leather and in the textile industry. It also represents the raw material of the production of sodium oxalate. Nickel formate is employed in the preparation of hydrogenation catalysts, and aluminum formate as a water repellent agent in the treatment of textiles and paper. Ammonium formate is an important analytical reagent.

Many of the formic acid esters find application as fumigants, solvents, flavoring agents, and components of perfumes. Methyl and ethyl formate serve as fumigants. Propyl, butyl, and pentyl formates find use as solvents for lacquers and polymeric materials. A variety of formate esters receive attention as flavoring agents for foods, pharmaceuticals, and as perfume ingredients.

Analytical Applications. Formic acid and its salts have found use in analytical chemistry both as a weak acid and as a reducing agent, and many applications have been reviewed by Welcher (8). Among the more prominent uses are the detection of cerium, rhenium, silver, and tungsten, and the determination of arsenic, bismuth, cobalt, copper, gold, indium, iron, lead, manganese, mercury, molybdenum, nickel, nitrate, palladium, platinum, silver, tungsten, and zinc.

Formate salts have been applied to the separation and determination of bismuth in mixtures with lead. The original method (11) states that bismuth may be completely separated, as a basic bismuth formate precipitate, from lead by boiling a nearly neutral solution of their salts with an excess of a solution of sodium formate containing a little formic acid. Basic bismuth formate is slightly soluble in solutions of sodium salts, in general, and in solutions of sodium formate, in particular. For this reason, ammonium formate has been substituted for the sodium salt (12).

Mercury, arsenic, and lead may be determined by visual comparison as their sulfides. Formic acid prevents the precipitation of small quantities of these metals as sulfides by hydrogen sulfide, yielding instead a colloidal suspension that is suitable for a colorimetric comparison (13). Molybdenum has been separated from tungsten by precipitation of molybdenum sulfide at pH 2.9 from a solution containing substantial concentrations of ammonium formate, tartaric acid, and formic acid (14). Zinc can be precipitated selectively with hydrogen sulfide from solutions also containing iron, cobalt, and nickel, if a large excess of formic acid is added to mask these metals as their formate complexes (15).

Fusion with lithium carbonate and sodium formate allows the detection of tungsten in dry mixtures by formation of a lithium–tungsten bronze (16).

The determination of a variety of noble metals by reduction to the metal using formic acid has been demonstrated. Platinum can be reduced to the metallic state by formic acid in an acetate buffer solution. Platinum is frequently isolated initially by precipitation of the sulfide followed by dissolution in aqua regia. Platinum is reduced by addition of sodium formate, and is ignited and weighed as such (17). Silver is similarly reduced by formic acid (18). Palladium is precipitated as the metal by sodium formate from slightly acidic solutions of palladium(II) chloride (19).

Copper and cadmium can be quantitatively separated utilizing the selective reducing action of potassium formate on a hot solution of the ions of both metals. Copper salts are quantitatively reduced to the metal while cadmium salts are not affected. The copper can be separated, dried, and weighed (20).

Formic acid has been used as a component of electrolytes in a variety of electrochemical procedures. Manganese has been separated from iron and zinc by quantitative electrolytic deposition as the dioxide from a formic acid–sodium formate solution (17). Indium can be deposited electrolytically on platinum from an indium salt solution containing formic acid. The accuracy of the method proved sufficient to establish the atomic weight of indium (21).

Iron has been separated from manganese, nickel, cobalt, and zinc by precipitation as a basic iron(III) formate (19). Nitrate has been determined gas volumetrically by reaction with formic acid to yield nitrous oxide, carbon dioxide, water, and potassium formate. The total volume of nitrous oxide and carbon dioxide is measured, carbon dioxide is then absorbed in potassium hydroxide solution, and the volume of nitrous oxide remaining is measured (22). A titrimetric procedure for nitric acid has been developed based on the reduction of nitrate by formic acid in the presence of sulfuric acid, removal of excess formic acid by warming, and the titration of the nitrosylsulfuric acid formed with either iodine or permanganate (23).

Formic acid finds occasional use as a buffer substance. Simple formate buffers have an effective buffering range of pH 2.7–4.7.

Methods of Manufacture

Formic acid was formerly manufactured by the decarboxylation of oxalic acid, often in the presence of glycerol. Today, formate salts are made by the direct reaction of a metal hydroxide and carbon monoxide at elevated temperature and pressure. The sodium formate is converted to formic acid by adding sulfuric acid to a slurry of this salt in 85–95% formic acid. The extensive decomposition encountered on the direct reaction of sodium formate with sulfuric acid is thereby avoided. The 85–95% formic acid is isolated by distillation. The overall conversion to formic acid on the basis of solid sodium hydroxide used is 90–95%.

Formic acid is also manufactured by the hydrolysis of methyl formate using catalytic amounts of sulfuric acid. Either essentially anhydrous or concentrated formic acid is obtained by a transesterification reaction of methyl formate with either oxalic or glutaric acid, using sulfuric acid as catalyst. Formic acid is liberated and the methyl esters of the dibasic acid are hydrolyzed to recover methanol and the dibasic acid. Methyl formate is produced by the direct reaction of methanol and carbon monoxide at about 200°C and a pressure of 25–50 atm.

Formic acid of 98–100% purity cannot be obtained by simple distillation of the dilute aqueous product since two constant-boiling azeotropes form, containing 76.5% and 83.2% formic acid, respectively. Azeotropic distillation offers a favorable approach. In one process distillation with propyl formate yields a nonaqueous propyl formate–formic acid phase that can be resolved by a second distillation. Concentration of formic acid by freezing offers another interesting possibility.

Sodium formate is recovered in significant quantities from the manufacture of pentaerthyritol by the aldol condensation of acetaldehyde and formaldehyde. Sodium formate is separated by concentration of mother liquors. Formic acid is also obtained as a by-product in the manufacture of acetaldehyde and formaldehyde from the catalytic oxidation of alkanes.

For details on the manufacturing processes of formic acid and its salts, see References 1–3.

Commercial Grades and Specifications

Formic acid is available in several grades. Bulk quantities are available as 85%, 90%, and 95% aqueous solutions, as a glacial (98%) technical grade, as a glacial (99.5%) pharmaceutical grade, and as a food processing grade. Reagent grade formic acid (88% and 98%) is also commercially available.

Typical manufacturers' specifications for bulk quantities of formic acid are shown in Table 4. Reagent specifications established by the American Chemical Society (24) and the specifications of the *Food Chemicals Codex* (25) are summarized in Table 5. The specifications and tests for formic acid reagent designated in the *U.S. Pharmacopeia* (26), are essentially identical to those for 88% formic acid meeting the ACS specifications.

Table 6 summarizes shipping data for 90% formic acid and for glacial formic acid.

Handling and Storage. Persons handling formic acid should appreciate its hazardous properties. It is at least twice as toxic as an equal concentration of acetic acid. Both concentrated and dilute formic acid can cause burns or irritation if allowed to come into contact with the skin or eyes. Breathing of formic acid vapors may result in irritation of the respiratory tract. The American Conference of Governmental Industrial Hygienists has suggested a threshold limit value of 5 ppm formic acid vapor

Table 4. Typical Specifications for Bulk Quantity Formic Acid

	90%	98% (glacial), technical grade	99.5% (glacial), pharmaceutical grade
assay, wt %, min	90–91.0[a]	98.0	99.5
acetic acid, wt %, max		0.8	0.4
toluene, ppm, max			5
water, wt %, max		1.0	0.5
suspended matter	substantially free	substantially free	substantially free
chloride, ppm, max	20	20	10
sulfate, ppm, max	10	10	10
heavy metals (as Pb), ppm, max	5	5	5
iron, ppm, max	3	3	3
color (APHA) Pt–Co, max	20	20	15

[a] By total acidity.

Table 5. Specifications of Reagent Grade and Food Processing Grade Formic Acid

	ACS reagent grade		Food processing grade
	88%	98%	
assay, wt%, min	88	98	85
dilution test	to pass	to pass	to pass
residue on evaporation, wt %, max	20	30	
acetic acid, wt %, max	0.4	0.4	0.4
ammonium (NH_4), ppm, max	50	50	
chloride, ppm, max	~10	~10	
sulfate, ppm, max	20	30	40
sulfite	to pass	to pass	
arsenic, ppm, max			3
heavy metals (as Pb), ppm, max	5	10	10
iron, ppm, max	5	10	
color (APHA), Pt-Co, max	15	15	

Table 6. Shipping Data for Commercial Grades of Formic Acid

	90%	Glacial (98%)
weight per gallon at 20°C, lb/gal	10.05	10.17
weight change, lb/gal-°C	0.00988	0.01050
coefficient of expansion, per °C		
20°C	0.00098	0.00103
55°C	0.00102	0.00107
flash point, °F		
Tag open cup[a]		138
Cleveland open cup[b]	185	
containers and net contents, lb[c]		
1-gal polyethylene jug, phenolic resin cap	10.0	[d]
5-gal ICC Cubitainer	50	[d]
55-gal ICC 2SL polyethylene drum		
with 37 A steel Overpak	510	[d]
freight description	"Formic Acid"	"Formic Acid"
Department of Transportation container description	"Corrosive Liquid"	"Corrosive Liquid"
ICC label required	white	white

[a] Cleveland open cup (Ref. 27).

[b] Tag open cup (Ref. 28).

[c] Also available in tank trucks and tank cars.

[d] Shipments of glacial formic acid are currently restricted to bulk quantities because of pressure buildup in sealed containers.

in air, based on a time-weighed average concentration for a conventional 8-hour working day.

Suitable materials for construction of tanks, pumps, valves, and piping in formic acid service include stainless steel, glass, rubber, ceramic ware, and a number of resin linings. Type 316 stainless steel is the most serviceable material for a wide variety of construction uses. Other materials such as zirconium or tantalum may be required where temperature, concentration, or oxidation levels depart greatly from normal conditions. Aluminum cannot be used for aqueous solutions of formic acid or for glacial formic acid at elevated temperature service.

During storage, glacial formic acid slowly decomposes, evolving carbon monoxide, and should not be stored in tightly sealed tanks or containers, since sufficient gas pressure can be generated to cause container rupture or leakage. Venting of drums should be accomplished in a manner that minimizes carbon monoxide accumulation and resulting health hazard. Particular care should be exercised in refilling bulk containers for glacial formic acid since the nearly empty tank may contain a considerable amount of carbon monoxide. The only safe procedure in storing anhydrous formic acid as a liquid is to employ vented containers.

Formic acid may be stabilized at temperatures as high as $35°C$ using a minimum water content of 1%. A 3% water content is required for stabilization at temperatures from $35°C$ to $55°C$.

Glacial formic acid (98%) has a fairly high freezing point, about $47°F$. The 90% solution freezes at about $21°F$. Suitable precautions are required to prevent freezing of formic acid or formic acid solutions in storage facilities or transfer systems. Circulation of warm water or controlled electrical heat are the preferred methods for heating bulk formic acid.

Methods of Analysis

SAMPLING

Since formic acid is a volatile acid, special care must be exerted to obtain a suitable analytical sample. Various methods for the weighing and transfer of such acids have been reviewed (5). The use of capillary-stem glass ampoules for this purpose is common.

Procedure

Accurately weigh a clean, dry glass ampoule (0.5-in thin walled bulb, 3 or 4 in. capillary stem), to the nearest 0.1 mg and insert the stem through a perforation in a small piece of thin metal or cardboard. Warm the bulb of the ampoule over a low flame and quickly insert the stem through the neck of the bottle containing the sample so that the tip is well submerged below the liquid surface. As the bulb cools, acid is sucked into the ampoule. When the desired amount of sample has been sucked into the ampoule, remove the stem from the bottle, seal the tip in a flame, wipe the outside of the ampoule clean, and reweigh accurately. Record the net weight of the sample.

IDENTIFICATION

Formic acid is usually considered an undesirable impurity in foods, drugs, and cosmetics. Since formic acid is injurious to health, it should not be present in wood vinegar. It is, in addition, an inadmissable fermentation product in fruit juices, jams, marmalades, etc. Several spot tests have been developed for the identification of formic acid (29) in such products and others.

Mercury Chloride Test. The reaction of the formate anion with mercury(II) chloride is recommended for the detection of formic acid in mixtures with carboxylic and sulfonic acids or their alkali metal salts; mercury(II) is reduced to mercury(I), which is subsequently detected by the reaction with ammonia. A positive test is indicated by the characteristic blackening associated with finely divided mercury arising from disproportionation of mercury(I) chloride. In a related test, formic acid is identified, having added mercury(II) chloride solution and warming, by the development of the white precipitate of mercury(I) chloride.

Chromotropic Acid Test. An alternate spot test for formic acid entails the reduction of formic acid to formaldehyde by nascent hydrogen (29). The test solution is mixed with a drop of 2 F (formal) hydrochloric acid, magnesium powder is added until the evolution of gas ceases. The formaldehyde produced can then be identified by the chromotropic acid test for formaldehyde. When formaldehyde is warmed with chromotropic acid, (4,5-dihydroxy-2,7-naphthalenedisulfonic acid), in concentrated sulfuric acid solution, a violet-pink color develops. A yellow to green color is produced by reducing sugars. Colored products should be decolorized with activated charcoal prior to the test.

Molybdenum Blue Test. Another spot test involves decomposition of formic acid and detection of the resulting carbon monoxide using the molybdenum blue formation that occurs when carbon monoxide is passed through a solution of phosphomolybdic acid containing palladium chloride as a catalyst.

Copper Acetate–Benzidine Acetate Test. Metal formates can be identified through pyrolytic decomposition in the presence of mercury(II) cyanide. When heated to 160–180°C, hydrogen cyanide is evolved from a dry intimate mixture of mercury(II) cyanide with a metal formate. The evolved hydrocyanic acid is detected by the copper acetate–benzidine acetate test procedure (30).

Cyanine Dyestuff Formation Test. A rather selective spot test for formic acid has been described in which a cyanine dyestuff is produced by the condensation of formic acid with a *p*-alkylquinaldinium salt. *N*-Methylquinaldinium *p*-toluenesulfonate is the recommended reagent. The limit of identification is reported to be 0.04 mg of formic acid. A large number of aldehydes and carboxylic acids do not interfere (31).

Thin-Layer Chromatography. Separation and identification of formic acid in the presence of acetic and lactic acids have been accomplished by thin-layer chromatography (32). The separations can be accomplished on silica gel G layers, using a solvent mixture of 1:2 pyridine–petroleum ether with R_f values of 0.52, 0.58, and 0.63, respectively. Separation with 20:1:4 ethanol–ammonia–water gave R_f values of 0.64, 0.66, and 0.51. Detection was accomplished using the disodium salt of dihydroindanthroazinedisulfonic acid ester.

ASSAY METHODS

If formic acid is present in aqueous solutions, either alone or with negligible amounts of other acids, an alkalimetric titration of the total acidity serves to establish the formic acid content. Where other acids that do not react readily with permanganate are present, the preferred method is a redox titration based on addition of permanganate to an alkaline solution followed by acidification, addition of an excess of oxalate, and back-titration with permanganate. By these steps both the volatilization of formic acid in acidic solution and its oxidation to carbon dioxide and water are avoided. Some workers prefer a redox titration method based on addition of an excess of permanganate to the alkaline solution, heating to 70°C with addition of a sufficient amount of potassium iodide, and back-titration with a standard sodium thiosulfate solution.

Alkalimetric Titration. The following procedure is applicable to all strengths and to all grades of formic acid. A precision of 0.25% or better can be attained (33).

Procedure

Run duplicate determinations. Use carbon-dioxide free water for all rinsings and dilutions. Obtain 1.2–1.5 g of the analytical sample by the ampoule method (see p. 124). Transfer the ampoule to a 500-ml heavy-wall conical flask containing about 150 ml of water, close the flask tightly with a clean rubber stopper, wrap the flask in a towel, and shake vigorously until the ampoule shatters, then continue to shake the closed flask for a few minutes until all vapors are absorbed. Loosen the stopper, rinse it and the sides of the flask with water, and completely crush any remaining fragments of the ampoule, using a heavy glass rod with a flattened end. Rinse the glass rod with water.

Add 2 or 3 drops of phenolphthalein indicator solution and titrate rapidly (about 1 ml/sec) with 0.33 N sodium hydroxide solution, best delivered from a chamber buret, with continual swirling to the first appearance of color throughout the solution. Note the temperature of the sodium hydroxide solution and add a correction of 0.00027 ml of 0.33 N sodium hydroxide solution for each degree centigrade below the standardization temperature or subtract an equivalent correction for each degree above.

$$\text{Formic acid, wt \%} = \frac{(V)(N)(MW)(100)}{(w)(1000)}$$

where V = volume of sodium hydroxide solution required for sample titration, in ml
N = normality of sodium hydroxide solution
MW = g-mol wt of formic acid (=46.026)
w = sample weight, in g

If small amounts of other acids are also present, express the result as "total acidity (as formic acid)."

Redox Titration. This procedure is recommended if the amount of other acids present would result in a false assay value if the determination is carried out by direct alkalimetric titration (5).

Procedure

Transfer 2 g of the sample in an ampoule (see p. 124) to a 500-ml volumetric flask containing about 200 ml of water and dilute to volume with water. Transfer a 50-ml aliquot to a conical flask and make it alkaline with sodium carbonate. Warm the solution and add a known, excess amount of 0.1 N potassium permaganate solution from a 100-ml buret. Add 0.1 N oxalic acid solution in excess of that needed to dissolve the precipitated manganese dioxide and then add 10 ml of 6 N sulfuric acid. Titrate the excess of oxalic acid with 0.1 N potassium permanagnate solution.

Add 1 ml of the 0.1 N oxalic acid solution to an Erlenmeyer flask, add some water, and titrate it with the 0.1 N potassium permanganate solution to determine its equivalency.

$$\text{Formic acid, wt \%} = \frac{(A - BC)(N)(MW)(100)}{(w)(2)(1000)}$$

where A = total volume of potassium permanganate solution added and used for the titration of the excess of oxalic acid, in ml
B = volume of oxalic acid solution added, in ml

C = volume of potassium permanganate solution needed for the titration
　　of 1 ml of the oxalic acid solution, in ml

N = normality of the potassium permanganate solution

w = sample weight in the aliquot, in g

MW = g-mol wt of formic acid ($= 46.026$)

DETERMINATION OF IMPURITIES

Acids. The procedure commonly used for the determination of acids other than formic present in amounts between 0.5 and 6.0 mole % is based on the titration with sodium hydroxide of the acidity remaining after quantitative oxidation of the formic acid with excess mercury(II) oxide (34). The acidic impurity present is generally expressed as acetic acid.

Procedure

If the amount of acidic impurity present is less than 2%, weigh a 5-g sample; if the amount is over 2%, use a 2-g sample. Transfer the sample to a 250-ml ground-glass-stoppered conical flask. Add exactly 5 ml of acetic acid solution, obtained by diluting 5 ml of glacial acetic acid with water to 1000 ml. Add 5.5 g of mercury(II) oxide for each gram of formic acid present in the sample then dilute with water to about 30 ml.

Fit the flask with a water-cooled reflux condenser and heat gently for 10 min. A fairly strong evolution of carbon dioxide occurs. Reflux gently for 30 min. Rinse each reflux condenser with 20–25 ml of water, cool the flask to room temperature and without filtering pour the contents into a 250-ml beaker. Rinse the flask with 20–25 ml of water and transfer the rinsings to the beaker. Stir the solution vigorously, preferably using a magnetic stirrer, and with continuous stirring, titrate the solution with 0.1 N sodium hydroxide solution using a pH meter equipped with a glass electrode. Take the end point of the titration at pH 8.6. A period of vigorous stirring is required to obtain a stable final pH value. Samples requiring more than 10–15 ml of 0.1 N sodium hydroxide solution do not give a very sharp end point. Carry out a blank determination with the amounts of reagents listed and handled under the conditions specified. Take the end point of the titration at pH 8.3 for the blank.

$$\text{Acidic impurity, as acetic acid, wt \%} = \frac{(A - B)(N)(MW)(100)}{(w)(1000)}$$

where　A = volume of sodium hydroxide solution used for sample titration, in ml

　　　　B = volume of sodium hydroxide solution used for the blank, in ml

　　　　N = normality of the sodium hydroxide solution

　　MW = g-mol wt of acetic acid ($= 60.054$)

　　　　w = sample weight, in g

The amount of acetic acid present can also be determined by gas chromatography. The ACS specifications (35) recommend the following instrumental conditions:

column	6 ft $\times$ ¼ in. OD packed
column packing	Porapak Q 80–100 mesh
temperature of	
injection port	190–200°C
column	150°C
detector	150°C
carrier gas and flow rate	helium, 40 ml/min
detector	thermal conductivity

From the chromatogram obtained, the amount of acetic acid and water present can be calculated. The amount of acetic acid present can also be determined together with the amount of toluene which may be present (see below).

Toluene. Toluene is used in one process for the concentration of formic acid; therefore, small amounts may remain in the product. The determination of toluene can be best accomplished by gas chromatography, and it also permits the simultaneous determination of the amount of acetic acid present. In the determination, Cellosolve acetate, in a concentration of 1%, is recommended as the internal standard for the quantitative evaluation of the chromatogram. Two types of columns have been found applicable for this determination to be used under the following conditions:

column	(a) 10 ft × 4 mm ID (¼ in. OD) packed
	(b) 12 ft × 2.4 mm ID packed
column packing	8 wt % Carbowax 6000 polyethylene glycol and 1 wt % docosanoic acid on Haloport F
temperature of	
injection port	190°C
column	130°C
detector	170°C
carrier gas and flow rate	helium: (a) 30 ml/min, (b) 25 ml/min
detector	flame ionization

With the first column, the approximate retention times are: toluene, 5 min; Cellosolve acetate, 13 min; acetic acid, 23 min; formic acid, 25 min. With the second column, the approximate retention times of toluene and acetic acid are 1.6 and 6 min, respectively, with Cellosolve acetate emerging between them, and formic acid as the last peak.

Water. The water content of glacial formic acid can be determined by the Karl Fischer titration. The procedure is outlined below and the sample size specified (36). For details on the Karl Fischer reagent, and the method see AQUAMETRY, Vol. 1, pp. 142–147.

Procedure

Transfer 50-ml portions of the glacial acetic acid to each of two *dry* 250-ml glass-stoppered conical flasks. Titrate the contents of each flask with the Karl Fischer reagent to the same light red-brown color. Reserve one of the flasks as the blank. To the other flask add the appropriate amount of formic acid as specified below:

Water content, wt %	Sample size, wt %
1.0	4
0.8	5
0.6	7
0.4	10
0.2	20
0.1	40

Weigh the specified amount of formic acid sample by means of a weighing pipet and titrate immediately with the Karl Fischer reagent until the color matches that of the blank. Calculate as usual.

The water content of formic acid (not only of glacial quality) can also be determined by gas chromatography, by using the conditions outlined above for the determination of the acetic acid impurity (p. 127).

Chloride.   The chloride impurity of formic acid is usually determined by a conventional turbidimetric approach, either as a determination or as a limit test.

Procedure

Transfer 10 ml of sample, measured by buret or pipet, to a 100-ml Nessler tube, dilute with water to about 50 ml, add 3 drops of concentrated nitric acid, then dilute with water to volume.   In case of samples containing less than 1 ppm of chloride, take a larger sample and evaporate to about 50 ml, thereby improving the sensitivity and precision by a factor as great as 5.

Prepare a series of standards in similar Nessler tubes by adding about 50 ml of water and 3 drops of concentrated nitric acid to each, then add increments of a standard sodium chloride solution containing 10 μg of Cl/ml to each tube as indicated in the following table, then dilute each to 100 ml:

Tube no.	NaCl solution, added ml	ppm Cl in 10-ml sample
1	1.0	1.0
2	1.5	1.5
3	2.0	2.0
4	2.5	2.5
5	3.0	3.0

Adjust the temperature of the sample solution and of the standards to the same value within the range of 25–30°C.   Add 3 drops of 10% silver nitrate solution to each tube and allow the tubes to stand in the dark for not more than 3–5 min.   The time of standing must be restricted since formic acid tends to reduce the silver salt. Compare the turbidity of the sample solution visually with that of the standards and select the standard that most nearly matches the sample.   Report the chloride content of the sample as ppm or % equivalent to the chloride content of the standard.

Sulfate.   The turbidimetric procedure prescribed by the ACS for establishing the sulfate content of reagent grade formic acid applies to a specification of 0.003 and 0.002% sulfate maximum for the 98% and 88% acids, respectively (24).   Greater sensitivity and reliability can be expected from a procedure that utilizes a mixed solvent system to reduce the solubility of the barium sulfate observed in the test.   A procedure utilizing this technique is given below (37).

Procedure

To a 10-g (8.3 ml of 90%) formic acid sample add 0.2 ml of N sodium carbonate solution and evaporate to dryness on a steam bath.   Dissolve the residue in 40 ml of water, 10 ml of absolute methanol and 1 ml of 5 N hydrochloric acid.   Mix the resulting solution and add 1 ml of 0.5 M barium chloride solution.   Mix thoroughly and allow to stand for 1 hr.   After this time compare any visible turbidity with that of standards prepared simultaneously with the sample, using a standard sulfuric acid solution prepared by diluting 20.8 ml of 0.1 N sulfuric acid with water to 1 liter; the SO_4^{2-} ion concentration of this solution is 0.1 mg/ml.

Heavy Metals. The classic hydrogen sulfide precipitation procedure for the determination of heavy metals (expressed as lead) is generally used for the determination of these impurities in formic acid. This proximate test is designed to confirm that the common heavy metals do not exceed a specified level. The following procedure is from *Reagent Chemicals* (24).

Procedure

To either 3.3 ml (4 g) of 88% formic acid or 1.6 ml (2 g) of 98% formic acid in a beaker add about 10 mg of sodium carbonate and evaporate to dryness on a steam bath. Dissolve the residue in about 20 ml of water and dilute to 25 ml. In a separate beaker, dilute a solution containing 0.02 mg of lead(II) ion to 25 ml. Using a pH meter, adjust both the standard and sample solutions to a pH between 3 and 4 with N acetic acid or 10% aqueous ammonium hydroxide solution, then dilute with water to 40 ml, and mix. Add 10 ml of freshly prepared hydrogen sulfide solution and mix. As a limit test any color in the solution of the sample should not exceed that in the standard. If the amount of heavy metals in the sample has to be determined prepare a series of standards with varying concentration and report the heavy metal content of the sample as the concentration of the standard with the closest color match.

Iron. The iron content of formic acid can be determined colorimetrically or photometrically as the thiocyanate. Usually limit tests are performed; the following is a representative procedure (24).

Procedure

To 5 ml (6 g) of formic acid sample in a beaker add about 10 mg of sodium carbonate and evaporate to dryness on a steam bath. Dissolve the residue in 6 ml of hydrochloric acid and dilute with water to 60 ml. Dilute 20 ml of the solution with water to 50 ml, add 30–50 mg of ammonium persulfate crystals, and 3 ml of an ammonium thiocyanate reagent solution prepared by dissolving 300 g of the salt in 1 liter of water. Any red color should not exceed that produced by 0.01 mg of iron(III) in an equal volume of solution containing the same quantities of reagents as used in the test. For quantitative determination, the comparison should be made with a series of appropriate standards.

Nitrogen Compounds. The nitrogen compounds present in formic acid as impurities are expressed as ammonia. According to the ACS specifications (24), the ammonia content of reagent grade formic acid is determined by the direct reaction of a sample neutralized with sodium hydroxide with Nessler reagent. A more rigorous procedure involves reduction of all nitrogen compounds to ammonium ion, distillation of ammonia, and subsequent colorimetric comparison, using the Nessler reagent (37).

Procedure

Dilute 8.3 ml (10 g) of 90% formic acid or 8.2 ml (10 g) of 98% formic acid with water to 100 ml. Transfer 5 ml of this solution to a micro-Kjeldahl distillation apparatus, add 25 ml of about 5 N nitrogen-free sodium hydroxide solution, and 0.5 g of aluminum wire. Pass steam into the distillation flask and collect any distillate in 5 ml of water containing 1 ml of 0.1 N hydrochloric acid. Continue to pass steam until the liquid boils. Disconnect the steam, allow the reaction to proceed for 1 hr, and then steam distill until a total volume of 50 ml is obtained during about 6 min. Prepare a standard in the same manner, using 1.29 ml of a freshly prepared standard ammonium chloride solution in place of the 5-ml aliquot of the sample solution.

Prepare the standard ammonium chloride solution by dissolving 2.97 g of ammonium chloride in 1 liter of water and diluting 1 ml of this solution to 100 ml; the NH_4^+ ion concentration of the final solution is 0.01 mg/ml.

To each distillate add 2 ml of 5 M ammonia-free sodium hydroxide solution and 2 ml of Nessler's reagent. As a limit test, any yellow color produced in the test should not be deeper than that produced in the standard. If the amount of nitrogen compounds in the sample has to be determined, compare the color produced in the sample with those produced in appropriate standards.

Reducing Substances. Reagent grade formic acid should contain no reducing substances. The ACS specifications (24) prescribe a simple limit test.

Procedure

Dilute 25 ml of formic acid sample with 25 ml of water and add 0.1 ml of 0.1 N iodine solution. The solution should retain a distinct yellow color.

According to the Analar Standards (37) the test should be performed by using 40 ml of sample and 40 ml of water. In this case, a positive result would correspond to 0.001% of sulfite ion.

Turbidity. The ACS specifications for reagent grade formic acid (24) prescribes that no turbidity should be observable when diluting 1 volume of sample with 3 volumes of water and letting the mixture stand for 1 hr.

Residue. For testing the residue which may be present in the sample, 50 g of formic acid is evaporated to dryness on a steam bath and then dried at 105°C for 30 min.

FORMIC ACID ESTERS

Methyl formate, $HCOOCH_3$, is a colorless flammable liquid with a pleasing odor, boiling at about 32°C. It is miscible with water and most organic solvents.

Ethyl formate, $HCOOC_2H_5$, is a colorless liquid with a characteristic odor. It is soluble in water with gradual decomposition, in most saponifiable oils, and in propylene glycol. It is sparingly soluble in mineral oil, and insoluble in glycerol.

Commercial pentyl formate (amyl formate), $HCOOC_5H_{11}$, is a mixture of isomers in which isopentyl formate, $HCOOCH_2CH_2CH(CH_3)_2$, predominates. It is a colorless liquid with a plum odor. It is soluble in most saponifiable oils, in mineral oil, and in propylene glycol. It is insoluble in glycerol.

Octyl formate, $HCOOC_8H_{17}$, which may be a mixture of isomers, is a colorless liquid with a fruity odor. It is soluble in most saponifiable oils, in mineral oil, and in propylene glycol. It is virtually insoluble in glycerol.

Geranyl formate, $HCOOCH_2CH:C(CH_3)CH_2CH_2CH:C(CH_3)_2$, is a colorless to pale yellow liquid having a fresh leaf rose odor. It is soluble in most saponifiable oils and in mineral oil. It is insoluble in glycerol and in propylene glycol.

Citronellyl formate, $HCOOCH_2CH_2CH(CH_3)CH_2CH_2CH:C(CH_3)_2$, is a colorless liquid with a strong fruity, somewhat floral odor. It is soluble in most saponifiable oils and in mineral oil. It is sparingly soluble in propylene glycol, but it is insoluble in glycerol.

Cinnamyl formate, $HCOOCH_2CH:CHC_6H_5$, is a colorless to slightly yellow liquid having a balsamic odor with a cinnamon-like background. It is miscible with alcohol, chloroform and ether, but is insoluble in water.

Table 7, according to the *Food Chemicals Codex* (38–44), lists the specifications of these formic acid esters.

Table 7. Specifications of Formic Acid Esters

Ester	Formula	Assay, wt %, min	Refractive index, n_{D}^{20}	sp gr	Free acids, max	Arsenic, ppm, max	Heavy metals, ppm, max	Lead, ppm, max
methyl[a]	$C_2H_4O_2$	97			0.04^d	3	10	
ethyl[b]	$C_3H_6O_2$	95	1.3590–1.3630	0.918–0.921	0.1^d	3	40	10
pentyl[b,c]	$C_6H_{12}O_2$	92	1.3965–1.3995	0.878–0.885	1^e	3	40	10
octyl[b,c]	$C_9H_{18}O_2$	96	1.4180–1.4200	0.869–0.872	1^e	3	40	10
geranyl[b]	$C_{11}H_{18}O_2$	85	1.4640–1.4660	0.906–0.914	3^e	3	40	10
citronellyl[b]	$C_{11}H_{20}O_2$	86	1.4430–1.4490	0.890–0.903	3^e	3	40	10
cinnamyl[b]	$C_{10}H_{10}O_2$	92	1.5500–1.5560	1.074–1.079	3^e	3	40	10

[a] Also specified to have a nonvolatile residue of 20 ppm max and a water content of 0.005% max.
[b] Also meets solubility in ethanol test.
[c] Mixed isomers.
[d] Percent acidity, expressed as formic acid.
[e] Acid value, mg KOH/g of sample.

Methods of Analysis

Assay Methods

The general assay procedure (39–44) is based on the saponification of the ester in an excess of base followed by back-titration of the excess base with acid. Commercial pentyl or octyl formate is usually a mixture of isomers. The assay does not resolve this isomeric mixture. Because of its volatility, methyl formate requires some procedural changes for its assay (38).

Procedures

GENERAL PROCEDURE. Transfer an approximately weighed amount of the sample (0.5 g for ethyl formate and 1 g for pentyl formate) into a tared 125-ml conical flask and weigh accurately. Add to the flask, and simultaneously to a similar flask for a blank test, 25.0 ml of 0.5 N ethanolic potassium hydroxide solution and a few boiling stones. Connect each flask to a reflux condenser and heat the mixtures on a steam bath for exactly 1 hr, and allow to cool. For ethyl formate, standing for 15 min at room temperature suffices. Add 10 drops of 1% ethanolic phenolphthalein solution to each flask and titrate the excess of base in each flask with 0.5 N hydrochloric acid.

$$\text{Ester, wt \%} = \frac{(B - A)(N)(MW)(100)}{(w)(2)(1000)}$$

where A = volume of hydrochloric acid required for sample titration, in ml
B = volume of hydrochloric acid required for blank titration, in ml
N = normality of hydrochloric acid
MW = g-mol wt of the ester
w = sample weight, in g

METHOD FOR METHYL FORMATE. From a buret transfer 100 ml of 0.5 N sodium hydroxide into a 100-ml volumetric flask. For the blank transfer 100 ml of the base into a 500-ml conical flask. Weigh the volumetric flask and its contents, pipet 2 ml of the methyl formate sample into that flask, mix and reweigh, to establish the weight of the sample added. Transfer the contents of that flask quantitatively with water rinses into a second 500-ml conical flask. Add sufficient water to the flask for the blank so as to match the volume in the sample flask. Add 10 drops of 1% ethanolic phenolphthalein solution to each flask, and titrate the excess base with 0.5 N hydrochloric acid. Calculate the methyl formate content as given above.

Determination of Impurities

Free Acids. In case of formate esters other than methyl and ethyl, the amount of free acids present is expressed as the *acid value*. The acid value is expressed as the milligrams of potassium hydroxide needed to neutralize the free acidity present in one gram of the sample. The following procedure is broadly applicable (45).

Procedure

Dissolve about 10 g of the accurately weighed sample in 50 ml of ethanol that has been previously neutralized to phenolphthalein with 0.1 N sodium hydroxide solution. Add 1 ml of 1% ethanolic phenolphthalein solution and titrate with 0.1 N sodium hydroxide solution until the solution remains faintly pink after shaking for 10 sec.

$$\text{Acid value} = \frac{(A)(N)(56.11)}{w}$$

where A = volume of sodium hydroxide solution used for the titration, in ml
N = normality of the sodium hydroxide solution
w = sample weight, in g

In case of methyl and ethyl formate, the amount of free acids present is determined and expressed as formic acid. This is the *acidity* of the sample. For methyl formate a titration with potassium hydroxide is effected in an alcoholic medium (38). For ethyl formate an iodometric titration is employed (39).

Procedures

METHYL FORMATE. Transfer a 50-ml sample into a 300-ml conical flask, containing 1 ml of a 0.1% solution of bromothymol blue in 1:1 ethanol–water and 50 ml of methanol that has been previously titrated with 0.1 N ethanolic potassium hydroxide solution to the first appearance of a blue color, and titrate the sample with the same base to the same blue color. The maximum permitted amount of free acid corresponds to 4.2 ml of the 0.1 N potassium hydroxide solution.

ETHYL FORMATE. Transfer about 5 g of accurately weighed sample to a glass-stoppered conical flask containing a solution of 500 mg of potassium iodate and 2 g of potassium iodide in 50 ml of water. Titrate the liberated iodine with 0.1 N sodium thiosulfate using starch as the indicator. Each ml of 0.1 N sodium thiosulfate is equivalent to 4.603 mg of formic acid.

$$\text{Free acids (as formic acid), wt \%} = \frac{(V)(N)(46.03)(100)}{(w)(1000)}$$

where V = volume of sodium thiosulfate solution used for titration, in ml
N = normality of sodium thiosulfate solution
w = sample weight, in g

Solubility in Ethanol. Except for methyl formate, the *Food Chemicals Codex* also prescribes checking the purity of the ester by its solubility in diluted ethanol (46).

Procedure

Transfer a 1.0-ml sample into a 10-ml glass-stoppered cylinder graduated in 0.1-ml subdivisions. Add, slowly, in small portions, ethanol–water mixture in the concentration specified below. Shake the cylinder after each addition. Record the volume of the mixture added which is needed to obtain a clear solution, then continue the addition until a total of 10 ml has been added. If opalescence or cloudiness occurs during the subsequent additions, record the volume of ethanol–water mixture at which this occurs.

Ester	Ethanol–water mixture	Volume of the mixture in which 1 ml of sample should completely dissolve	Remarks
ethyl	1:1	0.5 ml	
pentyl	6:4	4 ml	must remain in
octyl	7:3	5 ml	solution when
citronellyl	8:2	3 ml	diluted to 10 ml
geranyl	8:2	3 ml	
cinnamyl	8:2	2 ml	
	2:8	10 ml	

Heavy Metals and Lead. A conventional test for heavy metals is based on sulfide precipitation at pH 3.0–4.0; for details, see Vol. 8, pp. 438–439.

For esters except methyl, the *Food Chemicals Codex* also specifies a separate test for lead that is based on ashing of the sample, dissolution of the residue with cyanide and citrate present as complexing agents, and extraction with dithizone into chloroform. The purplish color of the solution is compared visually with that of standards. For details, see Vol. 8, pp. 440–441.

Arsenic. In formate esters intended as a food additive, arsenic is determined photometrically by the evolution of arsine and its reaction with silver diethyldithiocarbamate. For details, see Vol. 8, pp. 436–438.

FORMIC ACID SALTS

The most important formic acid salt is sodium formate; the specification of the reagent grade material is listed in Table 8. Sodium formate is utilized in the production of leather by the chrome tanning process; the formate ion reduces chromium(VI) to chromium(III) and solubilizes trivalent metals by complexation. The sodium salt is also used in the textile industry and is an ingredient of metal plating bath.

Ammonium formate is used in chemical analysis, especially to precipitate base metals (see p. 120).

Nickel formate is employed in the preparation of hydrogenation catalysts and has been considered for the production of alkaline storage batteries.

Table 8. Specifications of Reagent Grade Sodium Formate

assay, wt %, min	99.0
insoluble matter, wt %, max	0.005
chloride, wt %, max	0.001
sulfate, wt %, max	0.001
calcium, wt %, max	0.005
heavy metals, as lead, wt %, max	0.005
iron, wt %, max	0.005

Aluminum formate, usually in solution form, is used to impart water repellency to textiles and paper.

Methods of Analysis

Methods related to the analysis of sodium formate and ammonium formate are given below.

ANALYSIS OF SODIUM FORMATE

Assay Methods

Sodium formate is commonly assayed by a redox titration procedure (35).

Procedure

Weigh accurately about 1 g of sample, transfer it to a 200-ml volumetric flask, dissolve in 50 ml of water, dilute with water to volume, and mix. Transfer exactly 25 ml of this solution to a 250-ml glass-stoppered flask, add 3 ml of 10% sodium hydroxide solution and exactly 75 ml of 0.1 N potassium permanganate solution. Heat on a steam bath for 20 min, cool, add 5 ml of hydrochloric acid, 4 g of solid potassium iodide, 5 ml of starch indicator solution, and titrate the liberated iodine, corresponding to the excess of permanganate, with 0.1 N sodium thiosulfate solution. Carry out a blank determination with the reagents.

$$\text{Sodium formate, wt } \% = \frac{(B - A)(N)(MW)(100)}{(w)(2)(1000)}$$

where A = volume of sodium thiosulfate solution required for sample titration, in ml

        B = volume of sodium thiosulfate solution required for blank titration, in ml

        N = normality of sodium thiosulfate solution

   MW = g-mol wt of sodium formate ($=68.01$)

        w = sample weight in the aliquot

A special nonaqueous acidimetric procedure has been developed for the assay of sodium formate formed as a by-product in the manufacture of pentaerythritol. In this procedure the sample in glacial acetic acid is titrated with perchloric acid in acetic acid, using p-naphtholbenzein as the indicator.

Procedure

Prepare 0.5 N perchloric acid solution by adding 42 ml of 70–72% perchloric acid with cooling to a 1000-ml volumetric flask containing about 500 ml of glacial acetic acid, mixing, and diluting with glacial acetic acid to volume. Standardize this solution against potassium hydrogen phthalate in the following way. Accurately weigh 2.5–3.0 g of primary standard potassium hydrogen phthalate into a beaker, add about 50 ml of glacial acetic acid, heat to dissolve, then cool to room temperature, add 3–5 drops of a 0.1% solution of p-naphtholbenzein in glacial acetic acid, and titrate with the perchloric acid solution to a robin's egg blue color.

$$\text{Normality} = \frac{(W)(4.8967)}{V}$$

where W = weight of potassium hydrogen phthalate, in g

        V = volume of perchloric acid solution used for the titration, in ml

Weigh accurately a 1-g sample into a beaker and dissolve it in 50 ml of reagent grade glacial acetic acid. Add 5–7 drops of the 0.1% *p*-naphtholbenzein indicator solution and titrate with the 0.5 *N* perchloric acid solution to the first definite green color.

$$\text{Sodium formate, wt \%} = \frac{(V - 0.1)(N)(MW)(100)}{(w)(1000)}$$

where V = volume of perchlorate solution used for titration, in ml
N = normality of the perchlorate solution
MW = g-mol wt of sodium formate (=68.01)
w = sample weight, in g

Determination of Impurities

The procedures used for the determination of impurities such as chloride, sulfate, heavy metals, and iron closely parallel those discussed earlier for formic acid (pp. 127–131) and require no additional discussion. A separate method for the determination of calcium impurity is outlined below.

Calcium. The calcium content of sodium formate has been traditionally determined by a conventional turbidimetric oxalate procedure. Recently, interest has been, shown in carrying out the determination by atomic absorption spectrophotometry.

Procedure

Dissolve a suitable, weighed sample in water, add 5 ml of a 5% lanthanum chloride solution in 1:2 water–hydrochloric acid and dilute with water in a 25-ml volumetric flask to volume. Proceed similarly with three additional samples of the same weight, but add 1, 2, and 4 ml, respectively, of a freshly prepared calcium working standard solution with a calcium concentration of 0.01 mg/ml. Read the % absorption of each solution at 422.7 nm against water. Plot the absorbance against the amount of calcium added, draw the best fitting line through the points, and extrapolate the line to its intercept with the abscissa. The length of the abscissa between this intercept and the origin corresponds to the amount of calcium in the sample.

ANALYSIS OF AMMONIUM FORMATE

Assay Methods

The assay of ammonium formate is frequently established by independent determinations of both the ammonium and the formate contents.

Procedures

THROUGH THE AMMONIUM CONTENT. Weigh accurately about 3 g of sample and transfer to a 500-ml conical flask containing 50 ml of *N* sodium hydroxide solution and 75 ml of water. Add several boiling beads and boil the solution until the evolved vapors no longer turn moistened red litmus paper blue. Cool to room temperature and titrate the excess of sodium hydroxide with *N* sulfuric acid to the phenolphthalein end point.

$$\text{Ammonium formate, wt \%} = \frac{[(V_1)(N_1) - (V_2)(N_3)](MW)(100)}{(w)(1000)}$$

where V_1 = volume of sodium hydroxide solution added, in ml

   N_1 = normality of sodium hydroxide solution

   V_2 = volume of sulfuric acid required for titration, in ml

   N_2 = normality of the sulfuric acid

   MW = g-mol wt of ammonium formate (= 63.06)

   w = sample weight, in g

THROUGH THE FORMATE CONTENT. Weigh accurately a 1.0–1.2 g sample, transfer to a 250-ml volumetric flask, dissolve in water and dilute to volume. Pipet a 25-ml aliquot into an iodine flask, add 3 ml of sodium hydroxide solution containing 10 g of sodium hydroxide and 90 ml of water, and 50 ml of 0.1 N potassium permanganate solution. Heat on a steam bath for 20 min, cool, add 3 ml of concentrated hydrochloric acid, and 3 g of potassium iodide. Titrate the liberated iodine with 0.1 N sodium thiosulfate solution, adding starch indicator solution as the end point is approached. Run a blank determination using 50 ml of 0.1 N potassium permanganate solution to determine the exact equivalency of the 0.1 N potassium permanganate solution to the 0.1 N sodium thiosulfate solution.

$$\text{Ammonium formate, wt } \% = \frac{(B - A)(N)(MW)(100)}{(w)(1000)}$$

where A = volume of sodium thiosulfate solution required for sample titration, in ml

   B = volume of sodium thiosulfate solution required for blank titration, in ml

   N = normality of sodium thiosulfate solution

   MW = g-mol wt of ammonium formate (= 63.06)

   w = sample weight in the aliquot, in g

Bibliography

GENERAL REFERENCES

1. J. F. Walker and H. Lauderback, "Formic Acid and Derivatives," in A. Standen, ed., *Kirk-Othmer Encyclopedia of Chemical Technology*, Vol. 10, 2nd ed., Interscience Publishers, a division of John Wiley & Sons, Inc., New York, 1966, pp. 99–114.

2. K. O. Schmitt, "Ameisensäure," in *Ullmanns Encyclopadie der Technischen Chemie*, Vol. 3, 3rd ed., Urban & Schwarzenberg, Munich-Berlin, 1953, pp. 436–452.

3. W. L. Faith, D. B. Keyes, and R. L. Clark, "Formic Acid," in *Industrial Chemicals*, 3rd ed., John Wiley & Sons, Inc., New York, 1965, pp. 397–400.

4. H. W. Gibson, "The Chemistry of Formic Acid and Its Simple Derivatives," *Chem. Rev.* **69**, 673 (1969).

5. E. F. Joy and A. J. Barnard, Jr., "Commercial Acids and Bases," in F. J. Welcher, ed., *Standard Methods of Chemical Analysis*, 6th ed., Vol. IIA, Van Nostrand Co., Inc., Princeton, N.J., 1963, pp. 534–626.

6. *Research Center Technical Bulletins S63.6-1, -2, -3a, and -4*, Hercules Powder Co., 1964.

7. *Formic Acid*, Union Carbide Corporation, Chemicals and Plastics Division, 1967.

8. F. J. Welcher, *Organic Analytical Reagents*, Vol. 2, Van Nostrand Co., Inc., New York, 1947, pp. 33–41.

SPECIFIC REFERENCES

9. K. Bowden, E. A. Braude, E. R. H. Jones, *J. Chem. Soc.* **1946,** 948.

10. D. Chapman, *J. Chem. Soc.* **1956,** 225.

11. A. L. Benkert and E. F. Smith, *J. Am. Chem. Soc.* **18**, 1055 (1896).

12. S. Kallmann, *Ind. Eng. Chem., Anal. Ed.* **13**, 987 (1941).

13. H. R. Proctor and R. A. Seymour-Jones, *J. Soc. Chem. Ind.* **30**, 404 (1911).

14. H. Yagoda and H. A. Fales, *J. Am. Chem. Soc.* **58**, 1494 (1936).

15. P. von Berg, *Z. Anal. Chem.* **25**, 512 (1886); *Analyst*, **52**, 182 (1887).

16. E. Birk, *Z. Angew. Chem.* **41,** 751 (1928).

17. G. P. Scholl, *J. Am. Chem. Soc.* **25,** 1045 (1903).

18. A. Quartaroli, *Staz. Sper. Agrar. Ital.* **44,** 210 (1911).

19. W. Funk, *Z. Anal. Chem.* **45,** 489, 562 (1906).

20. E. I. Fulmer, *Ind. Eng. Chem., Anal. Ed.* **3,** 257 (1931).

21. L. M. Dennis and W. C. Geer, *Ber. Deut. Chem. Ges.* **37,** 961 (1904).

22. A. Quartaroli, *Staz. Sper. Agrar. Ital.* **44,** 157 (1911); *Gazz. Chim. Ital.* **41** (2), 53 (1911).

23. E. Vernazza, *Atti, Accad. Sci., Torino, Classe Sci. Fis. Nat.* **70,** 89 (1935).

24. *American Chemical Society Specifications*, 4th ed. 1967 Committee on Analytical Reagents, Reagent Chemicals, American Chemical Society, Washington, D.C., 1968, pp. 263–266.

25. *National Research Council Food Chemicals Codex*, 1st ed., Committee on Specifications, Food Protection Committee, National Academy of Sciences, Washington, D.C., 1966, pp. 289–290.

26. *The Pharmacopeia of the United States of America*, XVII, The United States Pharmacopeial Convention, Inc., Mack Publishing Co., Easton, Pa., 1965, p. 985.

27. *ASTM D 92-66, Flash and Fire Points by Cleveland Open Cup*, American Society for Testing and Materials, Philadelphia, Pa., 1970.

28. *ASTM D 1310-67, Flash Point of Volatile Flammable Materials by Tag Open-Cup Apparatus*, American Society for Testing and Materials, Philadelphia, Pa., 1970.

29. F. Feigl, *Spot Tests in Organic Analysis*, Elsevier Publishing Co., 7th ed., Amsterdam, 1966.

30. F. Feigl and D. Haguenauer-Castro, *Chemist-Analyst* **50,** 102 (1961).

31. E. Sawicki, J. W. Stanley, J. Pfaff, and J. Ferguson, *Anal. Chem. Proc. Intern. Symp., Birmingham Univ., England, 1962*, pp. 62–69.

32. V. Prey, H. Berbalk, and M. Kausz, *Microchem. Acta* **1962,** 449.

33. *Method No. F566,003* (effective 1963), E. I. du Pont de Nemours & Co., Inc., Industrial and Biochemicals Dept.

34. *Methods of Test for Formic Acid*, Standard 4341:1968, British Standards Institution.

35. Ref. 24, First Supplement; *Anal. Chem.* **41,** 2095–2103 (1969).

36. *Chemicals and Plastics Laboratory Manual, 1B-3A1, (1968)*. Union Carbide Corp., pp. 1–6.

37. *AnalaR Standards for Laboratory Chemicals*, 6th ed., AnalaR Standards Ltd., London, 1967, pp. 229–232.

38. Ref 25, pp. 439–440.

39. Ref. 25, pp. 256–257.

40. Ref. 25, pp. 47–48.

41. Ref. 25, pp. 476–477.

42. Ref. 25, pp. 299–300.

43. Ref. 25, pp. 196–197.

44. Ref. 25, pp. 185–186.

45. Ref. 25, p. 740.

46. Ref. 25, p. 746.

R. M. Speights
Geochemical Systems, Inc.
A. J. Barnard, Jr.
J. T. Baker Chemical Company

FOURIER TRANSFORM SPECTROSCOPY

Fourier transform spectroscopy, sometimes termed interference spectroscopy, multiplex spectroscopy, Fourier spectroscopy, or even interferometry, affords a means of obtaining spectral data in the UV to far-infrared ranges. With rare exceptions the data obtained or desired from the operation of a Fourier transform spectrometer system are in the form of conventional spectra, ie, plots of intensity versus wavelength or wave number. It is consequently not necessary to consider spectra per se; in this respect see INFRARED SPECTROMETRY, Vol. 2, p. 253; NEAR-INFRARED SPECTRO-PHOTOMETRY, Vol. 2, p. 648; REFLECTANCE SPECTROPHOTOMETRY, Vol. 3, p. 376; and ULTRAVIOLET AND VISIBLE ABSORPTION SPECTROMETRY, Vol 3, p. 726, for discussions of the theoretical background and utility of spectra. The various techniques used in preparing and handling samples, and the samples themselves, are generally like those used in conventional spectroscopy. Attention is therefore focused on the instrumental technique of Fourier transform spectroscopy itself. The subject will be briefly outlined; more detailed treatments are given in the general references (1–8).

The principles of Fourier transform spectroscopy have been known for a long time. Michelson was the first to use the technique in 1891, and showed that the intensity of the light emerging from a two-beam scanning interferometer is the Fourier cosine transform of the incident light (9,10). In order to produce the spectrum of the incident light one need, in principle, only make the cosine transform of the emerging light. Michelson recorded signals of relatively slight complexity by working in an extremely narrow spectral region, and was able to obtain evidence of hyperfine structure of narrow spectral lines. However, exceedingly complex signals are obtained by working in an extended spectral range, and the difficulties involved in carrying out the necessary computations by hand are insurmountable. Consequently, in the absence of modern digital computers or electronic analog devices used for Fourier analyses, Michelson's technique was not usable for obtaining spectra over an extended range and, although Rubens and Wood (11) recorded the first far-infrared spectra obtained by Fourier transform techniques in 1911, the technique lay dormant for a half century.

Interest was revived through two key contributions. Jacquinot showed that the light-gathering capacity of a spectrometer based on an interferometer could be much higher than that of a dispersion spectrometer using a slit (12), and Fellgett pointed out that using a Michelson interferometer allowed one to measure simultaneously all spectral elements of polychromatic radiation and thus obtain an important time advantage (13). Both contributions pointed to the potentially great sensitivity of the interferometer-based spectrometer and along with the capability of high resolution offered by the interferometer, as well as the availability of electronics and fast digital computers, spurred the construction of research-type Fourier transform spectrometer systems in the early and middle nineteen fifties. Some commercial Fourier transform spectrometers were available in the early and middle nineteen sixties but were not readily accepted by industrial analysts, probably because the techniques and instrumentation were strange and novel in contrast to the well-established and widely used dispersion spectrometers. Also, the data-handling and transformation techniques were still inadequate. Digital computation could be used but was cumbersome and time-consuming unless one's own computer was available. Analog methods of data reduction were rapid and permitted in-lab analyses to be made but were not precise enough. The bulk of the work involving Fourier transform spectroscopy thus remained in the hands of physicists and astronomers. However, the situation began to change when reliable and inexpensive minicomputers began to be available in the late sixties. It was then possible to incorporate a digital computer in the Fourier transform spectrometer and with improved software, to eliminate the data-processing troubles entirely. While the initial interest in Fourier transform spectroscopy involved the examination of weak sources or measurements at high resolution, the situation has now changed. The developments in both hardware and software have produced such excellent results, particularly in the infrared region, that Fourier transform spectroscopy promises to become the dominant infrared spectroscopic technique.

Theory

Before taking up the principles of Fourier transform spectroscopy it is useful to consider briefly the general aspects of spectrometry in what may be termed the optical region, ie, from the end of the microwave and the beginning of the far-infrared regions up to the end of the UV region. In contrast to radiometry, which is concerned solely with the intensity of radiation, the purpose of spectrometry is to supply information about the wavelength, wave number or frequency of the radiation as well as its intensity; for polychromatic radiation this means that the intensity of each component must be obtained. However, the frequencies of the radiations are so high (about 10^{12} Hz at the beginning of the far-infrared range and about 10^{15} Hz at the beginning of the UV range) that detectors cannot respond rapidly enough and consequently cannot discriminate between radiations of different frequencies, but merely respond by producing a signal proportional to the summed intensities of the radiations. Some sort of "ordering" or "separating" must therefore be done in order to carry out a spectrometric measurement, and this is usually accomplished by dispersing the radiation mixture into bundles of (almost) monochromatic radiation. The dispersed radiation bundles are then individually swept past a detector which produces a simple electrical signal proportional to the monochromatic radiation striking it. The spectrum obtained in this manner is therefore the result of a series of *radiometric* measurements. In contrast, the interferometer of a Fourier transform spectrometer carries out a "sorting" procedure by inducing phase differences between the various components of the radiation mixture. All components are processed and examined simultaneously, with significant advantages in sensitivity and efficiency in comparison to those of a dispersion instrument, but at the expense of simplicity. While the simple signal of the sequential radiometer need only be recorded, the signal or interferogram of the interferometer is complex and must be subjected to Fourier transformation. There are thus very great differences in the way Fourier transform and conventional dispersion spectrometers operate.

Although precise treatments of the way interferograms are produced and processed are complex (1–5), the way an interferometer can be used to produce a spectrum can be readily understood. Let a beam of monochromatic radiation of wavelength λ enter a Michelson interferometer as shown in Figure 1. The interferometer consists of two plane, first-surface mirrors M_1 and M_2 and a 50% transmitting, 50% reflecting beam splitter. Mirror M_2 is stationary, whereas mirror M_1 can be moved. On striking the beam splitter, the entering radiation is split into two equal components and each of the two rays is reflected at a mirror and then returned to the beam splitter, where their amplitudes will add. The rays r_1 and r_2 will be exactly in phase when the mirrors are equidistant from the beam splitter; they will interfere constructively, and a signal proportional to the sum of their amplitudes will be produced by the detector. If the mirror M_1 is moved either to the right or left from the "zero" position by a distance $\lambda/4$, then the path of ray r_1 is changed by an amount $\lambda/2$ so that, on recombination at the beam splitter, r_1 and r_2 will be 180° out of phase. Destructive interference will then

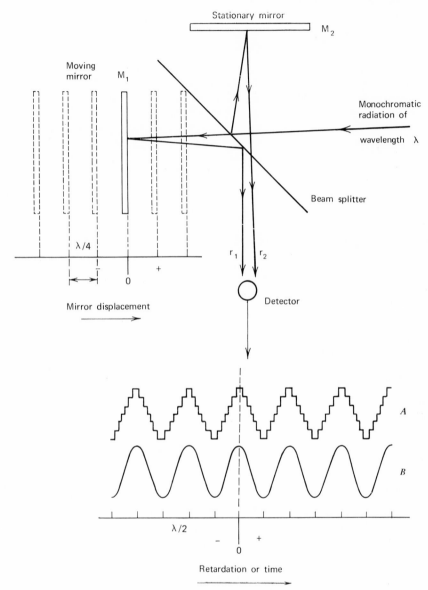

Fig. 1. Schematic representation of a Michelson interferometer and the signal produced. The incident ray is shown entering obliquely in order to avoid the overlapping of the rays r_1 and r_2. If the beam splitter consists of a transparent substrate bearing a beam splitting coating, then one of the rays would pass through the substrate once and the other three times. To compensate for this a "compensation plate" identical with the uncoated substrate is positioned parallel to the beam splitter; then each ray passes through the substrate material four times. Such a compensation plate has been omitted for simplicity. Trace A results if the mirror M_1 is moved incrementally; trace B results from a continuous motion.

occur and the detector output will be zero. This will happen for all mirror displacements which are precisely odd multiples of $\lambda/4$, ie, for optical path differences (termed retardations) of $\pm\lambda/2$, $\pm 3\lambda/2$, $\pm 5\lambda/2$, $\pm 7\lambda/2$. . . , the plus and minus signs indicating positive or negative retardations, ie, mirror displacement positions on either side of the zero position. Constructive interferences will similarly occur at mirror displacements which are even multiples of $\lambda/4$, at retardations of ± 0, $\pm\lambda$, $\pm 2\lambda$ . . . , and so on. Partial destructive or constructive interferences will occur at in-between positions. If mirror M_1 were moved in small identical steps there would be a stepwise change in the detector signal, shown schematically by the stepped plot A in Figure 1. That plot approximates a cosine wave, and the approximation becomes better as the mirror steps decrease in size and their number increases, and a continuous cosine wave will be produced if the mirror is moved continuously, eg, the lowest trace B in Figure 1. Such a detector signal, as well as more complex ones, is termed an interferogram. The simple cosine wave can be described by

$$I(X) = I(\nu) \cos 2\pi X\nu \tag{1}$$

where $I(X)$ is the intensity of the output signal as a function of mirror displacement X and $I(\nu)$ is the intensity of the source as function of optical frequency ν. The extension to polychromatic radiation now follows. If a radiation mixture enters the interferometer, each component will be subjected to retardation and the signal or interferogram produced by the detector is then the summation of all interferences. Or, for polychromatic radiation one sums all components, expressing this by

$$I(X) = \int_{-\infty}^{+\infty} I(\nu) \cos (2\pi X\nu) d\nu \tag{2}$$

$I(X)$ is the interferogram, and $I(\nu)$ is the spectrum of the source. Complex interferograms are shown in Figure 2. The center peak or central burst of the interferogram occurs in the vicinity of zero mirror displacement or retardation when all radiation components have the same phase. The peak amplitude of the interferogram is proportional to the total energy of the incident radiation which is modulated by the interferometer; the smaller amplitude peaks along each "wing" of the interferogram carry spectral information. The complement of equation 2 is

$$I(\nu) = \int_{-\infty}^{+\infty} I(X) \cos (2\pi X\nu) dX \tag{3}$$

and the Fourier transform pair, equations 2 and 3, provides the relation between the spectrum $I(\nu)$ and the interferogram $I(X)$. In practice it is found that interferograms are rarely symmetrical, so that the interferogram and spectrum are related by the complex pair

$$I(X) = \int_{-\infty}^{+\infty} I(\nu) e^{2\pi i X\nu} d\nu \tag{4}$$

$$I(\nu) = \int_{-\infty}^{+\infty} I(X) e^{-2\pi i X\nu} dX \tag{5}$$

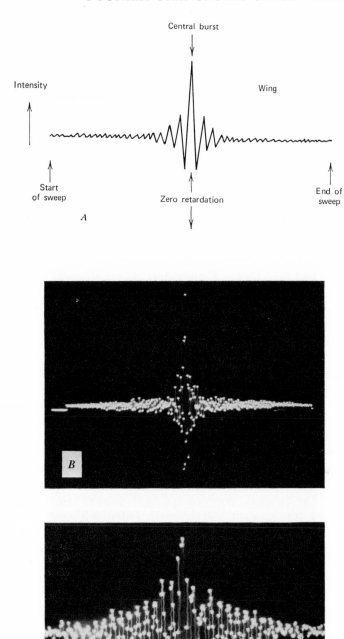

Fig. 2. Interferograms of broad-band sources. Trace *A* shows a stylized interferogram. For *B* and *C* the interferograms were digitized and stored in a computer core memory. The stored interferogram was then "read out," displayed on an oscilloscope screen, and photographed. Each white dot represents a bit of information stored in one memory channel.

In general, one measures intensity as function of mirror displacement and gets complex signals like those shown in Figure 2. Such a signal is expressed by equation 4. The spectrum is then derived by analyzing the interferogram by performing the transform, ie, equation 5.

Alternately, suppose that the mirror M_1 is moved at a constant velocity V. The cosine wave produced by the detector goes through one cycle if mirror M_1 is displaced by a distance $\lambda/2$. The frequency of the signal produced by the detector is then

$$f = V/(\lambda/2) = 2V\nu \qquad (6)$$

This means that, for a constant mirror velocity, there is a linear relation between the frequency ν in wave numbers of the incoming monochromatic radiation and the frequency of the detector signal. Alternately, one may consider the interferogram to arise from Doppler shifting. Again, let one mirror of the Michelson interferometer move with velocity V. The source in one "arm" of the interferometer will then appear to be moving away from the detector at a velocity $2V$, and the frequencies or wavelengths of the two rays r_1 and r_2 of Figure 1 will differ. For a monochromatic radiation of 3 μm wavelength the optical frequency is 10^{14} Hz, and this is changed in one arm of the interferometer to $(10^{14} - 2V/\lambda)$ Hz while it remains at 10^{14} Hz in the other. The detector is exposed to two frequencies differing by $2V/\lambda$ Hz. The detector cannot respond to the high frequencies of the individual incident radiations, but can respond to the beat frequency between the two signals. This is shown schematically in Figure 3, showing the production of a "wave packet" producing a beat frequency through the addition of two waves of differing wavelength. For each of the alternate approaches all detector frequencies are summed if polychromatic radiation is involved, and a complex interferogram results, again described by equation 4. Essentially what has been done is to cause a frequency shift. From equation 6, for example, with a mirror velocity of 0.5 mm/sec, monochromatic radiation of 10 μm wavelength (equivalent to 1000 cm^{-1} and a frequency of 3×10^{14} Hz) will produce a detector signal of 50 Hz. For 5 μm radiation, $f = 100$ Hz, and so on. For a polychromatic source each component is uniquely encoded and shifted "downstream" in frequency. Or, a complex signal of very high frequency (the incident polychromatic radiation) becomes modulated and shifted to a low audiofrequency range. The complex signal, rather than lying in the very high optical frequency range, now falls in a range easily handled by conventional audiofrequency electronics. The complex signal or interferogram is then analyzed or resolved into individual components to yield frequency–intensity information.

The resolution obtainable with an interferometer depends on many factors. Essentially, in simple theory the resolution for a centered interferogram can be defined by

$$\Delta\nu = \tfrac{1}{2}X$$

where X is the total path length traversed by the mirror. Note that the resolution in wave numbers is constant, rather than variable within the spectral range covered as in the case of dispersion instruments. In practice, resolution is a function of (a) the solid angle of the energy entering the instrument; (b) what may be termed the optical quality of the instrument, ie, planarity of mirrors, beam splitter, etc; (c) the linearity of mirror displacement or its equivalent, the degree to which mirror displacement is measured; (d) data-sampling and data-reduction procedures; (e) the retardation or maximum path difference. Although item (d) is beyond the scope of the present article, it is instructive to consider the other items.

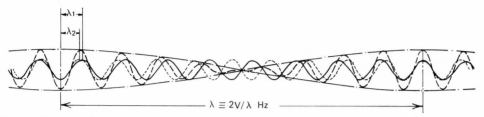

Fig. 3. The formation of a beat frequency. Two sinusoids of wavelengths λ_1 and λ_2 add to produce a beat frequency.

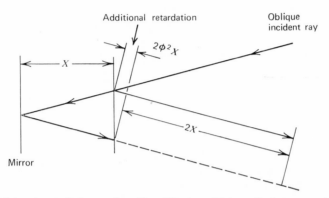

Fig. 4. Additional retardation produced by obliquity. If the radiation enters the interferometer not along the optical axis but obliquely, then an additional retardation $2\Phi^2 X$ is produced, resulting in decreased resolution.

The resolution is degraded if the beam entering the interferometer is not parallel. How this comes about is indicated in Figure 4. A ray entering along the optical axis would experience a retardation of $2X$ for a mirror displacement X. However, a ray entering at a small oblique angle, Φ, will experience (to a first approximation) an additional retardation equal to $2\Phi^2 X$. If one considers an extended monochromatic source which is large enough to fill the field of view of the instrument so that a converging cone of monochromatic light passes into the interferometer, then it is obvious that increasing the cone angle Φ will produce a continuous series of rays of different retardations. The radiation contributed by the peripheral region of the field of view at relatively high Φ values will give rise to rays which differ significantly from those coming in close to the optical axis. This means that a range of output frequencies is produced from a high monochromatic input frequency, so that the resolution is degraded. Similar effects are produced if the optical components of the instrument are not planar, similarly leading to a degradation of resolution.

The resolution is also affected by the degree to which the retardation is known, ie, measurements of mirror position. As is obvious from equation 4 and the previous description, two measurements are made: one is a measurement of radiation intensity, the other a measurement of retardation expressed as mirror displacement in terms of actual mirror position or the time required for a certain mirror displacement to occur at known velocity. If the retardation measurement is degraded, then resolution will be degraded. The ways in which attempts are made to insure high-quality retardation measurements by controlling the mirror motion will be briefly considered later. In practice, the degree to which the retardation measurement can be made is frequently tied to the item of major importance, the total retardation.

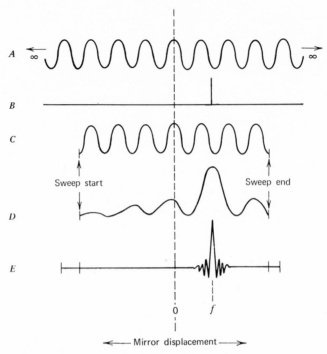

Fig. 5. Effect of truncation. An infinitely long wave train (trace *A*, produced by modulating monochromatic radiation by means of an infinitely long mirror travel) would lead to a spike of zero width on transformation (trace *B*). Transformation of a finite wave train (trace *C*) would lead to a band having width and side lobes (trace *D*). If a longer wave train is transformed, the width and side lobes decrease (trace *E*).

Note the integration limits of equation 5. They mean that the mirror displacement must occur from $-\infty$ to $+\infty$ in order to obtain a complete reproduction of the spectrum. The mirror travel is always limited, so that it is obviously impossible to meet the requirement, and the theoretical resolution is degraded. How this occurs can be outlined as follows. An ideal monochromatic radiation would give rise to an infinitely long cosine wave if the mirror excursion were infinitely long. This is indicated schematically by trace *A* of Figure 5, and represents the situation which is physically impossible. The Fourier transform of such an infinite wave is a spike of zero width, shown schematically by trace *B* in Figure 5. The mirror displacement is finite, therefore the duration of the cosine wave is finite and the wave form is truncated, eg, trace *C*. Such a truncated wave form contains a finite and usually relatively small number of wavelengths, and its Fourier transform takes the form of a function sin x/x. That function is centered at the same frequency as the spike of trace *B* but now has width and side oscillations. This is shown schematically in trace *D* of Figure 5. The width of the line is an inverse function of the number of wavelengths present in the truncated wave form and hence to the length of the mirror movement. If mirror displacement increases then the function narrows, eg, as shown in trace *E*, and resolution improves. This effect is nicely illustrated by Horlick's plots (14) shown in Figure 6. He simulated sweep-length effects by recording the interferogram of a polystyrene spectrum on magnetic tape and then carrying out the Fourier transform of portions of the interferogram. The latter is shown at the top of Figure 6. Spectrum *A* resulted from the transforma-

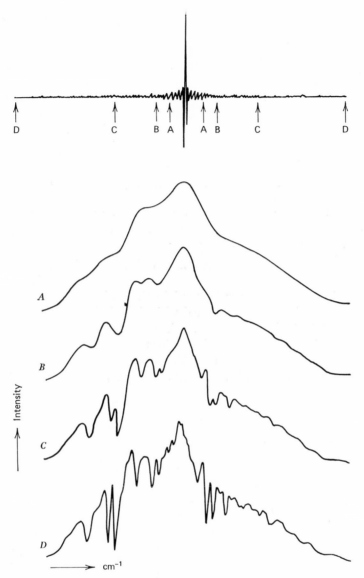

Fig. 6. Effect of truncation. The spectra A,B,C,D were produced by transforming segments of the interferogram shown at the top (14). The part between the A's resulted in spectrum A, and so on, the spectral structure becoming more apparent as the interferogram length increased.

tion of the part of the interferogram lying between the two A's marked at the top trace. Spectra B, C, and D resulted when interferograms of different lengths were transformed. As the length of the interferogram increases more spectral detail becomes visible, ie, the resolution increases.

Instrumentation

A Fourier transform spectrometer consists of a source (which may be the "sample" itself), an interferometer used to provide the necessary modulation, a detector,

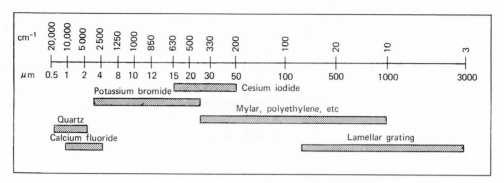

Fig. 7. Wavelength ranges covered by beam splitters.

various auxiliary electronic components such as mirror drives and amplifiers, a device for carrying out the Fourier transform, and some device for displaying or recording the spectrum. It is not necessary or feasible to describe all components, but instructive to consider some aspects of the instrumentation which are tied to the principles of the method.

Although interferometers can be used in the entire optical range, commercial instruments have mainly been concerned with the mid-infrared or "fingerprint" infrared region and the far-infrared region. The wavelength range which can be covered is determined by the beam splitter and detector used. The wavelength ranges covered by various beam splitters are shown in Figure 7. Interchangeable beam splitters are frequently used so that, along with a change in detector, different spectral regions may

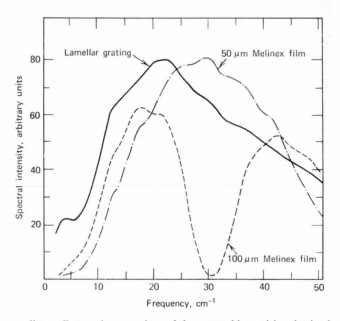

Fig. 8. Beam splitter effects. A comparison of the spectral intensities obtained with the Beckman FS-720 spectrometer fitted with 50- and 100 μm-thick Melinex film beam splitters with that obtained with the Beckman LR-100 lamellar grating spectrometer. Note the lower intensities obtained with film beam splitters at the low wave numbers region, and the failing of the 100-μm beam splitter near 30 cm⁻¹.

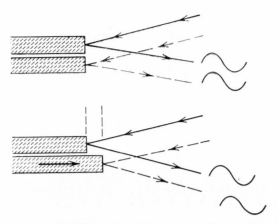

Fig. 9. Wave-front division by lamellar grating. If one plate is moved with respect to the other, interference of the two rays results.

be examined. Some difficulties are encountered in the very far-infrared region because the plastic-film beam splitters are inefficient and limited in the spectral range covered, illustrated by the plots of Figure 8. In order to counteract the failing of such beam splitters, some instruments have been built which cause modulation by wave-front division using a lamellar grating. The latter consists of a stack of parallel plates. Alternate plates are moved in unison so that, as is shown schematically by Figure 9, the incident radiation is divided into two parts and one part is retarded with respect to the other. Modulation occurs and interferograms result as described earlier. The schematic diagram of such an interferometer is given in Figure 10. The lamellar grating located in the spectrometer is made up of two sets of parallel intermeshing metal plates whose front surfaces have been lapped accurately flat. The plates are mounted so that these faces can be kept parallel to each other within a few seconds of

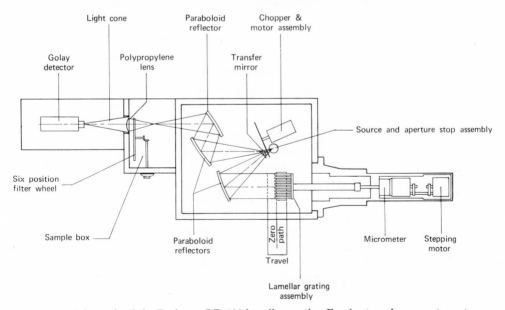

Fig. 10. Schematic of the Beckman LR-100 lamellar grating Fourier transform spectrometer.

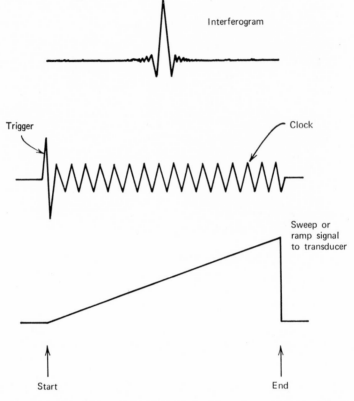

Fig. 11. Linear sweep with electronic time base. The mirror drive is mechanically and electronically adjusted so that the mirror velocity is constant. A trigger signal initiates the sweep and marks its beginning, and a precise clock signal is used as time base. The trigger and clock signals are used to measure retardation for the interferogram.

arc. The total area of the grating is 8 cm × 8 cm. The motion of the set of plates is equivalent to the motion of a mirror in producing interference effects.

In the far-infrared range the wavelengths encountered are of the order of hundreds of micrometers. It is therefore relatively easy to displace a mirror and precisely measure its displacement to fractions of a wavelength. This can be done by means of precise screws of the type used in micrometers. Consequently, a mirror drive for a far-infrared instrument is usually a suitable mechanical arrangement by which a mirror or mirror mount is coupled to a micrometer screw operated by an electronically controlled motor. The mirror motion could be continuous, resulting in a smooth signal like trace *B* of Figure 1, or be incremental. In an incremental or stepped drive the micrometer screw is advanced by, eg, 5 μm at regular intervals, resulting in a trace similar to trace *A* of Figure 1.

Such mechanical mirror positioning and measurements are not feasible at the shorter wavelengths, because the mirror position would have to be measured to fractions of a micron. This problem was partly overcome by using continuous drives. The mirror was mounted on a spring and displaced by a device similar to the voice coil

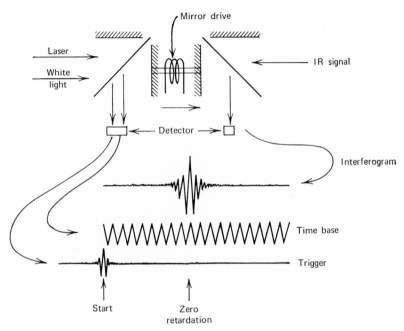

Fig. 12. Fringe-referenced interferometer. The two mirrors move simultaneously. Light from a white source produces a small interferogram, the central burst of which is used as trigger signal to indicate the beginning of the scan. Monochromatic radiation produces a sinusoidal signal which is used as time base.

of a loudspeaker, using complicated electronics to assure linearity of mirror motion. An electronic time base and trigger, shown schematically in Figure 11, were generated simultaneously. The relations are obvious: if the mirror is moved at constant velocity $V = X/\Delta t$, the displacement X is known because Δt is known by means of the electronic time base. Such instruments were successful and useful, but are now largely superceded. In order to be able to circumvent the severe requirements of a strictly linear drive and consequently be able to go to longer mirror excursions with attendant higher resolution, so-called fringe-referenced interferometers which generate their own time base were developed. How this is done is shown schematically in Figure 12.

One mechanism is used to move two mirrors simultaneously through identical displacements. The sample radiation to be processed is passed into one interferometer, and produces the "sample interferogram." Monochromatic light from a laser or a neon lamp is processed by the second interferometer and as in Figure 1, produces a cosine wave. White light from a small source is also passed into the second interferometer and produces a central burst when the light paths in the reference cube are symmetric. The two interferometers are aligned so that the white-light burst occurs at the beginning of a sweep. As the two mirrors move in concert, the three signals are "locked" together. Consequently, the requirement of a strictly linear drive is not necessary, and the mirror position can be determined by measuring the laser line interferogram, ie, counting the laser fringes as the mirror moves from the white-light burst reference position. Such fringe-referencing has made it possible to increase mirror sweep lengths

Fig. 13. Tandem interferometer. The two interferometer cubes used in the Block Engineering, Inc. Model 197 spectrometer are mounted so that one drive mechanism is used to displace the moving mirrors of both cubes simultaneously.

and consequently to increase resolution. Such a tandem interferometer pair is shown in Figure 13. Some instruments have been constructed so that only one interferometer cube was used and the infrared sample radiation and the laser and white-light reference beams shared the same beam splitter. This diminishes the light-gathering ability of the interferometer. Moiré fringes have also been used for fringe-referencing.

A fringe-referenced Michelson interferometer with 2-in.-diameter mirrors is shown in Figures 14 and 14a. The mirror drive is electromagnetic. A drag-free mirror drive is produced by floating the mirror shaft on an air cushion within a close-fitting sleeve.

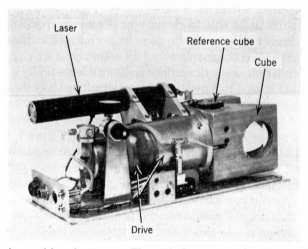

Fig. 14. Fringe-referenced interferometer. The optical system of the Digilab, Inc. Model FTS-14 spectrometer, side view.

Fig. 14a. Front view of the optical system of the Digilab, Inc. Model FTS-14 spectrometer.

Fig. 14b. Reference interferometer. The assembly shown is the reference interferometer used in the Digilab, Inc. Model FTS-14 spectrometer.

The plastic tubing, moisture trap, gas regulator, and gage are all associated with the air bearing. The black tube at the top left of Figure 14, seen end-on in Figure 14a, is the housing of the helium–neon laser used for fringe-referencing. The laser beam is deflected down into the large cube by a small mirror. The base of the second inter-

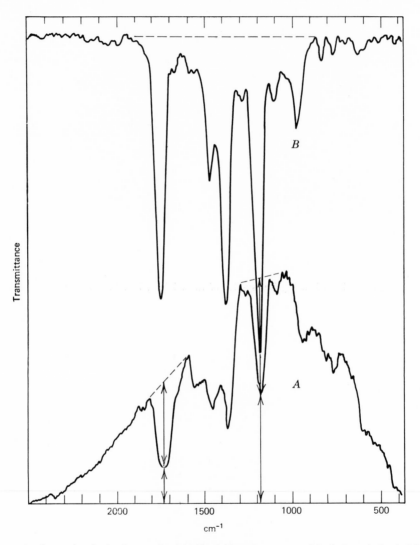

Fig. 15. Correction for background. (*A*) Single-beam spectrum of 2 µl of methyl ethyl ketone. (*B*) Background, ie, radiation passing through the empty cell, was subtracted from *A*. The spectra recorded with a Block Engineering, Inc. Model 200 spectrometer using analog data reduction.

ferometer used for fringe-referencing is the black rectangle fastened by four screws to the top of the cube. The reference interferometer itself is shown with its assembly in Figure 14b. The small glass cube is made of two prisms, the joined surfaces of which form the beam splitter. The moving mirror of this interferometer is a polished flat on the back of the main interferometer's moving mirror. The knurled rings at the back of the stationary mirror are slightly wedged so that mirror tilt can be adjusted. The wires come from two photodiodes which monitor the laser and a small white-light source built into the assembly.

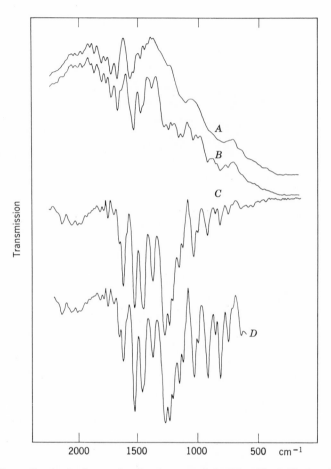

Fig. 16. Correction for background. Spectra recorded with a Block Engineering, Inc. Model 195 spectrometer with 100 scans and data reduction was carried out by digital computation. (*A*) Background (globar radiation passing through two potassium bromide flats). (*B*) 1 μl of eugenol was placed between the potassium bromide plates. (*C*) 100 scans of background as in *A* were subtracted from 100 scans of sample plus background as in *B*, resulting in the difference spectrum. (*D*) Ratio of spectra *A* and *B*.

Such a carefully constructed and precisely controlled drive is, essentially, the "heart" of the spectrometer and is directly responsible for the quality of the interferogram produced by the mirror sweep. The sweep time may be short (of the order of a fraction of a second to several seconds, as is usually the case with instruments operating at high-frequency ranges) or may be fairly long (min to hr for far-infrared instruments). Slowly scanning instruments usually incorporate a chopper (see Figure 10), but this is not needed if the scan time is short because the interferometer itself acts as chopper or modulator, as mentioned earlier.

The interferogram which is produced may be recorded in its analog form but is usually digitized prior to storage and transformation. As the mirror sweep proceeds, the detector signal is processed by an analog-to-digital converter. The digital signal may then be recorded on tape prior to storage in the memory of a large digital computer, be stored in the memory of the small computer, of the type used for time-averaging, or be stored in the memory of a minicomputer. The digitized, stored interferogram is then "reduced" to produce a spectrum by analog or digital procedures.

Data reduction done by analog means is feasible. The interferogram is reproduced repeatedly and each harmonic component is measured with a narrow band-pass electrical filter whose frequency can be varied over the region of interest. The device is, essentially, an electrical wave form analyzer or "wave analyzer" and functions, essentially, as a low-frequency spectrometer. The method is mechanized by changing the frequency of the wave analyzer at a constant rate and plotting the output on a strip chart recorder. The result is a graph of the spectral intensity of the source as a function of wave number.

The analog methods are useful in that a quick "readout" can be obtained in the laboratory if computing facilities are not readily available, but are imprecise. Further difficulties arise if analog-derived spectra are not ratioed against background but are used as single-beam spectra, ie, absorption bands superimposed on the spectrum of the source, or are corrected for background by subtracting the spectrum of the source. Some examples are shown in Figures 15 and 16.

Trace A of Figure 15 is a single-beam spectrum of methyl ethyl ketone measured with a Block Engineering, Inc. Model 200 Fourier transform spectrometer. The interferogram was stored in the core memory of the instrument's time-averaging computer and was then reduced by a wave analyzer. The spectrum is that of the source with the absorption bands of the sample superimposed on it, and suffers from all the disadvantages of single-beam spectra. It is possible to make some correction for "background" as follows: the interferogram of sample plus source is stored; the interferogram of the source is subtracted from the stored interferogram; the residual interferogram is then reduced. Such a procedure led to trace B of Figure 15. Trace B is of greater utility than trace A, but note that relative band intensities are affected by the subtraction procedure. Consider the two prominent bands near 1700 and 1200 cm^{-1}. In trace A the transmittance near 1700 cm^{-1} is about 30% and near 1200 cm^{-1} about 47%, so that the 1700/1200 band intensity ratio is 1.3. In trace B, however, the 1200-cm^{-1} band appears to be more intense than the 1700-cm^{-1} band, and the 1700/1200 ratio is 0.83. Another example of a spectrum corrected for background by subtraction is shown in trace C of Figure 16. When the correction was made by ratioing, the proper band intensity relations appear. This is particularly noticeable in the 1200–500 cm^{-1} region. The relatively small intensities of the bands below 1200 cm^{-1} of trace C is caused by the rapid fall-off of the single-beam source spectrum A.

Better analog results have been produced with more complex systems such as the Beckman-RIIC FTC-100 Fourier transform computer. While an interferogram is produced, the analog information is processed by an A/D converter and stored serially in one of two ferrite core matrix memories. Two sections of 1024-word capacity memory are available to enable a ratio of two spectra to be obtained by simultaneous transformation. (The paper-tape output of the spectrometer can be retained, so that more extensive processing of data by a large digital computer is possible.) Computation consists of cycling the stored information, passing the digitized data through a D/A converter, and then passing the analog output (the stored interferogram) through a scanning wave analyzer. The output of the wave analyzer is a spectrum and is recorded by an X-Y plotter. The program provides for either section of the memory to be transformed and displayed independently, or for simultaneous transformation to produce the ratioed spectrum. A "background" interferogram can be stored.

Even more complex systems have been used such as RIIC's Model FTC-300 control and data-handling system. The FTC-300 is made up of two major parts: the FS-300 unit contains all of the electronics for operating and controlling the spectrometer and produces a digitized interferogram, the latter being punched on tape for processing in an off-line computer, or is passed to the FTC-300 core memory; the FDP-300 data processing unit contains the logic control, memory circuitry, wave analyzer, and the flat-bed potentiometric recorder used to produce conventional spectra on preprinted charts. The FTC-300 system is more sophisticated and more complex than the earlier FTC-100 system, but is also a hybrid system. The digitized interferogram is stored in a 20k-bit memory. When complete, the digitized interferogram is converted by a D/A converter and the now analog signal is processed by a wave analyzer. As with the FTC-100, both background and sample interferograms can be stored, reduced individually or simultaneously, to produce single-beam or ratioed spectra. The ratioed spectra are claimed to be accurate to within $\pm 1\%$ when the background intensity has dropped to 3%.

Although wave analyzers have been used with good results, the computer method is much more versatile than analog methods. It is not only more precise, but corrections can be made, spectra can be ratioed and, in general, the data can be manipulated simply by writing the appropriate software. This capability gives the method a great versatility.

Digital data reduction can be carried out with large computers, but it is necessary to interface the spectrometer and computer. This can be done, for example, by digitizing the interferogram and punching the information on paper tape. The paper tape is then fed to the large computer which carries out the transform, and the spectrum is plotted out. Unless one has direct access to one's own computer, this method is obviously somewhat cumbersome. However, the advent of the minicomputer has alleviated that problem, and there have been great advances in digital methods. Some time ago, even with large digital computers, completing a Fourier transform calculation was costly. The reason for this is that the calculation of the transformation must include the contributions of each of the M data points which make up the interferogram for each of M spectral elements to be considered, so that the time required for computing the complete spectrum from the interferogram is proportional to M^2. However, as pointed out by Forman (15), the use of the so-called Cooley-Tukey algorithm (16) makes the computation time proportional to $M \log_2 M$. This greatly reduced the computing time, eg, it is possible to transform a 4096-point interferogram in about 15 sec whereas conventional techniques require 45 min. Processing interferograms has thus become an almost trivial operation and is readily accomplished by minicomputers built into the spectrometer systems. The minicomputer can then be used for data reduction, as well as to control the spectrometer system, to store data, and to enhance the signal-to-noise ratio (S/N) of data by multiple scanning.

The instruments operating in the visible to infrared ranges have short scan periods (of the order of seconds), so that multiple scanning becomes readily feasible. The signal proper is always positive *or* negative, while noise is positive *and* negative at random. If the same system is measured repeatedly and the results are added, then S grows linearly with the number of scans, while N increases only as the square root of the number of scans, so that S/N consequently increases as a function of the square root of the number of scans. With short scan periods it is therefore readily feasible to

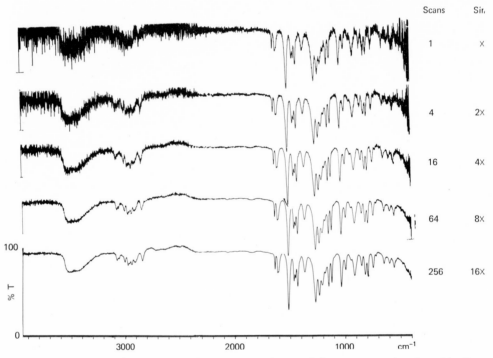

Fig. 17. Effects of multiple scanning. Spectra of eugenol, between potassium bromide discs, measured with a Digilab, Inc. Model FTS-14 Fourier transform spectrometer at a resolution of 2 cm^{-1}. The number next to each spectrum indicates the number of scans taken to produce the spectrum.

increase S/N by a factor of 10 or 20. However, provision has to be made to permit the coherent addition and storage of the multiple signals, and the built-in minicomputer can carry out these functions. An example of the signal-enhancing obtainable by multiple scanning is shown in Figure 17.

Multiple scanning can be used with any measurement technique and has been applied to nuclear magnetic resonance and electron spin resonance measurements and also to infrared measurements using a dispersion spectrometer (17). However, multiple scanning is really useful only when the individual scan is short. One rapidly reaches a point after which further S/N improvement is not really practical, as illustrated by Table 1. A ten- or twenty-fold S/N improvement is readily obtainable if the scan period is 1 sec, but having to wait for a thirty-fold S/N improvement begins to get tedious. It is readily apparent that if the individual scan periods are somewhat longer than a sec then the total scan time becomes quite long. A dispersion instrument could be set to cover a short spectral range in about 1 min with adequate resolution, but even with that scan period S/N improvements beyond a factor of 10 or so become unrealistic. An interferometer, on the other hand, will cover its entire spectral range in a relatively short time, so that multiple scanning becomes very beneficial.

Advantages. The Fourier transform spectrometer offers significant advantages in terms of S/N with respect to dispersion instruments based on the amount of signal which can be processed and the time used to process it.

Dispersion of radiation is not required so that energy-wasting slits are not needed. An interferometer has a relatively large, circular entrance aperture and relatively large mirrors. For example, the FTS-14 has 2-in. mirrors. The throughput, the amount of radiation which can enter the optics of the spectrometer, is therefore quite large in comparison to that of a dispersion spectrometer.

Table 1. S/N Enhancement by Multiple Scanning

| Number of scans | S/N | Total scanning time required for | | |
		1-sec scans	1-min scans	5-min scans
1	X	1 sec	1 min	5 min
4	$2X$	4 sec	4 min	20 min
16	$4X$	16 sec	16 min	$\sim$1.4 hr
64	$8X$	64 sec	$\sim$1 hr	$\sim$4 hr
256	$16X$	$\sim$5 min	$\sim$5 hr	$\sim$21 hr
1028	$32X$	$\sim$17 min	$\sim$17 hr	$\sim$3.5 days
4096	$64X$	$\sim$1 hr	$\sim$3 days	$\sim$2 weeks

The second major advantage also arises from the absence of the need to disperse radiation. In the dispersion spectrometer, each radiation bundle or resolution element of the spectrum is scanned across the detector. Therefore, if there are M resolution elements, the intensity of each element is measured for only a fraction T/M of the total scan time, T. The signal itself (the intensity of an element) is directly proportional to the time spent observing it, but noise, being random, is proportional to the square root of the observation time. The S/N is then proportional to $(T/M)^{1/2}$. With the interferometer, however, the incident radiation falls on the detector, so that each resolution element is observed throughout the entire scan period, with the result that S/N is proportional to $T^{1/2}$. The improvement by the factor of $M^{1/2}$ in the case of the interferometer can be quite large under conditions of relatively high, or high resolution. The improvement, termed Fellgett's advantage, is realized with detectors which are detector noise limited, ie, as the signal level increases there is no increase in detector noise. The improvement in S/N can be traded off for rapid response, so that the scan time can be decreased. A spectrum can be measured with a Fourier transform spectrometer in the same time as with a conventional spectrometer, but with better S/N, or in a much shorter time with an equivalent S/N.

In order to compare Fourier transform and conventional techniques, consider examining a spectrum composed of 2000 resolution elements. Suppose that an observation time of 1 sec per resolution element is needed to obtain an acceptable S/N. The dispersion spectrometer needs 2000 sec or 33 min to make the measurement; the interferometer makes the measurement in 1 sec. To improve S/N by a factor of 2 under the same conditions, the dispersion instrument would need 2 hr and 12 min, whereas the interferometer would require only 4 sec to carry out the measurement. If the resolution were to be improved by a factor of 2, the entrance and exit slit widths of the dispersion instrument must be halved. This decreases throughput by a factor of 4.

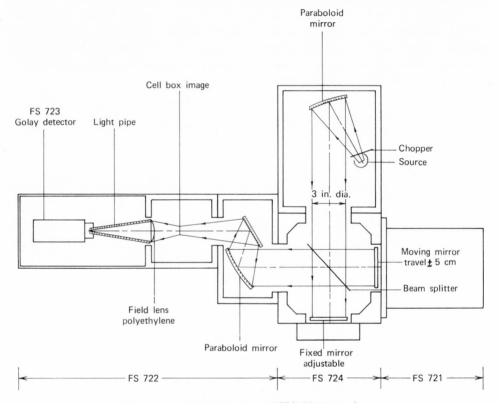

Fig. 18. Layout of Beckman-RIIC FS-720 optics.

In order to regain the desired S/N, the required measurement time is therefore increased by a factor of 16 to 8 hr and 48 min. In contrast, the resolution of an interferometer is doubled by doubling the length of traverse of the moving mirror. The resolution is doubled by going from a 1-sec measurement interval to 2 sec.

Such advantages in S/N make it worthwhile to use the Fourier transform techniques. Other advantages exist also, and some of these have already been mentioned. The resolution of the Fourier transform spectrometer is constant throughout the range covered by the instrument, for example. Also, it is possible to improve S/N through multiple scanning. The S/N advantage could be considered in terms of economics, ie, cost per spectrum, but it is difficult to do this because there are so many factors involved; instrument cost and capital-equipment depreciation rate, technician's salary, overhead, etc. However, for work situations involving the recording of numerous spectra, as in quality control, it seems likely that significant economic advantages arise through the use of a Fourier transform spectrometer. Especially with the computerized instruments, the digital nature of the spectral data and data-handling procedures lead to great flexibility and potential for storage of spectra, spectra files, and computerized search-match-identification and retrieval procedures.

Commercial Instruments

A variety of commercial Fourier transform spectrometers covering the spectrum from the UV to the far-infrared is available. Beckman Instruments, Inc. of Fullerton, California markets three spectrometers produced by Beckman-RIIC, Ltd., a British subsidiary. One of these was shown earlier in Figure 10. Models FS-720 and FS-820 spectrometers are similar and can be easily changed because of their modular nature. The beam splitter can also be changed. The location of the source and detector lends

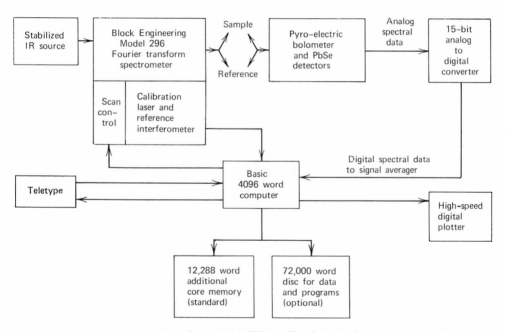

Fig. 19. Schematic of Digilab, Inc. Model FTS-14 Fourier transform spectrometer system.

itself to both source and detection studies. The instruments incorporate Michelson interferometers and use 7.5-cm diameter mirrors. The whole optical system can be evacuated to a pressure of below 0.1 torr, which is necessary to eliminate water vapor absorption. The FS-720 interferometer uses reflecting optics to maximize energy throughput. The FS-820 has a simplified optical system utilizing polyethylene lenses. The addition of a light pipe to both interferometers has also increased the light-collecting efficiencies of the instruments. The FS-720 modular interferometer is designed for use in the 10–500 cm^{-1} region and for resolutions up to 0.1 cm^{-1}. The Model FS-820 is designed for use in the 10–200 cm^{-1} region with resolutions up to 0.2 cm^{-1}. The layout of the FS-720 optics is shown in Figure 18. The various modules are largely interchangeable so that the spectrometer systems can be optimized for a particular application. For example, the FS-721 module contains a low-voltage synchronous

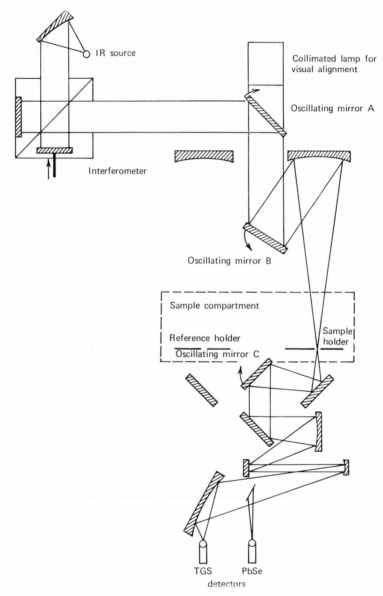

Fig. 20. Optical layout of FTS-14 spectrometer.

motor and multispeed gearbox used to produce mirror path difference speeds of from 0.5 μm/sec to 500 μm/sec. The path difference is ± 10 cm. The mirror motion is monitored through the use of a Moiré grating, the Moiré fringes produced by the system being used in a manner similar to the laser fringe-referencing described earlier. The

FS-722 sample, condenser, and detector modules house surface off-axis paraboloid and plane mirrors used to form an image of the source in the center of the accessory module, an electroformed copper light pipe used to increase the efficiency of the system, and a Golay detector fitted with a diamond window. The "sampling area" is a $5\frac{3}{4}$ in. cube and will house 10-cm gas cells, liquid cells, and solid sample holders. The source is imaged in the center of the module.

The FS-200 electronics module consists of a lock-in type amplifier, a digitizer, and a punch. A 12-bit analog-to-digital converter is triggered by the Moiré grating pulses and associated electronics. A punch records the interferogram on paper tape in 12-bit binary code. Data reduction can be carried out via an off-line digital computer, or by analog means using the FTC-100 or FTC-300 devices mentioned earlier. A variety of attachments including a variable temperature cell or a specular reflection device is available.

Several commercial systems are available from Digilab, Inc., a subsidiary of Block Engineering, Inc. of Cambridge, Massachusetts. The most advanced systems are built around the interferometer shown in Figures 14 and 14a, which is also the basis of the Model 296 system. The most interesting of the instruments is the Model FTS-14 Fourier transform spectrometer.

A block diagram of the FTS-14 is given schematically in Figure 19. The FTS-14 system consists, essentially, of the Model 296 spectrometer, a data-handling system, and the optical system shown schematically in Figure 20. Oscillating mirror A directs the beam from the interferometer into the sampling compartment. When rotated 45° clockwise, this mirror allows a collimated white light to pass through the sampling optics. Oscillating mirrors B and C are shown directing the beam through the sample path. During a ratio-recorded measurement they are flipped by computer command to their alternate positions, directing the beam first through the reference path, then through the sample path. The beam comes to a focus within the sample compartment. Two detectors are used, a lead selenide detector for the high-frequency region and a triglycine sulfate pyroelectric detector for the low-frequency region.

The Digilab FTS-14 data system is constructed around a Data General Nova minicomputer. The central processor has a 4096-word memory, a 16-bit word length, a cycle time of 2.6 μsec and a fully complemented software package. Several configurations of the Digilab data system are available for the FTS-14. An all-core unit consists of the central processor with 16k words of memory, a 15-bit A/D converter, a high-speed digital plotter, and a Teletype control unit. Working with the Model 296 spectrometer, this data system can calculate a fully ratio-recorded spectrum (3800–400 cm^{-1}) at 2-cm^{-1} resolution in 30 sec calculation time. In the half-wave number high-resolution mode, selected spectral intervals of the 3800–400 cm^{-1} region can also be calculated and ratioed in 30 sec. Another Digilab FTS-14 data system utilizes the 4096-word memory in the central processor, supplemented by a 72k-word expandable disc. This configuration is capable of first storing and then performing separate Fourier transform calculations on a pair of 16,000-word interferograms, yielding half-wave number ratio-recorded spectra of the entire 3800–400 cm^{-1} interval in under 120 sec calculation time. Survey spectra of 2 cm^{-1} resolution are calculated in 30 sec.

During the measurement cycle, while data are being accumulated, the large computational capacity required to carry out the Fourier transformation is used to operate the spectrometer and to monitor its performance throughout each measurement. It controls the mirror drive to take either high-resolution or lower-resolution scans as

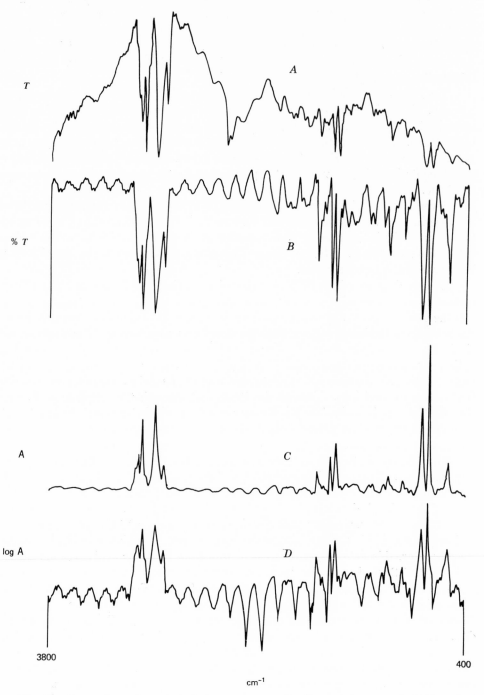

Fig. 21. Data presentation. A single-beam spectrum of polystyrene was recorded (*A*), ratioed against background and plotted as % *T* (spectrum *B*). The same data were then replotted as absorbance A (spectrum *C*) and log A (spectrum *D*).

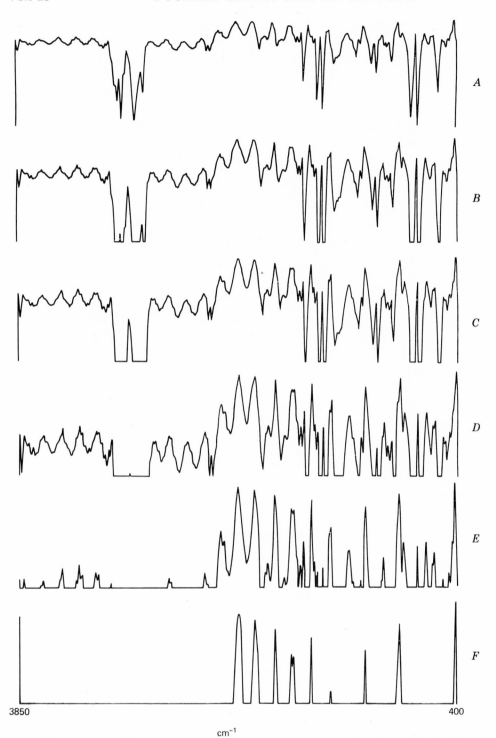

3850   400

cm⁻¹

Fig. 22. Ordinate scale expansion. A ratioed spectrum of polystyrene film was recorded with a FTS-14 system using eight scans at a resolution of 16 cm^{-1}. The limits set for the y axis were 0–100%T. In order to examine the bands falling in the high %T range more closely, the plot limits were changed. The lower plot limits were successively set to: B, 40; C, 50; D, 70; E, 80; and F, 90%T. The expanded plots resulted.

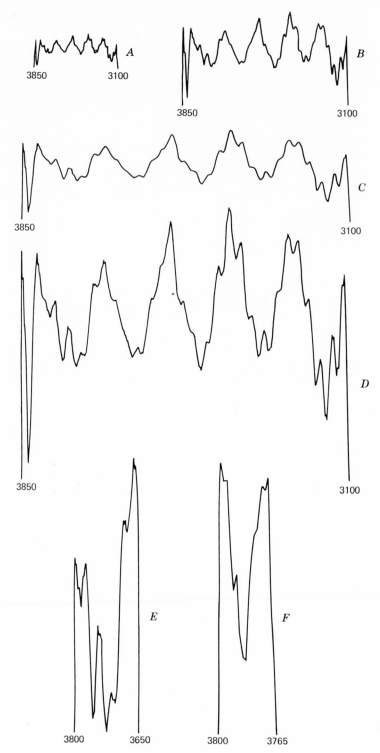

Fig. 23. Scale expansion. See the caption of Figure 22. A segment of spectrum A of Figure 22 was expanded and traced out to result in spectrum A in this figure. The computer was then instructed via Teletype to expand and replot the 3850–3100 cm^{-1} segment, resulting in traces B, C, and D. The spectral range was then narrowed and the x axis expanded to bring out the features of the small band in the 3780-cm^{-1} region, resulting in traces E and F. The computer print-out indicated that the maximum and minimum values for trace F were 79.64 and 78.27%T, respectively, so that the entire plot (arbitrarily printed out at a height of 6 in.) corresponded to 1.37%T.

directed via the Teletype by the operator; it counts off the number of scans requested by the operator and activates a solenoid which automatically switches the optical system between the sampling mode and the reference mode. At the end of the measurement the computer automatically branches into its transform calculations, ratios the sample and reference spectra if the operator has selected the double-beam mode, then

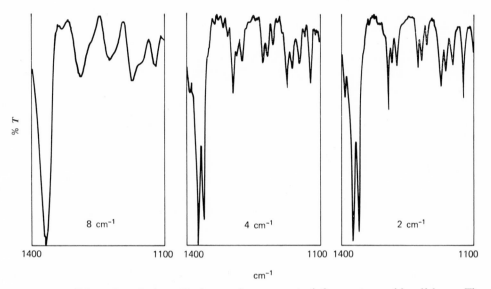

Fig. 24. Effect of resolution. Each trace is a segment of the spectrum of longifolene. The same sample was used but the resolution was varied by varying the sweep length. The resolution is given at the bottom of each trace.

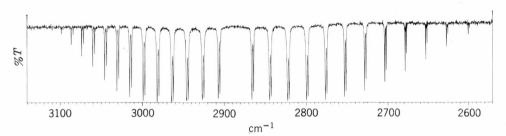

Fig. 25. Spectrum of hydrogen chloride. A segment of a hydrogen chloride spectrum recorded with a Digilab, Inc. FTS-14 spectrometer system is shown. The hydrogen chloride was in a 10-cm cell at a pressure of 40 torr; 128 scans each of 8-sec duration were summed. The spectrum was electronically ratioed against background and scale-expanded. Resolution is 0.5 cm⁻¹.

activates and drives the digital plotter to trace out a spectrum between the wave number limits requested by the operator. The computer also automatically traces out a wave number scale calculated from the reference laser information. If the operator so desires, the computer will find the spectral maximum, rescale it to 100%, and plot a scale-expanded spectrum. After plotting out the spectrum and wave number scale, the computer types out the maximum and minimum intensity levels which occur in the plotted spectral interval. The precise % transmission of any given spectral peak can therefore be learned simply by directing the computer to plot out the spectral interval in which it occurs; the % transmission will then be typed out automatically. The FTS-14 system as outlined above is completely automatic and, as its performance is computer-maximized, a highly skilled operator is not needed. Spectra of optimized quality and highly scale-expanded spectra can be obtained relatively quickly.

The built-in computer permits great flexibility for data presentation also. An example is shown in Figure 21. A spectrum of polystyrene was recorded and then ratioed against background to produce spectrum *B*. The computer was then instructed via Teletype to reproduce the spectrum in absorbance units (spectrum *C*), and then again in log A units (spectrum *D*). Scale-expansion capabilities are illustrated by the spectra of Figures 22 and 23. The various plots were produced from one spectrum stored in the computer memory. Resolution can be varied by changing the mirror travel, again by addressing the computer via Teletype. Examples are given by the

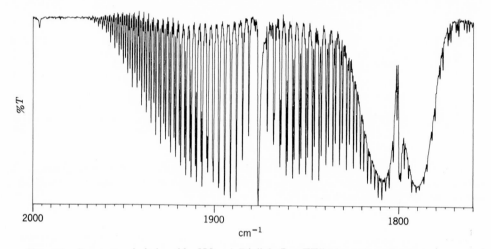

Fig. 26. Spectrum of nitric oxide, NO. A Digilab, Inc. FTS-14 spectrometer system was used to record the nitric oxide spectrum and to plot a portion of it; the nitric oxide was in a 10-cm cell at 10 torr pressure. 128 8-sec scans were used, electronically ratioed against background and scale-expanded. Resolution is 0.5 cm^{-1}.

plots of Figure 24. Two examples of high-resolution spectra measured with the FTS-14 system are shown in Figures 25 and 26. It must be remembered that only parts of the spectra are shown. The spectrometer recorded spectra over the entire 3900–400 cm^{-1} range at a constant resolution of 0.5 cm^{-1}, but only small segments of the spectrum stored in the computer memory were plotted as shown.

Block Engineering, Inc. offers a variety of modifications for the FTS-14 system and other Fourier transform spectrometers. For example, the FTS-14 system can be modified to operate in the far-infrared by changing beam splitter, source, detector, and software.

Grubb Parsons, Ltd. of England produces two instruments which are marketed in the United States by Edwin Industries Corporation, Silver Spring, Maryland. One is the Mark II "Cube" interferometer; an optical diagram is shown in Figure 27. The Mark II covers the 10–200 cm^{-1} range, using a Golay detector fitted with a quartz window. An extension of the range to 650 cm^{-1} is possible with special accessories. The resolution is variable at the operator's discretion to a maximum of 0.5 cm^{-1}, but can be improved to 0.1 cm^{-1} by means of a special mirror drive unit. The modular nature of the instrument makes it easy to adapt it to handle special sample cells.

The second instrument is the IS3 spectrometer; optical diagrams for the IS3 are shown in Figure 28. The range of the IS3 is 10–675 cm^{-1} if a diamond detector window is used, and 10–200 cm^{-1} if a quartz window is used. The resolution is variable to 0.1 cm^{-1} maximum. The moving mirror is accurately mounted on a glass block and moved in discrete steps of 5-μm path difference. These steps can be arranged by the operator to occur at time intervals of 0.5, 1, 2, 4 sec or longer. Poly(ethylene terephthalate)

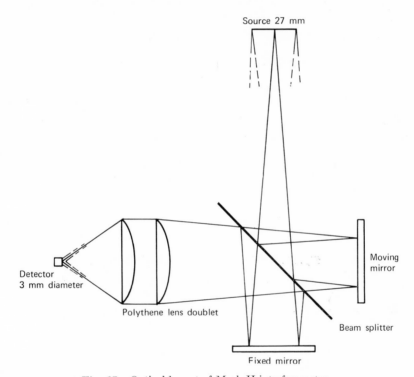

Fig. 27. Optical layout of Mark II interferometer.

beam splitters in a range of thicknesses are used. Different sample chambers are available as shown in Figure 28. The small-chamber SC1 will accommodate 10-cm gas cells as well as other cells. A rotary system accommodates up to six solid samples. The large-chamber SC2 accommodates larger attachments and heating or cooling devices. The IS3 electronics include a lock-in amplifier tuned to the chopper, an A/D converter, a pulse drive unit for driving the moving mirror system and A/D converter, and an Addo paper-tape punch. The necessary transforms are carried out by an off-line computer.

Idealab, Inc. of Franklin, Massachusetts supplies two standard interferometers and will tailor-make spectrometer systems. The essential difference between the standard Model IF-3 and IF-6 interferometers is that the Model IF-3 affords a max-

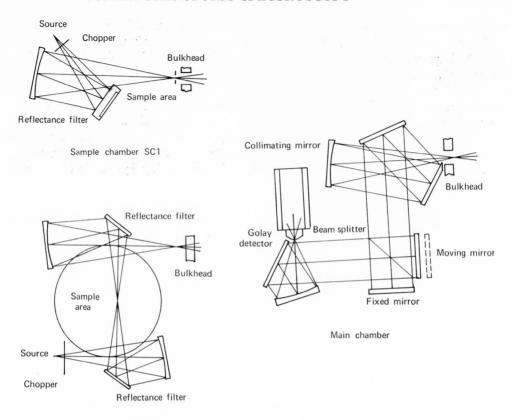

Fig. 28. Optical diagrams of IS3 spectrometer.

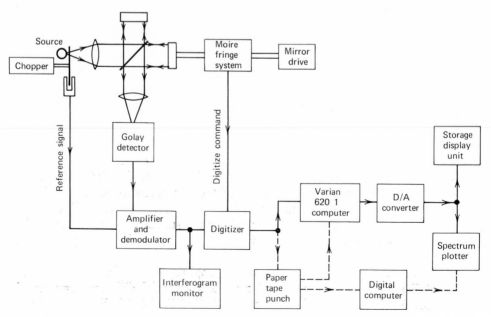

Fig. 29. Block diagram of MIR 2 spectrometer.

imum resolution of 0.5 cm^{-1} whereas the IF-6 can provide a maximum resolution of 0.1 cm^{-1}. In the IF-3 the interferometer mirror motion is kept linear by means of a tight servocontrol. The standard mirror velocity is continuously adjustable from 1 mm/ min to 1 cm/sec. A stepping control is also available for use with the basic IF-3 system. With this control the mirror travels a certain predetermined distance, is stopped and held for a certain time, and then moved again. The stepping can be either

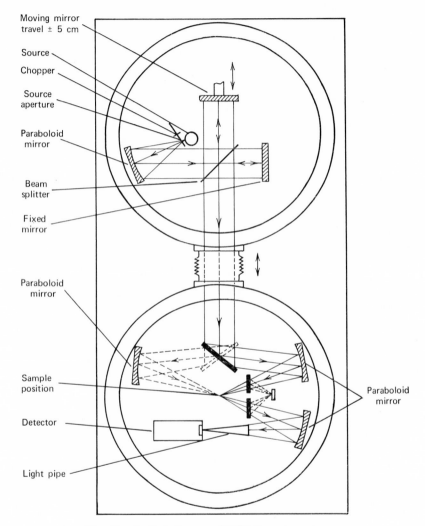

Fig. 30. Optical diagram of MIR-2 spectrometer.

preset or automatically varied as function of source intensity. Special IF-3 models may have a mirror velocity as low as 1 cm/ 5 hr. The standard Model IF-3 mirror drive provides a retardation of 2 cm, but modified versions and other drives are available. For example a special drive was developed by Idealab, Inc. with support from the U.S. Air Force Cambridge Research Labs in Bedford. It provides for an optical path difference of 2 m, and is capable of producing resolutions of 5 × 10^{-3} cm^{-1} in the near infrared. Optical components such as beam splitters can be readily interchanged.

Three "information channels" are provided: in addition to the interferogram a white light is used to provide a trigger signal and a laser provides a time base for fringe-referencing, in the manner described earlier. A single interferometer cube is used, however, the three signals being processed by the same mirrors and beam splitter.

The MIR-2 far-infrared spectrometer manufactured by CODERG (Société de Conversions des Énergies, Clichy, France) is marketed by Scientific Instrumentation, Inc., Palo Alto, Calif. A block diagram of the MIR-2 is given in Figure 29. The layout

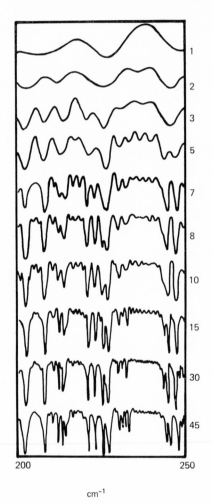

Fig. 31. Spectra of water recorded with MIR-2 spectrometer. Spectra displayed on the viewing screen of the instrument after certain scan times had elapsed. Scan times in min are given next to each spectrum.

of the optics is shown in Figure 30, and other sample space configurations are available. The optics are mounted in two chambers. A conventional Michelson interferometer with $f/2$ entrance aperture is used. The beam splitter is poly(ethylene terephthalate), and various thicknesses ranging between 6 and 100 μm are needed for complete coverage of the spectral region. The light source is a high-pressure water-cooled mercury vapor lamp, and the light-source unit can be removed so that a laser beam can be used for alignment purposes. The beam is modulated at 12.5 Hz, and a variable iris diaphragm controls the source aperture. The moving mirror is mounted on a high-precision slide bar. Mirror motion is provided by a stepping motor in 10-μm steps, or a continuous motion controlled by Moiré fringe-referencing is used. The beam emerging from the interferometer is parallel and enters a second chamber where, depending on the sampling configuration, the beam is reshaped. A Golay detector is used. The system can be evacuated to 10^{-6} torr. The instrument covers the range 800–10 cm^{-1}. The maximum resolution is 0.1 cm^{-1} over a 75-cm^{-1} region in the single-beam mode, or a 30-cm^{-1} region in the double-beam mode. Scanning rates vary.

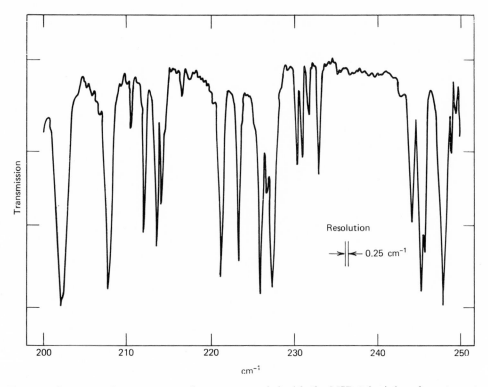

Fig. 32. Spectrum of water vapor. Spectrum recorded with the MIR-2 far-infrared spectrometer and obtained by plotting out the 45-min spectrum of Figure 31.

As shown in Figure 29, the MIR-2 can be used to produce digitized interferograms. These are punched out on tape, which serves to interface with an off-line computer. The more interesting system is the one incorporating a Varian 620/i minicomputer and a Tektronix storage display unit.

The computer of the MIR-2 system totally controls the entire interferometer, data-handling and processing systems. With the MIR-2 system, computation is continuous. The scan is started and produces a segment of the interferogram. The computer quickly performs a 750-value transform, stores the data, and also displays the rudimentary spectrum on a screen. This procedure is repetitive, and as the mirror continues to move and the computer continuously computes and adds data to those already stored, an increasingly refined spectrum appears on the viewing screen. This procedure is illustrated by the spectra of water shown in Figure 31. Each trace was displayed on the viewing screen and photographed. The time in minutes elapsed since the scan was started is shown beside each trace. When the spectrum has reached an acceptable S/N value, determined by examining the spectrum displayed on the viewing screen, the spectrum is plotted out. For example, when the water spectrum had reached the quality indicated by the lowest trace in Figure 31 after a 45-min scan period, the plotter was activated and the spectrum of Figure 32 resulted.

The MIR-2 system incorporating the minicomputer is completely computer-controlled. In practice, the operator would insert the sample and after a vacuum was

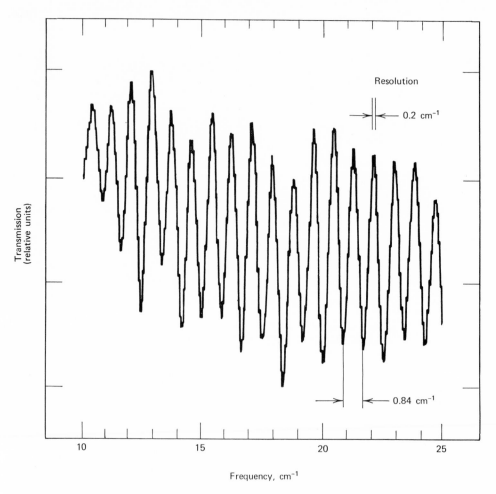

Fig. 33. Absorption spectrum of nitrous oxide, $^{14}N_2^{16}O$ recorded with the MIR-2 spectrometer.

established, would give the computer the required data about single- or double-beam operation; the spectral range; smallest separation between two points on the spectrum; number of points, being 750 points maximum for double-beam, or 1500 points maximum for single-beam; motor steps or continuous motion; apodising function (ten functions are available) for the transform. Operation thereafter is automatic, and the instrument shuts itself off when the required resolution is obtained. Scan times for 1500 points single-beam or 750 points double-beam spectra vary from, say, 5 min for a 50-cm^{-1} range at 1-cm^{-1} resolution to 2.7 hr for a 250-cm^{-1} range at 0.1-cm^{-1} resolution.   The instrument can be used for transmission or reflection measurements. Two sample spectra are shown in Figures 33 and 34.

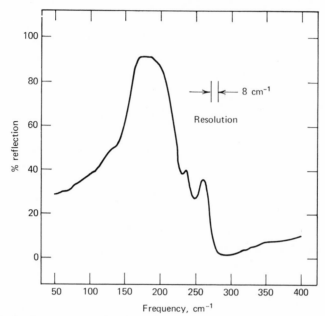

Fig. 34. Reflection spectrum of sodium chloride recorded with the MIR-2 spectrometer.

Some of the manufacturers offer a variety of sample holders, sample cells, and "attachments."   In general, these are very similar to sampling devices used with dispersion spectrometers and consequently need not be considered.

Bibliography

GENERAL REFERENCES

1. G. A. Vanasse and H. Sakai, in E. Wolf, ed., *Progress in Optics*, Vol. 6, John Wiley & Sons, Inc., New York, 1967, pp. 261ff.
2. J. Connes, *Rev. Opt.* **40,** 45, 116, 171, 231 (1961); (Engl. transl.) *NAV-WEPS Rept. No. 8099, NOTSTP 3157, number AD 409 869,* Clearing House for Federal and Technical Information, Springfield, Va., 22151, 178 pp.
3. L. Mertz, *Transformation in Optics*, John Wiley & Sons, Inc., New York, 1965.
4. R. Bracewell, *The Fourier Transform and Its Applications*, McGraw-Hill Book Company, New York, 1965.
5. G. A. Vanasse and J. Strong, in J. Strong, *Concepts of Classical Optics*, W. H. Freeman & Co., San Francisco, Calif., 1958, pp. 419–434.
6. A. E. Martin, *Infra Red Instrumentation and Techniques*, Elsevier Publishing Co., New York, 1966.
7. M. Françon, *Optical Interferometry*, Academic Press, Inc., New York, 1966.
8. A. Finch, P. N. Gates, K. Radcliffe, F. N. Dickson, and F. F. Bentley, *Chemical Applications of Far Infrared Spectroscopy*, Academic Press, Inc., New York, 1970.

SPECIFIC REFERENCES

9. A. A. Michelson, *Phil. Mag.* **31,** 256, 388 (1891).
10. A. A. Michelson, *Phil. Mag.* **34,** 280 (1892).
11. H. Rubens and R. W. Wood, *Phil. Mag.* **21,** 249 (1911).

12. P. Jacquinot and C. Dufour, *J. Rech. Centre Natl. Recherche Sci.* **6**, 91 (1948).
13. P. Fellgett, *M.S. Thesis*, Cambridge, 1951.
14. G. Horlick, *Appl. Spectros.* **22**, 617 (1968).
15. M. Forman, *J. Optical Soc. Am.* **56**, 978 (1966).
16. J. W. Cooley and J. W. Tukey, *Math. Comput.* **19**, 297 (1965).
17. A. Bluhm, J. A. Jousa, and J. Weinstein, *Appl. Spectros.* **18**, 188 (1964).

M. J. D. Low

New York University

FUMIGANTS

Fumigants are liquid or solid substances that vaporize to kill pests in the area in which the vapors are contained. Fumigants are used in greenhouses, in soil, in warehouses, in houses, and in offices. The compounds used must exist in the gaseous state in order to function effectively as fumigants. Compounds which boil near room temperature such as hydrogen cyanide, methyl bromide, and ethylene oxide are the most useful general fumigants. Higher-boiling compounds have proven effective for soil fumigation. A single compound or mixture may be highly selective regarding the pests it kills or it may kill a broad spectrum of pests such as insects, fungi, and weed seeds. Fumigants are generally very effective but the cost of material and application is high and they are generally very toxic.

The toxic nature of many of the fumigants used in closed spaces makes it essential to have simple methods for the rapid detection of these compounds for the safety of workers in the area. Commercial devices are available for this purpose which utilize glass tubes containing color reagents absorbed on a solid support. Measured volumes of air are drawn through the tube, and the length of the resulting colored zone provides an estimation of the concentration of the fumigant (1). Refrigerant leak detectors have also been recommended for the detection of fumigants (2).

CYANIDES

Hydrogen Cyanide

Hydrogen cyanide, HCN, was originally used for citrus orchard fumigation (3) and is now used for exterminating rodents and insects in ships and for killing insects in trees. It is manufactured by the catalytic oxidation of ammonia–methane mixtures (4). It is a colorless gas or liquid with a characteristic almond-like odor. It boils at 26°C and melts at -14°C. The density of the gas is 0.941 (air = 1.000) and the density of the liquid at 20°C is 0.687 g/ml. It is miscible with water or ethanol and slightly soluble in ethyl ether. It is highly toxic; 300 ppm will quickly cause death, 150 ppm for $\frac{1}{2}$–1 hr may endanger life, and the average fatal dose is 50–60 mg. The threshold limit is 10 ppm. For details, see HYDROGEN CYANIDE.

Calcium Cyanide

Calcium cyanide, $Ca(CN)_2$, was first used for citrus orchard fumigation (3) and was later recommended for insecticidal fumigation (5). It is prepared by the fusion of sodium chloride and calcium cyanamide or by the reaction of liquid hydrogen cyanide with calcium carbide to yield a product more like $CaH_2(CN)_4$. The commercial product, containing not less than 42% calcium cyanide, is a gray granular powder. It is decomposed by moisture to calcium hydroxide and hydrogen cyanide. The biological properties are the same as those of hydrogen cyanide.

Analysis of Cyanide

In the following method, cyanides, with the exception of cobalticyanides, are converted to hydrogen cyanide, separated from interferences by distillation, and collected in sodium hydroxide solution for further analysis (6). Silver nitrate titration can be used for concentrations as low as 1 mg/liter. The cyanide in the distillate reacts with silver nitrate to form the soluble cyanide complex, $Ag(CN)_2^-$. When all of the cyanide ion has complexed, the excess silver ion is detected by the silver-sensitive indicator, 5-(p-dimethylaminobenzylidene) rhodamine, which turns from a yellow to a salmon color. Lower concentrations should be measured colorimetrically. The pyridine–pyrazolone colorimetric method involves converting the cyanide to cyanogen chloride by reaction with chloramine-T and formation of a blue dye by reaction with pyridine–pyrazolone reagent (7). In the pyridine–benzidine colorimetric method, cyanide reacts with bromine to form cyanogen bromide which forms a complex with pyridine that gives a color reaction with benzidine (8). The latter method has a high degree of sensitivity.

Because of the extreme toxicity of cyanide compounds, all operations should be performed in a hood or a well-ventilated area. If samples cannot be analyzed immediately after collection, adjust to pH 11.0 or higher and store in a cool place.

Procedures

DISTILLATION. Assemble the apparatus as shown in Figure 1 (6). Add the sample, containing not more than 500 mg of cyanide, to the Claissen flask. In the case of liquid samples, dilute if necessary to 250–500 ml with water. For solid samples, add 250 ml of water. Place 50 ml of N sodium hydroxide solution in the gas-washing bottle, and if necessary to obtain an adequate volume, dilute with water. Connect the train to an aspirator and adjust the air flow to approximately one bubble/sec. If a higher rate is needed to keep liquid from backing up in the delivery tube, the air flow may be increased to two bubbles/sec without any loss in efficiency.

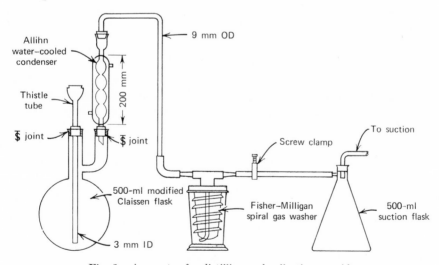

Fig. 1. Apparatus for distilling and collecting cyanide.

To the sample mixture in the main flask, add 20 ml of 0.25 M mercuric chloride solution and 10 ml of 2.5 M magnesium chloride solution by means of the air inlet tube. Rinse the inlet tube with water and allow the air flow to mix the contents of the flask for a few minutes. For each 100 ml of solution in the distillation flask, slowly add 5 ml of concentrated sulfuric acid and again rinse the inlet tube with water. Heat the Claissen flask at a rate that will produce rapid boiling of the sample, but at the same time does not permit vapors to rise over halfway into the condenser. Maintain the refluxing for 1 hr and then turn off the heat while maintaining the air flow for an additional 15 min. Pour the contents of the gas-washing bottle into a 250-ml volumetric flask. Rinse the gas-washing bottle and the tube from the condenser with water, add the washings to the volumetric flask, and dilute to volume.

The hydrogen cyanide content of air can be determined by absorbing the hydrogen cyanide in sodium hydroxide solution as described above, by passing a known volume of air through the gas-washing bottle. A hydrogen cyanide concentration of 10 ppm requires about 0.5 liters of air.

SILVER NITRATE TITRATION. Add 0.5 ml of indicator solution containing 0.02 g of 5-(p-dimethylaminobenzylidene) rhodamine in 100 ml of acetone to the absorption solution and titrate with 0.02 N silver nitrate solution until there is a color change from canary yellow to salmon. Also titrate a reagent blank containing the same amount of sodium hydroxide.

$$\text{Cyanide, as ppm of HCN} = \frac{(A - B)(N)(5.4 \times 10^4)}{w}$$

where A = volume of silver nitrate solution required for the sample, in ml
B = volume of silver nitrate solution required for the blank, in ml
N = normality of silver nitrate solution
w = sample size, in g or ml

If necessary, adjust the sample aliquot or silver nitrate concentration to require a titration of 2–10 ml.

PYRIDINE–PYRAZOLONE COLORIMETRIC METHOD. Prepare the cyanide standard solution as follows. Dissolve 2.51 g of potassium cyanide in 1 liter of water. Take a 10-ml aliquot, adjust to pH 11 with sodium hydroxide solution, and dilute to 250 ml. Titrate with silver nitrate solution to standardize. This solution will gradually lose strength and should be standardized weekly.

Prepare the colorimetric reagent as follows. Prepare a saturated aqueous solution of 1-phenyl-3-methyl-5-pyrazolone containing approximately 1.0 g/200 ml; heat to 75°C, cool, and filter to remove undissolved pyrazolone. Dissolve 0.050 g of bispyrazolone in 50 ml of pyridine, filter, and mix 25 ml with 125 ml of the saturated phenylmethylpyrazolone solution. Prepare fresh reagent daily; the pink color formed on standing will not affect the analysis.

Place an aliquot of the absorption solution containing 0.2–1.0 μg of cyanide into a 25- or 50-ml reaction tube and dilute to 15 ml with 0.2 N sodium hydroxide solution. Prepare a blank by adding 15 ml of sodium hydroxide solution to another tube. Also prepare a series of standard solutions containing 0.2, 0.4, 0.6, 0.8, and 1.0 μg of cyanide. Neutralize each solution to pH 6–7 with 1:4 acetic acid. The amount of acid required should be approximately the same for each solution. Add 0.2 ml of freshly prepared 1% chloramine-T solution to each tube, stopper, and mix. Let stand for 1–2 min and add 5.0 ml of the pyridine–pyrazolone reagent, and again stopper and mix. Allow 20 min for color development, dilute to volume with water and measure the absorbance at 620 nm.

Prepare a calibration curve with the values obtained for the standard solutions and determine the cyanide content of the sample from the standard curve.

Greater sensitivity is obtained by extracting the color with butyl alcohol. After color development, add 1 ml of 0.35 M disodium hydrogen phosphate solution and 10 ml of butyl alcohol, stopper and mix. If the emulsion that forms does not break within a few min, add more phosphate solution and mix again. Take an aliquot of the alcohol layer and measure the absorbance at 630 nm.

PYRIDINE–BENZIDINE COLORIMETRIC METHOD. Prepare the cyanide standard solution as follows. Dissolve 0.24 g of potassium cyanide in 1 liter of N sodium hydroxide solution. Dilute 1 ml of this stock solution to 100 ml with N sodium hydroxide solution. Prepare these solutions fresh each day.

Prepare the colorimetric reagent as follows. Mix 60 ml of pyridine and 40 ml of water and add 10 ml of concentrated hydrochloric acid; let cool to room temperature. Dissolve 5 g of benzidine dihydrochloride in 0.1 N hydrochloric acid and dilute to 100 ml with water. Prepare the pyridine–benzidine reagent just before use by diluting 5 ml of the benzidine solution to 25 ml with the pyridine mixture.

Pipet a 10-ml aliquot of the absorption solution in N sodium hydroxide solution into a large stoppered test tube. To this, add successively the following reagents, mixing thoroughly after each addition: 1 ml of glacial acetic acid, 1 ml of saturated bromine water, and 1 ml of arsenic trioxide solution prepared by refluxing 100 ml of water with 2 g of arsenic trioxide until the arsenic trioxide is dissolved. The volumes of these reagents are not critical since they are all added in considerable excess. Quickly adjust the volume to 20 ml with water, and then add 5 ml of the pyridine–benzidine reagent. Let the mixture stand for 15 min. During this time a red color is produced in the presence of cyanide, which is stable for 30 min. Measure the absorbance at 510 nm.

Do not leave the tubes unstoppered before the addition of the reagents. If the room temperature is above 20°C, cool the contents of the tubes in cold water before the addition of the acid.

Prepare a set of standards containing 1.0, 2.0, 4.0, 6.0, 8.0, and 10 ml of the diluted standard cyanide solution, dilute to 10 ml with N sodium hydroxide solution, and develop the colors as directed above. Prepare a calibration curve with the values obtained from the standard solutions and determine the cyanide content of the sample from the standard curve.

HALOGENATED HYDROCARBONS

Methyl Bromide

Methyl bromide (bromomethane, monobromomethane), CH_3Br, is an insecticidal fumigant (9) for use in railroad cars, mills, warehouses, under tarpaulins, and in cargo ships. It is also widely used as a soil fumigant. Methyl bromide is manufactured by the action of hydrobromic acid on methanol. It is a colorless gas which is usually odorless, but has a sweetish, chloroform-like odor at high concentrations and is nonflammable in air. The boiling point is 4.5°C, the melting point −93°C, and the density of the gas at 20°C is 3.974 g/liter. It is soluble in most organic solvents and soluble in water to the extent of 1.34 g/100 g at 25°C. The upper safe limit has been set at 17 ppm, above which respirators should be worn; the threshold limit is 20 ppm and the lethal concentration for rats in air is 514 ppm. The commercial name is Embafume. Small quantities of chloropicrin, usually 2 wt %, are sometimes added as a warning agent. See also Vol. 8, pp. 12–14.

Ethylene Dichloride

Ethylene dichloride (1,2-dichloroethane, ethylene chloride), $ClCH_2CH_2Cl$, is an insecticidal fumigant (10) for stored products, and has been suggested for use against the peach borer (*Sanninoidea exitiosa*) (11). The compound is manufactured by the action of chlorine on ethylene. It is a colorless liquid with an odor like chloroform. The physical properties are: boiling point, $83°C$; melting point, $-40°C$; specific gravity at $20/4°C$, 1.2569; refractive index, n_D^{20}, 1.4443; vapor pressure at $20°C$, 78 torr. The flash point (Abel-Penchy) is $12-15°C$. It is miscible with the common organic solvents and soluble in water to the extent of 0.43 g/100 g. The acute oral LD_{50} to rats is 770 mg/kg, to mice 870–950 mg/kg, and to rabbits 860–970. The threshold limit is 100 ppm. Commercial names are Dutch Liquid and Brocide. Ethylene dichloride is usually mixed with carbon tetrachloride to remove fire hazards; for example, Chlorasol (Union Carbide Chemical Co.) is 3:1 ethylene dichloride–carbon tetrachloride. See also Vol. 9, pp. 437–440.

Ethylene Dibromide

Ethylene dibromide (1,2-dibromoethane, ethylene bromide), $BrCH_2CH_2BR$, is an insecticidal fumigant (12,13) for stored products, fruits and vegetables, and for local treatment of equipment in flour mills. It is also used for soil treatment against some insects and nematodes. It is manufactured by the addition of bromine to ethylene. It is a heavy, colorless liquid which is nonflammable and has the following properties: boiling point, $131°C$; melting point, $9.3°C$; specific gravity, $25/25°C$, 2.172; refractive index, n_D^{20}, 1.5379; vapor pressure at $25°C$, 11 torr. It is miscible with most organic solvents and soluble in water to the extent of 0.43 g/100 ml at $30°C$. The acute oral LD_{50} to rats is 146 mg/kg. It is a vesicant and will cause severe burns if confined to the skin. The threshold limit is 25 ppm. Bromofume is the trade name of the Dow Chemical Company. Ethylene dibromide is usually marketed as mixtures with inert solvents for soil application; for example, Dowfume W-85 (Dow Chemical Co.) is 83% ethylene dibromide and 17% inert hydrocarbons. For mill or warehouse fumigation it is available as mixtures with carbon tetrachloride. Dichloropropene is also used in admixtures. See also Vol. 8, pp. 12–14.

Ethylene Chlorobromide

Ethylene chlorobromide (1-bromo-2-chloroethane), $BrCH_2CH_2Cl$, is used as a soil fumigant (14). It is a colorless liquid with the following properties: boiling point, $107-108°C$; melting point, $-16.6°C$; specific gravity, $19/4°C$, 1.689; vapor pressure, at $30°C$, 44 torr. It is miscible with ethanol and ethyl ether and soluble in water to the extent of 0.688 g/100 g at $30°C$. It is highly toxic to plants and mammals; it causes nausea and irritation of mucous membranes. It is generally sold as a 42% (v/v) solution in a volatile solvent.

Dichloropropene

1,3-Dichloropropene, $ClCH_2CH=CHCl$ (α,γ-dichloropropylene, γ-chloroallyl chloride), is used as a nematocide (15). The usual industrial preparation is by dehydration of 1,3-dichloro-2-propanol with phosphorus oxychloride or phosphorus pentoxide in benzene (16). The commercial product is a mixture of stereoisomers and is a colorless to amber liquid with the following properties: reflux boiling point, $104°C$; melting point, below $-50°C$; specific gravity, $25/4°C$, 1.217; flash point, $23°C$. It is miscible with methanol, acetone, benzene, carbon tetrachloride, and heptane, and is soluble in water to the extent of 0.1 g/100 g at $20°C$. It is a vesicant and very irritating and damaging to the eyes. The acute oral LD_{50} to rats is 250–500 mg/kg. Telone is the trade name of the Dow Chemical Company. Dorlone (Dow Chemical Company) is 1:5 ethylene bromide–Telone for use as a nematocide. See also Vol. 9, pp. 470–472.

Propylene Dichloride

Propylene dichloride (1,2-dichloropropane), $ClCH_2CHClCH_3$, is an insecticidal fumigant (17). It is manufactured by the chlorination of propylene. It is a colorless liquid with the following properties: boiling point, $95.4°C$; melting point, $-70°C$; specific gravity, $25/25°C$, 1.1593; refractive index, n_D^{25}, 1.437; vapor pressure at $19.6°C$, 210 torr; flash point, open cup, $21°C$. It is soluble in ethanol or ethyl ether and soluble in water to the extent of 0.27 g/100 g at $20°C$. The acute oral LD_{50} to mice is 860 mg/kg; the lethal concentration in air to rats is 2000 ppm; and the threshold limit is 75 ppm. Propylene dichloride is a component of D-D soil fumigant. Dowfume EB-5 (Dow Chemical Co.) is a mixture of 29.5% propylene dichloride, 7.2% ethylene dibromide, and 63.6% carbon tetrachloride.

D-D Soil Fumigant

D-D soil fumigant is a mixture containing 30–33% of the low-boiling isomer and 30–33% of the high-boiling isomer of 1,3-dichloropropene, 30–35% of propylene dichloride, and 5% of trichlorides. D-D is the trade name of the Shell Chemical Company and Vidden D, the trade name of the Dow Chemical Company. It is a general fumigant (18), especially effective for eelworms. It is obtained as a by-product in the manufacture of alkyl plastics. It is a black volatile liquid with a specific gravity, $20/4°C$, of 1.198 and a vapor pressure at $20°C$ of 31.3 torr. It is soluble in hydrocarbon and halogenated solvents, esters, ethers, and ketones, and practically insoluble in water. It is toxic to mammals but has sufficient odor to warn of danger.

Bromochloropropene

Bromochloropropene (1-chloro-3-bromo-1-propene), $ClCH{=}CHCH_2Br$, is used as a soil fumigant (19). It is manufactured by treating 1,3-dichloro-1-propene with an inorganic bromide. It is a liquid with a boiling range of 130–180°C and a density of 1.36–1.40 g/ml. The lethal vapor concentration for a 4-hr exposure is 260 ppm. It is commercially available as a mixture with related brominated and chlorinated C_3 hydrocarbons containing about 55% bromochloropropene.

Dichloroethyl Ether

sym-Dichloroethyl ether, $ClCH_2CH_2{-}O{-}CH_2CH_2Cl$, is an insecticidal soil fumigant (20). It is prepared by the treatment of ethylene chlorohydrin with sulfuric acid, by passing chlorine and ethylene into ethylene chlorohydrin at $80°C$ (21), or by the direct chlorination of ethyl ether. It is a colorless liquid with a pungent, irritating odor. The physical properties are: boiling point, $178°C$; melting point, $-50°C$; specific gravity, $20/20°C$, 1.22; refractive index, n_D^{20}, 1.457; vapor pressure at $20°C$, 0.73 torr; flash point, $55°C$. It is soluble in most organic solvents and soluble in water to the extent of 1.1 g/100 g at $20°C$. The acute oral LD_{50} to rats is 105 mg/kg and the threshold limit is 15 ppm. Chlorex is the trade name of Union Carbide Chemicals Company.

Dibromochloropropane

1,2-Dibromo-3-chloropropane, $CH_2BrCHBrCH_2Cl$, is a nematocide and soil fumigant (22,23,24). It is a brown liquid with the following properties: boiling point, 196°C; density at 14°C, 2.093 g/ml; refractive index, n_D^{25}, 1.5518; vapor pressure at 21°C, 0.8 torr; flash point open cup, above 88°C. It is miscible with hydrocarbon oils, isopropyl alcohol, 1,2-dichloropropane, and 1,1,2-trichloroethane and soluble in water to the extent of 0.1 wt %. The acute oral LD_{50} to rats is 172 mg/kg and to mice 257 mg/kg. Fumazone is a trade name of the Dow Chemical Company and Nemagon and Nemafume are trade names of Shell Chemical Company. Fumazone 70E contains 67% 1,2-dibromo-3-chloropropane. Nemagon is a technical product with 75% minimum assay. See also Vol. 8, p. 13.

p-Dichlorobenzene

p-Dichlorobenzene is used as an insecticidal fumigant (25). It is a colorless crystalline solid with a characteristic penetrating odor. It sublimes at ordinary temperatures, melts at 53°C, and boils at 174.12°C. The vapor pressure at 25°C is 1.0 torr and the specific gravity, 20/4°C, 1.4581. It is readily soluble in most organic solvents, slightly soluble in cold ethanol, and soluble in water to the extent of 0.008 g/100 g at 25°C. The acute oral LD_{50} to rats is 500–5000 mg/kg and to mice 2950 mg/kg. Commercial names include Dichloricide, Paramoth, and Paracide. See also Vol. 9, pp. 478–481.

o-Dichlorobenzene

o-Dichlorobenzene is used as a fumigant for the control of termites. It is a liquid with the following properties: boiling point, 180.5°C; melting point, -17°C; specific gravity, 20/4°C, 1.3059; refractive index, n_D^{20}, 1.5515; flash point, closed cup, 71°C. It is insoluble in water but miscible with ethanol, ethyl ether, and benzene. o-Dichlorobenzene is more toxic than the para isomer; it can cause injury to liver and kidneys and high concentrations cause central nervous system depression. See also Vol. 9, pp. 478–481.

Chloroform

Chloroform (trichloromethane), $CHCl_3$, is used as an insecticidal fumigant for grain and in mixtures with other fumigants. The acute oral LD_{50} to mice is 2180 mg/kg. The lethal inhalation concentration to mice is 28–42 mg/liter, to rabbits 59–79 mg/liter, and to dogs 100 mg/liter. See also Vol. 9, pp. 430–435.

Carbon Tetrachloride

Carbon tetrachloride (tetrachloromethane, perchloromethane), CCl_4, is used as a fumigant for nursery stock (26) and grain. It is also added to other pesticides to reduce fire hazards. The maximum allowable concentration is 10 ppm; vapors may cause acute poisoning at 1000 ppm. The lethal concentration in air for mice is 10,000 ppm. See also Vol. 8, pp. 320–330.

ANALYSIS OF HALOGENATED HYDROCARBONS

Fumigants in air have been analyzed by gas chromatography using the following operating conditions (27):

column	6 ft × ¼ in. OD, packed
column packing	10% SE-30 methyl silicone gum on 60/80 mesh Diatoport S
carrier gas and flow rate	helium, 50 ml/min
detector	thermal conductivity
sample size	1–2 µg of fumigant: direct injection of air sample or absorbed in n-pentane for compounds boiling below 80°C or o-xylene for compounds boiling above 80°C

	Absolute retention time, min
column temperature 60°C	
methyl bromide	1.00
n-pentane	1.18
ethylene dichloride	2.67
propylene dichloride	3.55
o-xylene	8.75
column temperature 125°C	
dichloroethyl ether	3.03
p-dichlorobenzene	4.05
o-dichlorobenzene	4.20

Ethylene oxide, phosphine, hydrogen cyanide, and acrylonitrile are also included in this study (27). Use of a more sensitive detector such as flame ionization or electron capture type should allow determination of fumigants in air at the ppb level. Absorption of fumigants by drawing the air sample over charcoal followed by extraction with carbon disulfide (28) has also been used as a preparation for gas chromatography.

Continuous monitoring of methyl bromide in air may be accomplished with thermal conductivity analyzers (1) or with flame ionization detectors (29).

Residues of halogenated hydrocarbon fumigants in soil can be extracted with hexane–water or xylene–water and determined by gas chromatography as described by Smith and Shigenaga (30).

Procedure

Transfer 25 g of the soil sample to a 50-ml volumetric flask. Add approximately 20 ml of water and exactly 2 ml of hexane or xylene and shake the flask on a rotary shaker for 30 min. Add sufficient water to raise the extractant into the neck of the flask, and filter it by pushing a plug of glass wool slowly down into the flask. Withdraw 5–50 µl of the clear hexane or xylene solution into a microsyringe and inject directly into the gas chromatograph.

The operating conditions and recovery data (30) are as follows:

Fumigant	*Extractant*	*Column*	*Column temperature, °C*	*% recovery*
D-D mixture	n-hexane	8-ft Apiezon	130	79–90
ethylene bromide	n-hexane	4-ft Apiezon	130	82–87
dibromochloropropane	n-hexane	4-ft Apiezon	190	91–93
chloropicrin	n-hexane	4-ft Apiezon	112	83–90
methyl bromide	o-xylene	4-ft Apiezon	140	44–51

Methyl bromide is not separated from *n*-hexane under these conditions and therefore *o*-xylene is used for extraction.

Johnson and Lear (31) reported a 100% recovery of dibromochloropropane from Yolo fine sandy loam spiked with 11.4 ng of the fumigant by extraction with 1:1 water–hexane. They used the following conditions for gas chromatography:

column	5 ft × ⅛ in., packed
column packing	5% DC-11 silicone grease on 60/80 mesh Chromosorb W, not acid-washed
column temperature	105°C
carrier gas and flow rate	nitrogen, 40 ml/min
detector	electron capture; 250 mCi of tritium
retention time	about 30 sec

Williams (32) reported a method for the determination of D-D mixture in which the soil sample is heated in a closed vessel and the air injected into the gas chromatograph. The chromatographic conditions employed were:

column	6 ft × ¼ in. OD, packed
column packing	5% Carbowax 20M on 70/80 mesh Anachrom SD
column temperature	90°C
carrier gas and flow rate	nitrogen, 60 ml/min
detector	electron capture, ^{63}Ni, operated at 290°C

This method gave relatively low recoveries of *cis*- and *trans*-1,3-dichloropropene, but extraction with acetonitrile did not improve the recoveries to a great extent.

Methyl bromide and ethylene bromide residues in soil have been recovered by high-vacuum distillation (33) but the technique is too complex for routine analysis.

Methyl bromide, ethylene oxide, ethylene dibromide, and ethylene dichloride are efficiently extracted from grains and flour with 5:1 acetone–water (49,50,51).

Procedure

Weigh about 10 g of wheat or 5 g of flour and transfer to a stoppered flask containing 30 ml of 5:1 acetone–water. Allow to stand at 20°C with occasional shaking. For methyl bromide or ethylene oxide allow 1 hr for flour and 6 hr for wheat. Ethylene dibromide requires 7 hr for wheat samples. Extraction of ethylene dichloride requires longer periods: 24 hr for wheat, barley, and sorghum, 48 hr for oats, and 72 hr for yellow maize.

Inject 2 μl of the supernatant solution into the gas chromatograph using either a U-tube injection device described by Heuser and Scudamore (50) or an injection block fitted with a removable glass liner (eg, a Perkin-Elmer F11) which can be cleaned periodically. Allow 12 min between injections for complete removal of water from the column since traces of water temporarily lower the sensitivity of the flame ionization detector.

For methyl bromide and ethylene oxide, use the following chromatographic conditions (34):

column	2 m × 4.6 mm ID, packed
column packing	15 wt % Ucon oil LB-550X poly(propylene glycol) on 60/80 mesh Chromosorb W
temperature	
of column	85°C
of injector	125°C
carrier gas and flow rate	helium, 80 ml/min
detector	flame ionization
absolute retention times	
ethylene oxide	42 sec
methyl bromide	45 sec
detection limit	
ethylene oxide	2×10^{-10} g
methyl bromide	5×10^{-10} g

For ethylene dichloride and ethylene dibromide use the following conditions (35):

column	4 m × ⅛ in. OD, packed
column packing	10 wt % Carbowax 1540 on Teflon 6
temperature of column	
for ethylene dichloride	65°C
for ethylene dibromide	120°C
temperature of injector	130°C
carrier gas and flow rate	nitrogen, 30 ml/min
absolute retention times	
ethylene dichloride	12.5 min
ethylene dibromide	8 min
detection limit	
ethylene dichloride	1×10^{-9} g
ethylene dibromide	5×10^{-11} g

Dibromochloropropane residues in cherries can be extracted by blending with acetone followed by partition into hexane (36). The hexane extract was used directly for gas chromatographic analysis using the following conditions (37):

column	6 ft, packed
column packing	20% ethyl acetate-fractionated Dow Corning high-vacuum silicone grease on 80/100 mesh Chromosorb W
temperature	
of column	200°C
of injector	265°C
of detector	235°C
carrier gas and flow rate	nitrogen, 60 ml/min
detector	electron capture, 56 μCi of ^{226}Ra

The detection limit is 5 ppb.

Dibromochloropropane in food crops has also been determined by petroleum ether extraction, treatment of the extract with Florisil, and gas chromatography using the following conditions (38):

column	5 ft $\times$ $\frac{1}{8}$ in, packed
column packing	5% SE-30 methyl silicone oil on 60/80 mesh Chromosorb W
detector	electron capture

As little as 10 pg fumigant could be detected.

CHLORONITROALKANES

Chloronitropropane

1-Chloro-2-nitropropane, $CH_2ClCHNO_2CH_3$, acts as a fungicide against soil-borne pathogens causing pre- and postemergent damping-off of seedling plants. It is manufactured by the light-induced chlorination of 2-nitropropane (39). It is a liquid with the following properties: boiling point, 172–173°C; melting point, below −70°C; specific gravity, 25/25°C, 1.2458; vapor pressure at 81–82°C, 25 torr; refractive index, n_D^{25}, 1.4419. It is miscible with most organic solvents and soluble in water to the extent of 8800 ppm at 20°C. The acute oral LD_{50} to rats is 197 $\pm$ 20 mg/kg, and to mice 105 $\pm$ 0.18 mg/kg; the acute inhalation LD_{50} to rats is 0.31 mg/liter on 4-hr exposure. Lanstan is the trade name of FMC Corp.

ANALYSIS OF CHLORONITROPROPANE

1-Chloro-2-nitropropane residues in crops are determined by gas chromatography after extraction into benzene–methanol (40).

Procedure

Macerate 50 g of plant sample in a homogenizer for 1 min. Add 100 ml of benzene and 50 ml of methanol and blend for 1 min. Separate the benzene layer, by centrifugation if necessary, and wash with 100 ml of water. To remove any interference which occurs in some green vegetables such as corn fodder, Brussels sprouts, or sugar beet tops, shake the benzene extract with about 30 g of Florisil. Dry the benzene extract over anhydrous sodium sulfate.

The conditions for gas chromatography are:

column	4 ft $\times$ $\frac{1}{4}$ in., packed
column packing	4% XE-60 cyanoethyl methyl silicone oil on 60/80 mesh Chromosorb W; preconditioned at 190°C for 3 hr and held at 95°C for 3 days
temperature	
of column	80°C
of injector	120°C
of detector	200°C
carrier gas	nitrogen, purified by passing through a 3-ft column of molecular sieve 2A (flow rate not given)
sample aliquot	5 μl containing up to 0.1 μg
detector	electron capture
retention time of chloronitropropane	3 min

This method gave a recovery of 75–105% after fortification with 10–100 ppb of the fumigant. The detection limit is about 25 pg. Traces of water in the benzene extract will change the detector characteristics and give anomalous results. Heavy oils and waxes which are present in the crop extract do not interfere at the low temperatures used; they collect in the injector and if not removed will bleed onto the column after several hours.

Chloropicrin

Chloropicrin (trichloronitromethane, nitrochloroform), CCl_3NO_2, is an insecticidal fumigant (41) used for soil, and stored grain and cereal products (42). It is also a nematocide (43) and is effective against most soil-borne pathogenic fungi except sclerotia-forming types (44). It is a colorless liquid with the following properties: boiling point, 112°C; melting point, −64°C; specific gravity, 20/4°C, 1.656; refractive index, n_D^{20}, 1.4611; vapor pressure at 0°C, 5.7 torr. It is soluble in most organic solvents and soluble in water to the extent of 2.27 g/liter at 0°C. Chloropicrin is very toxic and lachrimatory. It is so irritating to mucous membranes that it is used as a warning agent in other fungicides and 0.8 mg/liter for 30 min is lethal to mammals. Trade names are Picfum (Dow Chemical Company) and Larvacide (Morton Chemical Company of Canada, Ltd.).

ANALYSIS OF CHLOROPICRIN

Chloropicrin is hydrolyzed in hot alkaline peroxide medium to release nitrite ion which is reacted with sulfanilic acid and N-(1-naphthyl)ethylenediamine dihydrochloride and measured colorimetrically (45,46).

Procedure

Prepare a standard chloropicrin solution by weighing 2–4 mg in a sealed ampoule, break the ampoule under isopropyl alcohol in a 100-ml volumetric flask, and dilute to volume with isopropyl alcohol. Further dilute 10–100 ml with isopropyl alcohol.

The apparatus assembly to isolate chloropicrin from the sample is shown in Figure 2 (47). Prepare an absorber tube containing 2.5 ml of 2% sodium peroxide solution in N sodium hydroxide and 2.5 ml of isopropyl alcohol. Use 7.5 ml of each if U-tubes are used. Place the absorber tube in the apparatus train but do not attach the aeration flask. Maintain the temperature of the water circulating through the condenser at 85°C. Place in the aeration flask 100 ml of water, 10 ml of 6 N sulfuric acid, 10 ml of phosphotungstic acid solution containing 20 g of P_2O_5.-24 WO_3.$25H_2O$ in 80 ml of water, and approximately 0.5 g of defoaming agent. Make sure the stopcock of the flask is closed. Place 200 g of sample in a blender and add 200 ml of water. Grind until the sample is a slurry. If the sample is granular, as is wheat, it may be introduced directly into the aeration flask. Quantitatively transfer the slurry from the blender into the flask and connect the flask to the condenser and to a supply of nitrogen or clean compressed air. Open the stopcock of the flask to permit a slow stream of nitrogen or air to pass through the sample and water mixture. By means of a heating mantle controlled by a variable transformer, bring the contents of the aeration flask to boiling. Maintain the mixture at a brisk rate of boiling and increase the flow of gas to approximately 40 ml/min. Collect the distillate in the absorber tubes for 1 hr and then transfer the contents of the absorber tubes to a 100-ml volumetric flask. Wash each absorber with 10 ml of water and 15

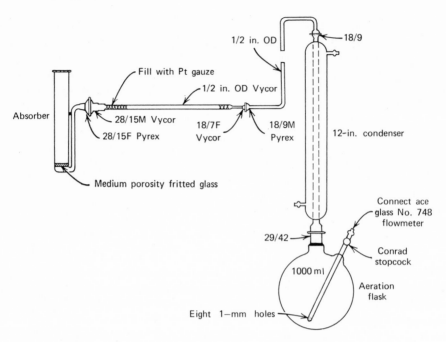

Fig. 2. Apparatus for isolation of chloropicrin.

ml of isopropyl alcohol and add the washings to the flask. Dilute to 100 ml with isopropyl alcohol.

Transfer a suitable aliquot of the distillate to a 125-ml boiling flask. Calculate the quantity of water, sodium peroxide solution, and isopropyl alcohol contained in the aliquot and adjust the contents to 3.5 ml of water, 5 ml of 2% sodium peroxide solution and 11.5 ml of isopropyl alcohol. A ratio of 11.5 of isopropyl alcohol to 8.5 ml of total water is critical. Place 1.0, 2.0, 3.0, 4.0, 5.0, 6.0, and 7.0 ml aliquots of the diluted standard solution into 125-ml boiling flasks containing 11.5, 10.5, 9.5, 8.5, 7.5, 6.5, 5.5, and 4.5 ml of isopropyl alcohol, respectively, and add 5 ml of 2% sodium peroxide solution and 3.5 ml of water. Place two or three glass beads in each flask. Also prepare a reagent blank. Use gas burners on which heat can be instantly adjusted. Attach reflux condensers sealing the joints with a small amount of glycerol. Adjust the boiling rate so that the vapors are well up in the condensers and reflux for 30 min. Rinse the condensers with 5 ml of isopropyl alcohol and remove flasks from the condensers. Cool the contents to room temperature and transfer the solutions to 50-ml volumetric flasks, keeping the solution to a volume of less than 45 ml. Add 1 drop of phenolphthalein indicator and neutralize with concentrated hydrochloric acid, then add 1 drop in excess. Cool to room temperature and add 1 ml of 1% aqueous sulfanilic acid solution. Mix by gently swirling, wait 2 min and then add 1 ml of 0.1% N-(1-naphthyl)ethylenediamine dihydrochloride solution. Dilute to volume with water and mix thoroughly. Allow 15 min for color development and then measure the absorbance at 550 nm versus water.

Prepare a calibration with the values obtained for the standard solutions and determine the chloropicrin content of the sample from the standard curve.

Volatile substances are obtained from some agricultural products during the distillation. Formation of a yellow or orange color during the refluxing step usually indicates the presence of such materials.   Neutralization with hydrochloric acid usually prevents any interference.

Dichloronitroethane

1,1-Dichloro-1-nitroethane, $CH_3CCl_2NO_2$, was developed as a fumigant by Commercial Solvents Corporation under the trade name Ethide (48).   It is prepared by the chlorination of the sodium salt of nitroethane.   It is a colorless liquid with the following properties: boiling point, 124°C; specific gravity, 20/20°C, 1.405; vapor pressure at 29°C, 16.9 torr; flash point, closed cup, 59°C.   It is soluble in water to the extent of 0.25% (v/v) at 23°C.   The acute oral LD_{50} to rats is 410 mg/kg and to rabbits 150–200 mg/kg.   The threshold limit is 10 ppm.   It is used as a storehouse fumigant by applying the undiluted liquid to suitable absorbent material and placing in the upper part of the area.

ANALYSIS OF DICHLORONITROETHANE

The colorimetric method of Jones and Riddick (49) involves decomposition of the halogenated nitroparaffin in sulfuric acid followed by formation of a red-blue color upon the addition of resorcinol.   It is believed that the sulfuric acid decomposition causes the release of nitrous acid, which in turn reacts with the sulfuric acid to give nitrosyl sulfuric acid.   The nitrosyl sulfuric acid then reacts with the resorcinol to give a *p*-nitrosophenolic compound.   These authors describe a procedure for the extraction of the fumigant from corn which they imply is applicable to other stored grains.

Procedure

The aeration assembly is shown in Figure 3 (49).   Use all glass apparatus, since rubber, cork, or metal is attacked by dichloronitroethane.   Weigh a suitable amount of corn sample, 50–500 g, depending upon the expected concentration of dichloronitroethane, and place in the aeration tube.   Connect three traps as shown, each containing 10.0 ml of concentrated sulfuric acid.   Adjust the air pressure to give 1 liter of air/min, as measured by a flowmeter.   Allow air to pass through the corn sample for 15 min.   Turn off the air and remove the first trap.   Replace with a fresh trap containing 10.0 ml of sulfuric acid and repeat the procedure.   Change tubes every 15 min until all of the dichloronitroethane has been removed.   To ensure complete removal of the fumigant from the grain, the aeration tube may be heated to 50–55°C.   It is convenient to develop the color complex in each trap as it is removed, to follow the extraction of the fumigant.   At the end of the aeration period remove the three traps from the train and analyze for the fumigant as described below.

Prepare a standard solution of 1,1-dichloro-1-nitroethane in concentrated sulfuric acid containing 10 µg/ml.   Place 1-, 2-, 3-, 4-, and 5-ml aliquots of the standard solution in glass-stoppered test tubes and dilute each to 10 ml with concentrated sulfuric acid.   Also take an aliquot of the sample solution, adjusting the concentration if necessary so that 10 ml contains not more than 50 µg of fumigant Also prepare a reagent blank.   Stopper the tubes and immerse in a boiling water bath for 5 min.   Remove the tubes from the bath, remove the stoppers, and immerse in a cooling (20–25°C) water bath for 2–3 min.   When the contents of the tubes are cool, cautiously stratify 5 ml of 1% aqueous resorcinol solution upon the acid.   Mix carefully, stopper the tubes, and immerse in the boiling water bath for 10 min.   Remove the tubes from the bath, remove the stoppers, and immerse the tubes once again in the cooling bath.   Measure the absorbance of each solution at

560 nm using the values obtained for the standard solutions to prepare the calibration curve.

A 93–99% recovery of dichloronitroethane in corn was observed by this method. The authors reported that a large number of secondary nitroparaffins and some tertiary nitroparaffins could be determined by this method, so that it might be extended to the analysis of 1-chloro-2-nitropropane (Lanstan) and chloropicrin. Quantitative results were achieved on 3–5 μg of fumigant, and the method could detect as little as 1 μg of material. The procedure has an accuracy of ±5% with a precision of ±1%.

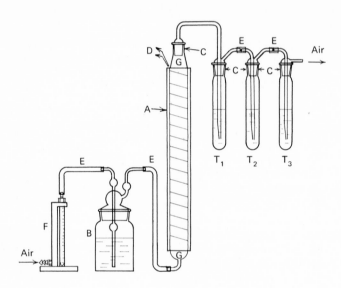

Fig. 3. Apparatus for extraction of fumigant. A, aeration tube. Inside tube: 67 cm long; OD, 32 mm; ID, 28 mm; wound with 43 turns of No. 22 Nichrome V resistance wire, ½ in. between turns. Outside jacket: 57 cm long; OD, 45 mm. B, air scrubbing bottle, filled with sulfuric acid, sp gr, 1.84. C, standard taper 24/40 glass joints. D, leads to Variac. E, Tygon tubing. F, flowmeter, Fisher Laboratory Model No. 11-163. G, glass wool plug. T, traps, 25 X 200 mm, borosilicate tubes, containing 10 ml of sulfuric acid, sp gr, 1.84.

1,1-Dichloro-1-nitroethane can also be determined by gas chromatography using the following operating conditions (50):

column	6 ft × ¼ in. OD, packed
column packing	20% DC 200 methyl silicone fluid (12,500 cSt) on 30/60 mesh Chromosorb P
temperature	
of injector	250°C
of column	50°C, then programmed at 3.7°C/min
carrier gas and flow rate	nitrogen, 120 ml/min
detector	microcoulometer, specific for halogen
retention time of	
dichloronitromethane	8–9 min

EPOXIDES

Ethylene Oxide

Ethylene oxide (1,2-epoxyethane), CH_2CH_2O, is an insecticidal fumigant (51) used in the vault fumigation of stored food products and for sterilization of hospital and laboratory equipment and spaces. It is manufactured by the oxidation of ethylene in the presence of a silver catalyst (52). Ethylene oxide is a colorless gas at room temperature and pressure. The physical properties are: boiling point, 10.7°C; melting point, -111°C; specific gravity, 7/4°C, 0.89; refractive index, n_D^{84}, 1.35988; vapor pressure at 20°C, 1095 torr. It is highly flammable at 73% in air. It is miscible with water and most organic solvents. The threshold limit is 50 ppm; it causes intolerable irritation to the eyes and nose. For fumigation purposes it is usually marketed as mixtures with carbon dioxide or fluorinated hydrocarbons to reduce the fire hazard; for example, Carboxide (Union Carbide Chemical Co.) is 1:9 ethylene oxide–carbon dioxide. Other commercial names are Oxirane and Anprolene. See also Vol. 12, pp. 317–340.

Propylene Oxide

Propylene oxide (1,2-epoxypropane, propene oxide, methyl oxirane),

$$
\begin{array}{c}
\text{O} \\
\diagup \; \diagdown \\
CH_2\!\!-\!\!CH\!\!-\!\!CH_3
\end{array}
$$

has been suggested as a soil fumigant (20) although it is generally regarded as less insecticidal than ethylene oxide. It is prepared by the action of alkali on propylene chlorohydrin. It is a colorless liquid with the following properties: boiling point, 35°C; specific gravity, 20/20°C, 0.8304; vapor pressure at 20°C, 445 torr. It is miscible with ethanol and ethyl ether and soluble in water to the extent of 40 wt % at 20°C. Repeated daily oral doses of 0.2 g/kg produced no toxic effect on rats, and single exposures of 2000 ppm for 2 hr or 1000 ppm for 7 hr produced no injury to rats. The threshold limit is 100 ppm.

ANALYSIS OF ETHYLENE AND PROPYLENE OXIDES

A sensitive colorimetric procedure has been developed for the determination of ethylene oxide in solid, liquid, and air samples (53,54). This method consists of first hydrolyzing the ethylene oxide to ethylene glycol and then oxidizing with sodium periodate to formaldehyde, which is then determined by the color produced by reaction with chromotropic acid or sodium chromotropate. The ethylene oxide is removed from solid and liquid samples by volatilization and trapping in hydroxylamine hydrochloride and triethanolamine solution. For air samples, the air is passed through a bubbler containing 1:4 sulfuric acid. The method of Critchfield and Johnson (53) is described in detail in Vol. 12, p. 328.

Adsorbed ethylene and propylene oxides can be determined by distillation and volumetric measurement (55). The adsorbed epoxides are released from the adsorbing material by distillation in monochlorobenzene and collected in glacial acetic acid. The distillate is then titrated with standardized hydrogen bromide solution, using crystal violet as an indicator. See Vol. 12, p. 331. The detection limits for ethylene and propylene oxide, using this procedure, are reported to be 0.04 mg and 0.06 mg, respectively.

Ethylene oxide residues on date fruit can be extracted with acetone and determined by gas chromatography (56). The operating conditions are given in Vol. 12, p. 332. Ethylene chlorohydrin, ethylene glycol, and diethylene glycol can also be determined by this method. Ethylene oxide can also be determined by the method of Heuser and Scudamore (34) which is given on p. 184.

OTHER FUMIGANTS

Vorlex

Vorlex is a mixture of 20% methyl isothiocyanate and 80% C_3 chlorinated hydrocarbons (dichloropropanes, dichloropropenes, and related compounds). The chlorinated hydrocarbon portion is essentially the D-D mixture. Vorlex is used as a preplant soil fumigant and has broad activity against fungi, nematodes, weeds, and soil insects.

ANALYSIS OF METHYL ISOTHIOCYANATE

Methyl isothiocyanate residues in soil samples can be determined by reaction with ammonia to form N-methylthiourea which is then allowed to react with pentacyanoamine ferrate to produce a blue color (57).

Procedure

Place a cooled mixture of 10 ml of concentrated ammonium hydroxide and 10 ml of absolute methanol in a 50-ml receiver tube. Lightly plug the mouth of the tube with glass wool to reduce loss of ammonia and partially immerse the tube in an ice bath. Weigh 50 g of soil sample and quickly transfer to a 100-ml conical distillation flask. Add 25 ml of 1:9 methanol–ethyl ether and connect the flask to a water-cooled condenser and to the receiver tube. Heat the flask and distill until 25 ml of distillate have been collected. Remove the receiver tube, stopper, and mix. Allow to stand at room temperature for approximately 20 min.

Transfer the contents of the receiver tube to a 150-ml beaker, rinse the tube with 5 ml of methanol, and add to the beaker. Evaporate the solution to approximately 4 ml, but not to dryness, by heating on a hot plate and applying a stream of air to prevent bumping. Transfer the concentrated solution to a 25-ml graduated cylinder, wash the beaker with several small portions of water, and add these to the cylinder until a volume of 10 ml is obtained. To this solution, add 2.0 ml of pH 7.4 0.1 M phosphate buffer and 1.0 ml of freshly prepared 0.1% sodium pentacyanoamine ferrate solution. Dilute to 15 ml with water, mix, and after 15 min measure the absorbance at 610 nm.

Determine the amount of N-methylthiourea in the samples from a standard curve similarly prepared from a range of solutions containing 2–50 μg of N-methylthiourea in 10-ml volumes of water.

In the following method, methyl isothiocyanate is extracted from soil samples with carbon tetrachloride and measured by infrared spectroscopy (58). The method is capable of determining residues greater than 1 ppm.

Procedure

Place 50 g of soil sample into a centrifuge bottle. Add 50 ml of water and 50 ml of carbon tetrachloride, stopper, and shake vigorously for approximately 3 min. Centrifuge for 10 min at 600 G. Decant the supernatant liquid into a 250-ml separatory funnel, being careful not to disturb the sediment. Allow the phases to separate and filter about 25 ml of the carbon tetrachloride layer through a glass wool plug into a 50-ml flask with a glass stopper. Add to the flask about 2 g of anhydrous sodium sulfate, stopper, mix, and allow to stand for at least 2–3 hr. Filter a portion of the dried extract through Whatman No. 1 filter paper and determine the absorption spectrum over the region of 3.5–5.5 μm. Determine the methyl isothiocyanate content from a standard curve using the net absorbance at 4.7 μm. The sensitivity of the method can be increased by using 100 g of sample.

Several isothiocyanates, including methyl isothiocyanate, have been separated by thin-layer chromatography (59). Isothiocyanates are extracted from the sample with carbon tetrachloride. The solvent systems used were: 1:1 ethyl acetate–methanol, 6:3 ethyl acetate–benzene, 19:1 chloroform–methanol, and 7:2 ethyl acetate–pyridine. The separated spots are visualized by exposing the dried chromatogram to gaseous chlorine and spraying with starch–iodine reagent. Methyl isothiocyanate shows up as a blue-black spot which gradually fades to brown. As little as 0.5 μg can be detected.

Acrylonitrile

Acrylonitrile (cyanoethylene, propene nitrile, vinyl cyanide), $CH_2{=}CHCN$, is used mainly as an insecticide in fumigation of individual machines in flour mills, for packaged cereal products, and stored tobacco (60). It is a colorless liquid with the following properties: boiling point, 77.3–77.5°C; freezing point, −83°C; specific gravity, 25/4°C, 0.801; refractive index, n_D^{25}, 1.3885; vapor pressure at 25°C, 105 torr; flash point, open cup, 0°C. It is miscible with most organic solvents and soluble in water to the extent of 7.5 wt %. The flammability limits in air are 3–17% (v/v). The acute oral LD_{50} to rats is 93 mg/kg. The threshold limit is 20 ppm. Commercial formulations are usually mixtures with carbon tetrachloride. See also Vol. 4, pp. 368–381.

Allyl Alcohol

Allyl alcohol (2-propen-1-ol), $CH_2{=}CHCH_2OH$, is used in formulations for soil fumigation, especially with D-D for the control of weed seeds, fungi, and nematodes. It is a colorless liquid with a pungent odor. The physical properties are: boiling point, 96.9°C; vapor pressure at 20°C, 17.3 torr; specific gravity, 20/4°C, 0.8540; refractive index, n_D^{20}, 1.41345; flash point, open cup, 21°C. It is miscible with water, ethanol, chloroform, and petroleum ether. The acute oral LD_{50} to dogs is 40 mg/kg, and to mice 85 mg/kg; the inhalation LD_{50} to rats is 1060 ppm for 1-hr exposure and 165 ppm for 4-hr exposure. See also Vol. 5, pp. 76–86.

Carbon Disulfide

Carbon disulfide (carbon bisulfide, dithiocarbonic anhydride), CS_2, is used as an insecticidal fumigant (61) for nursery stock and for soil treatment against the Colorado beetle and Japanese beetle. It is also used as a grain fumigant against weevils and moths. It is a colorless, volatile, and highly flammable liquid which boils at 46.5°C and melts at $-111.6°C$. The acute oral LD_{50} to rabbits is 300 mg/kg. The threshold value is 20 ppm (62). See also Vol. 8, pp. 268–279.

Formaldehyde

Formaldehyde (methanal, oxomethane, oxymethylene, methylene oxide, formic aldehyde, methyl aldehyde), HCHO, is used as a seed disinfectant (63) and as a space disinfectant (64) in hospitals and laboratories. It is manufactured by the catalytic oxidation of methanol by air. It is a colorless gas at ordinary temperatures with a pungent, suffocating odor. The physical properties are: boiling point, $-19.5°C$; melting point, $92°C$; density of gas, 1.067 (air = 1.000); specific gravity (of liquid), $-20/4°C$, 0.815; ignition temperature about $300°C$. It is soluble in ethanol or ethyl ether and soluble in water to the extent of 40 g/100 ml. It is irritating to mucous membranes. The acute oral LD_{50} to rats is 800 mg/kg. Paraformaldehyde or polymerized formaldehyde, $(CH_2O)_n$, is used for fumigation purposes; on heating it decomposes to formaldehyde monomer. See also FORMALDEHYDE.

Naphthalene

Naphthalene, $C_{10}H_8$, is used as a domestic fumigant and repellent for clothes moths, but it has doubtful value as a repellent (63). Impure grades are also used as soil fumigants. It is obtained commercially from coal tar fractions. Naphthalene is a colorless, flaky crystalline material, with a characteristic odor. The physical properties are: boiling point, $218°C$; melting point, $80°C$; vapor pressure at $20°C$, 0.0492 torr; specific gravity, $15/4°C$, 1.1517; flash point, open cup, $79°C$. It is soluble in ethyl ether, chloroform, or ethylene dichloride, slightly soluble in ethanol, and soluble in water to the extent of 0.003%. It is nontoxic to warm-blooded animals. See also NAPHTHALENE.

Phosphine

Phosphine (hydrogen phosphide), PH_3, is used as a fumigant for insects and rodents in stored grain. It is a colorless gas with an odor of garlic or decaying fish. The physical properties are: boiling point, $-87.7°C$; melting point, $-133°C$; vapor pressure at $-3°C$, 20 atm; density of gas at $0°C$, 1.529 (air = 1.000). It is spontaneously flammable in air if there is a trace of P_2H_4. It is slightly soluble in water. It is highly toxic. The lethal concentration for rats in air is 60 ppm; 2000 ppm is lethal to man in a few minutes; 400–600 ppm is dangerous to life after exposures of 30–60 min; 100–190 ppm can be tolerated for 60 min; 7 ppm can be tolerated without symptoms for several hours. The commercial preparation is Phostoxin, pellets containing 55% aluminum phosphide, 40% ammonium carbonate, and 5% aluminum oxide; in the presence of moisture, phosphine is liberated along with ammonia and carbon dioxide to give a nonflammable mixture. See also PHOSPHORUS COMPOUNDS.

Sodium Methyl Dithiocarbamate

Sodium methyl dithiocarbamate (N-methyldithiocarbamic acid sodium salt),

$$CH_3NHC(=S)-SNa,$$

is used as a fungicide and nematicidal soil fumigant (65,66). It is manufactured by the reaction of methylamine and carbon disulfide in the presence of sodium hydroxide. The salt decomposes in the soil to provide the volatile active agents, methyl isothiocyanate and hydrogen sulfide. Sodium methyl dithiocarbamate is a white crystalline solid with the odor of carbon disulfide. It is unstable in the solid state and in dilute or acid solutions, but is stable in concentrated alkaline solution. It is moderately soluble in methanol, sparingly soluble in other organic solvents, and soluble in water to the extent of 72.2 g/100 g at 20°C. The acute oral LD_{50} to rats is 820 mg/kg and to mice 285 mg/kg; the acute dermal LD_{50} to rabbits is 800 mg/kg. Commercial names include Vapam (Stauffer Chemical Co.), VPM (du Pont), metham sodium, and SMDC. See also Vol. 11, pp. 573–586.

Sulfuryl Fluoride

Sulfuryl fluoride, SO_2F_2, is used as an insectidal fumigant (67,68). It is more toxic to all stages of insect life than methyl bromide, and shows promise for the fumigation of buildings for termites. It is manufactured by the thermal decomposition of barium fluorosulfonate. It is a colorless, odorless gas with the following properties: boiling point, 55.4°C; melting point, −136.7°C; density of liquid, 1.7 g/ml; vapor pressure at 25°C, 260 psi. It is stable up to 400°C and in aqueous solutions, but is hydrolyzed by alkaline solutions. It is miscible with methyl bromide, sparingly soluble in ethanol and hydrocarbon solvents, and soluble in water to the extent of 0.75 g/100 g. It is highly irritating to the respiratory tract of man; test animals tolerated 100 ppm for 7 hr a day, 5 days a week for 6 months.

Analysis of Sulfuryl Fluoride

Sulfuryl fluoride in air can be determined by absorption in alkali solutions followed by the addition of excess titrant and back titration. The best method appears to be absorption in barium hydroxide solution (69):

$$2\,SO_2F_2 + 2\,Ba(OH)_2 \longrightarrow Ba(SO_3F)_2 + BaF_2 + 2\,H_2O$$

Barium fluoride and barium carbonate are precipitated when the air is bubbled through the absorbant. The addition of excess hydrochloric acid dissolves the barium fluoride, and the barium carbonate is decomposed with the partial evolution of carbon dioxide. Back titration with 0.02 N barium hydroxide solution to an end point of pH 5.0 gives the quantity of sulfuryl fluoride absorbed without interference from the carbon dioxide. Heuser (69) describes a correction for carbon dioxide contents greater than 1%.

Procedure

Prepare methyl red–bromocresol green indicator solution as follows. Dissolve 0.1 g of bromocresol green in 1.44 ml of 0.1 N sodium hydroxide solution and dilute to 50 ml with water. Dissolve 0.1 g of methyl red in 150 ml of absolute ethanol and mix with the bromocresol green solution. The indicator color changes are: pH 4.8, rose red; pH 5.0, colorless; pH 5.2, green.

Bubble the air sample containing sulfuryl fluoride through a known volume of 0.1 N barium hydroxide solution. Evacuate this solution and a reagent blank to 50 torr, then allow the solutions to stand for 48 hr. Add a known excess of 0.1 N hydrochloric acid to the sample and the reagent blank solutions, add 2 drops of the methyl red–bromocresol green indicator solution, and titrate with 0.02 N barium hydroxide solution to the colorless end point.

$$SO_2F_2, \text{ in mg} = (A - B)(N)(51)$$

where A = volume of 0.02 N barium hydroxide solution required for the sample, in ml

B = volume of 0.02 N barium hydroxide solution required for the blank, in ml

N = normality of 0.02 N barium hydroxide solution

The recovery of sulfuryl fluoride from normal air was found to be 98.7–101.6%. The accuracy of the method was found to be ±0.5% at 10 ng/l using a 1-liter adsorption flask.

Sulfuryl fluoride and a number of other inorganic gases have been determined by gas chromatography using the following conditions (70):

column	4 m × 6 mm, packed
column packing	30% halocarbon on silica gel preheated to 900°C
column temperature	30°C
carrier gas and flow rate	hydrogen, 150 ml/min
detector	thermal conductivity

Trichloroacetonitrile

Trichloroacetonitrile (trichloromethylnitrile), CCl_3CN, is an insecticidal fumigant (71) for the treatment of stored grains and has been suggested for household uses. It is manufactured by reacting hydrogen chloride, chlorine, and acetonitrile (72). It is a colorless to yellow nonflammable liquid with the following properties: boiling point, 85.7°C; melting point, −42°C; specific gravity, 25/4°C, 1.4403; refractive index, n_D^{20}, 1.4409. It is toxic to warm blooded animals but lachrimatory at low concentrations. The commercial name is Tritox. See also NITRILES.

Bibliography

1. T. Dumas and H. A. O. Monro, *Pest Control* **34**, 20 (1966).
2. A. A. Cristie, G. C. Hands, and R. G. Lidzey, *Chem. Ind.* (*London*) **1965**, 1935.
3. L. O. Howard, *Yearbook Agr.* (*U.S. Dept. Agr.*) **1899**, 150.
4. L. Andrussow, *Angew. Chem.* **48**, 593 (1935).
5. H. J. Quayle. *J. Econ. Ent.* **16**, 327 (1923).
6. *Standard Methods for the Examination of Water and Wastewater*, 11th ed., American Public Health Association, New York, 1960.
7. J. Epstein, *Anal. Chem.* **19**, 272 (1947).
8. W. N. Aldridge, *Analyst* **70**, 474 (1945).
9. LeGoupil, *Rev. Path. Veg.* **19**, 169 (1932).
10. R. T. Cotton and R. C. Roark, *J. Econ. Ent.* **20**, 636 (1927).
11. O. I. Snapp, *J. Econ. Ent.* **32**, 683 (1939).
12. U.S. Pat. 2,448,265 (1948), Kagy and McPherson (to Dow Chemical Co.).
13. U.S. Pat. 2,425,238 (1947), Fletcher and Kanaga (to Dow Chemical Co.).
14. M. W. Stone and F. B. Foley, *J. Econ. Ent.* **44**, 711 (1951).
15. J. R. Couch, *Down Earth* **12**, 7 (1956).
16. C. D. Hürd and C. N. Webb. *J. Am. Chem. Soc.* **58**, 2191 (1936).
17. I. E. Neifert, F. C. Cook, R. C. Roark, W. H. Tonkin, E. A. Back, and R. T. Cotton, *U.S. Dept. Agr., Agr. Infor. Bull.* **1925**, 1313.
18. W. Carter, *Science* **97**, 383 (1943).
19. U.S. Pat. 2,695,859 (1952), L. Hilmer (to Shell Development Co.).
20. R. C. Roark and R. T. Cotton, *U.S. Dept. Agr. Tech. Bull.* **1929**, 162.
21. Brit. Pat. 438,271 (1935), Perkins (to Carbide and Carbon Chemicals Corp.).
22. C. W. McBeth and G. B. Bergeson, *Plant Disease Reptr.* **3**, 223 (1955).
23. U.S. Pat. 2,937,936 (1955), Schmidt (to Pineapple Research Institute).

24. U.S. Pat. 3,049,472 (1962), Swezey (to Dow Chemical Co.).
25. W. Moore, *J. Econ. Entomol.* **9,** 71 (1916).
26. W. E. Britton, *Conn. Agr. Exp. Sta. Rept. No. 31,* 796 (1908).
27. B. Berck, *J. Agr. Food Chem.* **13,** 373 (1965).
28. F. H. Reid and W. R. Halpin, *Am. Ind. Hyg. Assoc. J.* **29,** 390 (1968).
29. K. Olah, J. Bodner, and S. Borocz, *Proc. Conf. Appl. Phys. Chem. Methods. Chem. Anal. (Budapest)* **2,** 177 (1966); *Chem. Abstr.* **68,** 62451 (1968).
30. D. H. Smith and R. S. Shigenaga, *Soil Sci. Soc. Am., Proc.* **27,** 602 (1963).
31. D. E. Johnson and B. Lear, *J. Chromatog. Sci.* **7,** 384 (1969).
32. I. H. Williams, *J. Econ. Ent.* **61,** 1432 (1968).
33. J. J. Jurinak and T. S. Inouye, *Soil Sci. Soc. Am., Proc.* **27,** 602 (1963).
34. S. G. Heuser and K. A. Scudamore, *Analyst* **93,** 252 (1968).
35. S. G. Heuser and K. A. Scudamore, *Chem. Ind. (London)* **1968,** 1154.
36. E. S. Goodwin, R. Goulden, and J. G. Reynolds, *Analyst* **86,** 697 (1961).
37. W. H. Gutenmann and D. J. Lisk, *J. Agr. Food Chem.* **11,** 301 (1963).
38. H. Beckman and A. Bevenue, *J. Agr. Food Chem.* **11,** 479 (1963).
39. U.S. Pat. 3,078,209 (1963), Willard and Maitten (to FMC Corp.).
40. T. E. Cullen and R. P. Stanovick, *J. Agr. Food Chem.* **13,** 118 (1965).
41. W. Moore, *J. Econ. Ent.* **11,** 357 (1918).
42. A. W. Linquist, *U.S. Dept. Agr. Circ. No. 351* (1935).
43. M. O. Johnson and C. H. Godfrey, *Ind. Eng. Chem.* **24,** 311 (1932).
44. F. L. Stark, *Cornell Univ. Agr. Exptl. Sta. Mem. No. 278* (1948).
45. L. Feinsilver and F. W. Oberst, *Anal. Chem.* **25,** 820 (1953).
46. M. E. Getzendaner, E. T. Wagoner, and M. Lambert, *J. Agr. Food Chem.* **13,** 565 (1965).
47. D. A. Mapes and S. A. Shrader, *J. Assoc. Offic. Agr. Chem.* **40,** 180–182 (1957).
48. W. C. O'Kane and H. W. Smith, *J. Econ. Ent.* **34,** 438 (1941).
49. L. R. Jones and J. A. Riddick, *Anal. Chem.* **24,** 1533 (1952).
50. J. Burke, *J. Assoc. Offic. Agr. Chem.* **46,** 198 (1963).
51. R. T. Cotton and R. C. Roark, *Ind. Eng. Chem.* **20,** 805 (1928).
52. U.S. Pat. 2,960,511 (1960), Courter and Mecorney (to Shell Oil Co.).
53. F. E. Critchfield and J. B. Johnson, *Anal. Chem.* **29,** 797 (1957).
54. N. E. Bolton and N. H. Ketcham, *Arch. Environ. Health* **8,** 711 (1964).
55. D. A. Gunther, *Anal. Chem.* **37,** 1172–1173 (1965).
56. S. Ben-Yehoshua and P. Krinsky, *J. Gas Chromatog.* **6,** 350–351 (1968).
57. G. A. Lloyd, *J. Sci. Food Agr.* **13,** 309 (1962).
58. M. G. Ashley and B. L. Leigh, *J. Sci. Food Agr.* **14,** 148 (1963).
59. C. Di Bello and E. Celon, *J. Chromatog.* **31,** 77 (1967).
60. U.S. Pat. 2,356,075 (1944), Migrdichian (to American Cyanamid Co.).
61. A. Garreau, *Science* **64,** 326 (1926).
62. *Am. Conf. Gov. Ind. Hyg.* **1962,** C1–C4.
63. W. S. Abbott and S. C. Billings, *J. Econ. Ent.* **28,** 493 (1953).
64. W. Bolle, *Vet. Med. Nachrichten* **1953** (3/4).
65. U.S. Pat. 2,766,554 (1956), Stauffer Chemical Co.
66. U.S. Pat. 2,791,605 (1957), Stauffer Chemical Co.
67. E. E. Kenaga, *J. Econ. Ent.* **40,** 1 (1957).
68. U.S. Pat. 2,875,127 (1959), Kenaga (to Dow Chemical Co.).
69. S. G. Heuser, *Anal. Chem.* **35,** 1476 (1963).
70. A. Engelbrecht, E. Nachbaur, and E. Mayer, *J. Chromatog.* **15,** 228 (1964).
71. G. Peters, *Chem. Ztg.* **64,** 485 (1940).
72. U.S. Pat. 2,745,868 (1956), Käbisch and Degussa.

B. G. Tweedy
J. A. Ross
G. A. Bozarth
University of Missouri

FUNGICIDES

Mercury-containing compounds.. 198
Quinones 200
Dithiocarbamates and thiuram disulfides................................. 202
Guanidines and imidazoles... 205
Chlorothiodicarboximides.. 209
Oxathiins... 212
Chlorinated and nitrated benzenes....................................... 214
Other fungicides.. 223
Bibliography.. 226

Fungicides are compounds used to control or prevent the growth and development of fungi on or in plants, animals, fibers, paints, wood products, and other materials. The first fungicides were very simple inorganic compounds, such as lime sulfur and copper sulfate. During the past few decades, many organic compounds have been developed for their fungicidal value. A slight change in the chemical structure generally does not improve and most commonly hinders its fungicidal value, but there are few instances where more than two chemicals belong to the same chemical class of compounds.

The quantitative analytical detection of fungicide residues is most important for plants used directly or indirectly for food purposes and is emphasized in this article. See also the general references (1–6).

MERCURY-CONTAINING COMPOUNDS

Bis(methylmercuric) Sulfate

Bis(methylmercuric) sulfate was introduced in 1958 as an experimental fungicide

$$CH_3—Hg—O \diagdown \quad O$$
$$S$$
$$CH_3—Hg—O \diagup \quad O$$

for control of seed-borne diseases of cereals, beets, potatoes, and bulbs by Farbenfabriken Bayer A.G. (7). It is prepared by the reaction of Grignard compounds or metallic organic compounds with mercuric salts. It is a white crystalline powder which melts at 260°C, decomposing with slow heating. It is soluble in water, insoluble in organic solvents, and recrystallizable from methanol. The acute oral LD_{50} to rats is 50 mg/kg and intraperitoneal 13.75 mg/kg. It is marketed as formulations containing 0.8 and 1.2% mercury. Alternate names are Cerewet and Areta-nieuw.

Methoxyethyl Mercuric Chloride

2-Methoxyethyl mercuric chloride was first developed by I. G. Farbenindustrie

$$CH_3—O—\overset{\overset{\displaystyle H}{|}}{\underset{\underset{\displaystyle H}{|}}{C}}—\overset{\overset{\displaystyle H}{|}}{\underset{\underset{\displaystyle H}{|}}{C}}—Hg^{+}Cl^{-}$$

about 1928 (8). It is used primarily as a seed treatment. It is prepared by introducing ethylene into a solution containing mercuric acetate and methanol, which forms methoxyethyl mercuric acetate. The chloride or silicate is then formed by precipitation. It is a white crystalline powder which melts at 65°C. It is soluble in acetone or 95% ethanol, is stable to alkali, but in the presence of halogen acids decomposes to ethylene, methanol, and mercuric salt. The acute oral LD_{50} to rats is 1140 mg/kg. It is marketed as a formulation containing 2.5% mercury. An alternate name is Ceresan.

Panogen

Panogen (methylmercury dicyandiamide) was first used in Sweden in the 1930s

$$CH_3—Hg—N—\overset{\overset{\displaystyle NH}{\displaystyle \|}}{C}—N—C\equiv N$$
$$\underset{\displaystyle H}{|}$$

as a seed disinfectant and was later used in the United States in the late 1940s. It is applied as a seed treatment and soil drench for control of several seed and soil-borne diseases or as a turf fungicide. It is prepared by reacting methylmercuric hydroxide and dicyandiamine and is precipitated by soluble chlorides. It forms white crystals which melt at 156–157°C and is stable under normal storage conditions. It is soluble in water, acetone, or ethanol and insoluble in benzene. The acute oral LD_{50} to rats is about 30 mg/kg. It is marketed as solutions containing 2.2, 4.4, and 6.3% and dust containing 0.9% active ingredient.

Emmi

Emmi (N-ethylmercuri-1,2,3,6-tetrahydro-3,6-endomethano-3,4,5,6,7,7-hexachlorophthalimide) was first introduced as an experimental fungicide in 1951 by the

Velsicol Corporation. Emmi is very active as a spore germination inhibitor and acts as an eradicant and protectant for powdery mildew and apple scab. It is prepared as follows (9): The condensation product of hexachlorocyclopentadiene and maleic anhydride, prepared via the Diels-Alder reaction, is reacted with ammonia to form the imide. Then the sodium salt of the imide is condensed with ethyl mercuric chloride. It is a white crystalline solid which melts at 140–141°C and is stable to heat and light. It is soluble in acetone and other ketones, moderately soluble in alcohols, slightly soluble in hydrocarbons, and practically insoluble in water. It is phytotoxic to rose plants. The acute oral LD_{50} to rats is 148 mg/kg. It is commercially available as a 10–34% emulsifiable concentrate and a wettable powder containing 10% active ingredient.

ANALYSIS OF MERCURY-CONTAINING FUNGICIDES

Mercury in fungicide and pharmaceutical preparations can be determined by the following method which utilizes isotope exchange of ^{203}Hg (10). The average recovery is 98.5 ± 1.12%.

Procedure

Place a sample containing 0.500–1.00 g of the organic mercury compound in a ground-glass double-neck flask and attach to a Friedrich condenser and a 50-ml dropping funnel. Add 10 ml of concentrated sulfuric acid to the flask. Then add about 25 ml of 50% hydrogen peroxide dropwise through the dropping funnel, cooling frequently between additions to prevent hazard. Allow the digestion to proceed in the absence of external heat until the sample is dissolved. Then heat the digest to full flame for 30 min. Allow the clear digest to cool and then transfer quantitatively with water rinses to a volumetric flask of such size that 5-ml aliquots will contain either microgram or milligram quantities of mercury.

Select a quantity of standard Hg^{2+} solution so that the aliquot measured contains 0.1–10 times the estimated amount of mercury in the sample solution. To sample and standard solutions add an amount of ^{203}Hg tracer not in excess of 0.01 times the Hg^{2+} content and enough concentrated sulfuric acid to make the acid concentration 2 N; the total volume should be 5–6 ml. Add 5.0 ml of carbon tetrachloride that has been analyzed for organic mercury content. Stir vigorously for 10 min and separate by centrifugation. Measure the ^{203}Hg in an aliquot of each phase by gamma scintillation counting. Normalize the count rate of each aliquot of the aqueous phase to a volume of 5.0 ml and calculate the isotope dilution.

QUINONES

Chloranil

Chloranil (2,3,5,6-tetrachlorobenzoquinone) was first introduced in 1939 by the

Naugatuck Chemical Co., Division of Uniroyal (11). It is used primarily as a seed protectant but is also used as a foliar fungicide. Chloranil is prepared by reacting *p*-phenylenediamine or phenol with potassium chlorate and hydrochloric acid or by the oxidation of trichlorophenol with chromic acid. Chloranil forms golden-yellow platelets when crystallized from acetic acid or acetone and monoclinic prisms when crystallized from benzene or toluene. It melts at 290°C with sublimation. It is soluble in carbon tetrachloride, chloroform, or carbon disulfide, and only slightly soluble, to the extent of 25 ppm, in water. It is stable in acid solution and reacts with alkali to form salts of chloranilinic acid. The acute oral LD_{50} to rats is 4000 mg/kg. It is commercially available as a wettable powder for spraying and dipping containing 48% active ingredient, a wettable powder for seed treatment containing 95% active ingredient, a dust for seed treatment containing 96% active ingredient, and a dust for foliar dusting containing 5 or 10% active ingredient. Trade names are Spergon and Vulklar.

ANALYSIS OF CHLORANIL

Chloranil residues in food crops are determined by extracting the chloranil into benzene and reacting with diphenyl-*p*-phenylenediamine to form a Wurster salt which is blue in aqueous acid solution and can be measured spectrophotometrically (12). The method is applicable to concentrations of 0.1–0.5 ppm.

Procedure

Purify crude diphenyl-*p*-phenylenediamine by vacuum distillation, collect the white crystalline platelets, and store in a brown bottle. The extracting solution contains 850 ml of glacial acetic acid, 50 ml of concentrated hydrochloric acid, and 100 ml of water; deaerate the solution before use by bubbling nitrogen through it for 1 hr. Adjust all reagents to 21–27°C.

Place a 1000 g crop sample and 500 ml of benzene in a glass gallon jar. Line the lid with cellophane or polyethylene. Roll on an automatic roller for 15 min. Decant the benzene and scrub it twice with 100-ml portions of water. Dry the benzene over anhydrous sodium sulfate and filter rapidly through a filter paper. Transfer 400 ml to a 500-ml separatory funnel and add 5 ml of the diphenyl-*p*-phenylenediamine reagent. Shake vigorously for 1 min and let stand for 5 min. A weak yellowish-orange color will appear due to oxidation of diphenyl-*p*-phenylenediamine by chloranil. Then add 50 ml of the extracting solution, shake for 1 min, and let stand for 1 or 2 min. The Wurster salt partitions into the aqueous acid phase as a blue color in approximately 10 ml of solution. The remaining extracting solution is lost by phase readjustment. Draw off the blue layer, filter through Eaton-Dikeman No. 613 paper if cloudy, place in a 1 cm cuvet, and read the absorbance at 700 nm, using extracting solution as a reference. This reading should be made exactly 10 min after addition of the diphenyl-*p*-phenylenediamine reagent as the blue color increases in intensity with time.

Run a standard curve just prior to the analysis or when a new batch of extracting solution is used. Plot absorbance against concentration of chloranil at 0.1, 0.2, 0.3 and 0.4 ppm. If initial analyses on samples indicate higher concentrations than the standard curve, dilute the blue solution with extracting solution.

Dichlone

Dichlone (2,3-dichloro-1,4-naphthoquinone) is used as a seed protectant and as a

foliar fungicide for controlling several fruit diseases. It is prepared by chlorination of 1,4-naphthoquinone (13), by oxidation of 2,3-dichloro-5,8-dihydro-1,4-naphthohydroquinone (14), or by oxidation of 2,3-dichloro-*p*-benzoquinone. It forms golden-yellow needles or leaflets when crystallized from ethanol. It melts at 193°C, is soluble in ethyl ether, dioxane, acetone, or benzene, moderately soluble in xylene or *o*-dichlorobenzene, and insoluble in water. The acute oral LD_{50} to rats is 1.5 mg/kg. It is commercially available as a wettable powder containing 50% active ingredient and a dust containing 3% active ingredient.

ANALYSIS OF DICHLONE

Dichlone is extracted into benzene solution and reacted with dimethylamine to form a red color which is specific for dichlone (15). The method is sensitive to 1 ppm and detectable to 0.05 ppm. Average recovery for untreated samples fortified with known amounts of dichlone was 91%.

Procedure

Place a 1000 g crop sample in a glass jar and add 500 ml of benzene. Line the lid with cellophane or polyethylene. Roll on an automatic rolling device for 15 min for surface extraction of dichlone. Decant the benzene and dry over anhydrous sodium sulfate for 10 min. Filter through a fast filter paper. The analysis should be carried out the same day to avoid decomposition of dichlone. Place 38 ml of the benzene extract in a 50-ml mixing cylinder with a ground-glass stopper. Dilute to 40 ml with anhydrous dimethylamine and mix thoroughly. Dilute a second 38-ml aliquot to 40 ml with benzene and mix thoroughly. Using benzene as a reference, measure the absorbance of both samples at 495 nm in 10 cm cells. Color measurements should be made 5–20 min after the addition of dimethylamine. Determine the dichlone content from a standard curve. Interference from natural plant components was found to be 0.02 ppm for untreated samples (15).

DITHIOCARBAMATES AND THIURAM DISULFIDES

Ferbam

Ferbam (tris(dimethyldithiocarbamate) iron) is used as a preventative foliar

$$\left[\begin{array}{c} CH_3 \\ CH_3 \end{array} \!\!\! > \!\! N\!-\!C \!\! < \!\! \begin{array}{c} S \\ S^- \end{array} \right]_3 Fe^{3+}$$

fungicide and is particularly good for control of black rot on grapes. It is prepared from sodium dimethyldithiocarbamate and a solution of a ferric salt (16). It is a black solid which decomposes before melting, above 180°C. The flash point is above 300°C. It is soluble in chloroform, acetone, pyridine, or acetonitrile, and to the extent of 120 μg/ml in water. The acute oral LD_{50} to rats is 4000 mg/kg, to mice 1000 mg/kg, and to guinea pigs and rabbits 700–3000 mg/kg. It is commercially available as a wettable powder containing 76% active ingredient and dusts containing 3.9, 7.6, and 11.5% active ingredient. Trade names include Ferbeck, Fermate, Ferradow, Karbam Black, and Vancide F.

Nabam

Nabam (disodium ethylene bisdithiocarbamate),

$$\underset{\displaystyle NaSCNH}{\overset{\displaystyle S}{\overset{\displaystyle \|}{}}}\!\!-\!CH_2CH_2\!-\!\underset{\displaystyle NHCSNa}{\overset{\displaystyle S}{\overset{\displaystyle \|}{}}}$$

is a broad spectrum protective fungicide (17). It was superseded by zineb. It is too phytotoxic to be used as a general foliar fungicide. It has been reported as having systemic activity against red stele of strawberry (18). It is also used in the preparation of several metal-containing dithiocarbamate fungicides. It is prepared by reacting ethylenediamine and carbon disulfide in the presence of sodium hydroxide (19). The hexahydrate forms colorless crystals which are unstable; upon aeration in aqueous solution, it forms elemental sulfur and ethylene thiuram monosulfide and its polymer (20). The acute oral LD_{50} to rats is 395 mg/kg. It is marketed as liquid solutions containing 18, 19, and 22% active ingredient and wettable powders containing 73 and 93% active ingredient. Trade names include Dithane D-14 and Parzate.

Maneb

Maneb (manganous ethylene bisdithiocarbamate) is a broad spectrum fungicide

used for prevention of many foliar diseases. It is prepared from nabam solution by neutralizing with acetic acid and adding manganese chloride or sulfate (21,22). It is a yellow crystalline solid which decomposes before melting. It is stable under most storage conditions but decomposes when exposed to moisture. It is slightly soluble in water, chloroform, or pyridine. It forms complexes irreversibly with strong chelating agents such as ethylenediaminetetraacetic acid sodium salts. The acute oral LD_{50} to rats is 6750 mg/kg. It is marketed as a wettable, dispersible powder containing 80% active ingredient. Trade names include Manzate D, Dithane M-22, and Vancide M. Dithane M-45 and Manzate 200 are zinc chloride and maneb complexes which improve performance.

Zineb

Zineb (zinc ethylenebisdithiocarbamate), like maneb, is a good broad spectrum

protective fungicide used generally for foliar diseases (23,24). It is prepared by reacting soluble zinc salts with nabam. It is a light colored powder which decomposes before melting. It is slightly unstable when stored in moist and hot areas, and there is evidence that photodecomposition occurs. It is soluble in pyridine and insoluble in water. The acute oral LD_{50} to rats is greater than 5000 mg/kg. It is marketed as a wettable powder containing 75% active ingredient. Trade names include Dithane Z-78 and Parzate C and D.

Ziram

Ziram (zinc dimethyldithiocarbamate) was originally developed as a rubber vulcanization accelerator. It is used as a foliar protectant fungicide for fruit and vegetables.

It is prepared by first reacting carbon disulfide with dimethylamine in a solution of sodium hydroxide, which results in the formation of sodium dimethyldithiocarbamate; ziram is then formed when soluble zinc salts are added. Ziram forms a white powder which melts at 246°C. It is compatible with most pesticides except those containing copper or mercury. It is soluble in dilute alkali, carbon disulfide, chloroform, or ethanol, slightly soluble in acetone, and insoluble in water. It is decomposed in acid solutions, but stable under most storage conditions. The acute oral LD_{50} to rats is 1400 mg/kg. It may irritate the skin and mucous membranes. It is marketed as a wettable powder containing 76% active ingredient. The trade name is Zerlate.

Mitiram

Mitiram (zinc-activated polyethylene thiuram disulfide) is a broad spectrum

$$\left[\text{+(CH}_2\text{—NH—C(S)—S—S—C(S)—NH—CH}_2\text{+)}_n \text{+(CH—NH—C(S)—S—Zn—S—C(S)—NH—CH}_2\text{+)}_m \right]_x$$

$n:m = 1:3$
$x = \text{unknown}$

protective foliar fungicide controlling several diseases on fruit, vegetables and turf. Its fungicidal properties were first discovered by Badische Anilin & Soda Fabrik A.G. in Germany and it was developed in the U.S. by Niagara Chemical Company. It is a solid which melts at 120°C with decomposition. It is insoluble in most solvents and decomposes in strong acid or alkaline solution. It is not compatible with liquid fertilizers; when using with malathion or Diazinon, it must be mixed immediately before use. The acute oral LD_{50} to rats is 10,000 mg/kg and to male mice above 5402 mg/kg. It is commercially available as a wettable powder containing 80% active ingredient and a dust containing 7% active ingredient. Trade names include Polyram and Polyram Combi.

Thiram

Thiram (bis(dimethylthiocarbamoyl) disulfide) is a broad spectrum foliar, soil,

$$\underset{H_3C}{\overset{H_3C}{\diagdown}} N\text{—C(S)—S—S—C(S)—N} \underset{CH_3}{\overset{CH_3}{\diagup}}$$

and seed protectant (25). It is manufactured by the oxidation of sodium dimethyldithiocarbamate by iodine or hydrogen peroxide (16). It forms white crystals when precipitated from chloroform or ethanol. The melting point is 155–156°C. It is soluble in chloroform, acetone, or benzene, slightly soluble in ethanol or ethyl ether, and insoluble in water. Thiram is compatible with most pesticides. It is commercially available under many trade names. Arasan is a wettable powder for use as a seed protectant containing 50–75% active ingredient. Arasan 42-S is a liquid suspension containing 4 lb/gal. Wettable powders for use as general fungicides are Tersan which contains 75% active ingredient, and Thylate which contains 65% active ingredient. Delsan is a seed protectant which contains 60% active ingredient thiram and 15% dieldrin. Tersan OM contains 45% active ingredient thiram and 10% hydroxymercurichlorophenol for use as a turf fungicide. Other trade names include TMTD, Thiurad, Thiosan, Thiuramyl, Puralin, Ferason, Nomersan, Pomasol, Resifilm, Pomorsol, Tuads, and Tulisan.

ANALYSIS OF DITHIOCARBAMATES

Dithiocarbamate residues are determined by colorimetric measurement of the carbon disulfide evolved from the acid hydrolysis of the dithiocarbamate. The method of Pease (26) covers the range of 20–160 μg of dithiocarbamate and is given in Vol. 11, pp. 580–582. A subsequent modification by Gordon et al. (27) permits determination of 1–10, 10–200, or 200–1000 μg ranges. See also DITHIOCARBAMATES, Vol. 11, pp. 573–602.

GUANIDINES AND IMIDAZOLES

Dodine

Dodine (n-dodecylguanidine acetate, laurylguanidine acetate),

$$\underset{\text{C}_{12}\text{H}_{25}-\text{NH}-\overset{\overset{\displaystyle \text{NH}}{\|}}{\text{C}}-\text{NH}_2 . \text{CH}_3-\overset{\overset{\displaystyle \text{O}}{\|}}{\text{C}}-\text{OH}}{}$$

was first introduced in 1956 as an experimental fungicide by American Cyanamid Company (28) and by 1960 it was proven to be an effective protectant and eradicative fungicide against fruit diseases, especially apple scab and cherry leaf spot. It is prepared by reacting dodecylamine with cyanamide and acetic acid. It is a white, slightly waxy solid which melts at 136°C at 99.5% purity and at 132–135°C at 97% purity. It is soluble in low molecular weight alcohols and in acids and slightly soluble in water. It is stable at 25°C in solid form or in solution and is stable under moderately alkaline or acid conditions, but the base is freed under highly alkaline conditions. It is incompatible with lime or chlorobenzilate, but compatible with most other pesticides. It is marketed as a wettable powder containing 65% active ingredient and a dust containing 75% active ingredient. Trade names are Cyprex and Melprex.

ANALYSIS OF DODINE

Dodine residues in fruit are determined by extraction with an ethanol–chloroform mixture and reaction with bromocresol purple to form a complex which is extracted into chloroform, hydrolyzed, and measured colorimetrically (29,30).

Procedure

Recrystallize indicator-grade bromocresol purple from boiling toluene at a concentration of about 2 g/100 ml. Dissolve 0.4 g in 75 ml of 0.01 N sodium hydroxide solution. If necessary, add more 0.01 N sodium hydroxide solution to adjust the pH to 6.0–6.1. Filter, if necessary, dilute to 500 ml with carbon dioxide-free water, and store in brown bottle. Prepare a pH 5.5 buffer solution by dissolving 15.2 g of disodium hydrogen phosphate, $Na_2HPO_4.7H_2O$, and 74.0 g of sodium dihydrogen phosphate, $NaH_2PO_4.H_2O$, in carbon dioxide-free water and diluting to 1 liter.

Grind the sample in a blender with 2:1 methanol–chloroform using 400 ml of solvent for each 100 g of sample. Suction filter it through two layers of Whatman No. 1 paper, and wash the pulp with an additional 100 ml of solvent for each 100 g of sample. Measure the volume of the extract, and transfer a portion equivalent to 50 g of sample to a 400-ml beaker. Add several glass beads and 1 ml of concentrated hydrochloric acid, and evaporate on a steam bath to 50 ml. Add 30 ml of 30% sodium chloride solution and 100 ml of methanol. Cool, transfer to a 500-ml separatory funnel, and extract gently with 50 ml of carbon tetrachloride by tipping the funnel six to eight times. After the phases separate, discard the carbon tetrachloride layer. Repeat the extraction three more times, shaking more vigorously each time, until the fourth extraction is shaken vigorously for 1 min; discard carbon tetrachloride each time. Adjust the pH to 5.5 with 4 N sodium hydroxide solution. Add 20 ml of pH 5.5 buffer solution and 20 ml of bromocresol purple solution. Readjust the pH to 5.5 and extract with two 50-ml portions of chloroform, shaking for 2 min each time. Shake the combined chloroform extracts for 30 sec with 25 ml of pH 5.5 buffer solution. Transfer the chloroform layer to another separatory funnel and shake for 1 min with 25 ml of buffer solution. After 10 min transfer the chloroform layer to another separatory funnel and shake with 20 ml of 0.05 N sodium hydroxide solution to remove all combined indicator and any organic acids which may persist. Recomplex the dodine present as free base in the chloroform by shaking for 3 min with 5 ml of bromocresol purple solution and 20 ml of pH 5.5 buffer solution. Wash the chloroform three times with 15 ml of buffer solution. Transfer to a 250-ml separatory funnel and shake for 2 min with 20 ml of 0.05 N sodium hydroxide solution. Combine the sodium hydroxide layers and read the absorbance at 590 nm. Determine the amount of dodine present from a standard curve.

Prepare the standard curve by adding 0.5, 1.0, 3.0, 4.0 and 5.0 ml of dodine of standard solution containing 13 μg/ml to a series of separatory funnels containing 100 ml of methanol, 50 ml of water, 30 ml of 30% sodium chloride solution, 20 ml of bromocresol purple solution, and 20 ml of pH 5.5 buffer solution. Adjust the pH to 5.5 and extract as outlined for the sample.

Benomyl

Benomyl (methyl 1-(butylcarbamoyl)-2-benzimidazolecarbamate) was intro-

duced in 1967 as an experimental fungicide by E. I. du Pont de Nemours & Co., Inc. (31). It is used as a protective and eradicant fungicide, particularly in annual crops, and is effective against a broad range of fungi, particularly on fruit, including apple scab and powdery mildew, and against mites, primarily as an ovicide. It is a white crystalline nonvolatile solid with a faint acrid odor. It is insoluble in water and oil. It is marketed as a wettable powder containing 50% active ingredient under the trade name Benlate.

ANALYSIS OF BENOMYL

Benomyl residues in plant and animal tissues and in soil can be determined by extraction, conversion to 2-aminobenzimidazole, and measurement by direct fluorometry or by colorimetry after bromination (32). Either method gives a sensitivity of 0.1 ppm based on a 50-g sample and an average recovery of 87%.

Procedure

Place 50 g of sample in a blender jar, add 150 ml of ethyl acetate, and blend at high speed for 5–10 min. Transfer the sample to a 250-ml centrifuge bottle, rinsing the blender jar with several small portions of ethyl acetate. Centrifuge at 2000 rpm for 10–15 min and decant the ethyl acetate extract through cotton into a 400-ml beaker. Rinse the blender jar with 100 ml of ethyl acetate and add to the centrifuge bottle. Shake vigorously for 2–3 min and centrifuge as before, combining the ethyl acetate extracts. Repeat the extraction procedure with 100 ml of ethyl acetate. Add 25 ml of 0.1 N hydrochloric acid to the combined ethyl acetate extracts. Place on a steam bath in a hood and evaporate to a volume of 10–15 ml. After evaporation, carefully wash down the sides of the beaker with small volumes of hot water, totaling approximately 15 ml, and transfer to a 125-ml separatory funnel. Cool to room temperature and add 50 ml of n-hexane. Shake for 2 min and allow the phases to separate, centrifuging if necessary for clean separation. Discard the hexane layer, and repeat the hexane wash twice more, discarding the hexane layer each time.

Transfer the aqueous phase to a 150-ml beaker, rinsing with small portions of water; the total volume is now about 40 ml. Add 15 ml of 6.5 N sodium hydroxide solution, cover, and boil gently on a hot plate for 15 min, using a glass rod to prevent bumping. While hot, wash the cover glass, stirring rod, and sides of the beaker with small portions of hot water. Carefully transfer the contents of the beaker to a 250-ml separatory funnel, rinsing with several small portions of water. Cool to room temperature and extract the aqueous hydrolyzate with four 75-ml portions of ethyl acetate, shaking for 2–3 min each time. After separation of the layers, filter the ethyl acetate through cotton into a 400-ml beaker. Concentrate to about 50 ml by evaporation at room temperature under a hood. Transfer the contents of the beaker to a 125-ml separatory funnel, rinsing with small portions of ethyl acetate. Finally, rinse the beaker with 10 ml of 0.1 N hydrochloric acid and add to the separatory funnel. Shake for 2 min. After the phases separate, drain the aqueous phase into a second 125-ml separatory funnel. Check the aqueous phase with pHydrion paper to verify that it is acidic and, if necessary, add 1 ml of N hydrochloric acid. Extract the ethyl acetate with a second 10-ml portion of 0.1 N hydrochloric acid and combine the acid phases.

Add 2 ml of 6.5 N sodium hydroxide solution to the combined acid extract and check with pHydrion paper to verify that the solution is now strongly basic. Extract with four 50-ml portions of water-saturated ethyl acetate, shaking for 2–3 min each time. After phase separation, filter the ethyl acetate extract through cotton into a 250-ml beaker. Evaporate in a hood to a volume of about 20 ml. Transfer quantitatively to a 50-ml beaker and continue evaporation to dryness. The sample is now ready for determination by one or both of the following methods. Determination should be made promptly after extraction.

Fluorometric Determination. Dissolve the residue in 9:1 methanol–aqueous 0.1 N sodium hydroxide solution. Transfer quantitatively to a 10-ml volumetric flask, washing with several small portions of the methanol–base mixture. Dilute to volume and mix. Determine the fluorescence of the solution at 335 nm, with an excitation wavelength of 285 nm. Compare the reading with a calibration curve prepared by measuring the fluorescence of 5, 10, 20, 30, and 50 μg of 2-aminobenzimidazole in 10 ml of 9:1 methanol–0.1 N sodium hydroxide solution. Determine the quenching factor on one or more control samples from each sample series by adding a known amount of 2-aminobenzimidazole to the untreated sample extract and comparing the relative intensity with the value obtained on a standard solution of the same apparent concentration. Calculate the benomyl content according to the following formula:

$$\text{Benomyl, ppm} = \frac{(c)(2.18)}{(q)(r)(w)}$$

where c = 2-aminobenzimidazole content in μg obtained from the calibration curve

q = quenching factor

r = recovery factor

w = sample weight, in g

Colorimetric Determination. Add 10 ml of saturated bromine water to the residue, cover, and place on a steam bath for 30 min. Uncover, and leave on steam bath until excess bromine is completely eliminated as determined by absence of odor. Transfer quantitatively to a 125-ml separatory funnel, rinsing with several small portions of hot water. Cool and dilute to 30 ml with water. Finally, rinse the residue beaker with 25 ml of water-saturated ethyl acetate. Add the rinsings to the separatory funnel and shake vigorously for 3–4 min. After phase separation, filter the ethyl acetate through cotton into a 50-ml beaker. Repeat the wash and extraction, using a second 25-ml portion of water-saturated ethyl acetate. Concentrate the combined extracts to a volume of about 1 ml and transfer to a 2-ml volumetric flask using a dropper and rinse the beaker with several small volumes of ethyl acetate. Dilute to volume and mix. Measure the absorbance at 445 nm, using semimicro quartz cells having a 10-mm light path versus ethyl acetate as a reference. Determine the 2-aminobenzimidazole content from a calibration curve prepared by carrying 5, 10, 20, 30, and 50 μg of the standard through the bromination procedure.

$$\text{Benomyl, ppm} = \frac{(c)(2.18)}{(r)(w)}$$

Glyodin

Glyodin (2-heptadecyl-2-imidazoline acetate) is a protective foliar fungicide used

primarily for the control of fruit diseases (33). It is prepared by reacting ethyl stearate with ethylenediamine to give *N*-2-aminoethyl monostearamide; water is then eliminated by heating, which results in a closure of the ring (34). It forms light orange crystals, which are soft and waxy and melt at 62–68°C. The free base melts at 94°C. It is soluble in 2-propanol or propylene glycol and insoluble in water. It is readily hydrolyzed under alkaline conditions to the monostearamide. It is compatible with most pesticides, but should not be used with oils or emulsifiable formulations. The acute oral LD_{50} to rats is 1300 mg/kg. It is marketed as a wettable powder containing 70% active ingredient as the free base and as a 2-propanol solution containing 30% active ingredient. Trade names are "Crag" Fruit Fungicide 341, Glyoxide, and Glyoxalidine. The activity of several analogs has also been investigated, but the fungicidal efficacy increased to a maximum as the aliphatic chain was lengthened to C_{17}.

ANALYSIS OF GLYODIN

Glyodin residues on fruit are determined by reaction with bromocresol purple and colorimetric measurement (35).

Procedure

Prepare the extraction tubes by sealing a No. 2 standard taper stopcock fitting to the end of 625-mm lengths of 32-mm glass tubing. Make four lateral indentations in the bottom of each tube to support a small plug of glass wool.

Prepare the bromocresol purple indicator solution by dissolving 0.100 ± 0.020 g of Eastman Kodak 5',5"-dibromocresolsulfonephthalein and 50 g of anhydrous sodium sulfate in 1 liter of water and shake until all of the indicator is in solution.

Cut samples of fruit of suitable size to fit in the tube. Ideally, 100–200 g of sample should be analyzed. The method is applicable to the analysis of samples containing 5.0–830 μg of the fungicide which is equivalent to 0.05–8.3 ppm for a 100-g sample. For samples containing higher concentrations, dilute the extract as necessary. After placing the sample in the tube, close the stopcock and extract by percolating 150 ml of chloroform over the sample three times with the stopcock half open. Filter the chloroform extract through Whatman No. 1 paper into a 500-ml graduated separatory funnel. Adjust the volume to 150 ml with chloroform. Add 100 ml of the indicator solution and shake vigorously. Allow to stand for 15 min at room temperature and then separate the chloroform layer into which the indicator has been extracted. Determine the absorbance at 410 nm. Prepare a reagent blank by shaking 150 ml of chloroform with 100 ml of the indicator. Determine the glyodin content present from a standard curve. Correction should be made for any absorbance of blanks prepared from control fruit.

CHLOROTHIODICARBOXIMIDES

Captan

Captan (N-trichloromethylthio-4-cyclohexene-1,2-dicarboximide, or N-trichloromethyl thiocyclohex-4-ene-1,2-dicarboximide) is a chlorinated compound first intro-

duced in 1949 by Chevron Chemical Company (Ortho Division of Standard Oil of California) for use primarily as a general purpose protective fungicide. It forms white crystals which melt at 172–175°C. It is soluble in ethylene dichloride or chloroform, partially soluble in acetone, benzene, or toluene, and soluble to the extent of 0.5 ppm in water. It is unstable under alkaline conditions, but it is compatible with most pesticides. The acute oral LD_{50} to rats is 10,000 mg/kg and to rabbits 3000 mg/kg. It has been reported that captan has some mutagenic activity when ingested into chicken eggs. It is marketed as a wettable powder containing 50% active ingredient, as dusts containing 5, 7.5, 10, and 20% active ingredient, and as a powder for seed treatment containing 75% active ingredient. The trade name is Orthocide. It is commonly mixed with other pesticides.

Difolatan

Difolatan (tetrachloroethylmercaptocyclohexenedicarboximide) was developed as a fungicide by the Ortho Division of Standard Oil of California (36). It is prepared by reacting ammonia and tetrahydrophthalic anhydride to form the imide which is then reacted with 1,1,2,2-tetrachloroethyl sulfonyl chloride. It forms white crystals which melt at 160–161°C, decomposing slowly at this temperature. It is slightly soluble in organic solvents and insoluble in water. It is stable under average storage conditions and in neutral and slightly alkaline solutions, but unstable in highly alkaline solutions. It is compatible with most pesticides. The acute oral LD_{50} to rats in 4600 mg/kg. It is commercially available as a wettable powder containing 80% active ingredient.

Folpet

Folpet (N-trichloromethylthiophthalimide) is a fairly broad spectrum foliar and

soil fungicide. It is remarkably nontoxic and is sometimes used for control of fungal disease in man. This fungicide was introduced by the Ortho Division of Standard Oil of California (37). It is prepared by reacting sodium phthalic anhydride and perchloromethylmercaptan with vigorous agitation (38). It forms white crystals which melt at 177°C. It is slightly soluble in aliphatic hydrocarbon solvents and insoluble in water. It is stable when dry but hydrolyzes slowly in water at room temperature and rapidly at high temperatures or under alkaline conditions. It is slightly phytotoxic to some crops when temperatures and humidity are high. It is compatible with most pesticides. The acute oral LD_{50} to rats is 10,000 mg/kg. It is marketed as wettable powders containing 50 and 75% active ingredient and as dusts containing 5 and 10% active ingredient. The trade name is Phalthan.

ANALYSIS OF CHLOROTHIODICARBOXIMIDES

Resorcinol Colorimetric Method. Captan or folpet reacts with resorcinol to give a yellow color which can be measured colorimetrically and is stable up to 24 hr. There are few interferences and the method is sensitive to as little as 5–10 μg of captan (37). If captan and folpet are both present, they can be separated by liquid chromatography on a silicic acid column.

Procedure

SAMPLE PREPARATION. Avoid high temperatures, alkaline conditions, and traces of water during the extraction, evaporation, and color development steps. Place a weighed sample in a jar and cover with a measured amount of benzene. Shake gently for 15–30 min and then filter through a folded paper containing a small amount of anhydrous sodium sulfate. For plant tissue samples, grind the sample and extract by shaking with 4 ml of benzene/g of sample for 30–60 min. Persistent emulsions may be treated with sodium sulfate. For blood or other biological solutions, extract with successive portions of carbon tetrachloride and condense the combined extracts by evaporation.

If fats are present, evaporate the extract to dryness. Dissolve the residue in hexane or heptane, remove an appropriate aliquot, and evaporate to 30 ml. Then extract with two 15-ml portions of acetonitrile containing 4 ml of acetic anhydride in 100 ml. Wash the combined extract with 10 ml of heptane or hexane. If the acetonitrile extract possesses any natural color, remove it by passing through a small column packed with 1 g of activated carbon.

SEPARATION OF CAPTAN AND FOLPET. Use a chromatography tube with a 15–20 cm stem and 25 mm OD. Partially fill with hexane and add 20 g of silicic acid. Prewash the column with two 50-ml portions of acetone, two 50-ml portions of ethyl ether, and two 50-ml portions of hexane. Stir the column with a glass rod to prevent formation of cracks and add a 1-cm layer of washed sand to the top. Percolate the sample extract in hexane solution through the column and then wash with four 50-ml portions of hexane discarding the washings. Elute folpet with six 50-ml portions of 1:3 ethyl ether–hexane. Then elute captan with four 50-ml portions of 1:1 ethyl ether–hexane.

COLORIMETRIC DETERMINATION. Evaporate the sample extract to dryness under vacuum and dissolve the residue in 5 ml or less of benzene. Transfer to a 50-ml test tube and add 4 ml of resorcinol solution containing 25 g in 100 ml of absolute ethyl ether. Place the tube in an oil bath, which is agitated and maintained at 143 ± 2°C. After 25 min, add 5 ml of glacial acetic acid, cool, and dilute to 25 ml, or more if color is too intense, with acetic acid. Use the same dilution for the reference blank. Measure the absorbance at 428 nm. Determine the captan or folpet content from a calibration curve of 0, 5, 10, 20, 30, and 50 ppm of standard sample.

Thin-Layer Chromatography. Captan, folpet, difolatan, and their degradation products can be determined by thin-layer chromatography on silica gel G plates, using 1% methanol in chloroform as the developing solvent (39).

Procedure

Coat silica gel G on 20 × 20 cm glass plates to a thickness of 250 μm and activate the plates by heating for 1 hr at 95–100°C. Store the activated plates in the presence of a desiccant until used. Line the developing tank with blotting paper, add the 1% methanol in chloroform developing solvent, and allow the tank to equilibrate for 30 min. Spot the sample extracts to allow development perpendicular to the direction of coat application. Develop the plates and air dry.

Table 1. Spray Reagents[a]

Compound	Permanganate	Resorcinol	DMPD	Chromic acid
captan	(0.2)	(1)		
folpet	(1)	(1)		
difolatan	(0.2)		(0.2)	
captan epoxide	(1)	(1)		
difolatan epoxide	(1)		(0.2)	
tetrahydrophthalimide	(0.5)			
phthalimide				(1)
tetrahydrophthalimide epoxide				(1–2)
				(1–2)

[a] Detection limits are given in parentheses, in μg. If no limits are indicated, there is no color development.

Apply the following spray reagents: (1) Aqueous potassium permanganate solution containing 1.5 g/25 ml diluted 1:99 with acetone results in a pink adsorbent layer, (2) resorcinol solution in glacial acetic acid containing 15 g/100 ml, (3) dimethyl-p-phenylenediamine (DMPD) solution prepared just before using by dissolving 0.25 g in a solution of 0.7 g of sodium hydroxide in 50 ml of absolute methanol, and (4) 10 g of potassium dichromate dissolved in 80 ml of concentrated sulfuric acid and diluted to 200 ml with water gives a yellow color to the adsorbent. Heating is required to develop spots with resorcinol (10–15 min at 110°C) and chromic acid (20–25 min at 130°C). The responses and limits of detection are shown in Table 1.

Gas Chromatography. Captan, folpet, difolatan, and selected degradation products can be determined by gas chromatography using two columns and electron capture detection. The operating conditions are as follows:

columns	1.8 m × 4 mm ID, packed
column packing	
column 1	20 wt % DC-200 methyl silicone on 80/100 mesh Gas Chrom Q, conditioned for 3 days at 250°C
column 2	15% QF-1 trifluoropropyl methyl silicone and 10% DC-200 on 100/120 mesh Gas Chrom Q, conditioned as column 1
temperature	
of injection port	225°C
of column 1	210°C
of column 2	200°C
of detector, for column 1	220°C
of detector, for column 2	200°C
carrier gas and flow rate	nitrogen, 120 ml/min

The relative retention times are as follows.

Compound	Column 1	Column 2
captan	1.00	1.00
folpet	1.06	0.97
difolatan	2.60	2.53
captan epoxide	2.20	3.32
difolatan epoxide	5.95	8.64
tetrahydrophthalimide	0.13	0.15
phthalimide	0.13	0.16
tetrahydrophthalimide	0.31	0.58

OXATHIINS

Carboxin

Carboxin (5,6-dihydro-2-methyl-1,4-oxathiin-3-carboxamilide) is primarily used as a seed treatment. Its action appears to be of a systemic nature and is particularly effective for the control of loose smut of small grains caused by the *Ustilago* species. It is prepared by reacting α-chloroacetoacetanilide and 2-mercaptoethanol, followed by acid-catalyzed cylization–dehydration (40). It is a white solid which melts at 91.5–92.5°C and 98.0–100°C, indicating two crystalline structures which revert to one when in solution. It is soluble in dimethyl sulfoxide, acetone, or methanol, slightly soluble in benzene or ethanol, and to the extent of 170 μg/g in water. It is compatible with all pesticides except highly acidic ones. The acute oral LD_{50} to rats is 3200 mg/kg and to rabbits is 8000 mg/kg. It is marketed as a wettable powder containing 75% active ingredient, a dust containing 10% active ingredient, and as a granular preparation containing 5% active ingredient. The trade name is Vitavax.

Oxycarboxin

Oxycarboxin (5,6-dihydro-2-methyl-1,4-oxathiin-3-carboxamilide-4,4-dioxide) is

an effective systemic fungicide which can be used to treat seed, soil, or foliage (41). This compound is somewhat specific for the control of rust of small grains, vegetables, and ornamentals. At the time of this publication, registration for use was pending. It is prepared by oxidation of 5,6-dihydro-2-methyl-1,4-oxathiin-3-carboxamilide (carboxin) with hydrogen peroxide. It is a white solid which melts at 127.5–130°C. It is soluble in dimethyl sulfoxide or acetone, slightly soluble in methanol or benzene, and very slightly soluble in water. It is compatible with pesticides which are not highly acidic or basic. The acute oral LD_{50} for rats is 2000 mg/kg and for rabbits 16,000 mg/kg. It is marketed as a wettable powder containing 75% active ingredient, as a dust containing 10% active ingredient, and as a granular preparation containing 5% active ingredient. The trade name is Plantvax.

ANALYSIS OF OXATHIINS

Carboxin and oxycarboxin hydrolyze in aqueous caustic to produce aniline, which is distilled and determined colorimetrically with *p*-dimethylaminobenzaldehyde (42). The following method is used to determine residues in green plants, potatoes, sugar beets, cottonseed, and grain meals. Satisfactory results are obtained at the level of 0.1 ppm.

Procedure

To a 2-liter flask add the following amounts of the sample, 50% sodium hydroxide solution, and water:

	Sample, g	50% sodium hydroxide solution, ml	Water, ml
green plants	200	500	100
cottonseed meal	200	400	100
sugar beets	250	400	100
potatoes	250	400	100

The following special cleanup procedure must be used for grain meal samples. Gently reflux 50 g of grain meal with 300 ml of methanol and 10 ml of concentrated hydrochloric acid for 30 min. Cool and filter through Eaton and Dikeman No. 615 paper and cheesecloth. Wring out as much methanol as possible and boil the recovered methanol with water until only 200 ml of water remains as indicated by a thermometer showing constant boiling at 100°C. Filter the cooled water extract through Whatman No. 1 paper into a 1-liter flask and add 300 ml of 50% sodium hydroxide solution and 200 ml of water.

After sample preparation, add to the flask 5 ml of 20% aqueous titanium trichloride solution, 2 g of granular zinc, 1 ml of Antifoam A paste (Dow Corning), and 1 ml of paraffin wax. Clean and coat the flask joint with silicone grease. Attach a distillation apparatus with an "Iowa State" type Kjeldahl spray trap incorporated in the distilling arm. Distill 150 ml into a 250-ml graduated suction flask attached to a slight source of vacuum. Add 5 g of sodium chloride to the distillate and extract with 50 ml of hexane. Retain the aqueous layer and re-extract with 30 ml of benzene. Wash the benzene layer three times with 50 ml of water, then extract with 10 ml of 1% oxalic acid solution. Transfer the extract to a 25-ml mixing cylinder. Add 2 ml of 2% p-dimethylaminobenzaldehyde solution in 1:9 hydrochloric acid and mix well. After 30 min, add 3 ml of glacial acetic acid and adjust the pH to 3.5 by dropwise addition of 50% sodium hydroxide solution. Adjust the volume to 16 ml with water. The color remains stable for several hours. If any fogginess is noted in the samples, filter through Whatman No. 1 paper before measuring the color.

Measure the absorbance of the samples in 5-ml cuvets against reagent blanks at 440 and 490 nm. The absorbance at 480 nm is used to correct for interferences. Determine the carboxin or oxycarboxin content from a calibration curve prepared by carrying 20, 40, 60, and 80 μg of a standard sample through the distillation, extraction, and color development procedure, as for the samples.

CHLORINATED AND NITRATED BENZENES

Terraclor

Terraclor (pentachloronitrobenzene) is chiefly a soil fungicide, but is commonly

used as a seed treatment and postemergence combination foliar and soil treatment. It is manufactured by the chlorination of nitrobenzene in chlorosulfuric acid at 60–70°C in the presence of iodine as a catalyst. It forms colorless crystalline needles which melt at 146°C and boil at 328°C with slight decomposition. The melting point of technical grade material is 142–143°C. It is soluble in aromatic and chlorinated hydrocarbons, ketones, or carbon disulfide, and almost insoluble in ethanol or water. It is stable to heat and acid and hydrolyzes to nitrite and pentachlorophenol in alkaline solution. It is highly stable in soil, and is compatible with all pesticides at pH 7 or less. The acute oral LD_{50} to rats is 30,000 mg/kg. Terraclor is marketed as a wettable powder containing 75% active ingredient, as an emulsifiable concentrate containing 2 lb/gal, and as dusts containing 10, 20 or 50% active ingredient. Under the trade name Brassicol it is marketed as a wettable powder containing 50 or 75% active ingredient, as an emulsifiable concentrate containing 20% active ingredient, and as a dust containing 20% active ingredient. Other trade names include PCNB, Folosan, Batrilex, Tilearex, Tritisan, and Turf-Tect.

ANALYSIS OF TERRACLOR

Colorimetric Method. Terraclor residues are determined by hydrolysis with ethanolic potassium hydroxide solution to nitrite. Nitrite diazotizes procaine hydrochloride and the diazonium salt is then coupled with 1-naphthylamine to give a magenta solution (43). The procedure will detect 10 μg of terraclor and is sensitive to 0.02 ppm. Beer's law is followed in the range of 10–50 μg. Tetrachloronitrobenzene interferes.

Procedure

Prewash petroleum ether with 1:1 hydrochloric acid, wash with water until neutral, and then dry over anhydrous sodium sulfate. Prepare Celite 545 by heating as a slurry with 1:1 hydrochloric acid for 10 min on a steam bath; cool, wash with water until neutral, and dry at 100°C. Prepare the magnesium oxide–Hyflo Super-Cel adsorbent mixture as follows: Heat magnesium oxide (Westvaco No. 2641) at 200°C for 1 hr and cool in a sealed jar. Combine 6 ml of water/100 g of magnesium oxide by grinding in a mortar and then mix in a sealed jar for 30 min. Add an equal volume of Hyflo Super-Cel and mix for 30 min. Age for 24 hr before use and discard after 4 days. Also prepare an adsorbent mixture of magnesium oxide and Celite 545 in the same way.

For crops such as lettuce, tomatoes, green beans, peppers, potatoes, and celery, blend 200 g of a sample with 250–300 ml of methylene chloride. Separate the solvent with a basket centrifuge using Whatman No. 2 filter paper and repeat the extraction on the pulp and paper matrix. Collect the aqueous material in a separatory funnel and wash with methylene chloride. Combine all methylene chloride extracts and dry with anhydrous sodium sulfate. Transfer the extract to a 150-ml pear-shaped acetylization flask and evaporate on a hot water bath. Evaporate to dryness with a stream of clean dry air, add 25 ml of petroleum ether, and reflux for 15 min. Use a 30 × 280 mm chromatographic column with a medium porosity filter disc and a vacuum side arm at the base. Pack the column with 2 cm of anhydrous sodium sulfate, 6 cm of magnesium oxide–Hyflo Super-Cel adsorbent, and 2 cm of anhydrous sodium sulfate. Prewash the column with 100 ml of petroleum ether, deliver the extract to the column, and collect the filtrate in a 150-ml acetylization flask. Add four 25-ml portions of petroleum ether, adding each as the previous one reaches the upper sodium sulfate layer. Concentrate the filtrate to 5 ml and proceed with the color development.

For forage crops with high wax and fat content, such as alfalfa, clover, and timothy, air-dry the sample and tumble 300 g with 1800 ml of *n*-hexane in an 80-oz jar for 45 min. Decant through a gauze filter, dry with sodium sulfate, and swirl with 10 g of a mixture of equal volumes of Celite 545 and Attaclay. Take a 900-ml aliquot, evaporate, and place in a 150-ml acetylization flask. Add 25 ml of petroleum ether and reflux for 15 min. Use a jacketed 30 × 280 mm chromatographic column and pack with 2 cm of anhydrous sodium sulfate, 3 cm of magnesium oxide–Celite 545 adsorbent mixture, and 2 cm of anhydrous sodium sulfate. Circulate methanol through the coils and place the column in a methylene dichloride–dry ice bath. Cool to −10°C and prewash the column with 100 ml of petroleum ether. Add 2 g of Celite 545 to the extract, swirl, and add to the column. After allowing the column to cool so that the waxes and fats solidify on the Celite, use positive pressure to force the extract into the column packing. Follow with four 25-ml aliquots of petroleum ether allowing the column to cool each time before forcing the extract into the packing. Concentrate the filtrate to 5 ml and proceed with the color reaction. After the color reagent is added, the solution should be heated to 80°C for a few minutes to liberate nitrogen from the waxes.

For materials such as cottonseed, which have a very high oil content, add 200 ml of petroleum ether to 100 g of finely ground sample and blend for 5 min. Filter through an asbestos pad, rinse thoroughly, and collect the filtrate in a 1-liter separatory funnel. Add 50 ml of concentrated sulfuric acid, mix, and allow 15 min for separation. Allow the sludge to fall and wash the aqueous layer with two 100-ml portions of petroleum ether. Combine the extracts and wash with water, 2% aqueous sodium bicarbonate solution, and water again until the washings are neutral. Dry the petroleum ether with sodium sulfate, evaporate to 5 ml, and continue with the color reaction. Check the pH before hydrolysis, as entrained acid may necessitate the use of more ethanolic potassium hydroxide solution.

Prepare the color reagent as follows: Dissolve 0.350 g of 1-naphthylamine in 88 ml of glacial acetic acid. Add 200 ml of water, and 7.500 g of procaine hydrochloride and dilute to 1 liter with water. Store in dark bottle in the cold. Prepare a series of standard solutions of terraclor in petroleum ether with concentrations of 2–10 ppm. Transfer a 5-ml aliquot of each standard and sample solution to 150-ml acetylization flasks. Also prepare reagent blanks. To each flask add 2 ml of 0.5 N ethanolic potassium hydroxide solution and 1 ml of acetone. Heat exactly 7 min at 80 ± 0.1°C with the flask immersed only ¼–½ in. Cool, add by pipet 20 ml of color reagent, and adjust the pH to 2–2.5 with concentrated hydrochloric acid. Add 25 ml of petroleum ether, stopper, and place on a shaker for 15 min. Transfer to a 60-ml separatory funnel and pass the aqueous layer through a 1 cm × 1 cm column of Celite 545. Collect the filtrate in a test tube and measure the absorbance of the solution in a 5-cm cell at 525 nm. Prepare a calibration curve of the values obtained on the standard solutions.

Polarographic Method. Terraclor residues in alfalfa–clover–Bird's foot trefoil forage are extracted with Skellysolve B and interferences are removed by chromatography on Attaclay and Florisil. The solvent is then evaporated and the residue dissolved in 2-propanol. Sodium acetate and acetic acid are added as the supporting electrolyte and the polarogram is recorded from 0.00 to −1.15 V versus a saturated calomel electrode (44). The half-wave potential for terraclor is −0.47 V, but a shift to about −0.53 V occurs during analyses of forage crops.

Dicloran

Dicloran (2,6-dichloro-4-nitroaniline) was introduced in 1959 by Boots Pure

Drug Co. as an experimental fungicide (45). It is particularly effective against Botrytis and is frequently used as a postharvest spray to control fruit rots of strawberry and stone fruits. It has very little effect upon spore germination and appears to act by intervening with cell division of hyphal growth. Dichloran is prepared by chlorination of p-nitroaniline (46). It is a crystalline solid which melts at 192–194°C. It is moderately soluble in acetone or methanol, slightly soluble in hexane or benzene, and insoluble in water. It is stable to oxidation and hydrolysis and is compatible with most other pesticides. The acute oral LD_{50} to rats is 10,000 mg/kg. It is marketed as a wettable powder containing 50% active ingredient and as dusts containing 4 and 8% active ingredient. The trade name is Botran.

Analysis of Dicloran

Colorimetric Method. Dicloran residues in plant materials can be determined from the deep yellow color which is characteristic of some mononitroaromatic compounds in the presence of strong alkali and acetone (47,48).

Procedure

Mix Florisil with sufficient water so that when 750 μg of dicloran in 15 ml of benzene is applied to the column, it moves through the column at such a rate that none is eluted with the first 100 ml of benzene and all is eluted in the following 300 ml.

Blend 60 g of macerated plant material with 180 ml of water-saturated benzene for 30–60 sec, depending on the firmness of the plant tissue. Centrifuge and withdraw 120 ml of supernatant. Evaporate to dryness and transfer the residue to a 100-ml mixing cylinder by dissolving it in successive portions of mutually saturated acetonitrile and petroleum ether so that a total of 50 ml of each solvent is used. Mix, remove the upper layer by pipet, and transfer the lower layer to the flask which contained the original residue. Evaporate the solvent and dissolve the residue in 3–5 ml of benzene. Transfer to a 19 mm $\times$ 28 cm column of Florisil. Add benzene to the column and discard the first 50 ml of eluent. Collect the next 300 ml of eluent and evaporate to dryness. Dissolve the residue in acetone and dilute to 5 ml. If insoluble material is present, drop a small piece of glass wool into the flask and withdraw the solution by pressing the pipet against this filter. Pipet 3 ml of the solution into a stoppered cuvet and measure the absorbance at 464 nm versus acetone. Add 2 drops of 4% potassium hydroxide solution to each cuvet and again measure the absorbance at the same wavelength. Determine the dicloran content from a calibration curve prepared from standard solutions containing 1–25 μg per 5 ml of acetone and using the difference in the two readings at 464 nm.

The distribution ration of dicloran between acetonitrile and petroleum ether is 20:1. Therefore the combined correction factor for aliquot of stripping solvent taken and for loss of dicloran in the solvent partition step is 1:58.

Gas Chromatography. Dicloran can also be determined by gas chromatography (49), using an electron capture detector. The benzene extract of the plant material, obtained as described in the previous colorimetric method, is injected directly without prior purification. The operating conditions are as follows:

column	$\frac{1}{8}$ in. $\times$ 5 ft glass, packed
column packing	5 wt % DC-11 silicone grease on acid-washed 60/80 mesh Chromosorb W
column temperature	185°C, isothermal
carrier gas	nitrogen at approximately 12 psig inlet pressure

The retention time for dicloran is about 4 min and the response is linear in the range of 40–400 $\times$ 10^{-12} g.

Chloroneb

Chloroneb (1,4-dichloro-2,5-dimethoxybenzene) is highly effective against seed-

ling diseases caused by *Rhizoctonia*, *Pythium*, and others (50,51). It is a white crystalline solid which melts at 133–135°C and boils at 268°C and is stable to the boiling point. It is moderately soluble in methylene chloride, dimethylformamide, acetone, or xylene, and soluble in water to the extent of 8 ppm at 25°C. It is stable in water, in the common organic solvents, and in dilute alkali and acid. It is compatible with most pesticides but not for use on foliage. The acute oral LD$_{50}$ for male or female rats is greater than 11,000 mg/kg. It is marketed as a wettable powder containing 65% active ingredient and as a dust containing 10% active ingredient. The trade name is Demosan.

ANALYSIS OF CHLORONEB

Chloroneb and a metabolite, 2,5-dichloro-4-methoxyphenol, are separated from soil and plant and animal tissues by stream distillation, extracted from the distillate with hexane, and determined by gas chromatography using programmed column temperature and a selective microcoulometric detector (52). Recoveries are about 90% and the method is sensitive to 0.02 ppm

Procedure

Place 50 and 100 g of soil, plant, or animal tissue sample in a 2-liter round-bottom flask. Add several boiling chips, 2–3 ml of Dow Corning Antifoam A, and 1 liter of 5 N phosphoric acid. Fill the U-tube of a distillation extraction head with water to the level of the lower arm and attach the flask to the lower arm. Add 400 ml of n-hexane and 1 boiling chip to a 1-liter flask and attach to the upper arm. Place a 24 in. water-cooled condenser on top of the head and apply heat to both flasks at such a rate that condensed hexane and water pass through the capillary in the form of small droplets. Continue the extraction for a minimum of 12 hr.

Upon completion of the extraction, remove the grease from the neck of the 1-liter flask and quantitatively transfer the hexane to a 600-ml beaker. Wash the flask several times with hexane and add the washings to the 600-ml beaker. Evaporate the hexane at room temperature in a hood to a volume of approximately 40 ml. Transfer the hexane solution to a 50-ml beaker and further evaporate to approximately 4 ml. Do not allow the solvent to evaporate to dryness because chloroneb and its metabolite are lost by volatility. Quantitatively transfer the hexane solution to a 5-ml volumetric flask, dilute to volume with hexane, and mix. Analyze the solution by gas chromatography using the following operating conditions:

column	4 ft $\times$ $\frac{3}{8}$ in. ID, packed
column packing	10 wt % DC-560 phenyl methyl silicone oil plus 0.2 wt % Epon 1001 epoxl resin on 80–100 mesh acid-washed and dimethyldichlorosilane-treated Chromosorb W; conditioned at 200°C for at least 72 hr before use
temperature	
of injection port	240°C
of column	100°C for 2 min, then programmed at 10°C/min to 180°C and held there isothermally until the end of the analysis
carrier gas	helium
flow rate through column	80 ml/min
purge flow rate	50 ml/min
detector	microcoulometer
furnace temperature	880°C
oxygen flow	50 ml/min
sample volume	100 μl for samples containing 0.4–1.0 μg/ml; smaller samples for higher concentrations
retention times	
chloroneb	10.7 min
the metabolite	9.3 min

Chloroneb can also be analyzed on a column containing 5 wt % XE-60 cyano-ethyl methyl silicone as the stationary phase, by using similar chromatographic conditions. However, the separation of interfering materials is not as complete and only 80% of the metabolite is recovered.

Dinocap

Dinocap (2-(1-methylheptyl)-4,6-dinitrophenyl crotonate) was first used for control

of apple scab but was later found to be highly effective for the control of mildew and mites. It is prepared by the nitration of the condensation product of phenol and capryl alcohol and esterification with crotonyl chloride (53). It is a dark brown liquid which boils at 138–140°C. It is soluble in most organic solvents but insoluble in water. Dinocap is compatible with most other fungicides and insecticides but incompatible with oil, oil-based sprays, and lime–sulfur mixtures. The acute oral LD_{50} to mammals is 2000 mg/kg, to male rats 980 mg/kg, and to female rats 1190 mg/kg. It is marketed as a wettable powder containing 22.5% active ingredient, as a dust containing 1.2 or 5% active ingredient, or as an emulsifiable concentrate containing 4 lb of active ingredient per gal. Other trade names are Karathane, Mildex, Arathane, and Isocothan. It is also marketed as a formulation with Dithane M-45 under the trade name Dikar.

Analysis of Dinocap

Dinocap is extracted with mixed hexanes, purified by either liquid chromatography or washing with sulfuric acid, and determined colorimetrically in N,N-dimethylformamide solution (54).

Procedure

Place 500 g of macerated tissue in a 1-gal tin equipped with a metal baffle and add 1 liter of mixed hexanes (bp 60–80°C). Use a rolling apparatus to extract the sample. Decant the extract into a beaker containing 200 g of anhydrous sodium sulfate and mix thoroughly. Then filter through fluted filter paper.

Purify the extracts by either of the following methods: (*1*) Prepare column containing 20 g of Florisil and prerinse with 50 ml of 6% ethyl ether in mixed hexanes. Pass 100-ml aliquot of the sample extract through the column and follow by rinses of 50, 100 and 150-ml portions of 6% ethyl ether in mixed hexanes. Discard the 50-ml rinse and collect the other two. (*2*) Add 20 ml of concentrated sulfuric acid to a 100- to 200-ml aliquot of the sample extract in a 500-ml separatory funnel. Shake gently for 3 min, allow the phases to separate, and discard the acid (lower) phase. Wash the upper phase with four 50-ml portions of water, discarding the water phase each time. Pass the remaining solution through a 2.5 × 25 cm column containing 100 g of anhydrous sodium sulfate. Rinse the separatory funnel with two 50-ml portions of mixed hexanes and add to column. Finally rinse the column with one 50-ml portion of mixed hexanes and add this to the column effluent.

After purification, evaporate under reduced pressure in a rotating evaporator with the flask partially immersed in a 40–50°C water bath. Dissolve the residue in 4 ml of N,N-dimethylformamide. Allow to stand for 20 min and then filter the solution through glass wool into a cuvet. Measure the absorbance at 440 nm versus that of N,N-dimethylformamide.

Prepare a calibration curve using solutions of dinocap in mixed hexanes containing 5–50 ppm. Evaporate and add 4 ml of N,N-dimethylformamide as for the sample. Beer's law is obeyed up to 50 μg of dinocap. Using chromatographic purification, the average recovery from treated fruits is 88.6%; the sulfuric acid wash method yields an average recovery of 90%.

Dexon

Dexon (*p*-dimethylaminobenzenediazo sodium sulfonate) is used for seed treat-

ment and turf diseases, and especially for *Pythium* (55). It is also effective against collar rot of apples (56). It is prepared by reacting sodium sulfite with diazotized *p*-aminodimethylaniline (55). It is a yellowish brown powder which is soluble in water, dimethylformamide, or ethanol, and insoluble in ethyl ether, benzene, or petroleum oils. It is stable in alkali media. The acute oral LD_{50} to rats is 60 mg/kg, and to guinea pigs 150 mg/kg. It is marketed as a wettable powder containing 70% active ingredient and as a granular formulation containing 5% active ingredient. It is also available as a wettable powder containing 35% each of Dexon and Terraclor.

Analysis of Dexon

Dexon residues in crop and seed samples are determined by reacting Dexon with resorcinol to form a fat soluble compound which is measured colorimetrically (57). The method detects 0.05–0.25 ppm of Dexon and recoveries are usually 75–100%.

Procedure

Grind approximately ½ lb of plant material in a Hobart food chopper or equivalent with an equal weight of dry ice. Store the material in a freezer for 16–20 hr so that the dry ice can sublime. Weigh approximately 100 g of the frozen material and transfer to a blender jar. Add a 1% sodium sulfite solution, 150 ml for most tissue samples, 250 ml for dried corn or sorghum, or 300 ml for sugar cane and blend the mixture at high speed for 2 min. For cottonseed samples, grind on a Wiley mill, weigh 25 g of sample, and blend with 100 ml of benzene and 200 ml of 1% sodium sulfite solution. Transfer the slurry of plant material to a cellulose dialysis tube which has been soaked prior to use for 5 min in 1% sodium sulfite solution. Fill the tubing one half full with the slurry and place in a 2-qt screw-capped glass bottle containing 600 ml of 1% sodium sulfite solution. Add approximately 5 drops of toluene as a preservative and cover the bottle with aluminum foil to prevent photodecomposition of the Dexon. Dialyze the slurry for 16–20 hr at room temperature. Measure the solution outside the dialysis tubing in a 1-liter graduated cylinder, quantitatively transfer to a shallow glass refrigerator tray, and place in a bath of chopped ice. For seeds, transfer the dialyzate to a 1-liter separatory funnel, add 100 ml of benzene, shake vigorously for 30 sec and allow the phases to separate; transfer the lower aqueous phase to a 1-liter graduated cylinder and then to a refrigerator tray. While stirring, add 15 ml of 4 M resorcinol solution to the cold dialyzate and then 25 ml of 4 N potassium hydroxide solution. Irradiate the solution in the tray for 30 min with two 150 W spotlights held 7 or 8 in. above the liquid surface. Transfer the solution to a 1-liter separatory funnel and add 60 ml of 0.6 M potassium dihydrogen phosphate solution and 30 ml of 4 N hydrochloric acid. Shake to mix thoroughly and then add 100 ml of benzene. Shake the mixture vigorously for 60 sec and allow the phases to separate. Slowly draw off and discard the lower aqueous phase. Transfer the benzene extract and any emulsion to a 250-ml centrifuge bottle and centrifuge at 1100 G for 5 min. Filter through a small pad of glass wool into a 250-ml separatory funnel and again separate and discard the aqueous phase. Measure the benzene extract, transfer to a 250-ml separatory funnel, and add 25 ml of N potassium hydroxide solution. Shake the mixture vigorously for 30 sec and allow the phases to separate. Draw off the aqueous phase into another 250-ml separatory funnel and repeat the extraction with an additional 25 ml of N potassium hydroxide solution. Discard the benzene solution. Combine the potassium hydroxide extracts and add 25 ml of 0.6 M potassium dihydrogen phosphate solution. Add 25 ml of 2 N hydrochloric acid and 10 ml of benzene and shake the mixture vigorously for 30 sec. Drain and discard the aqueous layer. Transfer the benzene layer to a 25-ml graduated cylinder containing 2–3 g of anhydrous sodium sulfate. Measure the absorbance 450 nm versus a blank prepared as above beginning with the irradiation step.

For the purpose of calculation it is assumed that dry materials do not contribute significantly to the volume of liquid in the dialysis system and that wet plants, such as pineapple, are composed entirely of water. This will result in a slight but relatively insignificant error. Alternatively, a determination of the water content of a separate sample can be made. Determine the Dexon content from a calibration curve prepared by carrying 0.2–0.8 µg standard samples through the procedure.

The Dexon content of formulations can be determined directly in 0.2 M sodium sulfite solution by measuring the absorbance at 435 nm (58).

Dyrene

Dyrene (2,4-dichloro-6-(*o*-chloranilino)-*s*-triazine) is a broad spectrum protective foliar fungicide, and is particularly effective against leaf diseases of tomatoes and potatoes, and dollar spot of turf (59). It is prepared by reacting cyanuric chloride with *o*-chloroaniline in an aqueous solution at 85°C (60). It is a white crystalline solid which melts at 159–160°C. It is soluble in toluene, xylene, or acetone, and insoluble in water. It is stable in neutral and slightly acidic solutions and hydrolyzed by alkali with heating; in N sodium hydroxide solution, the chlorine atoms are removed. It is compatible with most pesticides. The acute oral LD_{50} to female rats is 2710 mg/kg and to rabbits 460 mg/kg. It is marketed as a wettable powder containing 50% active ingredient and as a dust containing 5% active ingredient. The trade name is Kemate.

ANALYSIS OF DYRENE

Dyrene residues in crops are determined by hydrolyzing the Dyrene to form *o*-chloraniline, which is then diazotized and coupled with *N*-1-naphthylenediamine to yield an intense azo dye (61).

Procedure

Freeze the plant sample and then grind with an equal weight of dry ice in a Hobart food chopper. Return the powder to the freezer for 16 hr during which sublimation of the remaining carbon dioxide occurs. Place 100 g of the sample in a blender along with 100 ml of absolute 2-propanol and blend at high speed for 6 min or 15 min for onion tissue. Transfer the contents of the blender to a quart jar and wash the blender with several portions of water to total 400 ml. Add 200 ml of benzene and shake vigorously for 30 min. Centrifuge a portion of the mixture for 15 min to separate phases. Remove 40-ml aliquot of the benzene (upper) phase by pipet, and filter through Whatman No. 41 paper. Wash the filter paper with benzene and add to the filtrate in a 150-ml beaker. Evaporate the benzene to a volume of approximately 2 ml by placing it on a steam bath under a current of air. Wash the residue into a 100-ml volumetric flask with 10 ml of ethanol. For onion extracts an additional rinse with 5 ml of acetone is needed. Add 5 ml of 5 N hydrochloric acid, invert a beaker over the volumetric flask, and reflux for 5 hr on a steam bath. Then add 0.2 g of zinc dust and continue refluxing for 5 min more or until the solution is decolorized. Cool, dilute to 100 ml with water, pour into a beaker, and mix with 1 teaspoonful of filter aid. After 10 min, filter through Whatman No. 12 paper. Pipet two 40-ml aliquots into stoppered 50-ml graduated cylinders containing 1.0 ml of freshly prepared 0.25% sodium nitrite solution. Wait 10 min, then add 1.0 ml of 2.5% aqueous ammonium sulfamate solution. After an additional 10 min, add 2 ml of 1% aqueous *N*-1-naphthylethylenediamine dihydrochloride solution to one of the two cylinders. Dilute both solutions to 50 ml with water and mix thoroughly. After 1 hr measure the absorbance at 540 nm versus a reagent blank.

For more sensitive analysis, the *o*-chloroaniline can be separated by steam distillation after hydrolysis. Add 10 ml of 5 N sodium hydroxide solution to the hydrolyzate in about 10 ml of water. Steam distill into 5 ml of 5 N hydrochloric acid collecting about 50 ml of distillate. Dilute to 100 ml and proceed with the color development as described above.

OTHER FUNGICIDES

Cycloheximide

Cycloheximide (β-(2-(3,5-dimethyl-2-oxocyclohexyl)-2-hydroxyethylglutarimide)

was first isolated by Whiffen (62), who found that it was effective against certain fungi pathogenic to man. It was chemically identified by Leach et al. (63). It is active against many fungi at 100 ppm and recently has been used to induce the formation of the fruit abscission layer in citrus, thus making harvest much easier (64). It is produced by *Streptomyces griseus* and recovered as a by-product of streptomycin manufacture. It forms colorless crystals which melt at 115.5–117°C. Cycloheximide is soluble in chloroform or 2-propanol, and slightly soluble in water. It is stable in acid or neutral solutions but decomposes rapidly in alkaline solutions to form 2,4-dimethylcyclohexanone. It cannot be applied with chlorodane. The acute oral LD_{50} to rats is 2.5 mg/kg, to mice 133 mg/kg, and to monkeys 60 mg/kg. It is commercially available as a wettable powder containing 0.02 wt %, as water soluble tablets, and as a liquid concentrate. The trade name is Actidione.

ANALYSIS OF CYCLOHEXIMIDE

Bioassay. Cycloheximide residues in fruit are determined by extraction with chloroform and bioassay with *Saccharomyces pastorianus* (62,65,66). As little as 0.04 ppm in the fruit can be detected and the estimated average recovery is 75%, having a 95% confidence interval from 62 to 87%.

Procedure

Macerate 500 g of sample in a blender for 2–3 min. Transfer to a 2-liter flask containing 300 ml of chloroform and reflux the mixture for 45 min. Cool and transfer to a separatory funnel. Separate the chloroform layer and evaporate 250 ml to approximately 10 ml on a steam bath. Then evaporate to dryness with a stream of filtered air at room temperature. Suspend the residue in 1 ml of ethanol and dilute to 10 ml with water.

Prepare the assay medium containing 10 g of glucose, 2.5 g of Difco yeast extract, 1.0 g of potassium dihydrogen phosphate, and 20 g of agar in 1 liter of water and adjust to pH 6.0. Suspend the test organism *S. pastorianus* ATCC2366 in a medium containing the same ingredients as the assay medium without agar. Incubate at 37°C on a reciprocating shaker for 18–24 hr and store in a refrigerator. Innoculate the melted assay medium with this culture, pour into plates, and allow to harden. Place four paper discs on each plate and pipet 0.2 ml of the standard or sample onto each disc. Use standard solutions containing 1.5, 2.5, 4.0, and 6.0 μg of cycloheximide per ml in a pH 5.0, 1.0 M phosphate buffer.

Incubate the plates for 15–16 hr at 30°C and then measure the zone diameters to the nearest 0.5 mm. Plot zone diameters for the standards against log concentration. Ferbam and captan were the only other two of several pesticides which resulted in zones of inhibition.

Colorimetric Method. Cycloheximide can be determined by reaction with alkaline hydroxylamine to hydroxamic acid followed by conversion to the highly colored ferric hydroxamate (67). Beer's law is obeyed in the range of 0.2–2.2 mg/ml. Anhydrides, acid chlorides, lactones, esters, high concentrations of carboxyl, transition elements, and ions capable of forming complexes with ferric ion interfere.

Procedure

Prepare ferric perchlorate solution as follows: Mix 800 mg of iron powder with 3 ml of water, add dropwise 10 ml of 70% perchloric acid plus 7 ml of water, and gradually dilute to 100 ml with anhydrous ethanol. Further dilute 40 ml of this stock solution with 12 ml of 70% perchloric acid and 948 ml of anhydrous ethanol.

Weigh 40 g of sample into a 25-ml volumetric flask. Add anhydrous ethanol and dilute to volume. Transfer a 5-ml aliquot to a 50-ml volumetric flask and add 3 ml of 1:1 12.5% methanolic sodium hydroxide solution–12.5% methanolic hydroxylamine hydrochloride solution. Mix and stopper tightly. Immerse the flask in a 50°C water bath for 1 hr. Remove the flask and cool under running tap water with shaking while diluting the solution to approximately 40 ml with ferric perchlorate solution. Store in the absence of light for about 10 min and then add an additional 50 ml of ferric perchlorate solution and mix. Store in the dark if necessary and measure the absorbance at 530 nm within 1 hr. Determine the cycloheximide content from a standard curve prepared simultaneously.

Diphenyl

Diphenyl (biphenyl, phenylbenzene) was first recommended by Ramsey in 1944

(68) for the impregnation of citrus fruit wraps to inhibit the mycelial growth and spore formation of citrus fruit mold. It is prepared by the pyrolytic dehydrogenation of benzene. Diphenyl forms colorless leaflets which melt at 70.5°C and boil at 256.1°C. It is soluble in most organic solvents and insoluble in water. The acute oral LD_{50} to rats is 3280 mg/kg and prolonged exposure to human beings is considered harmful. See also DIPHENYLS AND TERPHENYLS, Vol. 11, pp. 524–537.

ANALYSIS OF DIPHENYL

The diphenyl content of fruit peel is determined by steam distillation followed by thin-layer chromatography and spectrophotometric measurement (69).

Procedure

Peel the fruit and weigh both the peeling and the fruit to determine the peel: fruit ratio. Place the peel in a blender and blend at high speed for 5 min. Take 300 g for extraction. Place in a 1-liter round-bottom flask with a ground-glass joint with enough water to yield a total volume of 500 ml and add a few boiling chips. Use the moisture test apparatus shown in Figure 1. Fill the flask and side arm with water to the overflow point. Place approximately 3 ml of *n*-heptane on top of the water layer and insert the cold finger. Wrap the exposed portion of the flask and the connector arm between the flask and the extraction unit with aluminum foil. Cool the cold finger with a rapid flow of cold water and gradually heat the flask, using a heating mantle equipped with a variable transformer until even boiling and then increase the temperature to vigorous boiling. Extract for 3 hr, then discontinue heating and drain the entire contents of the extractor into a 125-ml separatory funnel. Discard the lower aqueous layer and drain the heptane extract through a 2.5 cm, 8–10 mm ID column of granular anhydrous sodium sulfate into a 10-ml volumetric flask. Rinse the separatory funnel with 1 ml of n-heptane and add to the column. Rinse the cold finger and the extraction unit with five 2-ml portions of ethanol, collecting each rinse in the separatory funnel. Add 5 ml of n-heptane and shake vigorously for a few seconds. Add 50–75 ml of water, shake moderately for a few seconds, and allow the layers to separate. The lower layer may remain slightly cloudy, which is acceptable. Discard the lower layer and pass the heptane layer through the same sodium sulfate column. Rinse the separatory funnel and column with enough n-heptane to dilute to the 10-ml volume.

Fig. 1. Moisture test apparatus. Courtesy of Scientific Glass Apparatus Company.

Prepare a slurry of 40 g of silica gel GF-254 and 80 ml of water by shaking vigorously for 5 sec and then swirling for 30 sec to eliminate air bubbles. Coat 20 × 20 cm glass plates to a thickness of 300 μm. Air dry and then activate the adsorbent by heating for 2 min at 100°C. Store in the presence of a desiccant. Condition the developing tank with n-heptane for 1 hr before using. Spot approximately 100 μl samples 3 cm from the bottom edge of the plate. The size of the spot should be 1.5–2.0 cm in diameter. Pour 10–15 ml of n-heptane into the tank, insert the plate, and seal the tank. Develop until the solvent front is approximately 1 in. from the top of the plate. Air dry and view under ultraviolet light; diphenyl appears as a bright blue spot on a yellow background. Mark a rectangular area containing the biphenyl and an equal area containing no diphenyl for the reference. Remove the spots immediately by scraping and transfer to 10-ml volumetric flasks. Dilute to volume with ethanol, filter through Whatman No. 44 paper and measure the absorbance at 248 and 300 nm in 1-cm cells. Determine the diphenyl content from a calibration curve. The absorbance at 300 nm is used to correct for interferences.

Bibliography

GENERAL REFERENCES

1. P. G. Stecher, ed., *The Merck Index*, 8th ed., Merck and Co., Inc., 1968.
2. E. Y. Spencer, *Guide to the Chemicals Used in Crop Protection*, 5th ed., Canada Dept. of Agr., London, Ontario, 1968.
3. W. T. Thompson, *Agricultural Chemicals*, Vol. 4, Thompson Publications, Davis, Calif., 1967.
4. D. E. H. Frear, *Pesticide Index*, College Science Publishers, 1965.
5. *Farm Chemicals*, Meister Publishing Co., Willoughby, Ohio, 1969.
6. G. Zweig, *Analytical Methods for Pesticides, Plant Growth Regulators and Food Additives*, Vol. 3, Academic Press, New York, 1964.

SPECIFIC REFERENCES

7. U.S. Pat. 2,917,526 (1959), H. Klos and W. Schacht (to Farbenfabriken Bayer AG).
8. W. Bonnath, *Nachr. Schädllingkampf, Leverkusen* **10**, 73 (1935).
9. U.S. Pat. 2,598,562 (1952), M. Kleiman (to Velsicol Corporation).
10. S. Davis and A. Arnold, *J. Assoc. Offic. Anal. Chem.* **48**, 1134 (1965).
11. U.S. Pat. 2,349,771 (1944), Ter Horst (to Naugatuck Chemical Company, a division of Uniroyal).
12. J. R. Lane, *J. Agr. Food Chem.* **6**, 746 (1958).
13. U.S. Pat. 2,975,196 (1961), B. T. L. Sjöstrand (to Svenska Oljeslager Aktiebolaget).
14. U.S. Pat. 2,750,427 (1956), Gaertner (to Monsanto Chemical Co.).
15. J. R. Lane, *J. Agr. Food Chem.* **6**, 667 (1958).
16. U.S. Pat. 1,972,961 (1934), Tisdale and Williams (to E. I. du Pont de Nemours & Co., Inc.).
17. A. E. Dimond, J. W. Heuberger, and J. G. Horsfall, *Phytopathology* **33**, 1095 (1943).
18. E. M. Stoddard, *Phytopathology* **41**, 858 (1951).
19. U.S. Pat. 2,317,765, W. F. Hester (to Röhm & Haas Co.).
20. G. D. Thorn and R. A. Ludwig, *Can. J. Chem.* **32**, 872 (1954).
21. U.S. Pat. 2,504,404 (1950), Flenner (to E. I. du Pont de Nemours & Co., Inc.).
22. U.S. Pat. 2,317,765 (1943), W. F. Hester (to Rohm & Haas Co.).
23. U.S. Pat. 2,457,674 (1948), J. W. Hueberger (to Rohm & Haas Co.).
24. J. W. Heuberger and T. F. Manns, *Phytopathology* **33**, 1113 (1943).
25. W. H. Tisdale and A. L. Flenner, *Ind. Eng. Chem.* **34**, 501 (1942).
26. H. L. Pease, *J. Assoc. Offic. Agr. Chem.* **40**, 1113 (1957).
27. C. F. Gordon, R. J. Shuckert, and W. E. Bornak, *J. Assoc. Offic. Anal. Chem.* **50**, 1103 (1967).
28. U.S. Pat. 2,867,562 (1959), G. Lamb (to American Cyanamid).
29. N. R. Pasarela, *J. Assoc. Offic. Anal. Chem.* **47**, 300 (1964).
30. W. A. Steller, K. Klotas, E. J. Kuchar, and M. V. Norris, *J. Agr. Food Chem.* **8**, 460 (1960).
31. C. J. Delp and H. L. Klopping, *Plant Disease Rept.* **52**, 95 (1968).
32. H. L. Pease and J. A. Gardiner, *J. Agr. Food Chem.* **17**, 267 (1969).
33. R. Wellman and S. E. A. McCallan, *Contr. Boyce Thompson Institute* **14**, 151 (1946).
34. U.S. Pat. 2,540,171 (1951), B. W. Kiff (to Union Carbide and Carbon Corp.).
35. E. F. Hillenbrand, W. W. Sutherland, and J. N. Hogsett, *Anal. Chem.* **23**, 626 (1951).
36. W. D. Thomas, Jr., P. H. Eastburg, and M. D. Bankuti, *Phytopathology* **52**, 754 (1962).
37. A. R. Kittleson, *Science* **115**, 84 (1952).
38. U.S. Pa(. 2,553,770 (1951), A. R. Kittleson (to Standard Oil Development Co.).
39. I. H. Pomerantz and R. Ross, *J. Assoc. Offic. Anal. Chem.* **51**, 1058 (1968).
40. U.S. Pat. 3,249,499 (1966), B. V. Schmeling, M. Kulka, D. S. Thiara, and W. A. Harrison (to Uniroyal Company).
41. B. V. Schmeling and M. Kulka, *Science* **152**, 659 (1966).
42. J. R. Lane, *J. Agr. Food Chem.* **18**, 409 (1970).
43. H. J. Ackermann, H. A. Baltrush, H. H. Berges, D. O. Brookover, and B. B. Brown, *J. Agr. Food Chem.* **6**, 747 (1958).
44. C. A. Bache and D. J. Lisk, *J. Agr. Food Chem.* **8**, 459 (1960).
45. N. G. Clark, A. F. Hams, D. J. Higgons, and H. A. Stevenson, *Chem. and Ind., London* **21**, 572 (1960).
46. Brit. Pat. 845,916 (1960), Clark, Stevenson, Brookes, and Hams (to Boots Pure Drug Co., Ltd.).

47. W. W. Kilgore, K. W. Cheng, and J. M. Ogawa, *J. Agr. Food Chem.* **10**, 399 (1962).
48. G. A. Boyack, personal communication to W. W. Kilgore.
49. K. W. Cheng and W. W. Kilgore, The Upjohn Company, Kalamazoo, Mich., personal communications, 1970.
50. T. C. Ryker, M. J. Fielding, and R. L. Krause, *Proc. Cotton Disease Council* **25**, 137 (1965).
51. U.S. Pat. 3,265,564 (1965), (to E. I. du Pont de Nemours & Co., Inc.).
52. H. L. Pease, *J. Agr. Food Chem.* **15**, 917 (1967).
53. U.S. Pat. 2,526,660 (1950), W. F. Hester and W. E. Craig (to Rohm & Haas Co.).
54. W. W. Kilgore and K. W. Cheng, *J. Agr. Food Chem.* **11**, 477 (1963).
55. E. Urbschat, *Angew. Chem.* **72**, 981 (1960).
56. D. F. Millikan, personal communication (1970).
57. C. A. Anderson and J. M. Adams, *J. Agr. Food Chem.* **11**, 474 (1963).
58. D. MacDougall in G. Zweig, ed., *Analytical Methods for Pesticides, Plant Growth Regulators and Food Additives*, Vol. 3, Academic Press, 1964, pp. 51–53.
59. C. N. Wolf, P. H. Schuldt, and M. W. Baldwin, *Science* **121**, 61 (1955).
60. U.S. Pat. 2,720,480 (1955), C. N. Wolf (to Ethyl Corp.).
61. W. R. Meagher, C. A. Anderson, C. E. Gonter, S. B. Smith, and D. MacDougall, *J. Agr. Food Chem.* **7**, 558 (1959).
62. A. J. Whiffen, *J. Bact.* **56**, 283 (1948).
63. B. E. Leach, J. H. Ford, and A. J. Whiffen, *J. Am. Chem. Soc.* **69**, 474 (1947).
64. E. C. Kornfeld, R. G. Jones, and T. V. Parke, *J. Am. Chem. Soc.* **71**, 150 (1949).
65. G. C. Prescott, H. Emerson, and J. H. Ford, *J. Agr. Food Chem.* **4**, 343 (1956).
66. Y. H. Loo, R. S. Skell, H. H. Thornberry, J. Ehrlich, J. M. McGuire, G. M. Savage, and J. A. Sylvester, *J. Bact.* **50**, 701 (1945).
67. A. A. Forist and S. Theal, *Anal. Chem.* **31**, 1042 (1959).
68. G. B. Ramsey, M. A. Smith, and B. C. Heiberg, *Bot. Gas.* **106**, 74 (1944).
69. P. E. Corneliusser, *J. Assoc. Offic. Anal. Chem.* **50**, 934 (1967).

B. G. TWEEDY
CAROL LOEPPKY
University of Missouri

FURAN AND FURAN DERIVATIVES

Furan... 228
Tetrahydrofuran.. 230
Furfural... 232
Furfuryl alcohol... 240
Tetrahydrofurfuryl alcohol... 242
Polytetramethylene ether glycols..................................... 244
Bibliography... 250

Furan is a heterocyclic compound composed of four carbon atoms and one oxygen atom and is doubly unsaturated. The numbering system for the furan ring is shown below:

The most important furan derivatives are tetrahydrofuran, furfural, furfuryl alcohol, and tetrahydrofurfuryl alcohol (1); their structures follow.

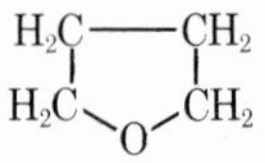

tetrahydrofuran

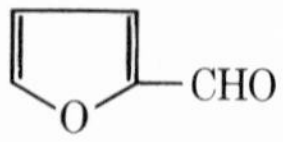

furfural

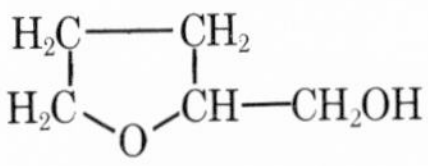

tetrahydrofurfuryl
alcohol

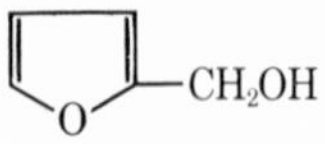

furfuryl alcohol

Polytetramethylene ether glycols prepared by ring-opening polymerization of tetrahydrofuran are also of commercial importance.

For more information of the manufacturing, properties, and application of these substances, the general references (1,2) should be consulted.

FURAN

Furan (furfuran), C_4H_4O, is a colorless liquid with a mild pleasant odor.

The solubility of furan in water at 25°C is 1 g/100 g of water; the solubility of water in furan at 25°C is 0.3 g/100 g furan. Furan is miscible with ethyl acetate, methanol, ethanol, isobutyl alcohol, n-amyl alcohol, acetone, methyl ethyl ketone, ethyl ether, heptane, petroleum ether, benzene, toluene, trichloroethylene, methylene chloride, and chloroform. It is soluble in ethylene glycol to the extent of about 12 wt %.

If not handled properly, furan is potentially hazardous for industrial use (3,4). The concentration of furan in the atmosphere should be kept to a minimum, and skin contact with liquid furan should be avoided in order to prevent possible local and systemic effects. It is recommended that workers with any abnormal circulatory, gastrointestinal, or liver conditions should not be exposed to furan.

Because of the low boiling point, low flash point, and high flammability of furan, it should be kept away from heat and open flame. Unless stabilized, furan on exposure to the air slowly forms an unstable peroxide. Consequently, it is wise to employ the usual precautions for the handling of ethers in using and distilling this material.

Some properties of furan are presented in Table 1 (4).

Table 1. Properties of Furan

melting point, °C	−85.68
boiling point, °C	31.3
specific gravity, 20/4°C	0.937
refractive index, n_D^{20}	1.4214
flash point, open cup, °C	−40
flash point, Tag, closed cup, °C	−35.5
heat of vaporization, at 31.2°C, cal/mole	95.5
heat of combustion, at constant vol, kcal/g-mole	500.1
heat of formation, kcal/g-mole	14.8
critical temperature, °C	214
vapor density, lb/ft³	0.170
flammability or explosive limits, in air, vol %	2.3–14.3

Methods of Manufacture

Furan may be manufactured from furfural by passing the vapors with steam over catalysts such as lime (5), or a mixed chromite of zinc and manganese (6), or by heating furfural in the liquid phase in the presence of a palladium catalyst (7). It can also be obtained by decarboxylation of 2-furoic acid.

Commercial Grades and Specifications

Commercial furan, a distilled product, is sold in one grade. Relevant specifications and a typical analysis are presented in Table 2.

Table 2. Commercial Specifications and Typical Analysis of Furan[a]

	Specification	Analysis
specific gravity, 20/4°C	0.936–0.940	0.938
moisture, wt %, max	0.2	0.02
methylfuran, wt %, max	0.2	0.02
tetrahydrofuran, wt %, max	0.05	
furfural, wt %, max	0.05	0.005

[a] Courtesy The Quaker Oats Co.

Methods of Analysis

Assay Methods

Furan is assayed by gas chromatography. Usually, the analysis also serves to determine the amount of impurities present. If the analysis is carried out isothermally, two different columns, each operated at different temperatures, are needed for a full determination:

column	(a) 10 ft × ¼ in. OD packed
	(b) 8 ft × ¼ in. OD packed
column packing	(a) 15 wt % di-*n*-decyl phthalate on Chromosorb W 80–100 mesh
	(b) 15 wt % Carbowax 20M on Chromosorb W 80–100 mesh
temperature of	
injection port	(a) 150°C (b) 260°C
column	(a) 50°C (b) 150°C
detector	(a) 150°C (b) 260°C
carrier gas and flow rate	helium, 50 ml/min
detector	flame ionization

In this case, two separate analyses are carried out. The amount of furan and of the low boilers (methylfuran, tetrahydrofuran) are established from the chromatogram obtained on the phthalate column, while the amount of furfural present is calculated from the chromatogram obtained on the Carbowax 20M column. It is also possible to use the Carbowax 20M column under temperature programmed conditions; in this case, all components present can be evaluated from one chromatogram.

DETERMINATION OF IMPURITIES

Impurities in furan are determined by gas chromatography, as discussed above.

Trace amounts of moisture are determined by the Karl Fischer method using a 50-ml sample size. The dead-stop back-titration method is preferred (see AQUA-METRY, Vol. 1, pp. 142–147).

The specific gravity is determined by the use of a Westphal balance (see Vol. 1, pp. 552–554).

TETRAHYDROFURAN

Tetrahydrofuran (tetramethyleneoxide), C_4H_8O, is a colorless liquid with an ethereal odor. It is a saturated cyclic ether, which is a good solvent for high molecular weight poly(vinyl chloride), poly(vinylidene chloride), and other difficultly soluble organic materials. Some properties of tetrahydrofuran are presented in Table 3 (8).

Tetrahydrofuran has reaction characteristics similar to those of an aliphatic ether, modified by its cyclic structure. Like most ethers, tetrahydrofuran forms an explosive peroxide when exposed to air (3,8). For this reason, commercial tetrahydrofuran is stabilized by the addition of an antioxidant. It should not be distilled or evaporated without testing for peroxides by the liberation of iodine from an acidified potassium iodide solution, and removing them, eg, by treatment with a mixture of ferrous sulfate heptahydrate and sodium hydrogen sulfate.

Tetrahydrofuran is used in large quantities as a solvent for high molecular weight poly(vinyl chloride) and poly(vinylidene chloride) in the preparation of printing inks, adhesives, lacquers, and other coating compositions. It is an excellent medium for reactions involving Grignard reagents, sodium acetylide, and lithium aluminum hydride. It is also used alone or in combination with water or other solvents as an extractant for physiologically active materials.

Tetrahydrofuran is miscible with most organic solvents and with water in all proportions. It forms an azeotropic mixture with 4.3 wt % water. This mixture is even better than tetrahydrofuran itself as a solvent for cellulose acetate, and for alkaloids such as caffeine.

Because of the low boiling point, low flash point, and high flammability, tetrahydrofuran should be kept away from heat and open flame. The threshold limit value for tetrahydrofuran is 200 ppm as recommended by the American Conference of Governmental Industrial Hygienists (*Threshold Limit Values for 1965*). This indicates that like similarly rated solvents, such as methanol, toluene, and xylene, tetrahydrofuran should be used in properly designed equipment in areas adequately ventilated.

Table 3. Properties of Tetrahydrofuran

melting point, °C	−108.5
boiling point, °C	65–67
density, d_4^{20}	0.887
refractive index, n_D^{20}	1.4073
flash point, open cup, °C	−17.2
flash point, closed cup, °C	−14.5
ignition temperature, °C	321
vapor density (air = 1)	2.5
explosive limits, in air, 25°C, vol %	1.8–11.8

Method of Manufacture

Tetrahydrofuran is manufactured by catalytic hydrogenation of furan and by a modified Reppe process.

Commercial Grades and Specifications

In the United States, tetrahydrofuran is produced by The Quaker Oats Company and by E. I. du Pont de Nemours, & Co., Inc. The specifications of their products are identical; they are summarized in Table 4.

Table 4. Specifications of Tetrahydrofuran

specific gravity, 20/4°C	0.886–0.889
boiling range at 760 torr	
first drop, ° C, min	65.5
95 ml evaporated, °C, max	66.7
water, wt %, max	0.03
acetone, wt %, max	0.05
isopropyl alcohol, wt %, max	0.05
n-propyl alcohol, wt %, max	0.05
n-butyl alcohol, wt %, max	0.05
peroxide (calculated as tetrahydrofuran hydroperoxide), wt %, max	0.015
color, APHA, max	20

Methods of Analysis

Assay Methods

Tetrahydrofuran is assayed by gas chromatography. The following analytical conditions are recommended.

column	10 ft × ¼ in. OD packed
column packing	15 wt % di-n-decyl phthalate on Chromosorb W 80–100 mesh
temperature of	
injection port	150°C
column	50°C
detector	150°C
carrier gas and flow rate	helium, 50 ml/min
detector	flame ionization

Determination of Impurities

Moisture. Trace amounts of moisture are determined by the Karl Fischer method using a 50-ml sample. The dead-stop back-titration method is preferred (see Aquametry, Vol. 1, pp. 142–147).

Volatile Organic Impurities. The organic impurities present can be determined from the gas chromatographic analysis carried out under the conditions listed above.

Peroxides. For the determination of the peroxide content of tetrahydrofuran, the following procedure is recommended (9).

Procedure

Place 100 ml of water in each of two 500-ml Erlenmeyer flasks. Add 25 ml of 32% sulfuric acid solution, and then add 25 ml of 10% potassium iodide solution to each beaker. Pipet 25 ml of tetrahydrofuran into one of the prepared flasks, stopper both flasks, shake and place in the dark for 15–20 min.

Titrate the contents of each flask with 0.02 N sodium thiosulfate solution to a colorless end point.

$$\text{Peroxides, wt } \% = \frac{(B - A)(N)(MW)}{(V)(s)(20)}$$

where B = volume of sodium thiosulfate solution used for blank, in ml
A = volume of sodium thiosulfate solution used for sample titration, in ml
N = normality of sodium thiosulfate solution
V = sample volume, in ml
s = specific gravity of sample
MW = g-mol wt of the peroxide (= 104.1)

Specific Gravity. Specific gravity is determined by the use of a Westphal balance (see Vol. 1, pp. 552–554).

FURFURAL

Furfural, C_4H_3OCHO (2-furaldehyde, fural, 2-furancarboxaldehyde, furfuraldehyde), is the most important member of the furan class. It is a colorless liquid when freshly distilled. It autoxidizes slowly on exposure to air, and especially in contact with iron, with gradual darkening in color and increase in acidity and polymer content. This autoxidation can be prevented by storage in the absence of oxygen (10).

Dobereiner reported the discovery of furfural in 1832, but commercial production was first achieved only in 1922 by The Quaker Oats Company.

Properties

Principal uses of furfural are as a selective solvent in oil refining, in butadiene operations, in the production of light-colored wood rosins, as a reactive solvent in the

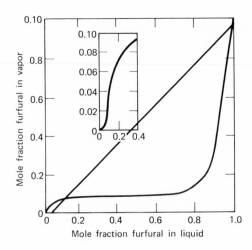

Fig. 1. Vapor–liquid composition for the furfural–water system.

Table 5. Properties of Furfural

melting point, °C	-36.5
boiling point, °C	161.7
specific gravity, 20/4°C	1.1598
refractive index, n_D^{20}	1.5261
flash point, open cup, °C	68.3
surface tension, at 30°C, dyn/cm	41.1
viscosity, cP	
at 25°C	1.49
at 38	1.35
at 54	1.09
at 99	0.68
heat of vaporization, kcal/g-mole, at 160.6°C	9.22
heat of combustion, kcal/g-mole	560.3
lower explosive limit in air, at 125°C, vol %	2.1
coefficient of expansion, per °C	0.00110
ignition temperature, °C	393
dielectric constant at 25°C, ϵ	38.0

vapor pressure	°C	torr	°C	torr
	39.9	8	154.4	625
	92.3	69	159.0	707
	120.3	214	160.9	744
	131.6	310	163.8	812
	140.2	411	170.6	966

Table 6. Mutual Solubility of Furfural and Water

Temperature, °C	Furfural, wt %	
	water phase	furfural phase
10	7.9	96.1
20	8.3	95.2
30	8.8	94.2
40	9.5	93.3
50	10.4	92.4
60	11.7	91.4
70	13.2	90.3
80	14.8	88.7
90	16.6	86.5
97.9[a]	18.4	84.1

[a] Boiling point at 760 torr.

manufacture of resin-bonded abrasive wheels and brake linings, and as a chemical intermediate for the production of other furan chemicals.

Some of the more important properties of furfural are given in Table 5 (2); Table 6 (11) presents the solubility data and Figure 1 the vapor–liquid equilibrium data for the furfural–water system.

Furfural undergoes the usual reactions of aldehydes. It condenses with compounds possessing active methylene groups, such as aliphatic carboxylic esters and anhydrides, aldehydes, ketones, nitriles, and nitroparaffins (12–14); resins are obtained with phenols.

Furfural is resistant to hydrolytic fission. High temperatures and long exposure are required to decompose furfural in dilute aqueous acidic medium (15).

Long experience in the handling of furfural indicates no particular health hazards under normal conditions. Its odor is usually sufficient warning of its presence, but a sensitive colorimetric test has been devised (16). Adequate ventilation should be provided, and if furfural is spilled on the body or clothes, it should be washed off with water. Furfural will stain the skin yellow-brown if left in contact and may be a local irritant.

The flammability of furfural is comparable to that of kerosene and may be controlled with water, foam, carbon dioxide, or dry chemicals.

Method of Manufacture

Manufacture of furfural is based on the following reactions:

$$\text{pentosan} + \text{water} \rightarrow \text{pentose}$$

$$\text{pentose} \rightarrow \text{furfural} + \text{water}$$

Commercially, it is produced in a single-step operation from agricultural residues, such as corn cobs and oat hulls. The raw material is charged to large rotary digestors and treated with dilute sulfuric acid. The furfural formed is removed by steam distillation. The vapors leaving the digestors are condensed and fed to a stripping column. Overhead vapors, rich in furfural, are condensed and cooled, separating into two layers. After removal of a small quantity of low-boiling fractions in a methanol column, the water layer is returned to the stripping column for recovery of furfural. The furfural layer, containing about 6% water, is sent to the dehydrating column, where the water is taken overhead, and dry furfural is drawn from the base and redistilled. Distillate from the dehydrating column is sent to the stripping-column decanter for recycling through the system.

Commercial Grades and Specifications

Specifications and a typical analysis of commercial grade furfural are given in Table 7.

Table 7. Specifications and Typical Analysis of Furfural[a]

	Specification	Analysis
specific gravity, 20/20°C, min	1.160	1.162
refractive index, n_{D}^{20}	1.152–1.527	1.526
acidity, eq/liter, max	0.020	0.013
residue, max %	0.50	0.04
moisture, max %	0.2	0.07

[a] Courtesy The Quaker Oats Company.

Methods of Analysis

Identification

Identification Through Derivative Forming. Furfural forms the usual derivatives of aldehydes (see Carbonyl compounds, Vol. 8, pp. 339–348), and these may be used for identification purposes. The melting points of the two most characteristic derivatives, phenylhydrazone and semicarbazone, are 97°C and 202°C, respectively.

Colorimetry. A quick qualitative test may be made by adding a few drops of a 25% solution of aniline in glacial acetic acid to an aqueous solution of furfural (17). An intense red color develops at once if furfural is present. It is not specific for furfural, since 5-methylfurfural and 5-hydroxymethylfurfural also give a positive test.

Infrared Spectroscopy. Furfural has a number of characteristic bands which permit its identification. Table 8 lists these bands (18–23).

Table 8. Characteristic Infrared Bands of Furfural[a]

Wave number, cm^{-1}	Remark
780–740	width and region both wide, sometimes split
885–870	sharp band and most characteristic
935–915	sharp band
1030–1000	ether linkage; very strong band
1075–1060	ether linkage; sharp band
1165–1140	ether linkage; sharp band
1250–1200	ether linkage; weak band
1370–1360	ether linkage; sharp band
1488–1466	C=C vibration of ring; strong band
3165–3125	C=C vibration of ring; strong band

[a] 0.015-cm cell

Assay Methods

Procedures for quantitative estimation may be divided into two groups based on the aldehyde group and ring reactions. The method selected should depend upon the nature of the other materials present.

There is no really specific method for assaying furfural. Assay methods, such as the sodium bisulfite method, which are dependent upon the aldehyde function, are affected by the presence of any contaminating aldehydes or ketones. The method of Hughes and Acree (24), which involves bromination of the furfural ring under controlled conditions, is affected by any contaminant which will accept bromine under the conditions of the method. Furfural can be isolated from many of these interfering substances by steam distillation.

Phloroglucinol Method. The official method of the AOAC for the determination of pentosans has been most generally employed (25). This involves distillation in the presence of hydrochloric acid under carefully controlled conditions, followed by precipitation of the aldehyde with phloroglucinol. Considerable practice is required to obtain concordant duplicate results within the range of 98–102% of the actual furfural content.

Procedure

Add 11 g of phloroglucinol to 300 ml of heated 12% hydrochloric acid in small portions with constant stirring until nearly dissolved. Pour the hot solution into enough cold 12 wt % hydrochloric acid to make a total volume of 1500 ml. Let it stand overnight, preferably several days, to permit any diresorcin to crystallize. Filter immediately before use.

Weigh a quantity of sample so that the acid distillate will not contain more than 140 mg of furfural corresponding to less than 300 mg of furfural phloroglucide. Transfer this sample quantitatively to a 300-ml distilling flask, add 100 ml of 12% hydrochloric acid solution, boiling chips, and a few drops of silicone oil or other antifoaming agent. Fit the distilling flask with a dropping funnel and condenser and distill at a rate of 3 ml/min for 120 min. Maintain the 100-ml volume in the distilling flask by incremental additions of 12% hydrochloric acid. Filter the distillate through a small filter paper, then add to the 360 ml distillate, with stirring, a quantity of the phloroglucinol solution containing twice the stoichiometric amount required for reaction. Dilute to 400 ml with 12% hydrochloric acid and let stand overnight.

Collect the amorphous black precipitate in a previously weighed Gooch crucible with an asbestos mat, wash carefully with 150 ml of water, and dry for 4 hr at 100°C. Cool and weigh in a weighing bottle.

Calculate the amount of furfural, pentoses, or pentosans from the weight of furfural phloroglucide precipitate by use of the following equations:

1. When weight of the phloroglucide precipitate is less than 0.03 g

$$\text{Furfural} = (A + B)(0.5170)$$
$$\text{Pentoses} = (A + B)(1.0170)$$
$$\text{Pentosans} = (A + B)(0.8949)$$

2. When weight of the phloroglucide precipitate is in the range of 0.03–0.300 g

$$\text{Furfural} = (A + B)(0.5185)$$
$$\text{Pentoses} = (A + B)(1.0075)$$
$$\text{Pentosans} = (A + B)(0.8866)$$

where A = weight of the phloroglucide precipitate, in g

B = solubility of the phloroglucide in 400 ml of reaction solution (0.0052 g)

Modified Hughes–Acree Method. A modified version of the method of Hughes and Acree, which is dependent upon the reaction of bromine with the furan ring under carefully controlled conditions of temperature and time (24), gives results within 1% of the correct value. Based upon accuracy and speed as well as ease of operation, it is preferred over the phloroglucinol method.

Procedure

Weigh samples of aqueous or organic solutions containing approximately 60 mg, but not more than 100 mg, of furfural, and transfer quantitatively to 500-ml wide-mouthed Erlenmeyer flasks, containing approximately 200 g of crushed ice. Add enough hydrochloric acid so that the resulting solution in the flask contains between 3 and 5% of the acid, and the total volume is about 125 ml. Pipet into the flask 25 ml of 0.1 N potassium bromate–bromide solution, mix thoroughly by swirling, and let stand for exactly 5 min. Add 10 ml of 10% potassium iodide solution, swirl, and titrate with 0.1 N sodium thiosulfate solution. When the brown color of the free iodine has faded to a straw color, add several ml of starch indicator solution and titrate to a colorless end point. Run a blank titration on the same solvent system used in the sample titration, including the ice.

$$\text{Furfural, wt \%} = \frac{(B - A)(N)(MW)(100)}{(w)(2000)}$$

where A = volume of sodium thiosulfate solution used for sample titration, in ml

B = volume of sodium thiosulfate solution used for blank titration, in ml

N = normality of sodium thiosulfate solution

MW = g-mol wt of furfural (= 96.04)

w = sample weight, in g

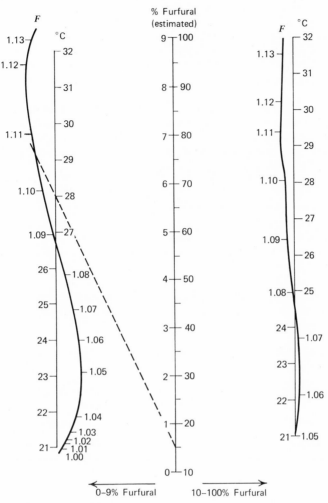

Fig. 2. Nomograph used for the sodium bisulfite method.

Sodium Bisulfite Method. A volumetric procedure, based on the reaction of furfural with sodium bisulfite (26), is useful in determining furfural in the presence of other furan compounds, especially furfuryl alcohol.

Procedure

Estimate the concentration of furfural in the solution to be analyzed from a determination of density or refractive index or by an approximate analysis. Select a sample size which will contain 1 g of furfural and dilute to 100 ml with water in a volumetric flask. Ethanol may be used as the solvent for water insoluble materials. Transfer 5 ml of the furfural solution to a glass-stoppered 125-ml Erlenmeyer flask. Add 25 ml of 0.1 *N* sodium bisulfite solution, swirl, and let stand for 15 ± 1 min. Add 3–4 drops of a starch indicator solution and titrate with 0.1 *N* iodine solution. Perform the titration within a period of 1–2 min. Carry out a blank determination by using 5 ml of water or solvent instead of the furfural solution.

$$\text{Furfural, wt \%} = \frac{(B - A)(N)(MW)(F)(20)(100)}{(w)(2)(1000)}$$

where A = volume of iodine solution required for sample titration, in ml
B = volume of iodine solution required for blank, in ml
N = normality of the iodine solution
MW = g-mol wt of furfural (96.04)
w = sample weight, in g
20 = dilution factor

Determine the correction factor F by laying a straight edge across the nomograph given in Figure 2, from the estimated point on the concentration line to the point representing the ambient temperature. The intersection of the straight-edge and the factor curve of the nomograph gives the value of F to the nearest hundredth.

Ultraviolet Absorption Method. This method is based on the measurement of the characteristic UV absorption of furfural at 276 nm.

Procedure

Prepare standard furfural solutions with a concentration of 1, 2, 3, 4, and 5 μg/ml. Determine the absorbances of these solutions at a wavelength of 276 nm and plot a calibration curve for some convenient temperature.

Steam distill a suitable aliquot of a furfural-containing sample to 200 ml of distillate. Dilute the distillate to a furfural concentration of approximately 4 μg/ml and measure the absorbance at 276 nm. Calculate the furfural concentration in the original sample from the calibration curve.

Gas Chromatography. Furfural can also be assayed by gas chromatography using either a di-n-decyl phthalate or a Carbowax 20M column. The following conditions are recommended:

column	(a) 10 ft × ¼ in. OD packed
	(b) 6 ft × ¼ in. OD packed
column packing	(a) 15 wt % di-n-decyl phthalate on acid-washed Chromosorb W 80–100 mesh
	(b) 15 wt % Carbowax 20M on Chromosorb W 80–100 mesh which was previously impregnated with 2 wt % potassium hydroxide
temperature of	
injection port	260°C
column	125°C
detector	260°C
carrier gas and flow rate	helium, 50 ml/min
detector	thermal conductivity or flame ionization

The chromatogram obtained also permits the determination of the impurities present (see below).

DETERMINATION OF IMPURITIES

Nonvolatiles. The amount of nonvolatiles is determined by heating the sample in an inert atmosphere.

Procedure

Pipet a 10-ml aliquot of furfural into a tared, disposable aluminum cup and weigh. Place the cup upon an aluminum block heater, recessed to receive and center the cup, and thermostatically maintained at 200°C.

Direct a stream of nitrogen upon the center of the liquid surface in the cup in sufficient volume to exclude all air.

Heat the cup for 4 or 5 min after apparent dryness is observed. It is then removed, cooled in a desiccator, and weighed.

Moisture. The moisture content of furfural is usually determined by the Dean and Starks method.

Procedure

Place 100 ml each of furfural and toluene in a 500-ml distilling flask, add boiling chips and connect to a Dean and Stark moisture test apparatus and condenser. Adjust the distillation rate to about 2 drops/sec initially, increasing to 4 drops/sec after most of the water has been distilled. The total time of distillation should be about 60 min.

Stop the distillation, rinse the condenser with toluene, and brush down any water droplets adhering to the walls by means of a small rubber policeman attached to a glass rod. Allow the receiver to cool to room temperature before reading the volume of water collected.

$$\text{Moisture, wt } \% = \frac{(100)(V_w)(s_w)}{(V_f)(s_f)}$$

where V_f = volume of the furfural sample, in ml
s_f = specific gravity of furfural at room temperature
V_w = volume of water collected, in ml
s_w = specific gravity of water at room temperature

Acidity. The acidity of furfural is expressed as acid equivalents per one liter of sample and determined by direct titration.

Procedure

In a 500-ml Erlenmeyer flask add 300 ml of water and a few drops of a 1% phenolphthalein indicator solution. Adjust the alkalinity of the water to a faint pink end point by careful drop-by-drop addition of 0.1 N sodium hydroxide solution. Then pipet 10 ml of furfural sample into the water, stir until dissolved, and titrate with 0.1 N sodium hydroxide solution to an end point which persists for 1 min.

$$\text{Acid equivalents/liter} = \frac{(V)(N)}{S}$$

where V = volume of sodium hydroxide solution used for the titration, in ml
N = normality of the sodium hydroxide solution
S = volume of the furfural sample, in ml

Volatile Organic Impurities. Commercial furfural contains traces of low-boiling substances and usually, some methylfurfural. Their amount can be evaluated from the chromatogram obtained under the conditions mentioned above, among the assay methods. The low boilers will emerge before furfural while the peak of methylfurfural will emerge just after the furfural peak.

FURFURYL ALCOHOL

Furfuryl alcohol, 2-furanmethanol, $C_4H_3OCH_2OH$, is a water-white liquid that gradually darkens in the presence of air. It is soluble in water and in many common organic solvents. Furfuryl alcohol was first prepared in the laboratory in 1864 by the reduction of furfural with sodium amalgam. Based on the high-pressure catalytic hydrogenation techniques developed by Peters, and by Adkins and Connor, furfuryl alcohol became commercially available in 1934. Its physical properties are summarized in Table 9 (2).

Furfuryl alcohol is used chiefly as a solvent and as a reagent, in the formation of resins. Although it has been used in substantial commercial quantities for the past 35 yr, there are no reports of impairment of the health of those who have handled it. Good ventilation should be provided and contact with the skin avoided. If spilled on the body it should be washed off promptly with water.

In the practice, furfuryl alcohol is produced by the catalytic hydrogenation of furfural.

Table 9.   Properties of Furfuryl Alcohol

melting point, metastable form, °C	−29
melting point, stable form, °C	−14.63
boiling point, at 760 torr, °C	170.0
density, d_{20}^{20}	1.135
refractive index, n_D^{20}	1.4868
flash point, open cup, °C	75.0
surface tension, at 25°C, dyn/cm	38.2
viscosity, at 25°C, cP	4.62
specific heat of liquid at 0°C, cal/(g)(°C)	0.472
heat of combustion of liquid, to yield H_2O and CO_2, at 25°C and constant volume, cal/g	6206.6
free energy of formation of liquid, ΔF_f° at 25°C, cal/g-mole	−36.880
entropy of formation of liquid from elements, at 25°C, cal/(g-mole)(°C)	−97.86
enthalpy of formation of liquid from graphite carbon, hydrogen and oxygen, ΔH_f°, at 25°C, cal/g-mole	−66,060
entropy of liquid, S, at 25°C, cal/(g-mole)(°C)	51.58

vapor pressure	°C	torr	°C	torr
	40	1.8	100	53.5
	60	6.3	120	127.4
	80	20.3	140	271.0

Commercial Grades and Specifications

The specifications of the commercial furfuryl alcohol and a typical analysis are listed in Table 10.

Table 10.   Furfuryl Alcohol Specifications and Typical Analysis[a]

	Specification	Analysis
specific gravity, 20/20°C	1.134–1.137	1.135
refractive index, n_D^{20}	1.485–1.488	1.487
moisture, wt %, max	0.3	0.05
furfural, wt %, max	0.7	0.14
cloud point, °C, max	10	6

[a] Courtesy The Quaker Oats Co.

Industrial grade furfuryl alcohol is pale yellow to amber in color and is completely miscible with water at temperatures above 21°C. It is stored and handled in steel without any special precautions. During storage it gradually becomes less soluble in water due to intermolecular dehydration (27), which is accelerated by heat and/or acidic materials, and may be retarded by addition of small amounts of organic or inorganic bases.

Deterioration of furfuryl alcohol due to autoxidation is indicated by the development of color, acidity, and increased moisture content. Deterioration may be inhibited by the addition of tri-*n*-propylamine or other basic material, or it may be prevented by the elimination of oxygen. Tri-*n*-propylamine causes an initial slight darkening of the furfuryl alcohol, but thereafter the color remains unaltered for extended periods, even on exposure to oxygen.

Methods of Analysis

Assay Methods

Furfuryl alcohol may be assayed by the modified Hughes–Acree bromination method in the absence of materials which can be brominated under the conditions of the method. For details on the procedure, see p. 236.

Furfuryl alcohol can be assayed by ultraviolet absorption at a wavelength of 216 nm. The presence of free phenol, phenolics, or free furfural in greater than 10% concentration by weight, or base or acid, will usually interfere with the determination.

Procedure

Prepare a calibration curve at some convenient temperature with aqueous furfuryl alcohol solutions containing a range of concentrations from 1 to 10 μg/ml. Measure the absorbance at a wavelength of 216 nm using a 1-cm cell. Samples of unknown furfuryl alcohol are diluted with water to an approximate concentration of this range, the absorbance measured at the reference temperature, and the concentration determined from the curve.

Gas chromatography permits not only the assay of furfuryl alcohol but also the determination of the impurities present. The following instrumental conditions are recommended:

column	6 ft $\times$ $\frac{1}{4}$ in. OD packed
column packing	15 wt % Carbowax 20M on Chromosorb W 80–100 mesh which was previously impregnated with 22 wt % potassium hydroxide
temperature of	
injection block	260°C
column	135°C
detector	260°C
carrier gas and flow rate	helium, 50 ml/min
detector	thermal conductivity or flame ionization

Determination of Impurities

Moisture. The moisture content of furfuryl alcohol is determined by the Dean and Starks method. For details, see p. 239.

Cloud Point. This test is an indication of the polymer content of the furfuryl alcohol.

Procedure

Place 15 ml of furfuryl alcohol and 30 ml of water in a 25×200 mm test tube with a thermometer. Cool the mixture in an ice bath while stirring until a distinct milky cloud is formed. Continue cooling and stirring until the mixture has been cooled an additional 1–2°C, then take the test tube from the bath and allow it to warm slowly with stirring. The temperature is taken when the milky cloud disappears and the mixture becomes clear. Note that the cloud point is sharp and reversible. The cloud may be reformed by barely touching the test tube to the ice bath. Report the cloud point in °C.

Furfural. Besides gas chromatography, (see p. 238), the furfural content of furfuryl alcohol can also be determined by a modified sodium bisulfite method.

Procedure

Pipet 2 ml of furfuryl alcohol and 25 ml of 0.1 N sodium bisulfite solution into a 125-ml Erlenmeyer flask. Mix thoroughly and let stand 15 min. Add several drops of starch indicator solution and titrate, in less than 2 min, with 0.1 N iodine solution until the blue color persists at least 10 sec. Also carry out a blank determination by substituting 2 ml of water for the sample.

For exact calculation, see the sodium bisulfite procedure given to assay furfural (p. 237); with small furfural concentrations, the following simplified calculation is adequate:

$$\text{Furfural, wt \%} = \frac{(B - A)(N)(5.0)}{V}$$

where A = volume of iodine solution required for sample titration, in ml
B = volume of iodine solution required for blank titration, in ml
N = normality of iodine solution
V = sample volume, in ml (2 ml)

Volatile Organic Impurities. The gas chromatographic analysis of the furfuryl alcohol sample also permits the evaluation of the amount of volatile organic impurities present. Low-boiling impurities as well as furfural will emerge prior to furfuryl alcohol, while a peak corresponding to traces of methylfurfuryl alcohol will follow the main peak.

TETRAHYDROFURFURYL ALCOHOL

Tetrahydrofurfuryl alcohol, $C_4H_7OCH_2OH$, is a high-boiling liquid with a mild, pleasant odor; it is completely miscible in water and with most common organic solvents. The commercial product is almost water-white and is handled and shipped in steel. On exposure to oxygen in iron or copper containers, tetrahydrofurfuryl alcohol discolors slowly, but it is not discolored when stored in contact with aluminum, even over an extended period of time.

Table 11. Properties of Tetrahydrofurfuryl Alcohol

boiling point, at 743 torr, °C	177.5
specific gravity, 20/20°C	1.064
refractive index, n_D^{20}	1.4505
flash point, open cup, °C	75–80
surface tension, at 25°C, dyn/cm	36.5 ± 0.5
viscosity at 25°C, cP	5.49
heat of combustion, kcal/g-mole	709.5
flammability limits, 72.5–122°C, vol %	1.5–9.7
dielectric constant, at 23°C, ϵ	37.1

Table 12. Tetrahydrofurfuryl Alcohol Specifications and Typical Analysis[a]

	Specification	Analysis
specific gravity, 20/20°C	1.055–1.057	1.055
refractive index, n_D^{20}	1.451–1.454	1.4532
color, APHA, max	50	1 0
furfuryl alcohol, wt %, max	0.1	0.07
1,2-pentanediol, wt %, max	1.6	0.53
moisture, wt %, max	0.3	0.05

[a] Courtesy The Quaker Oats Co.

The properties of tetrahydrofurfuryl alcohol are summarized in Table 11 (2). The commercial specifications of the distilled product, together with a typical analysis, are listed in Table 12.

Tetrahydrofurfuryl alcohol is produced by the catalytic hydrogenation of furfural or furfuryl alcohol. It is used as a solvent for cellulose esters, ethylcellulose, furfuryl alcohol polymers, styrene, phenol–aldehyde resins, vinyl acetate, and many dyes, lacquers, and coating materials.

Tetrahydrofurfuryl alcohol has been used in substantial quantities industrially for the past 20 yr without evidence of harmful effects to the health of the users; one should, nevertheless, provide good ventilation and avoid contact with the skin.

Methods of Analysis

Assay Methods

Tetrahydrofurfuryl alcohol is best assayed by gas chromatography; the following conditions are recommended:

column	10 ft $\times$ ¼ in. OD packed
column packing	15 wt % Carbowax 20M on Chromosorb W 80–100 mesh previously impregnated with 2 wt % potassium hydroxide
temperature of	
injection port	260°C
column	isothermal in the range between 135 and 150°C
detector	260°C
carrier gas and flow rate	50 ml/min
detector	thermal conductivity or flame ionization

The gas chromatographic analysis also permits the determination of volatile organic impurities present (see below).

(see below)

DETERMINATION OF IMPURITIES

The volatile organic impurities present can be determined from the gas chromatographic analysis. The peak of furfuryl alcohol emerges prior to the tetrahydrofurfuryl alcohol peak, while the peak of 1,2-pentanediol proceeds it.

The amount of furfuryl alcohol present can also be determined by the modified Hughes–Acree method (see p. 236). The amount of 1,2-pentanediol present may be determined by the following procedure.

Procedure

Dissolve 5.4 g of periodic acid in 100 ml of water contained in a 2-liter volumetric flask. Dilute with glacial acetic acid to volume and mix thoroughly.

Weigh 5 g of tetrahydrofurfuryl alcohol sample into a 100-ml volumetric flask and dilute to volume with chloroform. Transfer 50 ml of this solution to a 500-ml iodine flask, add 50 ml of the periodic acid solution, swirl to mix, stopper the flask, and let it stand for 30 min. Add 10 ml of 10% potassium iodide solution, mix thoroughly, and let it stand for 1 min, avoiding sunlight. Add 100 ml of water and a few ml of starch indicator solution, then titrate to a colorless end point with 0.1 N sodium thiosulfate solution.

Carry out blank determination with the amounts of reagents specified.

$$\text{1,2-Pentanediol} = \frac{(B - A)(N)(MW)(100)}{(w)(1000)}$$

where A = volume of sodium thiosulfate solution used for sample titration, in ml
B = volume of sodium thiosulfate solution used for blank titration, in ml
N = normality of sodium thiosulfate solution
MW = g-mol wt of 1,2-pentanediol (104.15)
w = sample weight, in g

POLYTETRAMETHYLENE ETHER GLYCOLS

Polytetramethylene ether glycols, $HO+CH_2-CH_2-CH_2-CH_2-O+_nH$, are polymeric diols ranging from liquids to waxy solids as the average molecular weight increases. The waxy solids melt to clear, viscous liquids at about 38°C. They are sold under the trade name of QO Polymegs (The Quaker Oats Co.).

Polytetramethylene ether glycols (PTMEG) are useful in polyurethan technology. Reaction with a molar excess of a diisocyanate results in NCO-terminated prepolymers which can be extended or crosslinked by subsequent reaction with polyols or polyamines. The resulting elastomers are used as thermoplastics, and in cast systems.

Highly elastic polyurethane fibers which are low in hydrolysis susceptibility are produced from PTMEG. When PTMEG with a molecular weight of 1000 reacts with isomeric toluene diisocyanates, the resulting prepolymers, with an approximate molecular weight of 2000, may react further with diamines to form elastic fibers.

The specific gravity of PTMEG at 35°C decreases with increasing molecular weight from 0.985 at 1000 molecular weight to 0.982 at a molecular weight of 2000. The viscosity of PTMEG varies with molecular weight and temperature, as indicated by the values listed in Table 13 (28).

Table 13. Viscosities of Polytetramethylene Ether Glycols

g-mol wt	Viscosity, cP	
	at 25°C	at 65°C
620	290	55
980	600	110
1460	1420	360
1900	2525[a]	440

[a] Supercooled liquid.

PTMEG is soluble in aromatic and chlorinated hydrocarbons, alcohols, esters, ketones, and nitroparaffins; very slightly soluble in aliphatic hydrocarbons; and slightly soluble in water, solubility decreasing with increasing molecular weight.

The open cup flash point is above 260°C.

No hazards have been encountered to date in handling PTMEG.

Commercial Grades and Specifications

PTMEG is manufactured by polymerizing tetrahydrofuran and is sold in the United States in four average molecular weight ranges. Their specifications are given in Table 14. Besides the items listed in this table, a number of other impurities are also controlled. Analysis of typical production lots is given in Table 15.

Table 14. Polymeg Specifications

Specification	QO Polymeg			
	650	1000	2000	3000
molecular weight	650 ± 50	1000 ± 50	2000 ± 100	3000 ± 150
hydroxyl number	160–187	107–118	53–59	35.6–39.4
acid number, wt %, max	0.05	0.05	0.05	0.05
moisture, wt %, max	0.05	0.05	0.05	0.05
volatiles, wt %, max	0.1	0.1	0.1	0.1
APHA color, max	100	100	100	200

Table 15. Typical Analysis of Commercial PTMEG Products

	QO Polymeg		
	650	1000	2000
peroxide (active oxygen), wt %		0.0018	0.0014
unsaturation, meq/g	0.0022	0.0011	0.0010
ash, ppm	10	10	10
calcium, ppm	1	3	3
iron, ppm	0.3	0.3	0.6
saponification number	0.00	0.00	0.00

Methods of Analysis

Polytetramethylene ether glycols are not assayed in the usual sense. Their analysis includes the determination of the molecular weight and further testing for impurities.

Molecular Weight Determination. Three methods are commonly used to determine the molecular weight of PTMEG. The preferred method is an acetylation procedure which determines a hydroxyl number which is used to calculate molecular weight (29).   A second method utilizing a phenyl isocyanate reaction can be used for most PTMEG and must be used for certain modified polytetramethylene ether glycols which are susceptible to cleavage of the ether linkage under the relatively harsh conditions of the acetylation procedure (30).   The third method utilizes vapor pressure osmometry, using methyl ethyl ketone as the solvent.   Methyl ethyl ketone effectively prevents association of the polymer molecules at the high concentrations necessary to evaluate PTMEG with average molecular weights in excess of 2000.   Procedures for the two methods are given below.   For vapor pressure osmometry, see MOLECULAR WEIGHT DETERMINATION, Vol. 2, pp. 627–636.

Procedures

ACETYLATION METHOD.   Using the following relationship,

$$\text{Sample size} = \frac{(56.1)(8)}{\text{approximate hydroxyl number}}$$

calculate the approximate sample size to be used in the determination.   Weigh the corresponding sample amounts into 250-ml iodine flasks.   Warm solid samples to facilitate sampling.   Add several glass beads as nonporous boiling chips.   Add 10 ml of 3:7 acetic anhydride–pyridine from a Koch automatic microburet to each flask and swirl to effect solution.   Attach air condensers to the flasks, seal the joints with pyridine in the wells, and reflux so gently that the vapors condense before reaching the neck of the flask for 30 min or more.

Cool the flasks in an ice bath.   Wash down the condensers and joints with 25 ml of pyridine followed by 50 ml of cold water.   Add 50 ml of N sodium hydroxide solution from an automatic pipet and 3–5 drops of a 1% phenolphthalein–pyridine indicator solution.   Finish the titration with N sodium hydroxide solution from a 10-ml microburet to a permanent pink end point.   Carry out blank determinations similarly, omitting the heating operation.

Calculate the uncorrected hydroxyl number, which is by definition the number of milligrams of potassium hydroxide equivalent to that amount of acid required to acetylate 1 g of sample, from the following equation:

$$\text{Hydroxyl number (uncorrected)} = \frac{(B-A)(N)(56.1)}{w}$$

where A = volume of sodium hydroxide solution required for sample titration, in ml

B = volume of sodium hydroxide solution required for blank titration, in ml

w = sample weight, in g

Hydroxyl number (corrected) = hydroxyl number (uncorrected) + acid number

$$\text{Molecular weight} = \frac{(56.1)(OH)(1000)}{(H)}$$

where OH = number of hydroxyls

H = corrected hydroxyl number

PHENYL ISOCYANATE METHOD.   The toluene and dimethylformamide used in this method must be distilled or dried over Linde molecular sieve 5-A until the water content is less than 0.01%.

Prepare N phenyl isocyanate reagent solution by adding 119 g of phenyl isocyanate to 500 ml of toluene and diluting to 1000 ml with toluene.

Prepare 2 N dibutylamine solution in toluene and 0.5 N perchloric acid solution in ethylene glycol monomethyl ether. Standardize the perchloric acid solution against 1.2 g of tris(hydroxymethyl)aminomethane (Fisher Primary Standard THAM) dissolved in water, using a 0.1% methanolic bromocresol green solution as the indicator for the titration.

Prepare a catalyst solution by diluting 2.1 g of stannous octoate (Catalyst T-9, M&T Chemicals, Rahway, N.J.) to 10 ml with toluene. Prepare this catalyst solution daily.

Pipet 25 ml of dimethylformamide into each of four 500-ml glass-stoppered Erlenmeyer flasks. Reserve two of these flasks for blank determinations. Into each of the sample flasks introduce an amount of sample calculated to contain not more than 11 meq of hydroxyl. Swirl each sample flask to effect solution. Pipet 20 ml of the N phenyl isocyanate reagent and 1 ml of the stannous octoate catalyst solution into each flask. Swirl to effect complete solution and allow to stand for 30 min.

Pipet 20 ml of the 2 N dibutylamine solution into each flask, swirl and allow to stand 15 min. Add 100 ml of ethylene glycol monomethyl ether and 6–8 drops of 0.1% methanolic bromocresol green indicator solution. Titrate with 0.5 N perchloric acid solution to the first definite yellow end point. The indicator changes color from blue to green to yellow.

$$\text{Molecular weight} = \frac{(w)(X)(1000)}{(B - A)(N)}$$

where w = sample weight, in g
X = number of hydroxyls per unit
A = volume of perchloric acid solution used for sample titration, in ml
B = volume of perchloric acid solution used for blank titration, in ml
N = normality of perchloric acid solution

Acid Number. The acid number of PTMEG is determined by titrating 10 g of sample in 50 ml of chloroform with 0.1 N potassium hydroxide solution to a phenolphthalein end point. A blank titration has to be carried out on the solvent.

$$\text{Acid number} = \frac{(A - B)(N)(56.1)}{w}$$

where A = volume of potassium hydroxide solution used for sample titration, in ml
B = volume of potassium hydroxide solution used for blank titration, in ml
N = normality of potassium hydroxide solution
w = sample weight, in g

Unsaturation. The unsaturation of PTMEG is determined by reaction with mercuric acetate and methanol producing acetoxymercuricmethoxy compounds and acetic acid. The amount of acetic acid released in this equimolar reaction is a measure of the unsaturation originally present. Before titration of the acetic acid, sodium bromide is added to convert the excess mercuric acetate to the bromide (29).

Procedure

Prepare mercuric acetate–methanol reagent by dissolving 40 g of mercuric acetate in methanol and diluting to 1 liter with methanol. Add 9–10 drops of glacial acetic acid, to require a blank titration of 1–10 ml of 0.1 N methanolic potassium hydroxide solution per 50 ml of reagent. Prepare the reagent weekly and filter before using.

Weigh duplicate 30-g samples of PTMEG into 250-ml glass-stoppered Erlenmeyer flasks. Dissolve each sample in 50 ml of methanol and titrate with 0.1 N methanolic potassium hydroxide solution to a phenolphthalein end point which persists for 15 sec. Record the average volume of titrants as A.

Pipet 50 ml of mercuric acetate solution into each flask, swirl, and allow to stand at room temperature for 30 min. Add 8–10 g of sodium bromide crystals to each flask and swirl to mix thoroughly. Add approximately 1 ml of 1% methanolic phenolphthalein indicator solution and titrate immediately with 0.1 N methanolic potassium hydroxide solution to a phenolphthalein end point which persists for at least 15 sec. Run two blank determinations in the same fashion. Record the average volume of titrants used for the sample titration as C and the average volume of titrants used for the two blank titrations as B.

$$\text{Unsaturation} = \frac{[C - (A + B)](N)}{w}$$

where A = average volume of potassium hydroxide solution used to neutralize the sample, in ml

B = average volume of potassium hydroxide solution used for two blank titrations, in ml

C = average volume of potassium hydroxide solution used for sample titration after the reaction, in ml

w = average weight of samples, in g

N = normality of potassium hydroxide solution

Peroxide Content. The peroxide content of PTMEG is determined by an iodine liberation procedure and back-titration with thiosulfate solution (30).

Procedure

Prepare a 1:9 solution of glacial acetic acid in isopropyl alcohol and a 20 wt/vol % solution of sodium iodide in isopropyl alcohol. Use a minimum amount of water to dissolve the sodium iodide prior to diluting to volume with isopropyl alcohol.

Accurately weigh duplicate 5–7 g of PTMEG samples into Erlenmeyer flasks. Pipet 25 ml of the acetic acid–isopropyl alcohol solution into each flask and swirl to dissolve the samples. Pipet 10 ml of the sodium iodide solution into each flask, add a boiling chip, attach to a condenser and reflux for 5–10 min.

Cool below the boiling point and add 5 ml of water. Titrate the contents of each flask with 0.02 N sodium thiosulfate solution to a colorless end point. Carry out a blank determination with the reagents.

$$\text{Peroxides, wt \%} = \frac{(A - B)(N)(16)(100)}{(w)(2)(1000)}$$

where A = volume of sodium thiosulfate solution used for sample titration, in ml

B = volume of sodium thiosulfate solution used for blank titration, in ml

N = normality of sodium thiosulfate solution

w = sample weight, in g

16 = atomic weight of oxygen

Moisture. The amount of trace moisture in PTMEG is determined by the Karl Fischer method. A back-titration with the dead-stop end point technique is used which permits titration of high impedance solutions (29). The principles of the determination are outlined below; for details on the reagent, such as standardization and calculation, see AQUAMETRY, Vol. 1, pp. 142–147.

Procedure

Warm the PTMEG sample, mix, and place 20–25 g in a Bailey weighing pipet. Weigh the sample and pipet.

Add 50 ml of 1:4 methanol–chloroform into the titration flask, add an excess of Karl Fischer reagent and titrate to a zero meter reading with the water–methanol standard solution.

Remove the flask from the titration assembly and add quickly 15–20 g of PTMEG from the weighing pipet. Determine and record the sample weight. Return the titration flask to the titration assembly and stir until dissolved. Add an excess of Karl Fischer reagent, about 10 ml, to the flask and titrate to a zero end point with the water–methanol standard solution.

Ash. The amount of ash is determined by a wet ashing procedure, with the addition of small amount of concentrated sulfuric acid (29).

Procedure

Weigh a 20–25 g sample of PTMEG into a tared crucible and add 5 drops of concentrated sulfuric acid. Warm on a hot plate to dryness or to a black residue. Transfer the crucible to a muffle furnace set at 250°C and burn off the sample gradually by increasing the temperature incrementally to 400°C. Do not permit the sample to ignite. Complete the ashing at 600°C for about 2 hr. Cool the crucible in a desiccator and weigh.

Volatile Substances. The volatile material in PTMEG is determined by subjecting a sample to a temperature of 150°C at 10 torr for a 10 min period (31) and determining the loss in weight.

Procedure

Set up a vacuum train by attaching a three-way stopcock to a trap cooled with dry ice by means of a vacuum hose containing a bleed valve. Connect the trap to a 2-liter suction flask which acts as a surge tank. Attach the surge tank to the manostat by a vacuum hose which is also attached to a McLeod gage and connect the manostat to a vacuum pump.

Add a magnetic stirring bar to a 200-ml distilling flask, place a thermometer in the neck of the flask by means of a rubber stopper, and determine the tare weight of the assembly on an analytical balance. Add 50–60 g of PTMEG and determine the weight of the flask assembly and sample to the nearest milligram.

Place a heating mantle around the flask and connect the side arm of the flask to the three-way stopcock of the vacuum train. Slowly decrease the pressure in the flask to 10 torr with stirring and then heat to 150°C and maintain for 10 min. Cool the flask to room temperature, allowing the pressure within the flask to return gradually to atmospheric pressure. Weigh the assembly and sample to the nearest mg.

$$\text{Volatiles, wt \%} = \frac{(W_2 - W_3)(100)}{(W_2 - W_1)}$$

where W_1 = tare weight of assembly, in g

$\qquad W_2$ = weight of flask plus sample, in g

$\qquad W_3$ = weight of flask plus sample after volatilization, in g

Bibliography

GENERAL REFERENCES

1. A. P. Dunlop and F. N. Peters, Jr., *The Furans, ACS Monograph 119*, Reinhold Publishing Corp., New York, 1953.
2. A. P. Dunlop, "Furfural and Other Furan Compounds," in A. Standen, ed., *Kirk-Othmer Encyclopedia of Chemical Technology*, Vol. 10, 2nd ed., Interscience Publishers, a division of John Wiley & Sons, New York, 1966, pp. 237–251.

SPECIFIC REFERENCES

3. *New Products Bulletins No. 4 (1949), No. 7 (1947)*, E. I. du Pont de Nemours & Co., Inc., Wilmington, Del.
4. *Q.O. Bulletin 149*, The Quaker Oats Co., Chicago, Ill., 1964.
5. O. W. Cass, *Chem. Ind.* **60**, 612 (1947).
6. U.S. Pat. 2,374,149 (April 17, 1945), G. M. Whitman (to E. I. du Pont de Nemours & Co., Inc.).
7. U.S. Pat. 3,007,941 (Nov. 7, 1961), H. B. Copelin and D. I. Garnett (to E. I. du Pont de Nemours & Co., Inc.).
8. *Q.O. Bulletin 148*, The Quaker Oats Co., Chicago, Ill., 1964.
9. *Bulletin FC4-362*, E. I. du Pont de Nemours & Co., Inc., Wilmington, Del.
10. A. P. Dunlop, P. R. Stout, and S. Swadesh, *Ind. Eng. Chem.* **38**, 705 (1946).
11. *Q.O. Bulletin 203*, The Quaker Oats Co., Chicago, Ill.
12. H. Gilman, R. E. Brown, and H. L. Jones, *Iowa State Coll. J. Sci.* **2**, 317 (1928).
13. *Ibid.*, **4**, 355 (1930).
14. A. Hinz, G. Meyer, and G. Schucking, *Chem. Ber.* **76**, 676 (1944).
15. D. L. Williams and A. P. Dunlop, *Ind. Eng. Chem.* **40**, 239 (1948).
16. J. E. Korenmann and S. B. Resnick, *Arch. Hyg. Bacteriol.* **104**, 344 (1930).
17. G. E. Youngberg and G. W. Pucher, *J. Biol. Chem.* **61**, 741 (1924).
18. A. H. J. Cross, S. G. E. Stevens, and T. H. E. Watts, *Chem. Abstr.* **52**, 4323b (1958).
19. R. Ercoli Mantica and L. Bicelli, *Chem. Abstr.* **53**, 3881c (1959).
20. L. W. Daasch, *Chem. Abstr.* **53**, 3882a (1959).
21. M. Fetizon and J. Guy, *Chem. Abstr.* **54**, 70d (1960).
22. K. Takano, *Chem. Abstr.* **56**, 10071d (1962).
23. Y. I. Khol'kin, *Chem. Abstr.* **61**, 15537f (1964).
24. E. Hughes and S. F. Acree, *Ind. Eng. Chem., Anal. Ed.* **6**, 123 (1934).
25. *Official Methods of Analysis*, 10th ed., Association of Official Agricultural Chemists, Washington, D.C., 1965, p. 336.
26. A. P. Dunlop and F. Trimble, *Ind. Eng. Chem., Anal. Ed.* **11**, 602 (1939).
27. A. P. Dunlop and F. N. Peters, Jr., *Ind. Eng. Chem.* **34**, 814 (1942).
28. *Q.O. Bulletin 150-B*, The Quaker Oats Co., Chicago, Ill.
29. *ASTM D 1638-67T, Testing of Urethane Foam Materials*, American Society for Testing & Materials, Philadelphia, Pa., 1969.
30. R. D. Mair and A. J. Graupner, *Anal. Chem.* **36**, 194 (1964).
31. *Publication WS 1034*, Bureau of Naval Warfare, Dept of U. S. Navy.

JOHN W. MADDEN
The Quaker Oats Company

FURFURAL.   See FURAN AND FURAN DERIVATIVES.

G

GADOLINIUM. See Rare earths.

GALLIUM

Gallium metal...251
Gallium alloys..269
Gallium compounds...275
Bibliography..283

GALLIUM METAL

Gallium, Ga, is a soft, silvery-white metal. It is a member of Group IIIA of the periodic table and possesses the electronic structure $[\mathrm{Ar}]3d^{10}4s^24p$. It exhibits three valences, $3+$ (common), $1+$, and $2+$, and its natural isotopic distribution is $^{69}\mathrm{Ga}$, 60.4 atom, %, and $^{71}\mathrm{Ga}$, 39.6 atom %.

Mendeleev in 1871 predicted the existence and properties of gallium (ekaaluminum). Four years later, Lecoq de Boibaudran discovered gallium by a spectroscopic method in zinc blende from the Hautes-Pyrénées, France. The properties of gallium observed by Boibaudran coincided almost exactly with those predicted by Mendeleev.

The average gallium content of igneous rocks is about 15 ppm. The only mineral that contains gallium as a major constituent is the very rare gallite, $CuGaS_2$. Germanite, $Cu_3(Fe,Ge)S_4$, another rare mineral, has been reported to contain a maximum of 1.85% Ga. Zinc blende formed at low temperatures and bauxite contain noteworthy amounts of gallium (about 100 ppm). Traces of gallium are found in many coals.

The most important use of gallium is the preparation of compound semiconductors such as gallium arsenide, gallium phosphide, etc. Gallium arsenide is used in various diodes. One such diode serves as a rectifier in microwave equipment. Gallium phosphide can be used as an electroluminescent diode. Gallium arsenide–phosphide, $GaAs_xP_{1-x}$, can be used as a semiconductor laser.

Other applications in research include the following. Gallium can be used as a thermometer for measuring high temperatures. Gallium forms low-melting alloys with indium, tin, zinc, etc. GaV_3 is a superconducting compound. Gallium halides, gallium oxide, and several other compounds of gallium show marked catalytic effects in Friedel-Crafts reactions, polymerizations, dehydrations, and the like.

Gallium oxide has been used in the emission spectroscopic analysis of U_3O_8 for impurity elements by the carrier–distillation method. In the presence of a small amount of gallium oxide, the uranium spectrum does not appear, but the spectra of the impurities are very distinct. For additional information, see the general references (1–7).

Properties

Selected properties of gallium are given in Table 1.

Gallium has a very low melting point and a very long liquid range. The density of the liquid near the melting point is greater than that of the solid and gallium solidifies with a 3.2% increase in volume.

The standard electrode potential ($E°$) for the reaction $Ga^{3+} + 3\,e \rightleftharpoons Ga$ is -0.56 V.

Gallium rather resembles aluminum in its chemical properties. In the cold, gallium is protected from atmospheric oxidation by a thin film of oxide. At red heat it is oxidized by air or oxygen. Water does not attack gallium. Gallium reacts with chlorine, bromine, and iodine to form gallium halides. Gallium dissolves in hot, concentrated hydrochloric, nitric, perchloric, and sulfuric acids. Gallium fluoride is formed by treating gallium with strong hydrofluoric acid. A mixture of hydrochloric and nitric acids is a good solvent for gallium. In sodium or potassium hydroxide solutions, gallium dissolves with the evolution of hydrogen and the formation of alkali metal gallates(III). Gallium forms alloys with many metals.

Hydrogen sulfide does not precipitate gallium in mineral acid solutions. Gallium sulfide is completely precipitated in weak acid solutions (eg, acetic acid–acetate) that contain precipitable elements such as arsenic or copper. Alkali hydroxides and ammonium hydroxide precipitate gallium hydroxide, but the hydroxide is soluble in an excess of alkali hydroxides, forming gallates. In dilute acid solutions, potassium ferrocyanide precipitates gallium in the form of the complex $Ga_4[Fe(CN)_6]_3$.

Table 1. Properties of Gallium

atomic number	31	coefficient of linear expansion, per °C	
atomic weight	69.72		
melting point, °C	29.78	for the a axis	1.65×10^{-5}
boiling point, °C	about 2000[a]	for the b axis	1.13×10^{-5}
crystal system	orthorhombic	for the c axis	3.1×10^{-5}
lattice constants, Å	$a = 4.5167$	coefficient of cubical expansion, per °C	
	$b = 4.5107$		
	$c = 7.6448$	0.10–29.65°C	5.5×10^{-5}
density, g/cm³		100°C	12.1×10^{-5}
solid, 20°C	5.907	vapor pressure, atm	
solid, 29.65°C	5.904	1179°K	1.53×10^{-7}
liquid, 29.8°C	6.095	1231°K	4.69×10^{-7}
liquid, 1100°C	5.445	1280°K	1.21×10^{-6}
Mohs hardness, 20°C	1.5–2.5	1332°K	3.47×10^{-6}
viscosity of liquid, cP		1357°K	5.11×10^{-6}
97.7°C	1.612	1383°K	8.75×10^{-6}
1100°C	0.578	reflectivity, %	
surface tension of liquid,		4360 Å	75.6
30–40°C, dyn/cm	735 ± 20	5890 Å	71.3
latent heat of fusion, cal/g	19.16	electrical resistivity at 0°C, $\mu\Omega$-cm	
latent heat of vaporization,			
cal/g	1014	along the a axis	16.1
specific heat, 29–127°C, cal/g	0.0977	along the b axis	7.5
thermal conductivity, 30°C,		along the c axis	50.5
cal/(sec)(cm²)(°C/cm)	0.07–0.09	ionization energy of $Ga \rightarrow Ga^+$, eV	6.00

[a] Literature values range from 1983 to 2400°C.

Methods of Manufacture

Gallium is usually recovered as a by-product in the zinc and aluminum metallurgical industries (1,3,4). Roasted zinc sulfide ore is leached with sulfuric acid to yield a crude zinc sulfate solution. Gallium is then precipitated from this solution as "iron mud" by neutralizing the excess of acid. The mud is then treated with sodium hydroxide solution to dissolve gallium and aluminum. Gallium is then separated from aluminum by ethereal extraction from hydrochloric acid solution. Gallium metal is deposited electrolytically from sodium hydroxide solution.

In the Bayer process, which uses bauxite as a starting material, aluminum hydroxide is crystallized from sodium aluminate solution. Gallium is concentrated in the waste liquor and finally is separated by electrolysis.

Another process for recovering gallium from sodium aluminate liquors in the Bayer process is based upon electrolysis with a mercury cathode. The mercury-containing gallium is then treated with sodium hydroxide solution to dissolve the gallium. Gallium is finally recovered from the alkaline solution by electrolysis.

Gallium can be purified by a variety of physical and chemical processes. These include treatment of the metal with hydrochloric or nitric acid, heating in vacuum, electrolysis, and fractional crystallization. Gallium chloride can be purified by zone refining.

Commercial Grades and Specifications

High-purity or semiconductor grade gallium available from American producers is said to be 99.9999% (8). Less pure grades, 99.999–99.9%, are also available.

Methods of Analysis

SEPARATION

Precipitation Methods. Precipitation methods are not very effective. Gallium can be separated from the alkali metals, magnesium, the alkaline earth metals, manganese, and nickel by precipitation with ammonium hydroxide in the presence of ammonium salts. Aluminum(III) and iron(III) precipitate with gallium.

Gallium is separated from aluminum, bismuth, cadmium, chromium, lead, manganese, mercury, and thallium by precipitation as gallium ferrocyanide from dilute (approximately 3 M) hydrochloric acid solution. Indium, zinc, and zirconium are also precipitated. The precipitate is fused with ammonium nitrate and the melt is treated with sodium hydroxide solution. Gallium is extracted as sodium gallate, leaving the iron as the oxide or hydroxide.

Gallium is separated from beryllium, cadmium, cobalt, manganese, nickel, thallium, and zinc by precipitation with tannin in 2% ammonium acetate–2% ammonium nitrate solution. The precipitate is ignited to oxide, and the oxide can be decomposed by fusion with potassium bisulfate.

Cupferron precipitates gallium in dilute (approximately M) sulfuric acid solution, but does not precipitate aluminum, chromium, indium, the rare earths, uranium(VI), or zinc. Iron, titanium, vanadium, and zirconium also are precipitated.

Camphoric acid or sodium camphorate precipitate gallium in dilute acetic acid solution. Gallium is thus separated from the alkaline earth metals, cadmium, chromium(VI), cobalt, lead, magnesium, manganese, nickel, and the rare earths, thallium(I), uranium(VI), vanadium, and zinc. Indium and iron(III) are precipitated.

Extraction Methods. Extraction of gallium from hydrochloric acid solution by ethyl or isopropyl ether is probably the most convenient method for the separation of μg and mg amounts of gallium from other elements, including aluminum. The empirical formula of the gallium complex in the ether phase is $HGaCl_4$ (9). The optimum hydrochloric acid concentration is 5.5–6.0 M for ethyl ether and 6.5–8 M for isopropyl ether. Under these conditions, iron(III), gold(III), and thallium(III) are extracted almost completely. Antimony, arsenic, germanium, molybdenum, tellurium, and tin are extracted to some extent. It has been reported that about 2% of indium of an original amount of about 100 mg is extracted before equilibration from 5.9–6.3 M hydrochloric acid into ethyl ether when using equal volumes of acid and ether (10). If iron(III) is reduced to iron(II) with a suitable reducing agent, eg, titanium(III) chloride, it is not extracted. At the same time, gold and thallium are reduced to metal and thallium(I), respectively, and they are then not extracted.

Gallium can be recovered from the ether phase by evaporating to dryness on a water bath. In the following procedure, ethyl ether can be used instead of isopropyl ether if the hydrochloric acid concentration is maintained at 5.5–6.0 M throughout the extraction.

Procedure

Transfer the sample solution to a separatory funnel and adjust the hydrochloric acid concentration to 6.5–7.0 M by having a total solution of about 50 ml. Add an excess of 15–20% titanium(III) chloride solution. After about 5 min extract twice with 50-ml portions of isopropyl ether. Wash the combined organic phase with a mixture of 1.0 ml of 7 M hydrochloric acid and 1 ml of the titanium chloride solution. Finally wash the organic phase with 10 ml of 7 M hydrochloric acid. Discard the aqueous phase and evaporate the organic phase to dryness on a water bath.

Another possibility is to form the 8-quinolinolate of gallium and extract it at pH 3.0 with chloroform. In this way, gallium can be separated from small amounts of aluminum, chromium(III), cobalt, lead, manganese, nickel, thorium, and uranium. Iron(III) will accompany gallium.

Ion Exchange Chromatography. Ion exchange chromatography provides a useful means of separating gallium. Both cation and anion exchange resins have been used.

Gallium is separated from antimony, copper, iron(II), lead, and zinc by passing a dilute (less than M) hydrochloric acid solution through a cation exchange resin, Dowex-50 (11). All the elements except gallium are eluted with M hydrochloric acid, and finally gallium is eluted with 1.3–1.5 M hydrochloric acid solution.

Anion exchange studies of a number of metals in hydrochloric acid solutions have been made by Kraus et al. (12,13). Gallium is very strongly adsorbed on strongly basic anion exchange resins from 5–12 M hydrochloric acid solution. Separation of aluminum, gallium, indium, and thallium(III) has been described (12). Approximately 4 ml of a 7 M hydrochloric acid solution containing 0.5 M Al(III), 0.15 M Ga(III), 0.15 M In(III), and 0.15 M Tl(III) is passed into a 20 cm $\times$ 0.4 cm^2 Dowex 1 column. Aluminum and indium are eluted with 7 M hydrochloric acid; the rate of elution of indium can be considerably increased by the use of 12 M hydrochloric acid. Subsequently, gallium is eluted with M hydrochloric acid and thallium(III) with 4 M perchloric acid. Iron(III) accompanies gallium, but iron(II) is eluted before gallium.

Thallium(I) will be eluted with aluminum and indium. Figure 1 shows a typical chromatogram obtained.

Table 2. Distribution Coefficients of Metal Ions in Two Solvents[a]

Metal ion	9:1 methanol–4.5 M HBr	0.45 M HBr
Mg(II)	2	2
Cd(II)	2	2
Sr(II)	2	2
Cu(II)	precipitation on the resin	precipitation on the resin.
Zn(II)	>400	5.5
Ca(II)	>1000	>600
Al(III)	2.1	2
Ga(III)	60	2.5
In(III)	165	9
La(III)	2.5	2
Yb(III)	2.5	2
Pb(II)	>1000	>400
Ti(IV)	2.1	2.1
Zr(IV)	3.9	3.8
Th(IV)		2
Bi(III)	>5000	>5000
U(IV)	2.1	2
Cr(III)	2.2	2
U(VI)	2.1	1.5
Mn(II)	2.2	2
Fe(II)	2.2	3
Co(II)	2.4	2.3
Ni(II)	2.3	2.3

[a] Column: 7 cm × 1.0 cm Dowex 1-X8, 100–200 mesh; sample size, 0.5 mg.

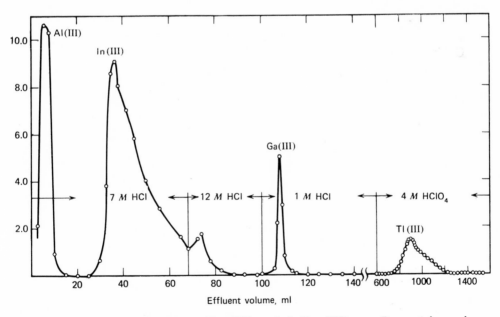

Fig. 1. Separation of indium(III), gallium(III), and thallium(III) on a Dowex 1 ion exchange column, at room temperature. Flow rate: 0.3–0.8 ml/min.

Gallium can be separated from aluminum, iron, uranium, and other elements by anion exchange chromatography, using a 9:1 mixture of methanol and 4.5 M hydrobromic acid as the solvent (14).   From this solution, gallium, together with copper, zinc, cadmium, indium, lead, and bismuth, is strongly adsorbed on the strongly basic anion exchange resin Dowex 1-X8.   Aluminum, iron(II), uranium(VI), and other elements pass into the effluent.   Subsequent elution with 0.45 M hydrobromic acid removes gallium, indium, and zinc, thus separating these metals from copper, cadmium, lead, and bismuth, which remain on the resin.   The effect of other acids or anions on the separability of gallium is not known.   The distribution coefficients of the various metal ions are listed in Table 2 (14); the procedure is given below.

Procedure

Treat Dowex 1-X8, 100–200 mesh, chloride form, with a concentrated solution of sodium carbonate until all the chloride ions are removed.   Wash the resin with hydrobromic acid, water, and methanol.   Soak the resin in 9:1 mixture of methanol and 4.5 M hydrobromic acid and then fill a 1.0 cm ID column to a height of 80 cm with the resin.

Dilute 5 ml of the sample solution in 4.5 M hydrobromic acid to 50 ml with methanol and add 100–200 mg of solid ascorbic acid.   Pass this sample solution through the resin column at a flow rate of approximately 0.4 ml/min.   After adsorption, wash the column with 20 ml of the methanol–4.5 M hydrobromic acid mixture containing a small amount of ascorbic acid.

Elute the gallium by means of 100 ml of 0.45 M hydrobromic acid.   Determine gallium in the eluate by titration with 0.01 M or 0.001 M solutions of ethylenediaminetetraacetic acid (EDTA) in the presence of a suitable indicator.

The anion exchange separation of aluminum, gallium, and indium in 2-methoxyethanol–hydrochloric acid or acetone–hydrochloric acid media is described in Vol. 5, pp. 210–211.

IDENTIFICATION

Gallium can be identified by spectrometric, colorimetric, and fluorescent methods (5,6).

Emission Spectroscopy.   Gallium can be detected by emission spectroscopy. The characteristic spectral lines are listed in Table 3.   Gallium can also be detected by a flame spectrophotometer, in an oxyhydrogen flame at 4172.1 and 4033.0 Å.

Colorimetric Methods.   Gallium gives characteristic colors with Rhodamine B, 8-quinolinol, and Pontachrome Blue Black R.

Detection by Rhodamine B.   Gallium in 6 M hydrochloric acid reacts with Rhodamine B, and the product is extractable with benzene (15).   The extract shows a red-violet color and an orange-red fluorescence in ultraviolet light.   The limit of identification is 0.5 μg of gallium.   Antimony(III), chromium(VI), gold(III), iron(III), mercury(II), thiocyanate, and tellurium(IV) interfere (16).   These ions may be re-

Table 3. Characteristic Spectral Lines of Gallium and Interfering Elements

Gallium line, Å	Interfering elements
4172.1	Cr, Fe, Ir, Mo, Os, Pd, Ti, V, CN-band
4033.0	Cr, Fe, In, Ir, Mn, Nb, Re, Sb, Ta, Ti
2943.6	Bi, Co, Fe, Ir, Mn, Ni, Ru, Ta, V, W
2874.2	Ag, Fe, Os, Pb, Pt, Re, Rh, Ru, Ta

moved by extracting gallium with ethyl or isopropyl ether from 6 M hydrochloric acid solution containing titanium(III) chloride.

Procedure

Prepare a 0.2% solution of Rhodamine B in 6 M hydrochloric acid. Transfer 1 drop of sample solution in 6 M hydrochloric acid to a small test tube. Add 3 drops of the Rhodamine B solution, 3–5 drops of benzene, and mix. If gallium is present, the benzene phase shows a red–violet color, or an orange–red fluorescence in ultraviolet light. Carry out a blank test.

Detection by 8-Quinolinol. Microgram amounts of gallium can be detected by adding 8-quinolinol to a solution having a pH of 2.6–3 and shaking with chloroform (17). In the presence of gallium, the chloroform layer shows a yellowish fluorescence in ultraviolet light. Small amounts of indium do not interfere if the extraction is done at pH 2.6. Iron(III) ions must be reduced to iron(II) by hydroxylamine hydrochloride. At pH 3, even 0.1 μg of gallium in 5–10 ml of the test solution gives a faint fluorescence (chloroform: 1 ml). The test is selective.

Detection by Pontachrome Blue Black R. Pontachrome Blue Black R is equivalent to CI Mordant Black 17 or CI 15705; it is 1-(2-hydroxy-1-naphthylazo)-2-naphthol-4-sulfonic acid (Calcon). This dye reacts with gallium in an acetate solution, and the product is extractable by amyl alcohol. The extract shows an orange fluorescence in ultraviolet light. The limit of identification is 0.5 μg of gallium (16). Aluminum, bismuth, cobalt, copper, gold, iron(II and III), and vanadium(IV and V) interfere.

Assay Methods

Gallium can be assayed by a number of gravimetric and volumetric methods. The purity of gallium metal can be checked by residual resistivity measurements (18).

Gravimetric Methods. Gallium can be determined by precipitation with various reagents.

Precipitation by Ammonium Hydroxide. An excess of ammonia must be avoided, for gallium hydroxide is appreciably soluble. The precipitation is preferably made in solutions that do not contain chlorides, because there is a possibility of losing gallium due to volatilization of gallium chloride. The following procedure is according to Hillebrand et al. (19).

Procedure

To about 200 ml of dilute sulfuric acid sample solution containing 10–100 mg of gallium, add a few drops of 0.2% ethanolic methyl red. Heat to boiling, and add a dilute ammonium hydroxide solution dropwise until the color of the solution changes to yellow. Add a small amount of paper pulp, boil for 1–2 min, and filter through a paper. Wash the precipitate with hot 2% ammonium nitrate solution, then dissolve the precipitate in as little hot dilute (eg, 3 M) sulfuric acid as possible, reprecipitate the gallium with ammonium hydroxide as before, and filter. Wash the precipitate with hot 2% ammonium nitrate solution. Transfer the paper and precipitate to a weighed platinum crucible, dry, char, and finally ignite at about 1000°C. Cool in a desiccator and weigh as Ga_2O_3. Repeat the ignition until a constant weight is obtained.

$$\text{Gallium, wt \%} = \frac{(W)(0.7439)(100)}{w}$$

where W = weight of Ga_2O_3 obtained, in g

w = sample weight, in g

Precipitation by Camphoric Acid. Gallium is precipitated as $Ga_2[C_8H_{14}(CO_2)_2]_3$ by camphoric acid or sodium camphorate from dilute acetic acid solution (20,21). The method is more selective than the precipitation by ammonium hydroxide. Gallium is conveniently separated by extraction with ether from hydrochloric acid solution containing a reducing agent (see p. 254) before its precipitation by camphoric acid (22,23).

Procedure

Evaporate a dilute hydrochloric acid or nitric acid solution of the sample, containing 5–70 mg of gallium, to dryness on a water bath. To the residue add 10 ml of 6 M acetic acid, 80 ml of water, and 20 ml of 10% ammonium nitrate solution. Heat the solution on a water bath and add 2 g of camphoric acid or 5 ml of 25% sodium camphorate solution. Allow to remain on the bath for 10 min, and then cool to room temperature. Filter the precipitate through filter paper and wash with a solution that contains 0.3 M acetic acid and 2% of ammonium nitrate. When sodium camphorate is used as a precipitant, wash the precipitate with an acetic acid–ammonium nitrate solution saturated with camphoric acid. Transfer the precipitate and paper to a weighed porcelain crucible, dry, char, and burn the paper and precipitate, and then ignite the residue at red heat. Cool in a desiccator and weigh the residue as Ga_2O_3.

Other Gravimetric Methods. Gallium hydroxide can be precipitated by sodium sulfite, urea, aniline, and pyridine. Tannin precipitates gallium from dilute acetate solution. In all cases, the precipitate is ignited and weighed as Ga_2O_3.

Cupferron precipitates gallium from dilute sulfuric acid solution. The precipitate, $[C_6H_5N(NO)O]_3Ga$, is ignited and weighed as Ga_2O_3. Gallium can be determined in the presence of aluminum by precipitating the former from M sulfuric acid (24). In the presence of zinc, the precipitation of gallium is made from 0.5 M sulfuric acid solution (24).

Determination of gallium with N-benzoyl-N-phenylhydroxylamine has been described (25). Other gravimetric reagents include 8-quinolinol, 5,7-dibromo-8-quinolinol, and sodium pyrrolidinedithiocarbamate.

Volumetric Methods. Gallium can be determined by titration with EDTA or with potassium ferrocyanide, and by titration of the gallium quinolinolate with potassium bromate.

Complexometric Titrations. Direct titrations of gallium with EDTA are carried out at pH 2–4. At higher pH, gallium is hydrolyzed. The pH range for back-titrations is wider. The reaction between gallium and EDTA is relatively slow, and the mixture is often heated to ensure rapid reaction.

Many indicators have been reported for the direct titration of gallium. They include copper–PAN (26), xylenol orange (27), pyrocatechol violet, gallocyanine, morin, and 8-quinolinol. A procedure using copper–PAN is described below.

Procedure

Prepare 0.01 M EDTA solution by dissolving 3.73 g of disodium ethylenediaminetetraacetate dihydrate in 1 liter of water. Standardize the solution against standard zinc solution in hydrochloric acid at pH 10 using aqueous ammonia–ammonium chloride buffer and eriochrome black T (EBT) as indicator. For the preparation of the EBT indicator solution, dissolve 0.4 g of EBT and 4 g of hydroxylamine hydrochloride in 100 ml of absolute methanol.

Prepare a copper–EDTA solution by mixing equivalent amounts of 0.01 M copper sulfate and 0.01 M EDTA solutions.

Prepare 1-(2-pyridylazo)-2-naphthol (PAN) solution by dissolving 0.1 g of PAN in 100 ml of ethanol.

Evaporate the sample solution, containing 1–10 mg of gallium, to dryness on a water bath. To the residue add about 90 ml of water, 2 ml of saturated sodium acetate solution, and about 14 ml of 1:1 acetic acid. Warm if necessary. Confirm or adjust the pH to 3.5 with sodium acetate or acetic acid, using test paper. Add 2 or 3 drops of the copper–EDTA solution and enough PAN solution to produce an intense violet color. Heat to boiling and titrate with 0.01 M EDTA solution until the color changes to yellow.

$$\text{Gallium, wt \%} = \frac{(V)(M)(AW)(100)}{(w)(1000)}$$

where V = volume of EDTA solution used for titration, in ml
     M = molarity of the EDTA solution
   AW = g at wt of gallium (=69.72)
    w = sample weight, in g

Many procedures have been described for the back-titration. Some of the indicators and standard metal solutions are: eriochrome black T, lead or zinc; xylenol orange, thorium; pyrocatechol violet, bismuth; potassium thiocyanate, cobalt; pyrogallol red or bromopyrogallol red, bismuth or lead.

Since many metals also react with EDTA, separation of gallium or masking of interfering ions is required in order to apply the titration methods to complex materials. Prior separations based on ether extraction and anion exchange from hydrochloric acid solution are useful (28). Fluoride sequesters aluminum in the EDTA titration of gallium at pH 1.6–2.0 (29) with copper–PAN indicator.

A method has been described for the determination of gallium in the presence of cadmium, cobalt, copper, indium, lanthanum, lead, nickel, zinc, and zirconium (30). In this method, gallium and other metals react with EDTA, at pH 6.5, then the pH is raised above 10.5, and the EDTA liberated by hydrolysis of the gallium complex is titrated. Aluminum is determined similarly and interferes with the determination of gallium.

Titration with Potassium Ferrocyanide. Gallium reacts with ferrocyanide in very dilute acid solutions to form a white precipitate of gallium ferrocyanide, $Ga_4[Fe(CN)_6]_3$. Gallium can be titrated potentiometrically with standard potassium ferrocyanide solution containing potassium ferricyanide (31,32).

The use of the dead-stop end point has been described in the titration of 0.05–0.17 mmoles of gallium nitrate (33). The optimum conditions are 230 mV, pH 2.0, and 50°C.

A redox indicator, 3,3′-dimethylnaphthidine or 3,3′-dimethylnaphthidinedisulfonic acid, can be used in the titration with potassium ferrocyanide (34). A small amount of potassium ferricyanide is added to the sample solution. The color change is from red to pale green. Gallium, in amounts of 0.7–2.9 mg, was determined with an average error of ±0.25 %.

The effect of other ions on the titration of gallium with ferrocyanide has not been throughly studied. At least zinc and indium are known to interfere.

Titration of the 8-Quinolinolate with Potassium Bromate. Gallium is precipitated quantitatively with 8-quinolinol, the oxine, or 8-hydroxyquinoline, from weakly acid, neutral, or slightly ammoniacal solution. Many elements, including copper, zinc, and iron(III), are also precipitated. The precipitate of gallium 8-quinolinolate, $Ga(C_9H_6NO)_3$, is dissolved in hydrochloric acid, and the 8-quinolinol liberated is titrated with potassium bromide–bromate solution:

$$BrO_3^- + 5\ Br^- + 6\ H^+ \longrightarrow 3\ Br_2 + 3\ H_2O$$

$$C_9H_7NO + 2\ Br_2 \longrightarrow C_9H_5Br_2NO + 2\ H^+ + 2\ Br^-$$

The standard potassium bromate solution containing potassium bromide is added to the sample solution in slight excess. Potassium iodide is then added, and the liberated iodine is titrated with standard sodium thiosulfate solution, using starch as indicator (35). The equivalent weight of gallium is $\frac{1}{12}$ the atomic weight. Gallium, in amounts of 14–28 mg, was determined with an error of $\pm 0.2\%$.

Determination in Trace Amounts

Gallium, in trace quantities, can be determined by a number of methods. Some of them are modifications of the methods already mentioned for the identification of gallium.

Spectroscopic Methods. Emission spectroscopy, as well as atomic absorption spectrophotometry, can be used for the determination of gallium.

Emission Spectroscopy. For the determination of gallium with arc or spark spectra, the following lines are usually used: 2874.2, 2943.6, 2944.2, 4033.0, and 4172.1 Å. The 4172.1 Å line is the most sensitive line of gallium, but the cyanogen band may interfere. This interference is alleviated by the use of an oxygen atmosphere (36). The next most sensitive gallium line, 4033.0 Å, is subject to the interference of manganese. In a dc arc, the 2943.6 Å line has been used by many analysts.

The ASTM standard method for the spectrochemical analysis of aluminum and its alloys by the point-to-plane technique includes the determination of 0.001–0.05% of gallium (37). Excitation is made with high-voltage spark or a condensed arc. Gallium lines of 2874.2 Å (spark) and 2943.6 Å (spark and arc) are used. The method is applicable primarily to the control analysis of chill-cast samples.

Flame Emission Spectroscopy. In an oxyhydrogen flame, less than 100 ppm of gallium in very dilute hydrochloric or nitric acid can be determined by the use of a flame spectrophotometer (38,39). The 4172 Å line is preferable to the 4033 Å line because of higher sensitivity and selectivity. The addition of acetone to the sample solution increases the sensitivity of the 4172 Å line (38).

Gallium can be determined by spraying the organic phase obtained by the solvent extraction into an oxyhydrogen flame. Gallium 8-quinolinolate in methyl isobutyl ketone (40) and gallium as $HGaCl_4$ in ethyl ether (41) have been utilized for the flame spectroscopic determination of gallium.

Atomic Absorption Spectrophotometry. Gallium can be determined in an air–acetylene flame. The sensitivity is 2 μg Ga/ml for 1% absorption at 2874 Å. The relative detection limit, which is defined as the concentration that produces absorption equivalent to twice the magnitude of the fluctuation in the background, is 0.1 μg/ml. As much as 0.5% of copper, magnesium, zinc, chloride, nitrate, phosphate, and sulfate do not interfere with the determination of 50 μg/ml of gallium. The recovery of gallium is 93% in solutions containing 0.5% aluminum (42).

Polarography. In acid solutions the polarographic wave for gallium is very close to the reduction wave of hydrogen. This makes the polarographic determination of gallium rather difficult. Nevertheless, several polarographic procedures have been developed.

In M ammonium hydroxide–M ammonium chloride solution gallium shows a wave whose half-wave potential ($E_{1/2}$) is about -1.6 V vs the saturated calomel electrode (SCE). Small amounts of gallium have been determined in 2.0 M ammonium hydroxide–saturated ammonium chloride solution after ion exchange separation (43).

Gallium can be determined in a pH 1 base electrolyte of perchloric acid, which is 0.1 M in sodium thiocyanate, 6.0 M in sodium perchlorate, and 0.1 M in toluene-sulfonic acid (maximum suppressor) (44). In this solution $Ga(SCN)_4^-$ is probably present. A reversible dc step is produced at $E_{1/2} = -0.781$ V vs SCE. The diffusion current is proportional to the gallium concentration in the range of 0.1–5×10^{-3} M.

A 1.3 M ammonium thiocyanate–1.1 M perchloric acid medium has been employed for an ac polarographic determination of gallium in iron and steel (45). A distinct peak is produced at -0.75 V versus the mercury pool. The peak height increases with increase in concentrations of thiocyanate and perchloric acid, and is proportional to concentration in the range 0.2–1.6 mg of gallium/25 ml of solution. Iron in amounts higher than 10 mg affects the peak of gallium, therefore gallium is previously separated by extraction with methyl isobutyl ketone. The absolute error is ±0.005% for 0.005–0.16% of gallium. In the following procedure, more than 1 mg of antimony and vanadium causes high results.

Procedure

Use a recording ac polarograph with the following settings: span voltage 2 V, parallel capacitance 0.4 μF. Use a 82.0 cm mercury head with the dropping-mercury electrode. Use a drop time of 4.32 sec and a flow rate of 0.634 mg/sec at -0.70 V vs the mercury pool in 1.3 M ammonium thiocyanate–1.1 M perchloric acid solution.

CALIBRATION. Weigh a number of gallium samples in the range between 0 and 1.6 mg into individual beakers, add 1 ml of 60% perchloric acid to each beaker, and evaporate just to dryness Dissolve the residues in small amounts of water and transfer each solution to a 25-ml volumetric flask. Add 0.3 ml of 60% perchloric acid and 5.0 ml of 50% ammonium thiocyanate solution to each flask and dilute to volume with water.

Transfer a portion of each standard solution into the electrolysis cell, holding the temperature at 23 ± 1°C. Deaerate with nitrogen and record the polarogram from -0.5 to -0.9 V vs the mercury pool. Plot the peak height at -0.75 V against gallium concentration. A straight-line calibration curve should be obtained.

GALLIUM IN IRON AND STEEL. Dissolve a 1.00 g sample in a mixture of 10 ml of concentrated hydrochloric acid and 3 ml of concentrated nitric acid. Add 10 ml of 60% perchloric acid and evaporate to strong fumes. Transfer the residue to a separatory funnel with 24 ml of water. To reduce iron(III), add 2 g of ascorbic acid and, after about 30 sec, add 30 ml of concentrated hydrochloric acid. Add 20 ml of methyl isobutyl ketone and shake for 1 min. Discard the aqueous phase. To back-extract gallium, shake the organic phase with two 10-ml portions of water for 1 min each. Combine the aqueous phases, add 2 g of ascorbic acid and, after about 30 sec, add 25 ml of concentrated hydrochloric acid. Shake with 20 ml of methyl isobutyl ketone for 1 min. Back-extract gallium with water as described above. Transfer the combined aqueous phase to a beaker, add 2 ml of concentrated nitric acid, and evaporate gently to dryness. Dissolve the residue in a small amount of water and transfer the solution to a 25-ml volumetric flask. Then complete the analysis as described for the calibration curve.

Other base electrolytes used for polarographic determination of gallium include: 1.0–2.0 M lithium chloride at pH 3.0–3.5 (46); 0.25 M glycine–0.1 M potassium chloride at pH 7.5–8.0 (47); 0.02–1.0 M catechol–0.1–1.0 M potassium chloride at pH 4–5 (48); and salicylate higher than 0.003 M at pH 2.8–3.4 (49).

Reduction of gallium–dye complexes has also been utilized for the determination of gallium. Superchrome Garnet Y has been used for determination of aluminum and gallium when both are present (50), and eriochrome violet for the determination of gallium in the absence of aluminum (51).

Anodic-stripping voltammentry of gallium has been studied (52). Traces of gallium in aluminum have been determined by this technique (53).

Neutron Activation Analysis. Traces of gallium can be determined by neutron activation. The pertinent data are shown in Table 4. Gallium-72 produced is usually used and its β activity or γ activity measured. For irradiation of 1 hr or less in a thermal neutron flux of 1.8×10^{12}, the estimated practical sensitivity is 0.005 μg Ga (54).

Table 4. Nuclear Characteristics of Gallium

Stable isotope	Abundance, %	Activation cross section, barns	Nuclide produced	Half-life	Major radiations and energies, MeV
^{69}Ga	60.4	1.4	^{70}Ga	21 min	β^- 1.65 max γ 0.173, 1.040
^{71}Ga	39.6	4.0	^{72}Ga	14.1 hr	β^- 3.15 max γ 0.601, 0.630, 0.835, 1.050, 1.465, 1.60, 1.860, 2.201, 2.50

Gallium-72 is produced by other nuclear reactions, for example, ^{72}Ge(n,p), ^{75}As-(n,α), and ^{235}U(n,f). However, the cross sections of all these reactions are likely to be low.

Gallium in aluminum, in concentrations of about 100 ppm, has been determined after radiochemical separation (55). Higher concentrations of gallium (0.02–0.1%) have been determined without separation (56). A procedure has been described for the determination of gallium in lead (57). Several methods have been developed to determine gallium in concentrations below 0.1 ppm and other impurities in a single sample of silicon by neutron activation analysis (58,59); these methods involve radiochemical separations and β counting.

Substoichiometric determination of traces of gallium in aluminum and silicon has been reported (60). After irradiation of the sample, interfering elements are removed by two extractions with cupferron and diethylammonium diethyldithiocarbamate. The 8-quinolinolate of gallium is formed and extracted into chloroform at a pH of 5.5, using a substoichiometric amount of 8-quinolinol.

Gamma activation has been used for determination of more than 200 ppm of gallium in indium or thallium (61). No separation is required.

Colorimetric Methods. Various reagents are used for the colorimetric determination of gallium.

Determination with Rhodamine B. The chlorogallate of Rhodamine B, (RH)-GaCl$_4$, where R represents the rhodamine dye, is extractable by either benzene (62), a mixture of chlorobenzene and carbon tetrachloride (63), or a mixture of benzene and ethyl ether (64). The intense red color and orange-yellow fluorescence of the extract provide sensitive means of determining small amounts of gallium. The optimum hydrochloric acid concentration for the extraction is about 6 M. The extractive efficiency of benzene also depends upon the Rhodamine B concentration. Because of incomplete extraction of gallium, the volume of the aqueous phase must be maintained constant. Beer's law is obeyed, and the sensitivity is 0.002 μg Ga/ml for an absorbance of 0.001 at 565 nm. The fluorometric determination is more sensitive than the absorptiometric.

Antimony(V), gold(III), thallium(III), and iron(III) interfere with the determination of gallium. Although these metals do not react if reduced to lower valences, it is more satisfactory to separate gallium from these and most other elements by ethereal extraction before applying the Rhodamine B reaction.

By the following procedure (62), 1–10 μg of gallium can be determined with an error of 5–10%.

Procedure

Dissolve 0.100 g of pure gallium or 0.134 g of Ga_2O_3 in a suitable amount of 6 M hydrochloric acid by heating gently. Dilute with 6 M hydrochloric acid to 100 ml in a volumetric flask. This solution has a gallium concentration of 1.00 mg/ml. Prepare a standard solution with a gallium concentration of 10 μg/ml by diluting 1.00 ml of this solution to 100 ml with 6 M hydrochloric acid. Prepare a Rhodamine B solution by dissolving 0.50 g of Rhodamine B in 100 ml of 6 M hydrochloric acid.

Evaporate the sample solution containing 1–10 μg of gallium to dryness on a water bath. Dissolve the residue in 5.0 ml of 6 M hydrochloric acid and transfer as completely as possible to a small, dry separatory funnel. Add 0.40 ml of Rhodamine B solution and 0.1 ml of 10% hydroxylamine hydrochloride solution and mix. Add 10.0 ml of benzene and shake for 1 min, allow to stand for a few min, and then drain off the aqueous phase and a small amount of the benzene phase. Transfer the benzene extract to a centrifuge tube and centrifuge for 3 min. Transfer the clear benzene extract to a clean, dry, 1-cm cell without rinsing. Rinse the cell several times with acetone between samples and dry by suction. Measure the transmittance of the solution at 565 nm, using benzene as a reference.

Establish the calibration curve by taking 0, 2, 4, 7, and 10 μg of gallium and proceeding as described above. Always carry out a blank determination.

Determination with 8-Quinolinol. Under proper conditions, gallium 8-quinolinolate can be quantitatively extracted into chloroform from aqueous solutions. Gallium can be determined in the pale yellow extract by either absorptiometric or fluorometric methods. The fluorometric method (yellowish fluorescence in ultraviolet light) is more sensitive and more selective than the absorptiometric method.

When an aqueous solution of pH 2.6–3.0 is extracted with chloroform, the only extractable 8-quinolinates that fluoresce are those of gallium, indium, and scandium (65,66). However, at a pH of 3.0, the fluorescence of indium is only about 1/500, and the fluorescence of scandium only about 1/40,000 of the fluorescence of an equal weight of gallium; thus, their interference is minor.

Procedure

Dissolve 2.04 g of potassium hydrogen phthalate in 100 ml of water. Dissolve 1.0 g of 8-quinolinol in 6 ml of glacial acetic acid by heating, and dilute with water to 100 ml.

Evaporate the sample solution containing 1–10 μg of gallium to dryness on a water bath, and dissolve the residue in 2.0 ml of 0.20 M hydrochloric acid. Transfer the solution to a small separatory funnel and wash with about 3 ml of water. Add 1 ml of 20% hydroxylamine hydrochloride solution, mix, and then add 6.0 ml of the potassium hydrogen phthalate solution. Mix and allow the solution to stand at room temperature for about 20 min.

Add 1 ml of 8-quinolinol solution, confirm that the pH of the solution is 2.6–3.0, and extract twice with 10-ml portions of chloroform. Filter the combined extracts through a small dry paper into a 25-ml volumetric flask. Dilute to the mark with chloroform. Measure the fluorescence intensity of the solution with a suitable fluorometer. Alternatively, compare the fluorescence intensity of the sample visually with that of the standards.

If 8-quinolinol in acetic acid solution is first added to a slightly acidic solution of gallium, and the pH is adjusted to 3.0–11.7 prior to the extraction with chloroform, an absorption maximum at 390 nm is obtained (67); for an absorbance of 0.001, the sensitivity is 0.010 μg of gallium/ml. Procedures utilizing extraction at pH 3.5 (68) or from a basic cyanide medium (69) have been described, from which the latter is more selective.

It should be mentioned that according to Nishikawa (70), 2-methyl-8-quinolinol (8-hydroxyquinaldine) is a more sensitive fluorometric reagent than either 8-quinolinol or the 5,7-dihalo-8-quinolinols.

Other Colorimetric Methods. Since the discovery of the reaction of gallium with Rhodamine B, many dyes have been proposed as reagents for the colorimetric and fluorometric determination of gallium. They include malachite green (71,72,45), crystal violet (73), and Astrazon Blue B (74). These dyes provide a sensitive and selective determination of gallium.

Gallium can be determined with 1-(2-pyridylazo)-2-naphthol (PAN) (75,76) and 4-(2-pyridylazo)-resorcinol (PAR) (77). These reactions are sensitive but not selective. However, the reaction with PAR can be made selective by first extracting gallium with a mixture of isopropyl ether and butyl acetate and then adding PAR to the separated organic phase (78).

Gallion, 2-(2-hydroxy-3-chloro-5-nitrophenylazo)-1-hydroxy-8-aminonaphthalene-3,6-disulfonic acid, has been used as a colorimetric reagent for gallium at pH 3 (79). Prior separation is generally required. Lumogallion, 4-chloro-6-(2,4-dihydroxyphenylazo)-1-hydroxybenzene-2-sulfonic acid, is a very sensitive fluorometric reagent for gallium (80,81). At pH 3, 1–5 μg of gallium in 25 ml can be determined by measuring the fluorescence intensity at about 580 nm. Aluminum, copper, iron(II and III), molybdenum, and vanadium interfere.

Other Methods. Gallium has been determined by x-ray fluorescence, by using the $GaK_{\alpha 1}$ line (82).

Electron probe microanalyzer has been used for determination of 0.1–2% of gallium in plutonium (83).

Mixtures of aluminum, gallium, and indium have been analyzed by solvent extraction with trifluoroacetylacetone in benzene followed by gas chromatography (84). The relative standard deviation was 2.0, 2.5, and 5.2% for 2.0 mg of aluminum, 5.0 mg of gallium, and 10 mg of indium, respectively. Copper interferes seriously with the determination of gallium.

Determination of Impurities

Physical Methods.   Emission, mass spectroscopy, and neutron activation analysis can be used for the determination of impurities in gallium metal.

Emission Spectroscopy.   Several methods have been described in the literature for the determination of impurities in gallium metal by emission spectroscopy (7,85–87).

Usually gallium is removed by ether extraction, and impurities that remain in the aqueous phase are determined by emission spectroscopy.   The procedure for the emission spectroscopic analysis of gallium arsenide (see pp. 275–278) should be applicable to gallium if the following dissolution procedure is carried out.

Procedure

Dissolve 1 g of sample by heating with a mixture of 10 ml of concentrated hydrochloric acid and 1 ml of 0.05 M sulfuric acid.   Evaporate the solution to about 5 ml, then transfer it to a 5-ml polyethylene bottle with 6 ml of 8 M hydrochloric acid.   Extract gallium with 15, 10, and 10 ml of isopropyl ether according to the procedure given on p. 254 and continue as described there.

Mass Spectroscopy.   Spark-source mass spectroscopy has been employed for the determination of less than 10 ppm of aluminum, boron, calcium, copper, indium, lead, magnesium, potassium, sulfur, tin, and zinc (88).

Neutron Activation Analysis.   Traces of impurity elements in gallium have been determined by neutron activation analysis (89).   For determination with long-lived nuclides, the sample is irradiated with a neutron flux of 6×10^{13} n(cm^{-2})(sec^{-1}) for 3–4 days.   For determination of elements with short-lived nuclides (Cd, Cu, Ge, Mn, and W), the sample is irradiated with a neutron flux of 1×10^{13} n(cm^{-2})(sec^{-1}) for 3–4 hr.   Chemical separation methods have also been developed for both long-lived

Table 5.   Activation Analysis of Gallium and Gallium Arsenide (sample, 500 mg) (89)

Element	Radionuclide determined	Lower limit of determination, ppm
Sb	^{124}Sb	2×10^{-4}
Cd	^{115}Cd	4×10^{-4}
Cr	^{51}Cr	4×10^{-5}
Co	^{60}Co	1×10^{-4}
Cu	^{64}Cu	5×10^{-5}
Ge	^{77}Ge	2×10^{-3}
Au	^{198}Au	2×10^{-6}
In	^{114m}In	4×10^{-4}
Ir	^{192}Ir	2×10^{-5}
Fe	^{59}Fe	2×10^{-3}
Mn	^{56}Mn	6×10^{-4}
Hg	^{203}Hg	1×10^{-5}
Ni	^{58}Co	2×10^{-3}
Sc	^{46}Sc	1×10^{-4}
Se	^{75}Se	1×10^{-4}
Ag	^{110m}Ag	4×10^{-4}
Ta	^{182}Ta	4×10^{-4}
Te	^{125m}Te	6×10^{-4}
Sn	^{113}Sn	8×10^{-4}
W	^{187}W	1×10^{-4}
Zn	^{65}Zn	1×10^{-4}

Table 6. Chemical Methods Applicable for the Determination of Impurities in Gallium Metal

Element	Method	Range, ppm	Reference
Ag	photometric titration with dithizone		(90)
Al	Ga removed by extraction; colorimetric determination as the 8-quinolinolate	>1	(91)
As	arsenic separated by extraction with diethyldithiocarbamic acid in chloroform; colorimetric determination as molybdenum blue	>0.25	(7)
Bi	photometric titration with thiourea		(90)
Cd,Cu,In, Pb,Zn	polarographic determination in 0.1 M hydrochloric acid—M potassium bromide or 0.1 M sodium acetate–0.1 M acetic acid		(90)
Co	photometric determination with nitroso-R salt		(90)
Cu	photometric determination with dithizone		(90)
Cu,Fe	photometric determination of Cu with bathocuproine, and of Fe with bathophenanthroline	>0.5	(91)
Fe	Fe separated by extraction of its cupferrate into chloroform; colorimetric determination with potassium thiocyanate	0.2–2	(7)
H	vacuum fusion	>3	see Vol. 8, pp. 616 and 681
In	In separated by coprecipitation with cobalt sulfide and by extraction with dithizone in carbon tetrachloride; polarographic determination in 0.2 M hydrochloric acid	2–10	(92)
Mn	photometric determination as permanganate		(90)
Ni	photometric determination with α-furildioxime	>0.1	(7)
O	vacuum fusion	>30	(7)
P	Ga removed by ether extraction; colorimetric determination as molybdenum blue	>0.2	(7)
Pt	photometric titration with dithizone		(90)
S	S separated as hydrogen sulfide; photometric (turbidimetric) determination as lead sulfide	>0.4	(7)
Sb	Sb separated by extraction with diethyldithiocarbamic acid in chloroform and by ether extraction of the pyridine–iodide complex; photometric determination with phenylfluorone	>0.5	(7)
Se	Se precipitated on As with hypophosphite; fluorometric determination with 3,3′-diaminobenzidine	>0.1	(7)
Si	Ga removed by volatilization as 8-quinolinolate; photometric determination as molybdenum blue	>1	(7)
Sn	Sn(II) extracted with diethyldithiocarbamic acid in chloroform; colorimetric determination with p-nitrophenylfluorone	>0.5	(7)
Te	Te coprecipitated with S by hydroxylamine hydrochloride; polarographic determination	>0.2	(7)
Zn	extracted with dithizone; photometric determination	>0.5	(91)

and short-lived radionuclides. Because highly radioactive [72]Ga and [76]As are formed, suitable shielding is required. The error of the determination is estimated to be about 20%. The lower limits of the determination are given in Table 5.

Chemical Methods. Table 6 summarizes the information related to the determination of impurities in gallium metal. The table lists the impurity element, the method which can be used for its determination, the concentration range where the method is applicable, and a reference where more information can be obtained.

Methods for the determination of the most important impurities—aluminum, copper, iron, and zinc are discussed in more detail below.

Aluminum. In the following procedure (91), gallium is removed completely by extraction with isopropyl ether and diethyldithiocarbamate–ethyl acetate. Aluminum is then determined photometrically with 8-quinolinol. The method is suitable for determination of more than 1 ppm of aluminum.

Procedure

Wash isopropyl ether with 8 *M* hydrochloric acid. Prepare an 8-quinolinol solution by dissolving 1.0 g of reagent in 3 ml of glacial acetic acid and diluting to 100 ml with water. Prepare a sodium diethyldithiocarbamate solution by dissolving 5 g of reagent in 100 ml of water.

Dissolve 2.00 g of sample by heating with a mixture of 10 ml of concentrated nitric acid and 10 ml of 6 *M* hydrochloric acid, and evaporate almost to dryness. Dissolve the residue in 20 ml of 8 *M* hydrochloric acid. Transfer the solution to a separatory funnel and wash the vessel with 10 ml of 8 *M* hydrochloric acid. Shake with 50 ml of isopropyl ether for 2 min. Transfer the aqueous phase to another separatory funnel and shake with two 25-ml portions of isopropyl ether. Transfer the aqueous phase to a beaker, add 1 ml of perchloric acid, and evaporate to dryness. Add 5 ml of 6 *M* hydrochloric acid and evaporate to a volume of about 2 ml. Add 5 ml of 10% sodium acetate solution and 10 ml of water and adjust the pH to 3 with ammonium hydroxide. Transfer the solution to a separatory funnel. Add 5 ml of the sodium diethyldithiocarbamate solution, mix, and allow to stand for about 10 min. Shake with 10 ml of ethyl acetate for about 2 min, and discard the organic phase. Add 5 ml of the diethyldithiocarbamate solution again and extract with 10 ml of ethyl acetate. Transfer the aqueous phase to a beaker, add 1 ml of 6 *M* hydrochloric acid, and boil down to a volume of about 20 ml. Cool.

Add 2 ml of 10% ammonium citrate solution, 3 ml of the 8-quinolinol solution, 1 ml of a 30% hydrogen peroxide solution, and 20 ml of water. Adjust the pH to 9.0 with ammonium hydroxide. Transfer the solution to a separatory funnel and shake with 10.0 ml of chloroform for about 2 min. Transfer the organic phase to an Erlenmeyer flask containing 0.5 g of anhydrous sodium sulfate. Measure the absorbance of the solution in a 1-cm cell at 390 nm against chloroform. Carry out a blank determination.

For the preparation of the calibration curve, weigh a number of pure aluminum samples in the range of 0–10 μg, add to each 1 ml of 6 *M* hydrochloric acid, 5 ml of 10% sodium acetate solution, 2 ml of 10% ammonium citrate solution, 3 ml of the 8-quinolinol solution and 1 ml of a 30% hydrogen peroxide solution. Dilute to about 40 ml with water, adjust the pH to 9.0, and continue as described above.

Copper and Iron. In the following procedure (99), copper is determined photometrically with bathocuproine (2,9-dimethyl-4,7-diphenyl-1,10-phenanthroline). After extraction of the copper(I)–bathocuproine complex, iron is determined photometrically with bathophenanthroline (4,7-diphenyl-1,10-phenanthroline). The method is suitable for determination of more than 0.5 ppm of copper and iron.

Procedure

PREPARATION OF REAGENTS. Prepare a 0.1% solution of bathocuproine in ethanol.

Prepare a 0.2% solution of bathophenanthroline in ethanol.

Prepare a hydroxylamine hydrochloride–ascorbic acid solution by dissolving 20 g of hydroxylamine hydrochloride and 20 g of ascorbic acid in 200 ml of water.

Purify the solution as follows. Adjust the pH to 5.5 with ammonium hydroxide and add 10 ml of bathophenanthroline solution and 20 ml of ethanol. Shake with 30-ml portions of isoamyl alcohol until the organic phase becomes colorless.

Prepare an ammonium citrate–ammonium acetate solution by dissolving 125 g of ammonium citrate and 63 g of ammonium acetate in 500 ml of water. Purify the solution as follows. Add 10 ml of hydroxylamine hydrochloride–ascorbic acid solution and adjust the pH to 5.5 with ammonium hydroxide. Heat on a water bath, add 10 ml of bathophenanthroline solution and 20 ml of ethanol, heat for about 10 min, and cool. Then extract with 30-ml portions of isoamyl alcohol until the organic phase has become colorless.

DETERMINATION. Dissolve 2.00 g of sample by heating with a mixture of 10 ml of concentrated nitric acid and 10 ml of 6 M hydrochloric acid, and evaporate almost to dryness. Dissolve the residue in 10 ml of 6 M hydrochloric acid and add 10 ml of water, 5 ml of the hydroxylamine hydrochloride–ascorbic acid solution, and 20 ml of the ammonium citrate–ammonium acetate solution. Adjust the pH to 5.5 with ammonium hydroxide, and transfer the solution to a separatory funnel.

Add 2 ml of the bathocuproine solution, mix, and allow to stand for about 10 min. Add 10 ml of isoamyl alcohol and shake for about 2 min. When the layers have separated, drain the aqueous phase into another separatory funnel and shake with 5 ml of chloroform. Discard the chloroform phase. Use the aqueous phase for the determination of iron. Wash the isoamyl alcohol phase with two 5-ml portions of water. Dilute the organic phase to 15.0 ml with ethanol. Measure the absorbance of the solution in a 2-cm cell at 476 nm against isoamyl alcohol. Determine the concentration of copper from the calibration curve.

Transfer the aqueous phase for the determination of iron to a beaker and heat to about 90°C on a water bath. Add 10 ml of ethanol and 4 ml of the bathophenanthroline solution, and heat for about 10 min. After cooling, transfer the solution to a separatory funnel. Add 10 ml of isoamyl alcohol and shake for about 2 min. When the layers have separated, drain off and discard the aqueous layer. Wash the isoamyl alcohol phase with two 5-ml portions of water. Dilute the organic phase to 15.0 ml with ethanol. Measure the absorbance of the solution in a 2-cm cell at 532 nm against isoamyl alcohol. Determine the concentration of iron from the calibration curve.

CALIBRATION. Establish the calibration curves by carrying a series of samples containing 0–10 μg each of copper and iron through the entire procedure.

Zinc. Zinc is first extracted with a carbon tetrachloride solution of dithizone (91) at a pH of 7.0–7.5 and then back-extracted with 1.2 M hydrochloric acid. This is followed by a second extraction with dithizone at pH 5.5 in the presence of N,N'-hydroxyethyldithiocarbamate as a masking agent. The excess of dithizone is removed by washing with sodium sulfide solution. The method is suitable for determination of more than 0.5 ppm of zinc.

Procedure

PREPARATION OF REAGENTS. Prepare a dithizone stock solution by dissolving 60 mg of the reagent in 100 ml of carbon tetrachloride. Before use prepare solutions containing 6 mg of dithizone/100 ml and 3 mg of dithizone/100 ml by diluting the stock solution with carbon tetrachloride.

Prepare an ammonium citrate solution by dissolving 250 g of the reagent in 500 ml of water. Purify the solution as follows. Adjust the pH to 7.0–7.5 with ammonium hydroxide and shake with 10-ml portions of the 60 mg/100 ml dithizone solution until the organic phase shows no color change.

Prepare an ammonium acetate solution by dissolving 30 g of the reagent in 300 ml of water. Purify the solution by shaking with 10-ml portions of the 60 mg/100 ml dithizone solution.

Prepare a N,N'-hydroxyethyldithiocarbamate solution by dissolving 0.6 ml of monoethanolamine in 12 ml of methanol, adding 0.3 ml of carbon disulfide, and diluting to 100 ml with water. Prepare fresh before use.

Prepare a sodium sulfide solution by dissolving 1 g of sodium sulfide in 100 ml of water. Before use dilute 4 ml of this solution to 100 ml with water.

DETERMINATION. Dissolve 2.00 g of sample by heating with 10 ml of concentrated nitric acid and 10 ml of 6 M hydrochloric acid, and evaporate almost to dryness. Dissolve the residue in 10 ml of 6 M hydrochloric acid and add 10 ml of ammonium citrate solution and 10 ml of water. Adjust the pH to 7.0–7.5 with ammonium hydroxide, and transfer the solution to a separatory funnel.

Shake successively with 10 and 5 ml of the 6 mg/100 ml dithizone solution. Combine the organic phases and shake with 10 ml of 1.2 M hydrochloric acid to back-extract zinc. Wash the aqueous phase with 5 ml of carbon tetrachloride. Transfer the aqueous phase to a beaker, add 5 ml of ammonium acetate solution, and adjust the pH to 5.5 with ammonium hydroxide. Transfer the solution to a separatory funnel and dilute to about 50 ml with water. Add 5 ml of the N,N'-hydroxyethyldithiocarbamate solution and shake successively with 10.0 and 5.0 ml of the 3 mg/100 ml dithizone solution. Combine the organic phases and wash with 5 ml of water and then with 5-ml portions of sodium sulfide solution until the aqueous phase has become colorless. Measure the absorbance of the organic phase in a 1-cm cell at 530 nm against carbon tetrachloride. Carry out a blank determination.

CALIBRATION. Establish a calibration curve by taking a graded series of zinc samples between 0 and 10 μg, adding 10 ml of 1.2 M hydrochloric acid and 5 ml of ammonium acetate solution, and then continuing as described above.

GALLIUM ALLOYS

Phase diagrams for binary alloys of gallium with one of the following elements are available (93,94): aluminum, antimony, arsenic, beryllium, bismuth, cadmium, cobalt, copper, germanium, gold, indium, lead, magnesium, manganese, mercury, nickel, palladium, praseodymium, silicon, silver, sodium, tellurium, thallium, tin, titanium, uranium, zinc, and zirconium.

For more details on the various gallium alloys, see Reference 4. The analytical methods related to the most important gallium alloys are discussed below.

ANTIMONY–ALUMINUM ALLOYS

Methods of Analysis

These alloys contain 65–81% of antimony, 0.8–16% of aluminum, and 2.9–34% of gallium. For the determination of antimony, the sample is dissolved in sulfuric acid and ammonium sulfate and the solution is titrated with potassium bromate.

For the determination of aluminum and gallium, the sample is dissolved in a mixture of hydrochloric acid and nitric acid, and antimony is oxidized with potassium bromate. Gallium and antimony are extracted with butyl acetate. Aluminum in the aqueous phase is determined in an acetate solution by adding excess of EDTA and back-titrating with standard thorium solution using Alizarin Red S as the indicator. Gallium in the organic phase is back extracted with tartaric acid solution. It is determined at pH 8 by adding excess EDTA and back-titration with standard zinc solution using eriochrome black T as indicator.   For details see Reference (95).

COPPER ALLOYS

The existence of CuGa$_2$ has been established.

Methods of Analysis

Gallium can be determined by precipitation with ammonia after precipitating the copper with hydrogen sulfide or sodium thiosulfate (96).   A more convenient method for gallium determination utilizes flame spectroscopy (39).   Copper causes a slightly positive interference, therefore copper is added to the standard gallium solutions used to obtain the calibration curve.   Iron, aluminum, and indium also cause slightly positive interferences, and zinc a slightly negative interference.   Thallium does not interfere.   Variation of the concentration of hydrochloric and nitric acids up to 0.5 M shows no effect.   The procedure is suitable to determine gallium in concentrations of 0.05–1%, with a maximum absolute error of 0.01%.

Procedure

Prepare a gallium stock solution by dissolving 1.00 g of the metal in a minimum amount of hydrochloric acid and diluting to 1 liter with water.   Prepare a copper solution by dissolving 4.00 g of the metal in a minimum amount of nitric acid and diluting to 1 liter with water.

Use an instrument such as a Beckman Model DU flame spectrophotometer with a Model 4300 photomultiplier attachment and a Model 4020 hydrogen burner, modified to have fine adjustment for the dark current control, a "bucking" circuit to balance the potential developed by the flame background, and an added 66-MΩ load resistor.   Warm up the instrument for about 1 hr, and allow the oxyhydrogen burner to burn for 10 min before running samples.   Adjust the oxygen pressure, the hydrogen pressure and flow, and the wavelength dial to give maximum sensitivity for gallium at 417.2 nm.

To obtain the calibration curve for 0–1% gallium in the alloy, prepare solutions containing 0–10 ppm of gallium and 995 ppm of copper.   Fix the slit width at 0.1 mm, and adjust the sensitivity so that the concentration range of 0–10 ppm of gallium represents about 100 units on the transmission scale.   Adjust the bucking circuit so that 0 ppm of gallium represents about 3 units on the transmission scale.   Place the selector switch in the 0.1 position at all times.   Plot the calibration curve which should be linear.

For the determination of gallium in samples, dissolve a 0.100 g sample in a minimum amount of nitric acid, and dilute to 100 ml with water.   Proceed as for the calibration curve.

GOLD ALLOYS

The existence of AuGa and AuGa$_2$ has been established and their structures studied.

Methods of Analysis

Gallium (1–5%) in gold–gallium alloys can be determined photometrically with 1-(2-pyridylazo)-2-naphthol (PAN) (97).   The color is developed in an acetone–water medium of pH 4.5.

Procedure

Prepare aqua regia immediately before use by mixing 3 vol of concentrated hydrochloric acid, 1 vol of concentrated nitric acid, and 4 vol of water.

Prepare an acetate buffer solution by dissolving 8.2 g of sodium acetate and 5 ml of glacial acetic acid in 100 ml of water.

Prepare a 0.1% PAN solution by dissolving the reagent in acetone.

Dissolve 25 mg of sample in 3 ml of aqua regia by heating on a water bath and dilute the solution to 250 ml with water. Transfer a 10-ml aliquot to a 25-ml volumetric flask, add 5 ml of the acetate buffer solution, 7.0 ml of acetone, 1.0 ml of the PAN solution, and dilute to volume with water. After about 10 min, measure the absorbance in a 1-cm cell at 540 nm against a reagent blank.

Construct a calibration curve with solutions containing a graded series of gallium samples between 0 and 80 μg.

INDIUM ALLOYS

The indium–gallium system has an eutectic at 24.5 wt % of gallium with a melting point at 15.7°C.

Methods of Analysis

Gallium in micro samples of indium–gallium alloys has been determined by emission spectroscopy using graphite electrodes, and molybdenum as an internal standard (98). For 0.2–1.0% of gallium, the error ranged from 11 to 22%.

Procedure

Prepare 3.8 cm $\times$ 0.46 cm graphite electrodes with flat ends. Prepare a standard indium solution by dissolving 200 mg of indium in 100 ml of concentrated hydrochloric acid. The concentration of the solution is 2 mg/ml. Prepare a standard gallium solution by dissolving 10 mg of gallium in 100 ml of concentrated hydrochloric acid. The concentration of the solution is 0.1 mg/ml.

Prepare a standard molybdenum solution by dissolving ammonium molybdate in water. The concentration of the solution is 0.005 mg/ml.

Use these indium and gallium standard solutions to prepare solutions having a gallium concentration ranging from 0.1 to 1.2%. This range is equivalent to an indium–gallium alloy sample solution with an alloy concentration of 0.100 mg/ml. Keep the hydrochloric acid concentration of the solutions between 1 and 2 M.

Weigh a microsample of indium–gallium alloy on a microbalance and transfer it to a 1-ml volumetric flask. Dissolve it by heating at 90–100°C with 0.1–0.3 ml of 8 M hydrochloric acid. Dilute the solution to between 1 and 2 M by diluting the sample with water and/or M hydrochloric acid in order to obtain a final alloy concentration of 0.100 mg/ml and an acid concentration between M and 2 M. For example, if the sample weighs 0.056 mg, dissolve it in 0.15 ml of 8 M hydrochloric acid and dilute with 0.41 ml of water.

Add 2 drops of a solution of 1 g of Apiezon grease in 200 ml of petroleum ether to both the upper and lower electrodes. Dry the electrodes with an infrared lamp and add 0.05 ml of the standard molybdenum solution to both electrodes. Dry the electrodes, add 0.05 ml of the sample solution to both electrodes, and dry again. Spark the samples within 30 min after they have been prepared on the electrodes. Keep the samples under an infrared lamp until they are sparked. Use the following conditions:

spectrograph	Bausch and Lomb Large Littrow Prism or equivalent
wavelength region	2490–3470 Å
slit width	30 μm
slit height	1.5 mm
source to slit distance	61 cm
aperture at collimator	16 mm
excitation unit	National Spectrographic Laboratories Spec Power, or equivalent
analytical gap	2 mm
auxiliary gap	2 mm
output voltage	8000 V
capacitance	0.005 μF
inductance	0.600 mH
secondary resistance	3 Ω
discharges/half cycle	7
exposure time	20 sec
plate	Kodak Spectrum Analysis 103–0 or equivalent
processor	National Spectrographic Laboratories Plate Processor or equivalent; processed according to standard procedures

Determine the transmittances of the gallium 2874.2 Å line and the molybdenum 2879 Å line with a nonrecording microphotometer. Convert these transmittance values to relative intensities using an emulsion calibration curve. Obtain the gallium content from the calibration curve.

To obtain the calibration curve, determine the intensity ratios of the Ga 2874.2 Å line vs the Mo 2879 Å line obtained on five indium–gallium standards containing 0.1, 0.2, 0.6, 1.0, and 1.2% of gallium and plot them on two cycle log–log graph paper against the gallium content. A straight line should be obtained.

An oscillopolarographic method has also been described for the determination of less than 1% of gallium in indium–gallium alloys (99). A polarogram is recorded in ethanolic 0.2 M tetraethylammonium iodide solution, and the peak height at -1.70 V vs the standard calomel electrode is measured.

MAGNESIUM ALLOYS

The existence of Mg_5Ga_2, Mg_2Ga, $MgGa$, and $MgGa_2$ has been established. Gallium in these alloys is determined by precipitation with ammonia (96) (see p. 257).

NIOBIUM ALLOYS

The existence of Nb_3Ga has been established. It possesses a cubic crystalline structure.

Methods of Analysis

Gallium in niobium–gallium alloys has been determined by complexometric titration after ethyl ether extraction (100). The sample is dissolved in the mixture of nitric and hydrofluoric acids and the solution is evaporated with sulfuric acid. Gallium is extracted with ethyl ether from 5 M hydrobromic acid solution. It is finally determined by back-titrating the excess of EDTA with a standard zinc solution at pH 8.5–9.0, using eriochrome black T as the indicator.

PLUTONIUM ALLOYS

Six intermediate phases of plutonium—gallium alloys are stable at room temperature.

Methods of Analysis

Gallium in plutonium–gallium alloys can be determined by complexometric titration after anion exchange separation using hydrochloric acid (27). Excess of EDTA is back-titrated with a standard thorium solution using xylenol orange as the indicator. Poirrier's blue is added in order to make the end point sharper. Repeated analyses of synthetic samples containing 1 g of plutonium and 0.010 g of gallium gave an average recovery of 100.2% and a relative standard deviation of 0.3%. If the sample contains more than 250 ppm of copper, it must be removed by sulfide precipitation. For more details on this pretreatment, the original publication should be consulted.

Procedure

Wash Dowex 1X4, 50–100 mesh, chloride form, ion exchange resin several times with ethanol, water, 8 M hydrochloric acid, and 0.5 M hydrochloric acid. Fill a 1.2 cm ID column to a height of 7 cm with the resin.

Prepare daily a fresh hydrochloric acid–ascorbic acid solution by dissolving 1 g of ascorbic acid in 100 ml of 5 M hydrochloric acid.

Prepare a buffer solution by dissolving 14 g of sodium acetate in 1 liter of water containing 114 ml of glacial acetic acid.

Prepare a xylenol orange solution by dissolving 0.02 g of the reagent in 100 ml of 2:3 ethanol–water.

Prepare a 0.02% aqueous solution of Poirrier's blue (available from National Aniline Division, Allied Chemical Corp.).

Prepare a 0.02 M thorium solution by dissolving thorium nitrate in water. Standardize the solution against a standard 0.1 M EDTA solution, using the procedure described below for the sample.

Dissolve 1.000 g of the sample, containing about 10 mg of gallium, in 5 ml of the hydrochloric acid–ascorbic acid solution. Heat if necessary. Pour the solution on the resin column that has just been conditioned by washing with 10 ml of the hydrochloric acid–ascorbic acid solution. Elute plutonium with about 20 ml of the hydrochloric acid–ascorbic acid solution at the rate of 4 ml/min, then elute gallium with 50 ml of 0.5 M hydrochloric acid.

Add 3 or 4 drops of a 0.1% bromophenol blue solution to the effluent, then add 6 M sodium hydroxide solution until the color of the solution just begins to turn blue. This corresponds to a pH of 3.5. Now add 15 ml of the buffer solution and exactly 5 ml of a standard 0.1 M EDTA solution, and boil for 2 min. Add 1 ml of the xylenol orange solution and 2 or 3 drops of the Poirrier's blue solution, and titrate the solution without cooling with the standard thorium solution.

Also carry out a blank determination.

URANIUM ALLOYS

The existence of UGa, UGa_2, and UGa_3 has been reported.

Methods of Analysis

In the following procedure (101), uranium is reduced to the tetravalent state by passing a hydrochloric acid solution of the sample through a lead reductor and is then titrated with a standard cerium(IV) solution. Gallium is determined by adding excess EDTA and back-titrating with standard iron(III) solution. Interference from uranyl ions, encountered in the visual detection of the end point, is overcome by using photometric detection. The methods are suitable for determination of wide concentration ranges of uranium and gallium.

Procedures

Dissolve 2.000 g of sample in concentrated nitric acid, add 20 ml of concentrated sulfuric acid, and evaporate to strong fumes. Cool, dilute slightly with water, and reheat to fumes. Dilute the solution to exactly 100 ml with water.

URANIUM. Prepare a lead reductor as follows. Prepare a column using a buret with an ID of approximately 1.0 cm. Insert a 1-cm plug of glass wool, followed by an approx 30 cm column length of 40–60 mesh lead particles (150–200 g). Shake down the lead particles and insert a 1-cm plug of glass wool. Insert the buret tip through a rubber stopper and couple it to a filtering flask. Wash the column with about 200 ml of M hydrochloric acid. Do not allow air to enter the lead column at any subsequent stage of the procedure. Always maintain the liquid level 2 or 3 cm above the upper glass wool packing.

If air enters the lead column, degas it before use. For degassing, remove the filtering flask and insert a beaker containing M hydrochloric acid under the lower end of the column. Apply vacuum to the upper connection of the column. Suck liquid up through the column to displace any air in the column. Replace the filtering flask, apply suction, and draw the M hydrochloric acid down the column. Repeat to ensure that the column is free from any air bubbles.

Prepare a 0.025 M ferroin solution by dissolving 0.7433 g of 1,10-phenanthroline and 0.3475 g of $FeSO_4.7H_2O$ in 50 ml of water. Prepare a 0.001 M ferroin solution by diluting 4 ml of the 0.025 M ferroin solution to 100 ml with water.

Prepare a 0.02 N cerium(IV) solution by dissolving 56.0 g of $Ce(NO_3)_4.2NH_4-NO_3$ in 500 ml of 0.5 M sulfuric acid. Standardize the solution against arsenic trioxide.

Take a suitable aliquot of the sample solution containing about 100 mg of uranium and dilute to about 60 ml with water. Add 20 ml of concentrated hydrochloric acid and pass the solution through the lead reductor. Wash with M hydrochloric acid. Transfer the reduced solution to a titration flask and wash the filtering flask with M hydrochloric acid. Add 1 drop of phosphoric acid (sp gr 1.69), 1.0 ml of the 0.001 M ferroin solution, and titrate with the 0.02 N cerium(IV) solution to the disappearance of the pink color. Then add 2 ml of phosphoric acid (sp gr 1.69) and 2–3 drops of the 0.02 N cerium(IV) solution to produce the full red color of the indicator again. Continue the titration to the disappearance of the red color. Carry out a blank determination through the entire procedure.

GALLIUM. Prepare a 0.1 M iron(III) solution by dissolving 5.585 g of pure iron in 20 ml of 10 M hydrochloric acid, oxidizing iron(II) by the dropwise addition of concentrated nitric acid, and diluting to exactly 1 liter with water. Dilute an aliquot of this solution to obtain a 0.02 M solution.

Prepare a 0.02 M EDTA solution according to the directions given earlier (see p. 258).

Prepare an indicator solution by dissolving 2.5 g of potassium benzohydroxamate in 100 ml of water.

Transfer a suitable aliquot of the sample solution containing 7–28 mg of gallium to a low-form beaker, dilute to about 300 ml, add a slight excess of the 0.02 M EDTA solution, and adjust the pH to 2.2, using a pH meter, by the addition of dilute ammonia solution. Add 1 ml of the indicator solution and position the beaker in an E.E.L. absorptiometer (Evans Electroselenium Ltd.). Adjust a stirrer to agitate the solution. Then adjust the absorptiometer to give zero reading with Ilford No. 605 filters (about 550 nm) in place and do not alter this setting during the titration. Make successive additions of the 0.02 M iron(III) solution from a buret with the tip touching the surface of the solution. Note the absorbance reading when the galvanometer needle has ceased oscillating after each addition of the titrant. Plot the volume of iron solution added against absorbance and determine the end point.

GALLIUM COMPOUNDS

Among the various gallium compounds, gallium arsenide has been studied most extensively, and detailed procedures have been developed for its analysis. Therefore, this compound is discussed here in more detail. The other gallium compounds are mentioned only briefly. For more information on the gallium compounds, see References 2–4.

GALLIUM ARSENIDE

Gallium arsenide, GaAs, crystallizes in the zinc blende structure, has a melting point of 1238°C, and can be prepared by direct reaction of the elements. It has semiconducting properties (energy gap at room temperature 1.35 eV). A phase diagram of the arsenic–gallium system has been described by Hansen and Anderko (93).

Methods of Analysis

ASSAY METHODS

Gallium in gallium arsenide can be determined by amperometric titration with N-benzoyl-N-phenylhydroxylamine (102).

No specific method has been reported for the determination of arsenic in gallium arsenide. Presumably arsenic can be determined by redox titrations after dissolution of the sample in an oxidizing acid or acids (eg, an excess of nitric acid over hydrochloric acid).

The purity of gallium arsenide can also be established by electrical measurements; Hall effect measurements and thermally stimulated current (TSC) measurements give correlations with the purity of the substance (18).

DETERMINATION OF IMPURITIES

Impurities in gallium arsenide can be determined by physical and chemical methods. For further details, see Reference 7.

Physical Methods. Emission spectroscopy and neutron activation analysis are used to determine trace metals in gallium arsenide.

Emission Spectroscopy. Traces of silicon and other impurities in gallium arsenide can be determined after chemical concentration by a spectroscopic procedure (103). The sample is dissolved in a mixture of hydrochloric acid, carbon tetrachloride, and bromine. Arsenic is removed by evaporating the sample solution to a small volume, then gallium is removed by extraction with isopropyl ether. Subsequently, the impurities are concentrated in the presence of sulfuric acid, dried on a carbon electrode, and excited in a dc arc in an atmosphere of argon and oxygen. Copper is used as the internal standard.

The schematic of the controlled atmosphere and optical system is shown in Figure 2 (103). It consists of a brass cylindrical chamber that can be screwed down into an O-ring seal in an insulating (Teflon) base. The cylinder is provided with a quartz window to transmit the light to the spectrograph and a ruby-glass window for inspection purposes. The base carries the electrode holders and the ports for evacuating the chamber and admitting the mixed gas.

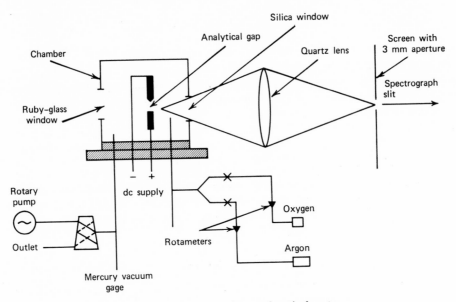

Fig. 2. Controlled atmosphere and optical system.

Special care is required to reduce the silicon blank value. The blank value comes both from the reagents and from airborne contamination. The latter may be eliminated by carrying out the concentration procedure in a closed chamber into which only filtered air is allowed to enter.

Typical recoveries of impurities from the following procedure (103) are as follows:

Element	Recovery, %
Al	
Be	
Bi	
Cr	80–100
Mg	
Mn	
Ni	
Si	
Co	60–80
Zr	
Cd	50

The lower limit of determination is dependent on the blank value. The following results have been obtained:

Element	Lower limit of detection, ppm	Element	Lower limit of detection, ppm
Al	0.1	Mg	0.01
Be	0.02	Mn	0.02
Bi	0.05	Ni	0.02
Cd	0.04	Si	0.02
Cr	0.02	Zr	0.1
Co	0.02		

Procedure

Prepare a carbon electrode (lower electrode) by cutting a suitable length from a 6.5 mm rod. Make the projecting tip 2 mm in diameter and 2 mm long. Support the carbon electrode in a graphite cup. Prepare a 6 mm diameter graphite rod (upper electrode) ending in a blunted 80° cone. If necessary pre-arc the electrodes at 4 A for 2 sec to remove surface contamination.

Table 7. Line Pairs Used for the Emission Spectroscopic Determination of Impurities in Gallium Arsenide

Element, Å		Copper, Å	Range, μg
Mg	2779.8		0.2–5.0
Mn	2798.3	(I) 2768.9	0.02–0.5
Mg(II)	2802.7		0.005–0.5
Cr(II)	2835.6	(I) 2858.2	0.1–5.0
Si	2881.58	(I) 2882.9	0.02–0.5
Mn	2933.06		0.2–5.0
Ni(I)	3050.8		0.05–0.5
Bi(I)	3067.7	(I) 3160.0	0.01–0.5
Al(I)	3082.1		0.05–1.0
Mo	3170.3		0.02–0.5
Ni(I)	3050.8		0.2–5.0
Bi(I)	3067.7		0.2–5.0
Al(I)	3082.1	(I) 3128.67	0.2–5.0
Be(II)	3130.42		0.005–0.2
Mo	3170.3		0.2–5.0
Ti(II)	3222.8		0.2–5.0
In(I)	3256.1	(I) 3223.4	0.05–5.0
Cd(I)	3261.0		0.2–5.0
Be(I)	3321.3		0.05–2.0
Zn(I)	3345.0	(I) 3319.7	0.2–5.0
Zr(II)	3391.95		0.2–5.0
Zn(I)	3345.0		0.10–5.0
Ti	3361.2	(I) 3375.7	0.02–0.3
Zr(II)	3391.95		0.05–1.0
Ni(I)	3414.77	(I) 3413.3	0.01–1.0
Co(I)	3453.51	3454.7	0.01–2.0
Cr(I)	3593.5	(I) 3545.0	0.02–0.5
Pb(I)	3683.47	3676.9	0.05–2.0
Cr(I)	4254.3	(I) 4249.0	0.02–0.2

Dissolve copper sulfate in water to yield a solution with a copper concentration of 1 mg/ml.

Weigh approximately 1 g of sample into a Teflon beaker and add 5 ml of 8 M hydrochloric acid, 5 ml of carbon tetrachloride, and 2 ml of bromine. Run a blank simultaneously. After the sample has dissolved, evaporate the solution to a syrupy appearance, then transfer it to a stoppered 50-ml polyethylene bottle with 6 ml of 8 M hydrochloric acid. Add 6 ml of peroxide-free isopropyl ether and shake for 5 min. When the phases have separated, draw off as much as possible of the ether phase with a polyethylene pipet. Transfer the aqueous phase to an 8-mm diameter polyethylene tube and remove the remaining ether. Transfer the aqueous phase to the polyethylene bottle and repeat extractions twice more. Finally add 2 ml of water to the polyethylene tube. This causes more ether to separate. Remove the ether as before. Transfer the aqueous phase to a Teflon beaker and add 1 ml of 0.05 M sulfuric acid and 1 ml of copper sulfate solution. Evaporate the solution to approximately 0.1 ml in a dust-free chamber.

Transfer the solution dropwise to the carbon electrode supported in a graphite cup placed in a stainless steel block. The block is on a hot plate beneath a 250 W infrared reflector lamp. Place the lamp 20 cm above the electrode head maintained at about 90°C.

Place the graphite cup supporting the impregnated carbon electrode in the lower positive electrode holder. Place the upper electrode and adjust the analytical gap to 3 mm. Evacuate the excitation chamber to a pressure of 0.5 torr and then fill by a steady flow (2 liters/min) of a 1:2 mixture of argon and oxygen. Arc the sample and develop the plate using the following conditions:

spectrograph	Hilger E478 or equivalent
wavelength region	2700–4300 Å
slit width	10 μm
slit height	3 mm
source to slit distance	1:1 image focussed on tile 30 cm from slit
analytical gap	3 mm
source	12 A dc arc (spark initiated) in 1:2 argon–oxygen mixture
exposure time	90 sec
plate	Kodak B10 or equivalent
development	Kodak D19b at 20°C for 3 min
step-sector spectrum	Fe–Fe arc, 4 A

With a densitometer, obtain galvanometer deflections for the element and internal standard lines and their adjacent backgrounds. Obtain the calibration curve at the appropriate wavelengths from an iron arc step-sector spectrogram exposed on the same plate as the sample. Convert the deflection values to Seidel densities, make background corrections, and convert the values of log (relative intensity of impurity/relative intensity of copper) to μg from previously prepared calibration (working) curves. Use the line pairs listed in Table 7.

Prepare the calibration curves by taking known amounts of standard solutions and carrying them through the entire procedure.

Less than the 1-ppm levels of rare earth elements in gallium arsenide can be determined by a dc arc in an argon and oxygen atmosphere (104). Standard samples have been prepared by addition of known amounts of rare earth elements to gallium arsenide.

Hall effect and resistivity measurements of zinc-diffused and cadmium-diffused gallium arsenide have been compared with spectroscopic determination of the diffusant concentrations in the samples (105).

Neutron Activation Analysis. Determination of traces of impurities in gallium arsenide by neutron activation analysis can be carried out according to the methods already discussed for gallium metal (p. 262). Different procedures have been employed for the determination of cadmium, cobalt, copper, indium, iridium, palladium, potassium, rhenium, silver, sodium, tungsten, and zinc (106). A method has been developed for determination of magnesium, silicon, and zinc after radiochemical separations (107). The half-lives of the active species measured are 9.5 min, 2.62 hr, and 55 min, respectively. A substoichiometric method has been used for the determination of 0.02–0.03 ppm of copper in gallium arsenide (108). Oxygen in gallium arsenide has been determined using the $^{16}O(T,n)^{18}F$ reaction. The tritons (T) are produced by the $^{6}Li(n,T)^{4}He$ reaction (109–111).

Polarography. Bismuth, cadmium, copper, and indium in gallium arsenide at concentrations of 1 ppm or less can be determined by square-wave polarography (112). In M hydrochloric acid the peak potentials for bismuth(III), copper(II), indium(III), and cadmium(II) are 0.08, 0.22, 0.59, and 0.64 V vs the mercury-pool anode, respectively. The waves of indium and cadmium overlap, but the peaks are distinguishable. It is considered that 0.5 μg amounts of bismuth, copper, indium, and cadmium can be determined with an error of 20%. However, selenium and molybdenum will interfere with the determination of bismuth, and uranium with the determination of copper. In the following procedure, a small amount of potassium bromate is added in order to oxidize any residual arsenic(III) to arsenic(V).

Procedure

Use a square-wave polarograph with a drop time of 3.5 sec in open circuit and a flow rate of 1.43 mg/sec.

Dissolve a sample of less than 0.5 g by heating it with a mixture of 5 ml of 3 M nitric acid and 1 ml of concentrated hydrochloric acid. Evaporate the solution to

Table 8. Chemical Methods Applicable for the Determination of Impurities in Gallium Arsenide

Element		Range, ppm	Reference
Cu	photometric or colorimetric determination with lead diethyldithiocarbamate	1–100	(113)
Cu, Te, Zn	stripping polarography	>0.1 Cu and Zn, >0.01 Te	(7)
H	vacuum fusion	>3	(7)[a]
O	vacuum fusion	>30	(7)[a]
P	arsenic is removed by volatilization; photometric determination as molybdenum blue	>0.5	(7)
Se	photometric determination with 3,3'-diaminobenzidine	>1	(7)
Se	colorimetric or polarographic determination		(113a)
S	arsenic is removed by distillation; S is separated as hydrogen sulfide; photometric (turbidimetric) determination as lead sulfide	>0.4	(7)
Te	Te is precipitated on As with tin(II) chloride and hypophosphite; photometric determination with diethyldithiocarbamate	>2	(7)

[a] See also Vol. 8, pp. 616 and 681.

dryness under an infrared lamp. Dissolve the residue at room temperature in a mixture of 4.0 ml of M hydrochloric acid and 0.4 ml of 0.005 N potassium bromate solution. The dissolution will take about 1 hr. Transfer the solution completely to a polarographic cell, and record a continuous square-wave polarogram at a suitable sensitivity setting of the polarograph. Measure the peak heights of the reduction waves on the polarograms, and determine the concentrations of bismuth, copper, indium, and cadmium from calibration curves. Run a blank determination.

To obtain the calibration curves, record polarograms on solutions containing 0, 0.5, and 1.0 μg each of bismuth, copper, indium, and cadmium in 5.0 ml of M hydrochloric acid. Plot the peak heights against the concentration (in μg/ml) of each element.

Chemical Methods. Table 8 summarizes the information related to the determination of impurities in gallium arsenide. The table lists the impurity element, the method which can be used for the determination, the concentration range where the method is applicable, and a reference where more information can be obtained.

GALLIUM ANTIMONIDE

Gallium antimonide, GaSb, crystallizes in the cubic, zinc blende structure, has a melting point of approximately 705°C, and can be easily prepared by direct reaction of the elements. Its phase diagram has been reported by Hansen and Anderko (93).

GALLIUM HALIDES

Physical properties of gallium halides are given in Table 9.

Table 9. Properties of Gallium Halides

Compound	Melting point, °C	Boiling point, °C	Color	Density, 25/4°C, g/cm³	Solubility in water
GaF_3	sublimes between 800–1000		none	4.47	slightly soluble
$GaCl_3$	77	201.2	none	2.47	very soluble
$GaBr_3$	122.3	279	none	3.69	soluble
GaI_3	212	346	yellow	4.15	soluble

Impurity elements in gallium chloride may be determined according to the methods for the analysis of gallium metal (pp. 265–269).

Gallium perchlorate, $Ga(ClO_4)_3 \cdot 6H_2O$, is also known.

LITHIUM GALLIUM HYDRIDE

Lithium gallium hydride, $LiGaH_4$, is a milder reducing agent than lithium aluminum hydride.

GALLIUM NITRATE AND NITRIDE

Gallium nitrate, $Ga(NO_3)_3 \cdot xH_2O$, is very soluble in water. It can be obtained by dissolving gallium in hot nitric acid.

Gallium nitride, GaN, forms hexagonal crystals; it decomposes at about 1000°C.

GALLIUM OXIDES

Gallium(III) Oxide. Five structural forms of gallium(III) oxide, Ga_2O_3, have been reported: α, β, γ, δ, and ϵ. The stable form between room temperature and the melting point (1725°C) is β-Ga_2O_3; it has a monoclinic crystalline structure and a density of 5.9. α-Ga_2O_3 is stable between 300 and 450°C; it has a rhombohedral structure and a density of 6.4.

Gallium oxide can be solubilized by fusion with sodium hydroxide, potassium hydrogensulfate, or potassium pyrosulfate.

Gallium Hydroxide. The gelatinous precipitate obtained when neutralizing gallium solutions contains $Ga(OH)_3$ and $Ga_2O(OH)_4$. It dissolves in dilute acids and alkalis.

Gallates(III). Gallium oxide as a complex anion gives salts called gallates(III). Gallates(III) of alkali metals, alkaline earth metals, rare earth elements, etc are known.

GALLIUM PHOSPHATE AND PHOSPHIDE

Gallium Phosphate. This substance is known in the anhydrous state, $GaPO_4$, as well as the dihydrate or trihydrate.

Gallium Phosphide. GaP is one of the more important gallium compounds. It has a cubic, zinc blende structure, has a melting point of 1350°C, and it can be prepared by direct reaction of the elements or by other methods. It has semiconducting properties; the energy gap at room temperature is 2.24 eV.

Gallium in gallium phosphide has been determined by amperometric titration with N-benzoyl-N-phenylhydroxylamine (102).

Silicon in gallium phosphide, in concentrations above 10 ppm, is determined by the photometric molybdenum blue method after anion exchange separation (114). Because recoveries of silicon are about 86%, the separation step is included in the procedure for the determination of the calibration curve. It is necessary to minimize the time required for the analysis in order to minimize the possible polymerization of silicate.

Procedure

COLUMN AND REAGENTS. Prepare a 17 cm long, 2 cm diameter column filled with weakly basic anion exchange resin, AG 3-X, 20–50 mesh, chloride form. Support the resin on a bed of granular silicon carbide in order to reduce the silicon blank from the glassware. Before initial use and after each analysis wash the column, at about 1 ml/min, with 30 ml of 1:1 ammonium hydroxide, 60 ml of water, 30 ml of 1:9 hydrochloric acid, and three 20-ml portions of water.

Prepare a standard silicon solution with a silicon concentration of 10 μg/ml by dissolving silicon dioxide in potassium hydroxide solution or by fusing silicon dioxide with sodium carbonate and dissolving the melt in water. Store the solution in a polyethylene bottle.

Prepare an ammonium molybdate solution by dissolving 10 g of $(NH_4)_6$-$Mo_7O_{24}.4H_2O$ in 200 ml of water.

Prepare a tin(II) chloride solution by dissolving 1 g of $SnCl_2.2H_2O$ in 2 ml of concentrated hydrochloric acid and diluting to 100 ml with water. Prepare fresh daily.

CALIBRATION CURVE. Heat gently a mixture of 3 ml of freshly prepared 4:1 hydrochloric–nitric acids with a series of silicon samples in the range between 0 and

50 μg for 5 min. Subsequently, destroy the nitric acid with the minimum amount of formic acid. When foaming ceases, boil the solution to a volume of 1.0–1.5 ml. Cool quickly, add 1 ml of 10% ammonium tartrate solution and 8 ml of water. Transfer the solution to the ion exchange column, elute at 2 ml/min, and discard the effluent. Continue the elution at about 5 ml/min with 10-ml portions of water until a total of 55 ml of effluent is obtained in a 100-ml volumetric flask. Then add 10 ml of ammonium molybdate solution to the effluent, mix, and allow to stand for 5 min. Add 30 ml of 1:3 sulfuric acid, mix, allow to stand for 30 sec, then add 1 ml of the tin(II) chloride solution, mix, and dilute to 100 ml with water. Immediately measure the absorbance of the solution in a 2-cm cell at 765 nm or 815 nm against water.

SAMPLE ANALYSIS. By heating gently, dissolve up to 0.1 g of a 150-mesh sample containing not more than about 40 μg of soluble silicon in 3 ml of 4:1 hydrochloric–nitric acids. Continue as directed above.

Traces of cadmium, copper, iron, lead, manganese, and nickel in gallium phosphide can be determined by excitation in a dc arc after chemical concentration of the impurity elements (115).

Spark-source mass spectroscopic analysis has also been made on gallium phosphide samples doped with germanium, selenium, silicon, sulfur, tellurium, tin, and zinc (116).

GALLIUM SELENATE AND SELENIDES

Gallium Selenates. The following gallium selenates are known: $Ga_2(SeO_4)_3.$-$16H_2O$ and $Ga_2(SeO_4)_3.22H_2O$.

Gallium Selenides. The following selenides of gallium(I, II, and III) are known: Ga_2Se, $GaSe$, and Ga_2Se_3 (mp 1020°C, d_4^{25} 4.9).

GALLIUM SULFATE AND SULFIDES

Gallium Sulfates, $Ga_2(SO_4)_3$, as well as its hydrated form, $Ga_2(SO_4)_3.18H_2O$, are known. With alkali metal sulfates and ammonium sulfate, gallium sulfate forms alums, $MGa(SO_4)_2.12H_2O$.

Gallium Sulfides. Gallium(I) sulfide, Ga_2S, forms gray, hexagonal crystals with a density of 4.2. Gallium(II) sulfide, GaS or Ga_2S_2, forms yellow, hexagonal crystals with a density of 3.75; they melt at 970°C. Gallium(III) sulfide, Ga_2S_3, has three known polymorphs: the α, β, and γ forms. Both α- and β-Ga_2S_3 form hexagonal crystals and are stable at higher temperatures whereas γ-Ga_2S_3 has a cubic structure and is stable at low temperatures. The α form corresponds to the ordered form of the β-form. The melting point of Ga_2S_3 is approximately 1255°C.

GALLIUM TELLURIDES

Four gallium tellurides are known: $GaTe$ is monoclinic, and has a mp of 824°C; Ga_2Te_3 has a cubic structure and a mp of 790°C: the two other tellurides (Ga_3Te_2 and $GaTe_3$) are unstable at room temperature. A phase diagram is given by Elliott (94).

ORGANIC GALLIUM COMPOUNDS

Gallium forms compounds with organic acids. Examples include the basic acetate, $4Ga(C_2H_3O_2)_3.2Ga_2O_3.5H_2O$, and the oxalate, $Ga_2(C_2O_4)_3.4H_2O$, as well as the oxalate, malonate, tartrate, and citrate complexes.

Gallium reacts with a number of reagents forming complexes. Examples for the reagents are 8-quinolinol, azo dyes, and EDTA.

Many complexes of the form $[GaL_4]^+[GaX_4]^-$ have been prepared, where L_4 represents four monodentate ligands, two bidentate ligands, or one quadrivalent ligand. The valency of gallium in $[GaL_4]^+$ is $+1$. An example for such a complex is $[Ga(CH_3COCH_2COCH_3)_2][GaCl_4]$. Analytically important compounds are $RHGaCl_4$, where RH^+ is the cation of a certain dye such as, eg, Rhodamine B or malachite green.

Gallium trihalides form addition compounds or complexes. For example, $GaCl_3.C_5H_5N$ and $GaCl_3.2C_5H_5N$ are obtained with pyridine, $GaCl_3.(CH_3)_2O$ and $GaBr_3.(CH_3)_2O$ with methyl ether, and $GaCl_3.CH_3Cl$ with chloromethane.

Organogallium compounds containing at least one Ga–C bond include trimethylgallium, $(CH_3)_3Ga$, triethylgallium, $(C_2H_5)_3Ga$, and triphenylgallium, $(C_6H_5)_3Ga$. Such compounds are highly reactive; they are violently hydrolyzed by water, and the lower trialkyls are spontaneously inflammable.

Bibliography

GENERAL REFERENCES

1. A. P. Thompson and J. R. Musgrave, "Gallium," in C. A. Hampel, ed., *Rare Metals Handbook*, 2nd ed., Reinhold Publishing Corp., New York, 1961.
2. N. N. Greenwood, "The Chemistry of Gallium," in H. J. Eméleus and A. G. Sharpe, eds., *Advances in Inorganic Chemistry and Radiochemistry*, Vol. 5, Academic Press Inc., New York, 1963, pp. 91–134.
3. I. A. Sheka, I. S. Chaus, and T. T. Mityureva, *The Chemistry of Gallium*, Elsevier Publishing Co., Amsterdam, 1966.
4. P. de la Bretèque, "Gallium and Gallium Compounds," in A. Standen, ed., *Kirk-Othmer Encyclopedia of Chemical Technology*, Vol. 10, 2nd ed., Interscience Publishers, a division of John Wiley & Sons, Inc., New York, 1966, pp. 311–328.
5. H. Onishi, "Gallium, Indium, and Thallium," in I. M. Kolthoff and P. J. Elving, eds., *Treatise on Analytical Chemistry*, Part 2, Vol. 2, Interscience Publishers, a division of John Wiley & Sons, Inc., New York, 1962, pp. 1–105.
6. E. B. Sandell, *Colorimetric Determination of Traces of Metals*, 3rd ed., Interscience Publishers, Inc., New York, 1959.
7. I. P. Alimarin, ed., *Analysis of High-Purity Materials*, Israel Program for Scientific Translations, Jerusalem, 1968 (original Russian ed. published 1965).

SPECIFIC REFERENCES

8. H. A. Wilhelm, *U.S. At. Energy Comm. IS-2029* (1967).
9. N. H. Nachtrieb and R. E. Fryxell, *J. Am. Chem. Soc.* **71**, 4035 (1949).
10. S. Ato, *Sci. Papers Inst. Phys. Chem. Res. (Tokyo)* **24**, 162 (1934).
11. R. Klement and H. Sandmann, *Z. Anal. Chem.* **145**, 325 (1955).
12. K. A. Kraus, F. Nelson, and G. W. Smith, *J. Phys. Chem.* **58**, 11 (1954).
13. K. A. Kraus and F. Nelson, *Proc. Intern. Conf. Peaceful Uses At. Energy, Geneva, 1955* **7**, 113 (1956).
14. J. Korkisch and I. Hazan, *Anal. Chem.* **37**, 707 (1965).
15. H. Onishi, *Anal. Chem.* **27**, 832 (1955).
16. I.U.P.A.C. Fifth Report, *Reagents and Reactions for Qualitative Inorganic Analysis*, Butterworths, London, 1964.
17. E. B. Sandell, *Ind. Eng. Chem., Anal. Ed.* **13**, 844 (1941).
18. L. R. Weisberg, "Electrical Measurements for Trace Characterization," in W. W. Meinke and B. F. Scribner, eds., *Trace Characterization: Chemical and Physical*, U.S. Government Printing Office, Washington, D.C., 1967, pp. 39–74.
19. W. F. Hillebrand, G. E. F. Lundell, H. A. Bright, and J. I. Hoffman, *Applied Inorganic Analysis*, 2nd ed., John Wiley & Sons, Inc., New York, 1953.
20. S. Ato, *Sci. Papers Inst. Phys. Chem. Res. (Tokyo)* **12**, 225 (1930).
21. *Ibid.*, **15**, 289 (1931).

22. *Ibid.*, **29,** 71 (1936).
23. *Ibid.*, **40,** 228 (1943).
24. E. Gastinger, *Z. Anal. Chem.* **140,** 244 (1953).
25. H. R. Das and S. C. Shome, *Anal. Chim. Acta* **27,** 545 (1962).
26. H. Flaschka and H. Abdine, *Chem. Anal.* **45,** 58 (1956).
27. F. J. Miner and R. P. DeGrazio, *Anal. Chem.* **37,** 1071 (1965).
28. G. R. E. C. Gregory and P. G. Jeffery, *Talanta* **9,** 800 (1962).
29. J. E. Mee and J. D. Corbett, *Chem. Anal.* **50,** 74 (1961).
30. K. L. Cheng and B. L. Goydish, *Talanta* **13,** 1161 (1966).
31. H. D. Kirschman and J. B. Ramsey, *J. Am. Chem. Soc.* **50,** 1632 (1928).
32. S. Ato, *Sci. Papers Inst. Phys. Chem. Res. (Tokyo)* **10,** 1 (1929).
33. N. R. Fetter and D. F. Swinehart, *Anal. Chem.* **28,** 122 (1956).
34. R. Belcher, A. J. Nutten, and W. I. Stephen, *J. Chem. Soc.* **1952,** 2438.
35. O. W. Rollins and C. K. Deischer, *Anal. Chem.* **26,** 769 (1954).
36. J. N. Weber, *Spectrochim. Acta* **17,** 669 (1961).
37. *ASTM E 227-67, Standard Method for the Spectrochemical Analysis of Aluminum and Its Alloys by the Point-to-Plane Technique using an Optical Emission Spectrometer*, American Society for Testing and Materials, Philadelphia, Pa., 1968.
38. H. Bode and H. Fabian, *Z. Anal. Chem.* **170,** 387 (1959).
39. V. W. Meloche and B. L. Beck, *Anal. Chem.* **28,** 1890 (1956).
40. H. Goto and E. Sudo, *Bunseki Kagaku* **10,** 456 (1961).
41. H. Brandenberger and H. Bader, *Helv. Chim. Acta* **47,** 353 (1964).
42. W. Slavin, *Atomic Absorption Spectroscopy*, Interscience Publishers, a division of John Wiley & Sons, Inc., New York, 1968, p. 107.
43. L. S. Nadezhina, *Zh. Anal. Khim.* **17,** 383 (1962).
44. E. D. Moorhead and G. M. Frame 2nd, *Anal. Chem.* **40,** 280 (1968).
45. O. Kammori, H. Kawase, and I. Inamoto, *Bunseki Kagaku* **14,** 1030 (1965).
46. T. A. Gorbatova and P. N. Kovalenko, *Zh. Anal. Khim.* **23,** 848 (1968).
47. P. Stantscheff, *Z. Anal. Chem.* **207,** 321 (1965).
48. A. I. Zelyanskaya and L. Ya. Kukalo, *Zh. Anal. Khim.* **18,** 726 (1963).
49. E. N. Vinogradova and N. N. Chudinova, *Zavod. Lab.* **22,** 1280 (1956).
50. B. A. Cooney and J. H. Saylor, *Anal. Chim. Acta* **21,** 276 (1959).
51. G. W. Latimer, Jr., *Anal. Chim. Acta* **29,** 480 (1963).
52. K. Zh. Sagadieva, *Zh. Anal. Khim.* **19,** 677 (1964).
53. L. N. Vasil'eva and E. N. Vinogradova, *Zh. Anal. Khim.* **18,** 454 (1963).
54. V. P. Guinn and H. R. Lukens, Jr., "Nuclear Methods," in G. H. Morrison, ed., *Trace Analysis: Physical Methods*, Interscience Publishers, a division of John Wiley & Sons, Inc., New York, 1965, p. 345.
55. W. A. Brooksbank, G. W. Leddicotte, and H. A. Mahlman, *J. Phys. Chem.* **57,** 815 (1953).
56. W. Kiesl, H. Bildstein, and H. Sorantin, *Mikrochim. Ichnoanal. Acta* **1963,** 151.
57. H. Jaskólska and J. Minczewski, *Acta Chim. Acad. Sci. Hung.* **32,** 9 (1962).
58. A. Kant, J. P. Cali, and H. D. Thompson, *Anal. Chem.* **28,** 1867 (1956).
59. B. A. Thompson, B. M. Strause, and M. B. Leboeuf, *Anal. Chem.* **30,** 1023 (1958).
60. A. Zeman, J. Růžička, and V. Kuvik, *Talanta* **13,** 271 (1966).
61. Y. Oka, T. Kato, and M. Sasaki, *Nippon Kagaku Zasshi* **86,** 612 (1965).
62. H. Onishi and E. B. Sandell, *Anal. Chim. Acta* **13,** 159 (1955).
63. F. Culkin and J. P. Riley, *Analyst* **83,** 208 (1958).
64. V. S. Saltykova and E. A. Fabrikova, *Zh. Anal. Khim.* **13,** 63 (1958).
65. E. B. Sandell, *Anal. Chem.* **19,** 63 (1947).
66. M. Ishibashi, T. Shigematsu, and Y. Nishikawa, *Bull. Inst. Chem. Res., Kyoto Univ.* **37,** 191 (1959).
67. K. Motojima and H. Hashitani, *Bunseki Kagaku* **9,** 151 (1960).
68. T. Moeller and A. J. Cohen, *Anal. Chem.* **22,** 686 (1950).
69. C. L. Luke and M. E. Campbell, *Anal. Chem.* **28,** 1340 (1956).
70. Y. Nishikawa, *Nippon Kagaku Zasshi* **79,** 631 (1958).
71. J. Jankovský, *Talanta* **2,** 29 (1959).
72. O. G. Koch and G. A. Koch-Dedic, *Handbuch der Spurenanalyse*, Springer-Verlag, Berlin, 1964, p. 577.

73. V. K. Kuznetsova, *Zh. Anal. Khim.* **18**, 1326 (1963).
74. V. Armeanu and P. Costinescu, *Talanta* **14**, 699 (1967).
75. T. Suzuki, *Bunseki Kagaku* **12**, 655 (1963).
76. K. L. Cheng and B. L. Goydish, *Anal. Chim. Acta* **34**, 154 (1966).
77. M. Hniličkova and L. Sommer, *Z. Anal. Chem.* **193**, 171 (1963).
78. K. Bansho and Y. Umezaki, *Bull. Chem. Soc. Japan* **40**, 326 (1967).
79. G. G. Karanovich, L. A. Ionova, and B. L. Podolskaya, *Zh. Anal. Khim.* **13**, 439 (1958).
80. A. M. Lukin and E. A. Bozhevol'nov, *Zh. Anal. Khim.* **15**, 43 (1960).
81. Y. Nishikawa, K. Hiraki, K. Morishige, and T. Shigematsu, *Bunseki Kagaku* **16**, 692 (1967).
82. A. N. Glotova and N. F. Losev, *Zavod. Lab.* **27**, 1107 (1961).
83. E. A. Hakkaila, G. R. Waterbury, and C. F. Metz, *U.S. At. Energy Comm. Rept. LA-3125* (1964).
84. G. P. Morie and T. R. Sweet, *Anal. Chem.* **37**, 1552 (1965).
85. W. M. Saltman and N. H. Nachtrieb, *Anal. Chem.* **23**, 1503 (1951).
86. E. B. Owens, *Appl. Spectrosc.* **13**, 105 (1959).
87. J. H. Oldfield and E. P. Bridge, *Analyst* **86**, 267 (1961).
88. W. A. Wolstenholme, *Appl. Spectry.* **17**, 51 (1963).
89. K. H. Neeb, H. Stöckert, R. Braun, and H. P. Bleich, *Z. Anal. Chem.* **245**, 233 (1969).
90. V. I. Lysenko and A. G. Kim, *Trudy Kom. Analit. Khim.* **15**, 200 (1965); *Anal. Abstr.* **13**, 2885 (1966).
91. Y. Ishihara, M. Koga, and H. Komuro, *Bunseki Kagaku* **15**, 372 (1966).
92. S. I. Sinyakova, N. A. Rudnev, Y.-C. Shen, and R. Dzhumaev, *Zh. Anal. Khim.* **16**, 32 (1961).
93. M. Hansen and K. Anderko, *Constitution of Binary Alloys*, 2nd ed., McGraw-Hill Book Co., Inc., New York, 1958.
94. R. P. Elliott, *Constitution of Binary Alloys*, First Supplement, McGraw-Hill Book Co., Inc., New York, 1965.
95. Yu. A. Chernikhov and T. V. Cherkashina, *Zavod. Lab.* **25**, 26 (1959); *Anal. Abstr.* **6**, 3870 (1959).
96. E. N. Kunenkova, *Trudy Inst. Metallurg., Akad. Nauk SSSR* **1958**, 289; *Anal. Abstr.* **7**, 913 (1960).
97. I. Dobeš and M. Salamon, *Chem. Listy* **60**, 68 (1966); *Anal. Abstr.* **14**, 2470 (1967).
98. E. M. Murt and J. C. Bready, *Appl. Spectry.* **15**, 1 (1961).
99. L. S. Kopanskaya, O. A. Arzhintar, and Yu. S. Lyalikov, *Zavod. Lab.* **34**, 132 (1968); *Anal. Abstr.* **16**, 2387 (1969).
100. I. E. Makasheva, I. S. Kirin, and Yu. A. Makashev, *Zavod. Lab.* **31**, 1192 (1965); *Anal. Abstr.* **14**, 609 (1967).
101. G. W. C. Milner, *Analyst* **81**, 367 (1956).
102. Z. A. Gallai, N. M. Sheina, and I. P. Alimarin, *Zh. Anal. Khim.* **20**, 1093 (1965).
103. J. H. Oldfield and D. L. Mack, *Analyst* **87**, 778 (1962).
104. M. S. Wang, *Appl. Spectry.* **22**, 761 (1968).
105. J. Black, *J. Electrochem. Soc.* **111**, 924 (1964).
106. P. I. Artyukhin, E. N. Gil'bert, and V. A. Pronin, *Radiokhimiya* **9**, 341 (1967).
107. D. E. Green, J. A. B. Heslop, and J. E. Whitley, *Analyst* **88**, 522 (1963).
108. K. Kudo, H. Araki, M. Fujimoto, and Y. Sato, *Radioisotopes (Tokyo)* **16**, 549 (1967).
109. R. F. Bailey and D. A. Ross, *Anal. Chem.* **35**, 791 (1963).
110. W. G. Leonhardt, *Anal. Chem.* **36**, 1879 (1964).
111. R. F. Bailey, *Anal. Chem.* **36**, 1879 (1964).
112. V. J. Jennings, *Analyst* **87**, 548 (1962).
113. V. G. Goryushina, E. Ya. Biryukova, and L. S. Razumova, *Zh. Anal. Khim.* **23**, 1044 (1968).
113a. E. L. Bush and E. H. Cornish, *Ultrapurif. Semicond. Mater. Proc. Conf., Boston, Mass., 1961; Chem. Abstr.* **57**, 6608a (1962).
114. C. L. Luke, *Anal. Chem.* **36**, 2036 (1964).
115. B. D. Brodskaya, M. A. Notkina, S. A. Korneeva, and N. P. Men'shova, *Zh. Anal. Khim.* **21**, 1447 (1966).
116. A. J. Ahearn, F. A. Trumbore, C. J. Frosch, C. L. Luke, and D. L. Malm, *Anal. Chem.* **39**, 350 (1967).

HIROSHI ONISHI
Japan Atomic Energy Research Institute

GASES, NOBLE

The noble gases are designated as that group of elements which belong to group VIII of the periodic table. The group consists of helium (He), neon (Ne), argon (Ar), krypton (Kr), xenon (Xe), and radon (Rn). These gases have also been referred to as the helium group, the rare gases, and the inert gases. The last two names are not entirely applicable, since helium and argon are produced in large quantities and since xenon, krypton, and radon form chemical compounds. Further information on the chemistry and technology of the noble gases can be found in the general references (1–2).

The first indication of the existence of the noble gases dates back to 1785, when Cavendish observed an inert residual volume of gas after repeatedly passing an electric discharge through air containing excess added oxygen to react with the nitrogen. Cavendish noted that the residue, which was not nitrogen, amounted to "not more than 1/120 part of the whole" quantity of air sampled. Later, in 1868, Janssen observed an unidentified yellow line in the solar spectrum. Lockyer concluded that this line represented a new element which he called helium from the Greek "helios" meaning sun. In 1891, Hillebrand obtained an inert gas from uranite, which gave yellow spectral lines differing from the mapped lines of that time. In 1894, Rayleigh noted that the density of nitrogen from the atmosphere was consistently higher than the density of nitrogen from chemical sources such as ammonia, nitrous oxide, and ammonium nitrate. This difference caused him to suspect the presence of a previously unidentified element in the atmosphere. Rayleigh and Ramsay worked cooperatively on the isolation and spectroscopic characterization of this new element, which they called argon from the Greek "argos" meaning inactive. In 1895, Ramsay showed that the gas Hillebrand isolated from the mineral uranite was identical with Lockyer's helium; at the same time, Kayser detected helium in the earth's atmosphere. In 1898, Ramsay and Travers discovered krypton, named from the Greek "kryptos" meaning hidden, by spectroscopic examination and density measurement of the residue from a sample of liquid air. They discovered neon, named from the Greek "neos" meaning new, as the volatile fraction of a sample of argon condensed with liquid air. About a month later that same year, they isolated xenon, named from the Greek "xenos" meaning strange, from the residue from the evaporation of liquid air. The family was rendered complete by the discovery of radon among the radioactive decay products of radium by Dorn in 1900 (3).

The atmosphere is the only known source of all the noble gases. Argon, neon, krypton, and xenon are all available commercially as products of the fractionation of liquid air. Commercial helium is obtained by recovery from certain natural gas sources. Radon is recovered in very small quantities as a radioactive decay product of radium.

The primary uses of the noble gases are associated with their inert characteristics. Helium and argon are used extensively in the metallurgical industry where inert atmospheres are needed. Argon, neon, krypton, and xenon are used in light sources for special applications where high intensity or longer filament life is required. Helium is used as a purge gas and pressurant gas in the missile and nuclear fields, and as a diluent in medical applications and breathing atmospheres. Helium and neon are used extensively as refrigerant fluids to establish and maintain very low temperatures in the cryogenic region for research and industrial applications. Xenon has strong anesthetic properties, but its use is limited by its high cost. In addition, all of the noble gases are used in a variety of laboratory and research applications.

The noble gases are commercially available in a variety of grades which include a high-purity grade, an ultrahigh-purity grade, a zero gas or instrument grade, an ultrapure carrier grade, and a research grade. Typical purity ranges and impurity levels for commercially available noble gases are listed in Table 1.

Table 1. Typical Purity Ranges and Impurities Levels for Commercially Available Noble Gases

impurity, ppm	Argon	Helium	Neon	Krypton	Xenon
nitrogen	<3–40	<5	<5	<5	<5
argon		<1	<1	<1	<1
helium	<5		<25–300	<5	<5
neon		<2–50		<20	<5
krypton					<25
xenon				<25	
hydrogen	<1	<1	<1	<1	<1
oxygen	<1–10	<1–5	<1	<1	<5
water	<1–4	<1–4	<1	<1	<1
methane	<0.5–1	<0.5	<0.5	<0.5	<5
acetylene	<0.05	<0.05	<0.05	<0.05	<0.05
total hydrocarbons	<1–3	<1	<1	<1	<5
carbon dioxide			<0.5		
carbon monoxide			<1		
nitrous oxide			<0.1		
purity range, %	99.995–99.999	99.995–99.9995	99.97–99.998	>99.99	>99.99

Properties

Physical Properties. All of the noble gas group elements are gases at room temperature and atmospheric pressure. They are colorless, odorless, and tasteless. The noble gases are monatomic molecules which are considered to have perfect spherical symmetry. Because of this molecular simplicity, much theoretical interest is shown in their physical properties. With the exception of radon, the physical properties of the noble gases have been relatively completely determined experimentally. Some pertinent physical properties are presented in Table 2. The values listed are for the naturally occurring isotopic mixtures of each element. More extensive compilations of physical properties data are available (1,4–6). Table 3 presents a listing of the naturally occurring isotopes of the noble gas elements along with their relative abundance. Heath (7) and Strominger et al. (8) include a complete listing of the unstable isotopes along with their decay schemes.

Chemical Properties. Chemically, the noble gas elements are considered nearly inert. A few stable chemical compounds have been prepared for radon, xenon, and krypton; none have been reported for helium, neon, and argon. Although hydrates or clathrates of water and hydroquinone with argon and the heavier noble gases have been well known for many years, chemists do not regard these structures as chemical compounds. In 1962, Barlett (9) observed the reaction of xenon with platinum hexafluoride, which was the first recorded true chemical reaction involving a noble gas. This report stimulated additional research leading to the synthesis of xenon tetrafluoride (10). Since then, scientists have prepared a variety of xenon fluorides and

Table 2. Physical Properties of the Noble Gas Elements

	He	Ne	Ar	Kr	Xe	Rn
atomic number	2	10	18	36	54	86
atomic weight	4.0026	20.183	39.948	83.80	131.30	222
normal boiling point (nbp), °K	4.215	27.09	87.28	119.80	165.04	211
triple point (tp)						
temperature, °K	no tp	24.54	83.81	115.77	161.38	202
pressure, atm	no tp	0.4273	0.68	0.7220	0.806	0.7[a]
critical point						
temperature, °K	5.199	44.40	150.86	209.4	289.74	378
pressure, atm	2.261	26.19	48.34	54.3	57.64	62
density, g/ml	0.0693	0.483	0.536	0.908	1.100	
density						
gas, at 1 atm 273.15 °K, g/liter	0.17850	0.90002	1.78380	3.7493	5.8971	9.73
gas, at nbp, g/liter	16.714	9.552	5.763	8.6	11.0	
liquid, at nbp, g/ml	0.1249	1.206	1.3936	2.415	3.057	4.4
gas/liquid volume ratio[b]	700	1340	781	644	518	452
heat of vaporization at nbp, cal/g-mole	19.4	429	1550	2154	3020	4325
heat of fusion at tp, cal/g-mole	no tp	80.1	283	392	548.5	776
thermal conductivity cal/(sec)(cm²)(°K/cm)						
gas, at 1 atm, 0°C	339.0	110.1	40.5	20.9	12.1	
liquid, at nbp	75	310	290	211	175	
first ionization potential, eV	24.586	21.563	15.759	13.999	12.129	10.747
min excitation energy, eV	19.818	16.618	11.548	9.915	8.315	6.772

[a] Estimated value.

[b] Volume of gas at 1 atm and 273.15°K (0°C) equivalent to unit volume liquid at nbp.

xenon oxyfluorides. A number of complex fluorides have been prepared by reaction of xenon with highly reactive hexafluorides like those of rhodium, ruthenium, and plutonium, as well as platinum. Only two compounds of krypton are known to have been isolated. These are the difluoride and the tetrafluoride which are both much more reactive than their xenon homologs. With radon, at least one volatile radon fluoride and one essentially nonvolatile fluoride have been established. A large number of other radon compounds have been claimed, but because of the self-decomposition of prepared materials through radioactive decay and the minute quantities of radon available, their preparations and the assessment of the product stoichiometry and properties are extremely difficult. A monograph on noble gas compounds by Moody and Thomas (11) and an article by Hyman (12) provide supplemental information on this subject.

Solubility. The solubility of the noble gases in water at 1 atm pressure and various temperatures is presented in Table 4 (13). These data show that, except for neon, the solubilities increase with increasing atomic number.

Minima occur at 10°C for helium, 0°C for neon, 40°C for argon, 35°C for krypton, and 40°C for xenon. At elevated pressures, solubilities increase with the ultimate formation of noble gas hydrates with the high molecular weight gases. Xenon hydrate forms at 1.15 atm at 0°C, krypton hydrate forms at 14.5 atm at 0°C, and argon hy-

Table 3. Naturally Occurring Isotopic Abundance of the Noble Gas Elements (7)

Element	Atomic number	Mass number	Abundance, atom %
He	2	3	0.00013
		4	99.9999
Ne	10	20	90.92
		21	0.257
		22	8.82
Ar	18	36	0.337
		38	0.063
		40	99.600
Kr	36	78	0.354
		80	2.27
		82	11.56
		83	11.55
		84	56.90
		86	17.37
Xe	54	124	0.096
		126	0.090
		128	1.919
		129	26.44
		130	4.08
		131	21.18
		132	26.89
		134	10.44
		136	8.87
Rn	86		no stable isotopes

drate forms at 150 atm at 0°C. No neon hydrate is reported at pressures up to 260 atm at 0°C.

All the noble gases exhibit high solubilities in cryogenic liquids. For example, helium is soluble in liquid oxygen to the extent of 1 part in 80 parts at −205°C. This high solubility in cryogenic liquids is the basis of a process for the recovery of krypton and xenon from air by scrubbing large quantities of gaseous air through relatively small quantities of liquid air to yield a product considerably enriched in krypton and xenon which can be more easily and economically refined.

The noble gases show higher solubilities in certain organic solvents than in water. For example, xenon solubility in p-xylene is reported as 2.95 ml/ml at 29°C, whereas krypton solubility in hexane is reported as 1.05 ml/ml at 25°C and 2.95 ml/ml at

Table 4. Solubility of the Noble Gases in Water at 1 atm[a] and Various Temperatures

Temperature, °C	Solubility, volume of gas[b] per volume of water				
	He	Ne	Ar	Kr	Xe
0	0.0134	0.0114	0.0561	0.1207	0.2189
10	0.0100	0.0118	0.0438	0.0921	0.1500
20	0.0138	0.0147	0.0379	0.0729	0.1109
30	0.0161	0.0158	0.0348	0.0679	0.0900
40	0.0191	0.0203	0.0338	0.0650	0.0812
50	0.0226	0.0317	0.0343	0.0716	0.0878

[a] 1 atm includes the partial pressure of the gas plus that of water.

[b] Volume of gas at 0°C and 760 torr.

$-90°C$. Additional data on solubility in organic solvents are reported by Steinberg et al. (14).

Toxicity. The noble gases are normal constituents of air and, at these extremely low concentrations, are not considered hazardous. They are regarded by Sax (15) as simple asphyxiants. The effect of simple asphyxiant gases is proportional to the extent to which they diminish the amount (partial pressure) of oxygen in the air that is breathed. The oxygen may be diminished to two thirds of its normal percentage before appreciable symptoms develop; when the simple asphyxiant reaches a concentration of 50%, marked symptoms can be produced. A concentration of 75% is fatal in a matter of minutes. The first symptoms produced by simple asphyxiant gases are rapid respiration and air hunger. Mental alertness is diminished and muscular coordination is impaired. Later, judgment becomes faulty and all sensations are depressed. Emotional instability often results and fatigue occurs rapidly. As the asphyxia progresses, there may be nausea and vomiting, prostration and loss of consciousness, and finally, convulsions, deep coma, and death.

Occurrence and Methods of Manufacture

The atmosphere is the commercial source of neon, argon, krypton, and xenon. Although helium exists in the atmosphere, its principal source in the United States is from certain natural gas wells. The abundance of the noble gases in the atmosphere is reported by Glueckauf (16), and is summarized in Table 5 (16).

The presence of helium in certain natural gases may be due to the entrapment of helium released by radioactive decay down through the ages. Certain minerals of a radioactive nature such as pitchblende, cleveite, and monazite also contain entrapped helium. Radon is produced in small amounts by radioactive decay of radium.

Helium is produced commercially primarily by separation from helium-bearing natural gases which contain about 0.4% helium or more. The production process (17) consists basically of lowering the temperature of the natural gas until all of the components except helium and a trace of hydrogen are condensed as liquids. The resulting helium-rich vapor is further purified to yield the desired quality product. Small amounts of helium can be recovered as a by-product of air-separation plants or by extraction from minerals such as monazite, but these sources are not economically competitive with the natural gas source.

Argon, neon, krypton, and xenon are produced commercially mainly as by-products from large scale oxygen and nitrogen plants. The recovery of the noble gas elements from the atmosphere is based upon a complex liquefaction and rectification process (18). In most air separation plants, the noble gases are separated as crude

Table 5. Abundance of Noble Gases in the Atmosphere

Element	Atmospheric concentration (dry air), ppm by vol
He	5.24
Ne	18.18
Ar	9340
Kr	1.14
Xe	0.086
Rn	6×10^{-14} [a]

[a] Average value. The concentration may vary from one location to another.

gases which must be further purified. A comparison of boiling points shows that the most volatile fractions of air will contain nitrogen, neon, and helium; oxygen, argon, krypton, and xenon will concentrate in the residual liquid. Further fractionation will yield an argon-rich stream that is introduced into separate argon columns in which the argon is further refined by distillation. Final oxygen removal may be accomplished by passage over hot copper, by selective adsorption, or by the addition of hydrogen, followed by catalytic combustion and reliquefaction of the argon to remove the excess hydrogen. The resulting argon is 99.99% pure or better.

The very small quantities of krypton and xenon, as well as hydrocarbons in the air, tend to accumulate in the reboiler. A liquid stream is continually withdrawn from the upper column and cycled through a rectifying column. The oxygen vapor from this krypton column is returned to the air-separation column, and the krypton–xenon enriched liquid from the bottom of the krypton column is passed through a catalytic combustion unit to remove the hydrocarbons. The resulting crude mixture contains about 1% krypton–xenon with the balance being oxygen. This crude mixture is withdrawn for further processing. The oxygen is usually removed from the crude krypton–xenon by chemical means, and the final separation of krypton from xenon is accomplished by cryogenic distillation.

Neon and helium accumulate in the condenser of the air-separation column. The gas stream withdrawn from the condenser has a neon–helium content which varies from less than 1 to 12%. The nitrogen content of this stream is reduced by passing the stream through a condenser which yields a crude neon stream composition about 46% neon, 19% helium, 2% hydrogen, and 33% nitrogen. This crude neon is withdrawn from the air-separation plant for further purification. In some processes, the small hydrogen content is removed by chemical oxidation followed by a drying step. The removal of nitrogen is generally accomplished by condensation from the pressurized crude gas in a liquid nitrogen-cooled trap followed by adsorption on liquid nitrogen-cooled charcoal. The remaining gas contains about 75% neon and 25% helium. Some of this is sold as technical grade neon. The final separation of neon from helium can be accomplished by differential adsorption. However, with the increase in the availability of very low-temperature refrigeration from liquid hydrogen, the components of the crude neon are separated by condensation at temperatures near the neon boiling point (19). This procedure is particularly advantageous when a liquefied neon product is desired.

Radon is normally prepared at the point of use in laboratory scale apparatus (20). Radium salts are dissolved in water, and the evolved gas is periodically collected. The gas contains radon, hydrogen, and oxygen. This gas is cooled sufficiently to condense the radon, and the gaseous hydrogen and oxygen are pumped away. ^{3}He, the rare isotope of helium, is obtained by separation from its parent element, tritium.

An important future source of krypton and xenon may result from nuclear power plant fuel reprocessing. These gases constitute a significant fraction of the products of thermal fission of nuclear power plant fuels (21). They accumulate in the fuel rods and are released during reprocessing of spent fuels. Processes are described in the literature for krypton and xenon recovery from this source (22).

Methods of Analysis

Because of the extreme chemical inertness of the noble gas elements, the qualitative and quantitative analyses of these materials are based upon their physical properties. The chemical reactions discovered for the higher molecular weight noble gases have not yet been utilized in analytical procedures.

IDENTIFICATION

Although the noble gas elements cannot be identified by chemical reaction, their presence can be detected indirectly by their resistance to chemical reaction. If a gas sample is thought to contain one or more noble gases, the sample may be reacted chemically to remove all components other than the noble gases. In the standard Orsat procedure (Vol. 2, pp. 139–145), after removal of acidic gases, oxygen, hydrogen, hydrocarbons, and carbon monoxide, the residue is a mixture of nitrogen and noble gases. This residue can be further treated to remove the nitrogen by reaction with active metal such as titanium, lithium, or calcium at high temperatures. Any gaseous residue after this treatment is one or more of the noble gases. This nonreactive gas residue may be a single noble gas or a mixture of several. Isolation and detection of the individual inert gases in the residue can be accomplished by fractional desorption from activated charcoal as described by Cady (23). The method is very tedious and depends upon the gradual replacement of less strongly adsorbed gas by more strongly adsorbed gas. With the availability of modern instrumentation, these methods are seldom used.

Emission spectroscopy is a less tedious technique for the identification of individual noble gases. Each noble gas will produce a characteristic emission spectrum when subjected to an electric discharge. The radiation from the discharge tube can be introduced through a suitable slit system into a spectrograph or spectrometer. For visual observations, the light may be viewed with the help of a laboratory spectroscope which is equipped with an eyepiece. The inert gases are identified by the pattern of the emission lines or, when a visual spectroscope is used, by the color of the lines. Spectra from unknown gas samples are readily obtained by filling a discharge tube with the gas to a few torr pressure, imposing a few thousand volts ac on the electrodes, and analyzing the emitted light.

Mass spectroscopy is another technique that can readily be used to identify noble gases. In a mass spectrometer, the gas sample is ionized and the ions are separated by the ratio of mass to electronic charge (m/e). In most modern instruments, the ion current for each value of m/e is measured by a scanning device and automatically recorded. The resulting mass spectrum is examined for m/e peaks characteristic of the noble gas isotopes. The principal peaks for the inert gases can be determined from Table 3, which presents the naturally occurring isotopic abundance for the noble gas elements. The peak heights in natural mixtures of isotopes are in proportion to their natural abundance. For example, neon will show its most intense peak at mass number 20, a second peak at mass number 22 with about $\frac{1}{10}$th the intensity of mass number 20, and a third peak at mass number 21 showing a very low intensity. With argon, mass number 40 will appear about 300 times as intense as mass number 36, whereas 36 will appear about $5\frac{1}{2}$ times as intense as mass number 38. Details of the quantitative aspects of mass spectroscopy as applied to noble gas analysis are presented in a later section.

Gas chromatography is probably the single most useful technique for the identification, separation, and determination of the noble gases. Specific conditions are described in the sections on Determination of Impurities (p. 293) and Determination in Mixtures (p. 304).

Assay Methods

A variety of techniques can be used to determine the purity of noble gases. Most approaches involve the measurement of the total impurities and establishing the purity by difference. Since impurity levels in commercially available noble gases are quite low, modern instrumentation is generally used to determine trace concentrations of each specific contaminant. These techniques are discussed in the next section. However, assay methods are available which permit the determination of total noninert gas impurities in noble gases based on the removal of the impurities by reaction with molten lithium or titanium sponge. Two of these procedures are discussed below.

Bowman-Hartley method. This method (24) was developed for determining the total impurities in the noble gases, argon and helium, that are used in arc welding, but is also applicable to the other noble gases. The method is based upon the fact that molten lithium absorbs nitrogen, oxygen, and water vapor. The gas sample is admitted into a constant volume apparatus where the impurities are removed by the molten lithium. The change in pressure produced by the removal of the impurities is used to determine the purity of the gas. A special apparatus is used to minimize errors due to small changes in atmospheric pressure and temperature. The apparatus is satisfactory for determining the purity of noble gases with a maximum error of about ±0.01% by volume. Since most present-day commercial sources of noble gases provide a purity of 99.99% or better, this procedure finds very limited use.

Titanium Absorption Method. This method was developed by Dombrowski (25) for the determination of trace nitrogen impurity and total impurities in noble gases. The method involves the absorption of all impurities in the noble gas on titanium metal sponge at temperatures between 900 and 1000°C. A measured volume of the noble gas sample is passed over a preweighed quantity of titanium metal. After absorption of the impurities, the metal sponge is reweighed and analyzed by a modified macro-Kjeldahl technique to determine the nitrogen content of the metal. The quantity of nitrogen absorbed by the sponge is calculated from the final weight of the titanium sponge and the difference in nitrogen analyses before and after absorption. The increase in weight of the sponge sample, the nitrogen pickup, and the volume of weight of noble gas sample permit calculation of the ppm of nitrogen and ppm of total impurities in the gas sample. This technique has been used effectively for impurity levels of 10–200 ppm by vol. The major disadvantages are the need for very large samples when measuring low-level impurities (600 STP liters in the 10 ppm range) and the long time required for analysis. With the availability of instrumental techniques, this procedure is seldom used.

Determination of Impurities

The listing of impurities in Table 1 (p. 287) shows that nitrogen and the noble gases themselves are the major contaminants in the high-purity products. Several other contaminants such as hydrogen, oxygen, hydrocarbons, and moisture are also generally monitored. In some cases, concern may exist about minor impurities of carbon dioxide, carbon monoxide, and nitrous oxide. In general, the total of these contaminants are present in concentrations which range from 10 to 100 ppm by vol with concentrations of any specific contaminant ranging from 0.1 to 25 ppm. Although some chemical procedures do exist for the determination of some of these contaminants, instrumental techniques are almost exclusively applied.

Infrared Spectroscopy

Infrared spectroscopy provides a very sensitive and accurate method for the identification and quantitative measurement of several impurities that may exist in the noble gases. Trace quantities of such strong infrared absorbing contaminants as carbon dioxide, carbon monoxide, nitrous oxide, and hydrocarbons such as methane and acetylene are readily determined by infrared absorption spectroscopy. Since noble gases do not absorb infrared radiation in the region between 2 and 15 μm, these contaminants can be measured with high sensitivity. The major absorption bands and minimum detectable limits of several typical gaseous contaminants that can be readily determined by infrared absorption spectroscopy are listed in Table 6.

Table 6. Major Absorption Bands and Minimum Detectable Limits for Gaseous Contaminants in Noble Gases by Infrared Spectroscopy

Gas	Major bands, μm	Minimum detectable limit, ppm[a]
CO_2	2.69, 2.76, and 4.22	0.5
CO	4.5 and 4.7	1.0
N_2O	4.45 and 4.5	0.1
CH_4	3.3, 7.65	0.5
C_2H_2	13.7	0.05
CF_4[b]	7.8	0.1
CH_2Cl_2[b]	7.95 and 13.35	1.0
SF_6[b]	10.6	1.0

[a] With a 10-m cell at 10 atm sample pressure.
[b] Contaminants generally found in krypton and xenon only.

Typical infrared spectra for high-purity helium are shown in Figure 1. These spectra were obtained from a Beckman IR-4 infrared spectrophotometer equipped with a Beckman high-pressure, long-path infrared gas cell and spectral recorder. These spectra were recorded with path lengths of 1, 5, and 10 m and a sample pressure of 10 atm. The spectra are labeled to show those contaminants that were present in the samples and to show where other contaminants would appear if they were present.

Gas Chromatography

Hydrogen, oxygen, nitrogen, and the noble gases are readily determined as contaminants in any specific noble gas by gas chromatographic methods. Molecular sieve 5A is the most frequently used adsorbent for the chromatographic separation of these components, although other materials are more effective for special separations as will be pointed out later. The selection of column packing, column size, and operating conditions as well as the carrier gas is dependent upon the bulk noble gas and the contaminants to be determined. Since each commercially available noble gas generally contains a different group of contaminants, a single gas chromatographic procedure cannot be used for the determination of impurities in all noble gases. Six different combinations of column configurations and operating conditions are listed in Table 7. These arrangements permit the measurement of most of the common trace impurities in the noble gases which are determinable by gas chromatographic methods.

Table 8 presents a summary of the chromatographic systems generally used to determine various contaminants in each of the noble gases, which are listed across

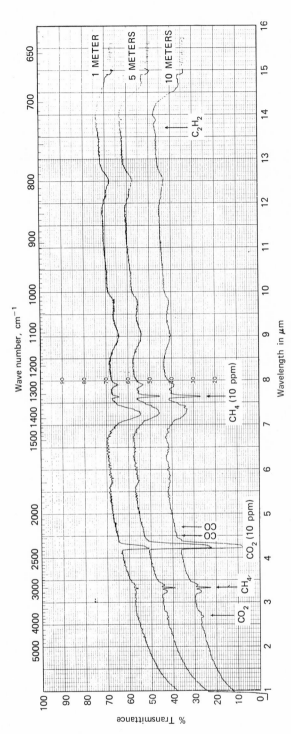

Fig. 1. Infrared absorption spectrum of impurities in helium with sample path lengths of 1, 5, and 10 meters at 10 atm pressure.

Table 7. Gas Chromatographic Systems Used for the Analysis of Noble Gases

System No. →	1	2	3	4	5	6
column dimensions	(a) 12 ft × ¼ in. OD + (b) 12 ft × ¼ in. OD in series	6 ft × ¼ in. OD	12 ft × ¼ in. OD	20 ft × ⅛ in. OD	8 ft × ¼ in. OD	8 ft × ¼ in. OD
column packing	molecular sieve 5A 30/60 mesh	molecular sieve 5A 30/60 mesh	molecular sieve 5A 30/60 mesh	molecular sieve 5A 30/60 mesh	molecular sieve 5A 30/60 mesh	Porapak R 80/100 mesh
column temperature, °C	(a) −78 (dry ice) (b) +40	40	40	40	40	40
carrier gas	helium or neon	helium	helium or neon	helium	argon	helium
inlet pressure, psig	35	20	20	20	20	20
flow rate, ml/min	50–60	50–60	50–60	50–60	50–60	50–60
sample volume, ml	10	10	5	5	1 (2 atm sample pressure)	10
filament current of the hot-wire detector, mA	250	400	400	400	160	400

Table 8. Summary of Chromatographic Systems for Determination of Various Contaminants in the Noble Gases[a]

Impurities	He	Ne	Ar	Kr	Xe
He		1	1	1[b]	1[b]
Ne	1, 3		1	1[b], 5	1[b], 5
H_2	1	1	1	1[b]	1[b]
$O_2 + Ar$	3	3[b]		4	2
N_2	3	3	[c]	4	2
Kr	3[b]	3[b]	[d]		2
Xe	3[b]	6[b]	[d]	6	
CO_2				6	6

[a] Numbers refer to chromatographic systems listed in Table 7.
[b] Method not widely practiced or measurement not generally made.
[c] Measurement not performed by gas chromatography for trace quantities.
[d] Measurements not generally needed.

the page in order of increasing retention time on molecular sieve. The impurities are listed vertically in order of increasing retention time on molecular sieve. The carbon dioxide is, of course, not eluted by molecular sieve under the listed conditions, and a Porapak R column is used for its determination. A brief discussion of the determination of the impurities in each of the noble gases is presented below. The procedures described provide rapid and sensitive methods for the routine analysis of the contaminant in the high-purity noble gases which are commercially available. In general, the detectable limits for the contaminants discussed above range from 2 to 5 ppm, depending primarily upon the retention time and the difference between the thermal conductivity of the contaminant and the carrier gas. More sensitive techniques are available for special purposes which utilize more sensitive detector systems, such as the helium ionization detector (26), which provides sensitivities on the order of 0.1 ppm or better for most permanent gases. The key to such analyses is the ability to make clear chromatographic separations using helium as the carrier gas. Another approach

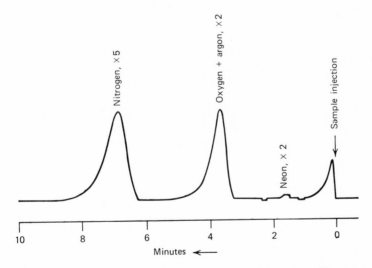

Fig. 2. Chromatogram of 900 ppm air in 5 ml of helium. Chromatographic system No. 3 (see Table 7); Carrier gas: helium. The attenuation of the recorder is indicated at the peaks.

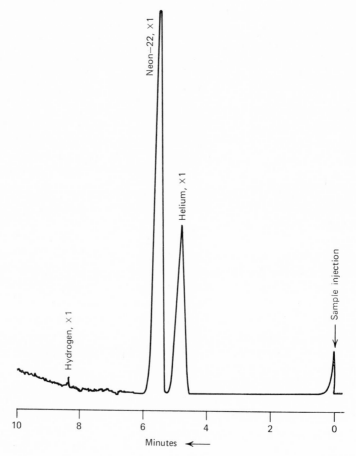

Fig. 3. Chromatogram of impurities in a 10-ml neon sample. Chromatographic system No. 1 (see Table 7); Carrier gas: neon. The attenuation of the recorder is indicated at the peaks.

to achieving higher sensitivities is to utilize the technique of preconcentration of impurities prior to injection into the chromatograph system. Purer (27) reports a procedure for the analysis of impurities in helium in the ppb range with a preconcentration method. This method is reported to be satisfactory for analyses in the ppb range for neon, hydrogen, argon, oxygen, nitrogen, krypton, methane, and xenon in helium.

Impurities in Helium. Helium is analyzed for traces of neon and hydrogen by chromatographic system No. 1 using a helium carrier; system No. 3 is used to determine neon, the oxygen–argon composite, and nitrogen. Krypton and xenon can also be determined with this arrangement if necessary. Figure 2 shows a typical chromatogram resulting from system No. 3 in which a laboratory standard containing 900 ppm of air in 5 ml of helium was used as the sample. The trace of neon shown was an original impurity in the helium.

Impurities in Neon. Neon is analyzed for traces of helium and hydrogen by chromatographic system No. 1, using neon as the carrier gas. Figure 3 shows a typical chromatogram for a commercial neon sample containing a trace amount of helium but no hydrogen. The peak immediately after the helium peak is reportedly due to ^{22}Ne, which exists in a higher concentration in the sample than in the carrier gas. The naturally occurring abundance for the isotopes of neon are shown in Table 3 (p. 289). During the processing of neon to obtain high-purity material, several concentration and distillation steps are performed which result in changes in the isotopic ratios. In Figure 3, a significantly higher concentration of ^{22}Ne existed in the neon sample gas as compared to the neon carrier gas.

Nitrogen in neon is readily determined with system No. 3 using helium or neon as a carrier gas. With helium carrier, the large peak from the bulk neon in the sample creates a large tail that masks the oxygen–argon composite. With neon carrier, the oxygen–argon composite, nitrogen, and krypton can readily be separated; the resulting chromatogram is similar to Figure 2. Xenon in neon is readily determined with system No. 6, should such a measurement be desired. This analysis is not usually performed on commercial neon, as xenon is generally not present as a contaminant.

Impurities in Argon. Argon is analyzed for traces of helium, neon, and hydrogen with system No. 1, using helium or neon as a carrier gas. If argon is used as the carrier, the three contaminants can be determined by a single analysis. Trace nitrogen in argon is not determined by gas chromatography because the large tail from the bulk argon overlaps the trace nitrogen peak which follows the argon. If argon carrier is

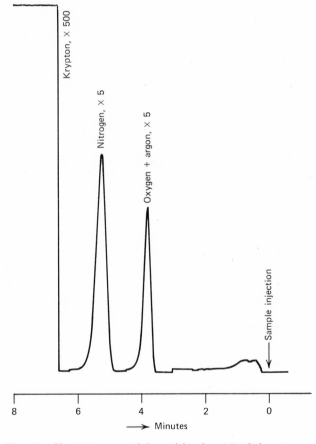

Fig. 4. Chromatogram of impurities in a 5-ml krypton sample. Chromatographic system No. 4 (see Table 7). The attenuation of the recorder is indicated at the peaks.

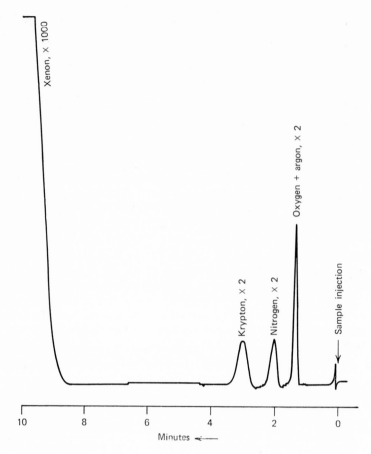

Fig. 5. Chromatogram of impurities in a 10-ml xenon sample. Chromatographic system No. 2
(see Table 7). The attenuation of the recorder is indicated at the peaks.

used, the nitrogen peak can be readily separated, but the sensitivity is very poor because of the similarity in thermal conductivity of the argon and nitrogen. Nitrogen in
argon is usually measured by special instruments involving emission spectroscopy and
ion mobility.

Impurities in Krypton. Krypton is analyzed for trace helium, neon, and hydrogen
with system No. 1, or these components may be analyzed as a composite peak using
system No. 5. The composite peak method is generally applied since these contaminants are generally not found in commercial krypton. System No. 4 permits the
separation of the argon–oxygen composite and nitrogen which are generally present in
commercial krypton. Figure 4 shows a typical chromatogram of krypton using system
No. 4. The nitrogen peak is followed by the large krypton sample peak. Xenon will
elute in this system after the krypton peak but the retention time is too long to provide
high sensitivity. Xenon and carbon dioxide are generally determined in krypton with
system No. 6; under these conditions the carbon dioxide peak will elute at 4.7 min,
followed by the xenon peak at about 8.0 min.

Impurities in Xenon. Xenon is analyzed for trace helium, neon, and hydrogen as
individual peaks with system No. 1, or more often as a composite peak with system
No. 5 as is described above for krypton. The oxygen–argon composite, nitrogen, and

krypton are generally determined in xenon with system No. 2 arrangement; a resulting chromatogram is shown in Figure 5. This chromatogram also shows the bulk xenon peak, which elutes well after the krypton peak and therefore provides no interference in the analysis. The carbon dioxide content of xenon is determined with system No. 6 as previously described for the carbon dioxide determination in krypton.

Mass Spectroscopy

The use of the mass spectrometer for the analysis of industrial gases has expanded rapidly with the appearance of a wide variety of residual gas analyzers and gas mass spectrometers on the market. A major advantage of the mass spectrometer for analytical work is the small quantity of sample required for complete analysis. This is of particular importance in the analysis of rare gases such as neon, krypton, xenon, and radon. For the analysis of ultrahigh-purity industrial gases, the more refined, reliable, and sensitive gas mass spectrometers must be employed. However, their use has been somewhat limited by the large initial investment and operating expenses.

A mass spectrometer can be used to determine those impurities which have different parent ion mass numbers than those produced by the noble gases. Table 9 lists the principal noble gas ions and their mass number (m/e) as produced in the mass spectrometer for the stable isotopes. Table 10 lists the principal contaminants usually found in noble gases and their respective parent ion mass numbers. As can be readily seen, only a few interfering situations exist. Traces of hydrogen in helium are obscured by the doubly ionized helium peak. Traces of carbon dioxide and/or nitrous oxide are obscured by the triply ionized ^{132}Xe. Traces of neon in argon are obscured by the doubly ionized ^{40}Ar, and traces of argon in krypton are masked by the doubly ionized ^{80}Kr. In addition, the analyst must recognize that two pairs of contaminant

Table 9. Principal Noble Gas Ions Produced in the Mass Spectrometer from Stable Isotopes

m/e	Ion	m/e	Ion
4	He$^+$	64	Xe^{2+}
18	Ar^{2+}	64$\frac{1}{2}$	Xe^{2+}
19	Ar^{2+}	65	Xe^{2+}
20	Ne$^+$, Ar^{2+}	65$\frac{1}{2}$	Xe^{2+}
21	Ne$^+$	66	Xe^{2+}
22	Ne$^+$	67	Xe^{2+}
36	Ar$^+$	68	Xe^{2+}
38	Ar$^+$	78	Kr$^+$
39	Kr^{2+}	80	Kr$^+$
40	Ar$^+$, Kr^{2+}	82	Kr$^+$
41	Kr^{2+}	83	Kr$^+$
41$\frac{1}{2}$	Kr^{2+}	84	Kr$^+$
42	Kr^{2+}	86	Kr$^+$
42$\frac{2}{3}$	Xe^{3+}	124	Xe$^+$
43	Kr^{2+}, Xe^{3+}	126	Xe$^+$
43$\frac{1}{3}$	Xe^{3+}	128	Xe$^+$
43$\frac{2}{3}$	Xe^{3+}	129	Xe$^+$
44	Xe^{3+}	130	Xe$^+$
44$\frac{2}{3}$	Xe^{3+}	131	Xe$^+$
45$\frac{1}{3}$	Xe^{3+}	132	Xe$^+$
62	Xe^{2+}	134	Xe$^+$
63	Xe^{2+}	136	Xe$^+$

Table 10. Principal Contaminants in Noble Gases and Their Parent Mass Spectrometer Peaks

Contaminant	Parent ion mass number (m/e)	Noble gas ion interferences
hydrogen	2	He^{2+}
methane	16	none
nitrogen	28	none
carbon monoxide	28	none
oxygen	32	none
carbon dioxide	44	Xe^{3+}
nitrous oxide	44	Xe^{3+}
other noble gases		
neon	20	Ar^{2+}
argon	40	Kr^{2+}

interferences also exist. These are nitrogen–carbon monoxide and carbon dioxide–nitrous oxide. If only the parent ion peak appears in the mass spectrum for these contaminant pairs, the analyst cannot be sure whether one or the other or both are present. If contaminant concentrations are high enough that secondary ion peaks appear, more positive detection is possible. Some specific applications of mass spectrometry to the determination of impurities in noble gases are discussed below.

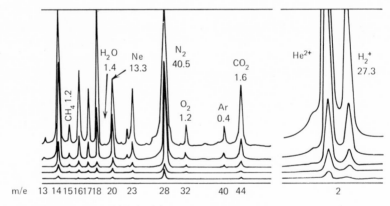

Fig. 6. Typical high-pressure, high-ionizing-current, mass spectrometer scan (25.0 torr, 100 μA) of impurities in helium.

In 1966, Suttle, Emerson, and Burfield (28) reported on the analysis of trace impurities in helium in the ppb range using a conventional mass spectrometer. To obtain the required sensitivity, the inlet sample pressure and the ionizing current were increased. The optimum conditions were found to be 25.0 torr inlet pressure and 100 μA ionizing current. A typical mass spectrometer scan for a specific helium sample is shown in Figure 6 (28). Peaks representing specific impurities are shown along with the average concentration in ppb as determined by a series of analyses. Sensitivities in the range of 0.1–1.0 ppm were easily achieved. As shown in the scan, the hydrogen analysis was made possible because of the high resolution of the instrument which permitted a separation of the He^{2+} and the H_2^+ peaks.

This technology was extended by Weems and Emerson (29) when they combined preconcentrating techniques and high-sensitivity mass spectrometry to develop a general analysis method for impurities in helium in the ppb range. Sensitivities in the range of 0.3–3.0 ppb were obtained. In this analytical method, the impurities in the helium are preconcentrated using a Bureau of Mines trace-impurity analyzer, as described by Kirkland et al. (30), in which the sample is passed through a trap cooled with liquid helium. The impurity trap is first evacuated and heated to about 260°C to remove moisture and other impurities. The trap is precooled with liquid nitrogen and then immersed in liquid helium. The helium sample is passed through the trap and all impurities in the helium freeze out as solids in the trap. Essentially all of the helium passes through the trap. After 12 liters of helium have passed through the trap, the inlet valve on the trap is closed, and the helium pressure in the trap reduced to 35 torr. The outlet valve is then closed, isolating the sample. When the sample has warmed to room temperature, the pressure in the trap is 50–60 psia. This pressure is sufficient to produce a 10 torr sample pressure when expanded directly into the 3-liter sample volume of the mass spectrometer. The sample is then analyzed using the mass spectrometer to produce a scan similar to Figure 6, but where the peaks represent considerably lower concentration levels in the original sample, since a 300-fold concentration of the impurities was accomplished by the pretreatment.

Other Methods

Water Content Determinations. Water vapor content is generally measured by dew point determination. The method is discussed in the article GAS, NATURAL on p. 327, and in Vol. 8, on p. 257. Table 11 provides some data relating dew point temperature at 1 atm to water vapor content.

Table 11. Several Dew Point Temperatures with the Corresponding Water Vapor Content at 1 atm

| Dew point temperature | | Water vapor content,[a] |
°F	°C	ppm by vol
+32	0	6000
0	−17.8	1250
−20	−28.8	420
−40	−40	126
−60	−51.1	34
−70	−56.7	16.6
−80	−62.2	7.8
−90	−67.8	3.6
−100	−73.4	1.55

[a] Values are based on water vapor pressure over ice at the respective temperature.

The water vapor content may also be determined by a gravimetric method based on the absorption of the water vapor in a weighed drying tube that is filled with an effective drying agent. This procedure is applicable to samples with reasonably high water vapor concentration. A discussion of the method is presented in Vol. 8, pp. 255–257.

Total Hydrocarbon Determination. The total hydrocarbon content of noble gases is generally measured with a hydrogen flame ionization detector similar to that used as a detector in a gas chromatograph but without the use of a separation column with the sample instead of the carrier gas being continuously fed into the detector. The technique is described in Vol. 8, p. 259.

Determination of Noble Gases in Mixtures

The two most popular techniques for noble gases in mixtures are mass spectrometry and gas chromatography, with the latter being the more generally applied. These two methods permit determination of the noble gases from concentration levels of less than 1 ppm to levels approaching 100%.

Mass Spectroscopy

From the data on naturally occurring isotopic abundance of the noble gases listed in Table 3 (p. 289), and the principal noble gas ions produced in a mass spectrometer for these isotopes, listed in Table 9 (p. 301), one can easily predict the typical mass

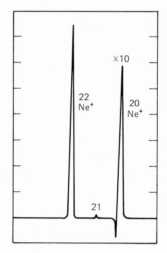

Fig. 7. Mass spectrum of atmospheric neon.

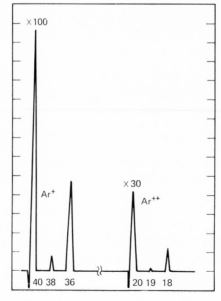

Fig. 8. Mass spectrum of atmospheric argon.

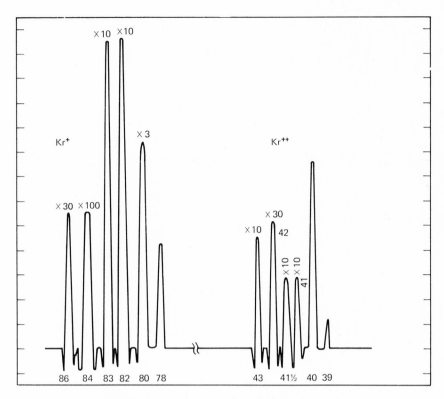

Fig. 9. Mass spectrum of atmospheric krypton.

spectra for natural mixtures of these isotopes with some indication of relative peak heights. Figures 7 (31), 8 (31), 9, and 10 illustrate graphically such data for neon, argon, krypton, and xenon, respectively. These data were taken from actual mass spectra that were obtained by running pure samples of the various noble gases. The peaks are labeled with the appropriate m/e values and the attenuation factors are shown above the peaks where they apply. Examination of these mass spectra and Table 9 reveals that overlapping of peaks for the natural isotopes occurs in only three cases. These occur at m/e values of 20, 40 and 43 for the Ne^+–Ar^{2+}, Ar^+–Kr^{2+}, and Kr^{2+}–Xe^{3+} ion pairs. When looking for characteristic isotope patterns for the noble gases, these situations must be borne in mind. For example, the quantitative estimation of the amount of neon in a mixture containing argon could not be based on the intensity of mass peak 20 unless the contribution of Ar^{2+} to that mass peak were subtracted. This can be done by estimating the argon concentration from mass peak 40 and calculating the contribution of Ar^{2+} to mass peak 20 from a knowledge of the mass spectrometer response and assuming that the argon isotopic distribution is in the naturally occurring ratios. A more direct approach is to use the mass 22 peak for neon estimation in the presence of argon interference with the major neon isotopic peak at mass 20. In the analysis of argon in a mixture containing krypton, the contribution of Kr^{2+} from isotopic mass number 80 must be considered. The problem is not as great in this case since mass number 80 accounts for only 2.27% of the isotopic abundance for krypton. This indicates that contribution of the doubly ionized Kr^{2+} peak to mass peak 40 is not very significant in comparison to the singly ionized Ar^+

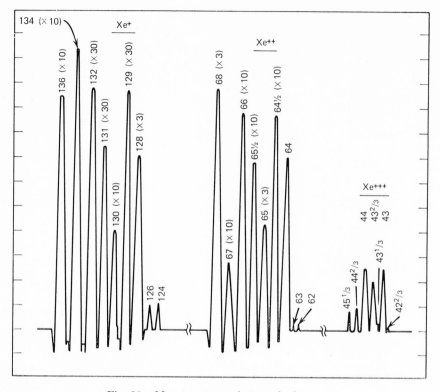

Fig. 10. Mass spectrum of atmospheric xenon.

with an isotopic abundance of 99.6%. Nevertheless, even this minor correction can be avoided by using the Ar^+ peak at mass number 36, but only with a significant loss of sensitivity, since the isotopic abundance of ^{36}Ar is only 0.337%.

Mass peak overlapping occurs with gases other than the noble gases. For example, carbon dioxide in the presence of neon will provide an overlap at mass peak 22 for CO_2^{2+} and Ne^+. However, this only creates a problem when the major neon peak at 20 is also obscured by argon. In general, the concentration of any gas in a gas mixture may be calculated from the height of a clear m/e peak that is compared with the height of the corresponding peak in a calibration run in which the gas pressure and other conditions are suitably controlled. A clear peak is one which is not partly due to some other gas. In the calibration run, either a sample of the pure gas or a mixture of known composition containing the desired gas may be used. If a clear peak is not available, a peak due mostly to the desired gas must be identified. If the concentrations of the impurity contributions can be obtained from other peaks, suitable allowances can be made for them and the concentration of the desired gas calculated.

Gas Chromatography

The chromatographic systems described under Determination of Impurities (p. 293) can be applied to the quantitative measurement of noble gases in gas mixtures. For example, the system represented by Figure 3 readily permits the measurement of helium in almost any gas mixture. Theoretically, a single column can be set up to provide for the complete separation of the five natural noble gases, but this is generally not practical because of the wide range in retention times for a given set of conditions. This problem is overcome somewhat with temperature programming, but subambient conditions are generally required for helium and neon separations. It is generally more practical to select a column and conditions for the solution of a specific problem or for the analysis of a specific gas mixture. All five noble gases are seldom encountered in a single sample. Several specific examples are discussed below.

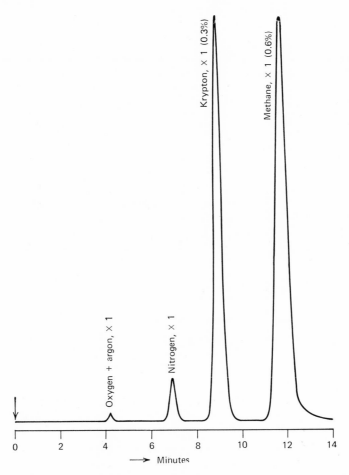

Fig. 11. Typical chromatogram of krypton and methane in 1.5 ml of helium with traces of air present. The attenuation of the recorder is given at the peaks. For conditions, see the text.

Figure 11 shows a typical chromatogram for krypton analysis in the presence of air and methane. The sample consisted of 0.3% krypton and 0.6% methane in helium which also contained a trace of air contamination. The column consisted of 12 ft $\times$ $\frac{1}{4}$ in. OD of molecular sieve 13X operated at 40°C. The setup used helium carrier gas at 20 psig to provide a 40 ml/min flow rate. A thermal conductivity detector was used with 300 mA filament current. A 1.5-ml sample loop was used to introduce the sample and a 0-1 mV strip chart recorder produced the chromatogram. The air component is resolved by this column into a composite argon–oxygen peak and a nitrogen peak. The air components are followed by a complete separation of the krypton and methane components. This setup allows measurements of krypton in a variety of gas mixtures, with krypton concentrations ranging from 0.01% to essentially 100%.

Figure 12 shows three typical chromatograms of samples containing krypton, oxygen, nitrogen, and xenon. These chromatograms were obtained with a 3 ft × ¼ in. OD molecular sieve 5A column operated at 40°C using a helium carrier gas and a

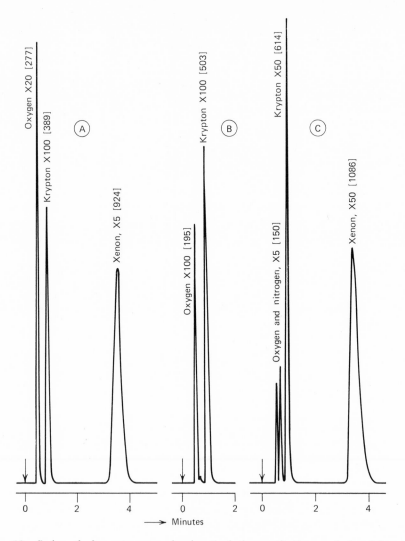

Fig. 12. Series of chromatograms showing typical quantitative analysis of krypton and xenon. The attenuation of the recorder is given at the peaks. Numbers in parentheses represent peak area in counts (arbitrary units). For conditions see the text.

1-ml sample. The detector was a thermal conductivity cell operated at a filament current of 180 mA. Chromatogram A represents a standard gas mixture containing 10.1% oxygen, 49.4% krypton, and 5.02% xenon in helium. Using the known percentage values from A, the concentration of the components in B and C can be calculated.

Bibliography

GENERAL REFERENCES

1. G. A. Cook, ed., *Argon, Helium, and the Rare Gases*, Vols. 1 and 2, Interscience Publishers, a division of John Wiley & Sons, Inc., New York, 1961.
2. R. A. Hemstreet and B. S. Kirk, "Helium-Group Gases," in A. Standen, ed., *Kirk-Othmer Encyclopedia of Chemical Technology*, Vol. 10, 2nd ed., Interscience Publishers, a division of John Wiley & Sons, Inc., New York, 1966, pp. 862–888.

SPECIFIC REFERENCES

3. M. W. Travers, *Discovery of the Rare Gases*, Edward Arnold & Co., London, 1928.
4. V. J. Johnson, ed., *A Compendium of the Properties of Materials at Low Temperature*, WADD Tech. Rept. 60-56, Part I (July 1960); Part 2 (Dec. 1961).
5. F. Din, *Thermodynamic Functions of Gases*, Vol. 2, Butterworth & Co., Ltd., London, 1956.
6. R. M. Gibbons and G. P. Kuebler, *Research on Materials Essential to Cryocooler Technology—Thermophysical and Transport Properties of Argon, Neon, Nitrogen, and Helium-4*, Tech. Rept. AFML-TR-68-370, (1968).
7. R. L. Heath, "Table of the Isotopes," in R. C. Weast, ed., *Handbook of Chemistry and Physics*, 47th ed., The Chemical Rubber Co., Cleveland, Ohio, 1966, p. B-4.
8. D. Strominger, G. M. Hollander, and G. T. Seaborg, *Rev. Mod. Phys.* **30**, 585–904 (1958).
9. N. Bartlett, *Proc. Chem. Soc.* **218** (1962).
10. H. H. Claassen, H. Selig, and J. G. Malm, *J. Am. Chem. Soc.* **84**, 3593 (1962).
11. G. J. Moody and J. D. R. Thomas, *Noble Gases and Their Compounds*, The MacMillan Company, New York, 1964.
12. H. H. Hyman, "Helium-Group Gases (Compounds)," in A. Standen, ed., *Kirk-Othmer Encyclopedia of Chemical Technology*, Vol. 10, 2nd ed., Interscience Publishers, a division of John Wiley & Sons, Inc., New York, 1966, pp. 888–894.
13. J. W. Mellor, *A Comprehensive Treatise on Inorganic and Theoretical Chemistry*, Vol. 7, John Wiley & Sons, Inc., New York, 1960, p. 942.
14. M. Steinberg and B. Manowitz, *Ind. Eng. Chem.*, **51**, 47–50 (1959).
15. N. I. Sax, *Dangerous Properties of Industrial Materials*, 2nd ed., Reinhold Publishing Corp., New York, 1963, p. 433.
16. E. Glueckauf, "The Composition of Atmospheric Air" in T. F. Malone, ed., *Compendium of Meteorology*, American Meteorological Society, Boston, 1951.
17. E. Guccione, *Chem. Eng.* **70** (20), 76–78 (1963).
18. M. Ruhemann, *The Separation of Gases*, Oxford at the Clarendon Press, London, 1949.
19. G. F. Hagenbach and J. H. Schiffhauser, "Commercial Production of Liquid Neon" in K. D. Timmerhaus, ed., *Advances in Cryogenic Engineering*, Vol. 9, Plenum Press, New York, 1964, pp. 557–560.
20. W. A. Jennings and S. Russ, *Radon: Its Technique and Use*, John Murray, London, 1948.
21. D. E. Deonigi, et al., *Isotope Production and Availability from Power Reactors*, Battelle Northwest (BNWL-716), Richland, Washington, July 1968.
22. M. Steinberg and B. Manowitz, *Ind. Eng. Chem.* **51**, 47–50 (1959).
23. G. H. Cady and H. P. Cady, *Ind. Eng. Chem., Anal. Ed.*, **17**, 760–766 (1945).
24. R. E. Bowman and C. B. Hartley, *Welding J.* **29**, 258-s–262-s (1950).
25. H. S. Dombrowski, *Anal. Chem.* **26**, 526–528 (1954).
26. *The Analyzer*, Beckman Instruments, Inc., Fullerton, Calif., May 1967, p. 6.
27. A. Purer, *J. Gas Chromatography*, **3**, 165 (1965).
28. E. T. Suttle, D. E. Emerson, and D. W. Burfield, *Anal. Chem.* **38**, 51 (1966).
29. G. W. Weems and D. E. Emerson, *U.S. Bureau of Mines Report of Investment 6779* (1966).
30. C. G. Kirkland, L. W. Brandt, and W. M. Deaton, *U.S. Bureau of Mines Report of Investment 5644* (1960).
31. Ref. 1, Vol. 2, pp. 496–498.

GEORGE E. SCHMAUCH
Air Products and Chemicals, Inc.

GAS, NATURAL

Natural gas is defined as a naturally occurring mixture of hydrocarbon and non-hydrocarbon gases found in porous geologic formations beneath the earth's surface, often in association with crude petroleum (1). The principal constituent is methane, but some ethane is almost always present. Minor constituents include heavier hydrocarbons and certain nonhydrocarbon gases, such an nitrogen, carbon dioxide, hydrogen sulfide, and helium. Oxygen and argon may be present, but generally in very small amounts. Some natural gases contain substantial amounts of saturated hydrocarbons heavier than ethane. A few are free of heavier hydrocarbons, and many contain significant quantities of one or more of the nonhydrocarbons mentioned above. Unsaturated hydrocarbons are nearly always absent.

Commercial natural gas supplied to fuel gas markets usually contains 80–95% methane and lesser amounts of ethane and propane. The balance is largely nitrogen. The heating values range from about 900 to 1200 Btu/ft^3 and the specific gravity varies from about 0.58 to 0.70 (2).

Natural gas was first discovered in the United States in 1775 in the Kanawha Valley, West Virginia. The natural gas industry has developed rapidly since about 1900, at which time it accounted for only 3.2% of the total energy produced in the States. Growth has been particularly rapid since 1948.

Marketed production in countries outside the Western Hemisphere has been relatively small until the last ten years. In 1961 nearly 75% of the world production was marketed in the United States and only 18% was outside the Western Hemisphere.

The Department of Statistics of the American Gas Association publishes annually a statistical record of the gas utility industry (3). For 1969 there were 40.9 million customers, up 1.8% from 1968. Sales reached a record 153.9×10^9 therms (1 therm is equivalent to a heating value of 100,000 Btu), up 6.3%.

Proved recoverable reserves of natural gas totaled 275.1×10^{12} ft^3 at the end of 1969. Net production of natural gas climbed to a record 21.2×10^{12} ft^3, a 7.0% increase since 1968.

Natural gas continues to represent an increasing portion of the nation's total energy production and consumption. Production of natural gas accounted for 38.0% of the total energy produced in the United States. Consumption of dry natural gas accounted for 31.9% of the total energy used.

Some common terms applicable to natural gas are defined as follows (3):

Associated natural gas is free natural gas in immediate contact, but not in solution, with crude oil in the reservoir.

Dissolved natural gas is natural gas in solution in crude oil in the reservoir.

Dry natural gas is gas in which the water content has been reduced by a dehydration process or gas containing little or no hydrocarbons commercially recoverable as liquid product. Gas in this second category should preferably be called *lean gas*. Specified small quantities of liquids are permitted by varying statutory definitions in certain states.

Liquids are hydrocarbon mixtures which are gaseous at reservoir temperatures and pressures, but are recoverable by condensation or absorption. Natural gasoline and liquefied petroleum gases fall in this category.

Nonassociated natural gas is free gas not in contact with, nor dissolved in, crude oil in the reservoir.

Sour natural gas is gas found in its natural state, containing such amounts of compounds of sulfur as to make it impractical to use without purifying because of its corrosive effect on piping and equipment.

Sweet natural gas is gas found in its natural state, containing such small amounts of compounds of sulfur that it can be used without purifying, with no deleterious effect on piping and equipment.

Wet natural gas is unprocessed natural gas or partially processed natural gas, produced from strata containing condensible hydrocarbons. The term is subject to varying legal definitions as specified by certain state statutes.

Properties

Natural gas, with few qualifications, is not harmful to plants or animal life. For example, animals kept in an atmosphere containing 25% natural gas for thirty days remained normal in every respect (4). Animals exposed to 80% gas for 8 hr were unaffected. In most cases plants and tree roots exposed to natural gas were not injured. Certain plants are affected and there may be injury to vegetation when considerable amounts of dry gas are forced through dry soil (5).

Methane and ethane are stable hydrocarbons which do not readily enter into chemical reactions other than combustion. Methane is the most stable hydrocarbon regarding resistance to thermal cracking. Ethane cracks less readily than hydrocarbons of higher carbon content. When it is subjected to cracking, ethylene and acetylene are among the reaction products. Some physical characteristics of interest (2,6) are listed in Table 1.

Table 1. Properties of Methane and Ethane

	Methane	Ethane
critical point		
temperature, °F	−116.5	90.1
pressure, atm	45.6	48.2
ft³/lb	0.099	0.079
heat of combustion,		
60°F, 30 in. Hg, dry, Btu/ft³		
gross	1012.0	1772.9
net	911.5	1622.1
density, lb/ft³	0.04237	0.07942
specific gravity (air = 1)	0.5539	1.0382
limits of flammability, % gas in air	5.0–15.0	3.0–12.5
boiling point, 1 atm, °F	−258.7	−127.5
spontaneous ignition temperature (air), °F	1301	968–1166

Production Transmission and Utilization

The six largest gas-producing states, which account for about 92% of the total marketed production, are Texas, Louisiana, Oklahoma, California, Kansas, and New Mexico.

Wells which produce dry gas present few processing problems, since such gas can usually be admitted to a pipeline with little or no treatment. Much natural gas is produced together with crude oil as a wet gas containing easily liquefiable heavier hydrocarbons. These natural gas liquids, such as propane and butane, are usually removed or reduced to low concentrations in processing plants before delivery of the gas for transmission.

Early production was utilized near the source owing to a lack of suitable means for distant transportation. Pipeline developments during the 1920s extended natural gas utilization more than 500 miles from its source. The manufacture of large-diameter, thin-walled, welded, seamless steel pipe capable of withstanding high pressure facilitated the construction of long-distance lines that now extend some 2000 miles or more from the source.

A convenient classification of ultimate consumers by type of service includes residential or domestic, commercial, and industrial. An important development in the third category is that of petrochemical usage, for example, in production of carbon black and hydrogen for ammonia synthesis.

Methods of Analysis

MEASUREMENT AND SAMPLING

The terms and conditions used in the measurement of natural gas are discussed in detail in ASTM D 1071 (7). In the practice, English units are used and standard conditions are specified as follows: temperature, 60.0°F; pressure, 30.00 in. Hg. (14.73 psia). The measurement is carried out usually at complete water-vapor saturation, which is equivalent to an absolute partial pressure of the dry gas of 29.478 in. Hg. A standard cubic foot of natural gas is the quantity of gas which fills a space exactly 1 cubic foot under these standard conditions.

When sampling natural gas, the measurement of pressure and temperature is of critical importance. For accurate pressure measurement, care must be taken in location and size of connection tapping on the pipe or vessel, and piping between it and the pressure measuring device. The article on PRESSURE MEASUREMENT AND CONTROL (Vol. 3, pp. 222–229) deals in detail with the various devices used for the actual measurement. The measurement of the temperature is also of special importance since there is an approximately 1% volume change for each 5°F change in the temperature. In practice, temperature measurement is usually done with help of thermocouples and resistance thermometers; for details see TEMPERATURE MEASUREMENT AND CONTROL, Vol. 3, pp. 599–642.

In the broadest sense, sampling natural gas consists of suitably conducting a flow of gas from the source into a properly purged container or containers and obtaining thereby a representative sample. Samples may be grab, spot, or snap samples. A series of grab samples, taken consecutively, may be considered as an average sample. An average sample may also be obtained by a continuous collection method. Purging of the sampling probe, sampling line, and sampling container may be done either by the gas to be sampled (air displacement), by water displacement, or by application of vacuum. Usually there is sufficient pressure on the system to purge and fill the container without the use of additional means. If not, some mechanical means must be provided.

The apparatus used for measuring gaseous samples can be classified according to this ASTM method as containers, gas meters of the displacement type, and gas meters of the rate-of-flow type. The ASTM method also describes procedures for their calibration.

Containers include cubic foot bottles of the immersion type or moving-tank type, portable cubic foot standard (Stillman type), fractional cubic foot bottle, burets, flasks, etc, for chemical and physical analysis, and calibrated gasometers (gas meter provers).

Displacement-type gas meters include liquid-sealed rotating drum meters, diaphragm or bellows-type meters, equipped with observation index, and rotary displacement meters.

Rate-of-flow-type gas meters include porous plug and capillary flowmeters, float (variable-area, constant-head) flowmeters, and orifice, flow nozzle, and Venturi-type flowmeters.

Cubic foot standards are used at or close to ambient temperature and pressure. Calibrated gasometers are used at or close to ambient temperature and within a few inches of the water column of the atmospheric pressure.

Liquid-sealed rotating drum meters are commonly known as wet test meters. Commercial sizes range from $\frac{1}{20}$ ft^3 to 7.0 ft^3 revolution. Operating capacities, or the volume of gas with a specific gravity of 0.64 that will pass through the meter in 1 hr with a pressure drop of 0.3 in. of the water column across the meter, range from 5 to 1200 ft^3/hr. When water is the sealing liquid, the useful temperature is from slightly above freezing to about 120°F. It is recommended that maximum operating pressure should not exceed 1 in. Hg or 13 in. water.

Diaphragm-type test meters have displacement capacities from about 0.05 to 2.5 ft^3 revolution. The volume of gas having a specific gravity of 0.64 that a meter will pass with a pressure drop of 0.5 in. of water column across the meter ranges from about 20 to 1800 ft^3/hr.

Rate-of-flow meters are especially useful where flow is steady, but they are neither suited for use in measurement of a specified quantity nor for flows that are subject to wide or more or less rapid variations of either rate or pressure. Flowmeters of the capillary tube and the porous plug (eg, sintered glass filter) types are useful for continuous sampling and sample measurement. They can satisfactorily meter rates as low as about 0.03 ft^3/min.

Wet test meters are not used when determining trace materials. Capillary flowmeters and orifice meters are superior in such cases.

Sampling connections and sample lines should be as short and as small as practicable to decrease purging time and contained volume. Material may be glass, rubber, plastic, or metal. Rubber should be used to a minimum extent and must be of a type which will not react with the sample. It should also have low permeability characteristics. Certain metals (eg, copper) should be avoided if sulfur compounds are to be determined.

In addition to being gas-tight, sample containers should be constructed of materials which do not react with the sample. The design and type of container may take any one of a number of forms. If the sample is to be shipped under pressure, the vessel must comply with requirements of and be approved by the Interstate Commerce Commission. Reference should also be made to shipping limitations of the Department of Transportation. Generally it is preferable to sample without the use of confining liquids, such as water or water solutions.

Test samples may be required from one or more of the following sources: gas wells, field gathering lines, before and after field processing, main transmission trunk pipelines, city distribution systems, storage holders, or similar piping, processing or storage systems. Pressure ranges may vary from subatmospheric to as high as 9,000–10,000 psi, as is found in some gas wells.

The volume of sample required depends both upon the analyses to be made and the apparatus used. In general the following minimum volumes, which include a volume for purging apparatus and two determinations, will normally suffice.

Process	Required sample volume
chemical gas analysis	1000 cm³
specific gravity, balance-type instrument	1.0 ft³
heating value determination	3–5 ft³
hydrogen sulfide (Tutwiler)	250–700 cm³
hydrogen sulfide (cadmium sulfate)	5 ft³
referee sulfur	10 ft³
gasoline content	5–10 ft³
fractional analysis	5–10 ft³
superexpansability tests	approximately 10 ft³

ASTM D 1145 (8) describes several sampling procedures. The method of sampling is intended to correlate the size or type of sample with the subsequent analysis. Separate procedures are included for natural gases containing primarily hydrocarbons and nitrogen, those containing hydrogen sulfide or organic sulfur compounds, or other sulfur contaminants, natural gas containing carbon dioxide, and natural gas containing gasoline and condensibles.

Consideration must be given to the purposes for which the samples are to be used and the conditions under which they must be obtained. Other considerations include required volume, size, design, and material of containers, the size, length and material of the sampling line and auxiliary equipment.

Account must be taken of the possible constituents, whether only hydrocarbons and inert gases or whether sulfur-containing compounds are present.

Samples for the determination of the hydrogen sulfide content of natural gases should preferably be taken directly from the line or well and analyzed in the field. When determining the gasoline content of natural gas, the adsorption of gasoline on charcoal must be accomplished in the field.

COMPOSITION ANALYSIS

The composition of natural gas may be determined by a chemical–volumetric method, mass spectrometry, IR spectroscopy, and gas chromatography. Today, all the previous methods have been largely supplanted by gas chromatography, and are therefore discussed only briefly.

Volumetric–Chemical Method

This method is described in detail in ASTM D 1136 (9), and may be useful in some instances where complete composition or higher accuracy is not required.

The method combines absorption and combustion techniques. Acid gases, oxygen, and unsaturated hydrocarbons are absorbed in saturated potassium hydroxide, fuming sulfuric acid, and alkaline pyrogallol (17 g/100 ml of saturated potassium hydroxide), respectively. Saturated hydrocarbons are then burned with excess oxygen over hot platinum. The contraction, the volume of carbon dioxide produced, and the volume of oxygen consumed are all measured.

If more than two saturated hydrocarbons are present, true composition is not found. Acid gases are determined as a group, as are unsaturated hydrocarbons, and inert gases. Data obtained are usually sufficient to calculate the heating value and specific gravity when the gas contains only small amounts of C_3 and heavier hydrocarbons. When the entire hydrocarbon content of a gas is calculated as methane and ethane only, the calculated heating value and specific gravity, as well as composition, may be in error. The extent of this error depends on the partial pressure of the C_3 and heavier hydrocarbons.

Mass Spectrometry

The composition analysis of natural gases by mass spectrometry is described in detail in ASTM D 1137 (10). The precision and accuracy of the measurement compare favorably with gas chromatography; however, since it is much more complicated and requires a more sophisticated and expensive equipment it is only rarely used. For details, the ASTM method should be consulted.

Infrared Spectroscopy

Light-saturated hydrocarbons have sufficiently different spectra to permit accurate analysis of their mixtures by infrared spectroscopy (2). By calibrating the attenuation of an infrared beam directed through a sample the concentration of each absorbing component can be measured. Spectrophotometers or nondispersion instruments can be used. The method is not generally used because of the advantages of gas chromatographic measurements.

Gas Chromatography

Gas chromatography is particularly well suited for the analysis of natural gas. The determination itself is simple, rapid, and precise, and test results are frequently used to calculate other characteristics, particularly specific gravity and heating value. Both the Natural Gasoline Association of America (11) and ASTM (12) published detailed procedures for this analysis.

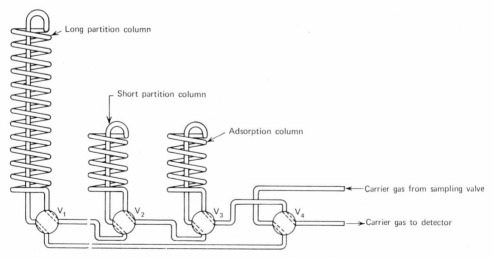

Fig. 1. Valve system and column arrangement recommended for the gas chromatographic analysis of natural gas.

Table 2. Partition Columns and Instrumental Conditions to be Used in Natural Gas Analysis

Stationary phase	Ratio of stationary phase:support, g/g	Column length,[a] ft	Column temperature, °C	Sample volume, ml	Carrier gas[b] inlet pressure, psig
hexamethylphosphoramide	20/100[c]	20	25	5	25
dimethylsulfolane	30/100	16 ⎫[d]	35	0.5	75[e]
diisodecylphthalate	30/100	8 ⎭			
DC-200/500 silicone oil	37.5/100	30	90	5	30

[a] OD = $\frac{1}{4}$ in.
[b] Helium.
[c] ml/g.
[d] The two columns are used in series.
[e] Flow rate, ml/min.

In the gas chromatographic analysis, the components up to *n*-pentane are separated individually while C_6 and higher hydrocarbons are usually grouped into irregular peaks by reversing the direction of the carrier gas through the column. Usually two such peaks are obtained, corresponding to the hexanes and to the heptanes plus heavier hydrocarbons. Methylcyclopentane and cyclohexane will also be included in the latter peak.

The chromatographic system should contain a sample inlet system permitting the introduction of sample volumes in the range of 0.25–0.5 ml as well as 2–5 ml, a valve system permitting the use of at least two columns and reversing the carrier gas flow, and a thermal conductivity detector with helium carrier gas. Figure 1 shows a four-valve system recommended for this type of analysis.

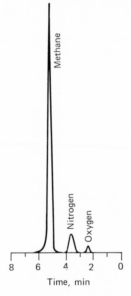

Fig. 2. Analysis of natural gas on a 5-ft molecular sieve column. Temperature, 30°C; carrier gas inlet pressure, 5 psig; sample size, 0.25 ml.

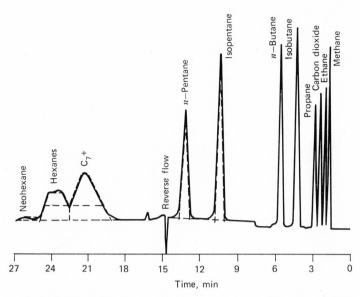

Fig. 3. Analysis of natural gas on a 20-ft long hexamethylphosphoramide column.

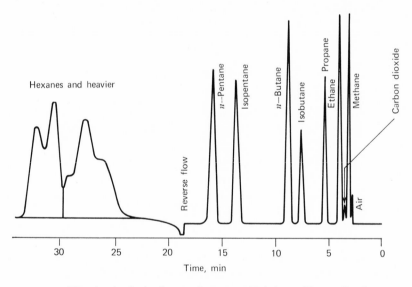

Fig. 4. Analysis of natural gas on a 30-ft long silicone oil column.

There are generally two columns necessary for a complete analysis: an adsorption and a partition-type column. A 5 ft × ¼ in. OD column packed with molecular sieve 5A or 13X 30/60 mesh is used for the first, and a number of partition columns have been recommended. Some typical specifications for the columns and the conditions to be used are listed in Table 2. The support material is always Chromosorb 30/60 or equivalent.

The adsorption column must completely separate oxygen, nitrogen, and methane, whereas the partition column must separate ethane through the pentanes and carbon dioxide. After the *n*-pentane peak, the carrier gas flow rate is reversed; thus, group

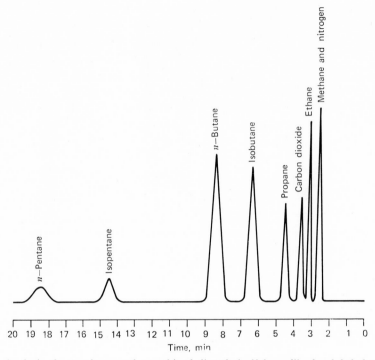

Fig. 5. Analysis of natural gas on the combined dimethylsulfolane–diisodecylphthalate column (8 ft + 16 ft).

peaks are obtained for the hexanes and the heavier components. Figures 2–5 show typical chromatograms obtained in the analysis of natural gas under the conditions listed in Table 2. As seen, the diisodecylphthalate plus dimethylsulfolane column only permits the analysis of the components up to *n*-pentane.

The reference sample should contain the components up to *n*-pentane in concentrations which generally do not differ more than 10 mole % from the concentration of the same component in the sample. Suitable gas standards are available commercially (13).

If more than 0.65 g of hydrogen sulfide is present in 100 ft³ of gas, a tube filled with Ascarite should be installed upstream the sampling valve of the gas chromatograph. Since Ascarite also absorbs carbon dioxide, the results in this case will be obtained on an acid-gas free basis. If the gas also contains some water, a drier containing phosphorus pentoxide should also be installed between the container and the sampling valve.

For the quantitative interpretation of the chromatogram, the following procedure is recommended.

Procedure

Analyze the sample and reference standard under identical conditions, and measure the heights of the peaks up to and including *n*-pentane. Calculate the concentration of each component up to and including *n*-pentane as follows:

$$C_i = \frac{H_i}{H_s} C_s$$

where C_i = concentration of the component in the sample, in mole %
C_s = concentration of the component in the standard, in mole %
H_i = peak height of the component in the sample, in mm
H_s = peak height of the component in the standard, in mm

For the reverse-flow peaks follow the following steps. Measure the areas of the reverse-flow peaks as well as of the isopentane and n-pentane peaks in surface units (mm²) or counts, then calculate the corresponding concentrations as follows:

$$\text{Hexanes, mole } \% = \frac{(A)(72)(C_1 + C_2)}{(86)(D_1 + D_2)}$$

$$\text{Heptanes plus heavier, mole } \% = \frac{(B)(72)(C_1 + C_2)}{(98)(D_1 + D_2)}$$

where A = area of the reversed-flow peak corresponding to the hexanes
B = area of the reversed-flow peak corresponding to heptanes plus heavier hydrocarbons
D_1 = area of the isopentane peak
D_2 = area of the n-pentane peak
C_1 = concentration of isopentane in the sample, mole %
C_2 = concentration of n-pentane in the sample, mole %

C_1 and C_2 are obtained from the previous calculation. In the above equation, 72 is the g-mol wt of the pentanes, 86 is the g-mol wt of the hexanes, and 98 is the average g-mol wt of the components giving the $C_7{}^+$ peak.

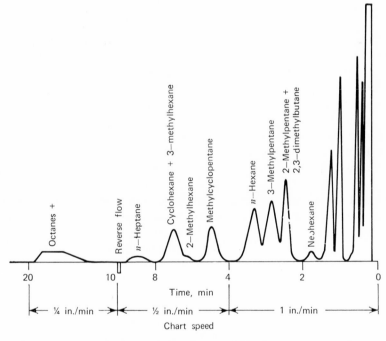

Fig. 6. Analysis of the hexanes, heptanes, and heavier components of natural gas on a 5-ft hexamethylphosphoramide column, at 30°C. Carrier gas inlet pressure, 10 psig; sample volume, 5 ml. The recorder chart speed was changed during analysis; it is indicated in the last line.

Finally, normalize the obtained mole % values by multiplying each value by 100 and dividing by the sum of the original values. The sum of the original values should not differ from 100.00% by more than ±1.00%.

If the separation of the C_6–C_7 and heavier components is desired, this can be accomplished on a 5-ft hexamethylphosphoramide column at 30°C. Here the carrier gas flow should be reversed after the emergence of n-heptane to obtain a composite peak for $C_8{}^+$. Figure 6 shows a typical chromatogram.

A typical composition of a natural gas obtained by gas chromatography is given in Table 3.

Table 3. Typical Composition of a Natural Gas as Determined by Gas Chromatography

Component	Concentration, mole %
nitrogen	0.32
methane	82.88
carbon dioxide	2.02
ethane	7.44
propane	4.39
isobutane	0.83
n-butane	1.08
isopentane	0.31
n-pentane	0.25
hexanes	0.17
heptanes plus heavier hydrocarbons	0.31
	100.00

DETERMINATION OF IMPURITIES

Gasoline Content

Wet natural gas, which contains more than about 150 gal of gasoline per million ft³, is usually treated for recovery of gasoline. The definition as to what constitutes gasoline in these cases is somewhat arbitrary. Before the development of gas chromatography, several methods were used for this evaluation. The standard compression test (2), also known as the test car method, is the oldest. The gas sample is compressed to about 250 psig and cooled. Any condensed liquid is measured, its specific gravity is determined, and sometimes other tests are made.

The charcoal adsorption test was commonly used for rough preliminary determination of potential production of liquids from new gas sources (14). A measured volume of gas is passed at a controlled rate through a standard size bed of coconut charcoal. The adsorbed gasoline is distilled from the charcoal by heating, and the vapors are largely condensed at 32°F. The quantity and quality of the liquid recovered give a fairly good indication of the value of the liquefiable content of the gas.

Low-temperature fractional distillation and mass spectrometry have also been utilized to determine the gasoline content of natural gas.

Today, these earlier techniques have been almost completely replaced by gas chromatographic analysis (15,16). In the gas chromatographic analysis, one does not determine the "gasoline content" but the groups of heavier hydrocarbons, or separates the individual components up to the octanes and determines the octanes and heavier components as one group. Details are given in a previous part of this article.

Sulfur Compounds

Hydrogen sulfide is present in natural gas from certain fields, and the level may vary from very low to relatively high concentrations in sour gas. Mercaptans and organic sulfides may also be present. Odorants added to natural gas before delivery to customers are generally mercaptans, cyclic sulfides, or linear hydrocarbon sulfides.

Hydrogen sulfide is undesirable because it corrodes equipment upon contact, it has deleterious effects on catalysts in organic synthesis, and its combustion products have toxic effects.

Usually only the hydrogen sulfide content of the natural gas is determined. Sometimes the determination of total sulfur and oxidizable sulfur is also required.

Hydrogen Sulfide. Sometimes a qualitative test for hydrogen sulfide suffices. The lead acetate test is frequently applied to other products as well and can be used on natural gas (17).

Procedure

Select a piece of glass tubing about 1.75 in. in diameter and 8 in. long. Fit the inlet end with a stopper and a glass baffle about 1 in. diameter. Fit the top stopper with a glass suspension hook for holding the test paper. Use glass connections for introducing gas into the system.

Dip a strip of white filter paper, 1 in. wide by 4 in. long, in 5% lead acetate solution. Press this strip between clean blotters to remove excess solution and then immediately suspend midway between the baffle and the outlet. Lead acetate paper, which needs only to be moistened, is available commercially. Pass gas at 4.5–5.5 ft^3/hr for 1 min. Immediately compare the exposed strip with a moistened blank. If the exposed strip is not distinctly darker, the gas shall be considered free from hydrogen sulfide.

This test is sensitive to 0.3–0.4 grains of hydrogen sulfide per 100 ft^3 of gas with 1 min exposure. For other exposure times this limit is about 0.45 for 30 sec and 0.2 for 30 min.

A hydrogen sulfide detector is available commercially from the Mine Safety Appliance Co. (18). The detector consists of glass tubes which contain granules of activated alumina impregnated with silver cyanide. An aspirator bulb draws the sample through one of these tubes. The granules turn dark gray if hydrogen sulfide is present and the length of discoloration is a measure of its amount. Detector tubes and calibration scale are available in two ranges, 0–50 ppm (0–3.2 grains/100 ft^3) and 0–0.04% (0–26 grains/100 ft^3).

For the quantitative determination of the hydrogen sulfide content of natural gas, three methods are generally available. The first, the so-called U.S. Steel Chemists' method (19), is based on the absorption of the hydrogen sulfide content of a given volume of gas and its determination with iodometric titration. The second, so-called Tutwiler method (2), is also an iodometric procedure but is based on the direct titration of the gas with a standard iodine reagent. If the sulfide concentration is at or above 0.65 g/100 ft^3, a 100-ml gas buret is used whereas for lower concentrations the use of a 500-ml gas buret is recommended. The third method, the so-called methylene blue method, is applicable to natural gas containing not more than 23 mg of hydrogen sulfide in 1 m^3 gas. In this method, the natural gas is bubbled through a zinc acetate solution, and subsequently, *N,N*-dimethyl-*p*-phenylenediamine in acid solution and ferric chloride are added to the solution. These react with any zinc sulfide resulting in methylene blue, the amount of which is determined by spectrophotometric measurement (19).   The procedures for the first and third methods are given below.

Procedures

IODOMETRIC METHOD.   Pass a measured volume of the gas, usually about 0.1 ft³ through one of the following solutions: (*1*) 2% sodium or potassium hydroxide solution;   (*2*) ammoniacal cadmium chloride solution prepared by dissolving 5 g of the salt in 375 ml of water and diluting to 1000 ml with concentrated ammonium hydroxide;   (*3*) ammoniacal zinc sulfate solution prepared by dissolving 10 g of the salt in 50 ml of concentrated ammonium hydroxide and diluting to 1000 ml with water.   Use 20 ml of the solution diluted with 200 ml water in a 500-ml flask. Record the temperature and pressure of the metered gas sample as well as the barometer reading.   Rinse the bubbling tube with acidified water, then add 5 ml of starch indicator and enough 1:1 hydrochloric acid to make the solution acidic. Titrate immediately with 0.1 *N* iodine solution.

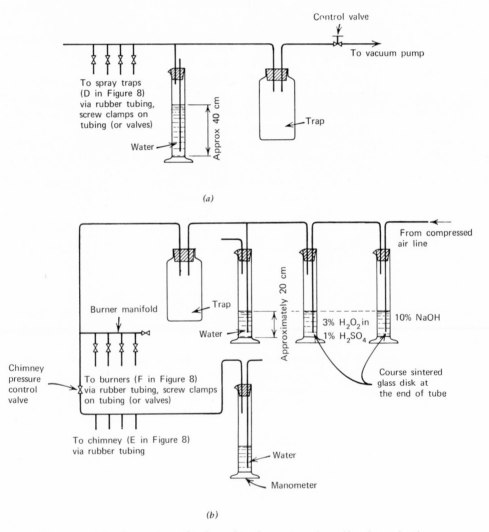

Fig. 7. (*a*) Suction system, (*b*) air purification system for sulfur determination.

METHYLENE BLUE METHOD. Place 30 ml of 2% zinc acetate solution, acidified with acetic acid, in a 50-ml absorption bottle, such as an Engler viscosity receiving flask. Prepare a two-hole stopper with a bubbler tube extending to the bottom of the flask. Connect the inlet to the sample container using aluminum or glass and a minimum of rubber or polyvinyl chloride tubing. Connect the outlet of the absorption bottle to a wet test meter or to a calibrated aspirator bottle.

Pass 0.1 ft³ (3 liters) of sample gas through the absorber at a rate not exceeding 1 ft³/hr. Use a larger sample for low concentrations of hydrogen sulfide. Maintain a meter temperature constant within ±0.5°F and record the barometric pressure.

Disconnect the absorber, add 10 ml of zinc acetate solution and cool in an ice bath to 5°C. Pipet 5 ml of the diamine solution consisting of 0.11 g of *N,N*-dimethyl-*p*-phenylenediamine sulfate dissolved in 100 ml of 2:1 sulfuric acid (stored in a brown bottle and freshly prepared every 2 weeks) into the absorber and mix completely with minimum agitation. Cool again to 5°C, then add 1 ml of a 2.7% ferric chloride solution and mix. Draw the solution in and out of the bubbler tube.

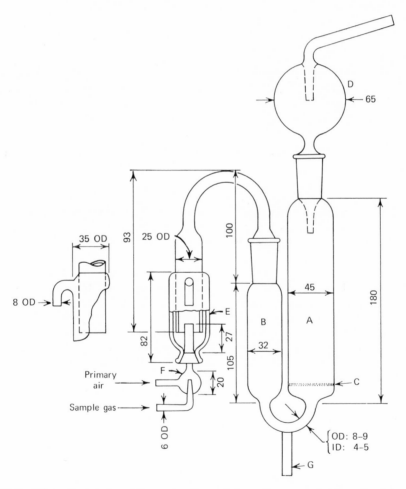

Fig. 8. Schematic drawing of the combustion and absorption apparatus for sulfur determination. A, B. Absorbers. C. Fritted disc. D. Spray trap. E. Chimney. F. Burner. G. Solid rod held in position by any suitable support. All dimensions are in mm.

Remove absorber from the cold bath and stand for 30–45 min. Remove the bubbler tube, rinse it with zinc acetate solution, dilute to volume with zinc acetate solution, and mix.

Prepare a blank solution containing the same amount of reagents as in the sample solution. Determine the absorbance of the sample at 745 nm against the blank using a suitable spectrophotometer. If a photometer is used, apply the proper color filter. Prepare the calibration curve by using known amounts of hydrogen sulfide.

Cells of longer or shorter path may be used or the sample may be diluted with a reference solution containing 5 ml of the diamine solution and 1 ml of the ferric chloride solution diluted to 50 ml with the zinc acetate solution. This reference solution should have an absorbance of 0.01 or less.

Total Sulfur. The amount of total sulfur is determined by combustion according to ASTM D 1072 (21) which is applicable to natural as well as manufactured gas. The apparatus required for this determination includes a special burner, chimney, absorbers, spray trap, a calibrated flowmeter, air purifying system, and manometer. Figure 7 gives the schematic of the suction system and air purification system and Figure 8 depicts the schematic of the all-glass system consisting of the burner, chimney, absorbers, and spray trap. The vacuum suction system may be fitted with a manifold for performing several burnings simultaneously. The capacity of the whole system should be sufficient to permit a steady gas flow of 3 liters/min through the absorbers and to maintain a constant manifold pressure of about 40 cm of water below atmospheric. The air purification system shown in Figure 8 consists of a series of scrubbers where the gas is passed successively through a 10% sodium hydroxide solution, a 3% hydrogen peroxide solution in 1:99 sulfuric acid, water, and finally, through a trap.

Procedure

In assembling the apparatus, connect the gas sample line by glass or aluminum tubing to the inlet of the flowmeter. Connect the outlet in a similar manner to the lower side arm of the burner. Adjust the valve which controls rate of flow so gas is burned at a rate to liberate about 250–500 Btu/hr. Use rubber or plastic tubing to connect the primary air from the purified air line to the upper side arm of the burner.

Rinse the spray trap, absorbers, and chimney well with water before each test. Add into the larger bulb of the absorber 20 ml of water and 10 ml of a sodium carbonate solution containing 3.306 g of the salt in 1000 ml of water. Attach the spray trap and chimney, and connect them respectively to the vacuum line and the purified air line by means of rubber or plastic tubing. Close the chimney opening with a cork.

Purge the flowmeter, burner, and connection with the gas sample and then light the burner flame. Adjust the gas flow rate and then the primary air flow to obtain a soft blue flame with no yellow tip. To start a determination, adjust suction and air flow, then insert the burner into the chimney, fastening it in place with rubber bands or springs. Check, readjusting if necessary, the indicated rate of gas flow and primary air flow to obtain a stable flame. Note time when burner was inserted, or meter reading if an integrating meter is used. Burn about 1 ft³ of gas. Maintain the flowmeter differential at a constant value during this period. Note time or meter reading when appropriate, then remove the burner from the chimney, replacing it with the cork, and continuing suction on the absorber until it attains room temperature. Extinguish the flame. Unless an integrating type meter was used, disconnect the burner from the flowmeter. Attach in its place a connection to a calibrated wet test meter (0.10 ft³ per revolution) that has been purged with 5 ft³ of the gas being tested.   Adjust flowmeter differential and manometer reading to that existing during the determination and determine with a stopwatch the time for one complete revolution of the meter.   Calculate the volume of gas burned as follows:

$$V = \frac{(t_d)(520)[P + (m/13.6) - w]}{(10)(t_c)(T_d)(30 - 0.522)}$$

where V = volume of sample burned in standard cubic feet at 60°F, 30 in. Hg, saturated

t_d = time for determination, in sec

t_c = time of one revolution of wet test meter during calibration, in sec

T_d = meter temperature, in °F absolute

P = barometric pressure, in in. Hg

m = manometer reading, in in. of water

w = vapor pressure of water at meter temperature, in in. Hg

If a calibrated integrating dry displacement meter is used for gas measurements, calculate the volume of gas burned as follows:

$$V = \frac{(V_m)(520)[P + (m/13.6) - w']}{(T_d)(30 - 0.522)}$$

where V_m = meter reading at end of determination minus the meter reading at the start of the determination, in ft³

w' = actual partial pressure of water vapor in gas at dry meter temperature, in in. Hg

After the absorber has cooled to room temperature, wash the chimney and trap with the smallest possible quantity of water, and add washings to the absorber. Add 3 drops of a methyl orange indicator solution and titrate the excess of sodium carbonate with a standard hydrochloric acid solution containing 2.275 g/liter; 1 ml of this solution is equivalent to 1 ml of the 0.3306% sodium carbonate solution when titrated against methyl orange.   Mix after each addition of the titrant by alternate sucking and blowing on one end of the absorber.

Discharge the tan color with a few drops of sodium carbonate solution, then add 50 ml of ethyl or isopropyl alcohol.   Add about 0.5 g of tetrahydroxyquinone indicator, mix well, start to titrate with standard barium chloride solution containing 7.634 g of $BaCl_2.2H_2O$/liter.   After the addition of 1–2 ml, add 1 ml of a 0.1 N silver nitrate solution and continue titration to the end point, where the color changes from yellow to rose which is persistent with good mixing.

$$\text{Total sulfur, grain/100 ft}^3 = \frac{(A - 0.2)(1.543)}{B}$$

where A = volume of barium chloride solution used in titration, in ml

B = volume of gas sample burned, in standard ft³

If the result in mg/100 ft³ is desired, multiply the above result by 64.7989.

Oxidizable Sulfur.   Trace quantities of oxidizable sulfur in natural gas are usually determined with an automatic recording titrator, the so-called Titrilog (22). This instrument may also be used for testing atmosphere.   The measurement is accomplished by titration with bromine generated electrically in solution. The limit of threshold sensitivity is about 0.1 ppm or 0.005 grains/100 ft^3. The instrument can be adjusted and calibrated for various levels of sulfur content.

Water Content

Practically all natural gas contains water vapor as it comes from the well. Sometimes liquid water is also entrained. Amounts of water vapor in gas under equilibrium conditions depend upon pressure and temperature.

Water presents a potential source of blockage in high-pressure pipelines. Partial or complete blocking of lines can occur when solid compounds, known as hydrates, are formed by chemical combination of hydrocarbons and water under pressure. These hydrates behave as solid solutions (23). Evidence suggests that molecules of natural gas occupy positions between the water molecules. In these natural gas complexes the water molecules are linked so that they form roughly spherical capacities which trap the natural gas; however, there is no chemical bond between the water and the natural gas. The ratio in these complexes is 46 water molecules to 6 gas molecules (24).

Many gases form solid hydrates that crystallize, usually at elevated pressures but also possibly at temperatures considerably above 32°F. Among the paraffin hydrocarbons, methane, ethane, propane, and isobutane form hydrates. Normal butane may be present only in a mixture with smaller molecules. Directionally larger molecules usually form more stable hydrates than those with fewer carbon atoms. Those of propane and isobutane are more stable than those of ethane, which are in turn more stable than those with methane.

Gas hydrate which forms in pipelines looks much like packed snow. It is very light and porous. Rather large volumes of gas are given off at atmospheric pressure. It burns quietly on ignition, leaving a small residue of water.

Natural gases with low inert content and high ethane and heavier gas content form hydrates at lower pressures. Natural gases with a high Btu will form hydrates more readily than those of lower heat value (2).

Dehydration to a dew point below any temperature the gas may encounter in transmission or distribution is one of several ways to insure against hydrate formation. In order that the dehydration be effective, water must be removed to the point where the dew point will not be reached at the lowest operating temperature and maximum pressure of the system. Dehydration may in some cases be accomplished by a combination of dehydration and desulfurization.

Several methods are available for the determination of the water content of natural gas. The direct gravimetric procedure is a basic one, and is adaptable to a fairly wide range of concentration (2). The gas containing the water vapor is passed through a desiccant such as calcium chloride or Dehydrite and the increase in weight is determined.

Another possibility is to place a stationary psychrometer or hydrometer in the gas stream and to register the wet and dry bulb temperatures. From the relative humidity, the % saturation at the temperature of the test can be determined, or read from suitable tables (25).

Changes in electrical conductivity can be related to dew point. An automatic dew point recorder using this principle is available commercially (19).

Hygroscopic salts such as lithium chloride, which absorb moisture, are the basis of another electrical measurement. When the lithium chloride coating is exposed to

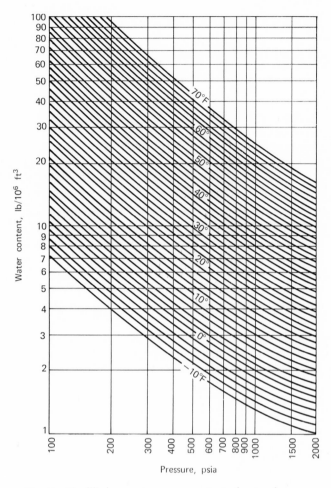

Fig. 9. Equilibrium water vapor content of natural gases.

varying water vapor concentrations, the change in electrical conductivity is measured in μA. Water vapor content is then derived from data correlating conductivity and relative vapor saturation. There are portable indicating models and recording instruments for this application. One such instrument was developed by the Bureau of Mines, and several instrument manufacturers have units designed for this determination (26).

Another direct chemical method involves passing the gas through ethylene glycol, followed by titration of absorbed water with Karl Fischer reagent. It was developed for referee use where conventional methods based on dew point fail to give definite and reproducible results.

Dew Point Method. The standard method used in the natural gas industry to determine the water content of the gas is based on the measurement of the dew point temperature. This is the temperature at which the gas is saturated with water vapor at the existing pressure. When a gas containing water vapor is at the water dew point temperature it is said to be saturated at the existing pressure. Saturated water vapor, or equilibrium water vapor content, represents the water vapor concentration in a gas mixture which is in equilibrium with a liquid phase of pure water that is saturated with the gas mixture.

Dew point apparatus must provide means (*1*) to permit a controlled flow of gas to enter and leave the apparatus while at a temperature at least 3°F above the dew point of the gas, (*2*) to cool and control the cooling rate of a portion (preferably a small one) of the apparatus with which the flowing gas comes in contact to a temperature low enough to cause vapor to condense from the gas, (*3*) to observe the deposition of dew on the cold portion, (*4*) to measure the temperature of the cold portion on which the dew is deposited, and (*5*) to measure the pressure of the gas within the apparatus or the deviation from the known existing barometric pressure. Construction should be such that the "cold spot," that is, the cold portion where dew is deposited, is protected from all gases other than that under test.

The sample should not be taken at a point where isolation would permit condensate to collect or would otherwise allow a vapor content to exist that is not in equilibrium with the main stream or supply of gas. Temperature of the pipelines leading the sample directly from the gas source to the dew point apparatus, and also the temperature of the apparatus, should be at least 3°F higher than the observed dew point. The determination may be made at any pressure as long as the gas pressure within the dew point apparatus is known with an accuracy appropriate to the accuracy of the test requirements.

Several commercial units are available for the measurement; the one corresponding to ASTM D 1142 method is the so-called Bureau of Mines apparatus. The method of measurement is briefly outlined below; for details, the ASTM procedure (27) should be consulted. The water content is determined from the dew point and pressure with help of nomograms such as shown in Figure 9. Complete sets of such charts covering the entire range of pressures and temperatures generally encountered are available from the Institute of Gas Technology (28).

Procedure

Introduce sample at a flow rate of between 0.05 and 0.5 ft³/min (measured at atmospheric pressure). Admit sufficient liquefied refrigerant gas which, when vaporized, will produce sufficient lowering in chiller temperature and target mirror. This rate may be comparatively rapid for the first trial run to get an approximate test. Repeat, controlling cooling and warming rate so it does not exceed 1°F/min as the dew point is approached. When dew has been deposited allow the target mirror to warm up at a rate comparable to the cooling rate. Repeat cooling and warming cycles several times. Consider the arithmetic average of the temperatures at which dew is observed to appear and disappear as the observed dew point.

Suspended Particles

Suspended particles may be iron oxide, dust, salt, tar, oil fog, gum, water vapor, light oil, scrubber oil, gasoline, or silica (2). Being colloidal in size, they are kept in suspension by Brownian movement, gravity, thermal gradients, electrical forces, acoustical forces, and centrifugal forces. They are referred to as aerosols or hydrosols.

Suspended particles are generally thought of as being objectionable because of possible service difficulties, but in some cases liquid particles (oil fog or water vapor) may be intentionally introduced into a stream.

With particles of comparatively large size, mass of material rather than number of particles or size distribution may be of greater importance.

Proper sampling is of extreme importance to obtain an accurate representation of the actual concentration of particles in the flowing gas stream (29). The main precautionary measures for isokinetic sampling include location of sampling point along a straight line where flow is undisturbed, location of sampling nozzle, feathering of leading edge of the probe nozzle, a short probe with a minimum number of bends, and temperature.

When dust from a measured amount of gas is filtered and weighed, the gas sample must be withdrawn without changing its velocity. The dust may be retained on filters which are ceramic, glass, or paper. Millipore filters are suggested (30) when direct microscopic observation is to be made. After weighing, it is sometimes desirable to incinerate the dust to determine mineral matter.

DETERMINATION OF PHYSICAL CONSTANTS

Specific Gravity

Weight per unit volume of natural gas is generally defined in terms of specific gravity. This is the ratio of the density of the fuel under the observed conditions of temperature and pressure, to the density of dried air of normal carbon dioxide content at the same temperature and pressure. Density is the mass per unit volume of the material being considered. For routine purposes, the specific gravity of natural gas is usually calculated from its composition determined by gas chromatographic analysis. If necessary, various methods are available for actual specific gravity measurements.

Calculation from Composition. The specific gravity of a natural gas can be calculated from its composition as determined by gas chromatography, by using the so-called ideal gas specific gravities of the components present in the gas (31). Table 4 lists these values; they differ from the real specific gravity of these substances because of the compressibility factor.

Table 4. Ideal Gas Specific Gravities of the Components of Natural Gas

Hydrocarbons	Specific gravity	Nonhydrocarbons	Specific gravity
methane	0.5536	carbon dioxide	1.5188
ethane	1.0377	helium	0.1381
propane	1.5217	nitrogen	0.9668
n-butane and isobutane	2.0058		
n-pentane and isopentane	2.4899		
hexanes (average)	2.9739		

The calculation of the specific gravity of a natural gas consists of two steps. First, using a 100.0% analysis, the mole fraction of each constituent is multiplied by the ideal specific gravity of that component. The sum of these products gives the ideal gas specific gravity of the sample. In the second step of the calculation, this value has to be multiplied by the gas compressibility factor. For most purposes, an average value is used which is 1.002 for natural gases low in pentanes and heavier material, and 1.003 for gases in which pentanes and hexanes are present in more than minimal amount.

Measurement of Specific Gravity.   There are a number of possibilities to measure the specific gravity of natural gases.   These techniques are discussed in detail in ASTM D 1070 (32) and will only be outlined here; see also DENSITY AND SPECIFIC GRAVITY, Vol. 1, pp. 546–560.

Generally, four types of techniques are applied for specific gravity measurements: in the first two, the measurement is carried out with help of pressure and displacement balances; the third technique is based on the centrifugal force, and the fourth is based on kinetic energy measurement.

Pressure Balances.   Here a beam carrying a bulb and counterweight is brought to balance successively in air and in the gas by adjusting the pressure within the balance case.   The absolute pressures are determined by means of a barometer and a mercury-filled manometer.   The specific gravity is then computed from the ratio of absolute pressures.   Pressure balance instruments vary in size, method of supporting the balance beam, sealing the balance case, and other details.   All are subject to corrections and errors of the same kind, but not necessarily the same magnitude.

Two commercial instruments are based on these principles.   The first is the four-spring type Ac–Me gravity balance.   Here, a pressure-tight cylindrical container is mounted on a baseboard.   Inside the container is a balance beam with a sealed float at the back and a graduated scale at the front.   The beam is suspended at the center by thin flat springs.   A window for viewing the scale is provided at the front of the container.   The balance beam may be locked by a cam mechanism when the instrument is not in use.   Valves for introducing gas and air samples are provided.

The second instrument in this category is the so-called Ac–Me recording gravitometer.   This is a continuous balancing instrument which weighs the difference between the weight of a fixed volume of air and the weight of the same volume of gas under the same temperature and pressure conditions.   A continuous sample and specific gravity record is obtained.

Displacement Balances.   These instruments depend upon the principle of balancing the weight of a given volume of gas at atmospheric pressure by displacement of the center of gravity of a balance beam.   The amount of this deflection, subject to correction, measures the specific gravity.

Apparatus of this general classification vary widely in construction and may be either of the indicating or recording type.   The Arcco-Anubis portable gas balance is an example for the first.   This is an indirect weighing instrument, designed primarily to meet the conditions of field service.   It may also be used in the laboratory.   Calculations require the usual applications of Boyle's and Charles' laws.   The Arcco-Anubis Recording Gas Gravitometer is a direct weighing instrument designed to produce a temperature, barometric pressure, and humidity compensated record of the specific gravity of the gas.   The unit is direct reading and no calculations are required.

Centrifugal Force Method.   This method measures the difference in centrifugal force between the natural gas and a reference air sample as both are accelerated by a specially designed wheel.   The manually operated Kimray gravitometer is an instrument utilizing these principles.

Kinetic Energy Method.   In this case, the ratio of the change in the kinetic energy is measured between an impeller and an impulse wheel operating in gas and another impeller and impulse wheel operating in air.   These measurements are in terms of the torques of the impulse wheels which are proportional, respectively, to the gas and air densities.   The Ranarex recording and Ranarex indicating gravitometers are instruments belonging to this category. The former is designed for use in a stationary location to determine and record while the latter is for portable service and indicates only.

Calorific Value

The calorific (heating) value is an important characteristic of natural gas and its price may depend upon it. The following terms are used by the industry; see also CALORIMETRY, Vol. 1, pp. 248–263.

Total calorific value is the number of British thermal units (Btu) evolved by the complete combustion, at constant pressure, of one standard ft³ of gas with air, the temperature of the gas, air, and the combustion products being 60°F, and all of the water formed by the combustion reaction becoming condensed to the liquid state.

Net calorific value is the number of Btu evolved by complete combustion, at standard pressure, of 1 standard ft³ of gas with air, the temperature of the gas, air, the combustion products being 60°F, and all of the water formed by the combustion reaction remaining in the vapor state. Thus the net value is its total calorific value minus the latent heat of evaporation at standard temperature of the water formed by the combustion reaction.

Observed calorific value is the number of Btu obtained by multiplying the lb of water heated in a calorific value test by its corrected temperature rise in °F, and dividing by the number of standard ft³ of gas burned.

Theoretical air is the volume of air that contains the quantity of oxygen, in addition to that in the gas itself, consumed in the complete combustion of a given quantity of gas. *Excess air* is the quantity of air passing through the combustion space in excess of theoretical air. *Combustion air* is that passing into the combustion space of the calorimeter, and is the sum of theoretical air and excess air.

Combustion products are all substances resulting from the burning of gas with its theoretical air, including the inert constituents of the gas and the theoretical air, but excluding excess air. *Flue gases* are the products of combustion remaining in the gaseous state together with the excess air.

The *standard rate of combustion* of any gas in the calorimeter is that which is equivalent to 3000 Btu/hr of total calorific value.

The calorific value can either be calculated from the composition of the natural gas as determined by gas chromatography or measured with help of a calorimeter.

Table 5. Calorific Values of Hydrocarbons Present in Natural Gas, in Btu/ft³

Substance	Calorific value, Btu/ft³	
	total	net
methane	1012.3	911.5
ethane	1773.4	1622.1
propane	2523.8	2322.0
n-butane	3270.7	3018.5
isobutane	3261.2	3009.0
n-pentane	4019.7	3717.2
isopentane	4010.7	3708.0
neopentane	3994	3692
n-hexane[a]	4760	4415

[a] Values for *n*-hexane are used for the C_6+ fraction.

Calorific Value Calculation.   The calculation is based on a 100.0% analysis but the noncombustibles such as nitrogen, helium, and carbon dioxide are disregarded. The mole fraction of the individual hydrocarbons is multiplied by the calorific value of the pure substances. The sum of the products is the calorific value at 60°F and 30 in. Hg, on a dry basis. For gases saturated with water vapor at 60°C, 1.74% of the calculated Btu value is to be deducted.

Different calorific values have been assigned by various authors to the hydrocarbons present in natural gas (2,6,33). In practice, the values listed in Table 5 are used most frequently (2).

Calorific Value Determination.   For the measurement of the calorific value of natural gases either the water flow calorimeter described in ASTM D 900 (34) or the continuous reading calorimeter described in ASTM D 1826 (35) is used. The first may be applied to gases having a total calorific value in the range of 475–3300 Btu/ standard ft³, while the second is generally applicable in the range of 900–1200 Btu/ standard ft³.

In the measurement of calorific values, the temperature, pressure, and the moisture content are determined on room air at the time of test in order to calculate a so-called humidity-correction factor which is applied to the observed calorific value to take account of the heat of vaporization of the difference in the amounts of water vapor entering and leaving the calorimeter. The humidity-control procedure involves artificially maintaining conditions such that the amounts of water vapor entering and leaving the calorimeter are equal or nearly so, and therefore the humidity correction is zero or very small.

MEASUREMENT WITH THE WATER-FLOW CALORIMETER. The apparatus consists of the following parts: (1) an 0.1 ft³ wet test meter for measuring the volume of gas burned; (2) a calorimeter unit in which the gas is burned, and where the heat produced is absorbed in a stream of water; (3) a balance and weights for weighing the water heated; (4) a psychrometer for measuring the humidity of the air; (5) thermometers for measuring temperatures of water, room, gas, and flue gases; (6) a 0.1 ft³ bottle for use in calibrating the wet test meter; (7) a gas pressure regulator; and (8) a graduated cylinder for measuring condensed water. Other essential items include a barometer for measuring atmospheric pressure, an apparatus for volumetric analysis of inlet gas and flue gases, a stopwatch or electric timer for measuring time of revolution of the meter index, and a humidifier for use in the humidity-control procedure.

Gas is burned at a uniform rate in the combustion chamber. Products of combustion and excess air rise, then are deflected and caused to flow downward through flue tubes of the heat exchange unit. A large part of the heat is transferred to the stream of flowing water so that the temperature of the flue gases is reduced nearly to that of the inlet water by the time they reach the products chamber. A small amount of water stands in the products chamber, forming a seal between the products chamber and the combustion chamber, and preventing recirculation of the flue gases with incoming air.

The calorimeter body is equipped with a damper so that the air drawn into the calorimeter can be maintained at 40% in excess of the theoretical air. Temperature of exhaust gases shall be not more than 1°F above that of inlet water. Outlet water temperature fluctuations shall not exceed 0.2°F when gas is burned at a uniform rate.

The products chamber shall be so constructed that all of the flue gases will pass through the dampered port without any recirculation with incoming air.

The diaphragm type of pressure regulator is preferable. If inlet pressure exceeds 12 in. water, a supplementary regulator shall be inserted for reducing gas pressure to about 12 in.

A thermometer graduated in intervals of 0.5°F from 54 to 101°F is used for the wet test meter, for the calorimeter flue, and for the ambient air temperature. More precise thermometers are required for the calorimeter inlet and outlet. For the inlet, ASTM thermometer 50F is used, which has a range of 54–101°F, with 0.1°F subdivisions and a maximum scale error of 0.2°F with a change in correction not more than 0.10°F for a 5°F range (36). For the outlet, ASTM thermometer 51F is recommended; this has a range of 69–116°F with 0.1°F subdivisions and the same limiting scale errors as mentioned for the inlet thermometer. Both thermometers are provided with a reading lens for improved precision and minimization of parallax.

Wet and dry bulb temperatures of combustion air are measured with a sling psychrometer, meeting the requirements of ASTM E 337 (37).

The equal-arm balance for determining weight of water heated during a test must have a capacity of 10 lb with a graduated beam reading to 0.001 lb and sensitive to this amount under full load. One pan is designed to hold weights, the other a bucket. The capacity of such buckets shall be about 10 lb of water.

Miscellaneous other equipment required includes a barometer (preferably mercurial), gas analysis apparatus such as the Bureau of Mines Gas Analyzer, and a 0.1 ft³ bottle for calibration of the wet test meter.

It is frequently necessary to increase the humidity in the combustion air. This may be accomplished either by increasing room humidity or by using a humidity controller on the combustion-air supply to the calorimeter.

The test room should preferably be used for this test only. Temperature should not be subject to sudden changes. It should be free from drafts, gas contamination, and direct sunlight.

Calorimeter inlet and outlet thermometers should be provided with certifications from a recognized standardizing laboratory, if possible from the National Bureau of Standards. A standard resistance thermometer is useful in checking constancy of corrections. Also the inlet and outlet thermometers should be checked against each other at a temperature slightly below room temperature. Any difference found should be applied to test data. The effect of water pressure on the bulb of the inlet-water thermometer causes an average increase of 0.01°F in its reading. This correction should be applied to the data obtained above except in those cases where the thermometers are compared in position in the system with no fuel being burned.

The wet test meter should be calibrated at approximately the same rate of flow used in the test. Air is preferable as the testing medium.

Procedure

Fill the water tank and adjust the temperature so that it will be close to room temperature, generally within ±1°F. The gas meter temperature should also be within ±1°F of room temperature. Pass sufficient gas through the meter to saturate the water. Fifteen to twenty ft³ passed at a rate of 6 ft³/hr is generally sufficient.

Check the system for leaks. When there is no leakage, light the burner and adjust the flow of gas to within ±2% of the standard rate. The standard rate is

120 sec/revolution of a 0.1 ft³ meter hand for an approximate calorific value of 1000 Btu. For other anticipated Btu values, use 12% of the expected heating value. After seven revolutions of the meter, adjust the primary air supply so that the luminous tip of the flame just disappears. Open the flue damper side and insert the burner in the calorimeter and clamp it in position so it is at the proper height and centered in the combustion chamber. Adjust the quadrant indicating valve so the temperature rise of the flowing heated water is $15 \pm 0.5°F$. Adjust the damper after thermal equilibrium has been reached so that air drawn into the combustion chamber is $49 \pm 5\%$ in excess of the theoretical air. After a constant rate of heat transfer is established, slowly withdraw a sample of flue gas into a portable gas analysis apparatus and analyze for carbon dioxide and oxygen. From a complete slow combustion or explosion analysis the theoretical volumes of oxygen consumed and carbon dioxide produced can be calculated, and subsequently the excess air %. If this varies by more than 5% from 40%, adjust the damper and bring to within this range. If necessary, adjust the water flow so the temperature rise is $15 \pm 0.5°F$.

Prepare the calorific test record, a suitable data sheet for recording the observations made by the operator. Data should include place, date, and time of test, kind of gas, purging time, type of calorimeter and serial number, wet test meter identification, level adjustment, last calibration, inlet- and outlet-water thermometer, serial numbers, immersion temperatures, date of last differential correction, damper setting, leak test, and signature of observer.

Make preliminary observations of barometric pressure (to 0.01 in. Hg), temperature of barometer (to 1°F), readings of wet and dry bulb temperatures (to 0.1°F), ambient room temperature, combustion air temperature, time per revolution of the meter index, pressure at the wet meter (to 0.1 in. water column), temperature of wet test meter water (to 0.1°F), and temperature of flue gases (to 0.1°F). This last figure should not differ by more than about 1°F from the inlet-water temperature after adjustment of other conditions.

For the first determination, if net calorific value is to be determined, start collection of condensate by placing the proper size graduated cylinder under the condensate drain tube at the instant the meter hand crosses zero. Record the meter reading. Adjust reading lenses, and make and record one or two preliminary readings of inlet- and outlet-water thermometers. Note whether temperature rise has remained in the range of $15 \pm 0.5°F$. As the meter index crosses the zero, shift the change-over device to divert effluent heated water to the weighing bucket.

Make and record three readings of the inlet-water thermometer and at least ten readings of the outlet-water temperatures. Readings may be scheduled by making them at the times the meter index passes suitably chosen graduations on the dial. It is preferable to make an estimate of the average reading of the outlet-water thermometer during each interval and to record this average as the reading rather than to record the readings observed at certain instants.

At the instant the index of the meter passes the zero mark at the end of the second revolution (end of the first revolution for gases above 1300 Btu/ft³), after the effluent water was diverted to the weighing buckets, shift the change-over device to divert the water back into the drain. It may be necessary to change the weighing bucket during the test period. Weigh the water collected to the nearest 0.001 lb.

Take a second and third series of observations as soon as convenient after the first series, repeating the full set of observations.

If net value is being measured, stop collection of condensate after the meter index has made at least ten revolutions. Remove the graduate from under the drain tube at the instant the meter index passes zero. Read and record meter reading and volume of condensate (to 0.1 ml). Repeat collection of condensate if necessary.

Before shutting down the apparatus, repeat the preliminary observations described earlier. To shut down, close the supply gas valve of the meter and then remove burner from calorimeter. Close the water valve from the supply tank and refill the tank. Be sure never to leave gas burning at the calorimeter when the apparatus is untended.

$$\text{Observed calorific value, Btu/standard ft}^3 = \frac{(W)(T)}{(V)(F)}$$

where W = amount of water heated, in lb
T = temperature rise of water, in °F (corrected)
V = observed gas volume, in ft^3
F = reduction factor to convert observed volume V to standard conditions

$$F = \frac{519.7}{459.7 + t} \frac{P - w_t}{29.4782}$$

where P = total gas pressures, in in. Hg
w_t = saturated vapor pressure of water at temperature t, in in. Hg
t = temperature of the gas, in °F

The observed calorific value is used for the calculation of either the total or the net calorific value. For these calculations, a number of correction factors are to be applied. These include C_m, which varies with the combustion-air temperature, C_d, which accounts for differences between the temperature of inlet water, combustion air and room, C_h, which accounts for the fact that in general the amount of water vapor entering the calorimeter is not equal to that leaving it, and finally C_w, which is the heat of vaporization of the water condensed in the calorimeter per standard ft^3 of gas

Table 6. Values of Correction C_h, in Btu/standard ft^3

Combustion-air temperature, °F	Values[a] of $\frac{fh}{100}$										
	0.0	0.1	0.2	0.3	0.4	0.5	0.6	0.7	0.8	0.9	1.0
40	6.4	6.1	5.6	5.2	4.8	4.4	4.0	3.6	3.2	2.7	2.3
45	6.5	6.0	5.5	5.1	4.6	4.1	3.6	3.2	2.7	2.2	1.7
50	6.8	6.2	5.6	5.1	4.5	3.9	3.4	2.8	2.2	1.6	1.1
55	7.4	6.8	6.1	5.3	4.7	4.0	3.3	2.6	1.9	1.2	0.5
60	8.4	7.6	6.8	5.9	5.1	4.3	3.5	2.7	1.8	1.0	0.2
65	9.7	8.8	7.8	6.8	5.8	4.8	3.8	2.9	1.9	0.9	−0.1
70	11.3	10.2	9.0	7.8	6.7	5.5	4.3	3.2	2.0	0.8	−0.4
75	13.2	11.8	10.4	9.0	7.7	6.2	4.8	3.5	2.1	0.6	−0.7
80	15.6	14.1	12.3	10.6	9.0	7.3	5.6	4.0	2.3	0.5	−1.1
85	18.1	16.3	14.3	12.2	10.4	8.4	6.4	4.5	2.5	0.5	−1.4
90	21.2	19.1	16.7	14.3	12.1	9.7	7.4	5.2	2.8	0.5	−1.8
95	24.9	22.3	19.5	16.7	14.1	11.4	8.6	6.0	3.2	0.4	−2.2
100	28.9	25.9	22.7	19.4	16.4	13.2	9.9	6.9	3.7	0.4	−2.6

[a] $f = \dfrac{30 - w_t}{30 - \dfrac{h}{100} w_t}$ where w_t = vapor pressure of water at t °F (see Table 9) and h = humidity of air entering the calorimeter, in %.

burned.   These calculations are outlined below; for more details and for the explana-
tion of the values listed in the tables, ASTM D 900 should be consulted.

Total Calorific Value.   In this calculation, two corrections are necessary, C_h and
C_d.   The value of C_h is taken from Table 6 and it has to be added to the observed
calorific value.   The values for C_d are listed in Table 7.   These are given as % anticipated total calorific value/°F difference in the inlet-water, and combustion-air temperatures.   The footnote to Table 7 is giving instructions when the correction calculated from C_d has to be added to or subtracted from the observed calorific value.

If the temperatures of the combustion air and the air surrounding the calorimeter
are not identical, the value of C_d has to be modified by an additional correction, which
is equal to 0.068% of the observed calorific value per °F difference, and is to be added

Table 7.   Values of Correction $C_d{}^a$

Mean of inlet-water and combustion-air temperature, °F	Total calorific value[b]	Net calorific value[b]
40	0.094	0.074
45	0.102	0.079
50	0.110	0.083
55	0.119	0.087
60	0.128	0.090
65	0.136	0.092
70	0.146	0.094
75	0.155	0.095
80	0.167	0.097
85	0.180	0.098
90	0.194	0.099
95	0.209	0.099
100	0.228	0.100

[a] The correction is added if the inlet-water temperature is higher than the combustion-air temperature, and is subtracted if the inlet-water temperature is lower.

[b] As % of anticipated total calorific value per °F difference between the inlet water and combustion air temperature.

Table 8.   Values of Correction C_m for the Calculation of the Net Calorific Value,
Btu/standard ft^3

Combustion-air temperature, °F	Value of C_m
40	0.53
45	0.42
50	0.34
55	0.27
60	0.22
65	0.19
70	0.16
75	0.15
80	0.13
85	0.12
90	0.12
95	0.13
100	0.14

Table 9. Latent Heat of Vaporization and Vapor Pressure of Water

Combustion-air temperature, °F	Heat of vaporization, Btu/ml	Vapor pressure, in. Hg
40	2.36	0.248
45	2.36	0.300
50	2.35	0.363
55	2.34	0.436
60	2.34	0.522
65	2.33	0.622
70	2.32	0.739
75	2.31	0.875
80	2.31	1.032
85	2.30	1.213
90	2.29	1.422
95	2.28	1.660
100	2.27	1.933

if the temperature of room air is lower than that of the combustion air and subtracted if it is higher.

Net Calorific Value. In this calculation three corrections are necessary, C_m, C_d, and C_w. The value of C_m is taken from Table 8 and added to the observed calorific value. The value of C_w is calculated by taking the heat of vaporization from Table 9 and multiplying it with the volume of condensate (in ml). The obtained value is to be added to the observed calorific value. Finally, the correction C_d is to be applied as mentioned above for the total calorific value calculation.

MEASUREMENT WITH THE CONTINUOUS READING CALORIMETER. The heating value is determined by imparting all of the heat obtained from combustion of the test gas to a stream of air and measuring its rise in temperature. The streams of test gas and heat-absorbing air are maintained in fixed volumetric proportion to each other by metering devices similar to ordinary wet test meters, geared together and driven from a common electric motor. The meters are mounted in a tank of water, the level of which is maintained, and the temperature of which determines the temperature of the entering gas and air. The flue gases resulting from combustion of the natural gas, including excess combustion air, is kept separate from the heat-absorbing air, and is cooled to a few degrees above the initial temperature of gas and air. The water formed in the combustion is practically all condensed to liquid. Consequently the temperature rise produced in the heat absorbing air is directly proportional to the heating value of the gas. Since all the heat from combustion of the sample, including latent heat of vaporization of water vapor formed in the combustion, is imparted to the heat-absorbing air, the calorimeter makes a direct determination of total heating value. The temperature rise is measured by nickel resistance thermometers and is translated into Btu/standard ft³.

In case of the continuous recording calorimeter, two additional definitions are used.

Heat-absorbing air is the heat exchange medium used to absorb the heat of combustion derived from the burning of gaseous fuel.

Saturated basis is the expressed total calorific value of a gas when it is saturated with water vapor at standard temperature and pressure; 1 ft³ is equivalent in dry gas content to 0.9826 ft³ of dry gas at the temperature and pressure.

The recording calorimeter consists of two major units, the tank unit or calorimeter proper in which the heating value is measured, and the recording unit which translates the heat measurements into an indication of calorific value and records it graphically. The unit should be installed in a draft-free room with side walls at least 10×13 ft with minimum ceiling height of 8 ft. The temperature should be 72–77°F. There shall be no direct sunlight on the unit; there should be no more than one window in the room, and that should have northern exposure.

When first installed, and after any major overhaul, the equipment is standardized against hydrogen. Subsequent restandardizations should be with pure methane, at least weekly.

The calorimeter, recording unit, and tank unit must be inspected regularly to insure good operating conditions. A cold balance test may be applied to check the complete temperature-measuring unit.

Because the calorimeter chart reading is a direct indication of the heating value of the gas, compensation in the instrument must be made either by standardization or by mechanical devices for all correction terms and other complicating factors.

Bibliography

1. *U.S. Bureau of Mines Minerals Yearbook*, Washington, D. C., 1969.
2. *Gas Engineers Handbook*, The Industrial Press, New York, 1965.
3. *Gas Facts*, American Gas Association, Dept. of Statistics, New York, 1970.
4. D. B. Tyler and D. Drury, "Natural Gas—Its Physiologic Action," *California and Western Medicine* **47**, 1 (1937).
5. M. M. Braverman et al., "Determining the Cause of Death of Vegetation by Analysis of Soil Gases," *Gas Age* **129**, 23 (1962).
6. *Physical Constants of the Components of Natural Gas and Natural Gasoline, T.S. 401*, Western Gas Processors and Oil Refiners Association, Long Beach, Calif., 1969.
7. *ASTM D 1071-55, Methods for Measurement of Gaseous Fuel Samples*, American Society for Testing and Materials, Philadelphia, Pa., 1969.
8. *ASTM D 1145-53, Method of Sampling Natural Gas*, American Society for Testing and Materials, Philadelphia, Pa., 1969.
9. *ASTM D 1136-53, Method for Analysis of Natural Gases by the Volumetric Chemical Method*, American Society for Testing and Materials, Philadelphia, Pa., 1969.
10. *ASTM D 1137-53, Method for Analysis of Natural Gases and Related Types of Gaseous Mixtures by the Mass Spectrometer*, American Society for Testing and Materials, Philadelphia, Pa., 1969.
11. *NGAA Tentative Method for Natural Gas Analysis by Gas Chromatography* (Publ. 2261-21), Natural Gasoline Association of America, Tulsa, Okla., 1961.
12. *ASTM D 1945-64, Method for Analysis of Natural Gas by Gas Chromatography*, American Society for Testing and Materials, Philadelphia, Pa., 1969.
13. Phillips Petroleum Corp., Bartlesville, Okla.
14. *Procedure for the Charcoal Test for the Determination of the Gasoline Content of Natural Gas*, T.S. 351, Western Gas Processors and Oil Refiners Association, Long Beach, Calif., 1947.
15. *Tentative Standard Chromatographic Test Procedure for the Determination of Propane, Butanes, and Pentanes-Plus in Natural Gas, T.S. 611*, Western Gas Processors and Oil Refiners Association, Long Beach, Calif., 1961.
16. *Tentative Standard Chromatographic Test Procedure for the Determination of Natural Gas Liquids Composition, T.S. 671*, Western Gas Processors and Oil Refiners Association, Long Beach, Calif., 1967.
17. R. S. McBride and J. D. Edwards, *Lead Acetate Test for Hydrogen Sulfide in Gas, T41*, National Bureau of Standards, Washington, D.C.
18. J. B. Littlefield et al., *Detector for Quantitative Estimation of Low Concentrations of Hydrogen Sulfide, RI 3271*, Bureau of Mines, Washington, D.C.
19. V. J. Altieri, *Gas Analysis and Testing of Gaseous Materials*, American Gas Association, New York, 1945.

20. *ASTM D 2725-68T, Method for Hydrogen Sulfide in Natural Gas (Methylene Blue Method)*, American Society for Testing and Materials, Philadelphia, Pa., 1969.
21. *ASTM D 1072-56, Method of Test for Total Sulfur in Fuel Gases*, American Society for Testing and Materials, Philadelphia, Pa., 1969.
22. *Titrilog—Operation and Maintenance Manual*, Consolidated Electrodynamica Corp., Pasadena, Calif., 1953.
23. C. B. Carson and D. L. Katz, "Natural Gas Hydrates (TP 1371)," *AIME Trans. (Pet. Dev. & Tech.)* **146**, 150 (1942).
24. J. F. Brown, Jr., "Inclusion Compounds," *Sci. Am.* **207**, 82 (1962).
25. F. M. Flanigan, "Comparison of the Accuracy of Humidity Measuring Instruments," *ASHRAE J.* **2**, 56 (1960).
26. W. M. Deaton, "Instrument for the Measurement of Water Vapor in Natural Gases," *Am. Gas Assoc. Proc.* **1953**, 1062 (1953).
27. *ASTM D 1142-63, Method for Water Vapor Content of Gaseous Fuels by Measurement of Dew-Point Temperature*, American Society for Testing and Materials, Philadelphia, Pa., 1969.
28. Institute of Gas Technology, Chicago, Ill.
29. Arthur D. Little, Inc., *Investigation of Sampling Procedure Requirements* (Project NFX-12; PF-15) (11P/R), American Gas Association, New York, 1957.
30. Millipore Filter Corp., Watertown, Mass.
31. "Calculation of Heating Value and Specific Gravity of Fuel Gases," *Research Bull. No. 32*, Inst. of Gas Technology, Mason and Eakin, Chicago, Ill.
32. *ASTM D 1070-67, Methods of Test for Specific Gravity of Gaseous Fuels*, American Society for Testing and Materials, Philadelphia, Pa., 1969.
33. L. Schnidman, *Gaseous Fuels*, American Gas Association, New York.
34. *ASTM D 900-55, Method for Calorific Value of Gaseous Fuels by the Water Flow Calorimeter*, American Society for Testing and Materials, Philadelphia, Pa., 1969.
35. *ASTM D 1826-64, Method for Calorific Value of Gases in Natural Gas Range by Continuous Recording Calorimeter*, American Society for Testing and Materials, Philadelphia, Pa., 1969.
36. *ASTM E 1-68, Specifications for ASTM Thermometers*, American Society for Testing and Materials, Philadelphia, Pa., 1969.
37. *ASTM E 337-62, Method for Determining Relative Humidity by Wet- and Dry-Bulb Psychrometer*, American Society for Testing and Materials, Philadelphia, Pa., 1969.

RALPH C. VOLLMAR

Consultant

GASOLINE

Gasoline is one of the major industrial products of the world, both in volume and dollar value. It is a complex liquid mixture of hydrocarbons, having a boiling range of 38–200°C, derived from crude petroleum by refining. Gasoline-type mixtures (synthetic gasolines) may also be obtained by processing from other natural organic sources such as coal, shale, tar sands, etc. These "synthetic gasolines" may become more important in the future as reserves of crude petroleum are expended. However, the specifications, testing, and analysis for gasoline will generally remain the same regardless of source.

Crude petroleum is refined by a number of processes resulting in various product streams, usually with given names derived from the nature of the process; ie, alkylate from the alkylation reaction, reformate from the reforming reactions, etc. A number of these streams are blended to produce commercial gasolines. Choice of the streams and the blending thereof is dictated by the type of refining facilities available and the requirements of the finished product.

A comprehensive view of the technology of gasoline can be found in the general references (1–6). In addition, a publication of particular interest is the *Motor Gasoline*

Survey (7). This survey is made twice yearly—summer and winter—in accordance with a cooperative agreement between the American Petroleum Institute and the Bureau of Mines of the United States Department of Interior. Surveys have been conducted since 1957 and results published since 1958. These surveys present a vast amount of information on individual fuels at the time of the survey and indicate trends over the years in important fuel characteristics. The type of information covered is indicated by Table 1 (7) and Figure 1 (7).

Table 1. Summary of Values for Various Properties

Test	Regular-price gasoline average	Premium-price gasoline average	Bibliography reference
gravity, °API	63.0	62.9	(8)
corrosion no.	1	1	(9)
sulfur content, wt%	0.043	0.020	(10)
gum, mg/100 ml	2	1	(11)
lead, g/gal	2.26	2.71	(12)
octane number, research	93.8	99.8	(13)
octane number, motor	86.3	92.2	(14)
Reid vapor pressure, lb	12.1	12.1	(15)
distillation test on evaporated basis, °F			(16)
initial boiling point	83	83	
5%	96	95	
10%	109	109	
20%	130	133	
30%	153	158	
50%	202	210	
70%	256	255	
90%	335	323	
95%	368	355	
end point	411	403	
residue, vol %	1.0	0.9	
distillation loss	2.1	2.3	

Since many of the properties used to define and specify gasoline are empirical or physical in nature, test methods involved therein are also empirical and physical tests rather than chemical tests. Therefore, while mention will be made of these and brief descriptions given of the properties which they define, procedures will be presented only for those methods which are basically chemical or physiochemical in nature.

Evaluation of Properties

Commercial gasoline is an extremely complex mixture of hydrocarbons and specific additives. The properties which are generally used to describe and specify gasolines are those related to performance. They include vapor pressure, distillation characteristics, octane number, lead content, sulfur content, specific gravity, and gum formation.

Vapor Pressure and Distillation Curve

An engine will start at the prevailing atmospheric temperature only if the gasoline forms a substantial amount of combustible vapor at that temperature. The generally

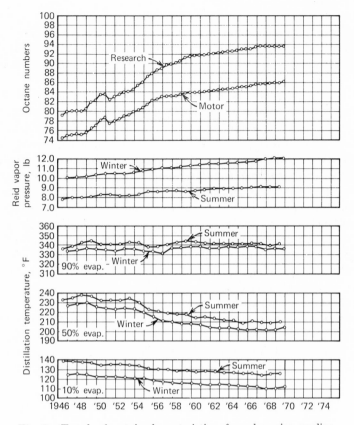

Fig. 1. Trends of certain characteristics of regular-price gasoline.

used U.S. measure of this ability to vaporize is the Reid vapor pressure test, given in ASTM D 323 (15). This test measures the vapor pressure exerted by the lowest boiling components of the gasoline using standardized apparatus under standard conditions, and indicates whether the gasoline will give off enough vapors to start an engine at a given temperature. The test also indicates, if the vapor pressure is too high, that there is danger of vapor lock which occurs when excessive premature vaporization in the fuel lines or the fuel pump causes partial or complete stoppage of the flow of liquid fuel to the carburetor.

Distillation characteristics are important since the gasoline must vaporize increasingly as carburetor and manifold temperature rise in order to provide fast warmup, even acceleration, and a proper distribution of fuel among the engine's cylinders. The method of choice for determining the distillation characteristics is ASTM D 86 (16), which consists of distilling a 100-ml sample of the gasoline, condensing the distillate, and recording the temperatures at which various percentages of the sample have distilled over. The temperature at which the first drop of gasoline evaporates and is condensed is called the initial boiling point (ibp). The final temperature achieved is called the end point. Normally, temperature readings are taken each time the level of condensed gasoline passes a 10-ml mark on a receiving 100-ml graduate. Thus, a record is obtained which shows the temperatures at which fractions such as 10, 20, and 30 vol % (see Table 1) of the sample have evaporated, and also the initial and end boiling points.

These two properties, as determined by the Reid vapor pressure test and the ASTM distillation curve, tell much about a gasoline's volatility and whether or not it will have the proper vaporizing characteristics for the climate and altitude where it will be used. The Reid vapor pressure and the 10 vol % point of the ASTM distillation curve are the main indicators of the front end volatility that determines the quick starting and vapor lock characteristics of the gasoline. The slope of the ASTM distillation curve from the 10 vol % point to the 50 vol % point indicates the ability of the gasoline to supply a proper fuel mixture during the warmup period, particularly during periods of acceleration. The 90 vol % point, or the slope of the 50 vol % to the 90 vol % portion of the curve, indicates the proportion of higher-boiling components of the fuel. Once the engine is up to normal operating temperatures, these components contribute high mileage per gallon. The end point or highest temperature reached during the ASTM distillation indicates the extent to which heavy ends are present in gasoline. If the difference between the 90 vol % point and the end point is greater than 70–80°F, some of the heavy ends may cause undue engine deposits and lubricant dilution. The distillation characteristics of the gasoline have assumed added importance in recent years since they also provide data for predicting potential evaporative losses from fuel distribution systems and also from fuel tanks and carburetor bowls of vehicles. These evaporative losses are one potential source of air pollutants.

Simulated Distillation by Gas Chromatography. Although ASTM D 86 is a rapid one-plate distillation of fair precision, the data obtained bears little relationship to the true boiling point distribution (TBP) of the sample. While many efforts have been made to correlate ASTM boiling range and true boiling point distillation data, none

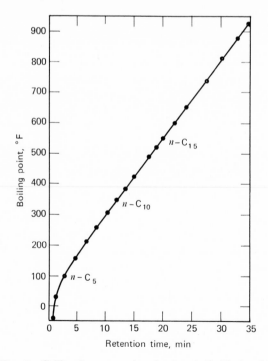

Fig. 2. Calibration curve for simulated distillation by gas chromatography.

have been completely satisfactory. For a more precise characterization of the sample a true boiling point distillation is used. Both the rather lengthy TBP distillation and the ASTM D 86 method fail to establish initial or final boiling points with any degree of accuracy, and only at or near the midpoint is there any agreement between the two methods. The obvious need for a better rapid distillation method has given rise to the development of gas chromatographic procedures to obtain boiling point distribution data; a number have been reported (17–20). In fact, simulated distillation by gas chromatography has advanced to the stage where a proposed tentative method has been published as ASTM D 2887 (21). This is a general method for petroleum products and fractions having a final boiling point of 1000°F or less; it may be used for gasoline range material with slight modifications. While simulated distillation cannot be directly related to either ASTM D 86 or TBP distillation, it does provide more accurate data on initial and final boiling points.

A sample is introduced into a gas chromatographic column which separates hydrocarbons in the order of their boiling point. The column temperature is increased by programming at a reproducible rate, and the area under the chromatogram is recorded throughout the run. A known mixture of hydrocarbons covering the boiling range of interest is also run under the exact same conditions and a calibration curve is plotted as shown in Figure 2 (21). Using this calibration curve, boiling points are assigned to the time axis of the runs. These data allow the boiling range distribution of the sample to be determined.

Any gas chromatographic system may be used to perform simulated distillation in the gasoline boiling range if it meets the following criteria:

1. A nonpolar column of limited efficiency is used. 2–4 ft long columns with $\frac{1}{8}$ or $\frac{3}{16}$ in. OD have been used; suitable liquid phases are UC W98 methyl vinyl silicone gum, GE SE-30 and OV-1 methyl silicone gums or OV-101 methyl silicone fluid.

2. The instrument is equipped with a temperature programming system capable of rigorous repeatable operation from −40°C to 300°C.

3. The system is equipped with either thermal conductivity or flame ionization detectors.

4. No cold spots exist between injection port and column, and column and detector.

5. The instrument supplies a stable baseline over the programmed temperature range.

6. The system also incorporates means of determining the accumulated area under the chromatogram. Electronic integration is preferred.

7. The recording potentiometer has a full scale response time of 2 sec or less.

8. The absolute retention times are exactly repeatable.

Procedure

Program the column temperature up to the maximum temperature to be used. Using a rigorous standard procedure, cool the column down to −40°C and hold for 5 min. Use a micro syringe which has been prechilled in dry ice to inject the desired volume of sample. Immediately start programming the column temperature up at a rate between 6 and 10°C/min. The recorder chart drive and the integrator must be turned on immediately with the injection. Record the peaks at a sensitivity setting that allows maximum peak height compatible with the method of measurement being used. Choose a sample size that does not allow any peaks to exceed the linear range of the detector. With hydrogen flame ionization detectors the usual sample size ranges from 0.2 to 1.0 μl. With thermal conductivity detectors 2 to 10 μl samples are usually satisfactory. Integrate the area under the chromatogram continuously. Record this area at intervals not greater than 5% of the total area across the boiling range. Continue the run until the chromatogram returns to a constant baseline. Run a calibration mixture of n-paraffins from C_4 through C_{16} by this procedure. Record the retention time of each component. Plot retention time versus atmospheric boiling points to obtain the calibration curve. From the calibration curve, assign boiling temperatures to each of the intervals at which area measurements were made.

Calculate the boiling point distribution data as follows:

Record the cumulative area under the chromatogram at each selected interval. At the end of the chromatogram where it has returned to baseline observe the total cumulative area counts. Move back along the chromatogram to a cumulative area count equal to 99.5% of the total. Mark this point as the final boiling point. Observe the area counts at the beginning of the run until a point at which the cumulative area is 0.5% of the total area. Mark this point as the initial boiling point of the sample. Subtract the cumulative area at the initial boiling point from the cumulative area at each selected interval to obtain a corrected cumulative area at each interval. Calculate the percent sample recovered at each interval by dividing the corrected cumulative area at each interval between the initial and final boiling points by the corrected total area at the final boiling point. Tabulate the percent recovered at each interval with the boiling temperature assigned to that interval from the calibration curve.

Octane Number

The fuel–air mixture in each engine cylinder should burn smoothly and evenly following the timed ignition by the spark plug, but sometimes as the flame front sweeps across the combustion chamber, the unburned portion of the fuel is heated and compressed to the point that it autoignites, detonating instantaneously. Instead of a smooth power stroke, the piston is given a hard rap to which it cannot respond because it is connected to the crankshaft and it, in turn, is connected to the other pistons going through different phases of the engine cycle at the engine speed then prevailing. This abrupt release of energy from the detonation causes high-frequency pressure fluctuations throughout the combustion chamber; these register on the ear as sharp metallic noises called knock. The energy that should have been released as useful power is dissipated in the form of pressure waves and increased heat radiated to surrounding engine parts and the cooling water. Knock not only produces an objectionable sound and wastes fuel, but prolonged knocking overheats valves, spark plugs and pistons and may substantially shorten their life. It has long been recognized that the chemical structure of fuel hydrocarbons largely determines their tendency to cause knock. Straight-chain paraffins are more knock-prone than branch chain paraffins, olefins or cyclic hydrocarbons. Naphthenes (saturated cyclics) are more knock-prone than aromatics (unsaturated cyclics). A knowledge of the relationship between hydrocarbon structure and knock potential has led to the development of processes, such as alkylation and reforming, widely employed in petroleum refining to produce better gasoline. Knock can also be combatted by negative catalysts, or an antiknock compound employed to head off or slow down precombustion reactions that might otherwise convert fuel hydrocarbons to autoigniting detonating compounds. The volatile alkyllead compounds are almost universally used for this application.

As gasoline became an important industrial product, it became evident that some yardstick was needed for measuring the antiknock quality of motor fuel. The octane scale, which was developed in 1926 (22), has become the worldwide standard for that purpose. This is an arbitrary scale based on the knocking characteristics of the two pure hydrocarbons, n-heptane and 2,2,4-trimethylpentane, in volumetric blends of the two. The straight-chain hydrocarbon, n-heptane, which is very knock-prone, is used to define the zero point on the scale. 2,2,4-Trimethylpentane, which is often referred to as isooctane and is nonknocking, was chosen to define the 100 point on the scale. Blending these hydrocarbons in varying percentages can produce primary reference fuels to match the knock resistance of any gasoline sample. Thus, if a blend of 80% isooctane and 20% n-heptane is required to match the knock resistance of a particular gasoline sample when both are run in a special knock test engine under specified conditions, the sample is said to have an octane number of 80. In other words, octane number is defined as the percentage of isooctane required in a blend with n-heptane to match the knocking characteristics of the gasoline being tested. In order to rate fuels of more than 100 octane number, a method has been devised which matches the octane quality of the test fuel with that of the reference fuel consisting of isooctane plus a known amount of tetraethyllead. The knock value of a fuel having the same antiknock quality as one gallon of isooctane plus 2 ml of tetraethyllead is expressed as $100 + 2$.

The antiknock quality of today's gasolines is rated by two laboratory knock test procedures, both of which employ the cooperative fuel research engine. The motor method, ASTM D 2700 (14), uses a set of standard operating conditions that correlated well with the severe requirements for fuels in automobile engines in the 1930s. The research method, ASTM D 2699 (13), uses a different, less severe set of operating conditions, which were adopted when it became apparent that the newer refining processes and engine improvements gave gasolines better road performance than their motor method ratings would indicate. Both methods have continued to be used, however, because together they predict the gasoline's road performance better than either does alone. If two fuels have equal motor method octane number (MON), the one with the greater research octane number (RON) will usually satisfy a greater percentage of cars. In the same manner, if the research octane ratings are equal, the fuel with the higher motor octane rating will usually perform better on the road. The difference between a fuel's research rating and its motor rating is called the sensitivity (RON − MON). This difference indicates how sensitive the gasoline is in terms of antiknock performance to more severe engine operating conditions. A gasoline's sensitivity depends on its hydrocarbon composition. As might be expected, since the reference fuels themselves are paraffins and by definition have the same octane numbers by either octane method, the paraffins contribute little or no sensitivity. On the other hand, olefins and aromatics are quite sensitive and, therefore, impart sensitivity to the cracked and reformed gasolines that contain them.

Hydrocarbon Composition

From the foregoing discussion, it can be seen that methods of analysis which will give us some insight to the hydrocarbon composition of gasoline are very important. The analytical methods employed generally fall into two categories: those which give broad hydrocarbon classifications; and those, usually instrumental, which give us detailed information on individual hydrocarbon components.

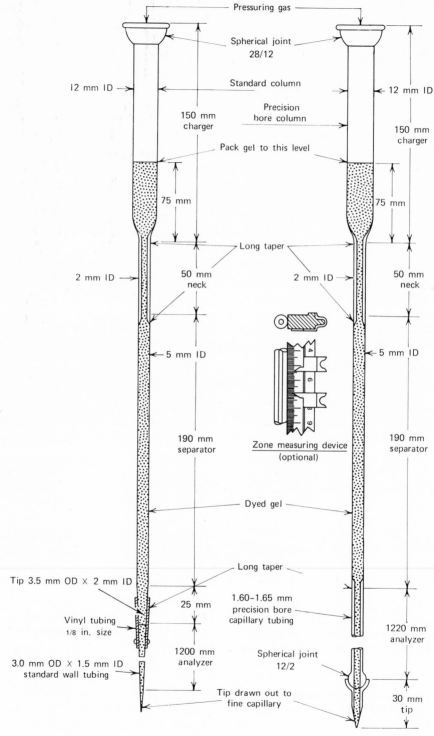

Fig. 3. Adsorption columns with standard wall (left) and precision bore (right) tubing in analyzer section.

Liquid Chromatographic Analysis. A widely used method for the separation of hydrocarbon types in gasoline is based on ASTM D 1319 (23). This procedure, called the FIA method, determines the saturates, nonaromatic olefins, and aromatics in depentanized gasolines. Aromatic olefins, some diolefins, and sulfur, nitrogen, and oxygen compounds are determined as aromatics.

A sample of the gasoline is charged to a glass adsorption column which is packed with activated silica gel. A small section in the column is packed with silica gel to which a mixture of fluorescent dyes has been added. Isopropyl alcohol is used to desorb the gasoline sample and transport it down the column. The gasoline is separated into aromatics, olefins, and saturates. The mixture of fluorescent dyes is also separated, selectively, along with the hydrocarbon types and makes the boundaries of aromatic, olefin, and saturate zones visible under ultraviolet light. The vol % of each hydrocarbon type can be calculated from the length of each zone in the column. Figure 3 (23) gives the dimensions for both standard and precision bore columns; either type can be used.

Procedure

Use a 100–200 mesh silica gel manufactured to insure minimum olefin polymerization. It is necessary to screen the gel to make certain that the gel size specification is met. Dry the gel in a shallow vessel at 350°F for 3 hr. Transfer the dried gel to an airtight container while still hot. Thereafter, exercise extreme caution to protect it from atmospheric moisture.

The gel containing the standard fluorescent indicator dyes is available from Patent Chemicals, Inc., 335 McLane Boulevard, Patterson, New Jersey by requesting "standard dyed gel for the FIA method of hydrocarbon type analysis."

Pack two standard wall columns for duplicate analysis of each sample, or a single column if the precision bore column is used. (See Figure 3). To pack the columns with gel, suspend each column from a loose-fitting clamp placed immediately below the spherical joint of the charger section. Add small increments of silica gel through a glass funnel, while vibrating the column along its entire length, using an electric vibrator. Continue until the separator section is half full. Stop the vibrator and add a 3–5 mm layer of the dyed gel. Start the vibrator and add additional silica gel while vibrating the column. Continue to add silica gel until the tightly packed gel extends 75 mm into the charger section. Occasionally, wipe the length of the column with a damp cloth. This aids in packing the column by removing static electricity. Continue to vibrate the column after the filling is completed: an additional 4 min is usually satisfactory when an electric vibrator is used. Place the filled columns in a darkened area. Chill the sample and a suitable hypodermic syringe to 2–4°C. Draw 0.75 ± 0.03 ml of sample into the syringe and inject the sample 30 mm below the surface of the gel in the charger section. Fill the charger section to the spherical joint with isopropyl alcohol which has been refined to 99%, conforming to ASTM specification D 770 (24) for isopropyl alcohol. Connect the column to a source of pressurizing gas, either air or nitrogen, and apply two psig for $2\frac{1}{2}$ min to move a liquid front down the column. Increase the pressure to 5 psig for another $2\frac{1}{2}$ min. Adjust the gas pressure to give a total transit time of approximately 1 hr. Usually, 4–10 psig is needed for gasoline samples. Carefully wipe the outside of the column with a cloth dampened with ethanol. Avoid handling the column with bare hands thereafter. After the red isopropyl alcohol aromatic boundary has advanced 350 mm into the analyzer section, make a set of readings by quickly marking the boundary of each hydrocarbon type zone, observed in ultraviolet light, from a source with radiation predominantly at 3650 Å. Ordinary wax

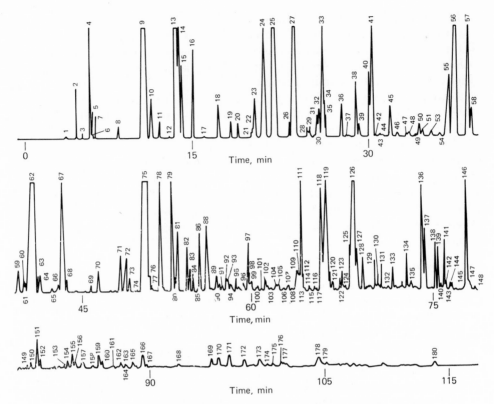

Fig. 4. Chromatogram of a typical premium grade gasoline.

glass-marking pencils may be used to mark these boundaries. For the nonfluorescent saturate zone, mark the front of the charge at the point where the yellow fluorescence first reaches its maximum intensity. For the upper end of the olefin zone, mark the point where the blue fluorescence first appears or reaches its maximum intensity. For the third or aromatic zone, mark the upper end of a reddish or brown zone. When the sample has advanced another 50 mm down the column, make a second set of readings by marking the zones in the reverse order as done previously, so as to minimize errors due to the advancement of boundary positions during readings. If the markings are made with glass-marking pencils, two colors can be used—one for each set of measurements—and the distances can be measured at the end of the test. Release the gas pressure, disconnect the column, lay it horizontally on the bench, and measure off in mm the length of the aromatic zone, the length of the olefin zone, and the length of the saturate zone.

$$\text{Aromatics, vol \%} = \frac{L_a}{L}\,(100)$$

$$\text{Olefins, vol \%} = \frac{L_o}{L}\,(100)$$

$$\text{Saturates, vol \%} = \frac{L_s}{L}\,(100)$$

where L_a = length of aromatic zone, in mm
       L_o = length of olefin zone, in mm
       L_s = length of the saturate zone, in mm
       L = sum of L_a plus L_o plus L_s

Average the respective values for each type and round to the nearest whole percent. If necessary, adjust the result for the largest component so that the sum of the components is 100%.

Gas Chromatographic Analysis. Gas chromatography is by far the most widely used instrumental analytical method for determining detailed individual hydrocarbon composition of gasoline-type materials. There is no general method for the gas chromatographic analysis of gasoline. However, a number of methods have been published (25–31). Those which give the most detailed analysis, often identifying 150–200 individual hydrocarbon compounds in gasoline, employ open tubular columns of high efficiency, and sophisticated commercial gas chromatographs capable of temperature programming over a wide range from subambient to a 150–200°C. The techniques of gas chromatography are discussed in Vol. 2, pp. 157–194. Figure 4 (26) is a chromatogram of a typical regular grade gasoline. This chromatogram was obtained under the following conditions (26):

column	200 ft × 0.010 in. ID open tubular coated with squalane liquid phase
temperature of	
injection port	300°C
stream splitter	270°C
column	isothermal at −5°C until the emergence of peak 9 (isopentane), then heated as rapidly as possible to 25°C, held isothermal until the emergence of peak 40 (benzene), then heated at 2°C/min to 90°C, held there isothermally until the emergence of peak 150 (n-decane), then heated at 3°C/min to 105°C and held there until the end of analysis
detector	240°C
carrier gas (He) flow rate	1.3 ml/min until the elution of peak 126 (o-xylene), then increased to 3.5 ml/min and held there until the elution of peak 169 (n-undecane), then increased to 5.0 ml/min
sample size	1–2 μl, split $\frac{1}{200}$
detector	flame ionization

Table 2 (26) lists the individual hydrocarbons corresponding to the individual peaks. It must be emphasized that this is only one of many high-resolution-type chromatographic techniques available for the analysis of individual hydrocarbon components of gasoline. The choice of a specific method will be dictated by the availability of equipment and how detailed an analysis is required. Table 3 (26) indicates the type of quantitative information that can be acquired from this analysis.

Table 2. Hydrocarbon Identification of Chromatographic Peaks Shown in Figure 4

Peak number	Component[a]	Boiling point, °C	Peak number	Component[a]	Boiling point, °C
1	propane	−42.07	44	2,4-dimethyl-1-pentene	81.64
2	isobutane	−11.73	45	1-methylcyclopentene	75.8
3	isobutylene	−6.90		+ 2-methyl-*cis*-3-hexene	86
	+ butene-1	−6.26	46	2,4-dimethyl-2-pentene	83.26
4	*n*-butane	−0.50		+ 3-ethyl-1-pentene	84.11
5	*trans*-2-butene	0.88		+ 3-methyl-1-hexene	84
6	neopentane	9.50	47	2,3-dimethyl-1-pentene	84.28
7	*cis*-2-butene	3.72	48	2-methyl-*trans*-3-hexene	86
8	3-methyl-1-butene	20.06		+ 5-methyl-1-hexene	85.31
9	isopentane	27.85	49	3,3-dimethylpentane	86.06
10	pentene-1	29.97	50	cyclohexane	80.74
11	2-methyl-1-butene	31.16		+ (4-methyl-*cis*-2-hexene)	87.31
12	2-methyl-1,3-butadiene	34.07	51	4-methyl-1-hexene	86.73
13	*n*-pentane	36.07		+ 4-methyl-*trans*-2-hexene	87.56
14	*trans*-2-pentene	36.35	52	3-methyl-2-ethyl-1-butene	86.1
15	*cis*-2-pentene	36.94	53	5-methyl-*trans*-2-hexene	88.11
16	2-methyl-2-butene	38.57	54	cyclohexene	82.98
17	3,3-dimethyl-1-butene	41.24	55	2-methylhexane	90.05
18	2,2-dimethylbutane	49.74		+ (5-methyl-*cis*-2-hexene)	89.5
19	cyclopentene	44.24	56	2,3-dimethylpentane	89.78
20	3-methyl-1-pentene	54.14		+ (1,1-dimethylcyclopentane)	87.85
	+ 4-methyl-1-pentene	53.88		+ (3,4-dimethyl-*cis*-2-pentene)	87.9
21	4-methyl-*cis*-2-pentene	56.30	57	3-methylhexane	91.85
22	2,3-dimethyl-1-butene	55.67	58	1-*cis*-3-dimethylcyclopentane	91.73
23	cyclopentane	49.26		+ 2-methyl-1-hexene	91.95
24	2,3-dimethylbutane	57.99		+ 3,4-dimethyl-*trans*-2-	
	+ (4-methyl-*trans*-2-pentene)[a]	58.55		pentene	90.5
25	2-methylpentane	60.27	59	1-*trans*-3-dimethylcyclopentane	90.77
26	2-methyl-1-pentene	60.72		+ 1-heptene	93.64
27	3-methylpentane	63.28		+ 2-ethyl-1-pentene	94
	+ (hexene-1)	63.49	60	3-ethylpentane	93.48
	+ (2-ethyl-1-butene)	64.66		+ 3-methyl-*trans*-2-hexene	94
28	*cis*-3-hexene	66.47	61	1-*trans*-2-dimethylcyclopentane	91.87
29	*trans*-3-hexene	67.08	62	2,2,4-trimethylpentane	99.24
30	3-methylcyclopentene	65.0		+ (*trans*-3-heptene)	95.67
31	2-methyl-2-pentene	67.29	63	*cis*-3-heptene	95.75
32	3-methyl-*cis*-2-pentene	67.70	64	3-methyl-*cis*-3-hexene	95.33
33	*n*-hexane	68.74		+ 2-methyl-2-hexene	95.44
	+ (4,4-dimethyl-1-pentene)	72.49		+ 3-methyl-*trans*-3-hexene	93.53
34	*trans*-2-hexene	67.87	65	3-ethyl-2-pentene	96.01
35	*cis*-2-hexene	68.84	66	*trans*-2-heptene	97.95
36	3-methyl-*trans*-2-pentene	70.44	67	*n*-heptane	98.43
37	4,4-dimethyl-*trans*-2-pentene	76.75		+ (3-methyl-*cis*-2-hexene)	94
38	methylcyclopentane	71.81	68	2,3-dimethyl-2-pentene	97.40
	+ 3,3-dimethyl-1-pentene	77.57		+ *cis*-2-heptene	98.5
39	2,2-dimethylpentane	79.20	69	1-*cis*-2-dimethylcyclopentane	99.57
	+ 2,3-dimethyl-2-butene	73.21	70	methylcyclohexane	100.93
	+ (2,3,3-trimethyl-1-butene)	77.87		+ 2,2-dimethylhexane	106.84
40	benzene	80.10		+ 1,1,3-trimethylcyclopentane	104.89
41	2,4-dimethylpentane	80.50	71	2,5-dimethylhexane	109.10
42	4,4-dimethyl-*cis*-2-pentene	80.42		+ ethylcyclopentane	103.47
43	2,2,3-trimethylbutane	80.88	72	2,4-dimethylhexane	109.43

Table 2 (*continued*)

Peak number	Component[a]	Boiling point, °C	Peak number	Component[a]	Boiling point, °C
73	2,2,3-trimethylpentane	109.84	106	2,2-dimethyl-3-ethylpentane	133.83
74	1-*trans*-2-*cis*-4-trimethyl-cyclopentane	109.29		+ 2-methyl-4-ethylhexane	133.8
75	toluene	110.63	107	2,6-dimethylheptane	135.21
76	3,3-dimethylhexane	111.97		+ (1-*cis*-2-dimethyl-cyclohexane)	129.73
77	1-*trans*-2-*cis*-3-trimethyl-cyclopentane	110.2	108	*n*-propylcyclopentane	130.95
78	2,3,4-trimethylpentane	113.47	109	ethylcyclohexane	131.78
79	2,3,3-trimethylpentane	114.76	110	2,5-dimethylheptane	136.0
80	1,1,2-trimethylcyclopentane	113.73		+ 3,5-dimethylheptane	136.0
81	2,3-dimethylhexane	115.61	111	ethylbenzene	136.19
	+ 2-methyl-3-ethylpentane	115.65	112	2,4-dimethyl-3-ethylpentane	136.73
82	2-methylheptane	117.65	113	3,3-dimethylheptane	137.3
83	4-methylheptane	117.71	114	1,1,3-trimethylcyclohexane	136.63
84	3,4-dimethylhexane	117.73	115	2,3,3-trimethylhexane	137.68
	+ (1-*cis*-2-*trans*-4-trimethylcyclopentane)	116.73	116	1-*cis*-3-*cis*-5-trimethyl-cyclohexane	138.41
85	3-ethylhexane	118.53	117	2-methyl-3-ethylhexane	138.0
86	3-methylheptane	118.93	118	*p*-xylene	138.35
	+ (3-methyl-3-ethylpentane)	118.26	119	*m*-xylene	139.10
87	1,1,3-*trans*-4-tetramethyl-cyclopentane	121.6		+ (3,3,4-trimethylhexane)	140.46
88	2,2,5-trimethylhexane	124.08	120	2,3-dimethylheptane	140.5
	+ (1-*cis*-2-*cis*-4-trimethyl-cyclopentane)	118	121	3,4-dimethylheptane	140.6
89	1,1-dimethylcyclohexane	119.54	122	4-methyloctane	142.48
	+ 1-*trans*-4-dimethyl-cyclohexane	119.35	123	2-methyloctane	143.26
90	1-*cis*-3-dimethylcyclohexane	120.09	124	3-ethylheptane	143.0
91	1-methyl-*trans*-3-ethyl-cyclopentane	120.8	125	3-methyloctane	144.18
92	2,2,4-trimethylhexane	126.54	126	*o*-xylene	144.41
93	1-methyl-*trans*-2-ethyl-cyclopentane	121.2		+ (2,2,4,5-tetramethyl-hexane)	147.8
	+ 1-methyl-*cis*-3-ethyl-cyclopentane	121.4	127	2,2,4-trimethylheptane	147.88
94	cycloheptane	118.79	128	2,2,5-trimethylheptane	148
95	1-methyl-1-ethylcyclopentane	121.52		+ 2,2,6-trimethylheptane	148
96	1-*trans*-2-dimethylcyclohexane	123.42	129	2,5,5-trimethylheptane	152.80
	+ 1-*cis*-2-*cis*-3-trimethylcyclo-pentane	123.0		+ 2,4,4-trimethylheptane	153
97	*n*-octane	125.67	130	isopropylbenzene	152.39
98	1-*cis*-4-dimethylcyclohexane	124.32	131	*n*-nonane	150.80
99	1-*trans*-3-dimethylcyclohexane	124.45	132	3,3,5-trimethylheptane	155.68
100	2,4,4-trimethylhexane	130.65	133	2,4,5-trimethylheptane	157
101	isopropylcyclopentane	126.42		+ 2,3,5-trimethylheptane	157
102	2,3,5-trimethylhexane	131.34	134	*n*-propylbenzene	159.22
103	2,2-dimethylheptane	132.69	135	2,2,3,3-tetramethylhexane	160.31
104	1-methyl-*cis*-2-ethylcyclopentane	128.05		+ 2,6-dimethyloctane	158.54
105	2,4-dimethylheptane	133.5	136	1-methyl-3-ethylbenzene	161.31
	+ 2,2,3-trimethylhexane	133.6	137	1-methyl-4-ethylbenzene	161.99
			138	3,3,4-trimethylheptane	164
				+ 3,4,4-trimethylheptane	164
				+ 3,4,5-trimethylheptane	164
			139	1-methyl-2-ethylbenzene	165.15
				+ 5-methylnonane	165.1
			140	4-methylnonane	165.7
			141	1,3,5-trimethylbenzene	164.72

(*continued*)

Table 2   (*continued*)

Peak number	Component[a]	Boiling point, °C	Peak number	Component[a]	Boiling point, °C
142	2-methylnonane	166.8	161	2-methylindane	184
143	*tert*-butylbenzene	169.12	162	1,4-dimethyl-2-ethylbenzene	186.91
144	unidentified C$_{10}$ alkylate peak		163	1-methylindane	186.5
145	3-methylnonane	167.8	164	1-methyl-3-*tert*-butylbenzene	189.26
146	1,2,4-trimethylbenzene	169.35		+ unidentified C$_{11}$ alkylate	
147	*sec*-butylbenzene	173.31		peak	
148	isobutylbenzene	172.76	165	1,3-dimethyl-4-ethylbenzene	188.41
149	1-methyl-3-isopropylbenzene	175.14	166	1,3-dimethyl-2-ethylbenzene	190.01
150	*n*-decane	174.12		+ 1,2-dimethyl-4-ethyl-	
151	1,2,3-trimethylbenzene	176.08		benzene	189.75
	+ 1-methyl-4-isopropyl-		167	1-methyl-4-*tert*-butylbenzene	192.76
	benzene	177.10	168	1,2-dimethyl-3-ethylbenzene	193.91
152	1-methyl-2-isopropylbenzene	178.15	169	*n*-undecane	195.89
	+ indane	177	170	1,2,4,5-tetramethylbenzene	196.8
153	1,3-diethylbenzene	181.10	171	1,2,3,5-tetramethylbenzene	198.0
154	unidentified C$_{11}$ alkylate peak		172	isopentylbenzene	198.9
155	1-methyl-3-*n*-propylbenzene	181.80	173	5-methylindane	199
156	*n*-butylbenzene	183.27	174	4-methylindane	203
157	1,2-diethylbenzene	183.42	175	*n*-pentylbenzene	205.46
	+ 1,4-diethylbenzene	183.30	176	1,2,3,4-tetramethylbenzene	205.4
	+ 1-methyl-4-*n*-propyl-		177	tetralin	205.57
	benzene	183.75	178	naphthalene	217.96
158	1-methyl-2-*n*-propylbenzene	184.80	179	1,3-dimethyl-5-*tert*-butylbenzene	205.1
159	1,3-dimethyl-5-ethylbenzene	183.75	180	*n*-dodecane	216.28
160	unidentified C$_{11}$ alkylate peak				

[a] Chemical name in parenthesis indicates a minor component also present in the peak.

Lead Additives

Alkyllead antiknock fluids are added to nearly all commercial fuels in amounts up to the level of 4.23 g lead/gal of fuel (the amount of metallic lead in 4 ml of tetraethyllead). Octane number increases of 10–15 are fairly typical at this concentration, although each type of gasoline component has its own response to antiknock fluid. Many chemical compounds have been found to have antiknock properties; however, none of the thousands investigated to date provide as much effectiveness at as little cost as do the alkyllead compounds. The original antiknock agent was tetraethyllead (TEL). However, in recent years tetramethyllead (TML), and its physical mixtures with TEL, and chemically redistributed equilibrium mixtures of the two, have been introduced commercially and gained wide acceptance both in the United States and abroad. TML and TEL–TML mixtures are more volatile than TEL and provide more even distribution of antiknock quality throughout the gasoline boiling range. They are particularly desirable where the lighter components of a gasoline are of relatively low octane number. By distributing their antiknock action more evenly throughout the vaporizing fuel as it goes to each of the engine cylinders, TML and TEL–TML mixtures often provide superior antiknock performance in modern automobiles. In addition, the synergistic effects between TEL–TML mixtures and the individual hydrocarbon composition of a particular fuel provide opportunities to optimize octane improvement while minimizing lead addition. This ability to optimize octane improve-

Table 3. Hydrocarbon Compositions of Typical Premium and Regular Grade Gasolines[a,b]

Component	wt % regular grade	wt % premium grade	Component	wt % regular grade	wt % premium grade
propane	0.14	0.01	2,4-dimethyl-2-pentene + 3-ethyl-1-pentene + 3-methyl-1-hexene	0.05	0.05
isobutane	0.30	0.37			
isobutylene + butene-1	0.02	0.04			
n-butane	3.93	4.29	2,3-dimethyl-1-pentene	0.01	0.02
trans-2-butene	0.16	0.20	2-methyl-trans-3-hexene + 5-methyl-1-hexene	0.05	0.04
neopentane	0.02	0.04			
cis-2-butene	0.13	0.17	3,3-dimethylpentane	Trace	0.02
3-methyl-1-butene	0.08	0.12	cyclohexane + 4-methyl-cis-2-hexene	0.36	0.17
isopentane	7.88	10.17			
pentene-1	0.34	0.45	4-methyl-1-hexene + 4-methyl-trans-2-hexene	0.08	0.09
2-methyl-1-butene	0.35	0.22			
n-pentane	7.27	5.75	3-methyl-2-ethyl-1-butene + 5-methyl-trans-2-hexene	0.03	0.04
trans-2-pentene	0.52	0.90			
cis-2-pentene	0.43	0.67	cyclohexene	0.03	0.03
2-methyl-2-butene	1.09	0.96	2-methylhexane + (5-methyl-cis-2-hexene)	1.25	1.48
2,2-dimethylbutane	0.17	0.46			
cyclopentene	0.13	0.18	2,3-dimethylpentane + (1,1-dimethylcyclopentane) + (3,4-dimethyl-cis-2-pentene)	0.47	4.17
2-methyl-1-pentene + 4-methyl-1-pentene	0.16	0.18			
4-methyl-cis-2-pentene	0.05	0.04	3-methylhexane	1.41	1.77
2,3-dimethyl-1-butene	0.10	0.08	1-cis-3-dimethylcyclopentane + 2-methyl-1-hexene + 3,4-dimethyl-trans-2-pentene	0.41	0.27
cyclopentane	0.58	0.51			
2,3-dimethylbutane	0.59	1.55			
4-methyl-trans-2-pentene	0.30	0.18	1-trans-3-dimethylcyclopentane + 1-heptene + 2-ethyl-1-pentene	0.40	0.27
2-methylpentane	3.85	3.76			
2-methyl-1-pentene	0.22	0.22			
3-methylpentane + (hexene-1) + (2-ethyl-1-butene)	2.72	2.23	3-ethylpentane + 3-methyl-trans-2-hexene	0.25	0.16
cis-3-hexene	0.13	0.11	1-trans-2-dimethylcyclopentane	0.20	0.16
trans-3-hexene	0.15	0.12	2,2,4-trimethylpentane + (trans-3-heptene)	0.32	4.58
3-methylcyclopentene	0.08	0.04			
2-methyl-2-pentene	0.32	0.27	cis-3-heptene	0.17	0.16
3-methyl-cis-2-pentene	0.45	0.37	3-methyl-cis-3-hexene + 2-methyl-2-hexene + 3-methyl-trans-3-hexene	0.35	0.31
n-hexane + (4,4-dimethyl-1-pentene)	3.50	1.51			
trans-2-hexene	0.36	0.18	3-ethyl-2-pentene	0.04	0.04
cis-2-hexene	0.24	0.15	trans-2-heptene	0.10	0.06
3-methyl-trans-2-pentene	0.44	0.34	n-heptane + (3-methyl-cis-2-hexene)	1.92	1.96
4,4-dimethyl-trans-2-pentene	Trace	Trace			
methylcyclopentane + 3,3-dimethyl-1-pentene	1.50	0.62	2,3-dimethyl-2-pentene + cis-2-heptene	0.14	0.12
2,2-dimethylpentane + 2,3-dimethyl-2-butene + 2,3,3-trimethylbutene	0.20	0.14	1-cis-2-dimethylcyclopentane	0.13	0.09
			methylcyclohexane + 2,2-dimethylhexane + 1,1,3-trimethylcyclopentane	0.61	0.31
benzene	1.35	0.81			
2,4-dimethylpentane	0.32	1.71	2,5-dimethylhexane	0.24	0.42
2,2,3-trimethylbutane	Trace	0.04	ethylcyclopentane	0.14	0.18
4,4-dimethyl-cis-2-pentene	0.02	Trace	2,4-dimethylhexane	0.34	0.50
2,4-dimethyl-1-pentene	Trace	0.03	2,2,3-trimethylpentane	Trace	0.23
1-methylcyclopentene + 2-methyl-cis-3-hexene	0.37	0.32	1-trans-2-cis-4-trimethyl-cyclopentane	0.16	0.04

(continued)

Table 3 (*continued*)

Component	wt % regular grade	wt % premium grade	Component	wt % regular grade	wt % premium grade
toluene + (3,3-dimethyl-hexane)	5.92	12.30	2,5-dimethylheptane + 3,5-dimethylheptane	0.14	0.16
1-*trans*-2-*cis*-3-trimethylcyclo-pentane	0.25	0.06	ethylbenzene	2.70	1.70
2,3,4-trimethylpentane	0.11	2.26	2,4-dimethyl-3-ethylpentane	0.05	0.03
2,3,3-trimethylpentane	0.05	2.28	3,3-dimethylheptane	0.08	0.04
1,1,2-trimethylcyclopentane	0.11	0.09	2,3,3-trimethylhexane	0.12	0.05
2,3-dimethylhexane + 2-methyl-3-ethylpentane	0.39	0.60	2-methyl-3-ethylhexane	0.13	0.04
2-methylheptane	1.05	0.48	*p*-xylene	1.54	1.58
4-methylheptane	0.52	0.22	*m*-xylene + (3,3,4-trimethyl-hexane)	3.87	3.83
3,4-dimethylhexane + (1-*cis*-2-*trans*-4-trimethylcyclopentane)	0.20	0.16	2,3-dimethylheptane	0.39	0.13
3-ethylhexane	Trace	0.01	3,4-dimethylheptane	0.33	0.07
3-methylheptane + (3-methyl-3-ethylpentane)	1.54	0.63	4-methyloctane	0.55	0.11
2,2,5-trimethylhexane + (1-*cis*-2-*cis*-4-trimethylcyclopentane)	0.17	0.74	2-methyloctane	0.62	0.14
1,1-dimethylcyclohexane + 1-*trans*-4-dimethylcyclohexane + 1-*cis*-3-dimethylcyclohexane	0.27	0.17	3-ethylheptane	0.16	0.02
			3-methyloctane	0.85	0.60
1-methyl-*trans*-3-ethylcyclopen-tane	0.12	0.06	*o*-xylene + (2,2,4,5-tetra-methylhexane)	2.05	1.94
2,2,4-trimethylhexane	0.18	0.11	2,2,4-trimethylheptane	0.12	0.17
1-methyl-*trans*-2-ethylcyclopen-tane + 1-methyl-*cis*-3-ethyl-cyclopentane	0.13	0.07	2,2,5-trimethylheptane + 2,2,6-trimethylheptane	0.07	0.27
cycloheptane + 1-methyl-1-ethylcyclopentane	0.11	0.05	2,5,5-trimethylheptane + 2,4,4-trimethylheptane	0.06	0.21
1-*trans*-2-dimethylcyclohexane + 1-*cis*-2-*cis*-3-trimethylcyclo-pentane	0.18	0.12	isopropylbenzene	0.23	0.10
			n-nonane	0.83	0.14
n-octane + (1-*cis*-4-dimethyl-cyclohexane)	1.43	0.42	3,3,5-trimethylheptane	0.05	0.02
1-*trans*-3-dimethylcyclohexane	0.12	0.08	2,4,5-trimethylheptane + 2,3,5-trimethylheptane	0.07	0.17
2,4,4-trimethylhexane	0.04	0.02	*n*-propylbenzene	0.72	0.24
isopropylcyclopentane	0.02	0.01	2,6-dimethyloctane + (2,2,3,3-tetramethylhexane)	0.12	0.06
2,3,5-trimethylhexane	0.05	0.15	1-methyl-3-ethylbenzene	1.84	0.83
2,2-dimethylheptane	0.08	0.01	1-methyl-4-ethylbenzene	1.00	0.42
1-methyl-*cis*-2-ethylcyclo-pentane	0.11	0.07	3,3,4-trimethylheptane + 3,4,4-trimethylheptane + 3,4,5-trimethylheptane	0.08	0.35
2,4-dimethylheptane + 2,2,3-trimethylhexane	0.24	0.08	1-methyl-2-ethylbenzene + 5-methylnonane	0.90	0.34
2,2-dimethyl-3-ethylpentane + 2-methyl-4-ethylhexane	0.09	0.02	4-methylnonane	0.26	0.04
			1,3,5-trimethylbenzene	0.76	0.39
2,6-dimethylheptane + (1-*cis*-2-dimethylcyclo-hexane)	0.20	0.07	2-methylnonane	0.41	0.06
			3-methylnonane	0.32	0.06
n-propylcyclopentane	0.06	0.01	1,2,4-trimethylbenzene	2.83	1.61
ethylcyclohexane	0.36	0.17	*sec*-butylbenzene	0.13	0.01
			isobutylbenzene	0.06	0.01
			1-methyl-3-isopropylbenzene	0.12	0.03
			n-decane	0.50	0.08
			1,2,3-trimethylbenzene + 1-methyl-4-isopropylbenzene	0.68	0.32

Table 3 *(continued)*

Component	wt % regular grade	wt % pre-mium grade	Component	wt % regular grade	wt % pre-mium grade
1-methyl-2-isopropylbenzene + indane	0.35	0.15	n-undecane	0.22	0.07
1,3-diethylbenzene	0.25	0.08	1,2,4,5-tetramethylbenzene	0.21	0.10
1-methyl-3-n-propylbenzene	0.48	0.16	1,2,3,5-tetramethylbenzene	0.42	0.17
n-butylbenzene	0.25	0.05	isopentylbenzene	0.17	0.07
1,2-diethylbenzene + 1,4-diethylbenzene + 1-methyl-4-n-propylbenzene	0.44	0.09	5-methylindane	0.30	0.11
			4-methylindane	0.16	0.03
1-methyl-2-n-propylbenzene	0.16	0.05	n-pentylbenzene	0.14	0.03
1,3-dimethyl-5-ethylbenzene	0.42	0.18	1,2,3,4-tetramethylbenzene	0.19	0.03
2-methylindane	0.10	0.02	tetralin	0.14	0.02
1,4-dimethyl-2-ethylbenzene	0.36	0.09	naphthalene	0.24	0.10
1-methylindane	0.17	0.07	1,3-dimethyl-5-tert-butylbenzene	0.16	0.02
1-methyl-3-tert-butylbenzene	0.11	0.03	n-dodecane	0.09	0.05
1,3-dimethyl-4-ethylbenzene	0.27	0.13	total saturates identified	56.38	62.30
1,3-dimethyl-2-ethylbenzene + 1,2-dimethyl-4-ethylbenzene	0.50	0.19	total olefins identified	7.69	7.50
			total aromatics identified	32.91	28.50
1-methyl-4-tert-butylbenzene	0.13	0.04	total components unidentified	3.02	1.70
1,2-dimethyl-3-ethylbenzene	0.09	0.03	total	100.00	100.0

[a] Trace components less than 0.01 wt%.

[b] Chemical name in parenthesis indicates a minor component also present in the peak.

ment while minimizing lead addition will assume greater importance in future years as restrictions are placed on the total amount of lead allowable in motor fuels.

Determination of Total Lead Content. Total lead in gasoline can be determined by a method based on ASTM D 526 (12) or D 2547 (32). The alkyllead compound is extracted from the gasoline and converted to lead chloride by refluxing with concentrated hydrochloric acid. The acid extract is evaporated to dryness and any excess organic material present is removed by oxidation with nitric acid. The lead is then precipitated as lead chromate and either determined gravimetrically, by weighing the chromate precipitate, or volumetrically by iodometric titration.

Procedure

Assemble the apparatus shown in Figure 5. All components should be made of borosilicate glass. Measure the temperature of the gasoline sample to the nearest 0.5°C. Pipet 50 ± 0.05 ml of the gasoline into the flask through the thistle tube, and add approximately 50 ml of a heavy petroleum distillate. Add 50 ml of hydrochloric acid and reflux the mixture for 30 min. Adjust the heat carefully to maintain vigorous boiling but avoid bumping in the flask or flooding in the condenser. After refluxing, turn off the heat and allow the sample to cool. Drain the acid layer into a 400-ml beaker. Add 50 ml of water and reflux the water and gasoline–oil mixture for 5 min. Drain the water into the 400-ml beaker and repeat the water extraction. Evaporate the aqueous extract to dryness. Add 3 ml of concentrated nitric acid to the residue. Cover the beaker with a watch glass and heat to oxidize any organic material present.

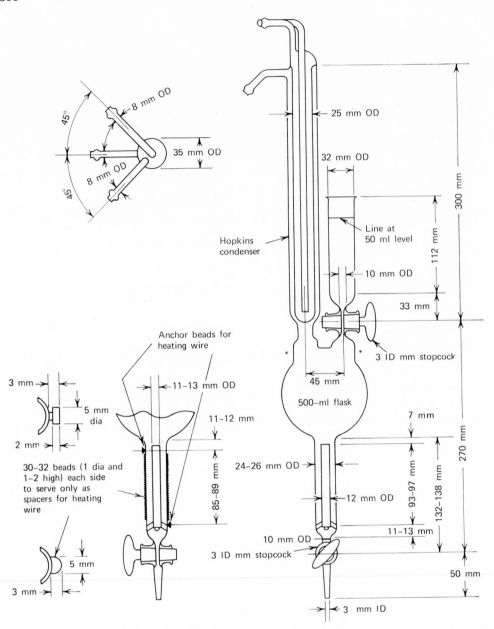

Fig. 5. Extraction apparatus for total lead determination. *Condenser and thistle funnel may be fitted to flask by means of B19 (or equivalent) ground glass joints if desired.

If the residue flashes on being heated with nitric acid, discard the sample and repeat the acid extraction with another sample of gasoline; then evaporate the extract until crystallization commences, but not to complete dryness. Prepare a potassium chlorate–nitric acid solution by dissolving 78 g of potassium chlorate in 550 ml of concentrated nitric acid. Add 10 ml of this solution, cover the beaker with a watch glass, and evaporate the mixture almost to dryness. Repeat this treatment, if necessary, to obtain a white residue. Repeat the nitric acid treatment.

Add 4 ml of 1:20 nitric acid and 25 ml of water to the white residue and heat until all of the lead salt is in solution. Cool, add 6 drops of 0.5% p-nitrophenol indicator solution, and add 1:1 ammonium hydroxide until the indicator changes color. Then add approximately 4–5 ml in excess. Add acetic acid to neutralize the ammonium hydroxide; then add 1–2 ml in excess. Dilute this solution to 300–350 ml with water. Heat to boiling on a hot plate and add 10 ml of 10% potassium dichromate solution dropwise from a pipet. Continue boiling until the precipitated lead chromate is deep orange in color, approximately 5–7 min. Allow the precipitate to settle for a minimum of 3–4 hr. Filter the sample through a filtering crucible previously dried at 110–120°C and weighed. Wash the beaker and precipitate with hot water. Dry the precipitate and crucible in an oven at 110–120°C for 1 hr. Cool in a desiccator and weigh. Calculate the concentration of lead in grams per U.S. gallon at 60°F by the following equation:

$$\text{Lead, g/U.S. gal, } 60°\text{F} = 48.41\ G\ [1 + 0.00065\ (t - 60)]$$

where G = weight of lead chromate, in g
        t = temperature of the gasoline when pipetting the sample, in °F

If a volumetric determination is preferred, proceed as follows: After filtering the lead chromate precipitate through the filtering crucible, wash the precipitate and beaker with hot water until no turbidity is produced when 1 drop of a 10% solution of lead acetate, $Pb(C_2H_3O_2).3H_2O$, is added to 1 drop of filtrate. To prepare a lead chromate solvent, dissolve 300 g of sodium chloride in 1 liter of water, then add 200 ml of concentrated hydrochloric acid to 350 ml of water, and combine the acid and salt solutions. Dissolve the lead chromate in the filter and the beaker in 50 ml of the lead chromate solvent, adding the solvent in small portions. Wash the filter and beaker several times with small portions of cold water, keeping the solution volume to 200–250 ml. Add 1 g of potassium iodide to the solution and titrate the liberated iodine immediately with 0.05 N sodium thiosulfate solution to a pale yellow color. Add 1 ml of 1% starch indicator solution and continue the titration until the blue color just disappears. Calculate the concentration of lead in terms of grams per U.S. gallon at 60°F by the following equation:

$$\text{Lead, g/U.S. gal, } 60°\text{F} = 75.71\ FV\ [1 + 0.00065\ (t - 60)]$$

where F = thiosulfate factor, equivalent grams of lead/ml of thiosulfate solution
        V = volume of thiosulfate solution used to titrate the sample, in ml
        t = temperature of the gasoline when pipetting the sample, in °F

Total lead in gasoline can also be determined instrumentally by either atomic absorption spectrophotometry or x-ray absorption spectroscopy. The methods employed are essentially standard methods for these techniques for determining lead.

Determination of Individual Alkyllead Compounds. A method has been developed based on work reported by Kolbe and co-workers in Germany (33) and Ballinger and Whitmore in the United States (34) which determines the distribution of individual alkyllead compounds in gasolines as weight percentages of the total lead. This method combines a gas chromatographic separation with atomic absorption spectrophotometry to determine the lead. In essence, the atomic absorption spectrophotometer is used as a highly specific detector for the gas chromatograph.

Any gas chromatograph capable of being temperature programmed in the range of 80–200°C may be used. The chromatographic conditions are as follows:

column	10 ft × ¹/₈ in. packed
column packing	20 wt % 1,2,3-tris(2-cyanoethoxy)propane on 60–80 mesh KOH-treated Chromosorb P
temperature of	
injection port	100°C
column	programmed from 100°C to 160°C at 12°C/min
carrier gas and flow rate	nitrogen, 40 ml/min
sample volume	approximately 3 μl

The exit of the gas chromatographic column is connected to the nebulizer inlet of the atomic absorption spectrophotometer by a short length of capillary tubing. Any available instrument capable of determining lead at the 2170 Å absorption line can be used. Operating conditions for the atomic absorption spectrophotometer are as follows:

flame	acetylene/air
absorption line	2170 Å
absorption units	0–0.2 = recorder full scale

The output signal from the spectrophotometer is recorded on a 0–1 mV potentiometric recorder. The recorder trace appears as the familiar chromatogram; see Figure 6. Peak areas are proportional to weight of lead.

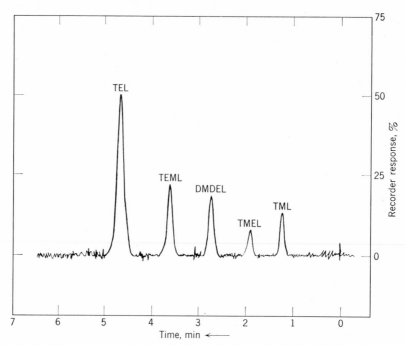

Fig. 6. Typical chromatogram obtained in determination of individual alkyllead compounds by combined gas chromatography and atomic absorption spectroscopy.

TEL   = tetraethyllead
TEML = triethylmethyllead
DMDEL = dimethyldiethyllead
TMEL = trimethylethyllead
TML   = tetramethyllead

Other Additives

Commercial gasolines, in addition to the basic hydrocarbon mixture and the alkyl-lead octane improver additives, can also contain a variety of other additives. These fall into the following categories: deposit modifiers, antioxidants, metal deactivators, antirust agents, anti-icing agents, detergents, multipurpose additives, dyes, and proprietary additives.

The action of *deposit modifiers* is to reduce or prevent spark plug fouling by engine deposits, or uncontrolled ignition due to glowing combustion chamber deposits. Compounds used for this are usually organophosphorus compounds.

Antioxidants are added to improve the oxidation stability of the gasoline. The most widely used compounds for this purpose are phenylenediamine, aminophenols, and dibutyl-*p*-cresol.

Metal deactivators are usually added along with the antioxidants. The compounds used are usually amines and prevent trace amounts of copper, picked up from piping on the engine fuel system, from accelerating gum formation by acting as catalysts in gasoline oxidation.

Because rusting and corrosion can cause problems in fuel distribution systems of refineries and fuel companies and in the fuel systems of engines, several types of hydrocarbon-soluble compounds are used as *antirust agents* in gasolines. Most of these compounds are surfactants such as fatty acid amines, sulfonates, alkyl phosphates, and amine phosphates.

Anti-icing agents, which are added to prevent ice formation in engine fuel lines and on the carburetor, are of two types: Either freezing point depressants such as alcohols or glycols, or surface active agents which prevent the formation of ice deposits. These include amides, amines, and amine or ammonium salts of organophosphates.

Detergent additives are now used almost universally to improve cleanliness in fuel jets, antipollution valves, etc, in the engine. These detergents are generally surface active materials such as amides or alkyl ammonium dialkyl phosphates.

Many refiners now use a *multipurpose additive* which combines detergent, de-icing, and anticorrosion properties in a single formulation. Most of these formulations gain their properties from their surface active ingredients, typically aminohydroxy amides.

As can be seen from the foregoing discussion, most of the minor additives employed in gasoline contain active functional groups. Analysis for these additives, therefore, is usually carried out by employing standard techniques for determining the functional groups.

Sulfur Content

Sulfur is determined by a ASTM D 1266 (10). In this procedure, a carefully measured quantity of gasoline is burned in a wick-type lamp and the products of combustion are recovered quantitatively so that the quantity of sulfur in the original gasoline can be determined. The recovered combustion products are treated with peroxide to make sure that all of the sulfur oxides are in the sulfate form. Then the sulfate is determined either by titration with a standard alkali solution or by precipitation as barium sulfate. Results are expressed as sulfur, wt %.

Gum Content

Gum can form in gasoline when hydrocarbons which are unstable either begin to oxidize, or combine with each other in a type of polymerization. Gum-forming materials eventually settle out of the gasoline as resinous deposits in the fuel system or on engine parts. These gum deposits can interfere with the operation of the carburetor or the intake valves. Fortunately, modern refining techniques minimize the gum forming potential of our gasolines. The amount of existent gum in a gasoline can be determined by the following procedure.

Procedure

Pipet a 50-ml sample of gasoline into a 250-ml beaker which has been previously weighed. Evaporate the sample to near dryness with a jet of heated air. Wash the residue with several portions of *n*-heptane. The heptane wash will remove any high-boiling additives that are present but will leave the gum content intact. Dry and reweigh the beaker, and determine the weight of the gum residue by difference. Gum is expressed in terms of mg of air jet gum/100 ml of sample.

API Gravity

An additional property which the analyst will often come across in reference to gasoline is the API gravity. API gravity is a system of expressing gravity in arbitrary numbers derived from the formula: API gravity equals 141.5 over specific gravity at 60°F minus 131.5. For example, if a petroleum product has a specific gravity of 0.70, then

$$\text{API gravity} = \frac{141.5}{0.70} - 131.5 = 70.6$$

Bibliography

GENERAL REFERENCES

1. J. C. Lane, "Gasoline and Other Motor Fuels," in A. Standen, ed., *Kirk-Othmer Encyclopedia of Chemical Technology*, Vol. 10, 2nd ed., Interscience Publishers, a division of John Wiley & Sons, Inc., New York, 1966, pp. 463–498.
2. W. A. Gruse, *Motor Fuels*, Reinhold Publishing Corp., New York, 1967.
3. *The Story of Gasoline*, Ethyl Corp., New York, 1964.
4. K. K. Papok and Ye. G. Semendio, *Motor, Jet, and Rocket Fuels*, Moskva, 1962.
5. D. A. Williams and G. Jones, *Liquid Fuels*, Oxford, Pergamon Press, Macmillan, New York, 1963.
6. *CRC Handbook*, 3rd ed., Coordinating Research Council, New York, 1946.

SPECIFIC REFERENCES

7. *Motor Gasolenes, Winter 1969–1970, Petroleum Products Survey No. 66*, Mineral Industry Surveys, U.S. Department of the Interior, Bureau of Mines, Bartelsville, Okla., 1970.
8. *ASTM D 287–67, API Gravity of Crude Petroleum and Petroleum Products (Hydrometer Method)*, American Society for Testing and Materials, Philadelphia, Pa., 1969.
9. *ASTM D 130–68, Copper Corrosion by Petroleum Products, Copper Strip Test*, American Society for Testing and Materials, Philadelphia, Pa., 1969.
10. *ASTM D 1266–69T, Sulfur in Petroleum Products (Lamp Method)*, American Society for Testing and Materials, Philadelphia, Pa., 1969.
11. *ASTM D 381–64 (1968), Existent Gum in Fuels by Jet Evaporation*, American Society for Testing and Materials, Philadelphia, Pa., 1969.
12. *ASTM D 526–66, Lead in Gasoline, Gravimetric Method*, American Society for Testing and Materials, Philadelphia, Pa., 1969.
13. *ASTM D 2699–68, Knock Characteristics of Motor Fuels by the Research Method, in ASTM Manual for Rating Motor Fuels by Research and Motor Methods*, 1969 ed., American Society for Testing and Materials, Philadelphia, Pa., 1969.

14. *ASTM D 2700–68, Knock Characteristics of Motor and Aviation-type Fuels by the Motor Method, in ASTM Manual for Rating Motor Fuels by Research and Motor Methods,* 1969 ed., American Society for Testing and Materials, Philadelphia, Pa., 1969.
15. *ASTM D 323–58 (1968), Vapor Pressure of Petroleum Products (Reid Method),* American Society for Testing and Materials, Philadelphia, Pa., 1969.
16. *ASTM D 86–67 Distillation of Petroleum Products,* American Society for Testing and Materials, Philadelphia, Pa., 1969.
17. J. C. Worman and L. E. Green, *Anal. Chem.* **37**, 1620 (1965).
18. L. E. Green, L. J. Schmauch, and J. C. Worman, *Anal. Chem.* **36**, 1512 (1964).
19. J. A. Petrocelli, T. J. Puzniak, and R. O. Clark, *Anal. Chem.* **36**, 1008 (1964).
20. F. T. Eggertsen, S. Groennings, and J. J. Holst, *Anal. Chem.* **32**, 904 (1960).
21. *ASTM Book of Standards, Part 17,* 1970, p. 1176.
22. G. Edgar, *SAE J.* **20**, 245 (1927).
23. *ASTM D 1319–69, Hydrocarbon Types in Liquid Petroleum Products by Fluorescent Indicator Adsorption,* American Society for Testing and Materials, Philadelphia, Pa., 1969.
24. *ASTM D 770–64, Specification for Isopropyl Alchol (Isopropanol),* American Society for Testing and Materials, Philadelphia, Pa., 1969.
25. R. E. Leveque, *Anal. Chem.* **14**, 1811 (1967).
26. W. N. Sanders and J. B. Maynard, *Anal. Chem.* **3**, 527 (1968).
27. D. J. McEwen, *Anal. Chem.* **38**, 1047 (1966).
28. R. D. Schwartz and D. J. Brasseaux, *Anal. Chem.* **35**, 1374 (1963).
29. R. D. Schwartz, R. G. Mathews, and D. J. Brasseaux, *J. Gas Chromatog.* **5** (5), 25 (1967).
30. L. R. Durrett, L. M. Taylor, and I. Dvoretzky, *Anal. Chem.* **35**, 687 (1963).
31. R. L. Martin and J. C. Winters, *Anal. Chem.* **35**, 1930 (1963).
32. *ASTM D 2547–67, Lead in Gasoline, Volumetric Chromate Method,* American Society for Testing and Materials, Philadelphia, Pa., 1969.
33. B. Kolbe, G. Kemmner, F. H. Schleser, and E. Wiedeking, *Z. Anal. Chem.* **22**, 166 (1966).
34. P. R. Ballinger and I. M. Whitmore, *Preprints, Division of Petroleum Chemistry, 156th Natl. Meet., Am. Chem. Soc., Atlantic City, N.J., Sept. 1968,* pp. 133–139.

DAVID L. CAMIN
Sun Oil Company

GELATIN

Gelatin is a protein derivative obtained by boiling collagen, the principal fibrous protein constituent of animal skin, bones, and white connective tissue. The word *gelatina* is of medieval Latin origin, meaning frozen, or thickened; it aptly describes the properties of this substance. The many and varied uses of gelatin depend upon its characteristic tendency to set to a firm gel in a cooled aqueous medium. Nutritionally, gelatin is not a complete protein. It lacks tryptophan, and is markedly deficient in tyrosine, methionine, and several other important amino acids. In spite of this inadequacy, however, almost three fourths of the gelatin manufactured in the United States is used as a food or in food products. Powdered and flavored, it is commonly used for the preparation of gelatin desserts; unflavored, it is widely used in recipes to impart its jelling or thickening effect to other foods. As a protective colloid, it is a stabilizer in ice cream. It is an important ingredient in jellies, marshmallows, confectioneries, and bakery products, and it is a "protein extender" in meat products. Jelling and specific nutritional properties are the bases for its use in bacteriological culture media. In the pharmaceutical industry, both hard and soft gelatin capsules form absorbable containers for unit dosages of a variety of drugs. Gelatin has been recommended as a remedy, taken orally, for brittle fingernails. Sterile gelatin solutions are administered intraveneously as a blood plasma extender and for the treatment of shock, and sterile absorbable sponges of gelatin are employed routinely in surgery for hemostasis. A significant proportion of gelatin produced is used in photographic films as the emulsion support medium for photosensitive silver halides. In wines and juices it is a clarifying agent. It is used in lithographic and printing inks, textiles, papers, adhesives, cements, light filters, matches, and numerous other products.

Properties

Available as translucent, brittle sheets, flakes or shreds, or as a coarse to fine powder, gelatin is faintly amber in color. It has a characteristic faint odor, described as boullion-like. Insoluble in cold water, it swells therein and absorbs from five to ten times its weight of water. Gelatin is soluble in hot water, in acetic acid, and in a hot mixture of glycerin and water. It is insoluble in ethanol, in chloroform, in ethyl ether, and in fixed and volatile oils (1).

Aqueous gelatin "solutions" are fluid colloidal dispersions, or sols. Upon cooling in an ice bath or refrigerator, sols containing as little as one percent of gelatin form firm gels. The sol–gel transformation is completely reversible.

"Pure gelatin" is refined collagen which has been hydrolyzed incompletely. The average chain lengths and molecular weights of the polypeptide molecules are diminished as the boiling of collagen aqueous dispersions is prolonged during the manufacturing process. Molecular weights of gelatins thus are reported to range from low values of 10,000 or 25,000 to high values reaching 250,000. Higher molecular weight gelatins produce sols of relatively high viscosity which form relatively more firm gels on cooling. The firmness of the gel which is formed is referred to commonly in terms of jelly strength, or gel strength.

Occurrence and Methods of Manufacture

The common commercial sources of gelatin, ie, sources of collagen, are porkskin, calfskin, and oxbone. Cleaned pigskins are pretreated by digesting several hours with dilute mineral acids, whereas pretreatment of bovine tissue usually involves liming in a calcium hydroxide slurry for a prolonged period. Following suitable pretreatment, the collagen is thoroughly washed with water to remove acid or alkali residues. Gelatin is obtained by hot water fractional extraction of the collagen. A detailed description of this manufacturing process is given by Marks (2).

High jelly strength and high viscosity are characteristics of gelatins of higher molecular weight. Many commercial uses of gelatin depend upon a high jelly strength; premium grades are, therefore, generally obtained from the first, lower temperature extracts of collagen. Successive fractions are obtained following prolonged hydrolysis with increasing temperature.

Commercial Grades and Specifications

Commercial grades of gelatin are classified as edible, photographic, technical, and USP. Edible and USP grades are ingested or absorbed by humans and animals. Limits are therefore placed on potentially toxic substances which are likely to be found. Table 1 summarizes specifications which have been published in the USP (1) and in the BP, the *British Pharmacopoeia* (3).

Table 1. Specifications for Gelatin

Specification	USP XVIII	1968 BP
residue on ignition (sulfated ash), % max	2	3.25
loss on drying, % max		16.0
arsenic, ppm max	0.8	2
copper, ppm max		30
lead, ppm max		5
zinc, ppm max		100
heavy metals, ppm max	50	
sulfur dioxide, ppm max	40	1000
jelly strength, g	to pass test[a]	150
microbial limits:		
total bacterial count per g, max	5000	
test for *Escherichia coli* on a 10-g sample	negative	

[a] See p. 368.

Koch first used gelatin as a solidifying agent for bacteriological culture media in 1881. Solutions of 12% gelatin, commonly used as bacterial culture media, melt between 28 and 30°C; the gelatin is selected so as to produce pH 6.8 solutions (4).

Methods of Analysis

IDENTIFICATION

Gelatin may be precipitated selectively from its sols by several reagents, thus affording means for convenient identification. Tannic acid, trinitrophenol, and chromium trioxide are precipitating reagents specified in identification tests found in the USP (1) and the BP (3).

Procedures

TEST A. To a 1% solution of gelatin add 1% trinitrophenol solution. A yellow precipitate is formed.

TEST B. To a 1% solution of gelatin add a solution consisting of 1 g of potassium dichromate in 15 ml of water, mixed with one fourth its volume of 10% (w/v) hydrochloric acid. A yellow precipitate is formed.

TEST C. To a 0.05% solution of gelatin add freshly prepared tannic acid reagent, consisting of 1 g of tannic acid dissolved in 1 ml of ethanol and diluted with water to 10 ml. Turbidity is produced.

The BP further states that gelatin is not precipitated by other acids, alum, lead acetate solution, or ferric chloride solution.

The official AOAC method for the identification of gelatin in liquids, such as milk and ice cream, involves the precipitation of extraneous protein with mercuric nitrate, filtration, and precipitation of gelatin from the filtrate with trinitrophenol (5). If curdiness is a characteristic of the sample, eg, cottage cheese, it is first macerated with water (6).

Procedures

FOR LIQUID SAMPLES. Prepare a mercuric nitrate reagent by dissolving mercury in twice its weight of concentrated nitric acid, and diluting the solution with water to 25 times its volume.

To 10 ml of sample add 10 ml of mercuric nitrate reagent. Shake, add 20 ml of water, shake again, let stand 5 min, and filter. If a substantial quantity of gelatin is present, the filtrate will be opalescent. To a portion of the filtrate in a test tube add an equal volume of a saturated aqueous solution of trinitrophenol. A yellow precipitate is produced in the presence of a considerable amount of gelatin; lesser quantities are indicated by cloudiness.

FOR COTTAGE CHEESE AND SIMILAR SAMPLES. Thoroughly mix 5 g of sample and 10 ml of water at 50–60°C, add 5 ml of mercuric nitrate reagent (see above), and shake. After standing 5 min filter through medium-fast retentive paper. To the filtrate add another 5 ml of mercuric nitrate reagent, and proceed as directed for liquids.

SEPARATION

Separation of gelatin can be effected through the judicious choice of precipitants for the components of mixtures. Examples are given below.

Gelatin is not precipitated by 4% trichloroacetic acid solution (slightly higher concentrations of the acid are needed), whereas globular proteins are totally precipitated by 3% trichloroacetic acid solution (7). The use of this reagent for the removal of unwanted proteinaceous material prior to the analysis of the sample is reported by Kashiwada and Kakimoto (8).

Procedure

To the gelatin solution add trichloroacetic acid until its concentration is 2%. Filter the resulting precipitate, neutralize the filtrate with sodium hydroxide solution, and add a 10% lead acetate solution. Filter, and precipitate the excess lead ion from the filtrate with 10% sulfuric acid. Filter again, and neutralize the filtrate with sodium hydroxide solution. Treat the filtrate with Folin-Wu reagent, which consists of one part sodium tungstate and 2.7 parts 0.66 N sulfuric acid. Assay the filtered residue by the Kjeldahl method (p. 367).

A procedure for the isolation of gelatin from meat extract and meat stocks was proposed by the Analytical Methods Committee (9). It depends on the formation of a gelatin–formaldehyde complex, which is nearly insoluble in water, by evaporating the sample solution to dryness in the presence of formalin.

Procedure

Weigh a 10-g sample and transfer it to a 250-ml beaker containing 125 ml of water. Bring to a boil while stirring, and add 0.5 ml of glacial acetic acid. Heat the mixture on a steam bath for 15–30 min, filter, and wash with hot water. Cool the filtrate and dilute it to 250 ml in a volumetric flask. Transfer a 25-ml aliquot to a porcelain evaporating dish, add 0.25 ml of 40% formaldehyde, mix, and evaporate to a thick consistency. Spread the mass over the dish surface to within 1 in. of the rim and bake it hard on a steam bath, continuing the heating for 2 hr. Extract twice with 100 ml of 1% formaldehyde solution at 40°C, allowing 1 hr for each extraction. Filter, wash with 1% formaldehyde solution at 40°C, and determine the gelatin in the residue by the Kjeldahl method (p. 367).

For the analysis of paper for gelatin, Abribat et al. (10) separated the gelatin by precipitation with 5% tannic acid from a boiled, acidified extract. Tannic acid was also used by Jaulmes et al. (11) to precipitate gelatin from sodium chloride solutions acidified to pH 3 with citric acid. Gelatins containing a minimum of residual nitrogen, following tannic acid precipitation, are selected for the clarification of wines. Fruit juice concentrates are similarly clarified with gelatin. Brunner (12) observed that juice concentrates clarified with lower grade gelatin developed a secondary turbidity within two weeks. The secondary turbidity was attributed to low molecular weight components which were found on chromatographing low grade gelatins on Sephadex columns.

Assay Methods

Assay by Hydroxyproline Content. Collagen is unique among animal tissues in that it contains significant amounts of hydroxyproline (13). This amino acid (or imino acid) is not found in noncollagenous tissues, and body fluids contain none or, at most, trace residues of it. Upon conversion of collagen (av mol wt 1,500,000) to gelatin (av mol wt 50,000–70,000) an insoluble protein residue remains. Eastoe (14) demonstrated, however, that no change in amino acid composition results from this conversion. He reports 14.1% by weight hydroxyproline in ox-hide gelatin and 13.6% by weight in Difco "Bacto" microbiological gelatin. Jackson and Cleary (15) report an average of 14.4% by weight hydroxyproline in all collagenous tissues of most mammals.

Complete hydrolysis of gelatin is essential for the quantitative recovery of hydroxyproline. McFarlane and Guest (16) found either acid or alkaline hydrolysis to be satisfactory, provided sufficient time is allowed. Acid hydrolysis, claimed by Wierbicki and Deatheridge (17) to be superior, is most commonly employed. Kadoyama (18) demonstrated, by paper chromatography and ultraviolet spectrophotometry, that no significant decomposition resulted from boiling hydroxyproline in 6 N hydrochloric acid for 20 hr. McFarlane and Guest observed that autoclaving gelatin in 3 N hydrochloric acid at 150°C and 70 psig was effective if continued for 6 hr. Leach (19) hydrolyzed gelatin in 1.5 hr by autoclaving gelatin solutions with equal volumes of concentrated hydrochloric acid in sealed tubes at 150°C and 70 psig.

Many analytical procedures for hydroxyproline are modifications of a colorimetric method developed by Neuman and Logan (20, 21). Hydroxyproline is oxidized, in the presence of cupric sulfate, by hydrogen peroxide to yield a pyrrole-2-carboxylic acid. This chromogen is coupled with p-dimethylaminobenzaldehyde (Ehrlich's reagent) to produce a red color; and Beer's law is obeyed over a broad concentration range. This method suffers somewhat from lack of reproducibility, due to difficulty in controlling the oxidation, and to incomplete elimination of the excess peroxide. If peroxide is not entirely decomposed prior to color development, there is lessening of color intensity. Addition of ferrous sulfate (22), distillation of the pyrrole chromogen into Ehrlich's reagent (23), and heating the oxidation mixture at reduced pressure (24) are some of the recommendations for satisfactory elimination of excess peroxide. Bekhor and Bavetta (25) found sodium peroxide to be a satisfactory oxidant. Various investigators have used hydrogen peroxide concentrations ranging from 1.8% (26) to 6% (27). Any concentration within this range may be used, with apparently equal success, when analyzing isolated hydrolyzates; however, concentrations of less than 4% may be inadequate in the presence of unknown hydrolyzates, which, in some instances, catalyze the decomposition of peroxide (24). Color is developed in a sulfuric acid solution in propanol and water, usually at an elevated temperature (27). Color stability has been observed to be least satisfactory in aqueous solution, and optimum in 54.5% (v/v) propanol (24). For improved color stability it has been further recommended that sulfuric acid not exceed 0.8 N in the mixed solvent, and that cooling to 20°C should follow the color development at 70°C. Proline does not interfere. Color due to tyrosine in gelatin does not exceed 1.5% (20) or 2% (27) of the total color. However, tyrosine and tryptophan from other sources may be expected to interfere significantly; their elimination is therefore necessary. Column chromatography (19) or liquid extraction (24) may be effective means of separating tyrosine. Tryptophan is destroyed during acid hydrolysis; therefore alkaline hydrolysis is not recommended if tryptophan is likely to be present.

In their review of the determination of collagen, Jackson and Cleary (28) present a modification of the colorimetric method devised by Leach (19). Snell and Snell (29) describe a method which incorporates ferrous sulfate for the elimination of excess peroxide. The method of Hutterer and Singer (24) is presented here. Alternate procedures are described for colorimetric evaluations: Method A, for direct spectrophotometric analysis, is satisfactory if tyrosine is previously separated or does not interfere significantly; however, Method B, for differential spectrophotometric analysis, may be employed in lieu of prior separation of nonspecific chromogenic materials in the hydrolyzate.

Procedures

Prepare a 4% (w/v) solution of hydrogen peroxide on the day of use by diluting 30% hydrogen peroxide with water; store in a refrigerator between analyses.

Prepare a 5% (w/v) solution of p-dimethylaminobenzaldehyde in 1-propanol. If a colorless solution does not result, purify the reagent as follows. Dissolve 100 g of p-dimethylaminobenzaldehyde in 200 ml of ethanol by heating at 70°C. Add charcoal, stir with continued heating for 5 min, and filter by suction. Add an excess of water to precipitate the p-dimethylaminobenzaldehyde, filter, and wash with water. Repeat as necessary to obtain a white product, when dried in vacuo, which gives a colorless solution in 1-propanol.

Transfer 1 ml of a solution containing 1–10 μg of hydroxyproline to a test tube with a side arm. Add 0.2 ml of 0.05 M cupric sulfate solution, 0.5 ml of 2.5 N sodium hydroxide solution, and 0.5 ml of 4% hydrogen peroxide solution. Shake, and allow the mixture to stand at room temperature for 5 min. Immerse the tube in a 70°C water bath for 10 min; after the first 5 min at 70°C apply vacuum and agitate the tube for about 30 sec to complete the removal of hydrogen peroxide. Cool in ice. Add 0.8 ml of 8.0 N sulfuric acid and 2.5 ml of 5% p-dimethylaminobenzaldehyde in 1-propanol. Place the tube in the 70°C water bath for 40 min. For the completion of the analysis, use either spectrophotometric Method A or B.

SPECTROPHOTOMETRIC METHOD A. Cool the solution to 20°C and measure the absorbance against a blank at 560 nm. If the hydrolyzate is known to contain a significant amount of tyrosine or nonspecific chromogenic material, extract the solution with chloroform or ethyl ether and measure the absorbance of the aqueous phase at 560 nm. Repeat the procedure using known concentrations of pure hydroxyproline, and plot a standard curve. Determine the hydroxyproline content of the sample by comparison with the standard curve.

SPECTROPHOTOMETRIC METHOD B. Cool the solution to 20°C and measure the absorbance against a blank at 500 nm and at 560 nm. The corrected absorbance, X, is obtained using the following formula:

$$X = A_{560} - \left\{ [A_{500} - (A_{560} \times R)] \frac{1}{(Q - R)} \right\}$$

where A = the absorbance of the sample at the wavelength indicated

$$R = \frac{\text{absorbance of hydroxyproline standard solution at 500 nm}}{\text{absorbance of hydroxyproline standard solution at 560 nm}}$$

$$Q = \frac{1}{R}$$

Use of the above equation is valid provided R is a constant ratio for each of the standard hydroxyproline solutions.

Determine the hydroxyproline in the sample by comparison with a previously prepared standard curve.

CALCULATION OF GELATIN CONTENT. Calculate the amount of gelatin in the sample by dividing the amount of hydroxyproline by 0.14, ie, by assuming 14% by weight hydroxyproline in gelatin.

Chloramine-T (sodium p-toluenesulfonchloramide) may be used for the oxidation of hydroxyproline prior to color development by coupling of the oxidation product with Ehrlich's reagent. Several modifications of methods developed by McFarlane and Guest (16) and later by Stegemann (30) are reviewed by Jackson and Cleary (31). Better precision is claimed for these procedures, one of which is presented on p. 372.

Hydroxyproline may also be determined using naphthoquinone sulfonate reagent after other amino acids in the mixture, except proline, are destroyed with nitrous acid. Both hydroxyproline and proline are determined by this method, which is presented in Vol. 8, p. 518.

Assay by Nitrogen Content. The nitrogen content of gelatin from any given source is essentially constant. Commercial gelatin, from bovine bone and hide and from pigskin, is reported to contain 18% nitrogen by weight. This value obtained by determination of nitrogen in previously isolated gelatin is commonly used in the determination of the gelatin content of samples (10–14). Chatt (32) reports on the routine analysis of jellies, without pretreatment, by the Kjeldahl method. The weight of nitrogen found, multiplied by 5.55, equals the weight of gelatin in the sample. Of course, if the source of the gelatin in a sample is known, and its average nitrogen content is determined, the factor 5.55 should be corrected appropriately.

An improved Kjeldahl method for nitrate-free samples, described here, is the official AOAC method for determining nitrogen in gelatin (33).

Procedure

Transfer a weighed sample containing approximately 1 g of gelatin to a 500–800-ml Kjeldahl digestion flask and add 0.7 g of mercuric oxide (or 0.65 g of metallic mercury), 15 g of powdered potassium sulfate, and 25 ml of concentrated sulfuric acid. If the sample weight exceeds 2.2 g, increase the amount of sulfuric acid by 10 ml for each gram of sample. Heat the contents gently, with the flask in an inclined position, until frothing ceases. If necessary, add a small amount of paraffin to reduce frothing. Boil briskly until the solution clears, and continue to boil for 2 hr longer. Cool the solution, add about 200 ml of water, and cool it to below 25°C. Add 25 ml of an 8% (w/v) solution of sodium thiosulfate pentahydrate, and mix to precipitate the mercury as the sulfide. Add a few zinc granules to prevent bumping, tilt the flask, and without agitation, add a layer of sodium hydroxide solution (25 g of pellets or enough saturated sodium hydroxide solution to make the contents strongly alkaline). Immediately connect the flask to a Kjeldahl distilling bulb on a condenser, and keeping the tip of the condenser immersed in 50.0 ml of standardized 0.3 N hydrochloric or sulfuric acid in the receiver, rotate the distilling flask to mix the contents thoroughly. Heat the mixture until all the ammonia has distilled, collecting at least 150 ml of distillate. Titrate the excess acid with 0.1 N sodium hydroxide solution.

$$\% \text{ gelatin} = \frac{[(V_a)(N_a) - (V_b)(N_b)](14.008)(5.55)(100)}{(w)(1000)}$$

where V_a = volume of standard acid, in ml
V_b = volume of standard base, in ml
N_a = normality of the standard acid
N_b = normality of the standard base
w = sample weight, in g

DETERMINATION OF PROPERTIES

The value of gelatin in commerce resides principally in its gel-forming capacity. Jelly strength is, therefore, an important index of gelatin quality. Jelly strength is expressed in Bloom grams, and represents the weight in grams that is required to depress a flat plunger, 12.7 mm in diameter, a distance of 4 mm into a gel of 6.67% (w/v) gelatin at 10°C, under the prescribed conditions, in a Bloom gelometer (34). Careful preparation of a gel is of as great importance as is the measurement itself. Excessive heat is avoided, since significant hydrolysis of the gelatin might otherwise occur. The official AOAC method for the determination of the jelly strength of powdered or sheet gelatin is described below (35).

Procedure

Pipet 105 ml of water, at 10–15°C, into a standard Bloom bottle, add 7.5 g of gelatin, and stir. Let the mixture stand 1 hr, and then bring it to 62°C in 15 min by placing it in a water bath regulated at 65°C (sample may be swirled several times to aid solution). Finally mix by inversion and let the sol stand 15 min. Place it in a water bath controlled at 10 ± 0.1°C, and let it stand for 17 hr. Determine the jelly strength in a Bloom gelometer adjusted for 4 mm depression and to deliver 200 ± 5 g shot each 5 sec, using the 0.5 in. (12.7 mm) plunger.

Gel strength, which is described in the USP (1), is not expressed in quantitative terms as is jelly strength; however, gelatin which meets the USP requirement has a Bloom rating of at least 200 Bloom grams (36).

Procedure

Transfer 1.0 g of gelatin and 99 ml of water to a 200-ml flask, allow it to stand for 15 min, place the flask in a water bath at 60°C, and swirl occasionally until solution is complete. Transfer 10 ml of the solution to a test tube having an internal diameter of 12 mm, and place the tube in an ice bath, making certain that the top of the solution is below the level of the ice and water. Place the bath containing the tube in a refrigerator, and maintain it at about 0°C for 6 hr. When the tube is removed from the bath and inverted, there should be no visible movement of the gel.

The USP procedure for gel strength may be used with other concentrations of gelatin as well. Table 2 (36) gives approximate Bloom ratings of gels, based upon the minimum concentration of gelatin needed to produce a firm gel as prescribed by the USP test.

Table 2. Bloom Ratings of Variously Treated Gelatins

Minimum % gelatin needed to produce a firm gel	Bloom rating for gelatin	
	from acid-treated precursor	from alkali-treated precursor
1.3	100	
1.2	150	100
1.1	200	150
1.0	250	200
0.9	>250	250

DETERMINATION OF IMPURITIES

Several toxic substances may be carried through the manufacturing stages from the source of the collagen, or they may be left as a residue from chemical treatment of the collagenous tissues.

Arsenic. The colorimetric determination of arsenic by the silver diethyl dithiocarbamate method is covered in detail in Vol. 8, pp. 436–438. The modifications in procedure necessary to adapt this method to gelatin (1) are given below.

Procedures

PREPARATION OF REAGENTS; PREPARATION OF STANDARD SOLUTIONS; PREPARATION OF APPARATUS. See Vol. 8, pp. 436–437.

PREPARATION OF SAMPLE. Mix 1.5 g of gelatin with 10 ml of water in the arsenic generator flask. Add 10 ml of concentrated nitric acid and 10 ml of 72% perchloric acid, mix, and heat cautiously to the production of strong fumes of perchloric acid. Cool, wash down the sides of the generator with water, add 10 ml of concentrated nitric acid, and again heat to strong fumes. Cool, wash down the sides of the generator with water, and again heat to fumes. Cool, dilute with water to 52 ml, add 3 ml of concentrated hydrochloric acid, and mix.

DETERMINATION. To the solution in the generator flask, add 2 ml of 15% potassium iodide solution and 0.5 ml of the acid stannous chloride solution, and mix. Allow the mixture to stand for 30 min at room temperature, and proceed as directed in Vol. 8, pp. 437–438.

Residue on Ignition. The *Food Chemicals Codex* procedure for residue on ignition (49), similar to the USP procedure, is given in Vol. 8, p. 442. This procedure is conducted on a 5.0 g sample of gelatin, but without the use of sulfuric acid. Reserve the residue for testing for heavy metals.

Heavy Metals. In the USP heavy metals test (1), the sample solution is treated with hydrogen sulfide, and visual comparison is made with a standard solution of lead nitrate similarly treated with hydrogen sulfide.

Procedure

Prepare the standard lead stock solution as follows. Dissolve 159.8 mg of lead nitrate in 100 ml of water containing 1 ml of concentrated nitric acid, and dilute with water to 1 liter. Prepare and store this stock solution in glass containers.

Prepare the standard lead solution as follows. Pipet 10 ml of standard lead stock solution into a 100-ml volumetric flask and dilute to volume with water. Pipet 2.5 ml of this solution into a 50-ml Nessler tube, add water to make 25 ml, and adjust the pH to between 3 and 4 using 6% (v/v) acetic acid or 40% (v/v) ammonium hydroxide solution. Dilute to 40 ml with water, and mix.

Prepare the sample solution as follows. To the residue from the test for residue on ignition (from a 5.0 g sample of gelatin) add 2 ml of concentrated hydrochloric acid and 0.5 ml of concentrated nitric acid, and evaporate to dryness on a steam bath. Add 1 ml of N hydrochloric acid and 15 ml of water, warm for a few minutes, and filter, collecting the filtrate in a 50-ml volumetric flask. Wash the residue, using the washings to dilute the filtrate to volume. Pipet 5 ml of this solution into a 50-ml Nessler tube, add water to make 25 ml, and adjust the pH to between 3 and 4, as for the standard lead solution. Dilute to 40 ml with water, and mix.

To each of the solutions contained in the Nessler tubes add 10 ml of freshly saturated hydrogen sulfide solution, mix, allow to stand for 5 min, and view downward over a white surface. The color of the sample solution should be no darker than that of the standard lead solution.

Copper.   Analytical methods capable of detecting a few parts per million of copper are necessary for the evaluation of photographic gelatin. Traces of copper and other common metallic impurities have a profound effect on photographic emulsions.

A relatively simple polarographic procedure is described by Michel and Maron (37). The gelatin sample is ignited to destroy the organic matter; copper, lead, and zinc are subsequently determined quickly and accurately. See also Vol. 10, p. 616.

Colorimetric methods are commonly employed for metals in gelatin. Vinogradova et al. found sodium diethyldithiocarbamate useful for the colorimetric determination of small amounts of copper in the absence of iron(III), nickel, cobalt, and bismuth (38). Saulnier describes a technique whereby analyses for copper, zinc, and lead are performed without prior destruction of gelatin (39). The metal ions, retained on a cation exchange resin, are subsequently eluted with hydrochloric acid and the metals are determined, after separation, using dithizone.

Russell and Hart (40) conducted a systematic evaluation of several complexing agents which are frequently used for the colorimetric determination of copper. They found 2,2′-biquinoline to offer distinct advantages in specificity, sensitivity, chemical stability, and color stability of the copper complex when compared with dithizone, sodium diethyl dithiocarbamate, zinc dibenzyldithiocarbamate, biscyclohexanone oxalyldihydrazone, and neocuproine. More sensitive than most of the other complexing agents, 2,2′-biquinoline is the most selective for copper. Only the ferric ion was observed to interfere in complexation with 2,2′-biquinoline and neocuproine; and the interference due to ferric ion is easily eliminated by adding tartaric acid to the solution. Absorbances of the copper complex with 2,2′-biquinoline are measured in isoamyl alcohol. The extraction of the complex from its aqueous solution into the alcohol is facilitated by a large partition coefficient. Temperature control is desirable, however, so as to minimize the solubility of isoamyl alcohol in water.

Procedure

Since the complexing reagent is sensitive to oxidizing agents that may occur in the alcohol, the following treatment of isoamyl alcohol may be necessary. Shake 800 ml of isoamyl alcohol with 100 ml of 10% sodium metabisulfite solution. Separate the layers and dry the alcohol overnight in contact with anhydrous magnesium sulfate. Filter and distill, collecting the fraction which boils between 128 and 132°C. Store in an amber bottle.

Prepare a 0.02% (w/v) solution of 2,2′-biquinoline in isoamyl alcohol, and store in an amber bottle. The solution may be used for several months.

Heat a 2-g sample of gelatin and 10 ml of concentrated nitric acid in a 100-ml conical flask on a hot plate, until vigorous evolution of brown fumes is observed. Remove the flask from the hot plate, add 2 ml of concentrated sulfuric acid, and resume heating until brown fumes are no longer visible and charring begins. Add 4 ml of 72% perchloric acid, heat until the liquid is colorless or pale yellow, and then maintain the same temperature for an additional 3 or 4 hr to ensure elimination of all excess perchloric acid. Cool, dilute the solution with 10 ml of water, boil for a few minutes, and finally cool the solution. Add 2 ml of 50% tartaric acid solution and 2 ml of 15% hydroxylamine hydrochloride solution, adjust the pH to between 4 and 7 with 30% sodium hydroxide solution, and dilute with water to about 50 ml. Adjust the solution to $25 \pm 0.5°C$ in a thermostatically controlled water bath and transfer it to a separatory funnel. Pipet 10 ml of 2,2'-biquinoline reagent (also at $25 \pm 0.5°C$) into the separatory funnel and shake the mixture for 3 min. Separate the alcohol layer and measure its absorbance at about 535 nm. Determine the copper content of the gelatin from a previously constructed standard curve.

Lead and Iron. The *Food Chemicals Codex* procedures for lead (50) and iron (51), given in Vol. 8, pp. 440–441, are used for gelatin. In addition, the determination of iron in gelatin as the ferrous complex with 2,2'-bipyridyl is reported by Benes (41).

Sulfur Dioxide. Sulfur dioxide may be present as a preservative in gelatin. A polarographic method for the determination of sulfur dioxide is reported by Stevan (42). In the USP method, described here, sulfur dioxide is distilled from the sample, oxidized to sulfate, and determined gravimetrically (1).

Procedure

Dissolve 20 g of gelatin in 150 ml of hot water in a long-necked round-bottom flask. Add 5 ml of 85% phosphoric acid and 1 g of sodium bicarbonate, and immediately connect the flask to a condenser. Distill, collecting 50 ml of distillate under the surface of 50 ml of 0.1 N iodine solution. Acidify the distillate with a few drops of concentrated hydrochloric acid, add 2 ml of 12% barium chloride solution, and heat the mixture on a steam bath until the liquid is nearly colorless. Collect the precipitate on ashless filter paper and wash it with 25 ml of hot water. Ignite at 700°C to constant weight, and calculate the sulfur dioxide, in ppm, by the formula:

$$\text{Sulfur dioxide, ppm} = \frac{p(64.06)(1000)}{w(233.4)}$$

where p = weight of barium sulfate, in mg
w = weight of gelatin sample, in g

Thiosulfate. Because of its sensitizing effect on silver halides, thiosulfate is important as a contaminant in photographic gelatins. A direct polarographic analysis of a trypsin hydrolyzate of gelatin is reported by Janus and Nellist (43) for the determination of thiosulfate. Bossignana et al. (44) describe an iodimetric method for thiosulfate in photographic gelatins. Thiosulfate is separated by ion exchange chromatography, formaldehyde is added to suppress sulfite, the solution is acidified with acetic acid, and it is titrated with iodine. In a comparison of methods, Timson et al. (45) found polarography to be more specific and precise; iodimetric determinations following ion exchange chromatography gave consistently low results.

The method given here is the colorimetric determination of Warburton and Przybylowics (46). Thiosulfate is reduced to sulfide by sodium borohydride in an alkaline medium; the excess borohydride is destroyed, and the sulfide reacts with *p*-dimethylaminoaniline to form methylene blue, which is subsequently determined colorimetrically.

Procedure

Combine 1 g of gelatin and 49 ml of water in a 100-ml beaker. Allow the gelatin to swell at room temperature and heat gently to dissolve it. Add 2 g of Amberlite IR-120-H cation exchange resin and stir the mixture rapidly for 15 min. Allow the resin to settle and transfer 5-ml aliquots of the supernatant liquid to each of two 3-dram disposable plastic vials with tightly fitting polyethylene caps—one for the sample and the other for a blank. To the blank vial add 0.50 ml of acetone, and 0.25 ml of each of the following reagents: (a) 0.2 *N* sodium hydroxide solution; (b) 3% ferric sulfate in 15% sulfuric acid; (c) 1% *p*-dimethylaminoaniline in 15% sulfuric acid, decolorized with Florosil. Cap the vial, and mix.

To the sample vial add 0.25 ml of a freshly prepared 1.5% (w/v) sodium borohydride in 0.2 *N* sodium hydroxide solution. Swirl to mix. Add 0.50 ml of acetone, swirl, and wait exactly 15 sec. As rapidly as possible, add 0.25 ml each of the iron and amine reagents, cap the vial tightly, and shake it vigorously until color development is complete. Vent carefully, cap the vial securely, and shake a second time to dispel supersaturated gas. Measure the absorbance at 667 nm against the blank, and convert to ppm sodium thiosulfate by reference to a standard calibration curve.

DETERMINATION IN MIXTURES

It is convenient to determine gelatin in mixtures by analyzing for hydroxyproline. Gelatin may be expected to be the only hydroxyproline-containing protein in tissue, blood, urine, or other biological samples. The many modifications of the Neuman and Logan method, including the procedure of Hutterer and Singer (see pp. 365–367), are satisfactory for the determination of gelatin in mixtures. Except for tyrosine, other amino acids do not interfere.

The reaction of Ehrlich's reagent with hydroxyproline following oxidation of the sample with chloramine-T rather than hydrogen peroxide (30), was found to be affected less by nonspecific chromogens from other sources such as tyrosine, tryptophane, etc. A modification of this method, reported by Woessner (47), is suggested for analyzing mixtures, particularly those in which hydroxyproline concentrations are small. Two methods of determination are described: Method I for mixtures in which the hydroxyproline concentration exceeds 2%, and Method II for those of lower hydroxyproline content.

Procedure

REAGENTS. Prepare a buffer solution as follows. Combine 50 g of citric acid monohydrate, 12 ml of glacial acetic acid, 120 g of sodium acetate trihydrate, and 34 g of sodium hydroxide with sufficient water to provide 1 liter of solution. Adjust the pH to 6.0 and store in a refrigerator under toluene.

Prepare 0.05 *M* chloramine-T reagent as follows. Dissolve 1.41 g of chloramine-T (sodium *p*-toluenesulfonchloramide) in 20 ml of water. Add 30 ml of methyl Cellosolve and 50 ml of buffer solution, mix, and store in a glass-stoppered bottle. Use on the day of preparation.

Prepare 3.15 *M* perchloric acid as follows. Add 27 ml of 70% perchloric acid to 50 ml of water in a 100-ml volumetric flask, mix, and dilute to volume.

Prepare 20% *p*-dimethylaminobenzaldehyde (Ehrlich's reagent) as follows. Just before it is to be used, mix 20 g of *p*-dimethylaminobenzaldehyde with enough methyl Cellosolve to make 100 ml. Warming in a 60°C water bath may be necessary to solubilize.

Prepare standard solutions as follows. Dissolve 25 mg of vacuum-dried L-hydroxyproline in 0.001 *N* hydrochloric acid, and dilute to 250 ml with the 0.001 *N* acid. Dilute with water to provide solutions containing 0.5–2.5 ppm of hydroxyproline. Use on the day of preparation.

DETERMINATION. Prepare sample solutions as follows. Mix a small weighed sample with sufficient hydrochloric acid to produce 6 *N* acid, seal in a small Pyrex tube, and hydrolyze at 130°C for 3 hr. Wash the hydrolyzate from the opened tube into a volumetric flask with water, add several drops of 0.02% methyl red indicator, and mix. Add a volume of 2.5 *N* sodium hydroxide solution calculated to just neutralize the solution, adjust to pH 6–7 (slightly yellow color) with hydrochloric acid or sodium hydroxide solution, and dilute to volume with water.

METHOD I. Pipet 2 ml of the sample solution, previously adjusted to contain 1–2.5 ppm hydroxyproline, into a 16 × 150 mm test tube. (The concentration of sodium chloride resulting from pH adjustment must not exceed 0.4 *M*, or color development may be inhibited.) Add 1.0 ml of 0.05 *M* chloramine-T reagent, mix, and allow to stand 20 min at room temperature. Add 1.0 ml of 3.15 *M* perchloric acid to destroy excess chloramine-T, mix, and allow to stand 5 min. Add 1.0 ml of 20% *p*-dimethylaminobenzaldehyde solution, mix thoroughly, and place the tube in a 60°C water bath for 20 min. Cool in tap water for 5 min, and within 1 hr measure the absorbance at 557 nm. Determine the hydroxyproline content directly from a calibrated standard curve obtained by similar treatment of 2-ml volumes of standard solutions of 0.5–2.5 ppm of hydroxyproline. Use this value to calculate the gelatin content (see p. 363).

METHOD II. The total amino acid content in the 2-ml portion taken should not exceed 1.5 mg; higher concentrations depress chromogen formation. Proceed as directed under Method I, including the color development at 60°C for 20 min. Cool in tap water for 5 min, and remove the tube from the bath. Add 10 ml of benzene, stopper the tube, shake briskly for about 5 sec, and remove the major portion of benzene by suction. Repeat the extraction with benzene, and separate the phases by centrifuging at slow speed. Carefully insert a pipet below the interface, and transfer 3.5 ml of aqueous solution to a cuvet. Measure the absorbance within 10 min after extraction was started; gradual fading may be expected beyond this time. Immediately after reading the absorbance, add 0.2 ml of 30% hydrogen peroxide, mix, and exactly 5 min thereafter, determine the blank absorbance. Subtract the blank absorbance from the initial reading and determine the hydroxyproline content directly from a calibrated standard curve obtained by similar treatment of 2.0-ml volumes of standard solutions containing 0.5–2.5 ppm of hydroxyproline. Use this value to calculate the gelatin content (see p. 363). A small empirical correction is recommended when using Method II, to correct for the slight fading (about 12%) of interfering chromogens from other amino acids:

$$\text{Corrected absorbance} = (A - B) - 0.12(B - C)$$

where A = absorbance of sample after extraction with benzene
      B = absorbance of sample after treatment with peroxide
      C = absorbance of water blank after treatment with peroxide

Woessner recommends recrystallizing *p*-dimethylaminobenzaldehyde if the reagent solution is colored deep blue or purple. In another modification, however,

Bergman and Loxley (48) found this precaution to be unnecessary. Increased sensitivity and the added convenience of eliminating careful temperature control characterize the alternate procedures they described. One method is a rapid determination; the other involves overnight color development.

Bibliography

1. *The Pharmacopeia of the United States*, XVIII, Mack Publishing Co., Easton, Pa., 1970, p. 278.
2. E. M. Marks, "Gelatin," in A. Standen, ed., *Kirk-Othmer Encyclopedia of Chemical Technology*, Vol. 10, 2nd ed., Interscience Publishers, a division of John Wiley & Sons, Inc., New York, 1963, pp. 499–509.
3. *The British Pharmacopeia*, General Medical Council, The Pharmaceutical Press, London, 1968, pp. 435–436.
4. *Difco Manual*, 9th ed., Difco Laboratories, Inc., Detroit, Mich., 1953, pp. 290–291.
5. *Official Methods of Analysis*, 11th ed., The Association of Official Analytical Chemists, Washington, D.C., 1970, p. 257.
6. *Ibid.*, p. 276.
7. J. L. Jacobs, *J. Am. Leather Chem. Assoc.* **44,** 722–737 (1949); *Chem. Abstr.* **44,** 3733e (1950).
8. K. Kashiwada and D. Kakimoto, *Bull. Japan. Soc. Sci. Fisheries*, **18,** 203–207 (1952); *Chem. Abstr.* **48,** 1897d (1954).
9. Analytical Methods Committee, *Analyst* **78,** 134–135 (1953).
10. M. Abribat, J. Pouradier, J. David, and, A. M. Venet, *Chim. Anal.* **33,** 245–247 (1951); *Chem. Abstr.* **45,** 9861i (1951).
11. P. Jaulmes, S. Brun, and M. Coupet, *Trav. Soc. Pharm. Montpellier* **29**(1), 21–26 (1969); *Chem. Abstr.* **71,** 100362d (1969).
12. H. Brunner, *Schweiz. Z. Obst-Weinbau* **105**(12), 277–284 (1969); *Chem. Abstr.* **71,** 69425a (1969).
13. W. F. Harrington and P. H. Von Hippel, "Structure of Collagen and Gelatin," in C. B. Anfinsen, M. L. Anson, K. Bailey, and J. T. Edsall, eds., *Advances in Protein Chemistry*, Vol. 16, Academic Press, Inc., New York, 1961, p. 31.
14. J. E. Eastoe, *Biochem. J.* **61,** 589 (1955).
15. D. S. Jackson and E. G. Cleary, "The Determination of Collagen and Elastin," in D. Glick, ed., *Methods of Biochemical Analysis*, Vol. 15, Interscience Publishers, a division of John Wiley & Sons, Inc., New York, 1967, p. 31.
16. W. D. McFarlane and G. H. Guest, *Can. J. Research* **17**[B], 139–142 (1939).
17. E. Wierbicki and R. E. Deatherage, *J. Agr. Food Chem.* **2,** 878 (1954); *Chem. Abstr.* **48,** 13120c (1954).
18. H. Kadoyama, *Nagasaki Igakkai Zasshi* **33,** 595 (1958); *Chem. Abstr.* **52,** 15633b (1958).
19. A. A. Leach, *Anal. Biochem.* **2,** 529–534 (1961).
20. R. E. Neuman and M. A. Logan, *J. Biol. Chem.* **184,** 299–306 (1950).
21. *Ibid.*, pp. 549–556.
22. C. J. Martin and A. E. Axelrod, *Proc. Soc. Exptl. Biol.* **83,** 461 (1953); *Chem. Abstr.* **47,** 11296i (1953).
23. F. Serafini-Cessi and C. Cessi, *Anal. Biochem.* **8**(4), 527 (1964).
24. F. Hutterer and E. J. Singer, *Anal. Chem.* **32,** 556–558 (1960).
25. I. J. Bekhor and L. A. Bavetta, *Anal. Chem.* **33,** 1807 (1961).
26. R. M. Lollar, *J. Am. Leather Chem. Assoc.* **53,** 2 (1958); *Chem. Abstr.* **52,** 19201e (1958).
27. D. S. Miyada and A. L. Tappel, *Anal. Chem.* **28,** 909–910 (1956).
28. Ref. 15, pp. 36–38.
29. F. D. Snell and C. T. Snell, *Colorimetric Methods of Analysis*, Vol. IV-A, D. Van Nostrand Co., Inc., Princeton, N.J., 1967, pp. 299–303.
30. H. Stegemann, *Hoppe-Seylers Z. Physiol. Chem.* **311,** 41 (1958); *Chem. Abstr.* **52,** 15345b (1958).
31. Ref. 15, pp. 39–45.
32. E. M. Chatt, *Analyst* **77,** 335–340 (1952).
33. Ref. 5, p. 16.
34. "Standard Methods (Revised) for Determining Viscosity and Jelly Strength of Glue," *Ind. Eng. Chem., Anal. Ed.* **2,** 348 (1930).
35. Ref. 5, p. 390.

36. A. Osol and G. E. Farrar, Jr., eds., *The United States Dispensatory*, 25th ed., J. B. Lippincott Co., Philadelphia, Pa., 1955, p. 599.
37. G. Michel and N. Maron, *Anal. Chim. Acta* **4**, 542–550 (1950).
38. A. D. Vinogradova, M. E. Koval'skaya, and V. I. Sheberstov, *Zh. Nauchu. i Prikl. Fotogr. i Kinematogr.* **6**, 450–452 (1961); *Chem. Abstr.* **58**, 12107b (1963).
39. J. Saulnier, *Sci. Ind. Phot.* **35**, (1), 1–7 (1964); *Chem. Abstr.* **61**, 7690a (1964).
40. G. Russell and P. J. Hart, *Analyst* **83**, 202–207 (1958).
41. J. Benes, *Chem. Prumysl* **8**, 84–85 (1958); *Chem. Abstr.* **52**, 13531e (1958).
42. V. Stevan, *Chem. Prumysl* **12**, 652–655 (1962); *Chem. Abstr.* **58**, 11957g (1963).
43. J. W. Janus and D. R. Nellist, *J. Photogr. Sci.* **15** (6), 270–276 (1967).
44. P. Bassignana, G. B. Tagliafico, L. Valbusa, and F. Pocchiari, *J. Photogr. Sci.* **9**, 372–374 (1961).
45. W. J. Timson, P. O. Kliem, A. E. Steigemann, and W. D. Kelly, Jr., *Phot. Sci. Eng.* **10** (5), 270–277 (1966); *Chem. Abstr.* **65**, 16297f (1966).
46. C. D. Warburton and E. P. Przybylowics, *J. Photogr. Sci.* **15** (5), 201–206 (1967).
47. J. F. Woessner, *Arch. Biochem. Biophys.* **93**, 440–447 (1961).
48. I. Bergman and R. Loxley, *Anal. Chem.* **35**, 1961–1965 (1963).
49. *Food Chemicals Codex*, National Academy of Sciences, National Research Council, Washington, D. C., 1966, p. 786.
50. *Ibid.*, pp. 772–774.
51. *Ibid.*, p. 707.

C. H. Barnstein
National Formulary

GERMANIUM

Germanium... 375
Germanium alloys.. 398
Germanium compounds... 399
Bibliography... 401

GERMANIUM

Germanium, Ge, is of considerable historical interest because its existence was predicted by Mendeleev in 1871 and confirmed by Winkler fifteen years later. Its properties and those of its compounds corresponded closely to those predicted by Mendeleev for his "eka-silicon." It thus played an important part in the early history and final confirmation and general acceptance of the periodic law.

Germanium is in the fourth group of the periodic table, between silicon, a non-metal with some metallic properties, and tin, a metal which nevertheless has a non-metallic allotrope. It is classified as a semimetal, and its semiconducting properties are the principal basis for its utility. See the general references for additional information (1–8).

The abundance of germanium in the lithosphere is variously estimated at between 1 and 10 ppm (1–10 g/metric ton). Thus it is only a little less abundant than boron or arsenic, and more so than antimony, zinc, or selenium. Its commercial rarity and high price (GeO_2 about \$170/kg) (9) are due not to inherent scarcity in the earth's crust, but to its wide distribution in trace amounts and the lack of any primary sources; it is not concentrated in ores of which it forms a major constituent, and, with rare exceptions, is always recovered as a by-product from the winning of other metals, or occasionally from coal residues.

Few minerals contain appreciable quantities of germanium, and even these are seldom found in amounts sufficient to justify direct recovery from them, since they are usually associated with other ores. Principal germanium minerals are shown in Table 1 (1).

Table 1. Principal Germanium-Bearing Minerals

Mineral	Type	% Ge[a]	Country of origin
argyrodite	Ag, Ge sulfide	5–7	Germany
canfieldite	As, Sn, Ge sulfide	1.8	Bolivia
enargite	Cu, As sulfide	1.0	western U.S.
germanite	Cu, Fe, Zn, As, Ge sulfide	5–10	Southwest Africa
renierite	Cu, Fe, Ge, As sulfide	5–7	Congo Republic, Southwest Africa

[a] Approximate values.

Principal U.S. production of germanium is derived from smelter residues resulting from the retorting and refining of zinc concentrates from the tri-state area of Missouri, Oklahoma, and Kansas, and from fluorspar–zinc–lead ores from the Kentucky–Illinois area. Eagle-Picher Industries, Inc., operates a refinery in Oklahoma. As shown in Table 2 (1), Africa is the other main source of germanium-containing ores, which are refined in Belgium, Luxembourg, West Germany, Italy, Japan, and the United Kingdom (10).

Table 2. Principal Ores from which Germanium Is Produced

Ore	Location	% germanium	Note
sphalerite	U.S.: Missouri, Oklahoma and Kansas	0.005–0.015	Ge present as impurity
zinc sulfide	U.S.: Mississippi Valley	0.001–0.01	Ge present as impurity
Pb–Zn–Cu ores	Southwest Africa: Tsumeb	0.015	Ge present as germanite and renierite
Cu–Zn–sulfides	Congo Republic: Katanga	0.01	Ge present as renierite

Many coals contain traces of germanium, which is concentrated when the coal is burned and can be recovered from fly ash, flue dusts, and similar residues. Recovery from this source has been practiced in England, and if the volume of published literature is any criterion, this is an important source of germanium in the Soviet Union.

With the exception of occasional finds of workable germanite deposits, primary germanium is always recovered as a by-product of the work-up of zinc, copper–lead–zinc, or fluorspar–lead–zinc ores, or from fly ash, flue dust, or other residues from the burning of coal. The manufacture of semiconductor devices generates scrap, which is refined on a toll basis. Because of the high economic value of the metal, the germanium content of such scrap must be determined accurately.

Details of the process depend on the source; References 2 and 8 may be consulted for details. The final steps are usually the volatilization of germanium as the tetrachloride, which is purified by repeated distillation and hydrolyzed by water to yield germanium dioxide. This is reduced to the metal by heating to 650°C in a hydrogen atmosphere, and the metal powder is melted at 1100°C in an inert atmosphere to form ingots. For electronic applications the metal is further purified by zone refining.

Germanium owes almost all of its commercial importance to its semiconducting properties; the first crystal diodes and transistors were developed using germanium.

Early power rectifiers were likewise based on germanium elements, but silicon has almost entirely displaced it in this application. Although silicon is displacing germanium in transistors also, and has done so in the more sophisticated branches of electronics, germanium appears to be holding its own in the entertainment (TV, hi-fi, etc) field, and shipments of germanium have been fairly steady (10). Significant quantities of gallium-doped germanium are used in the production of radiation detectors.

Glasses in which germanium dioxide replaces silica have a high index of refraction and high dispersion, and are used in some specialized optical equipment. Some organo-germanium compounds have been investigated as catalysts for polyester resins; this use, though not significant in the United States, is commercial in Europe and Japan (10).

Germanium is transparent to infrared radiation, leading to its use for radiation detectors; these uses are classified. Lithium-drifted germanium is used for detecting γ-rays (11).

Germanium–gold alloys have been investigated for dental applications, and the germanium–gold eutectic alloy has some application as a solder.

Properties

The properties of germanium are intermediate between those of silicon and tin. It is a semiconductor, defined (briefly and somewhat imprecisely) as a material whose electrical conductivity is intermediate between that of a metal (10^{-6} Ω-cm resistivity) and that of an insulator (over 10^{10} Ω-cm resistivity) (12). Its principal physical constants and properties are listed in Table 3 (1).

Table 3. Properties of Germanium

atomic number	32
atomic weight	72.59
isotopes and abundance, %	
mass no. 70	20.4
mass no. 72	27.4
mass no. 73	7.8
mass no. 74	36.6
mass no. 76	7.8
color	silvery
crystal structure	octahedral
index of refraction	4.068–4.143
hardness, Mohs scale	6.25
ductility	frangible
density at 25°C, g/cm³	5.32
specific volume at 25°C	0.188
melting point, °C	936
boiling point, °C	2700 (approx)
latent heat of fusion, g-cal/g	111.5
latent heat of vaporization, g-cal/gal	1200
specific heat at 25°C, cal/g	0.086
volume resistivity at 25°C, Ω-cm	60
electrochemical equivalent, Ge^{4+}, mg/coulomb	0.1881
electrode potential, Ge^{4+} ($H_2 = 0.0$ V)	-0.15 (estd)
atomic radius, nm	0.122
atomic volume, ml/mol	13.2

Germanium is relatively resistant to attack by most acid and alkali solutions at room temperature; at higher temperatures it is dissolved slowly by sulfuric acid, and more rapidly by nitric acid and aqua regia. Molten caustic alkalis dissolve it readily; it also dissolves in sodium or potassium hydroxide solutions in the presence of hydrogen peroxide. Halogens react with it readily to form the tetrahalides.

Germanium forms two series of compounds, in which its valence is 2+ and 4+, the latter being much more stable. A titrimetric procedure depends on this property; the germanium is reduced to the bivalent state and titrated with an oxidant.

The regular progression of properties is noted in descending Group IV of the periodic table. Silicon is almost universally tetravalent and nonmetallic; germanium exhibits some metallic behavior and forms some relatively unstable bivalent compounds; tin is metallic, although it has a nonmetallic allotrope, and its bi- and tetravalent compounds are of almost equal stability; finally, lead is entirely metallic and is bivalent in practically all its stable compounds except the organometallics. It may also be noted that many of the bivalent compounds in this group are ionic in character, whereas most of the tetravalent compounds are covalent; thus the solution chemistry of tetravalent germanium is concerned principally with complex, coordinate, and heteropoly anions, rather than with simple salts.

All members of Group IV readily form covalent bonds with carbon, and hence exhibit an extensive organometallic chemistry; but although the silanes, silicones, organotins, and organoleads have established commercial uses, the high price of germanium has limited interest in organogermanium compounds, mainly to academic studies; there is much literature on organogermanium chemistry.

Specifications

There appear to be no chemical specifications for germanium metal or germanium dioxide (9). ASTM specifications rely on performance tests; in ASTM Recommended Practice F 27 (13), the quality of germanium dioxide is judged by the properties of the germanium metal made from it by hydrogen reduction and zone refining. A "super purity grade" germanium, with only about 1 part per trillion ($1/10^{12}$; 5×10^{10} atoms/cm^3) of impurity, is being marketed at an announced price of \$20/kg (14).

Many acceptance tests are purely empirical; the germanium metal is satisfactory if a device made from it performs correctly (9). A number of ASTM specifications prescribe the electrical testing of semiconductor materials such as germanium (15–17).

Methods of Analysis

From a practical standpoint, analytical methods are relevant to the following types of materials: (1) germanium-bearing ores, containing 0.001–2% Ge; (2) concentrates and in-process streams, containing up to 25% Ge; (3) scrap and residues from processing, 1% to fairly pure Ge; (4) germanium dioxide; (5) germanium metal; (6) organogermanium compounds, with 5–20% Ge content. Although methods are available for all of these types of samples, the problem of analyzing semiconductor grade germanium presents the analytical chemist with a challenge that he has still not fully met. Impurity levels are often in the parts per billion range, sometimes less than 1 ppb; and, as stated by Kane and Larrabee (3), in semiconductor materials it is conventional to refer all impurity concentrations to atoms/cm^3 rather than the weight–weight basis

familiar to chemists.   Concentration in ppb and atoms/cm³ are related by the following equation:

$$1 \text{ ppb} = \frac{M \times 10^9}{(A)(d)} \text{ atoms/cm}^3$$

where M = atomic weight of impurity
   A = Avogadro's number
   d = density of bulk material

Since $A = 6 \times 10^{23}$ and for germanium, $d = 5.32$, 1 ppb impurity is equal to
$(0.313 \times 10^{-15} M)$ atoms/cm³.

Because standard analytical techniques, even the most refined instrumental ones,
are at best only marginally sensitive enough to provide useful information concerning
the quality of semiconductor grade germanium, specifications for the metal are usually
expressed in terms of electrical properties rather than chemical purity.   Methods requiring access to nuclear reactors, such as neutron activation analysis, are also recommended, but these are beyond the reach of most laboratories.

Germanium ores and inorganic materials containing germanium are put into
solution by digestion with sulfuric acid, with or without nitric acid as oxidant.   If
much silica is present, hydrofluoric acid may be added.   If presence of chlorides is
known or suspected, precautions must be taken to prevent loss of germanium by
volatilization of the tetrachloride; alkali fusion may be used.

Germanium metal and alloys may be dissolved in nitric–sulfuric acid mixtures or
by fusion with caustic alkalis or sodium carbonate.   Because germanium metal may
attack platinum, use of nickel crucibles is preferred.

The volatility of germanium tetrachloride is a most useful property for separating
germanium from most other elements, either in preparation for final determination or to
remove it so that minor impurities can be determined.

Once the sample is in solution, most analytical methods rely on the distillation of
germanium tetrachloride or its extraction by organic solvents; final determination may
be colorimetric, volumetric, or gravimetric, although the first named appears the most
popular.   A useful review of standard methods up to 1953, just about the time its
semiconducting properties were becoming important, was presented by Krause and
Johnson (4).

IDENTIFICATION

Emission spectrography is the most useful method for the indentification of germanium in unknown samples.   Since the method is the same for both detection and determination, detailed procedure is given later (p. 385).

Dressel (18) has described a rough but useful field test.   The procedure is given
below.

Procedure

Dissolve a thimbleful of powdered hematein (6a,7-dihydro-3,4,6a,10-tetra-
hydroxybenz[b]-indeno[1,2-d]pyran-9(6H)-one) in 5 ml of 6 N sulfuric acid, and
add this solution slowly to 95 ml of ethanol.

Grind the sample to pass 200 mesh.   Put into solution by appropriate method:
for coal ash, flue dusts, and the like, add one spoonful to a test tube containing 10–15

ml of 6 N sulfuric acid, heat to boiling, cool, and filter. For sulfide minerals and other less soluble materials, fuse with potassium pyrosulfate, leach, and filter.

Transfer the clear filtrate to a tapered centrifuge tube. Add about 6 drops of the hematein reagent and 15 drops of carbon tetrachloride to the solution in the centrifuge tube; insert a rubber stopper, shake vigorously for 15–30 sec, and let stand. A purple layer in the bottom of the tube indicates the presence of germanium.

Molybdenum and antimony give purple complexes with hematein but are not extracted with carbon tetrachloride. Phenylfluorone can be used instead of hematein; the resulting test is more sensitive but less selective; tin, indium, antimony, and titanium give complexes of similar color.

Separation

Two methods, distillation and solvent extraction, are used almost exclusively for the analytical separation of germanium from other elements present in solution (5). Other methods, such as ion exchange and coprecipitation, have been investigated and occasionally recommended, but are much less important because of their lack of selectivity.

Extraction

From solutions in hydrochloric acid, 8 N or higher in strength, germanium is extracted to the extent of about 95% by carbon tetrachloride (19). The extraction coefficient is decreased when the germanium concentration is greater than 2.6×10^{-3} M. Equilibrium is established quickly, after 1–2 min shaking. Extraction is also decreased by the presence of fluoride ion at concentrations more than ten times that of germanium, but the addition of aluminum ion at concentration about equal to that of fluoride eliminates the interference. Although the extraction is not quantitative, this is compensated in analytical procedures by establishing standard calibration curves for spectrophotometry using the same procedure.

Trivalent arsenic is the only important metal coextracted with germanium. Osmium and ruthenium tetroxides are also coextracted, but would rarely be encountered in practice. Interference by arsenic is avoided by running the extraction under oxidizing conditions, in presence of bromine or potassium chlorate, so that the arsenic is oxidized to the pentavalent state, which is practically insoluble in carbon tetrachloride. If large amounts of pentavalent antimony are present, it should be reduced to the trivalent state, for example with hydrazine sulfate, before extraction of the germanium.

After extraction into the organic phase has separated the germanium from the other elements, it is back-extracted into water.

Extraction is just as specific as distillation, and has the advantages of speed and simplicity. By two extractions—first into the organic phase from 8 N hydrochloric acid, then into the aqueous phase using pure water—the germanium is obtained almost free of excess hydrochloric acid, so that the possibility of loss by volatilization is decreased.

Various other extractants have been investigated; in particular, methyl isobutyl ketone has been recommended. But although the completeness of extraction is higher (98 vs 95%), many more interferences are encountered: vanadium, arsenic, iron(III), zirconium, antimony, and tin must be absent. Germanium can be separated from arsenic by extraction with dioctyl methylene bisphosphonic acid in ligroin (20).

Extraction with carbon tetrachloride from hydrochloric acid solution forms the basis of many reported analytical procedures, some of which are discussed in detail below. A large proportion of them are colorimetric, but in one method (21) ores are dissolved in phosphoric acid, concentrated hydrochloric acid is added, and the germanium extracted into carbon tetrachloride. Back-extraction is with an ammonium oxalate–oxalic acid solution, and the germanium is finally determined by weighing as GeO_2.

Distillation

The other common method of separating germanium from interfering elements is distillation of germanium tetrachloride from solutions 6 N in hydrochloric acid. This method is as specific as extraction, and is quantitative when proper precautions are observed; it is not as rapid, and requires considerably more care to avoid loss of germanium. It has been shown (22) that the concentration of the hydrochloric acid from which distillation takes place is critical if sodium chloride is also present, as it will inevitably be if the original sample was taken into solution via a fusion with sodium carbonate or sodium hydroxide. Significant amounts of germanium can be lost if the medium is 6.2 N in hydrochloric acid instead of 5.8 N. This criticality is avoided by using a long delivery tube on the distillation apparatus, and dipping the end of the delivery tube into a few ml of water in the receiver, subsequently maintaining it just below the surface of the distillate.

Distillation is not quantitative in the presence of insoluble matter like amorphous silica or lead sulfate. Silica is removed by treatment with hydrofluoric and sulfuric acids.

The only element that codistills with germanium is arsenic in the trivalent state. Therefore distillation is carried out under oxidizing conditions such that arsenic is converted to the pentavalent state. Excess chlorine may be introduced as such, but more often the distillation is performed after the addition of potassium permanganate or potassium chromate.

The application of distillation for separation of germanium is coterminous with that of solvent extraction; choice is largely a matter of the analyst's preference. It has the advantage of being quantitative and thus does not rely on compensating internal standardization as does extraction; it is the basis of the volumetric determination (23).

Other Methods

Cation exchangers have been used to separate germanium, which is not retained on such nonchelating resins as Dowex 50, from dilute hydrochloric acid solutions, and thus can be separated from lead, zinc, copper, and iron; but arsenic and antimony are also not retained and will be found in the effluent along with the germanium. Separation on anionic resins, where germanium is held as a chloro complex while many other elements are not, has also been proposed.

Luke (24) has proposed an interesting method for the determination of trace elements, including germanium, by coprecipitation with a "carrier." Based on these principles, germanium, in concentrations of 2–10 $\mu g/ml$, is quantitatively coprecipitated with iron(III) hydroxide when the iron–germanium ratio is 25:1. The iron–germanium separation is then performed by distillation or solvent extraction, as previously discussed (5). Using other carriers, Luke (24) has proposed to determine trace elements, including germanium, by coprecipitation followed by x-ray fluorescence spectroscopy, a method also described by Wlotska (25).

Chromatographic methods have also been described. For a more complete discussion of these other methods, the book of Korkisch (5) and the references therein cited should be consulted.

DETERMINATION AS A MAJOR CONSTITUENT

In the case of germanium, "major constituent" means concentrations at or above the 1% level. Materials included in this category are in-process streams, scrap, germanium compounds both organic and inorganic, and germanium metal and its alloys. For the determination of germanium at this level, gravimetric and volumetric methods are most useful. Although colorimetric methods could be used, they would involve so much dilution of the sample that accuracy would probably not be satisfactory.

Gravimetric Methods

Many gravimetric methods for the determination of germanium have been described in the literature; among the precipitants mentioned are tannin, magnesium ion, molybdates and tungstates, and various organic reagents. Many of these methods have their special applications but have not found wide acceptance. The tannin precipitate is bulky and tends to trap other materials; magnesium oxide may coprecipitate with the magnesium germanate; the molybdogermanic and tungstogermanic acid precipitates are not stoichiometric, and empirical factors must be used in calculations.

In the generally used method, germanium is precipitated from 6 N sulfuric acid solution by saturation with hydrogen sulfide; the solution must be truly saturated and the precipitate must stand for at least 12 hr for reasonably complete precipitation. The sulfide is not weighed as such but is converted to germanium dioxide. This may be accomplished in various ways; the sulfide may be dissolved in ammonium hydroxide and oxidized with hydrogen peroxide; the solution is evaporated to dryness and the dry residue ignited in a muffle furnace at 800°C. Alternatively, the sulfide may be ignited directly to the oxide at 375°C. In either case, oxidizing conditions must be maintained throughout the ignition to prevent loss of germanium as the relatively volatile monoxide. Not too much precipitate should be ignited, since conversion may not be complete; about 200 mg of germanium sulfide is the maximum that should be handled.

The gravimetric procedure given below is suitable for samples containing 0.01–100% of germanium; sample size should be such as to contain 50–100 mg of germanium. Accuracy is 2–3% at the lower ranges and within 0.1% in the higher range.

Procedure

Fit a 500-ml Kjeldahl flask with a three-hole rubber stopper, which carries a piece of glass tubing extending to the bottom of the flask, through which chlorine is passed, a separatory funnel for adding hydrochloric acid, and a spray trap connecting the flask to a vertical water-cooled condenser. The lower end of the condenser is connected to a glass tube that extends to the bottom of a 500-ml Erlenmeyer flask fitted with a two-hole rubber stopper. Mark this flask to indicate its 300-ml level and connect it to a similar flask with a glass tube leading from the stopper of the first and extending through the stopper to the bottom of the second. The second hole in the stopper of the second flask is the outlet for chlorine. Place both receiving flasks in an ice bath and keep them as cold as possible during the distillation. Use this apparatus only in a fume hood.

Place an air trap and a bubbling bottle between the chlorine cylinder and the above apparatus; place the air trap next to the cylinder to prevent any water from being drawn back into the regulating valve; place the bubbling bottle, containing water, next to the apparatus as an aid in regulating the flow of chlorine.

Weigh accurately an amount of sample that contains 50–100 mg of germanium. Mix with 5 g of sodium peroxide and transfer to a nickel crucible. Add 1 g of sodium hydroxide pellets. If the sample weighs more than 2 g, add an additional 5 g of sodium peroxide and 1 g of sodium hydroxide pellets for each 2 g of sample over 2 g. Fuse the mixture at a moderate temperature; allow to cool, and leach with 50 ml of hot water. Transfer the leach solution and any undissolved solids to the distilling flask in the apparatus described.   Rinse the crucible with a little dilute hydrochloric acid and add the rinsings to the Kejldahl flask.

Add three or four glass beads to the Kjeldahl flask and set up the apparatus. Turn on the chlorine from a cylinder and saturate the solution in the Kjeldahl flask, then reduce the flow of chlorine to one or two bubbles/sec. Using the separatory funnel, add slowly 70 ml of concentrated hydrochloric acid. Heat the flask and boil gently until three fourths of the liquid has distilled over. Then add 30 ml of concentrated hydrochloric acid and continue distillation until the flask is almost dry.

Discontinue heating and the flow of chlorine, then disconnect the Kjeldahl flask. Rinse the condenser with a little water, collecting the washings in the receiving flasks. Add the distillate in the second receiving flask to the first, dilute to 300 ml, and add 80 ml of 18 N sulfuric acid. Saturate this solution with hydrogen sulfide gas, allowing the gas to bubble through the solution for at least 30 min. Stopper the flask and let it stand overnight.

Prepare a fritted glass crucible by boiling in 6 N sulfuric acid, washing well with 6 N sulfuric acid, and igniting to constant weight. Filter the germanium sulfide through the tared crucible and wash several times with 6 N sulfuric acid saturated with hydrogen sulfide. Ignite at 375°C for 3–4 hr, to constant weight. The ignited precipitate is germanium dioxide.

$$\text{wt \% Ge} = \frac{(G)(69.40)}{w}$$

where G = weight of the ignited precipitate, in g
       w = sample weight, in g

Volumetric Methods

Germanium in solution forms complex acids with polyhydric alcohols; the acid then can be titrated with standard alkali, and methods based on this reaction have been proposed (25,26). A widely recommended method (23) is a redox titration; germanium is reduced to the bivalent state by sodium hypophosphite and titrated with standard potassium iodate. The method is useful for samples with germanium contents in the 0.01–100% range, about the same as for the gravimetric method. Accuracy is about 0.2%, depending on the volume of the titration. The method has been studied in detail by Cheng (28). The procedure given below is according to Abel (23). The description of Musgrave (1) differs in minor detail.

The distillation apparatus consists of a 500-ml Erlenmeyer flask connected by a distillation head to a water-cooled condenser. The distillation head contains a thistle tube which extends to the bottom of the flask. The condenser has a tip about 20 cm long. The reduction flask is a 500-ml Erlenmeyer capped with a siphon tube that can be immersed in a sodium bicarbonate solution.

A heating unit that will produce a distillation rate of 3–5 ml/min is recommended.

Procedure

REAGENTS. Prepare a standard germanium solution in the following way. Ignite about 5 g of high-purity germanium dioxide at 800°C for 30 min. Cool in a desiccator and transfer 3.458 g to a 1-liter volumetric flask. Add 15–20 g of sodium hydroxide and 150–200 ml of water, and heat gently until solution is complete. Cool, and dilute to the mark with water. Store in a polyethylene bottle. One ml of the solution is equivalent to 2.400 mg of germanium. Prepare a standard potassium iodate solution by transferring 0.4 g of sodium carbonate, 3.0 g of potassium iodate, and 40 g of potassium iodide to a 1-liter flask, dissolving in water and diluting to volume.

Standardize the potassium iodate solution in the following way. Transfer by pipet 50 ml of the standard germanium solution to a 500-ml Erlenmeyer flask. Add 170 ml of 6 N hydrochloric acid, about 5 g of sodium hypophosphite, NaH_2-$PO_2.H_2O$, and one or two boiling stones. Cap with a reduction head and mix. Heat to boiling and boil for 5–10 min. Remove from the heat, place the siphon tube in a beaker containing saturated sodium bicarbonate solution, and cool to 15–20°C in a water bath. Remove the reduction head, add 3–5 ml of 5% starch solution, and titrate immediately with the potassium iodate solution to a blue end point that persists for 10–15 sec. Use a magnetic stirrer for the titration. Calculate the germanium equivalent of the potassium iodate solution from this titration.

DETERMINATION. Dissolve the samples in any appropriate manner; select the sample size to contain 50–100 mg of germanium. Fusion with sodium hydroxide–sodium peroxide, digestion with 25% aqueous sodium hydroxide solution followed with 5% hydrogen peroxide, or treatment with concentrated nitric–sulfuric acid mixtures is suitable for ores, oxides, and similar materials. Carry out the fusion in nickel crucibles using 5–6 g of sodium peroxide and 1–2 g of sodium hydroxide at dull red heat. Dissolve concentrates by boiling with 15 ml of 25% sodium hydroxide solution for 3–5 min, then adding 30 ml of 5% hydrogen peroxide and boiling again. Dissolve metal samples with a mixture of 15–20 ml of concentrated nitric acid and 10 ml of concentrated sulfuric acid and taking to fumes of sulfur trioxide.

Transfer the sample solution to the distillation apparatus. Adjust the volume to 85–90 ml and add about 0.3 g of potassium permanganate. To the receiving flask add 125 ml of 1:3 hydrochloric acid, about 10 g of sodium hypophosphite, and 10 ml of 48% hydrobromic acid. Connect the apparatus and add 120 ml of 12 N hydrochloric acid through the thistle tube. Start the distillation and collect 70–75 ml of the distillate. Disconnect the apparatus, rinse the condenser with a minimum amount of water, and remove the receiving flask. Add one or two boiling stones to the flask and cap with a reduction head. Reduce and titrate as given for the standardization of the potassium iodate solution.

DETERMINATION IN MINOR AND TRACE AMOUNTS

For determination of germanium in minor and trace quantities, such as occur in ores, coal residues, and electrolytic zinc solutions, emission spectrography is widely applicable, and colorimetric methods are both sensitive and accurate.

Polarographic and chromatographic determinations, as well as the use of atomic absorption spectrophotometry, have also been proposed (29–31).

Spectrographic Methods

By using emission spectrography, germanium contents between 0.001 and 1% can be determined within about 10%, the usual limit of accuracy of the spectrograph; suitable dilution with an appropriate matrix enables higher percentages to be handled.

In a method (32) for the detection and determination of volatile trace elements, including germanium, in silicate rocks, bismuth is used as the internal standard, and the germanium line at 2651.18 Å is the analytical line. The detection limit is said to be 0.5 ppm of germanium.

Musgrave proposed the following spectrographic procedure (1).

Procedures

PREPARATION OF STANDARDS. Prepare a matrix by thoroughly mixing the following compounds in the amounts shown: calcium oxide, 20.0%; silica, 20.0%; zinc sulfide, 20.0%; alumina, 10.0%; magnesium carbonate, 10.0%; iron(II) sulfide, 10.0%; lead monoxide, 5.0%; copper(II) sulfide, 5.0%.

Prepare a 1% germanium solution by dissolving 1.440 g of germanium dioxide in a 10% sodium hydroxide solution and diluting to 100 ml. Make up a series of standards ranging from 0.005 to 1.0% germanium: to 100-mg portions of the matrix, add appropriate volumes of the standard germanium solution so that, after drying, the standards will contain known percentages of germanium within this range. Mix thoroughly and dry overnight at 110°C. Mix standards with buffer and arc, according to the procedure following. Plot a curve of relative intensity versus concentration of germanium.

Make up buffer by thoroughly mixing 2 parts by weight of pure lithium carbonate and 1 part of pure graphite powder; both solids must pass 100 mesh before mixing. Mix 20 mg of the prepared sample, or of the standard, thoroughly with 100 mg of buffer in an agate mortar. Weigh 15 mg of this mixture into the anode and tamp firmly.

SAMPLE PREPARATION. Grind solid samples to pass 200 mesh; for liquid samples, take to dryness and grind the solid to pass 200 mesh. If chlorides are present or suspected in the liquid, neutralize and add a strong oxidizing agent during the evaporation.

INSTRUMENT CONDITIONS. Use the following instrument conditions and settings:

(1) *Electrodes*
anode
  length   1.50 in. (38.1 mm)
  rod diameter   0.242 in. (6.14 mm)
  inside diameter of cup   0.094 in. (2.39 mm); $\frac{3}{32}$ in. (2.38 mm) drill
  outside diameter of cup   0.156 in. (3.96 mm)
  inside depth of cup   0.188 in. (4.78 mm)
  outside depth of cup   0.322 in. (8.18 mm)
cathode
  length   1.50 in. (38.1 mm)
  rod diameter   0.120 in. (3.05 mm), flat end
  material   National Carbon Company stock AGKS rods or equivalent

(2) Spectrograph settings

power	10 A on 300-V line, under standard ignitor conditions
intensity control	filters Nos. 4 and 7 (8%)
height limiting aperture	C-1
slit width	50 μm
analytical gap	3 mm, maintained throughout burn
filter	13% nominal transmission at 3230 Å
grating aperture	10–10 (fully open)

(3) Exposure and photography

pre-arc	none
exposure period	complete vaporization (about 3 min)
wavelength range	2300–4500 Å
film	SA No. 1 with standard processing

DETERMINATION. Using standard photometric procedure, read and record % transmission for the appropriate lines listed below:

Concentration range, %	Reference line, Å	Element line, Å
0.0025–0.010	Li 3232.6[a]	Ge 2651.18
0.02–0.5	Li 3232.6	Ge 3039.06
0.1–1.0	Li 3232.6	Ge 2691.34

[a] Passed through 13% filter on front of camera.

Using the current emulsion response curve derived by the step filter method, calculate the relative intensities, R, for the line pairs and determine the percentage concentration from the appropriate working curve. Draw the working curves for R vs concentration % on log–log paper. Report the average of the duplicates.

Colorimetric Methods

The combination of the ease with which germanium can be separated from most other elements by distillation and solvent extraction, and the availability of several organic reagents that form colored complexes with germanium renders colorimetric procedures attractive for both the identification and the determination of the element. Many color-forming reagents have been proposed, but phenylfluorone (2,6,7-tri-hydroxy-9-phenyl isoxanthene-3-one) has been by far the most thoroughly investigated and widely recommended (1,6,19,33–37). Oxidized hematoxylin has an advantage over phenylfluorone in that it does not require quite such an accurate spectrophotometer.

Spectrophotometry appears to be the method of choice among the strictly chemical procedures when it is applicable. However, if the germanium content of the sample is much greater than 1% or so, dilution of the sample solution is required and this can be carried only so far before accuracy will suffer. The lower limit of usefulness is about 0.0001%.

Determination with Phenylfluorone. Many variations of detail have been published for determining germanium by the phenylfluorone method. The procedure given below was recommended by Luke (19). A somewhat simplified procedure was described by Musgrave (1).

Procedures

REAGENTS. *Standard Germanium Solution*. Transfer 0.1441 g of pure germanium dioxide to a 100-ml platinum dish. Add 3 ml of 5% sodium hydroxide solution, stir with a polyethylene rod until all has dissolved, then add about 75 ml of water. Neutralize to Congo red paper by adding 1:9 sulfuric acid dropwise. Add 3 or 4 drops in excess after the paper has turned blue. Remove the paper, transfer the solution to a 1-liter volumetric flask, and dilute to the mark. Transfer 50 ml of this solution to a 500-ml volumetric flask and dilute to volume. The germanium concentration of this solution is 10 μg/ml.

pH 5 Buffer Solution. Dissolve 900 g of sodium acetate trihydrate or 540 g of the anhydrous salt in about 700 ml of water by warming. Filter with suction and transfer to a 2-liter volumetric flask containing 480 ml of acetic acid. Cool and dilute to volume with water.

Gum Arabic Solution. Dissolve 0.5 g of powdered gum arabic (gum acacia) in 50 ml of hot water and filter. Prepare fresh daily.

Phenylfluorone Solution. Transfer 50.0 mg of phenylfluorone to a 100-ml beaker. Add 50 ml of methanol, 1 ml of concentrated hydrochloric acid and stir to dissolve. Transfer to a dry 500-ml volumetric flask and dilute to volume with methanol. The solution is stable for about a month; do not store in polyethylene.

CALIBRATION. Transfer 0, 0.5, 1.0, 2.0, 3.0, and 4.0 ml of the standard germanium solution to 60-ml separatory funnels. Add 2 ml of 1:1 sulfuric acid, dilute to 7 ml with water, and add 19 ml of concentrated hydrochloric acid. Add 20 ml of carbon tetrachloride, stopper, and shake vigorously for 1 min. Allow the layers to separate and run the carbon tetrachloride layer into a second 60-ml separatory funnel that is dry or has been rinsed with 9 N hydrochloric acid. Add 2 ml of carbon tetrachloride to the acid solution in the first funnel, shake 10 sec, allow to separate, and run the lower layer into the second funnel. Wash the combined carbon tetrachloride solutions by shaking 10 sec with 2 ml of 9 N hydrochloric acid. Allow the layers to separate and transfer the lower layer to a third 60-ml separatory funnel which has been dried in an oven or by an air jet. Add 12.0 ml of water from a buret to the carbon tetrachloride solution in the third funnel. Stopper and shake vigorously for 1 min. Allow the layers to separate and discard the lower layer.

Filter the aqueous layer through a small dry paper and collect the filtrate in a dry 50-ml conical flask. Pipet 10.0 ml of the filtrate into a 50-ml volumetric flask. Add 1.5 ml of 1:1 sulfuric acid, then 10 ml of buffer solution, and then 1 ml of the gum arabic solution from measuring pipets, swirling after each addition. Add 10.0 ml of the phenylfluorone solution, stopper, and mix. Ignore any precipitate of sodium acetate; this will dissolve upon subsequent acidification. Let stand 5 min. Dilute to volume with 1:9 hydrochloric acid. Transfer a portion of the solution to a 1-cm absorption cell and make the photometric measurement as soon as possible at 510 nm, using water as the reference solution. Prepare a calibration curve.

SAMPLE ANALYSIS. Select a sample containing no more than 40 μg of germanium. Dilute larger samples by taking aliquots after dissolving. Dissolve the sample in a small excess of suitable acid or alkali in a 50-ml conical flask. Do not use halogen acids or their salts at any stage in the preparation of the sample solution. If organic matter is present, destroy it by wet oxidation. Finally, add 2 ml of concentrated sulfuric acid and evaporate on a Meker-type flame to about 1.25 ml. Carry a reagent blank through all the steps of the analysis. If the sample is known to contain less than about 0.25 mg of antimony, add 5 drops of concentrated perchloric acid and evaporate on the flame to 0.75–1.0 ml. Otherwise add 2 ml of concentrated sulfuric acid and about 0.1 g of hydrazine sulfate and evaporate on a flame to 0.75–1.0 ml. Cool. If a precipitate of iron or chromium sulfate is present, add 1 ml of water and heat uncovered on a low-temperature hot plate until fumes of acid just appear; if necessary, repeat the addition of water and heating just to fumes one or more times to dissolve the precipitate completely. Cool. Ignore insoluble sulfates of lead, barium, or calcium. Add 6 ml of water, pour into a 60-ml separatory funnel, and wash in with 19 ml of concentrated hydrochloric acid. Add 20 ml of carbon tetrachloride and continue as given for the preparation of the calibration curve.

Although the phenylfluorone procedures described are generally satisfactory for quantities of germanium in the 1–10 μg range, they encounter difficulties when smaller amounts must be determined. By forming the germanium–phenylfluorone species and separating it from the excess of the reagent before dissolution in an organic solvent, the procedure given below (38) is said to obviate these difficulties. The germanium is extracted as the chloro complex into carbon tetrachloride; this separates it from interfering metals. It is then back-extracted into aqueous solution of pH 5; phenylfluorone is added as a methanol solution. The germanium precipitate is agglomerated at the interface by shaking; most of the carbon tetrachloride layer is drained off, and the aqueous layer, which contains the excess of the organic reagent, is decanted and the remaining precipitate is dissolved in a known volume of acetone–water and the absorbance measured. It is claimed that as little as 0.05 μg of germanium can be determined in this manner with reasonably good accuracy.

Procedure

Prepare a standard germanium solution, a pH 5 buffer solution, and a phenylfluorone solution as detailed in the earlier procedure.

Transfer the sample solution containing up to 1.5 μg of germanium in 15 ml of 9 N hydrochloric acid to a 75-ml separatory funnel. Add 5 ml of carbon tetrachloride, shake vigorously for 1 min, then allow the phases to separate, swirl, and drain off the carbon tetrachloride layer completely into a 75-ml separatory funnel which is modified so that the narrow neck just above the stopcock is cylindrical (4 mm ID) for a distance of about 13 mm. Add 5 ml of the pH 5 buffer solution and 5 ml of water, and shake for 1 min. Add 0.75 ml of 1:1 sulfuric acid and 5 ml of the phenylfluorone reagent. Mix by gentle swirling and allow to stand for 5 min. Add 10 ml of 1:9 hydrochloric acid and shake for 15 sec. Allow the phases to separate, swirl, and slowly drain off all of the carbon tetrachloride layer which is discarded. If gas bubbles form at the interface during this step, tap the funnel to dislodge them.

Decant off the aqueous layer carefully by tipping the funnel, and finally invert it on a piece of filter paper for a few seconds to blot up the liquid that runs down the funnel walls; but stop this blotting operation before traces of carbon tetrachloride containing the germanium precipitate leave the funnel. Return the funnel to its upright position, add exactly 5 ml of 4:1 acetone–water and shake for a few sec to dissolve the precipitate. Drain the solution through the stopcock into a small, clean, dry beaker; swirl. Fill a 1-cm cuvet, cover, and measure the absorbance at 497 nm vs water.

Calculate the amount of germanium from a calibration curve prepared by carrying known amounts of germanium through the same procedure.

Determination with Oxidized Hematoxylin. Although the most widely used colorimetric method for determination of germanium uses phenylfluorone to develop the color, oxidized hematoxylin ($C_{16}H_{20}O_7$) is said to have certain advantages; whereas the determination of the transmittance of the phenylfluorone solution is critical and requires a good spectrophotometer, the complex with oxidized hematoxylin has a a wider absorbance range which can be observed with a less sensitive colorimeter. The two methods give about equivalent results and are useful in the same range of germanium content, 0.0001–1.0%. Larger percentages can be estimated by dilution of the solution, with concomitant sacrifice of accuracy, which is about 10%—satisfactory for the lower ranges but useful only for estimates in the higher percentages. The procedure given below was recommended by Musgrave (1).

Procedure

REAGENTS. *Oxidized Hematoxylin Solution.* Dissolve 3.00 g of pure hematoxylin in a solution of 500 ml of water and 200 ml of ethanol. Add 20 ml of 3% hydrogen peroxide and heat on a boiling water bath for 20 min. Cool, transfer to a 1-liter volumetric flask and dilute to volume with water. The solution keeps indefinitely if stored in a glass bottle fitted with a screw cap or ground-glass stopper.

Standard Germanium Solutions. Dissolve 0.1441 g of pure germanium dioxide in the minimum amount of 0.1 N sodium hydroxide solution; acidify to pH 3.2 with hydrochloric acid and dilute with water to 1 liter in a volumetric flask. The germanium concentration of this solution is 100 μg/ml. Dilute 10 ml of this solution to 1 liter. The germanium concentration of the final solution is 1 μg/ml.

pH 3.2 Buffer Solution. Dissolve 10.2 g of potassium hydrogen phthalate in the minimum amount of water, add 147 ml of 0.1 N hydrochloric acid, and dilute to 1 liter.

Gelatin Solution. Dissolve 0.500 g of plain gelatin in hot water and dilute to 50 ml. Make up fresh every 3–5 days.

CALIBRATION. By proper dilution of the standard germanium solutions, prepare standards containing 0.5–10 μg/5 ml. Transfer each 5 ml of standard solution to a 25-ml volumetric flask and add 1 ml of the gelatin solution and 1.0 ml of the oxidized hematoxylin reagent solution. Allow to stand for exactly 45 min at 25°C, then dilute to volume with the buffer solution. Prepare a blank solution as described for sample analysis and use it as the reference for 100% transmittance. Determine the transmittance of the standard solutions and plot a curve of transmittance versus germanium content.

SAMPLE ANALYSIS. Carry out sample preparation and extraction with carbon tetrachloride as described for the phenylfluorone method (p. 386). Adjust the concentration so that the final carbon tetrachloride extract should contain 2–20 μg of germanium. Shake the carbon tetrachloride extract with 10.0 ml of water for 2 min, allow the phases to separate, then take a 5-ml aliquot of the aqueous phase. Adjust the aliquot to pH 2.5–3.0 and dilute to 10 ml with the buffer solution. Transfer a 5-ml aliquot to a 25-ml volumetric flask, add 1 ml of the gelatin solution and 1.0 ml of the oxidized hematoxylin reagent solution, and allow to stand at 25°C for exactly 45 min. Dilute to volume with buffer solution, mix, and measure the transmittance at 630 nm with any standard colorimeter, using 1-cm absorption cells.

Set the transmittance at 100% for reference, with a blank solution containing 5 ml of the buffer solution instead of the germanium solution, which has been carried through the same procedure (addition of gelatin and hematoxylin, standing for 45 min at 25°C, and diluting). Compare the transmittance with the standards curve.

DETERMINATION OF IMPURITIES

The principal use of germanium is in semiconductors, and the principal use of germanium dioxide is as a precursor of the metal. In this application, impurities must be as low as 1 ppb or less, and chemical methods are usually not adequate. For one thing, even the best reagents often contain more impurity than it is sought to determine. Even emission spectrography is of doubtful utility (3); impurity levels lie at the very limit of sensitivity of the method. Mass spectrometry has been used, and recently the technique of activation analysis has been intensively investigated, in particular neutron activation analysis (3,7,39,40).

Activation analysis, however, suffers from several practical drawbacks. The samples after irradiation are sufficiently high in activity to require a license for their handling. Few laboratories have a reactor or accelerator, and thus, one would have to rely on the services offered by laboratories that are suitably equipped. Some elements, eg, boron, either have no active isotopes or their isotopes are so short-lived that they have decayed before the sample returns from the reactor.

There is an extensive literature on emission spectrography for determining impurities in germanium; see Reference 7 for citations. According to Kane and Larrabee (3) this technique is not sensitive enough for impurities or dopants in the ppb range. Sensitivity can be improved by distilling off the germanium as tetrachloride and running the analysis on the residue.

In view of these considerations, it is evident why tests for the acceptability of germanium for semiconductor applications rely on physical, usually electrical, properties rather than chemical analysis. In the same category are tests for the suitability of a sample of germanium dioxide for the production of germanium by hydrogen reduction.

In spite of the limitations of chemical analysis, methods have been developed for determining many impurities in germanium or germanium dioxide. These methods are applicable to both the metal and the oxide; only the methods for dissolving the sample will differ.

Although it is taken for granted that chemicals used will be of reagent quality, even further precautions are required in many of the methods specified for the detection and determination of impurities in germanium at the ppm level. Water should be not only distilled but then deionized; a resistivity of 14 MΩ-cm is desirable, although the presence of dissolved carbon dioxide is of no consequence (7). Reagents should be the purest available; some manufacturers offer "semiconductor grade" materials, which should be used. Liquids such as chloroform and carbon tetrachloride should be redistilled.

Scrupulously clean bench tops and working areas are necessary; reagent racks above the working surface should be avoided. Rooms should be reasonably free of dust, and drippings from fume hoods must be guarded against.

Equally important is meticulous care of the analyst's tools, to avoid contamination of the very dilute solutions employed, particularly if they are stored for long periods. Hard glass is generally satisfactory, but it should be leached with aqua regia and thoroughly rinsed before use. Teflon and polyethylene containers should be used for storage of some reagents. Very dilute solutions such as standards may tend to deplete by adsorption on the container walls and must therefore be made up fresh. Conversely, containers that have been used for stronger solutions may desorb ions into weaker ones: very dilute solutions should therefore be prepared in new and freshly leached containers. In pipetting a series of standards, the most dilute should be taken first, working up the series to the more concentrated.

In working with samples of metallic germanium, it should be assumed that the surface is contaminated; for the most exacting work every procedure should be initiated by etching the surface before proceeding with the analysis. A suitable etch for germanium is a 15:5:2 (vol) mixture of concentrated nitric acid, acetic acid, and hydrofluoric acid.

The methods outlined below are in general capable of determining impurities at about the 1 μg level, and since samples weigh about 1 g, sensitivity is of the order of 1 ppm.

Arsenic. Luke and Campbell (41) proposed a method involving separation of the arsenic from germanium and other interfering elements by extraction from a hydrochloric–oxalic acid solution with diethylammonium diethyldithiocarbamate in chloroform. Copper, bismuth, and mercury accompany the arsenic, but they cause no interference in the subsequent photometric determination using the molybdenum blue complex. Although the method gives good results, it is long and tedious. The following procedure (42) retains the photometric determination with molybdenum blue, but eliminates the germanium by distilling it off as the chloride rather than by extraction.

Procedure

Prepare a standard arsenic solution in the following way. Transfer 0.0660 g of arsenious oxide, NBS standard sample, to a 100-ml platinum dish and add 20 ml of water and 1 pellet of sodium hydroxide. Cover and warm to dissolve the arsenious oxide completely. Cool, add 5 ml of 70–72 wt % perchloric acid, transfer to a 500-ml volumetric flask, and dilute to volume with water. Transfer 10.0 ml of this solution to a 1-liter volumetric flask, add 10 ml of perchloric acid, and dilute to volume with water. The final solution has an arsenic concentration of 1 μg/ml.

Prepare a graduated series of standards by adding 1, 2, 4, etc, ml of the standard arsenic solution to 25-ml volumetric flasks. Carry a reagent blank through the entire procedure. Add 0.5 ml of 70–72 wt % perchloric acid and dilute to about 10 ml with water. Add 1 drop of 0.02% methyl red solution and neutralize carefully with concentrated ammonium hydroxide added dropwise until the solution just turns yellow. Blow out the ammonia fumes from the interior of the flask. Add 2:3 hydrochloric acid dropwise to bring back the red color and then 1.25 ml of this dilute acid in excess. Add 0.2 ml of 0.030% aqueous potassium bromate solution, warm and swirl to decolorize the solution. Cool, add 1.25 ml of a 1% aqueous ammonium molybdate solution (1.000 g in 100 ml of solution) stored in a polyethylene bottle and mix. Add 1.25 ml of a 0.160% aqueous hydrazine sulfate solution and dilute to volume with water. Place unstoppered in vigorously boiling water in a beaker on a hot plate and allow to remain for exactly 5 min. The water level in the beaker should cover the mark on the flask.

Remove to the bench for a few minutes and cool to room temperature in a water bath. Pour the sample into a clean 5-cm Corex absorption cell, and immediately measure the absorbance at 840 nm using water as the reference solution; use the red-sensitive phototube and a slit width of 0.015 mm. Prepare a calibration curve. The reagent blank should give a transmittance of about 95%; if it is much lower than this, prepare fresh reagents.

Transfer 0.1–0.5 g of germanium or germanium oxide, ground to 60 mesh or finer, to a 125-ml conical Vycor flask. Add 0.5 ml of perchloric acid, 12 ml of hydrochloric acid, and 3 ml of nitric acid. Evaporate without cover under a hood on a hot plate whose surface temperature is about 175°C until perchloric acid fumes begin to appear. If the sample was larger than 0.1 g, add 10 ml of hydrochloric acid and 1 ml of nitric acid and repeat the evaporation. Finally, add 5 ml of hydrochloric acid and evaporate to expel nitric acid. When fumes of perchloric acid appear, heat on a flame until the acid is condensing near the top of the flask; avoid unnecessary expulsion of the acid. Cool, wash into a 25-ml volumetric flask with about 10 ml of water, and determine arsenic by the procedure given above for calibration.

In a spectrographic method for the determination of traces of arsenic and bismuth in germanium or germanium oxide (43), the arsenic is first extracted into a chloroform solution of diethylammonium diethyldithiocarbamate; the extract is evaporated on graphite powder, mixed with a buffer of graphite and antimony oxide, and arced. A method for the determination of arsenic by neutron activation analysis has also been published (44).

Phosphorus. In the determination of phosphorus, antimony, and copper, germanium is quantitatively removed by distillation of the chloride. Phosphorus is determined by the molybdenum blue method. Most interfering elements are complexed and rendered harmless by addition of fluoborate. Arsenic and selenium are removed by distillation as bromides; silicon is inactivated by dehydration of silica with perchloric acid; copper and gold are plated out on lead (41).

Procedure

REAGENTS. *Standard Phosphorus Solution.* Dissolve 0.4260 g of pure dry diammonium hydrogen phosphate in water and dilute to 1 liter in a volumetric flask. Transfer 10.0 ml of this solution to a 1-liter volumetric flask, and dilute to volume. This final solution has a phosphorus concentration of 1 μg/ml.

Sodium Fluoborate Solution. In a 500-ml flask add 5 g of sodium fluoride and 30 g of boric acid to 300 ml of water and dissolve. Filter and dilute to 500 ml. Store in polyethylene bottles.

Redistilled Hydrochloric Acid. Transfer 2 g of iron(II) ammonium sulfate, a few boiling stones, 1 liter of concentrated hydrochloric acid, and 500 ml of water, to a 2-liter round-bottomed flask. Distill the mixture, discarding the first and last 50 ml portions. The distillate contains about 24 wt % of hydrochloric acid.

Redistilled Nitric and Hydrobromic Acids. Redistill 1 liter of the concentrated acids, by discarding the first and last 50 ml.

CALIBRATION. Transfer 0, 1.0, 2.0, 3.0, 4.0, and 5.0 ml of the standard phosphorus solution to 25-ml volumetric flasks and dilute to about 10 ml with water. Add 0.5 ml of 70–72 wt % perchloric acid, followed by 1.25 ml of the sodium fluoborate solution and 1 drop of a 0.02% methyl red solution, and continue the procedure as outlined above for arsenic (p. 391). The transmittance of the blank should be about 85%.

SAMPLE ANALYSIS. *Germanium Metal.* Transfer 2.000 g of the sample, ground to pass 150 mesh, to a 125-ml Vycor conical flask. Carry a reagent blank through the whole procedure. Add 2 ml of 70–72% perchloric acid and 50 ml of 1:5 nitric–hydrochloric acid mixture, prepared fresh from redistilled acids. Cover and heat to boiling on a hot plate at 250°C. When violent solution has ceased and most of the remaining metal has collected at the bottom of the flask, remove the cover and boil vigorously down to a volume of 5–10 ml. When the solution starts to get cloudy, add 15 ml of redistilled hydrochloric acid, cover, and heat to boiling to redissolve the precipitated germanium dioxide. When the volume has been reduced to about 2 ml, remove the cover and heat until copious fumes of perchloric acid start.

Cool somewhat, add 15 ml of redistilled hydrochloric acid, and heat on a hot plate without cover to expel the remaining traces of germanium. When perchloric acid fumes again appear, cool, and add 3 ml of hydrobromic acid.

Boil down on a flame to a volume of 0.5 ml to expel arsenic, antimony, and selenium. Cool, add 15 ml of water and 0.2 g of fine grain test lead, cover, and boil gently for 15 min to plate out any copper. Without removing the sample from the plate, add 1.25 ml of the sodium fluoborate solution, cover, and boil 1 min to dissolve any precipitated zirconium phosphate. Cool and filter through paper into a 25-ml volumetric flask, washing twice with water. Add 1 drop of a 0.02% methyl red solution and continue with the neutralization and color development as in the preparation of the calibration curve. Correct for a reagent blank.

Germanium Dioxide. Transfer 3.000 g of the powdered sample to a 125-ml conical Vycor flask. Carry a reagent blank through the whole procedure. Add 2 ml of 70–72% perchloric acid and 50 ml of 1:99 nitric acid–hydrochloric acid mixture, prepared fresh from redistilled acids. Cover and heat to boiling on a hot plate at about 200°C. When the solution is boiling smoothly, remove the cover and allow the solution to evaporate. When the solution is nearly clear, increase the hot plate temperature somewhat, cover, and continue to boil until all traces of germanium dioxide have been redissolved. Remove the cover and continue heating to fumes of perchloric acid; finally heat on a flame to the appearance of copious fumes of perchloric acid. If there is any doubt about the removal of all traces of germanium, add 5 ml of hydrochloric acid and repeat. Cool and add 3 ml of hydrobromic acid. Continue the procedure as outlined above for germanium metal starting with "Boil down on a flame..."

Antimony. If the temperature of the hot plate does not exceed 200°C during the solution and distillation of germanium, no loss of antimony occurs. After removal of the germanium, antimony is determined by the photometric rhodamine B–benzene method. The antimony must be in the pentavalent state before addition of the indicator. The procedure described below (41) is designed to eliminate interference by most elements. After removal of germanium, antimony is reduced to the trivalent state and separated from thallium and iridium by a cupferron–chloroform extraction. Iron is removed by a second extraction with the same reagents, and gold is removed by precipitation as the metal using selenium as the coprecipitant. Antimony is oxidized with perchloric acid and cerium(IV) sulfate and determined photometrically. The samples used for the preparation of the calibration curve are carried through all the separations, in order to compensate for the slight losses of antimony that occur therein.

Procedure

REAGENTS. *Standard Antimony Solution.* Dissolve 1.000 g of pure powdered antimony metal by heating with 10 ml of concentrated sulfuric acid in a 500-ml conical flask. After complete solution, take to copious white fumes to expel sulfur dioxide. Cool and add 300 ml of cool 1:2 sulfuric acid. Cool, transfer to a 1-liter volumetric flask, and dilute to volume with water. Transfer 10 ml of this solution to a 1-liter volumetric flask, add 300 ml of 1:2 sulfuric acid, and dilute to volume with water. The antimony concentration of the final solution is 1 μg/ml.

Selenium Nitrate Solution. Dissolve 0.5 g of pure powdered selenium in 5 ml of concentrated nitric acid by gentle warming. Add 10 ml of concentrated sulfuric acid and evaporate to copious white fumes to expel the nitric acid. Cool, add 10 ml of water, and reevaporate to fumes. Cool and add 100 ml of water.

Cerium(IV) Sulfate Solution. Dissolve 0.2 g of cerium(IV) sulfate in 10 ml of 1:4 sulfuric acid by gentle warming. Cool, transfer to a 100-ml volumetric flask, and dilute to volume.

CALIBRATION. Transfer 0, 1.0, 2.0, and 3.0 ml of the standard antimony solution to 125-ml conical Vycor flasks, add 2 ml of concentrated sulfuric acid to each and evaporate the water. Add about 30 mg of pure powdered sulfur and concentrate the solutions on a flame to about 1 ml. Cool, add 10 ml of water, and heat if necessary to dissolve any salts. Cool and transfer to a 60-ml separatory funnel whose stem has been cut off so that only about 1 cm is left below the stopcock. Dilute to 20 ml and add 2 ml of cupferron solution prepared fresh daily by dissolving 1 g of cupferron in 100 ml of water. Add 10 ml of redistilled chloroform and shake vigorously for 30 sec. After phase separation is accomplished, drain off the lower layer through a plug of fine glass wool into a 125-ml conical Vycor flask. Add 4–5 ml more chloroform to the funnel, shake, and again drain into the flask. Discard the aqueous layer.

Add 1 ml of concentrated nitric acid to the chloroform solution and boil on a low-temperature hot plate to expel the chloroform. Add 2 ml of concentrated sulfuric acid and 0.25 ml of 70–72 wt % perchloric acid and concentrate to 1 ml on a flame to expel all organic matter. Cool and add 10 ml of water. Heat if necessary to dissolve salts; cool, transfer to a 60-ml separatory funnel, and dilute with water to 20 ml. Repeat the cupferron–chloroform extraction, but this time discard the chloroform layers and washings. Transfer the aqueous solution to a 125-ml conical Vycor flask.

Add 1 ml of nitric acid and boil down to fumes of sulfuric acid. Add 1 ml of sulfuric acid and 0.25 ml of perchloric acid and boil down to 1 ml. Cool to room temperature, add 1 ml of selenium nitrate solution, and mix. Add 5 ml of 6% sulfurous acid solution and heat to 95–100°C. Allow to stand 5 min and filter through paper into a 125-ml conical Vycor flask. Wash well with water and discard the paper and precipitate. Boil down to sulfuric acid fumes, then add 3.0 ml of concentrated sulfuric acid and 0.25 ml of 70–72% perchloric acid. Concentrate on a flame to 2.5 ml.

From this point on, carry out the steps as rapidly as possible. Cool to room temperature; wash down the inside of the flask with 5 ml of 1:1 hydrochloric acid, and pour the contents into a 100-ml volumetric flask. Repeat the washing with 8 ml of 1:99 phosphoric acid and pour it into the same volumetric flask. Cool under a stream of water. Add 1 ml of the cerium(IV) sulfate solution, stopper, and invert the flask. Add 5 ml of 0.1% filtered rhodamine B solution, stopper and invert. Add 1 ml of a 1:2 mixture of butyl Cellosolve and water and 15.0 ml of benzene. Stopper and shake vigorously for 30 sec. Pour the solution into a separatory funnel and allow the layers to separate. Drain off and discard all of the lower layer plus about 0.5 ml of the benzene layer. Pour the benzene layer through a dry filter paper into a 5-cm Corex absorption cell. Without delay measure the absorbance photometrically at 565 nm, using benzene as the reference solution; use the ultraviolet-sensitive phototube and a slit width of 0.02 mm. Plot a calibration curve.

SAMPLE ANALYSIS. Dissolve and distill the germanium or germanium dioxide as directed in the method for phosphorus (p. 392), using the low-temperature hot plate (200°C) throughout. When the germanium has been expelled, add 2 ml of concentrated sulfuric acid and heat until copious fuming of sulfur trioxide takes place, to expel perchloric acid. Cool somewhat, add about 30 mg of sulfur, and proceed from this point as in the preparation of the calibration curve. Carry a reagent blank through the entire procedure and correct for it in reading the calibration curve.

Copper. A method said to be completely specific for copper, with no interference from 56 metals, is based on the photometric measurement using neocuproine (2,9-dimethyl-1,10-phenanthroline) as the color former. The procedure is given below (41).

Procedure

Prepare a standard copper solution in the following way. Dissolve 0.1000 g of pure copper in 3 ml of redistilled nitric acid (see p. 392) in a 125-ml conical Vycor flask. Add 10 ml of 70–72% perchloric acid and heat to copious fumes to expel all nitric acid. Cool, transfer to a 1-liter volumetric flask and dilute with water to volume. Transfer 10 ml of this solution to a 500-ml volumetric flask and dilute to volume. The copper concentration of the final solution is 2 μg/ml.

CALIBRATION. Transfer 0, 2.0, 4.0, 6.0, 8.0, and 10.0 ml of the standard copper solution to 100-ml beakers, add 0.5 ml of 70–72 wt % perchloric acid, and dilute to 50 ml with water. Add 2 ml of a 10% aqueous hydroxylamine hydrochloride solution and 2 ml of a 30% aqueous sodium citrate solution. Neutralize by dropwise addition of ammonium hydroxide until just definitely red to Congo paper (pH about 4). Remove the paper and add 2 ml of a solution of 0.100 g of neocuproine in 100 ml of absolute ethanol.

Transfer the solution to a 150-ml separatory funnel and add 150 ml of redistilled chloroform. Shake for 30 sec. Allow the layers to separate; insert a fairly compact plug of fine glass wool in the stem of the funnel and drain about 14 ml of the chloroform solution into a 5-cm Corex absorption cell; the solution should be clear. Measure the absorbance photometrically at 457 nm using chloroform as the reference solution, the ultraviolet-sensitive phototube, and a slit width of 0.025 mm. Plot a calibration curve.

SAMPLE ANALYSIS. Dissolve and distill the germanium or germanium dioxide as directed in the method for phosphorus (p. 392). Reduce the volume to 0.5 ml on a flame, cool, add 50 ml of water, and continue as given above, for the preparation of the calibration curve. Carry a reagent blank through the analysis. Correct the reading for this blank.

Gallium. Small amounts of gallium are determined by extraction with a chloroform solution of oxine (8-quinolinol) followed by photometric measurement. The reagent is not specific for gallium, but the procedure avoids interferences. Because extraction into the organic layer is not quantitative, compensation is made by including the same steps in the preparation of the calibration curve. The procedure is given below (45).

Procedure

REAGENTS. Prepare a standard gallium solution in the following way. Transfer 0.0134 g of gallium oxide to a 125-ml conical Vycor flask. . Add 5 ml of concentrated hydrochloric acid, cover, and warm gently to dissolve. Cool, transfer to a 200-ml volumetric flask, and dilute to volume with 1:1 hydrochloric acid. Pipet 50 ml of this solution to a 500-ml volumetric flask and dilute to volume with 1:1 hydrochloric acid. The gallium concentration of the final solution is 5 μg/ml.

Prepare acid-washed ethyl ether in the following way. Transfer 200 ml of anhydrous ethyl ether to a 500-ml separatory funnel and add 30 ml of 1:1 hydrochloric acid in which about 50 mg of sodium sulfite has been dissolved. Drain and discard the acid layer. Repeat the washings with two more 30-ml portions of sodium sulfite-containing acid.

CALIBRATION. Transfer 0, 1.0, 3.0, 5.0, and 7.0 ml portions of the standard gallium solution to 125-ml separatory funnels. Add sufficient 1:1 hydrochloric acid to bring the volume in each to 25 ml. Working individually, add 25 ml of acid-washed ether to the funnel; drain and discard the lower layer. Add 2 ml of 1:1 hydrochloric acid and again discard the lower layer. Repeat twice more. Add 15 ml of water and run the lower layer into a 125-ml conical Vycor flask. Repeat the extraction with 10 ml of water and drain the aqueous layer to the flask. Place the flask on a low-temperature hot plate for a few minutes until the solution no longer smells of ether. Cool and transfer with minimum washing to a 125-ml separatory funnel.

Add 1 drop of 0.1% aqueous m-cresol purple indicator solution and add ammonium hydroxide dropwise until the solution just turns yellow. Immediately add 5 ml of a 10% aqueous sodium cyanide solution; mix, then add 20 ml of freshly prepared solution of 1.000 g of 8-quinolinol in 100 ml of chloroform, and shake. After phase separation is accomplished, drain all but about 2 ml of the chloroform layer through a dry filter paper to a dry 50-ml conical flask. Mix well and transfer to a 5-cm absorption cell and measure the absorbance photometrically at 400 nm, using chloroform as the reference solution. Plot a calibration curve.

SAMPLE ANALYSIS. Dissolve and distill the sample of germanium or germanium dioxide as described in the method for phosphorus (p. 392), omitting the distillation with hydrobromic acid. Carry a reagent blank through all steps. When the germanium has been completely removed, evaporate to dryness on a flame to expel all perchloric acid. Cool, add 25 ml of 1:1 hydrochloric acid, heat almost to boiling, cool, and proceed with the extraction and photometric measurement as described in the preparation of the calibration curve. Correct for the reagent blank.

Indium.   Indium can be determined photometrically by dithizone–chloroform or oxine–chloroform extraction. Neither is specific for indium, but by separating the indium first by dithizone extraction and then determining it by oxine extraction, the desired specificity is obtained. Rhodium and iridium interfere seriously, leading to very low results. Beryllium interferes if present in amounts greater than about 0.1 mg. The procedure is given below (45).

Procedure

REAGENTS. *Standard Indium Solution.* Dissolve 0.1000 g of indium metal in 5 ml of concentrated nitric acid by warming. Boil to expel brown fumes. Cool, transfer to a 1-liter volumetric flask, and dilute to the mark. Transfer 50 ml of this solution to a 1-liter volumetric flask and dilute to volume with water. The indium concentration of this final solution is 5 μg/ml.

pH 3.5 BUFFER SOLUTION. In 2 liters of water in a 4-liter container, dissolve 40 ml of concentrated nitric acid, 40 ml of concentrated ammonium hydroxide, and 4 g of potassium acid phthalate, then dilute with water to 4 liter. Neutralize carefully with ammonium hydroxide until the pH is 3.5 as measured with a pH meter.

REDISTILLED CHLOROFORM. To a round-bottom flask add a few grains of 20–30 mesh silicon carbide, about 0.1 g of calcium oxide, and 800 ml of reagent grade chloroform. Distill gently on a water bath. Discard the first 25 ml of distillate, and collect the next 700 ml in a dark bottle to which 7 ml of ethanol has been added as a preservative. Use this whenever chloroform is called for in this procedure.

CALIBRATION. Transfer 0, 2.0, 4.0, 6.0, 8.0, and 10.0 ml of the standard indium solution to 125-ml conical flasks and add 2 ml of 1:9 perchloric acid to each. Dilute to 20 ml, then add 1 drop of 0.1% aqueous m-cresol purple indicator solution plus a small piece of Congo red paper. Neutralize carefully by dropwise addition of 1:9 ammonium hydroxide until the solution just starts to turn yellow. Continue adding ammonium hydroxide until the edges of the Congo red paper just turn red. Pour the solution into a 125-ml separatory funnel. Wash down the sides of the flask with 25 ml of the pH 3.5 buffer solution and add the washing to the funnel. Add 20 ml of freshly prepared solution of 1.000 g of 8-quinolinol in 200 ml of chloroform, and proceed with the extraction and photometric determination of indium as described for the preparation of the calibration curve for gallium (p. 395).

SAMPLE ANALYSIS. Dissolve and distill the germanium or germanium dioxide as described in the method for phosphorus (p. 392), but omitting the distillation with hydrobromic acid. When the germanium has been completely removed, expel all but about 0.2 ml of the perchloric acid by heating on a flame. Cool, wash down the sides of the flask with 10 ml of water, and pour into a 125-ml separatory funnel. Repeat the wash transfer with two more 5-ml portions of water. Add 2 ml of 10% aqueous ammonium citrate solution and 1 drop of 0.1% m-cresol purple indicator solution. Neutralize by dropwise addition of ammonium hydroxide until the solution just turns yellow. Add 5 ml of 1:9 perchloric acid. Add 10 ml of 0.1% solution of dithizone in chloroform, shake, and allow the phases to separate. Drain and discard the chloroform layer. Rinse the inside walls of the funnel with about 2 ml of chloroform and again drain and discard the chloroform layer. Repeat the extraction with a second 10-ml portion of the dithizone solution to ensure complete removal of bismuth. Rinse the walls with 2 ml of chloroform, shake, allow to settle, and drain and discard the chloroform layer. If the aqueous layer is very pink because of the presence of chromium, add 1 or 2 drops of the m-cresol purple indicator solution to ensure a more pronounced color change in the subsequent neutralization.

Neutralize by dropwise addition of ammonium hydroxide until the solution just turns yellow and then just purple. Add 5 ml of 10% aqueous sodium cyanide solution, then 10 ml of a 0.01% solution of dithizone in chloroform, and shake. After phase separation is accomplished, drain off the lower layer to a second separatory funnel. Wash down the walls of the funnel with about 2 ml of chloroform and again drain the lower layer to the second funnel. Repeat the extraction and chloroform washing twice more with 10-ml portions of the 0.01% dithizone solution, collecting the chloroform extracts and washings in the same 125-ml funnel. After the last washing, discard the aqueous solution.

Add 50 ml of a solution of one drop of concentrated ammonium hydroxide in 500 ml of water, prepared daily, shake, and allow the phases to separate. Drain the lower layer to a 125-ml conical Vycor flask. Wash down the walls of the funnel with about 2 ml of chloroform and drain to the flask. Discard the aqueous phase. Add 0.5 ml of concentrated nitric acid to the chloroform solution and place on an asbestos pad on a low-temperature hot plate. Boil gently until the chloroform is completely expelled. Add 1 ml of 70–72 wt % perchloric acid and move to a warmer part of the plate; evaporate to copious fumes of perchloric acid. Do not rush the evaporation; oxidation of the organic matter may not be complete and high values for indium will result. Finally swirl over an open flame to expel all but about 0.2 ml of the acid. Cool and wash down the sides of the flask with 20 ml of water. The solution should be colorless. Add 1 ml of a 1% aqueous sodium metabisulfite solution and a small piece of Congo red paper, plus 1 drop of 0.1% m-cresol purple indicator solution, and proceed with the neutralization, extraction, and photometric determination as given for the preparation of the calibration curve. Correct for the reagent blank.

Boron. A photometric determination of boron in germanium and germanium oxide has been developed, but the method is long and tedious (46). Spectrographic determination, preceded by distillation to expel the germanium while keeping the boron from distilling over by complexing it with mannitol, is claimed to have a sensitivity of 4×10^{-8} g of boron (47,48).

Selenium. By distilling off the germanium tetrachloride in the presence of hydrazine, selenium is kept behind. Potassium bromide and sulfuric acid are then added, and the selenium distilled as the tetrabromide into dilute ammonium hydroxide. It is determined spectrophotometrically with sodium *p*-hydrazinebenzenesulfonate at 520 nm (49) (see SELENIUM).

GERMANIUM ALLOYS

In the usual meaning of the word, few germanium "alloys" are of importance. In semiconductor applications, germanium may be "doped" with extremely small amounts of other metals, principally those of groups III and V of the periodic system; the determination of these "alloying" elements has already been discussed above, in so far as chemical methods are applicable to them.

Little has been published on the analysis of germanium alloys. Most of the methods for the determination of germanium, particularly the gravimetric and volumetric procedures outlined earlier (pp. 382–385), are applicable to germanium alloys. The two following procedures, one gravimetric and the other volumetric, are directed specifically to the determination of germanium in germanium-rich alloys.

Gravimetric Method. This procedure (50) is based on the fact that germanium dioxide is insoluble in concentrated nitric–sulfuric acids, while the sulfates of most metals are soluble. Germanium-rich alloys are most conveniently dissolved in nitric–hydrofluoric–sulfuric acid mixtures; evaporation of such solutions must be carried out at low temperatures to avoid loss of germanium as the fluoride. Overnight evaporation is recommended.

Procedure

In a 250-ml high-temperature polypropylene beaker dissolve a sample containing 100–1000 mg of germanium alloy in the form of small chips, using a solution of 25 ml of water and 10 ml each of concentrated hydrofluoric, nitric, and sulfuric acids. Place a polyethylene cover on the beaker and let the reaction proceed for 15 min. Remove the cover while washing it with a minimum amount of water. Start the evaporation on a constant-temperature water bath, at a sample temperature of 70–75°C, and continue for about 18 hr (overnight). When most of the nitric and hydrofluoric acids have evaporated, the sulfuric acid will cause the temperature to rise and stabilize at 85–90°C.

Wash down the sides of the beaker with 8–10 ml of water and evaporate the suspension for 2 hr more. Transfer the precipitate to a 250-ml glass beaker using water to wash it in; police with a plastic scraper. Add 1.5 g of granular boric acid and 2 ml of nitric acid to the glass beaker and evaporate without a cover to fumes of sulfur trioxide. Cool, add 100 ml of concentrated nitric acid, warm to 70–75°C, and maintain at this temperature for 10–15 min so that all sulfate salts dissolve. Stir occasionally.

Cool to 25°C and vacuum filter the germanium dioxide through a weighed fritted 30-ml porcelain Gooch crucible previously heated in a muffle furnace at 750–800°C. Police the beaker and wash the precipitate with 10–15 ml of concentrated nitric acid. Dry the crucible at 250°C for 10 min on a hot plate, then transfer to a muffle furnace and heat for 10 min at 750–800°C. One g of germanium dioxide is equivalent to 0.6940 g of germanium.

Volumetric Method. This method is particularly recommended for germanium–gold alloys, which are soluble only in aqua regia, and the presence of chloride and nitrate ions introduces a complication with many procedures. This method is based on the reaction of mannitol with germanic acid to form a titratable monoprotic acid, which can be titrated with standard alkali (27).

Procedure

Weigh a sample containing 20–35 mg of germanium and place it in a flask connected to a condenser. Add 20 ml of 12 N hydrochloric acid and 5 ml of 16 N nitric acid. Allow it to react at room temperature for 1 hr, with the outlet of the still immersed in 75 ml of water cooled in an ice bath. When the sample is nearly dissolved, heat to boiling, and continue until only about 3 ml of liquid is left in the flask. When the distillation is complete remove the stopper of the distilling flask, allow to cool, disconnect the flask, and wash germanium oxide from the sides and tip of the condenser tube with 25 ml of 6 N sodium hydroxide solution. Wash the condenser tube with water to prepare it for the next sample. Allow the distillate to cool in ice water. Wash the gold solution out of the sample flask for recovery if desired. This cooling prevents loss of germanium chloride and helps prevent formation of a colored gold solution from traces of gold that sometimes distill over.

To the cold distillate add a few drops of 0.5% ethanolic phenolphthalein indicator solution. Add 6 N sodium hydroxide solution just to a red color; about 15 ml will be needed. Immediately add 6 N hydrochloric acid dropwise just to clear the color, then add 5 drops of a 0.1% aqueous *p*-nitrophenol indicator solution. If the solution is yellow, add 1 more drop of 6 N hydrochloric acid. From a buret add 0.02 N sodium hydroxide solution until the solution is yellow (pH 5.5). Take the initial reading of the buret at this point. Add 1.0 g of mannitol and begin the titration. When the yellow color has returned, add 5 drops of a saturated aqueous phenol red indicator solution. A deeper yellow results; continue the titration until a definite red tint is seen by looking horizontally through the solution (pH 6.8). Alternatively carry out the titration with a potentiometer or a pH meter, using pH 5.5 and 6.8 as the start and end point of the titration.

Standardize the 0.02 N sodium hydroxide solution against pure germanium by carrying it through the procedure, except that the reaction time with the hydrochloric–nitric acids must be increased from 1 hr to 4 hr.

GERMANIUM COMPOUNDS

The germanium compounds of importance are germanium dioxide, germanium tetrachloride, and the numerous organogermanium compounds.

Germanium Dioxide. The principal use of germanium dioxide, GeO_2, is as a precursor of the metal. As already stated (p. 378), the principal specification for germanium dioxide merely requires that satisfactory metal can be made from it by hydrogen reduction (13).

Germanium dioxide exists in two forms, so-called soluble and insoluble. The properties of these two forms are listed in Table 4 (1). Germanium dioxide can be reduced, especially at high temperature under reducing conditions, to the monoxide, GeO; this is considerably more volatile, leading to the danger of loss of germanium under improper conditions.

There are several ASTM standards related to germanium dioxide; however, none of them gives chemical properties. In a standard method of test for the volatile content of germanium dioxide (51), the loss on ignition at 800°C is determined, and

Table 4. Properties of Germanium Dioxide

	Soluble	Insoluble
crystal structure	hexagonal	tetragonal
density, g/cm³	4.7	6.2
solubility in water, 25°C, %	0.45	0.00045
action of hydrochloric acid	reacts to form soluble $GeCl_4$ or H_2GeCl_6	none
action of sodium hydroxide solution	reacts to form soluble Na_2GeO_3 (or $Na_2Ge(OH)_6$)	none

another standard (52) specifies a test for the bulk density of the dioxide. A recommended practice (13) gives instructions for the preparation of a test ingot of germanium from a sample of germanium dioxide by hydrogen reduction and zone refining. The suitability of the ingot prepared in this way is then tested by two electrical tests (53,54).

The determination of germanium in germanium dioxide or of the trace impurities present follow the procedures outlined earlier, in the Methods of Analysis section.

Germanium Tetrachloride. Germanium tetrachloride has a low boiling point and thus high volatility; Table 5 (1) lists the vapor pressure of $GeCl_4$ at various temperatures. For this reason, it is utilized in many analytical procedures as well as in the recovery and purification of the metal.

Table 5. Vapor Pressure of Germanium Tetrachloride

Temperature, °C	Torr	Atm
−49	0.76	0.001
−19	7.6	0.01
0	26	0.034
21	76	0.1
62	380	0.5
83.1	760	1.0

Organogermanium Compounds. Over 750 organogermanium compounds have been synthesized but they are mostly of academic interest. For more details, see References 55–58.

In the determination of the germanium content of organogermanium compounds, the principal problem is to dissolve the compounds without loss of germanium in a volatile form, while at the same time destroying the organic matter. Fusion in a nickel bomb with sodium hydroxide or sodium hydroxide–sodium carbonate mixtures at temperatures as high as 940°C has been proposed (59). The specific nature of the organic moieties will determine the nature of the precautions required. Phenyl compounds seem to be especially difficult to decompose. Once the germanium is in solution, it may be determined gravimetrically, by precipitation as the sulfide which is then ignited to the oxide for weighing; see p. 382. Reduction to germanium(II) followed by oxidimetric titration can also be used. For details, see p. 383.

A procedure (60) having wide applicability uses fuming sulfuric acid plus 30% hydrogen peroxide to decompose the sample. The normality of the sulfuric acid is then adjusted to 6 N, after which precipitation by hydrogen sulfide and ignition to the oxide proceed as already described.

In another method (60) the sample is decomposed with nitric and sulfuric acids; hydrochloric acid is then added and the germanium distilled as the tetrachloride into hydrochloric acid solution. Any of the methods previously described can then be used for the final determination of germanium.

Chalmers and Sinclair (61) found that the germanomolybdic acid formed when ammonium molybdate is added to a germanium-containing solution is stabilized by acetone. According to these authors, organogermanium compounds can often be simply analyzed by adding 5–20 mg of sample to a mixture of 10–12 ml of acetone and 4 ml of 2 N sulfuric acid in a 50-ml standard flask, shaking until the sample has dissolved, and then adding 6–7 ml of an 8% ammonium molybdate solution prepared and stored in polyethylene and measuring the absorbance in a 1-cm cell at 430 nm.

Bibliography

GENERAL REFERENCES

1. J. R. Musgrave, "Germanium," in I. M. Kolthoff and P. J. Elving, eds., *Treatise on Analytical Chemistry*, Vol. 2, Part 2, Interscience Publishers, a division of John Wiley & Sons, Inc., New York, 1962, pp. 207–245.
2. H. R. Harner, "Germanium," in C. A. Hampel, ed., *Rare Metals Handbook*, 2nd ed., Reinhold Publishing Corp., New York, 1961, pp. 188–197.
3. P. F. Kane and G. B. Larrabee, *Characterization of Semiconductor Materials*, McGraw-Hill Book Co., New York, 1970.
4. H. H. Krause and O. H. Johnson, *Anal. Chem.* **25**, 134 (1953).
5. J. Korkisch, *Modern Methods for the Separation of Rarer Metal Ions*, Pergamon Press, New York, 1969, pp. 345–356.
6. E. B. Sandell, *Colorimetric Determination of Traces of Metals*, 3rd ed., Interscience Publishers, Inc., New York, 1959, pp. 482–493.
7. P. F. Kane, "Semiconductors," in F. J. Welcher, ed., *Standard Methods of Chemical Analysis*, Vol. 3, 6th ed., Part B: *Instrumental Methods*, Van Nostrand Co., Inc., Princeton, N.J., 1966, pp. 1764–1811.
8. H. R. Harner and A. W. Laubengayer, "Germanium," in A. Standen, ed., *Kirk-Othmer Encyclopedia of Chemical Technology*, Vol. 10, 2nd ed., Interscience Publishers, a division of John Wiley & Sons, Inc., New York, 1966, pp. 519–527.

SPECIFIC REFERENCES

9. J. R. Musgrave, Eagle-Picher Industries, private communication, 1970.
10. *Minerals Yearbook*, U.S. Department of Commerce, Washington, D.C., 1968.
11. F. S. Goulding and Y. Stone, *Science* **170**, 280 (1970).
12. D. J. Fink and J. M. Carroll, eds. *Standard Handbook for Electrical Engineers*, 10th ed., Sect. 4, McGraw-Hill Book Co., New York, 1968, para. 589.
13. *ASTM F 27-68, Preparing a Test Ingot of Germanium by Hydrogen Reduction of Germanium Dioxide*, American Society for Testing & Materials, Philadelphia, Pa., 1969.
14. *Chem. Week* **107** (18), 35 (Oct. 28, 1970).
15. *ASTM F 28-66, Minority-Carrier Lifetime in Bulk Germanium and Silicon*, American Society for Testing & Materials, Philadelphia, Pa., 1969.
16. *ASTM F 76-68, Hall Mobility in Extrinsic Semiconductor Single Crystals*, American Society for Testing & Materials, Philadelphia, Pa., 1969.
17. *ASTM F 81-70, Bulk Semiconductor Radial Resistivity Variation*, American Society for Testing & Materials, Philadelphia, Pa., 1970.
18. W. M. Dressel, *U.S. Bureau Mines RI 5907* (1962).
19. C. L. Luke and M. E. Campbell, *Anal. Chem.* **28**, 1273 (1956).
20. D. Grdenić and V. Jagodić, *J. Inorg. Nucl. Chem.* **26**, 167 (1964).
21. A. Tchakirian, *Ann. Chim.* **12**, 415 (1939).
22. H. B. Rayner, *Anal. Chem.* **35**, 1097 (1963).
23. G. J. Abel, Jr., *Anal. Chem.* **32**, 1886 (1960).
24. C. L. Luke, *Anal. Chem.* **41**, 237 (1968).
25. F. Wlotzka, *Z. Anal. Chem.* **215**, 81 (1966).
26. H. J. Cluley, *Analyst* **76**, 517 (1951).

27. J. F. Reed, *Anal. Chem.* **38,** 1085 (1966).

28. K. L. Cheng, *Anal. Chim. Acta* **35,** 293 (1966).

29. D. C. Manning, *At. Absorption Newsletter* (*Perkin-Elmer Co.*), **6** (2), 35 (1967).

30. J. Ramirez-Munoz and M. Roth, *Flame Notes* **2** (1), 18 (1967).

31. R. E. Popham and W. G. Schrenk, *Spectrochim. Acta,* Part B **23** (8), 543 (1968).

32. W. C. Tennant, *Appl. Spect.* **21,** 282 (1967).

33. M. A. Menkovskii, S. A. Gordon, and N. N. Nurminskii, *Zavodsk. Lab.* **28,** 1321 (1962); *Chem. Abstr.* **59,** 345 (1963).

34. K. P. Medvedev, L. M. Khar'kina, V. M. Petropol'skaya, and K. A. Nikitiva, *Zavodsk. Lab.* **29,** 805 (1963); *Chem. Abstr.* **59,** 9695 (1963).

35. E. Pungor and A. Halász, *Magy. Kém. Folyóirat* **73,** 451 (1967); *Chem. Abstr.* **67,** 122002 (1967).

36. V. A. Oshman and V. M. Volkov, *Zavodsk. Lab.* **27,** 1341 (1961); *Chem. Abstr.* **56,** 10899 (1962).

37. T. Toyoguchi and H. Shimizu, *Bunseki Kagaku* **16,** 565 (1967); *Chem. Abstr.* **68,** 18358 (1968).

38. C. L. Luke, *Chemist-Analyst* **54,** 109 (1965).

39. R. Pietra, S. Sabbioni, and J. Paul, *U.S. At. Energy Comm. EUR* 2753f (1967).

40. R. DeNeve, D. DeSoete, and J. Hoste, *Anal. Chim. Acta* **40,** 379 (1968).

41. C. L. Luke and M. E. Campbell, *Anal. Chem.* **25,** 1568 (1953).

42. C. L. Luke, Bell Telephone Laboratories, private communication, 1970.

43. T. J. Veleker, *Anal. Chem.* **34,** 87 (1962).

44. A. Foldzinska and J. Malinowski, *Nukleonika* **8,** 233 (1963); *Chem. Abstr.* **60,** 11363 (1964).

45. C. L. Luke and M. E. Campbell, *Anal. Chem.* **28,** 1340 (1956).

46. C. L. Luke, *Anal. Chem.* **27,** 1150 (1955).

47. O. P. Malkova, A. N. Zhukova, and N. K. Budnewskii, *Tr. po Khim. i Khim. Tekhnol.* **1,** 188 (1963); *Chem. Abstr.* **60,** 7446 (1964).

48. O. P. Malkova, A. N. Tumanova, and N. K. Rudnevskii, *Zh. Anal. Khim.* **20,** 130 (1965); *Chem. Abstr.* **62,** 12430 (1965).

49. V. I. Rigin, N. N. Mel'nichenko, and V. K. Yanitskii, *Zavodsk. Lab.* **33,** 1370 (1967); *Chem. Abstr.* **68,** 84096 (1968).

50. W. W. White, *Anal. Chem.* **38,** 512 (1966).

51. *ASTM F 5-60* (*1968*), *Volatile Content of Germanium Dioxide,* American Society for Testing & Materials, Philadelphia, Pa., 1969.

52. *ASTM F 6-60* (*1968*), *Bulk Density of Germanium Dioxide,* American Society for Testing & Materials, Philadelphia, Pa., 1969.

53. *ASTM F 42-69, Conductivity Type of Semiconductors,* American Society for Testing & Materials, Philadelphia, Pa., 1969.

54. *ASTM F 43-70, Resistivity of Semiconductor Materials,* American Society for Testing & Materials, Philadelphia, Pa., 1970.

55. F. Rijkens, *Organogermanium Compounds,* Germanium Research Committee, Utrecht, Netherlands, 1960.

56. R. K. Ingham and H. Gilman, "Organogermanium Polymers," in F. G. S. Stone and W. A. G. Graham, eds., *Inorganic Polymers,* Academic Press, Inc., New York, 1962, p. 353.

57. G. E. Coates, *Organo-Metallic Compounds,* 2nd ed., Methuen & Co., London, 1960, p. 165.

58. D. L. Venezky, "Inorganic Polymers," in H. F. Mark, N. G. Gaylord, and N. M. Bikales, eds., *Encyclopedia of Polymer Science and Technology,* Vol. 7, Interscience Publishers, a division of John Wiley & Sons, Inc., New York, 1967, pp. 664–691.

59. V. A. Klimova and M. D. Vitalina, *Zh. Anal. Khim.* **19,** 1254 (1964); *Chem. Abstr.* **62,** 1070 (1965).

60. C. L. Wilson and D. W. Wilson, *Comprehensive Analytical Chemistry,* Vol. 1 B, Elsevier, New York, 1960, p. 594.

61. R. A. Chalmers and A. G. Sinclair, *Anal. Chim. Acta* **33,** 384 (1965).

Frederick A. Lowenheim
Consultant

GERMICIDES.   See Disinfectants and antiseptics, Vol. 11, pp. 537–572.

GIN.   See Alcoholic beverages, distilled, Vol. 4, pp. 462–494.

GLASS AND GLASS–CERAMICS

Constitution of glasses.. 405
Methods of analysis... 412
　Composition analysis... 414
　　Chemical methods for individual constituents........................... 416
　　Redox state determinations.. 443
　　Chelometry.. 444
　　Flame spectroscopy... 449
　　Emission spectroscopy.. 453
　　X-ray emission spectroscopy.. 454
　　Spark source spectrometry.. 456
　　Electroanalytical methods.. 457
　Determination of properties... 459
　　Spectrophotometry.. 459
　　X-ray diffraction... 465
　　Microscopy... 471
　　Electron microprobe analysis... 475
　Analysis of gases in glass.. 478
Bibliography... 481

Glass is a noncrystalline solid; it is characterized by an absence of long-range order in its atomic structure. Although a definition on the basis of this concept would thus include organic as well as inorganic glasses and the metastable state of a variety of normally crystalline elements and compounds, consideration will be given here only to those glasses of major commercial importance, namely, oxide glasses. Consequently, the definition of the American Society for Testing and Materials that describes glass as "an inorganic product of fusion which has cooled to a rigid condition without crystallizing," is appropriate. Equally applicable, but more descriptive is an alternate definition which states, "a glass is an inorganic substance in a condition which is continuous with, and analogous to, the liquid state of that substance, but which, as the result of having been cooled from a fused condition, has attained so high a degree of viscosity as to be, for all practical purposes, rigid."

Occurring in nature as obsidian, natural glass evidently found widespread application during the Stone Age for weapons and tools. Further attesting to the ubiquity of glass as well as its antiquity is the recent discovery of glass, much of it as spherules, among the prominent phases comprising certain of the lunar soil samples returned by Apollo 11. Man's involvement with glassmaking probably did not commence until about 12,000 BC when he undertook decorative glazing of stone beads. From this he moved, around 7000 BC, to manufacture of articles made completely of glass. From the first, glass seemed to find primary application as a decorative or artistic form, as glazes, jewelry, and amphoras, suitable as luxuries afforded only by the very rich. Although later gradually diversifying in application to such uses as containers, drinking vessels, window glazing, and optical components, glass remained largely a luxury material empirically produced and primarily serving artistic purposes until early in this present century. With the inception, around 1900, of research specifically oriented to the study of glass, technical progress promptly accelerated. Results of this research and additional information about the chemistry and technology of glass can be obtained from the general references (1–12). Also see CERAMICS, Vol. 9, pp. 189–232.

The significant position held today by glasses and glass–ceramics in the field of engineering materials is due to the wide variety of physical and chemical properties that can be designed into these substances. Thermal expansion, thermal stress resistance, thermal shock resistance, viscosity, Young's modulus, Poisson's ratio, impact abrasion resistance, volume resistivity, dielectric constant, loss factor, power factor, refractive index, and color constitute some of the more important and controllable properties of glasses and glass–ceramics. Of these properties, among the more basic are viscosity and thermal expansion. Viscosity is of considerable importance in all phases of glass manufacture inasmuch as it determines practically all the

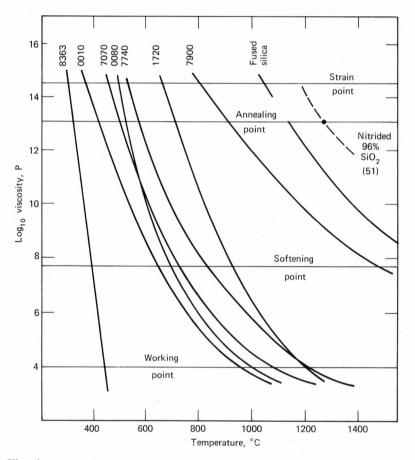

Fig. 1. Viscosity versus temperature for some commercial glasses. Courtesy Corning Glass Works. The four digit numbers are Corning Glass Works code numbers.

melting, forming, annealing, sealing, and upper use temperatures of glass. Figure 1 illustrates the behavior of viscosity with temperature for several commercial glasses over a wide temperature range, as well as the rheological basis for the working point, softening point, annealing point, and strain point (13). Thermal expansion is of prime importance to such considerations as sealing and where thermal stress and thermal shock resistance are involved. Figure 2 shows the expansion–temperature relationships of some typical glasses and glass–ceramics (14). Indicated by the open circles are the setting points, that is, the temperature at which the glass "sets up" and below which strain cannot be relieved by plastic flow.

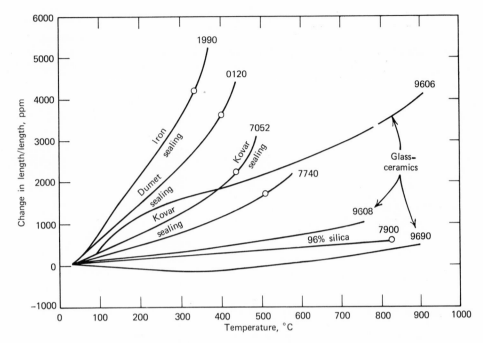

Fig. 2. Expansion versus temperature for some commercial gasses and glass–ceramics. Courtesy Corning Glass Works. The four digit numbers are Corning Glass Works code numbers.

Chemical durability or corrosion resistance is an additional property often of considerable practical importance to the application of these materials. A rather comprehensive review of the chemical durability of a variety of commercial glasses as it relates to glass composition, the process of fabrication, and the service conditions has been published by Bacon (15).

Constitution of Glasses

Accounting for the diversity and range of properties and adaptability of glasses and glass–ceramics is their complex makeup. Few materials are so diversely constituted. Practically every element in the Periodic Table can be incorporated into a glass. The majority of the elements actively participate in the structure of glass either as network former, intermediate, or modifier (see Fig. 13, p. 466). The latter class of elements is ionic and interstitial in the structure, whereas the former classifications are characteristically covalent in nature and combine to form the random network "backbone" structure of glass. The identity and classification of several of the elements that commonly combine to form stable glasses are shown in Table 1 (11). With regard to composition, glass, unlike inorganic compounds, considered integrally, is nonstoichiometric. It is really most analogous to a solution, hence its ability to accommodate wide ranges of concentrations of such a variety of elements. Elements that do not "dissolve" into the glass structure can often be dispersed colloidally. Permanent gases do have a finite but very low solubility (16) in glass; otherwise, gaseous elements and compounds exist as tiny bubbles, called seeds or blisters.

Table 1. Classification, Valence, and Coordination of Oxides Constituting Glass

Structural role	Metal in oxide	Valence	Coordination number
glass formers	B	3	3
	Si	4	4
	Ge	4	4
	Al	3	4
	B	3	4
	P	5	4
	V	5	4
	As	5	4
	Sb	5	4
	Zr	4	6
intermediates	Ti	4	6
	Zn	2	2
	Pb	2	2
	Al	3	6
	Th	4	8
	Be	2	4
	Zr	4	8
	Cd	2	2
modifiers	Sc	3	6
	La	3	7
	Y	3	8
	Sn	4	6
	Ga	3	6
	In	3	6
	Th	4	12
	Pb	4	6
	Mg	2	6
	Li	1	4
	Pb	2	4
	Zn	2	4
	Ba	2	8
	Ca	2	8
	Sr	2	8
	Cd	2	4
	Na	1	6
	Cd	2	6
	K	1	9
	Rb	1	10
	Hg	2	6
	Cs	1	12

In addition to the glass-formers, intermediates, and modifiers, another important ingredient usually present in glasses and glass–ceramics at trace to minor levels is the fining agent. Fining is that part of the melting process during which gaseous inclusions are removed from the molten glass. Occurring as bubbles such gaseous inclusions constitute defects that affect the appearance, light transmittance, and strength of the final product. Fining agents, by either evaporation or a chemical reaction, evolve a gas within the melt which accelerates fining by causing existing bubbles to become larger. Arsenic or antimony oxide (in combination with nitrate) are fining agents which release oxygen; sulfur trioxide is given off by the sulfates; halides such as

Table 2. Chemical Composition Ranges of Major Types of Commercial Glasses and Glass–Ceramics[a]

Element oxide	soda-lime 0080, 0081, 7220, 7250, IA-9, X-4, T glass	borosilicate 7740, 7800, 7050, 7720, N-51A, K-705, K-772, G-20, E-glass	alumino-silicate 1720, 1723, 0315, 0312, 0331, EZ-1, S-glass	opal 6720, 6810, 8601	colored 2405, 2475, 3530	lead/barium 0010, 0014, 0120, 8871, 9010, EG-4, TM-5, KG-12	special 7280, 8603, RL-1, 8096, 8097	glass-ceramics 9608, 9606, Cervit, Neoceram
SiO_2	65–75	65–82	60–70	60–70	65–75	5–70	50–80	50–80
Al_2O_3	0.2–3	0.2–6	10–30	0–10	1–3	0–5	4–30	15–30
B_2O_3	0–8	5–30	0–8	0–5	–	+	0–20	0–3
Na_2O	13–18	0–6	0–15	1–20	5–20	5–10	0–15	0–15
K_2O	0–2	0–5	0–2	0–8	1–15	5–10	0–5	–
Li_2O	+	0–2	0–10	–	–	0–2	0–10	0–10
MgO	0–8	0–5	5–15	+	1–5	+	–	0–15
CaO	5–20	0–20	0–10	0–15	2–10	+	–	0–1
BaO	0–1	0–5	0–10	–		0–25	1–10	0–15
PbO	–	0–5	–	0–3		0–82	0–5	0–80
TiO_2	–	–	–	–		–	–	4–10
ZrO_2	–	–	–	–		–	0–20	0–5
ZnO	0–5	0–10	–	0–20	5–15	–	0–5	0–5
CdO	–	–	–	–	0.3–2	–	–	–
P_2O_5	–	–	–	0–5		–	–	0–5
As_2O_3	+	+	+	0–10	+	+	+	+
Sb_2O_3	+	–	+	+	+	+	+	–
S or SO_3	+	–	–	+	0–0.5	+	–	–
Se	–	–	–	–	0–0.5	–	(b)	–
Cl, Br	–	–	–	(c)	–	–	(b)	–
Ag	–	–	–	(c)	–	–	(b)(c)	–
Au	–	–	–	–	–	–	(c)	–
Ce	–	–	–	(c)	–	0–2	(c)	–
F	–	0–1	–	0–10	(a)	0–1	+	0–1
colorants[b]								

[a] + May be present in minor amounts.
– Usually not present.
(a) Present in amounts ranging from 0.001 to 1% to produce appropriate color.
(b) Present in photochromic compositions.
(c) Present in photosensitive compositions.
[b] Co, Ni, Cu, Fe, U, Cr, V, etc.

The 4-digit code corresponds to Corning Glass Works released glasses.
IA, K, N, EZ, EG, TM, KG, RL glasses are Owens–Illinois, Inc. compositions.
E, T, S are Owens-Corning fibrous glasses.
G is Jena glass.
X is a glass produced by General Electric Co., Great Britain.

sodium and potassium chloride fine by an evaporation process. Depending on the glass composition and the type of fining agent, the retention of the fining agent in the final glass may range from 0.01% for chlorides and sulfates to the order of 1% for arsenic or antimony.

Color is imparted, sometimes unintentionally from batch contaminants, through dissolution of such transition elements as iron, chromium, nickel, cobalt, manganese, vanadium, copper, cerium, and uranium. Oxidation state, coordination number, and the presence of auxiliary elements such as titanium will also alter the color of a particular ion. Black glass is obtained with high concentrations of a combination of manganese and chromium, or relatively high concentrations of lead sulfide, iron sulfide, or cobalt polyselenide. Color is also imparted through controlled nucleation and growth of such species as cadmium sulfoselenide, cadmium selenide, selenium, or metallic crystals, eg, gold, copper, and silver, to colloidal particle size dimensions.

Although oxygen is never determined during an analysis, in keeping with the convention long established by the rock analysts, the compositions of glasses and glass–ceramics are always given in terms of the elemental oxides. Until an accurate procedure is developed for major amounts of oxygen in inorganic oxide materials, or unless one is considering nonoxide glasses, the assumption that the metallic elements constituting glasses or glass–ceramics exist as their common oxides will have to suffice. Several elements, notably the transition elements, arsenic, antimony, sulfur, selenium, fluoride, and chloride can exist in glass in other than their highest oxidation state. Analytical methods have been developed to deal with many of these constituents and their presence is duly reported in the proper oxidation state as the oxide, or as is often the case for sulfur, and always the case for the halogens, as the negative element ion. As previously pointed out, glasses and glass–ceramics are not discrete stoichiometric compounds. Hence, rational analysis in which the appropriate anions and cations are matched to manifest the conditions as they exist in the glass is at present impossible.

There are no industry-wide standardized compositions; glass compositions are usually highly proprietary and traditionally they are specified by properties rather than composition. Nevertheless, it may be useful to classify the commercially impor-

Table 3. Concentration Ranges of Components in Optical Glasses

Elements	Oxide concentration range, wt %
Li, Na, K	0.1–20
Be, Mg, Ca, Sr, Ba	0.1–50
Y, La, Ce	1–30
Ti, Zr	0.1–20
Ta, Nb	1–30
W	1–10
Zn, Cd	0.5–10
B, Al	1–50
Si, Ge, Pb	1–100
P, As, Sb, Bi	0.1–60
S, Se, Te	0.1–1[a]
Th	1–30
F^-, I^-	0.1–10[b]

[a] Sometimes present in their lowest oxidation state.
[b] Always present in their lowest oxidation state.

Table 4. Typical Compositions of Commercially Important Glasses and Glass-Ceramics

Element oxide	Chemical composition, wt %							
	soda-lime container	TV bulb glass	chemically resistant borosilicate	heat-resistant aluminosilicate	phosphate opal	optical barium crown	glass-ceramic for cooking	glass-ceramic for technical applications
SiO_2	74.2	66.5	80.5	58.5	75.9	45.0	58.6	56.0
Al_2O_3	1.8	3.9	2.2	19.0	1.4	0.1	27.9	19.7
B_2O_3			12.9	5.1	12.8	4.5		
Na_2O	12.5	7.1	3.8	0.9	5.9	0.6	0.4	
K_2O	0.4	6.9	0.4		0.3	6.8	0.1	
Li_2O		0.2					2.8	
MgO	0.5	0.3		8.8	0.1		2.6	15.0
CaO	10.6	0.6		7.2	1.4			0.1
SrO		0.2						
BaO		11.2				22.4		
PbO		2.2				4.7	0.4	9.0
TiO_2							1.9	
ZrO_2							2.5	
ZnO						15.5		
P_2O_5					1.6		3.0	
As_2O_3		0.1					0.5	0.3
Sb_2O_3		0.4			0.2			
SO_3	0.2	0.8						
F					0.4		0.1	

tant products into the following nine categories: soda-lime, borosilicate, alumino-silicate, opal, colored, optical, lead/barium, and special glasses, and glass–ceramics. Table 2 shows the approximate composition ranges in weight percent for some of the leading members of each category, except optical glasses. The range of optical glass compositions is a field in itself and is indicated in Table 3 (17). Table 4 gives typical compositions of some commercially important glasses and glass–ceramics. Additional glass compositions are tabulated in the CERAMICS article, Vol. 9, on pp. 198–201.

Soda-lime–silica glasses lead all the other glass compositions in tonnage production. Consisting chiefly of silica, but also including soda, lime (sometimes of dolomitic limestone origin), and a small amount of alumina, there is relatively minor variance between the compositions employed for sheet (window glass), plate, containers, and lamp bulbs. The advantages of these compositions are that lime glasses are relatively easy to melt and fabricate, and the raw materials are inexpensive.

The *borosilicate* glass family is an outgrowth of a concept in chemically resistant glass that was introduced by Corning Glass Works in 1915 to replace the then dwindling supply of Jena chemically resistant laboratory ware, originating from Germany. The composition, essentially unchanged, continues as a major factor in the production of ware for the laboratory and chemical process industry. This heat and chemically resistant glass is high silica in composition and contains a significant amount of boric oxide together with relatively minor amounts of alkalies and alumina. Modifications of the basic composition have been made to provide a very stable chemically resistant glass that withstands autoclaving and hence is specially suited for pharmaceutical ampoules. Other members of the borosilicate family have been developed for molybdenum, tungsten, and Kovar sealing, and hence are important in the lamp and electronic vacuum tube industries. Still other borosilicates are important for their low dielectric loss and yet others, particularly those containing lanthanum and/or barium, for their optical properties.

Aluminosilicates, containing a major amount of silicate and about 20% alumina together with minor amounts of the alkaline earths and boric oxides, constitute a family of extremely hard glasses used for top-of-stove cooking, combustion tubes, and gage glasses for high-pressure steam boilers. A newer but substantially softer family recently added to this category are the alkali alumino silicates. Containing major amounts of lithia or soda, this latter type of aluminosilicate has the property of undergoing chemical strengthening (18) whereby in a molten salt bath, higher atomic weight alkali ions displace and "stuff" into positions occupied by the lower atomic weight alkali ions originally present in the glass. Thus strengthened, such glasses can have flexural strengths over 100,000 psi. Chemically strengthened glass has already found prominent use as pipets, centrifuge tubes, and automobile windshields and backlights.

Opal glasses achieve their opacity by thermal nucleation and precipitation of crystals with an index of refraction different from that of the base glass. Opal dinnerware and the white stripe on thermometer tubing contain about 5% of a second phase such as zinc sulfide, calcium fluoride, or calcium phosphate. Some opals are the result of the separation of an immiscible glass.

Optical glasses constitute perhaps the most diverse families of glasses. Compositions exist in unlimited variety, ranging from fused silica to multicomponent rare earth optical glasses containing oxides of lanthanum, thorium, tantalum, tungsten, and zirconium. See Table 3 for a summary of their range of compositions. The paramount consideration in formulating refractive optical glasses is the achievement of the desired refractive index and dispersion. Batch cost and simultaneous optimization of other properties, such as chemical durability, must sometimes be compromised by the formulation in order to meet the desired optical specifications. Glasses having a dispersion, ie, a v value, of 55 or above are defined as crown glasses; those having a v value below about 50 are defined as flint glasses. Characteristic of optical glasses, in addition to their designed optical properties, is their high degree of homogeneity and freedom from glass defects such as bubbles, crystalline inclusions, striae, etc. For use in reflective optics, specifically telescope mirrors, the requirements are not quite so stringent. Mirror glasses must mainly possess a low expansion, be weathering resistant, and capable of taking a high surface polish. Of the newer applications of refractive optical glasses, perhaps the most salient is fiber optics; this development has contributed basically to electronic image intensification and medical viewing devices for examining body cavities.

Photosensitive glasses (19,20) are produced by establishing a carefully poised redox system, involving cerous ions, tin or antimony oxide, and dissolved metal ions. Absorption of ultraviolet radiation by the cerium initiates a photochemical reduction of metal and consequent formation of metal nuclei. Subsequent heat treatment causes the latent image to develop by further thermal reduction of the metal with antimony as the electron source. The consequent growth of the metal nuclei to the colloidal size range produces the colored image. Either gold, silver, or copper are suitable metal species. Using silver as the metal ion in conjunction with the appropriate glass system, after the initial "photographic" development process, additional heat treatment will heterogeneously precipitate either a sodium fluoride or a lithium metasilicate opal phase, depending on the glass. The resulting photograph-in-glass consists of an opal glass image that persists through the thickness of the glass, affording an interesting three-dimensional effect. With the lithium metasilicate glass, chemical machining is possible, since the crystallized lithium metasilicate is much more soluble in hydrofluoric acid than the surrounding glass. Thus, precisely patterned parts for such applications as fluid amplifiers and master plates for the flexographic printing process can be accurately shaped.

Photochromic glasses (21,22), which darken on exposure to light and fade when the light intensity decreases, derive their property from the presence of small amounts of silver mixed-halide crystallites, doped with a trace amount of copper. Light from about 3000–6000 Å wavelength acting upon the glass interacts with the dispersed crystals of silver halide, reducing a small amount of silver ion to the metal and producing a corresponding amount of free halogen. Upon removal of the light source the metallic silver and the atomic halogen recombine and the color fades. Using this principle in an appropriate opthalmic glass, prescription-ground "eye comfort" Photochromic lenses have been achieving increasing popularity.

Reconstructed 96% silica glass (23) is made by acid leaching the alkali borate-rich microimmiscible phase that results after heat treating certain sodium borosilicate glasses, and consolidating the resulting silica-rich skeleton by a high-temperature firing. The 96% silica glassware produced in this way has a durability and refractoriness approaching that of fused silica, but can be produced in complex shapes at less cost. A few percent boric oxide and a fraction of a percent each of alumina and zirconia account for the 4% nonsilica portion of the glass.

Glass–ceramics, representing a new field of glass technology, results from the integral conversion of glass to fine-grained (more than 50% crystalline) bodies by homogeneous and heterogeneous nucleation and controlled crystal growth. The process, discovered by Stookey (24,25), is effected by incorporation of a minor ingredient, the nucleating agent, which can be precipitated as multitudinous tiny crystals or immiscible liquid droplets. "Ceramming" takes place at a temperature at which the minor nucleating phase can cause the major constituents of the glass to nucleate and crystallize. Besides metallic colloids, titanium dioxide and titanates, chromic oxide, phosphorus pentoxide, zirconium dioxide, zinc sulfides, and fluorides, incorporated into the base glass to the extent of 1–10 wt % can also serve as nucleating agents. Since normal glass-forming operations can be applied, new materials having unique and useful properties can be fabricated that otherwise would not be manufacturable.

Methods of Analysis

Bulk composition by complete or partial chemical analysis constitutes perhaps the most important component of total characterization of glass and glass–ceramic materials. It determines whether intolerable volatilization losses or dissolution of the refractory melting vessel has occurred; it also detects batching errors. Chemical analysis, although long recognized as an optimal tool for control, was not widely implemented in the past due to the slowness of wet chemical methods. Rheologically significant properties which are composition dependent—such as working range, softening point, annealing point, and strain point—along with careful specification of methods for measuring them (26,26a), have been and continue to be essential in the production control and engineering applications of glass. However, such tools as new rapid chemical methods, electroanalytical methods, flame spectroscopy, direct reading emission spectroscopy, and x-ray spectrometry are now providing rapid and accurate chemical analysis for many production operations. Control by composition is fast approaching standard practice.

The compositions of commercially significant glasses and glass–ceramics normally include only those elements delineated in Table 5. Using the techniques indicated in the table, it is becoming increasingly common to sample and determine each element separately. Not only are such techniques intrinsically more accurate, but cumulative errors are avoided and the total analysis can be accomplished rapidly by this direct unitized approach. However, many occasions still exist where extensive separations are essential. When the more classical approach is mandatory, such newer techniques as ion exchange, electrolysis, solvent extraction, pyrohydrolysis and combustion have helped to relieve the separation problems.

Often the chemical composition alone, unsupported by other information, provides an inadequate description of the material. This is particularly true of glass–ceramics, where the identity and quantity of the crystal phases is of particular significance in the overall characterization. To a considerable degree, the same may be said of opal glasses, whose opacifying phase is much less than 50%, and which may be comprised of crystallites or small immiscible glass droplets. In either instance, the techniques of microscopy, particularly the replica electron microscopic methods, are used for establishing the microstructure, morphology, phase relationships, and crystallinity. In addition, x-ray diffraction is indispensable to the proper characterization of crystal species in either opal glasses or glass–ceramics.

Sampling and Sample Preparation. The hazards of sampling commercial glasses and glass–ceramics are greatly reduced by the fact that the product of large tank-scale production melts is generally quite homogeneous. However, glass–ceramics in their usual cerammed state do present some special problems, due to their multi-phased-polycrystalline nature. To avoid possible segregation, representative pieces

Table 5. Constituent Ranges in Glasses and Glass–Ceramics and Preferred Analytical Methods[a]

| Oxide | Range, wt % | | |
	0.01–1	1–10	10–100
SiO_2	s,c	c,g	g,c
Al_2O_3	s,c	g,cp	g,cp
B_2O_3	s,c,t	t	t
Li_2O	f	f	g,f
Na_2O	f	f	g,f
K_2O	f	f	g,f
CaO	f,c,cp,g	f,cp,g	cp,g,f
MgO	a,c	a,cp,g	cp,g,a
TiO_2	s,c,e	c,g,t,e	g,t
ZrO_2	s,c	g,cp,c	g,t
PbO	c,e,cp	e,cp,g	e,cp
BaO	s,f	g,f	g,f
ZnO	s,a,e,c	cp,a,g,e	e,cp
CdO	s,a,e,	e,cp,a	e,cp
P_2O_5	c	c,g	g
As_2O_3	c,e,t	t,e	
Sb_2O_3	c,e,t,a	t,e,a	
Cl,Br,I	t	t,g	
SO_3	cb,g		
F	p	p	
Fe_2O_3	c,s,a	t,cp	
Cr_2O_3	c,s,e		
Ni	c,s,e		
Co	c,s,e		
Ag,Au	c,e,a		
Se,Te	s,c,e,a		

[a] a = atomic absorption
c = colorimetry
cb = combustion–titrimetry
cp = complexometry
e = electroanalytical, including coulometry, polarography
f = flame emission spectroscopy
g = gravimetry
p = pyrohydrolysis–titrimetry
s = spectrography
t = titrimetry, other than complexometry, eg, redoximetry, acidimetric, precipitation.

of glass–ceramics should be crushed and ground completely to the fineness required for decomposition; sieving should be avoided. If sieving is deemed essential, the sample of a glass–ceramic must be completely ground until all the powdered material goes through the sieve, and then thoroughly blended in the sample vial. The finer the sample is ground, the less likely it will be that segregation of the various phases of glass–ceramics will occur.

Subdivision or comminution of glasses and glass–ceramics is essential to efficient and expeditious conversion of the sample to a water-soluble form. To minimize undue pickup of water and carbon dioxide, as well as oxidation of polyvalent constituents to be determined, such as ferrous iron, a fairly coarse grind of 60–80 mesh is recommended, particularly if an acid decomposition is the intended route. If, however, fusion decomposition is planned, a much finer grind, approximating 200 mesh or even 400 mesh is preferred; otherwise, a protracted fusion may be the consequence that even then does not fully flux the sample. For these materials, powdering may be rapidly accomplished using, in order of preference, a corundum mortar, an agate mortar (percussion to be avoided!), a hardened steel percussive mortar (Plattner, Ellis, or diamond-type), or a mullite mortar. Boron carbide is a superior mortar, but expensive, and due to its brittleness, will not withstand any percussive action; it introduces the least contamination. The choice of mortar should be such that the inevitable contamination (27) will have the least effect on the results. A steel mortar obviously should not be used if one plans to determine trace iron content. On the other hand, the pickup of alumina from a corundum mortar will probably have an undetectable effect on the determination of alumina at the 10 wt % level. Always preclean the mortar and pestle by thoroughly grinding a small portion of the sample to a fine powder, which is then discarded. Automatic mortars, such as the Spex Mixer Mill or the Angstrom Disk Mill, utilizing cobalt-bonded tungsten carbide grinding containers together with balls or pucks, are rapid and well suited to preparation of large quantities of sample. Sampling for analysis should be done as soon as possible after the sample has been ground. Otherwise, an ignition loss determination at 1000°C should be run to correct for water and carbon dioxide pickup. If sampling of the powdered glass must be deferred, storage in a desiccator over sintered barium oxide is recommended.

Composition Analysis

Preliminary Testing. Prior to commencing any compositional characterization it is of utmost importance to obtain at least a qualitative survey of the elements present. It is especially essential to the development of the correct wet analytical chemical strategy. A qualitative or semiquantitative emission spectrographic examination (see p. 453) will usually suffice for the metallic elements and phosphorus. Other important nonmetals, fluorine in particular, must be detected by chemical means. Since the presence of fluorine in amounts greater than 2 wt % demands a revision of the procedure for the silica determination, a qualitative procedure for fluoride (27a) is given here.

Procedure

Prepare zirconium alizarin test paper by soaking Schleicher and Schüll No. 589 White Ribbon or equivalent filter paper in a solution containing two volumes of 2% aqueous sodium alizarin sulfonate solution and one volume of 5% zirconium oxychloride in 1:19 hydrochloric acid. After the reddish purple lake is fully and uniformly deposited onto the filter paper fibers, rinse thoroughly with water. Allow to dry, then cut into 4 mm × 10 cm strips.

Introduce 50 mg of powdered glass and 150 mg of anhydrous boric oxide into a 1 cm × 9 cm 96% silica glass test tube. Insert a strip of the zirconium alizarin paper moistened with N hydrochloric acid 3 cm into the upper part of the test tube. Quickly heat the lower part of the test tube with a concentrated gas–oxygen flame until the glass–boric oxide melts and becomes quiescent. Sop up all moisture accumulating in the upper part of the test tube. The presence of fluoride is indicated by a distinct color change of the indicator paper from a dark pink to a light yellow. The length of the yellow coloration can be employed as a rough estimate of the amount of fluoride in the sample. Complete discoloration of 2–3 cm indicates the presence of 0.5% fluoride, whereas discoloration of 1 cm implies 0.1% fluoride.

Phosphorus, if suspected as a constituent, should also be determined first, by an appropriate method (see p. 432), since the spectrographic examination, due to spectral interference and/or insensitivity, may not reveal its presence. Phosphorus pentoxide in amounts greater than 1 wt % will also require certain modifications in the silica determination, and in other determinations as well.

Decomposition. All silicate glasses are decomposed by either acid attack with a mixture of hydrofluoric acid and another mineral acid, or by fusion with sodium carbonate followed by digestion with a mineral acid. The choice of approach is dependent on the elements to be determined and the method. Flame spectroscopy, for example, cannot tolerate alkalies such as are introduced by fluxes, and perchlorate is the preferred anion. Table 6 summarizes the common elements to be determined in glasses and glass–ceramics and the corresponding usual mode of sample decomposition. Obviously a compromise must be made when preparing the sample for the determination of titanium in a barium–titanium-containing glass, since perchloric acid is optimal for barium glasses and sulfuric acid is best for glasses containing titanium. In such instances, it is common to substitute perchloric acid for sulfuric acid. In doing so, however, it is essential that the fuming step which removes hydrogen fluoride and silicofluoride be especially thorough and repeated no less than three times with intervening water rinses of the walls of the platinum vessel. The higher the tri- and tetravalent metallic oxide content, the more tenaciously fluoride is likely to be retained in the sample. In some instances where complete fluoride volatilization is a problem, it may be more expedient to resort to the classical approach of

Table 6. Common Elements/Oxides in Glasses and Glass–Ceramics and the Corresponding Mode of Sample Decomposition

Element/oxide to be determined	Preferred decomposition mode
SiO_2	fusion
Al_2O_3	$HF + H_2SO_4$
B_2O_3	fusion
$Li_2O, Na_2O, K_2O, Rb_2O, Cs_2O$	$HF + HClO_4$
MgO, CaO	$HF + HClO_4$
BaO, PbO, SrO	$HF + HClO_4$
TiO_2, ZrO_2	$HF + H_2SO_4$
ZnO, CdO	$HF + HClO_4$
P_2O_5	$HF + HClO_4$
As_2O_3, Sb_2O_3	$HF + H_2SO_4$
$Fe_2O_3, Cr_2O_3, MnO, Co_2O_3, NiO, CeO_2$	$HF + H_2SO_4$ or $HClO_4$
CuO	$HF + H_2SO_4$ or $HClO_4$
SO_3	$HF + HClO_4$
S^-, Se^-, Te^-	HF
F^-	fusion
Cl^-, Br^-, I^-	HF (cold)

decomposing the sample by sodium carbonate fusion and removing the silica by dehydration.

Chemical Methods for Individual Constituents

It is evident, considering the great diversity of elemental combinations which may constitute glass materials, that no simple all-embracing classical chemical scheme can be given. However, the procedures given here are applicable to most of the commercial glasses and glass–ceramics, such as might be typified by the compositions shown in Table 2 (p. 407).

Silica. The following method is used for the determination of silica in glass samples which do not contain phosphorus.

Procedure

Weigh a 0.5 g sample of the powdered glass into a 150-ml platinum dish containing 3 g of anhydrous sodium carbonate. If base metals, such as lead, antimony, etc, are present, add 25 mg of sodium nitrate. Mix thoroughly with a platinum stirring rod. Starting with a low (oxidizing) flame and gradually increasing the heat, cautiously heat the sample–flux mixture over an air–gas blast burner until the fusion reaction is complete as evidenced by a homogeneous-appearing quiescent melt. Cover with a watch glass and allow to cool. Add 30 ml of water and digest, covered on a steam bath. If the sample contains greater than 0.5% fluoride, add 0.3 g of aluminum chloride, $AlCl_3.6H_2O$, for each 10 mg of fluoride present. With the watch glass in place, cautiously add 1:1 hydrochloric acid by pipet until the effervescence abates; then add 10 ml of 1:1 hydrochloric acid in excess. Rinse the watch glass and the sides of the dish with 1:49 hydrochloric acid. If the sample contains 2% or more titania, add 5 ml of 30% hydrogen peroxide. Place the dish on a steam bath and allow the contents to evaporate to dryness. Cover the dish and to the cooled dry residue add 10 ml of 1:1 hydrochloric acid. Add 30 ml of water and digest for 15 min. During the digestion, stir occasionally, and with a flattened glass stirring rod, crush and break up all clumps. Filter through a Whatman No. 41 ashless filter paper, collecting the filtrate in a 250-ml platinum evaporating dish. Wash the silica on the filter thoroughly with near-boiling 1:49 hydrochloric acid and then finally with near-boiling water. Police the original platinum dish with pieces of moist ashless filter paper and add them to the precipitate on the filter paper. Place the precipitate in a 30-ml platinum crucible that previously has been ignited to 1200°C with its cover and weighed.

If titania is present in excess of 2%, add 5 ml of 30% hydrogen peroxide to the filtrate. Place the 250-ml dish containing the filtrate on the steam bath and evaporate to dryness. Place in a 110°C oven and bake for 30 min. Cover, then after the dish is cool, add 5 ml of concentrated hydrochloric acid and 50 ml of water. Digest on a steam bath for 15 min, then filter through a Whatman No. 42 filter paper. As before, wash well with near-boiling 1:49 hydrochloric acid and near-boiling water. Transfer the second silica precipitate to the weighed crucible containing the first precipitate. Police the dish and watch glass with moist filter paper and combine the pieces of filter paper with the precipitates.

Add 4 drops of 1:1 sulfuric acid to the contents of the crucible and place in a cold muffle furnace. Allow the temperature of the furnace to gradually increase until the paper chars, then allow the temperature to go to 1000°C until all traces of the paper have burned off. Cover the crucible, heat it in the furnace at 1200°C for 30 min, then cool and weigh. Add 5 ml of water, 5 drops of 1:1 sulfuric acid, 15 ml of 48% hydrofluoric acid to the contents of the crucible and evaporate to dryness.

Replace the lid, ignite for 5 min at 1200°C, cool and weigh. The weight loss after the hydrofluoric acid treatment divided by the sample weight and multiplied by 100 equals the % silica.

If phosphate, fluoride, and antimony are absent and the titania content is low, the second silica separation can be accomplished more expediently by addition of 25 ml of 72% perchloric acid to the filtrate, which in this case is collected in a 400-ml 96% silica glass beaker, and evaporating to perchloric acid fumes and boiling (covered) for 20 min. After adding 100 ml of water and digesting for a few minutes, the silica is recovered by filtration and carried through the rest of the procedure as before. Care must be taken to remove all perchloric acid in the washing step, otherwise an explosion may result during ignition of the filter papers.

When lead, zinc, cadmium, zirconium, titanium, and large amounts of aluminum are not present, an expedient approach is to collect the filtrate from the first dehydration in a 200-ml volumetric flask, take a 20-ml aliquot, and develop and measure colorimetrically the absorbance of the yellow silicomolybdate complex. The silica thus found in the filtrate is added to that recovered gravimetrically, following the standard procedure, to obtain the total silica content of the sample (28).

If the glass sample contains more than 2% phosphate, the following procedure is used for silica determination.

Procedure

Fuse 0.5 g of the finely powdered sample with 3 g of anhydrous sodium carbonate in a 150-ml platinum dish over an air–gas blast burner until the reaction is complete as evidenced by a uniform-appearing melt. Cover the dish with a watch glass, and to the cooled melt add 30 ml of water and digest to break up the fluxed mass. If the sample contains greater than 0.5% fluoride, add 0.5 g of aluminum nitrate, $Al(NO_3)_3.9H_2O$, for each 10 mg of fluoride present. By pipet add 1:1 nitric acid slowly enough so that the effervescence is kept under control, until neutralization is complete. Then add 10 ml of 1:1 nitric acid in excess. If titania and zirconia are present in amounts greater than 1%, add 5 ml of 30% hydrogen peroxide. Place the covered dish on the steam bath to expel the carbon dioxide. Remove the watch glass and wash down the cover and sides of the dish with water. Evaporate to dryness on a steam bath, then bake in a 110°C oven for 30 min. Drench the dry residue with 10 ml of 1:1 nitric acid, add 30 ml of water and digest with the dish covered to dissolve the soluble salts. Filter through a Whatman No. 41 ashless paper, collecting the filtrate in a 250-ml platinum dish. Wash thoroughly with hot 1:49 nitric acid. Then wash once with 1:19 ammonium hydroxide and finally with a little warm water. To the combined washings, add 25 ml of 72% perchloric acid. If more than 2% titania and/or zirconia is present, add 5 ml of 30% hydrogen peroxide. Evaporate to strong fumes, cover the dish, and boil gently for 20 min. Cool, add 75 ml of water, digest for 5 min, and then filter through a Whatman No. 42 filter paper. Wash well with warm 1:99 nitric acid and finally hot water, taking care to wash the upper portion of the funnel and paper thoroughly so that all the perchloric acid is washed away. Place the combined silica precipitates in a platinum crucible, add 4 drops of 1:1 sulfuric acid and place in a cold muffle furnace. Ignite slowly to burn off the paper, and proceed as described in the above procedure.

Boron. The method for boron determination given here is based on precipitation of interfering cations, followed by titration with sodium hydroxide solution. Promising alternatives to this approach include ion exchange separation of interfering cations (29), and the use of EDTA masking without separation (30), prior to the usual acidimetric finish.

Procedure

Weigh a 0.5 g sample of the powdered glass if the boric oxide content is greater than 5%; weigh a 1-g sample if the content is less than 5%. The sample is weighed into a 75-ml platinum dish containing three to four times the sample weight of anhydrous sodium carbonate. If the glass contains fluoride, for each 10 mg of fluoride in the sample, add 50 mg of boron-free calcium carbonate. Mix the sample and flux thoroughly with a platinum stirring rod. Cover the dish tightly with a platinum–10% rhodium lid and fuse at 1000–1100°C just until reaction is complete and a uniform melt is obtained. Rotate the dish as it cools so that the melt solidifies in a thin layer. Cool to room temperature with the lid in place. Add 25 ml of water and digest until the melt is completely disintegrated. If lead or zinc is present, filter through Whatman No. 40 paper, using suction if desired; collect the filtrate in a 400-ml 96% silica glass beaker; wash the precipitate with 0.5% sodium carbonate solution. If lead or zinc is not present, transfer the contents of the dish directly into the 400-ml 96% silica glass beaker, rinsing the dish and lid with hot water. Cover the beaker with a watch glass and carefully make the solution distinctly acid to methyl red with 1:1 hydrochloric acid. About 5 ml of 1:1 hydrochloric acid is needed for each gram of sodium carbonate flux. Use some of the acid to rinse the platinum dish and lid. If the sample contains phosphates add 50 mg of ferric chloride, $FeCl_3 \cdot 6H_2O$, for each 10 mg of phosphorus pentoxide present. Heat the solution to boiling, add a wad of dry filter paper pulp and adjust the pH to 5.0–5.4 (the orange color of methyl red) with 6 N sodium hydroxide solution. Digest on a hot plate or steam bath at 65–95°C, with occasional stirring, for 0.5–1 hr, always maintaining the pH at 5.0–5.4 by the addition, if necessary, of 0.1 N hydrochloric acid. Filter the hot solution through a Whatman No. 40 filter paper, using a Büchner funnel and suction. Collect the filtrate in a 400-ml 96% silica glass beaker containing 10 drops of 0.1 N hydrochloric acid. Wash out the beaker and precipitate with six to eight 10-ml portions of hot water. Boil the acid filtrate for a few seconds to eliminate carbon dioxide. Use of a bump rod is recommended. Cool to room temperature with a cold water bath. Using a pH meter, adjust the pH to 5.4 with carbonate-free 0.1 N sodium hydroxide solution. Add about 20 g of mannitol for each 100 ml to saturate the sample solution. Titrate with carbonate-free 0.1 N sodium hydroxide solution that has been standardized against potassium biphthalate primary standard, to a pH of exactly 6.8. Add more mannitol to saturate the solution and further titrate until the pH remains at 6.8. The volume of standard sodium hydroxide solution required between pH 5.4 and 6.8 provides a measure of the boron contained in the sample. Make a blank determination, repeating the entire procedure with a glass such as National Bureau of Standards SRM No. 80, known to contain no boron. Correct for the blank determination, and calculate the boron content as boric oxide.

Barium, Lead, Zinc, Aluminum, Calcium, and Magnesium. In order to determine barium, lead, zinc, aluminum, calcium, and magnesium by classical means, taking into account the possible presence of arsenic, antimony, titanium, zirconium, and iron, a separation scheme is essential.

General Scheme. Should significant amounts of phosphate be present in the sample, and particularly when titanium and zirconium are also present, it is recommended that this constituent be removed as the orthophosphate (31) by precipitation from strongly acid solution with an excess of zirconium, prior to the sulfate precipitation of lead and barium. No allowance has been made for the rare earths; if present, there are a number of separation approaches suggested in Vol. 9, pp. 264–269. In addition, attention is called to the nitrate separation of alkaline earths from other elements, including lanthanum, developed by Willard and Goodspeed (32).

A method for magnesium is included in this scheme; however, determination of magnesium is preferably accomplished directly on a separate sampling by atomic absorption flame spectroscopy (p. 449) or by complexometric titration (p. 447).

Procedures

LEAD PLUS BARIUM. Weigh a 1-g sample into a 150-ml platinum dish. Treat with 10 ml of water, 5 ml of 72% perchloric acid, and 10 ml of hydrofluoric acid. Heat on a steam bath until most of the water evaporates, then transfer to a hot plate and heat to strong perchloric acid fumes. Wash down the sides of the dish with water and repeat the evaporation and fuming. Add 0.3 g of boric acid, rinse down the dish with water and repeat the evaporation, then fume to near dryness. Treat the residue with water, digest on a steam bath to dissolve, and transfer to a 400-ml 96% silica glass beaker.

If arsenic or antimony is present and phosphate is absent, add 15 ml of 72% perchloric acid and evaporate to light fumes. Slowly add 15 ml of 48% hydrobromic acid and increase the temperature until heavy fumes are evolved. If, on slight cooling, the solution becomes cloudy, repeat the hydrobromic acid-fuming treatments until the solution remains clear on cooling. Continue fuming until all but 1 ml of the perchloric acid is volatilized. If titania is present in substantial amounts the solution may grow cloudy on heating.

Add 10 ml of 1:1 sulfuric acid and evaporate to strong sulfuric acid fumes on a hot plate. Cool, and dilute with 100 ml of water (or with enough water to make the solution 5% in sulfuric acid). Cover the dish, digest on a steam bath for 1 hr, and allow to stand until cool. Filter through a Whatman No. 42 filter paper washing with 1:99 sulfuric acid. Reserve as filtrate A. Transfer the precipitate and paper back to the precipitation beaker, add 15 ml of concentrated nitric acid and 5 ml of concentrated sulfuric acid. Cover and wet ignite by gradually increasing the heat until copious fumes of sulfuric acid are evolved. Add a few milliliters of concentrated nitric acid and fume off. Repeat this step until a colorless solution is obtained, fuming finally so that the sulfuric acid refluxes up the wall of the beaker. Rinse down the beaker and cover with water and bring to fumes repeatedly to drive off the nitrous acid. Reprecipitate by adding 100 ml or another appropriate volume of water to make the solution 5% in sulfuric acid. Digest for 1 hr on the steam bath and allow to stand until cool. Filter on a tared fine-porosity porcelain filter crucible, washing with 1:99 sulfuric acid. Reserve as filtrate B. Ignite the crucible and contents slowly to constant weight at 600°C. Cool in a desiccator for 1 hr and weigh. Using the weight of mixed barium-lead sulfates, and the % lead oxide found in the separate sampling (see procedure below), calculate the % barium oxide.

ZINC. Combine filtrates A and B from the sulfate precipitation, add bromine water and boil to a volume of about 100 ml, so that a solution of 1:10 sulfuric acid is attained. Cool to 0–10°C and slowly add, with stirring, cold 6% cupferron solution until no further precipitation takes place. Disperse a small amount of filter pulp and allow to settle for 2 or 3 min. Filter through Whatman No. 40 paper using a filtering cone and suction and collecting as filtrate C in a 600-ml 96% silica glass beaker containing a little cupferron reagent solution to indicate whether precipitation has been complete. Use of a bell-jar-type suction filtering apparatus is recommended. Wash the precipitate with cold 1:10 sulfuric acid containing 1.5 g of cupferron per liter. Apply suction to dry the precipitate as much as possible.

Alternately, transfer this precipitate and paper to a tared 75-ml platinum dish, carefully dried, slowly ignited to burn off the carbon, and finally heated to 1000°C for 30 min, cooled and weighed.   The resulting value gives an estimate of iron, titanium, and zirconium oxides plus some antimony that may have escaped the hydrobromic acid volatilization treatment.   Otherwise, discard the precipitate, since the components will be determined separately later.

If zinc, arsenic, and antimony are all known to be absent, proceed directly to the procedure for aluminum.   If any of these elements are present, evaporate filtrate C by boiling covered with a raised watch glass until the volume approaches 20 ml, or until the solution starts to foam severely.   Cool, add 25 ml of concentrated nitric acid and carefully evaporate to sulfuric acid fumes.   Repeatedly add a few milliliters of concentrated nitric acid with intervening heating to sulfuric acid fumes until the solution is clear and colorless.   Cool, rinse down the beaker and cover, and add 10 ml of 72% perchloric acid.   Heat to boiling and evaporate once more to strong fumes of sulfuric acid.   If arsenic or antimony are not present in the sample, proceed to the next paragraph.   Cool, add 0.5 g of elemental sulfur and boil the concentrated sulfuric acid solution for 10 min.   Cool and dilute to approximately 6 N sulfuric acid.   Remove any residual sulfur with the aid of a plastic spoon or stirring rod, then boil to remove sulfur dioxide.   Adjust the volume of the 6 N sulfuric acid solution to at least 100 ml and gas with hydrogen sulfide for 30 min. Using a bell-jar-type filtration apparatus, filter through Whatman No. 42 paper supported on a platinum filtering cone using gentle suction.   Wash with 6 N sulfuric acid saturated with hydrogen sulfide.   Collect the filtrate and washings, D, in a 400-ml beaker and reserve.   Discard the sulfide precipitate.

If zinc is absent, proceed directly to the aluminum procedure.   If zinc is present, boil filtrate D down to sulfuric acid fumes and continue fuming until the sulfuric acid volume is reduced to a few milliliters.   Cool, dilute to 200 ml, add a few milliliters of bromine water to oxidize and clear the solution, and then boil out the excess bromine.   Add ammonium hydroxide until a precipitate just fails to redissolve.   Add 2 g of citric acid to the cooled solution and adjust to pH 2.4 with ammonium hydroxide using a pH meter.   Gas rapidly with hydrogen sulfide for 30 min.   Add 10 ml of 0.02% gelatin solution and continue gassing with hydrogen sulfide for five more minutes.   Let stand until the precipitate settles and filter on a tared fine-porosity porcelain crucible.   Wash with 0.5% citric acid solution adjusted to pH 2.4 with ammonium hydroxide, saturated with hydrogen sulfide, and containing 5 ml of 0.02% gelatin per 100 ml of wash solution.   Collect and reserve filtrate and washings, E.   Convert the precipitate to zinc oxide by igniting slowly to 950°C in a muffle furnace to constant weight.

As an alternative to a gravimetric finish, the zinc sulfide precipitate may be dissolved in dilute acid, the solution boiled to remove hydrogen sulfide, and then titrated complexometrically with ethylenediaminetetraacetate at pH 4.6, using xylenol orange indicator.

ALUMINUM.   Depending on the composition of the glass, boil filtrate and washings, C or D or E, to reduce the volume to about 100 ml.   Add 50 ml of concentrated nitric acid and 25 ml of concentrated hydrochloric acid, cover the beaker, and warm gently until vigorous evolution of gas ceases, and then heat more strongly to fumes of sulfuric acid.   Add a few milliliters of concentrated nitric acid and heat again to strong fumes of sulfuric acid.   Repeat until the solution is clear and colorless.   If ultimate removal of organic material is difficult to achieve, add 2–3 ml of 72% perchloric acid, after the nitric acid is added, and heat to strong fumes of sulfuric acid.   Dilute wet ignited filtrate to 200 ml with water.   Add 2 g of ammonium chloride and heat the solution to boiling.   Add a few drops of methyl red indicator and then treat with ammonium hydroxide until the indicator just turns from red to a distinct yellow. With a bump rod inserted and the beaker covered, boil for 2 min. Stir in filter paper pulp and allow the precipitate to coagulate. Using a bell-jar suction apparatus, filter through Whatman No. 40 paper applying gentle suction. Collect and reserve the filtrate and washings, F, in a 600-ml beaker. Wash the precipitate with hot 2% ammonium chloride solution that has been treated with ammonium hydroxide to bring the pH to the just-yellow side of methyl red. Return the paper and precipitate back to the precipitation beaker. Add 10 ml of 1:1 hydrochloric acid to dissolve the precipitate. Macerate the filter paper, dilute to about 150 ml, and heat to boiling. Add a few drops of methyl red indicator and reprecipitate at once by adding ammonium hydroxide until the indicator just turns from red to yellow. Insert a bump rod, cover, and boil for 2 min. Suction filter, as before, using Whatman No. 40 paper and wash with hot 2% ammonium chloride neutralized to the just-yellow side of methyl red. Collect and reserve the filtrate and washings, G, in a 400-ml beaker. Police the beaker using moist pieces of filter paper. Ignite the filter paper and precipitate slowly in a tared platinum crucible until the paper has been completely burned off, then cover the crucible and ignite at 1200°C for 30 min. Cool in a desiccator and weigh. The ignited oxide is calculated as aluminum oxide since titanium, zirconium, and iron have been removed by the cupferron separation.

CALCIUM. Combine filtrate G with filtrate F, acidify to methyl red, and evaporate to about 200 ml. Add 1.5 g of ammonium oxalate, $(NH_4)_2C_2O_4 \cdot H_2O$, then heat to boiling, and add ammonium hydroxide slowly until the solution is alkaline to the methyl red indicator. Digest for 1 hr on the steam bath, cool to room temperature, then filter through Whatman No. 42 paper. Wash with 0.1% ammonium oxalate solution that has been neutralized to methyl red. Collect and reserve the filtrate and washings, H, in a 600-ml beaker. Return the precipitate and paper to the precipitation beaker, add 10 ml of 1:1 hydrochloric acid, pulp the paper to dissolve the precipitate, and dilute to about 150 ml. Add 0.5 g of ammonium oxalate, $(NH_4)_2C_2O_4 \cdot H_2O$, heat to boiling, make just alkaline to methyl red with ammonium hydroxide, digest for 1 hr on the steam bath, cool to room temperature, and filter as before through Whatman No. 42 paper. Wash with 0.1% ammonium oxalate solution that has been neutralized to methyl red. Collect the filtrate and washings, I, in a 400-ml beaker. Place the paper and precipitate in a 30-ml platinum crucible that has been weighed with its cover, which should fit snugly. Heat the crucible with the cover off slowly in a ventilated electric muffle furnace until the paper is fully charred and burns off. After ignition of the paper is complete, cover the crucible and ignite at 1200°C for 10 min. Cool in a desiccator containing phosphorus pentoxide for 30 min, then weigh. The ignited precipitate is highly hygroscopic calcium oxide. Reignite at 1200°C for 5 min, cool in a desiccator, and reweigh. Repeat to constant weight.

Alternative to a gravimetric finish, the calcium oxide may be dissolved in dilute acid and titrated compleximetrically with EDTA at pH 10 using hydroxynaphthol blue (Mallinckrodt) as indicator.

MAGNESIUM. Acidify the combined filtrates, H and I, with hydrochloric acid and evaporate to about 200 ml. Cool in an ice bath, add 2 g of diammonium hydrogen phosphate and stir. After the reagent has dissolved, treat the solution with ammonium hydroxide until alkaline, then add 20 ml excess. Allow to stand at about 0°C in an ice bath or refrigerator overnight. Filter through Whatman No. 42 paper and wash with cold 1:19 ammonium hydroxide. The filtrate and washings may be discarded. Place the beaker in which the precipitation was made under the filter funnel and dissolve the precipitate with 50 ml of hot 1:9 hydrochloric acid. Save the filter paper. Add 0.1 g of diammonium hydrogen phosphate and dilute to 100 ml. Cool in an ice bath, make alkaline with ammonium hydroxide while stirring vigorously, then add 10 ml of ammonium hydroxide in excess. Let stand in an ice bath or refrigerator at least 4 hr, filter through Whatman No. 42 paper, and wash with cold 1:19 ammonium hydroxide. The filtrate and washings may be discarded. Police the beaker with small pieces of damp filter paper and add them to the precipitate. Place filter papers from both precipitations in a tared platinum crucible. Ignite very slowly in a well-ventilated muffle furnace until the paper chars and burns off completely, then ignite at 1100°C for 30 min to constant weight. Cool and weigh the magnesium as magnesium pyrophosphate ($Mg_2P_2O_7$). Calculate the magnesium content as magnesium oxide, MgO; 1 mg of magnesium pyrophosphate is equivalent to 0.3622 mg of magnesium oxide.

Separation of Lead from Barium. In the general scheme, lead and barium are separated as a mixed sulfate. Therefore, if both elements are present, either lead or barium must be determined on a separate sampling in conjunction with the general scheme. A procedure for lead is given below.

Procedure

For glasses containing about 5–10% lead oxide, decompose a 2-g sample with 10 ml of water, 10 ml of 72% perchloric acid and 20 ml of 48% hydrofluoric acid in a 150-ml platinum dish. For samples containing greater than 10% lead oxide, take a 1-g sample. Evaporate on a steam bath to remove most of the volatiles and water, then transfer to a hot plate and gradually increase the temperature to the point where copious fumes of perchloric acid are evolved. Continue fuming for 5 min. Cool, wash down the dish with water, add 0.3 g of boric acid and repeat the evaporation and fuming to near dryness. Treat the residue with water, digest on a steam bath to dissolve, and transfer to a 400-ml 96% silica glass beaker.

If arsenic or antimony is present, add 15 ml of 72% perchloric acid and evaporate to light fumes. Slowly add 20 ml of 48% hydrobromic acid and increase the temperature until heavy fumes are evolved. If, on cooling slightly, the solution becomes cloudy, repeat treatments with hydrobromic acid and fuming until the acid solution remains clear on cooling. Continue to evaporate to remove most of the perchloric acid.

Dilute to 200 ml with water. Adjust the acidity to 0.2 N hydrochloric acid by first neutralizing to the just-alkaline color of methyl red, and then adding 6 ml of 1:1 hydrochloric acid. Heat to 60–70°C and gas with hydrogen sulfide for 30 min. Cool to room temperature and allow to settle for 30 min. Filter through a Whatman No. 42 paper and wash with 0.2 N hydrochloric acid saturated with hydrogen sulfide. Return the precipitate and paper to the precipitation beaker. Treat with 15 ml of concentrated nitric acid, then 5 ml of sulfuric acid. Insert a stirring rod, cover with a watch glass, and heat to strong sulfuric acid fumes. From time to time cautiously add a few ml of concentrated nitric acid through the lip of the beaker and fume off. Continue this treatment until the precipitate redissolves and the solution is clear and colorless. Repeatedly cool, wash down the sides and cover of the beaker with water, evaporate and fume, until all nitrous acid has been removed. Finally, cool, dilute with water to obtain a 1:19 sulfuric acid solution, adding the water dropwise initially, in order to obtain a coarse crystalline precipitate. Digest on the steam bath for 1 hr and then let stand until cool. Filter through a tared fine-porosity porcelain filtering crucible. Wash with 0.7% ammonium sulfate solution. Ignite slowly to 500°C to constant weight. Cool in a desiccator for 1 hr and weigh. Calculate as lead oxide.

Lithium, Sodium, and Potassium. As a preliminary, anion and cation exchange chromatography may be advantageously employed for separating phosphate and cationic interferences such as lead and barium (33), and for separating the alkalies from each other (34).

In the procedure which follows, sodium is separated from potassium by precipitation with zinc uranyl acetate reagent. Since lithium, like sodium, is precipitated by the triple acetate reagent, a separate procedure is necessary when both lithium and sodium accompany potassium.

Procedures

SODIUM AND POTASSIUM (LITHIUM ABSENT). *Reagent and Sample Preparation.* Prepare a zinc uranyl acetate reagent by dissolving 100 g of uranyl acetate, $UO_2(C_2H_3O_2)_2 \cdot 2H_2O$, and 300 g of zinc acetate, $Zn(C_2H_3O_2)_2 \cdot 2H_2O$, in 810 ml of warm water containing 90 ml of 30% acetic acid, adding a few crystals of sodium chloride, shaking well, then allowing the solution to age for 24 hr before use.

Weigh a finely powdered sample, estimated to contain 50–100 mg of sodium oxide, into a 75-ml platinum dish. For a 1-g sample, decompose with 10 ml of water, 3 ml of 72% perchloric acid, and 10 ml of 48% hydrofluoric acid. Add 2 ml of 1:1 sulfuric acid after the first fuming with perchloric acid only if barium is present; use perchloric acid preferentially even for high-lead glasses. Sulfuric acid must be used to remove barium and may be used for lead–barium glasses. Evaporate and heat to strong fumes three times, with intervening water rinse-downs of the dish between fumings. Add 0.2 g of boric acid to the acid mixture just prior to the final fuming and fume to a syrup that crystallizes on cooling. If barium is present, dilute, digest, and filter the insoluble sulfates through Whatman No. 42 filter paper, washing with 0.2 N sulfuric acid. If lead is present, adjust the acidity of the filtrate to 0.2 N perchloric acid, gas with hydrogen sulfide for 30 min, filter off the precipitate on Whatman No. 42 paper, washing with hydrogen sulfide-saturated 0.2 N hydrochloric acid, and discard; remove the hydrogen sulfide in the filtrate by boiling, then adding bromine water with continued boiling.

If phosphate is present, add ammonium hydroxide until the solution is neutral or until a permanent precipitate just forms and then add hydrochloric acid dropwise until the precipitate dissolves. Add a 10% solution of ferric chloride hexahydrate drop by drop until the liquid above the yellowish-white precipitate of ferric phosphate becomes distinctly brown in color. Then add concentrated ammonium hydroxide until the solution is ammoniacal in order to separate the excess iron that was added. Boil for about 2 min, allow to settle, filter through Whatman No. 40 paper, and wash sparingly with warm 1% ammonium chloride solution. Transfer precipitate and paper back to the beaker. Pulp the paper and dissolve the precipitate in a minimum amount (about 10 ml) of 1:1 hydrochloric acid. Dilute to about 100 ml and reprecipitate by making the hot solution ammoniacal with concentrated ammonium hydroxide. Boil, filter, and wash sparingly with warm 1% ammonium chloride solution. Combine the filtrates and washings from both precipitations and acidify with concentrated hydrochloric acid. Evaporate, as necessary, to enable transfer to a 100-ml volumetric flask; dilute to volume.

Sodium Determination. Evaporate a suitable aliquot, containing about 10 mg of sodium oxide, to dryness in a platinum dish, then ignite gently to remove ammonium salts. Dissolve the residue with a few milliliters of 1:1 hydrochloric acid and evaporate to dryness on a steam bath. Add 1 ml of water to dissolve most of the residue and then add 20–25 ml of freshly filtered zinc uranyl acetate reagent. Stir the sample solution 1 min after addition of the reagent, cover to prevent evaporation, and allow to stand 30 min. Filter with suction using a previously weighed medium porosity fritted glass filtering crucible. Use a policeman to effect quantitative transfer, wash five times with 2-ml portions of freshly filtered zinc uranyl acetate solution, and then wash five times with freshly filtered 99:1 ethanol–acetic acid that had been shaken and equilibrated with pure sodium uranyl acetate crystals. Finally, wash twice with anhydrous ethyl ether. Draw air through the crucible to dry the precipitate, place the crucible in the balance case, and weigh after 10 min. Draw air through the precipitate and weigh again until the weight remains constant. Treat the precipitate with warm water, then dry with ethanol, ethyl ether, and air, in succession, using suction. After allowing to stand in the balance case for 10 min, weigh as before. The difference in weight is sodium uranyl zinc acetate, $NaZn(UO_2)_3(C_2H_3O_2)_9.6H_2O$. Calculate the sodium content as sodium oxide, Na_2O; 1 g of sodium uranyl zinc acetate is equivalent to 0.0215 g of sodium oxide.

Potassium Determination. Pipet an aliquot of the sample stock solution previously sampled for sodium, containing 5–100 mg of potassium oxide, into a 75-ml platinum dish. Evaporate the solution to dryness, then ignite in a muffle furnace at about 600°C to remove ammonium salts. Decompose the residue with 2–5 ml of ammonia-free concentrated hydrochloric acid and a little water. Prepare chloroplatinic acid reagent by dissolving 15 g of chloroplatinic acid, $H_2PtCl_6.-6H_2O$, in 50 ml of water containing 5 ml of 1:1 hydrochloric acid. Add an excess of the chloroplatinate reagent over that required to react with both the potassium and sodium in the sample solution; 1 ml is required for each 50 mg of potassium oxide and 1.6 ml for each 50 mg of sodium oxide present in the aliquot. Evaporate to a thick syrup in an ammonia-free atmosphere. Treat the residue with 20–25 ml of 80% ethanol; mix well to dissolve all but the potassium chloroplatinate, which is insoluble. Let stand 30 min with occasional stirring. The supernatant alcohol should be colored by the excess of reagent. Suction filter through a medium porosity fritted glass filter. Wash the precipitate with 80% ethanol three or four times by decantation, transfer it to the filter and wash two or three more times with the 80% ethanol. Reserve the filtrate and washings for recovery of the platinum.

Using a clean 250-ml beaker as the receiver, dissolve any residue remaining on the dish with hot water and pour through the filter to dissolve the precipitate cake. Repeat this rinse-wash step to thoroughly dissolve all traces of the yellow potassium chloroplatinate. Adjust the volume in the 250-ml beaker to about 150 ml, add 5 ml of concentrated hydrochloric acid, and reduce all of the chloroplatinate to free platinum with magnesium ribbon previously washed in water. About 0.1 g of magnesium will be required for each 50 mg of potassium oxide. Press the ribbon into a small ball and hold it at the bottom of the beaker with a stirring rod. When action has ceased, add a small piece in excess to ascertain complete reaction. Finally, boil the solution for a few minutes to coagulate the precipitate. The supernatant liquid should be colorless and clear. Filter through a Whatman No. 42 paper, washing the platinum several times with hot water. Ignite to constant weight at 1000°C in a tared porcelain crucible. Cool in a desiccator and weigh the platinum. One gram of platinum is equivalent to 0.4829 g of potassium oxide, K_2O.

LITHIUM, SODIUM, AND POTASSIUM. *Reagent and Sample Preparation.* Prepare zinc uranyl acetate reagent for lithium determination by dissolving 108 g of zinc acetate, $Zn(C_2H_3O_2)_2.2H_2O$, and 95 g of uranyl acetate, $UO_2(C_2H_3O_2)_2.2H_2O$, in 400 ml of warm water and 600 ml of glacial acetic acid. Mix thoroughly and allow to stand several hours to cool to room temperature; stir the solution, which will contain undissolved crystals, for a half hour before use.

Select a sample size that will afford suitable aliquots for each of the alkalies. Decompose 1 g of powdered glass in a 75-ml platinum dish by treating with 10 ml of water, 5 ml of 72% perchloric acid, and 8 ml of 48% hydrofluoric acid. Evaporate to fumes on a steam bath, then fume for at least 5 min on a hot plate. Rinse down the sides of the dish with water, evaporate and fume as before. Wash down the sides of the dish with water, add 0.3 g of boric acid, and finally evaporate and fume to dryness. Ignite very gently, using a flame, to remove perchloric acid from the sides of the dish. Add 25 ml of 1-butanol, digest and stir on the steam bath 2–3 min or until the residue is well dispersed. To the hot solution, add dropwise, with stirring, 2 ml of 1-butanol saturated with dry hydrogen chloride, then add 6 ml more. Cool, filter through a sintered-glass filtering crucible. Wash with ten 2-ml portions of a 5:2 mixture of 1-butanol and 1-butanol saturated with dry hydrogen chloride. Reserve the filtrate, which contains the lithium.

Dissolve the precipitate residue from the filtering crucible with hot water. If barium or lead is present, add a slight excess of 1:1 sulfuric acid, digest on a steam bath, filter through Whatman No. 42 paper, and wash with water. Transfer the solution to a 100-ml volumetric flask and dilute to volume.

Sodium and Potassium Determinations. Follow the procedures given on p. 423. If phosphate is present, it must first be removed (see the paragraph immediately preceding Sodium Determination).

Lithium Determination. Transfer the 1-butanol filtrate to a 75-ml platinum dish using water rinsing. Treat the solution with 1 ml of concentrated sulfuric acid and evaporate very slowly on the steam bath with occasional additions of small amounts of water to facilitate complete removal of 1-butanol. Evaporate to dryness, then gently ignite to burn off traces of organic matter. Dissolve the residue with water containing a few drops of 1:1 sulfuric acid. Filter off any barium or lead sulfates that separate at this point, on a Whatman No. 42 paper, washing with water. Adjust the final volume to 100 ml in a volumetric flask. Transfer an aliquot of the solution containing between 0.2 and 3.5 mg of lithium oxide to a 50-ml beaker and evaporate to dryness. Dissolve the residue with 3 ml of 1:1 hydrochloric acid and evaporate to dryness on the steam bath. Treat the residue with a freshly filtered 10-ml portion of the zinc uranyl acetate reagent, and allow to stand 30 min with frequent stirring. Suction filter through a tared sintered-glass filtering crucible. Wash five times with 2-ml portions of filtered reagent, using these washes to effect quantitative transfer. Then wash five times with 2-ml portions of freshly filtered ethanol wash solution that is prepared by shaking 100 ml of 99:1 ethanol—acetic acid with lithium zinc uranyl acetate crystals until saturated. Wash twice with anhydrous ethyl ether and dry with suction. If more than 30 mg of calcium oxide is present in the aliquot, redissolve the precipitate with 10 ml of 0.1 N hydrochloric acid, wash the filtering crucible with three small portions of water, and evaporate the solution until it films over. Then reprecipitate, filter, and wash as before. Draw air through the filter cake, after the ether wash, until the precipitate is dry. Allow the crucible to stand in the balance case 10 min, then weigh. The weight of the precipitate corresponds to lithium zinc uranyl acetate hexahydrate, $LiZn(UO_2)_3(C_2H_3O_2)_9.-6H_2O$; 1 g of this compound is equivalent to 0.009816 g of lithium oxide, Li_2O.

Titanium. Titanium in amounts greater than 5–10% as titanium dioxide is best determined gravimetrically, after cupferron precipitation and ignition to the oxide. Unless iron, zirconium, and other reacting metals are absent, they must be determined in either the precipitate or separate samples, and subtracted from the weight of the ignited cupferron precipitate. Since iron is often only present at contaminant levels of 0.01–0.1% as ferric oxide, its presence is often ignored except for the most accurate referee analyses.

For materials containing less than 5% titanium, a colorimetric method is given. A second colorimetric method (35), using Tiron (1,2-dihydroxybenzene-3,5-disulfonate), is recommended for titanium at concentrations of 0.005–1%.

Procedures

FOR MAJOR LEVELS. Adjust the volume of a sulfuric acid or perchloric acid solution of the sample, containing 50–100 mg of titania, to 200 ml. The sample should previously have been fumed free of all fluorides; addition of 0.3 g of boric acid prior to the final fuming is recommended. Use perchloric acid only if sulfate-insolubles such as lead or barium are present. Add a sufficient amount of the corresponding acid to make the sample solution 1:9 in either sulfuric or per-chloric acid. Treat with dilute permanganate until the solution is tinted a faint pink. If phosphate is present, add 1 g of tartaric acid. Stir in a large pinch of ash-less filter paper pulp, cool to 10°C, then, while stirring, slowly introduce 6% cup-ferron solution until no further precipitation occurs as evidenced by the appearance of a "flash" of a fine white precipitate that redissolves. Filter immediately through a Whatman No. 40 paper supported on a platinum filter cone using gentle suction. Wash the precipitate with chilled 1:9 sulfuric or hydrochloric acid containing 1.5 g of cupferron per liter. Transfer the paper and precipitate to an ignited and tared 30-ml platinum or porcelain crucible. Dry in a 110°C oven, transfer to a cold muffle furnace, then cautiously increase the heat until all effervescence has sub-sided. Increase the heat further until charring has occurred, then bring the tem-perature up to 1000°C for the final ignition. Ignite to constant weight, cool in a desiccator, and weigh.

Calculate as titanium dioxide, TiO_2, correcting for other oxides if they are present.

FOR MINOR LEVELS. Weigh a sample of powdered glass estimated to contain 5 mg of titanium dioxide into a 75-ml platinum dish. Treat a 1-g sample with 5 ml of water, 3 ml of 1:1 sulfuric acid, and 2 ml of 48% hydrofluoric acid. Cover, and digest on a steam bath for 1 hr. Rinse the cover with water, evaporate to strong sulfuric acid fumes, then fume on a hot plate for 5 min. Cool, rinse down the sides of the dish with water, bring to sulfuric acid fumes, and repeat the strong fuming on the hot plate. Cool, add 0.1 g of boric acid, and repeat the water wash-ing, evaporation, fuming process, adding more 1:1 sulfuric acid, if necessary, to prevent the solution from going to dryness. Add 18 ml of 1:1 sulfuric acid and digest until a clear solution is obtained. Transfer to a 100-ml volumetric flask with water rinses. Add 20 drops of 30% hydrogen peroxide and dilute to volume while mixing well. Allow to cool to room temperature and complete dilution.

If barium or lead is present, decompose the sample with 3 ml of 72% per-chloric acid instead of sulfuric acid, and with intervening water rinsing, evaporate and fume strongly, the second time to dryness. Ignite, add 1 g of 1:1 (w/w) boric acid–sodium carbonate flux mixture, and fuse until the residue is completely dis-solved. Treat the melt with a little water and 5 ml of 72% perchloric acid and digest on a steam bath until clear. Transfer to a 100-ml volumetric flask, add 5 ml of 72% perchloric acid, add hydrogen peroxide as above, and dilute to volume. Mea-sure the absorbance of the solution in a 1-cm cell at 410 nm. Run a reagent blank through the entire procedure and subtract its absorbance from that of the sample. Obtain the titanium content from the observed net absorbance by referring to a concentration–absorbance calibration curve.

Prepare the calibration curve by taking suitable aliquots of a stock titanium solution at dilutions ranging from 1 to 20 mg of titania per 100 ml. The same kind and quantities of acid must be used in preparation of the standards for color de-velopment as was employed for the samples. Prepare the stock solution by fusing 0.5000 g of titanium dioxide in 5 g of 1:1 sodium carbonate–anhydrous sodium borate in a platinum dish, dissolving the melt by digestion with water and either 30 ml of concentrated sulfuric acid or 85 ml of 72% perchloric acid, and diluting to 500 ml in a volumetric flask.

If the iron or chromium content is high, prepare duplicate aliquots of the sample, omitting only the peroxide from one aliquot, and read the peroxidized aliquot versus the other aliquot as the reference. Correct this reading for the reagent blank.

FOR TRACE TO MINOR LEVELS. Weigh 0.1–0.5 g of the powdered sample into a 75-ml platinum dish. Treat with a few milliliters of water, 5 ml of 1:1 sulfuric acid or perchloric acid, and 10 ml of 48% hydrofluoric acid. Use perchloric acid if either lead or barium is present. Heat to fumes of sulfuric (or perchloric acid), then fume strongly for 5 min. Cool, rinse down with water, and repeat the fuming step at least two more times with intervening water rinses. If lead is present, evaporate to 2–3 ml volume, transfer to a 125-ml Erlenmeyer flask, neutralize with 50% sodium hydroxide solution, dilute to 30 ml, add 2.5 ml of 72% perchloric acid, and gas with hydrogen sulfide for 30 min. Filter off the lead sulfide precipitate on a Whatman No. 42 paper, and wash the precipitate with 0.3 N perchloric acid saturated with hydrogen sulfide. Retain the filtrate and boil to remove the hydrogen sulfide, adding a slight excess of bromine water to remove the last traces. Evaporate, if necessary, to 30 ml.

Transfer the filtrate from the lead sulfide precipitation (or the fumed down sample solution, if lead is absent) to a 100-ml volumetric flask and dilute to volume. Pipet a suitable aliquot into a 50-ml beaker and add 5 ml of 4% Tiron solution. Neutralize to the basic side of Congo Red with 1:1 ammonium hydroxide. Cool, add 5 ml of pH 5 buffer that is prepared by mixing equal volumes of M sodium acetate solution with M acetic acid. Adjust the pH of the sample solution to 5.0 with ammonium hydroxide, using a pH meter. Transfer to a 50-ml volumetric flask, dilute to about 40 ml, and mix. Add 5 drops of thioglycollic acid and mix. Dilute to volume, then allow the color to develop for 10 min. Measure the absorbance at 410 nm using a 1-cm cell. Carry a reagent blank through the entire procedure and subtract its absorbance from that of the sample. Read the amount of titania in the sample from a calibration curve prepared from suitable dilutions of a standard titania stock solution carried through the same procedure to cover the concentrations from 10 to 100 μg of titania per 50 ml. (See Procedure for Minor Levels for the preparation of titania stock solution).

Zirconium. Gravimetry (36) is the preferred approach for determining zirconium dioxide at the 1% and higher range. For concentrations of 1% or less, gravimetry becomes less satisfactory; analysis is better accomplished colorimetrically using pyrocatechol violet (37).

Procedures

FOR MAJOR LEVELS. Weigh a 0.5–1 g sample containing 20–100 mg of zirconium into a 150-ml platinum dish. Decompose with about 5 ml of water, 10 ml of 48% hydrofluoric acid, and 10 ml of 1:1 sulfuric acid. Fume down in the usual manner with intervening cooling, water rinse-downs, evaporations, and refuming. For the final fuming, add 0.3 g of boric acid. If sulfate precipitable metals are present, add 8 ml of 1:1 sulfuric acid and digest on a hot plate near the boiling point for 10 min, then add 100 ml of water and digest on a steam bath for 1 hr; filter hot through a Whatman No. 42 paper, washing with 0.2% sulfuric acid. Evaporate the sample solution or filtrate to dryness in the platinum dish, then bake, heating to red heat with an air–gas blast burner. Cover the residue with 10–15 times its weight of 2:1 sodium carbonate–sodium borate flux mixture and heat over an air–gas burner until a clear melt is obtained. Then digest the sample with 40 ml of 1:1 hydrochloric acid, heating on a steam bath and stirring occasionally until the melt is completely in solution.

If phosphate is present in substantial amounts, do not add acid to the fluxed residue, but digest the melt with water on a steam bath with stirring. After digestion, filter through a Whatman No. 40 paper and wash thoroughly with hot water. Ignite the precipitate in the dish and fuse once more with 1–2 g of the 1:2 sodium carbonate–anhydrous sodium tetraborate flux mixture. Add 40 ml of 1:1 hydrochloric acid to the phosphate-free residue and digest to fully dissolve the melt.

Transfer the acidified sample solution to a 250-ml beaker and evaporate or dilute to obtain about 50 ml. Add 50 ml of 13% mandelic acid solution, heat the mixture to 85–95°C, and digest for 20 min. Cool to room temperature and filter through a Whatman No. 40 paper. Wash with a solution that contains 2 ml of concentrated hydrochloric acid and 5 g of mandelic acid per 100 ml, policing thoroughly. Transfer the paper with precipitate to a tared 30-ml platinum crucible and carefully ignite in a muffle furnace situated in a hood. Allow the temperature to slowly increase until the paper is charred, then bring the temperature to 1000°C and hold for 30 min. Remove the crucible, cover, and place in a desiccator to cool, then weigh. The ignited residue is zirconium dioxide.

FOR MINOR TO TRACE LEVELS. Weigh a sample of powdered glass containing 25–75 μg of zirconium into a 75-ml platinum dish. Add 5 ml of water, and for each 0.1 g of sample, add 2 ml of 1:1 sulfuric acid and 2 ml of 48% hydrofluoric acid. Evaporate on a steam bath then heat to strong fumes on a hot plate. Cool, rinse down with water, and repeat evaporation and fuming. Rinse down and then finally evaporate and fume to dryness. If sulfate precipitable metals are present, substitute an equal volume of 72% perchloric acid for sulfuric acid and bring to fumes one more time than specified for sulfuric acid. Cool, add 10 ml of 7 N nitric acid, and digest on a steam bath or hot plate until the sulfate residue is dissolved. Cool and transfer to a 125-ml separatory funnel with an additional 10 ml of 7 N nitric acid. Add 5.00 ml of freshly prepared 0.1 M tri-n-octylphosphine oxide (TOPO) in cyclohexane, prepared by dissolving 1.93 g of TOPO in 50 ml of reagent grade cyclohexane. Stopper the separatory funnel and extract on a mechanical shaker for 15 min. Drain and discard the aqueous phase. Add 20 ml of 7 N nitric acid and shake for an additional 10 min. Drain and discard the aqueous phase. Withdraw a 2-ml aliquot of the organic phase and transfer to a 25-ml volumetric flask. Add 10 ml of ethanol, 1.5 ml of 0.05% (w/v) ethanolic pyrocatechol violet solution, and 5 ml of pyridine. Mix after each addition, then dilute to volume with ethanol. After allowing the color to develop for 10 min, measure the absorbance at 655 nm using 1-cm cells. Run a reagent blank through the entire procedure. Using the net absorbance, interpolate the amount of zirconium per 5.00 ml of TOPO solution from a calibration curve prepared from a stock zirconium metal solution aliquoted and treated exactly as the sample, except that no additional hydrofluoric acid need be added prior to fuming to dryness. Zirconium metal dissolves readily in 48% hydrofluoric acid to which 1 ml of concentrated sulfuric acid and a few drops of concentrated nitric acid have been added; after the metal has dissolved, fume strongly to rid the solution of all traces of fluoride.

Calculate the zirconium content as zirconium dioxide, ZrO_2.

Arsenic and Antimony. A distillation method, using the apparatus shown in Figure 3, is recommended for the determination of arsenic in glass (38); if antimony is also present it is determined by further treatment of the same sample in the same apparatus. If arsenic is absent, the titrimetric method described below can be used for antimony. In addition, a colorimetric method (39) is given for trace amounts of antimony. This procedure, though perhaps not quite so precise as the titrimetric method, has the advantages of being specific for antimony in the presence of arsenic, and also being unaffected by the presence of lead or barium.

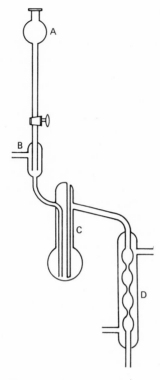

Fig. 3. Scherrer-type still for the separation of arsenic, antimony, and tin.

Procedures

ARSENIC. Weigh 3 g of finely powdered glass into a 150-ml platinum dish. Treat
with 25 ml of water, 25 ml of concentrated nitric acid, 20 ml of 1 : 1 sulfuric acid, and
30 ml of 48% hydrofluoric acid; add 5% potassium permanganate solution until the
solution remains pink. Stir and warm on a steam bath until the sample has dissolved. Evaporate, adding permanganate solution as necessary to maintain a pink
coloration. When most of the water has evaporated, transfer to a hot plate and
fume for at least 5 min. Cool, add 1 g of boric acid, dilute with 25 ml of water, and
then digest for about 10 min on the steam bath. While still hot, transfer to a
Scherrer-type still (see Figure 3) via the funnel A. The condenser delivery tube
should extend through a two-hole stopper to the bottom of a 500-ml Erlenmeyer
receiver containing 75 ml of water. The other hole of the two-hole stopper should
accommodate a glass delivery tube leading from the vapor space of the receiver
into a trap consisting of a 125-ml Erlenmeyer flask containing 50 ml of 5% sodium
bicarbonate solution. Place the receiver in position and surround it with an ice
bath. Add 1 g of hydrazine hydrochloride and 3 g of potassium bromide to the
platinum dish and transfer to the still with a minimum amount of water. Add 50
ml of concentrated hydrochloric acid to the still using the acid to rinse the platinum
dish. Pass a slow stream of carbon dioxide into the apparatus at the rate of 6–8
bubbles per sec through the sidearm at B. Heat the solution in the distillation
flask C until almost all the water is distilled over. Finally, add a total of 125 ml of
concentrated hydrochloric acid in 25–35 ml portions, using each portion to rinse the
platinum dish. Maintain the temperature between 110 and 111°C while each
portion distills. Without interrupting heating or the flow of carbon dioxide, remove
the receiver and rinse the end of the condenser with a little water. If antimony is to
be determined on the same sample, place another receiver containing 75 ml of water
in position.

Rinse the delivery tube to the trap and combine all washings and the contents of the trap with the distillate. Add 5 ml of 0.01 M iodine monochloride solution and titrate the arsenic potentiometrically with 0.02 N potassium bromate solution that has been standardized against arsenious oxide, using the platinum-saturated calomel electrode system. Run a reagent blank through the entire procedure and subtract from the volume of titrant consumed by the sample. Calculate the arsenic as arsenic trioxide, As_2O_3.

ANTIMONY (ARSENIC PRESENT). If arsenic is present, it must be separated as described above under Arsenic. The antimony-containing sample remains in the boiling flask, C, of the still. Add 2 g of tartaric acid to the receiving flask which contains 75 ml of water and surround it with ice. Fill the 125-ml Erlenmeyer flask trap with 50 ml of 5% sodium bicarbonate solution and connect to the outlet delivery tube from the distillate receiver. With the carbon dioxide running in at B at the rate of 6–8 bubbles per sec, add 10 ml of 1:1 sulfuric acid. The total amount of concentrated sulfuric acid in the boiling flask should be 15 ml. Heat the distillation flask as before and distill until the temperature is 200–220°C. Then add 15–20 ml of 40% hydrobromic acid dropwise at the rate of 1 drop every 3 sec. After the hydrogen bromide has been added during the course of about 20 min, allow the distillation to run a few more minutes and then stop, leaving the carbon dioxide stream going. Rinse the condenser and contents of the trap into the distillate and neutralize the distillate and washings with ammonium hydroxide to the methyl red color change. Boil gently to remove any sulfur dioxide and then make the solution 3% (v/v) hydrochloric acid. Gas rapidly with hydrogen sulfide for 15 min, heating the solution to near boiling during the treatment. Allow to stand until the precipitate settles, filter through Whatman No. 42 filter paper, and wash with 2% (v/v) sulfuric acid saturated with hydrogen sulfide. Transfer the precipitate and beaker back to the flask, cover, and add 10 ml of concentrated sulfuric acid and 15 ml of concentrated nitric acid. Heat and boil vigorously on a hot plate to rapidly effect oxidation of most of the organic matter. The solution should remain dark when the fumes of sulfuric acid appear. Fume strongly, cool somewhat, and treat with a few drops of 30% hydrogen peroxide, and reheat to strong fumes to oxidize the remaining organic matter. Repeat peroxide treatment and fuming until the solution is colorless, then cool, wash down the cover and sides of the flask with water, and again fume well. Add 0.5 g of powdered sulfur and boil the concentrated sulfuric acid solution for 10 min. Cool, add about 30 ml of water, boil about two min, add 5 ml of concentrated hydrochloric acid, 25 ml of water, and 2 g of tartaric acid. Filter through a Whatman No. 41 paper and wash with about 75 ml of 1:19 hydrochloric acid. Boil the filtrate 5 min, cool, and add 35 ml of concentrated hydrochloric acid for each 100 ml of solution. Introduce 5 ml of 0.005 N iodine monochloride solution and titrate the reduced antimony potentiometrically with potassium bromate solution which has been standardized against arsenious oxide, using the platinum-saturated calomel fiber junction electrode system. Carry a reagent blank through the entire procedure and subtract from the sample titration.

Calculate the antimony as antimony trioxide, Sb_2O_3

ANTIMONY (ARSENIC ABSENT). Weigh 3.000 g of the powdered glass sample into a 150-ml platinum dish. Treat with 15 ml of water, 10 ml of 1:1 sulfuric acid, and 30 ml of 48% hydrofluoric acid. If sulfate precipitable metals are present, substitute 72% perchloric acid for sulfuric acid. Evaporate on a steam bath and then to strong fumes on a hot plate. Cool, wash down the sides of the dish, add 0.25 g of boric acid, then repeat evaporation and fuming as before. Dilute with about 50 ml of water, neutralize to methyl red with ammonium hydroxide, then add 6 ml of concentrated hydrochloric acid. Transfer to a 400-ml 96% silica glass beaker with water rinses, then dilute to 200 ml. Gas with hydrogen sulfide for 20 min, heating the solution to near boiling during the hydrogen sulfide treatment, then digest on a steam bath to coagulate the precipitate. Filter through a Whatman No. 42 paper, washing with 2% (v/v) acetic acid saturated with hydrogen sulfide. Put the filter paper plus precipitate back into the precipitation beaker. If perchloric acid has been employed, fuse the residue remaining in the bottom of the platinum dish with 1 g of sodium bisulfate, dissolve in about 10 ml of 1:1 sulfuric acid, and then transfer to the beaker containing the sulfide precipitate and filter paper. Add 10 ml of concentrated sulfuric acid and 15 ml of concentrated nitric acid. Heat and boil rather rapidly to oxidize most of the organic matter. Continue heating to strong sulfuric acid fumes. Cool, add cautiously a few drops of 30% hydrogen peroxide, and reheat to strong fumes. Repeat peroxidation and fuming until the solution is colorless. Heat to fumes of sulfuric acid, cool, wash down the cover and sides of the beaker with water, and again fume well. Add 0.5 g of sulfur and boil the concentrated sulfuric acid for 10 min. Cool, rinse down cover and walls of beaker with 30 ml of water, and boil for 2 min. Add 5 ml of concentrated hydrochloric acid, 25 ml of water, and 2 g of tartaric acid. After the tartaric acid is dissolved, filter through a Whatman No. 41 paper, and wash with about 75 ml of 1:19 hydrochloric acid. Boil filtrate 5 min, cool, and add 35 ml of concentrated hydrochloric acid for each 100 ml of solution. Add 5 ml of 0.005 N iodine monochloride solution and titrate potentiometrically with 0.02 N potassium bromate that has been standardized against arsenious oxide using the platinum-saturated calomel electrode system. Run a reagent blank through the entire procedure. Calculate total antimony as antimony trioxide, Sb_2O_3.

ANTIMONY AT TRACE LEVELS. Treat a 0.1 g sample of powdered glass in a small platinum dish with 2 ml of water, 2 ml of 72% perchloric acid, 3 ml of concentrated nitric acid, 5 ml of 48% hydrofluoric acid, and enough drops of 5% potassium permanganate solution to impart a permanent pink color to the solution. Evaporate and fume to a volume of about 1 ml. Cool, add 10 ml of concentrated hydrochloric acid, and digest on a steam bath until the solids dissolve. Transfer to a 50-ml volumetric flask with concentrated hydrochloric acid. Dilute to volume with concentrated hydrochloric acid. Withdraw an aliquot containing 10–70 μg of antimonous oxide and transfer to a 60-ml separatory funnel. Add enough concentrated hydrochloric acid to make up the total solution volume to 17.0 ml. Add several drops of a 1.6% solution of ammonium hexanitratocerate, $(NH_4)_2Ce(NO_3)_8$, and mix. Allow the solution to stand a few minutes to allow complete oxidation. Pipet 25 ml of isopropyl ether into the separatory funnel, stopper, and shake for 30 sec. Add 7.0 ml of water and mix immediately. Cool in a 25°C water bath for 10 min, then shake again for 30 sec. After separation of the two phases, draw off the lower (aqueous) layer and discard. Add 20 ml of 0.01% (w/v) Rhodamine B in 0.5 N hydrochloric acid. Stopper the separatory funnel and shake for 30 sec. Allow the phases to separate and again discard the lower (aqueous) layer. Quickly filter the ether layer through a dry Whatman No. 41 filter paper, into a dry stopper-type spectrophotometer cell. Use a 1-cm cell for 10–70 μg levels of antimonous oxide, and a 5-cm cell for levels between 0 and 12 μg. Measure the absorbance at once at 550 nm. Run a blank through the procedure and subtract to obtain the net absorbance. Read the amount of antimony from a calibration curve obtained by treating aliquots of an antimony metal standard solution exactly in the same manner as the sample, omitting the decomposition steps. Prepare the standard antimony stock solution by dissolving the pure metal in a mixture of 5 ml of concentrated nitric acid and 10 ml of concentrated hydrochloric acid.

Calculate the antimony content of the sample as antimonous oxide, Sb_2O_3.

Nonmetallic Constituents.   Methods for important nonmetallic constituents of glass are described below.

Procedures

PHOSPHORUS BY GRAVIMETRIC METHOD.   Decompose 1 g of powdered glass in a 75-ml platinum dish with 10 ml of water, 5 ml of 72% perchloric acid, and 8 ml of 48% hydrofluoric acid.   The sample should contain 25–100 mg of phosphorus pentoxide.   Stir, then evaporate on a steam bath to remove most of the water. Transfer to a hot plate and fume not too vigorously for 5 min.   Wash down the sides of the dish with water, add 0.3 g of boric acid, and digest to dissolve.   Neutralize the excess perchloric acid present with ammonium hydroxide, then add 20 ml of 1:1 nitric acid and dilute with 100 ml of water.   Cover the dish and digest on a steam bath for several hours.   If the solution is not clear, filter through a Whatman No. 40 filter paper into a 500-ml Erlenmeyer flask.   Wash the insoluble residue on the filter paper with hot water.   Reserve filter paper, A.   Add to the filtrate 15 g of ammonium nitrate, followed by 35 ml of a 10% solution of ammonium molybdate tetrahydrate.   Stopper the flask and shake on an automatic shaker for 30 min. Allow the precipitate to settle at least 30 min or overnight.   Filter through Whatman No. 42 paper and wash with 5% ammonium nitrate solution made just acid with nitric acid.   Discard the filtrate.   Dissolve the precipitate on the filter paper, and any remaining in the flask, into a 400-ml beaker by treatment with 1:1 ammonium hydroxide, followed successively with small volumes of hot water, hot 1:4 hydrochloric acid, 1:1 ammonium hydroxide, and finally hot water.   Reserve filter paper, B.   To the dissolved phosphomolybdate precipitate, add 0.5 g of citric acid and adjust the volume to 150 ml.   Acidify to bromthymol blue (yellow color) with 1:1 hydrochloric acid.   Prepare a magnesia mixture by dissolving 200 g of magnesium chloride hexahydrate and 150 g of ammonium chloride in 750 ml of warm water and adding ammonium hydroxide until the solution is alkaline to litmus; allow to stand 1 hr, filter through Whatman No. 40 paper, acidify the filtered solution to a red litmus color, then dilute to 1 liter.   Add 25 ml of the magnesia mixture and cool in an ice bath.   Add ammonium hydroxide until the bromthymol blue indicator turns blue, then add 5 ml of ammonium hydroxide in excess for each 100 ml of solution.   Stir occasionally for 3–4 hr, filter through Whatman No. 42 paper, and wash with 1:19 ammonium hydroxide.   Dissolve the precipitate on the filter paper with about 50 ml of hot 1:4 hydrochloric acid followed by 50 ml of hot water, collecting the filtrate in the precipitation beaker.   Reserve filter paper, C. Add 1 ml of the magnesia mixture to the solution, cool in an ice bath, make alkaline to bromthymol blue indicator with ammonium hydroxide, and then add 5 ml of ammonium hydroxide in excess.   Stir occasionally for at least 2 hr, and allow to stand 4 hr, or preferably overnight.   Collect the precipitate on a Whatman No. 42 filter paper and wash with 1:19 ammonium hydroxide.   Place the paper and precipitate in a tared platinum crucible and slowly ignite in an electric muffle furnace. Char the paper without flaming, burn it off below 900°C, then ignite to constant weight at 1100°C.   Cool in a desiccator and weigh as magnesium pyrophosphate, $Mg_2P_2O_7$.   One gram of magnesium pyrophosphate is equivalent to 0.6378 g of phosphorus pentoxide, P_2O_5.

Place the three reserved filter papers, A, B, and C, in a weighed platinum crucible.   Burn off the paper, ignite to 1100°C, then cool and weigh.   If the residue recovered from the filter papers is about 1 mg, it may be ignored, except for the most accurate work.   If it is substantial, fuse the residue with a little sodium carbonate and leach the cooled melt by digestion with hot water.   Filter off the residue using Whatman No. 40 paper and washing with hot water, then determine the phosphorous content in the filtered and acidified leachate by the colorimetric method, which follows; accordingly correct the total amount of phosphorous recovered gravimetrically.

PHOSPHORUS BY COLORIMETRIC METHOD. Weigh 0.1 g of powdered glass into a 75-ml platinum dish. Optimally, the sample should contain 2–7 mg of phosphorus pentoxide. Treat with 2 ml of water, 5 ml of 72% perchloric acid, and 2 ml of 48% hydrofluoric acid, and evaporate the water on a steam bath. Transfer to a hot plate and fume strongly. Rinse down the sides of the dish, evaporate and fume at least two more times. Transfer with minimal water rinses to a 100-ml volumetric flask, add 1 drop of 0.1% aqueous p-nitrophenol indicator solution, and neutralize with 10% sodium hydroxide solution. Prepare a 0.25% vanadic acid solution by dissolving 2.5 g of ammonium metavanadate and 20 ml of nitric acid in enough water to provide 1 liter of solution. Also prepare a sodium molybdate reagent consisting of 69.6 g of sodium molybdate dihydrate dissolved in enough water to make 500 ml of solution. To the sample in the volumetric flask, add in order with mixing, 10 ml of 1:2 nitric acid, 10 ml of 0.25% vanadic acid solution, and 5 ml of sodium molybdate reagent. Mix and dilute to volume. Measure the absorbance of the solution at 470 nm. Use a 1-cm cell for 2–7 mg of phosphorus pentoxide or a 5-cm cell if the level is between 0.5 and 1 mg. Run a reagent blank through the entire procedure and subtract the absorbance from the sample absorbance. Prepare a calibration curve using suitable aliquots of a solution containing 1.917 g of potassium dihydrogen phosphate per liter, equivalent to 1.01 mg of phosphorus pentoxide per milliliter. Interpolate the amount of phosphorus pentoxide in the sample from its net absorbance.

FLUORIDE BY STEAM DISTILLATION. *Preparation of Reagents and Standard Solutions.* Prepare a cobalt stock solution by dissolving 5 g of cobaltous nitrate hexahydrate in enough water to make exactly 500 ml of solution; prepare a chromate stock solution by dissolving 0.125 g of sodium dichromate tetrahydrate in enough water to make 1 liter of solution. Mix 24 ml of water with 6 ml of cobalt stock solution and 20 ml of chromate stock solution to provide the neutralization color standard. Mix 35 ml of water with 10 ml of cobalt stock solution and 5 ml of chromate stock solution to provide the equivalence point color standard.

Prepare a buffer solution by dissolving 50 g of monochloroacetic acid in water, adjusting the pH to 3.4 with 50% sodium hydroxide solution, and diluting to 500 ml.

Prepare a 0.05 N thorium nitrate solution by dissolving 13.81 g of thorium nitrate tetrahydrate in water containing 2 ml of concentrated nitric acid, and diluting to 2 liters. Since the titer of the thorium nitrate varies somewhat with the amount of fluoride being titrated, a correction graph must be constructed. Take 1-, 2-, 3-, 4-, and 5-ml aliquots of primary standard 0.05 N sodium fluoride solution, and dilute each aliquot to 50 ml in an Erlenmeyer flask. To each, add 1 ml of 0.025% sodium alizarin sulfonate solution, and 0.5 N sodium hydroxide solution dropwise until the indicator turns pink. Then add 0.05 N hydrochloric acid dropwise until the color of the solution matches the neutralization color standard. Add 2 ml of monochloroacetic acid buffer solution. Using a 10-ml microburet, titrate with 0.05 N thorium nitrate solution to a color that matches the equivalence point color standard. Perform a blank determination and make the necessary corrections. Plot the apparent thorium nitrate normality found for each titration versus the milliliters of thorium nitrate consumed for each sodium fluoride aliquot.

Determination. Grind 4 g of sodium carbonate and 0.75 g of zinc oxide in an agate mortar, then add 0.5 g of powdered glass and grind to mix thoroughly. A larger or smaller sample may be chosen, but no more than 5 mg of fluoride should be taken. Transfer to a 75-ml platinum dish. Grind an additional gram of sodium

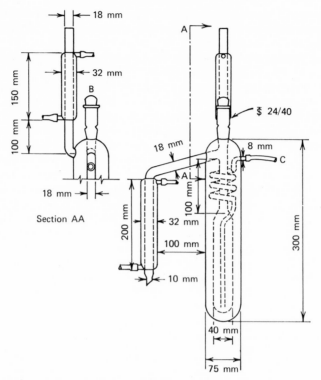

Fig. 4. Constant temperature steam distillation apparatus for isolation of fluoride.

carbonate to clean the mortar, then add it to the contents of the dish. Fuse in an electric furnace at 850–900°C for 20 min. Digest the melt with 25 ml of water, warming on a hot plate to hasten decomposition. Assemble the steam distillation apparatus (43) shown in Figure 4. Charge the apparatus with 35 ml of 72% perchloric acid. Filter the hot leachate of the melt, using a fluoride-free Whatman No. 31 filter paper, through sample access port B. Wash the dish and paper four times with 5–7 ml portions of hot 1% sodium carbonate solution. Place in position a 125-ml Erlenmeyer flask receiver containing 1 ml of 0.025% sodium alizarin sulfonate indicator solution.

Use constant boiling *sym*-tetrachloroethane as the heat transfer liquid to maintain the sample chamber at 146°C. With the bypass to the atmosphere closed, start heating the steam generator and the electric heater of the still simultaneously so that the steam begins passing into the still at C about the same time as the heat transfer liquid surrounding the sample chamber commences to reflux in its condenser. After all systems are up to temperature and operating smoothly, through adjustment of the heat, regulate the steam-generator bypass to the atmosphere so that about 5 ml of distillate collects per min. Collect five 50-ml portions and titrate each fraction as described for the standardization of the 0.05 N thorium nitrate solution, starting with the dropwise addition of 0.5 N sodium hydroxide solution. Run a complete reagent blank through the entire procedure and subtract the blanks corresponding to the respective fractions. Using the net volume of thorium nitrate required by each fraction, interpolate the proper thorium nitrate normality corresponding to that fraction. By summing the corrected milliequivalents of thorium nitrate consumed for each fraction, the amount of fluoride in the sample can be computed.

FLUORIDE BY PYROHYDROLYSIS (40). *Preparation of Reagents and Standard Solutions.* Follow the procedure as given for Fluoride by Steam Distillation.

Determination. Grind the sample to a uniformly impalpable powder (less than 425 mesh), with an agate mortar and pestle. Weigh 0.3 g of fluoride-free uranium oxide, U_3O_8, into a 65-mm agate mortar. For a sample containing 3–6% fluoride, weigh 0.1 g of the powdered glass into the agate mortar containing the uranium oxide. For 0.5–3% fluoride, mix a 0.2 g sample with 0.4 g of uranium oxide; for 0.1–0.5% fluoride, use a 0.5 g sample and 0.6 g of uranium oxide. Grind the two powders thoroughly together, then using a camel's hair brush, transfer to a small platinum boat. Assemble a pyrohydrolysis distillation apparatus (276) similar to that shown in Figure 5. Fill the boiling flask with fluoride-free water and adjust the heat so that the condenser is delivering 3.5–4.5 ml/min. Adjust the power to the tube furnace so that the temperature inside the reaction tube with steam flowing is

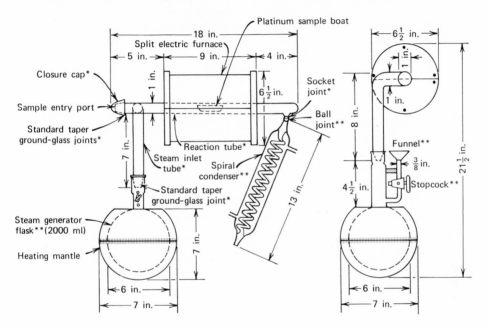

Fig. 5. Glass still for fluoride analysis by pyrohydrolysis separation. *Items are Corning Code 7900 96% silica glass. **Items are Corning Code 7740 borosilicate glass.

1050°C. With a push rod, slide the sample through the sample entry port to the position previously established as the zone of maximum temperature. Quickly close the sample entry port. Collect succeeding 50-ml portions of the distillate in 125-ml Erlenmeyer flasks containing 1 ml of 0.025% sodium alizarin sulfonate and 1 drop of 0.1 N sodium hydroxide solution. Add 0.1 N sodium hydroxide dropwise as required during the run to maintain the distillate on the alkaline side of the indicator (magenta). Prepare each aliquot for titration as it is collected by acidifying to the neutralization-color standard by dropwise addition of 0.05 N hydrochloric acid. Add 2.0 ml of monochloroacetic acid buffer solution and, using a 10-ml microburet, titrate with 0.05 N thorium nitrate solution as described in the procedure above.

CHLORIDE, BROMIDE, AND IODIDE. Dissolve 5 g of powdered glass with 20 ml of water and 40 ml of 48% hydrofluoric acid in a 150-ml platinum dish. If the halide level is expected to be higher than the usual contamination level of 0.05% chloride, take a smaller sample and proportionately less hydrofluoric acid; for a sample containing 0.1% chloride, take a 1-g sample and use 8 ml of 48% hydrofluoric acid. Stir with a Teflon stirring rod until dissolved. Moderate heating at low steam bath temperatures can be applied. When the sample has decomposed completely as evidenced by the disappearance of all gritty particles, cool to room temperature and add 1 g of boric acid for each 8 ml of 48% hydrofluoric acid. Place the dish in an ice bath, agitate the sample with a magnetic stirrer, and using a microburet, potentiometrically titrate the sample with 0.01 N primary standard silver nitrate solution. Use a silver–silver bromide indicating electrode and a reference electrode consisting of a silver–silver bromide electrode immersed in a 10% sodium sulfate solution saturated with silver bromide crystals, and contained in a 10-cm length of 7-mm polyethylene tubing loosely plugged at the lower end with a polyethylene or Teflon plug; the drip junction can be facilitated by interposing a piece of thread between the plug and plastic tubing inner wall. Prepare each silver–silver bromide electrode by connecting a piece of silver wire in series through a 470 Ω resistor to a 1.5 V dry cell and anodizing it in a 1% potassium bromide solution for 1 hr with platinum wire as the cathode. An expanded scale pH meter is particularly well suited to this titration. The equivalence point is taken as the point of maximum change of potential. Run a reagent blank. Calculate the amount of chloride in the sample from the volume of silver nitrate solution used, corrected for the blank.

If bromide is present, two end point inflections will be observed, the first corresponding to the bromide present. The volume of silver nitrate subsequently required from the bromide end point to the next inflection corresponds to the chloride present.

If iodide is present, or suspected, add sulfur dioxide-saturated water to the sample prior to the addition of hydrofluoric acid. If all three halides are present, three inflections will be observed, the first potential break corresponding to iodide, the second to bromide, and the third to chloride.

TOTAL SULFUR BY GRAVIMETRIC METHOD. If the sample does not contain lead, decompose 5 g of the powdered glass in a 150-ml platinum dish by treating with 25 ml of water, 0.5 g of calcium carbonate acidified with a little perchloric acid, 50 ml of 48% hydrofluoric acid, and 10 ml of 72% perchloric acid. If sulfide sulfur is present, carry out the decomposition in a Teflon beaker, but add bromine water instead of water prior to addition of hydrofluoric acid. Stir and digest on a steam bath for about 15 min, then add 1 ml of concentrated nitric acid, 15 ml of 72% perchloric acid, and 0.2 g of magnesium nitrate hexahydrate. Evaporate on a steam bath to remove most of the nitric and hydrofluoric acids, then fume on a hot plate for about 5 min. Cool, wash down sides of the dish with water, and evaporate and fume to near dryness. Cool, treat the moist residue with 25 ml of 1:19 hydrochloric acid, digest on a steam bath, to effect solution, and finally transfer to a 400-ml beaker and dilute to about 200 ml.

If the glass contains lead, decompose by mixing 3 g of the powdered sample with 6 g of sodium carbonate and 0.5 g of potassium nitrate in a platinum dish. Fuse in a furnace for 15 min at 1000°C. Leach the melt with water saturated with carbon dioxide. Filter and wash the insoluble residue with 1% sodium bicarbonate solution. Discard the insoluble residue containing most of the lead, acidify the filtrate with hydrochloric acid, then add 10 ml of concentrated hydrochloric acid in excess. Evaporate the acidified filtrate to dryness to dehydrate the silica. Quench the dry residue with 4 ml of 1:1 hydrochloric acid, add 25 ml of water, digest a few minutes on a steam bath, then filter off the silica on a Whatman No. 40 paper, washing with hot water. Dilute the filtrate to 200 ml.

Irrespective of the mode of sample decomposition, the sample is now ready for the final pH adjustment prior to precipitation with barium. Neutralize the solution with ammonium hydroxide until the hydrous oxide precipitate just forms.

If antimony or other easily hydrolyzed ions are present, adjust the pH to the neutral color of methyl red, boil for a few minutes, then filter through a Whatman No. 40 filter paper. Wash with hot 2% ammonium chloride solution that has been neutralized to methyl red. To the filtrate or unfiltered solution, as the case may be, add 2 ml of concentrated hydrochloric acid for each 200 ml of solution volume. Heat to boiling and add slowly with stirring 10 ml of 10% barium chloride solution. Digest near the boiling point for 1 hr and then allow to stand at least 4 hr at room temperature. Filter through Whatman No. 42 paper or through a tared fine-porosity porcelain filtering crucible. Wash with small volumes of 1:99 hydrochloric acid, and finally with water, minimizing the volumes of wash liquids. If filter paper is used, transfer to a tared platinum crucible, place in a cold muffle furnace, then ignite slowly to char off the paper. For either mode of collecting the precipitate, ignite to constant weight at 700°C. Weigh the total sulfur content as barium sulfate; calculate as sulfur trioxide. One gram of barium sulfate is equivalent to 0.343 g of sulfur trioxide.

TOTAL SULFUR BY RAPID COMBUSTION METHOD (41). Use of the Laboratory Equipment Corporation (LECO), St. Joseph, Michigan, induction combustion apparatus, which basically consists of the Model 521-400 high-frequency induction furnace and a Model 532 automatic photometric titrator, is assumed.

Prepare a primary standard titrant by dissolving 0.444 g of potassium iodate in water and diluting to 1 liter. Prepare a starch indicator solution by mixing 9 g of Arrowroot starch with 10 ml of water, slowly pouring the resulting paste into 1 liter of boiling water, cooling to room temperature, then adding 15 g of potassium iodide, stirring until it is dissolved.

Weigh a suitable-size sample of powdered glass into a LECO No. 528-35 ceramic crucible. A sample size larger than 1 g is not recommended and, if more than 0.2% sulfur is present reduce the sample size proportionally. Add 1.3 g of iron accelerator and about 2.5 g of granulated tin. If arsenic is present in the sample, add about 0.5 g of magnesium oxide. Place a LECO No. 528-42 porous refractory lid on the crucible and position the sample in the combustion chamber by setting the crucible on the pedestal and operating the pedestal raising (and lowering) mechanism. This operation seals the sample, then properly situated in the induction coil, in a gas-tight combustion chamber. Start the oxygen flow and adjust the rate to 1 liter/min. Fill the titration vessel into which the exit gases are delivered with 1.5% (v/v) hydrochloric acid and add 2 ml of starch–iodide solution. Adjust the sensitivity knob of the titrator so that enough potassium iodate is automatically added to produce and maintain a deep blue color. Henceforth, do not change the setting of the sensitivity knob. Refill the buret. Activate the automatic timer controlling the power to the furnace by setting the switch to the "titrate" position and pushing the button which initiates a 6 min combustion cycle. During this time, all forms of sulfur in the sample are converted to sulfur dioxide which is carried by the oxygen stream into the titration vessel where a photocell-controlled buret delivers sufficient iodate to effect stoichiometric reaction. If the crucible has been positioned correctly within the induction coil, the amount of iron accelerator is sufficient, and the sample size is not too large, the plate current meter should register 400–500 mA during the burn. At the conclusion of the timer cycle, lower the pedestal and remove the hot crucible using crucible tongs; then read the buret which is calibrated directly in terms of % sulfur per gram of sample. Run a blank on the same proportions of iron and tin and subtract from the sample reading. Calculate the total sulfur as % sulfur trioxide.

The chief interference in the application of this method is chloride, which causes low results by simultaneously generating free chlorine along with the sulfur dioxide produced from the sample.

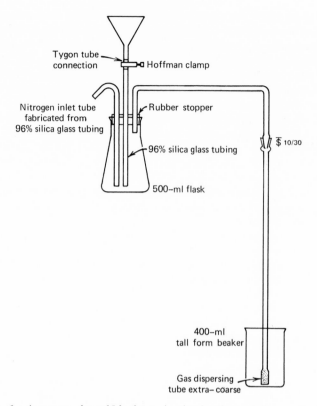

Fig. 6. Apparatus for sulfide determination by the evolution method.

SULFIDE BY EVOLUTION METHOD (42,227). Introduce a suitable size sample—
5 g for 0.05% sulfide, 2 g for 0.5% sulfide—ground to pass an 80-mesh sieve, into a
500-ml 96% silica glass Erlenmeyer flask, and position in the apparatus shown in
Figure 6. A heat-resistant chemical borosilicate flask is also satisfactory, but, due to
hydrofluoric acid attack, will have to be replaced more frequently, perhaps after
five runs. To the 400-ml beaker, add 200 ml of water and 25 ml of absorbing solution
prepared by dissolving 25 g of zinc sulfate heptahydrate in 100 ml of water, adding
100 ml of concentrated ammonium hydroxide, mixing, and adding enough water to
make the final volume 250 ml. Surround the beaker with an ice bath and position
the fritted glass element of the delivery tube as near the bottom of the beaker as
possible. Purge the apparatus with a slow stream of nitrogen for about 1 min, then
add, via the funnel, 80 ml of 1:1 hydrochloric acid. Finally, add 10 ml of 48%
hydrofluoric acid for each gram of sample. Rinse down the funnel with a volume of
water equal to the volume of hydrofluoric acid added. Clamp off the Tygon tube
connection to the funnel by means of the Hoffman clamp and heat the flask contents to boiling. When the solution boils, clamp off the nitrogen inlet and discontinue the nitrogen; continue boiling for 2 min. Remove the heat source and resume
the nitrogen flow for 3 min. Detach the delivery tube at the standard taper joint
and remove the beaker. Add 5 ml of 1% starch solution and 50 ml of 1:1 hydrochloric acid and carefully mix using the delivery tube as a stirrer. Quickly over-
titrate to a blue color with 0.03 N primary standard potassium iodate solution,
consisting of 1.070 g of potassium iodate and 15 g of potassium iodide in 1 liter of
water. Rinse out the delivery tube two or three times by drawing up portions of the

solution. Add more standard iodate solution to restore the blue color, if necessary. Back titrate until colorless with 0.02 N sodium thiosulfate solution. Add 0.03 N potassium iodate solution until a pale blue end point is reached. Compute the net volume of potassium iodate required by subtracting the volume of sodium thiosulfate utilized, multiplied by the iodate/thiosulfate titer ratio from the total volume of iodate added. Run a reagent blank similarly through the entire procedure and make the necessary correction. Calculate as % sulfide, S^{2-}.

SELENIUM. Prepare a 0.03 N primary standard potassium iodate solution by dissolving 1.070 g of potassium iodate and 15 g of potassium iodide in water and diluting to 1 liter.

Prepare a 0.04 N sodium thiosulfate solution by dissolving 9.92 g of sodium thiosulfate pentahydrate in water and diluting to 1 liter. Standardize the thiosulfate solution against the iodate solution, using 5 ml of 1% starch solution as indicator.

For glasses containing about 0.1% selenium, weigh 5 g of powdered sample into a Teflon beaker. Treat with 5 g of tartaric acid, 20 ml of saturated bromine water, and 40 ml of 48% hydrofluoric acid. Stir until the sample is dissolved and add 100 ml of concentrated hydrochloric acid saturated with sulfur dioxide. Continue stirring, then allow the solution to stand from 30 min to 4 hr. Filter through a Gooch crucible prepared with a thick pad of asbestos and wash four times with water. Dissolve the selenium precipitate by adding to the contents of the filtering crucible 2 ml of bromine–hydrobromic acid—prepared by dissolving 5 ml of bromine in 15 ml of 48% hydrobromic acid—and refiltering, collecting the reoxidized selenium in the original Teflon beaker. Wash the Gooch crucible several times with small portions of water, then repeat the bromine–hydrobromic acid treatment of the Gooch crucible and water rinsing to ensure complete dissolution and transfer of the precipitate. Add water saturated with sulfur dioxide dropwise until the brown color fades to a pale yellow color. If the solution becomes completely decolorized add bromine water dropwise until a pale yellow persists. Finally discharge the yellow color by adding a few drops of 5%(w/v) phenol. Titrate the selenious acid, H_2SeO_3, present as follows. Pipet 15 ml of standardized 0.04 N sodium thiosulfate solution into the sample solution. Stir, add 5 ml of 1% starch solution, and titrate the excess thiosulfate with 0.03 N potassium iodate solution. Calculate the selenium content from the net volume of thiosulfate solution consumed.

Coloring Additives and Contaminants. The following methods are given for trace levels of metals which are present as color additives, or as contaminants which may affect color.

Procedures

IRON (44). Weigh a sample containing 0.05–0.25 mg of iron as ferric oxide into a 75-ml platinum dish. For a 0.1 g sample, add a few ml of water, 2 ml of 1:1 sulfuric acid, 2 ml of 48% hydrofluoric acid, and evaporate and fume in the customary manner. Rinse down and repeat fuming at least twice, continuing the final fuming just to dryness. If sulfate precipitable metals are present, use 2 ml of 72% perchloric acid in place of 1:1 sulfuric acid. Add 0.5 ml of hydrochloric acid and a few ml of water to the residue and digest briefly on a steam bath until dissolved. Transfer to a 50-ml volumetric flask and add in succession 2 ml of 14% hydroxylamine hydrochloride solution, 10 ml of a reagent consisting of 113.1 g of diammonium hydrogen citrate and 93.1 g of disodium EDTA in 1 liter of aqueous solution, and 4 ml of 1.2% (w/v) ethanolic 1,10-phenanthroline monohydrochloride solution. Swirl to mix, then add 6 ml of pyridine. Dilute to volume, mix well, and then allow to stand for 30 min.   Read the absorbance at 510 nm using appropriately either a 1-cm or 5-cm cell.   Run a reagent blank through the entire procedure and subtract from the sample absorbance reading.   If ions such as Cu(II), Cr(III), Mn(II), Ni(II), V(IV,V), or Ti(IV) are present in substantial amounts (not often the case for ordinary glasses), also subtract from the sample absorbance reading a sample blank prepared by processing a duplicate sample to which all reagents have been added except 1,10-phenanthroline.   Read the amount of iron corresponding to the net absorbance reading from a calibration curve prepared by similarly treating suitable aliquots of a known iron solution prepared by dissolving 0.1000 g of pure iron in hydrochloric acid and diluting to 1 liter.   Calculate the iron content as ferric oxide, Fe_2O_3.

If cobalt or other coloring ions are present in amounts that cause the sample blank to be appreciable, it is recommended that the EDTA component be omitted and citrate alone be employed for masking.   A corresponding calibration curve should then be prepared.

CHROMIUM (45).   Weigh a sample containing between 0.02 and 0.1 mg of chromium into a 75-ml platinum dish.   For a 0.1 g sample, add 5 ml of water, 3 ml of 1:1 sulfuric acid, and 2 ml of 48% hydrofluoric acid, and heat to fumes of sulfuric acid.   Cool, rinse down the sides of the dish and then fume strongly until most of the sulfuric acid has evaporated and the contents of the dish crystallizes on cooling.   Cool, transfer with a minimal amount of water (no more than 40 ml) to a 250-ml beaker.   Add 5 ml of 85% phosphoric acid and sufficient additional sulfuric acid to total approximately 20 meq of this acid.   If necessary, adjust the volume of the solution to about 40 ml.   Heat just to boiling, then add 1 ml of 0.1 M potassium permanganate solution and allow to digest on a steam bath for 20 min.   Destroy the excess permanganate by adding 1 drop of 1% sodium azide solution every 10 sec until the sample solution becomes colorless.   Cool to room temperature, add 5 ml of 4 M sodium dihydrogen phosphate solution and dilute to about 90 ml.   Add 4 ml of 0.25% diphenyl carbazide in 1:1 acetone–water.   Transfer to a 100-ml volumetric flask and dilute to volume.   If this solution is cloudy at this point due to the presence, for example, of insoluble sulfates, provide a clear solution by centrifuging a suitable portion.   Read the absorbance of the solution in either a 1-cm or 5-cm cell, whichever is appropriate, at 540 nm.   Subtract the absorbance obtained for a reagent blank carried through the entire procedure.   Read the amount of chromium corresponding to the net absorbance from a calibration curve prepared by similarly (except for decomposition steps) developing and reading the absorbance of suitable aliquots of a standard chromium solution.   Prepare the standard chromium solution by dissolving 0.0283 g of primary standard potassium dichromate in water and diluting to 1 liter.   Calculate the chromium content of the glass as chromic oxide.

NICKEL (42,46).   Weigh a sample containing between 0.025 and 0.15 mg of nickel in a 75-ml platinum dish.   For 0.1 g of glass, add 5 ml of water, 2 ml of 72% perchloric acid, and 2 ml of 48% hydrofluoric acid.   Evaporate and fume just to dryness.   Rinse down the walls of the dish with water, add 1 ml of 72% perchloric acid, and evaporate and fume just to dryness once more.   Dissolve the residue by adding 4 ml of 1:1 hydrochloric acid and warming.   Cool, add 5 ml of 10% hydroxylamine hydrochloride solution, 5 ml of 10% citric acid, neutralize to litmus with 1:1 ammonium hydroxide, and then add 5 ml in excess.   Transfer to a 125-ml separatory funnel, dilute to 50–75 ml and add 5 ml of 1% (w/v) ethanolic dimethylglyoxime solution.   Extract three times with 5-ml portions of chloroform.   Shake the combined chloroform extracts in a separatory funnel with 20 ml of 0.5 M ammonium hydroxide.   Drain and reserve the scrubbed chloroform phase in another separatory funnel.   Add another 5 ml of chloroform to the separated aqueous phase, and after shaking, add this portion of chloroform to the portion already reserved. Reextract the nickel from the chloroform phase by shaking for 1 min with 5 ml of N hydrochloric acid. Drain the aqueous phase into a 50-ml beaker. Repeat the extraction with a second 5-ml portion of N hydrochloric acid. Dilute the combined aqueous phases in the 50-ml beaker to 25 ml, add, with mixing, 1 ml of 10% citric acid solution, 3 ml of 2% potassium persulfate solution, 15 ml of 2 M sodium hydroxide solution, and 1 ml of 1% (w/v) ethanolic dimethylglyoxime solution. Heat to 60°C for 5 min, and transfer to a 50-ml volumetric flask. Cool, and dilute to volume. Measure the absorbance at 465 nm using a 1-cm cell; a 5-cm cell may be used if the amount of nickel is below the recommended range. Obtain the net absorbance of the sample by subtracting the absorbance of a reagent blank carried through the entire procedure. Read the amount of nickel corresponding to the net absorbance of the sample from a calibration curve prepared from suitable aliquots of a standard nickel solution that have been carried through the entire color development starting with the addition of hydroxylamine hydrochloride solution. Prepare the standard nickel solution for aliquation by making a one-tenth dilution of a stock solution consisting of 0.1000 g of pure nickel metal dissolved in hydrochloric acid and diluted to 1 liter. Calculate the nickel content as nickel oxide, NiO.

COBALT (42,47). Weigh a suitable size sample, containing 0.015–0.10 mg of cobalt, in a 75-ml platinum dish. For a 0.1 g sample, treat with 5 ml of water, 3 ml of 1:1 sulfuric acid, and 0.5 ml of concentrated nitric acid, and evaporate to strong fumes of sulfuric acid. Rinse down with water and repeat heating to strong fumes at least once more. If the sample contains lead or barium, substitute 72% perchloric acid for sulfuric acid, bring to fumes at least three times, and finally fume to near dryness. Add 1 ml of hydrochloric acid and 5 ml of water and digest, covered on a steam bath, to dissolve all soluble salts. Then add 2 ml of 10% sodium citrate solution and continue heating with occasional stirring until the solution is clear. Neutralize to litmus with 1:1 ammonium hydroxide. Transfer to a 60-ml separatory funnel, add 0.2 ml of 1:1 ammonium hydroxide and shake 1 min with 5 ml of 0.01% (w/v) dithizone in carbon tetrachloride. Drain off the carbon tetrachloride phase into another separatory funnel and repeat, with additional portions of 0.01% (w/v) dithizone, successive extractions of the aqueous sample solution until the carbon tetrachloride layer appears brownish-green. Wash the combined organic extracts by shaking vigorously with 5 ml of water, then draw off the carbon tetrachloride layer into a 50-ml beaker. Evaporate the carbon tetrachloride solution to dryness on a steam bath, then add 0.25 ml of concentrated sulfuric acid, 2 ml of concentrated nitric acid, and 0.5 ml of 72% perchloric acid. Cover with a watch glass, then evaporate and fume to dryness, but do not bake. Dissolve the evaporated residue with 0.60 ml of 1:1 hydrochloric acid, 0.60 ml of 1:10 nitric acid, and 12 ml of water. Add 1.3 ml of 0.2% nitroso-R salt solution, mix, then add 2.5 g of sodium acetate, $NaC_2H_3O_2 . 3H_2O$. The pH should, at this point, be about 5.5. Boil for 1 min, add 1.0 ml of concentrated nitric acid, and boil again for 1 min. Allow to cool in the dark to room temperature, then transfer to a 25-ml volumetric flask and dilute to volume. Measure the absorbance at 540 nm using a 1-cm cell; use a 5-cm cell for levels of cobalt below the recommended range. Run a reagent blank through the procedure and subtract its absorbance from the sample reading to obtain the net absorbance. Read the amount of cobalt corresponding to the net absorbance from a calibration curve prepared by using suitable aliquots of a standard cobalt solution (10.0 mg/liter) that have been carried through the color development procedure starting with the addition of sodium citrate solution. Prepare the cobalt standard solution by making a one-tenth dilution of a stock solution consisting of 0.1000 g of the pure metal dissolved in hydrochloric acid and diluted to 1 liter with water. Calculate the cobalt as cobaltous–cobaltic oxide, Co_3O_4.

MANGANESE. Decompose a suitable size powdered sample containing 0.5–2.5 mg of manganese in a 75 ml platinum dish. For a 0.5 g sample, treat with 5 ml of water, 5 ml of 1:1 sulfuric acid, and 5 ml of 48% hydrofluoric acid. Evaporate to fumes on a steam bath, then fume strongly on a hot plate to a volume of about 1 ml. If the glass contains lead or barium, substitute for 1:1 sulfuric acid an equivalent amount of 72% perchloric acid. Cool, rinse down the sides of the dish with water, and bring to strong fumes again. If perchloric acid was used, add 50 mg of boric acid after rinsing with water, then evaporate and fume a third time to dryness, but do not bake. Dissolve the residue by digestion with 18 ml of 1:1 nitric acid, then transfer to a 250-ml beaker. Adjust the volume to about 30 ml. Add 5 ml of 85% phosphoric acid and 0.3 g of potassium periodate. Cover and boil gently for 10 min after the pink color starts to develop. Cool, transfer to a 50-ml volumetric flask, and dilute to volume. Measure the absorbance at 525 nm using a 1-cm cell; use a 5-cm cell if the manganese level is below the recommended range. Process a reagent blank through the entire procedure and subtract its absorbance from that of the sample. Using the net absorbance, read the manganese content from a calibration curve prepared by processing suitable aliquots of a standard manganese solution for color development, starting with the addition of nitric and phosphoric acids and potassium periodate. Prepare the manganese standard solution by dissolving 0.1000 g of manganese metal in 1:1 nitric acid and diluting to 1 liter. Calculate the manganese as manganese oxide, MnO.

Persulfate can be used in place of periodate to improve the rate of oxidation of very low levels of manganese.

CERIUM (48–50). *Preparation of Standard Curves.* Prepare a stock cerate solution by dissolving 1.53 g of tetrasulfatoceric acid, $H_4Ce(SO_4)_4$, in N sulfuric acid and diluting to 1 liter; standardize this approximately 0.03 N solution against primary standard arsenious oxide in N sulfuric acid using a few drops of 0.01 M osmic acid as catalyst and a drop of 0.025 M ferrous 1,10-phenanthroline as the indicator. The stock cerate standard will contain about 0.421 mg/ml of cerium. Take aliquots of a 1:5 dilution of the stock standard, and measure the absorbance of the resulting solutions at 320 nm using a 5-cm cell. Plot a calibration curve.

Prepare a $6 \times 10^{-4} M$ potassium permanganate solution by dissolving 95 mg in water and diluting to 1 liter. Take 1-, 2-, and 3-ml aliquots of this solution and dilute them to 100 ml. Measure the absorbance of these solutions in 5-cm stoppered cells at 320 nm and at 525 nm. Plot the absorbance of each solution at 320 nm versus its absorbance at 525 nm.

Determination. Decompose a suitable size sample, containing between 0.05 and 0.25 mg cerium as ceric oxide, in a 75-ml platinum dish. For a 1-g sample, treat with a few ml of water, 5 ml of 1:1 sulfuric acid and 10 ml of 48% hydrofluoric acid. Carry a reagent blank through the procedure with the sample. Evaporate on a steam bath, then transfer to a hot plate and heat to dense white fumes of sulfuric acid. Add a few drops of concentrated nitric acid during fuming to destroy organic matter. Cool, rinse down the sides of the dish thoroughly with water, evaporate, and repeat fuming until the final volume is 1–2 ml. Cool and rinse down the sides of the dish with about 20 ml of water. Cover with a watch glass and digest until the sample is completely dissolved, then transfer to a 100-ml beaker. At this point, the solution in the beaker must be less than 3 N sulfuric acid. Add 5 ml of 4% potassium persulfate solution and 2 drops of 0.4% silver sulfate solution. Heat to boiling and boil for 10 min using a bump rod to prevent bumping. After cooling to room temperature, transfer to a 50-ml volumetric flask and dilute to volume with water. Measure the absorbance of the blank and the sample at 320 and 525 nm, using 5-cm stoppered cells, against a 5-cm cell filled with water. Add 2 drops of 1% (w/v) hydrogen peroxide solution to the cells containing the sample and blank solutions and mix each thoroughly. Remeasure the absorbance of both sample and blank at 320 and 525 nm. Subtract the corresponding blank absorbance readings from those of the sample. Then compute the true absorbance due to cerium as follows:

$$\text{True absorbance of cerium} = [A_{320}^{\text{I}} - A_{320}^{\text{II}}] - A_{320}^{\text{Mn}}$$

where A_{320}^{I} = initial absorbance reading of the sample at 320 nm

A_{320}^{II} = absorbance of sample at 320 nm after addition of peroxide

A_{320}^{Mn} = computed absorbance of manganese at 320 nm corresponding to the observed difference in absorbance at 525 nm before and after addition of peroxide; this is obtained by comparison of this difference with the previously prepared permanganate standard curve

Using the true absorbance of the sample, read the cerium content of the sample from the previously prepared cerium standard curve. Calculate the cerium as ceric oxide, CeO_2.

Redox State Determinations

The redox equilibria that are established during the melting process for certain minor and trace ingredients can play an important role in both the manufacture of glass and its ultimate properties. Ferrous iron, for instance, has a strong optical absorbance at about 1.1 μm in the infrared. Consequently, the presence of this species severely affects the melting process because considerably more heat is then required to bring the glass melt up to the desired temperature. The economics of the process is therefore greatly improved by incorporating into the batch oxidants that convert the iron to the ferric state. Removal of gas bubbles from the molten glass during the fining stage is often accomplished by the inclusion of arsenic and/or antimony in the batch. The pentoxides of these elements release oxygen at an appropriate temperature and proper viscosity to assist the glass in purging itself of entrapped gas bubbles. The effectiveness of the fining process as well as the conditions for its optimization can therefore be judged by analytical determination of the relative amounts of the tri- and pentavalent species. Redox equilibria affect the optical absorbance spectra of glasses containing minor amounts of such metals as copper, titanium, vanadium, chromium, cerium, and manganese. Smith and Cohen (51) have studied the spectra of these and several other cations in alkali silicate glasses. The redox equilibria for nonmetals, notably sulfur and selenium, are of paramount importance to the production of the proper color in red and yellow cadmium sulfoselenide, and cadmium sulfide glasses. Sulfide is also critical to the production of zinc sulfide opals and carbon–amber glasses.

Determination of the redox state of the various species of metals and nonmetals in glass is an exceedingly complex and difficult analytical problem due to the drastic chemical action needed to decompose the sample. A further complication arises when more than one multivalent species is present, since new equilibria can result when the glass is brought into solution, caused by interactions. Consequently, this type of analysis is attempted relatively rarely, usually by glass technologists undertaking special studies. Several investigators have been successful in the determination of ferric and ferrous iron (52–55) which happens to be one of the more tractable systems.   Douglas and workers have reported success in the determination of tri- and hexavalent chromium (56), ceric and cerous ion (57), and even pairs of redox equilibria involving chromium–iron, manganese–arsenic, chromium–arsenic, chromium–cerium, and cerium–manganese (58); but in all cases the glass matrices were simple, being either alkali–silicate or alkali–borate glasses.   Close et al. (53) have reported classical methods for determining the various valence states of arsenic, antimony, and selenium as well as iron in glass.   Wise and Williams (59,60) have reported constant-current coulometric methods for the valence states of arsenic and antimony in glasses.   In general, for all of these analytical approaches, the combined total of all valence species of the element is determined and then, by suitable specific techniques, the amounts of one or more of the other redox species are determined. One of the redox species is almost always taken by difference.   It is rare that more than two valence states of the element exist simultaneously in a glass; selenium apparently is exceptional in that all four species have been observed (53) in the same glass.   The methods employed are generally slight variations of those procedures described in the preceding sections.

Chelometry

Chelometry or chelometric titrations, which utilize the ability of certain multi-dentate ligands, notably aminopolycarboxylic acids, to form very stable, soluble 1:1 complexes with many metal ions has, since about 1950, developed into a very important tool for the analysis of glasses and glass–ceramics.   The principles of the technique have been covered in detail under COMPLEXATION IN AQUEOUS MEDIA, Vol. 1, pp. 376–428.   Cluley (61) reported a rapid method for the chelometric determination of calcium and magnesium in soda-lime glasses following a chloroform-8-quinolinol extraction of the iron and aluminum interferences.   Later Přibil (62) demonstrated that these and other metal interferences could be masked with triethanolamine enabling the direct determinations of lime and magnesia without separations.   Applying triethanolamine and other masking agents including cyanide and dimercapto-propanol, Flaschka (63) outlined an elaborate rapid chelometric analytical scheme for the determination of not only calcium and magnesium, but also for manganese, iron, aluminum, and several other metals.   Results obtained by Friedrich and Fáborský (64) and Holmberg (65) by the masking-chelometric method demonstrated the speed and soundness of this approach as applied to window and similar glass compositions.

Using yet another masking approach, specifically fluoride, Lange (66) suggested a method for the determination of zinc in glass; procedures for calcium, and magnesium in the presence of zinc and aluminum, are also discussed.   A rapid and reasonably selective chelometric method for determining aluminum in opal glasses has been described by Cluley (67).   Based on work by Přibil and Veselý (68), the procedure involves a preliminary stoichiometric titration of all reactable metals, including aluminum, with EDTA at pH 5.5, and the subsequent recomplexation of aluminum with fluoride which releases an equivalent amount of EDTA.   Su (69) utilized the specificity of mandelic acid to separate zirconium from complex glass and refractory systems and then ascertained the zirconium content by decomposing the precipitate with excess boiling EDTA, and backtitrating the excess chelon.   Investigation of rapid methods for the determination of calcium and magnesium in soda-lime glasses continued (70) and, now, procedures have advanced close to the point of adoption as standard methods (71) for these elements. The paper by Sales (70) also makes recommendations for determing lead and aluminum in lead crystal glasses.

More complex glasses have been analyzed by chelometric titrations, utilizing a combination of masking and classical separations to achieve selectivity. Málat et al. (72) have described a method for determining thorium in a complex optical glass and later Málat and Múčka (73) described an entire chelometric scheme for the analysis of a thorium–lanthanum–barium–borate nonsilica optical glass. A similar silica-containing glass was analyzed for thorium, lanthanum, and barium by Přibil and Veselý (74) using disodium triethylenetetraminehexaacetate (HTPA) which forms a sufficiently stable complex with thorium to permit, with suitable pH adjustments, sequential titration of lanthanum (pH 5–6) with HTPA and barium (pH 9–11) with EDTA. Zirconium, thorium, lanthanum, aluminum, calcium, and barium were determined on an even more complex optical glass by a scheme developed by Přibil and Veselý (75). According to this scheme, aluminum is determined by EDTA back titration after separation of zirconium, thorium, and lanthanum as hydroxides. Thorium and lanthanum are determined in the redissolved hydroxide precipitate by stoichiometrically masking zirconium with diethylenetriaminepentaacetate (DTPA) and successively titrating thorium at pH 2.5–3.5 and lanthanum at pH 5–5.5. Zirconium is determined on a separate sample using EDTA, after removal of the interfering hydroxides by precipitation and masking with triethanolamine; calcium and barium are titrated in one aliquot using EDTA at a pH of 9; barium is determined on another aliquot after separation as barium chromate.

Table 7. Conditions for Potentiometric EDTA Titration of Metal Ions

pH	Buffer systems	Metals that may be titrated[a]
2	nitric or chloroacetic acid	*direct titration with EDTA* Th, Hg, Bi (use NH_4NO_3 in salt bridge of calomel cell to avoid introduction of chloride ion)
4–5.5	acetic acid or hexamethyl-enetetramine	*direct titration with EDTA* Sc, Y, La, rare earths in 3+ oxidation state, VO^{++}, Mn^{++}, Cu, Zn, Cd, Hg, Pb, Bi *back-titration with Cu, Zn, Cd, Hg, or Pb standard solutions* Cr^{+++} (heat near boiling with excess EDTA for 10 min before back-titration) Fe^{+++}, Ni, Al, Ga, In, Zr, Hf, Th, Sc, Y, La, rare earths in 3+ oxidation state, VO^{++}, Mn^{++}, Cu, Zn, Cd, Hg, Pb, Bi
8–10	ammonia, triethanolamine, ethanolamine	*direct titration with EDTA* Mg, Ca, Sr (pH 10), Ba (use pH 10 and remove dissolved oxygen by bubbling out solution with nitrogen) Co, Ni, Cu, Zn, Cd, In, Pb (add tartrate to keep lead and indium in solution during titration) *back-titration with Zn, Ca, Mg, Cu, or Cd standard solutions* Cr^{+++} (boil for 10 min in presence of excess EDTA before back titration) Sc, Y, La, rare earths in 3+ oxidation state, Hg, Bi, Mg, Ca, Sr (pH 10), Ba (pH 10 and remove O_2 first), Co, Ni, Cu, Zn, Cd, Pb, Tl (oxidize first to 3+ by boiling with nitric acid)

[a] Most of the metal ions listed under pH 4–5.5 or pH 8–10 will not interfere with titrations at pH 2. Alkaline earth ions do not interfere with titrations at pH 4–5.5.

An alternate to metallochromic end point indication is the potentiometric approach, using the mercury pM electrode (278–280). Besides its obvious applicability for colored solutions, it has, due to fewer competitive equilibria being involved, an intrinsically better selectivity. In addition, the pM electrode lends itself readily to sequential titration of two or more cations in the same solution by making full use of the pH effect. Table 7 (279) gives the conditions for pM potentiometric EDTA titrations using the mercury–mercury–EDTA electrode.

Several chelometric methods which are commonly used in glass analysis are detailed below.

Procedures

ALUMINUM IN THE PRESENCE OF IRON, TITANIUM, AND ZIRCONIUM.   Weigh a powdered glass sample containing 20–50 mg of alumina into a platinum dish. For a 0.1 g sample, add a few ml of water, 2 ml of 72% perchloric acid, and 2 ml of 48% hydrofluoric acid. If no sulfate precipitable elements are present, 1:1 sulfuric acid should be substituted for 72% perchloric acid. Evaporate to strong fumes of perchloric acid and fume for 5 min, but not to dryness. Add more perchloric acid, if necessary, rinse down the sides of the dish and fume again. Repeat as before, but add 0.1 g of boric acid for the final fuming. Add a few ml of water, digest the contents in the dish until a clear solution is obtained. Transfer into a 125-ml separatory funnel. Using water rinsings of the platinum dish, dilute the sample in the separatory funnel to about 40 ml. Add 15 ml of 72% perchloric acid and cool the separatory funnel and its contents in an ice bath for 30 min. Add 5 ml of 6% cupferron and 10 ml of 1:1 chloroform–n-hexanol. Stopper the funnel, shake for 1 min, then return to the ice bath to allow the layers to separate. If an emulsion forms that does not break, add a few ml of chloroform. Drain the organic (lower) phase into another separatory funnel. Similarly reextract the original aqueous phase with 10 ml of 1:1 chloroform–n-hexanol. Finally, wash the original aqueous phase with 10 ml of chloroform. Collect all organic extracts in the second separatory funnel. Extract the combined organic phases with 10 ml of 4 N perchloric acid. Separate the organic phase and collect the aqueous phase in a 200-ml tall-form beaker. If the alumina content of the sample is greater than 10%, repeat the extraction with 10 ml of 4 N perchloric acid. To the aqueous phase collected, add 15 ml of pH 4.6 acetate buffer solution, consisting of 82 g of sodium acetate and 70 ml of glacial acetic acid per liter of aqueous solution. Prepare 0.1 M EDTA by dissolving 37.2 g of disodium ethylenedinitrilotetraacetate dihydrate in water and diluting to 1 liter. Pipet into the sample solution enough 0.1 M EDTA to stoichiometrically react with the aluminum present and provide a 20% excess. Using a pH meter, adjust the pH to 4.6 with 50% sodium hydroxide solution. Cover the beaker, and boil for 10 min. Cool to room temperature.

Prepare a 0.05 M primary standard zinc solution by dissolving 6.5370 g of high-purity zinc metal in 40 ml of 1:1 perchloric acid and diluting with water to 2000 ml. Prepare a 0.05 M mercury–EDTA complex solution by reacting 0.10 M EDTA solution with an equal volume of 0.10 M mercuric nitrate solution. Add 5 drops of the 0.05 M mercury–EDTA complex solution to the sample solution. Insert a mercury electrode–fiber junction saturated calomel electrode pair connected to a pH meter, preferably of the expanded scale type. Titrate the excess EDTA with primary standard 0.05 M zinc solution, taking the end point as the greatest potential change per unit titrant added.

Obtain the volumetric titer ratio of EDTA to zinc and calculate the exact normality of the EDTA solution.

$$\% \ Al_2O_3 = \frac{[A - (B)(R)](N)(5.098)}{w}$$

where A = volume of EDTA solution added, in ml

B = volume of zinc solution required, in ml

R = volumetric titer ratio

N = normality of EDTA solution

w = sample weight, in g

The extraction procedure can be omitted if both titanium and zirconium are absent and provided the iron content is less than 0.05%.

ALUMINUM IN THE PRESENCE OF LEAD, ZINC, AND IRON. Weigh a sample of powdered glass containing 20–50 mg of alumina into a platinum dish. For a 0.2 g sample, add a few ml of water, 2 ml of 72% perchloric acid, and 3 ml of 48% hydrofluoric acid. If no sulfate-precipitable elements are present, 1:1 sulfuric acid should be substituted for 72% perchloric acid. Evaporate, then fume strongly on a hot plate for 5 min. Rinse down the sides of the dish, then repeat the evaporation and fuming. Add 0.1 g of boric acid, rinse down, and evaporate and fume for 5 min but not to dryness. Cool, add 10 ml of water, 5 ml of 72% perchloric acid, and dissolve by warming and stirring. Transfer to a 200-ml tall-form beaker and dilute to about 50 ml with water.

Prepare 0.1 M EDTA solution, pH 4.6 acetate buffer solution, and 0.05 M primary standard zinc solution as described in the previous procedure. Pipet in a known amount of 0.1 M EDTA solution, about 20% in excess of that required to complex all cations that form stable EDTA complexes at pH 4.6. Add 15 ml of pH 4.6 acetate buffer. Using a pH meter, adjust the pH to 4.6 by dropwise addition of 50% sodium hydroxide solution. Boil for 10 min, cool to room temperature, then add 4 drops of 0.1% aqueous xylenol orange indicator. Titrate to a yellow-to-red color change using 0.0500 M primary standard zinc solution. Add 2 g of potassium fluoride dihydrate and boil the solution for 20 min. Cool to room temperature and titrate again with primary standard zinc solution to the yellow-to-red color change. The volume of zinc solution required for the second titration is equivalent to the amount of aluminum in the sample.

$$\% \ Al_2O_3 = \frac{(A)(N)(5.098)}{w}$$

where A = volume of zinc solution required for second titration, in ml

N = normality of zinc solution

w = sample weight, in g

The above procedure will tolerate the presence of the alkaline earths, lead, zinc, iron, cobalt and nickel. However, potentiometric end point detection is recommended if the colored transition metals are present in significant amounts.

CALCIUM AND MAGNESIUM IN SODA–LIME GLASS. Prepare a 0.025 M primary standard calcium solution by dissolving 2.5020 g of calcium carbonate, previously dried at 110°C, in a minimal amount of 1:1 hydrochloric acid and diluting to 1 liter. Prepare a 0.025 M EDTA solution by dissolving 9.3 g of disodium ethylenedinitrilotetraacetate dihydrate in water and diluting to 1 liter. Standardize the 0.025 M EDTA solution by taking a 25-ml aliquot of a 0.02500 M primary standard calcium solution, and titrating exactly as directed for determination of calcium in the sample solution.

Weigh about 1 g of powdered glass into a platinum dish. Add a few ml of water, 5 ml of 72% perchloric acid, and 15 ml of 48% hydrofluoric acid. Evaporate to fumes of perchloric acid, then fume strongly for 5 min. Rinse the sides of the dish down with water, then repeat evaporation and fuming. Fume until the perchloric acid has completely evaporated. Cool, add 1 ml of concentrated hydrochloric acid and 10 ml of water. Agitate and warm if necessary to dissolve, then transfer to a 50-ml volumetric flask. Cool to room temperature and dilute to volume.

Pipet a 20-ml aliquot of the sample solution into a 250-ml Erlenmeyer flask and dilute to 100 ml with water. Add 10 ml of 30% (v/v) triethanolamine and, using a pH meter, adjust the pH to 12.5 by dropwise addition of 50% sodium hydroxide solution. Add 0.2 g of hydroxynaphthol blue (Mallinckrodt Code 5630) and, stirring with a magnetic stirrer, titrate with 0.025 M EDTA solution to a clear blue color. The volume of titrant corresponds to the calcium content. Pipet a second 20-ml aliquot of the sample into a 250-ml Erlenmeyer flask and dilute to 100 ml. Add 10 ml of 30% (v/v) triethanolamine. Prepare an ammonia buffer solution by dissolving 67.5 g of ammonium chloride in 250 ml of water, mixing with 570 ml of concentrated ammonium hydroxide, and diluting to 1 liter. Add 10 ml of the ammonia buffer to the sample solution, followed by 0.04 g of methyl thymol blue indicator mixture, which consists of 0.2 g of methyl thymol blue mixed intimately with 20 g of potassium nitrate. Titrate with 0.025 M EDTA solution to a change in color from blue to smoky-gray. The volume of titrant corresponds to the sum of the calcium and magnesium contents of the sample.

$$\% \text{ CaO} = \frac{(A)(M)(56.08)}{(w)(4)}$$

$$\% \text{ MgO} = \frac{(B - A)(M)(40.31)}{(w)(4)}$$

where A = volume of EDTA solution required for the first titration, in ml
B = volume of EDTA solution required for second titration, in ml
M = molarity of EDTA solution
w = sample weight in aliquot, in g

If such metals as lead, zinc, cadmium, other alkaline earths, or rare earths, are present, the method requires modification. Separations and/or masking would be essential.

ZINC. Weigh a powdered glass sample containing 50–100 mg of zinc oxide into a platinum dish. For 0.5 g of sample, add a few ml of water, 1 ml of 72% perchloric acid, and 5 ml of 48% hydrofluoric acid. Evaporate on a steam bath, then fume on a hot plate. Cool, rinse down the sides of the dish, then evaporate and fume to moist dryness. Dissolve the solids with water, heating if necessary. Transfer to a 100-ml Teflon beaker containing a Teflon-coated stirring bar. Add 5 ml of 48% hydrofluoric acid. Dilute to 25 ml with water, then, using magnetic stirring, add 3 g of sodium borate decahydrate, $Na_2B_4O_7.10H_2O$, and 4 drops of 0.1% methyl orange indicator solution. Adjust the pH to the just yellow side of methyl orange by dropwise addition of 50% sodium hydroxide; use 1:1 perchloric acid if acidification is necessary. Add 10 ml of pH 4.6 acetate buffer (consisting of 82 g of sodium acetate and 70 ml of glacial acetic acid per liter of aqueous solution). Add 5 drops of 0.05 M mercury–EDTA solution, insert mercury pool–fiber junction saturated calomel electrodes connected to an expanded scale pH meter, and titrate with 0.05 M EDTA. Take the end point at the point of greatest change in potential per unit volume. Record the volume of EDTA. Standardize the EDTA solution by pipetting a 20-ml aliquot of 0.05 M primary standard zinc solution (see first Aluminum procedure above for preparation) into a 100-ml Teflon beaker and, starting with the addition of 5 ml of 48% hydrofluoric acid, treat exactly as described for the sample.

$$\% \; ZnO \; = \; \frac{(A)(N)(8.137)}{w}$$

where A = volume of EDTA solution used for sample, in ml
N = normality of EDTA solution
w = sample weight, in g

This method is reasonably specific. Alkaline earths, aluminum, and trace to minor levels of titanium, zirconium, and lead do not interfere. If lead is present in substantial amounts, substitute 1:1 sulfuric acid for perchloric acid, and after decomposition, filter off the lead sulfate before proceeding.

Flame Spectroscopy

Flame spectroscopy in its general sense embraces all those optical processes that occur in a flame, including emission from excited atoms, resonance absorbance of monochromatic light by ground-state atoms, and fluorescent emission by suitably irradiated ground-state atoms. The last named phenomenon, utilized in atomic fluorescent spectroscopy, has not yet found practical application to glass analysis and hence will not be considered further. On the other hand, few techniques have had the impact on the analytical technology of a class of materials as have flame emission and atomic absorption spectrometry on the analytical chemistry of glasses and glass–ceramics. The principles of the methods have been considered in the articles ATOMIC ABSORPTION SPECTROPHOTOMETRY, Vol. 1, pp. 160–186, and FLAME PHOTOMETRY, Vol. 2, pp. 12–88.

Application of flame emission spectroscopy (FES) to silicate systems followed soon after Lundegårdh's demonstration (76) of the capabilities of his innovative implementation of the flame source for spectroscopy. Representative of earliest application of the technique to silicates was the work of Elving and Chao (77), who in 1949 reported use of the technique for the determination of soda in silica catalyst materials. Biffen (78) applied the method to the determination of sodium and potassium in refractory materials, among them glass, and Broderick and Zack (79), in 1951, utilizing a statistically designed approach, developed a procedure specifically directed to the determination of sodium, potassium, and lithium in glass. Wide recognition and adoption of this significant new technique by analysts in the glass industry soon followed. Close and co-workers applied the Beckman DU spectrophotometer in conjunction with the hydrogen–oxygen total-consumption burner to the determination of magnesium (80) and potassium (81). In 1954, Williams and Adams (82) introduced a versatile approach to the determination of lithium, sodium, potassium, rubidium, and cesium. This method, in fact, is still in use and continues under consideration by ASTM (83) for designation as a standard method. Subsequently, these same workers (84), employing an ammonium hydroxide precipitation to separate R_2O_3 and RO_2 interferents, expanded their approach to include the alkaline earths, magnesium, calcium, and barium. This too remains as a suggested ASTM method (85). Broadening of the scope of application of flame spectroscopy to glass continued with the work of Roy (86), who determined manganese as well as the alkalies and alkaline earths in glass and raw materials. Dean and Burger (87) determined iron, even at trace levels, in siliceous materials, including glass, using flame emission. In 1958, Hegemann et al. (88) reported the successful flame emission determination of aluminum in a 4% (v/v) 1-butanol solvent system, after separating aluminum from the glass matrix by a hydroxide precipitation. Employing similar approaches involving use of organic solvents, Ishida (89) and later Menis et al. (90), in conjunction with improved optics and electronic instrumentation (91), reported the determination of lanthanum in complex glasses by emission flame spectrometry. Dobes (92) further extended application of flame emission in glass to the determination of boron and phosphorus.

Since the introduction of atomic absorption spectroscopy as an analytical tool, applications have followed at a rapid rate. Of special significance to the glass analyst are the enhanced detectabilities of magnesium, zinc, cadmium, lead, and iron. Recognizing this potential, Passmore and Adams (93) developed direct, rapid, and precise atomic absorption procedures for major and minor amounts of zinc and iron in glass and refractory systems. They also undertook a study of the critical factors needing control when applying atomic absorption spectroscopy to the determination of the alkaline earths in glass (94), which provided the basis for their recommendation of several highly adaptable methods for measuring magnesium, calcium, strontium, and barium in complex glasses. Combining the results of these two studies these same workers have published, for consideration by ASTM, a suggested method for analyzing glasses and ceramic materials for magnesium and zinc (95). The broad capability of atomic absorption spectroscopy for analysis of complex glasses was amply demonstrated by Jones (96), who describes the determination of lithium, sodium, potassium, magnesium, calcium, barium, lead, zinc, iron, cobalt, nickel, and manganese in glass and ceramic frit. Even more comprehensive analyses have been found possible as typified by the publications by Langmyhr and co-workers (97–99) and Medlin et al. (100), who have successfully undertaken complete analyses of silicate rocks by atomic absorption spectroscopy. There is little doubt but that a major contributing factor in the success of these and other comprehensive analytical schemes has been the nitrous oxide–acetylene flame, introduced by Willis (101), without which the more refractory elements could not have been determined so well.

A unified treatment of the analysis of glass by the atomic absorption and flame emission spectroscopic techniques was presented by Adams (102) who indicated a potential capability of atomic absorption and flame emission spectroscopy for determining some 62 elements. More recently, some 67 elements were determined by both of these techniques with reasonably good detectability (103).

In summary, the flame methods enable the glass analyst, without complex manipulations, to accomplish in a matter of hours what formerly required up to two or three days. Since the usual precision of both methods is of the order of ± 1 to 2% of the amount present, application of flame spectroscopy to glasses and glass–ceramics is usually limited to the minor (1–20 wt %) and trace (less than 0.1 wt %) constituents. Improvements in the techniques are continuing, particularly in the area of precision, such that even now, taking special care, a precision as low as ± 0.5 relative % can be achieved in special instances.

Sample Treatment. Since flame spectroscopy requires presentation of the sample in solution form, glasses and glass–ceramics must receive much the same chemical pretreatment as for wet chemical analysis. See the earlier discussion under Decomposition, on p. 415. One redeeming feature is that rarely must the sample size exceed 0.1–0.2 g. A complicating factor, however, is that there are some restrictions as to the choice of reagents. Generally, an acid attack is preferred, but mineral acids such as sulfuric or nitric acids should usually be avoided because their anions have a suppressive effect on the flame spectra. Consequently, perchloric acid is the normal choice in conjunction with hydrofluoric acid to effect the decomposition. Minimal amounts of these acids should be employed since they do contribute to the blank, particularly for sodium. Usually for a 0.1–0.2 g sample contained in a small platinum dish, after addition of 2 ml of water, 10 drops of 72% perchloric acid and 1–2 ml of 48% hydrofluoric acid will suffice. Decomposition is accomplished in the customary manner as previously described, and the sample is transferred to a volumetric flask of the appropriate size and diluted to volume with water and enough 72% perchloric acid to make the solution 0.25% (v/v) in 72% perchloric acid. Since residual fluoride and silicon also have deleterious effects on flame spectra, it is important to ensure that the sample be completely reacted and heated so that all the silicon and volatile fluorides are completely expelled prior to dilution. Problems with insoluble residues may be encountered after fuming samples containing antimony or titanium (in excess of 5% titanium oxide) with perchloric acid. One can try to avoid the problem by taking a smaller sample, attempting a milder fuming, or resorting to sulfuric acid as the fuming acid. In the latter case, compensatory modifications, ie, addition of buffers to the sample solution, should be made to correct for the suppressive effect of the sulfate on the spectra of certain analytes. One interesting variation on the normal acid attack is to decompose the sample under pressure in a Teflon-lined bomb as described by Langmyhr (97) and Bernas (104), who have demonstrated applicability of the approach to a wide variety of silicates and other materials.

Fusion decomposition has been normally avoided since, aside from blank considerations, high salt-containing solutions tend to clog up burners and also introduce both a high spectral radiation background and potential line interferences. Nevertheless, utilizing the intrinsic advantage of atomic absorption spectroscopy in overcoming these handicaps, a number of workers (100,105,106) have made expedient use of the fusion decomposition approach to comprehensively analyze silicate rocks and minerals. One disadvantage that cannot be overcome is that the elements in the sample common to the flux cannot be determined. Of the available fluxes, lithium metaborate (107) appears to be the best. This decomposition approach is well worth considering for the more refractory titania–zirconia–alumina–low silica-containing glasses.

Table 8. Elements and Concentration Ranges for Flame Emission Spectrometry for Alkalies

Element	Concentration range in which radiation measurements are most useful, ppm	Concentration range of element oxide in glass, %
lithium	0–20	0–15
sodium	0–25	0–20
potassium	0–25	0–20
rubidium	0–20	0–15
cesium	0–20	0–15

Method for Alkali Metals in Glass by Flame Emission Spectrometry.
Shown in Table 8 are the elements and concentration ranges in the glass and glass–
ceramics to which this method is adapted (83). Also given are the approximate
corresponding solution concentration ranges to which the sample must be converted
to obtain useful analytical data by this method. About 8–10 ppm is the optimum
range of concentration for lithium, sodium, and potassium.

Procedure

PREPARATION OF STANDARDS. Prepare stock standard solutions as indicated below:

Element	Salt	Weight, g	Diluted volume, ml	Final element concentration, ppm
lithium	Li_2CO_3	2.6617	500	1000
sodium	NaCl	2.5418	1000	1000
potassium	KCl	1.9069	1000	1000
rubidium	Rb_2SO_4	0.7810	1000	500
cesium	Cs_2SO_4	0.6807	1000	500

Dissolve and dilute the chloride and sulfate salts with water. Dissolve the lithium
carbonate in a slight excess of dilute hydrochloric acid, evaporate to dryness, and
then dissolve in water and dilute to volume.

Prepare 1:10 dilutions of the stock standard solutions. From the resulting
solutions take aliquots that, when diluted to volume, will bracket the unknown alkali
concentrations within 20 relative percent. If sodium and potassium are present
simultaneously in the sample, allow for their mutual interference by preparing
mixed standards containing both of these alkalies. Unless the ratio of a diverse ion
to the alkali being analyzed is unusually high, eg, fiftyfold, there is usually no need
to more closely match the standard to other matrix concomitants. Before diluting
the bracketing standards to final volume, add sufficient perchloric acid to make the
final solutions 0.25% (v/v) with respect to this acid.

SAMPLE PREPARATION. Taking care in all handling to avoid alkali (sodium)
contamination, decompose 0.1 g of powdered glass with 2 ml of water, 10 drops of
72% perchloric acid, and 2 ml of 48% hydrochloric acid in the customary manner.
Multiple fumings with intervening dropwise additions of perchloric and hydrofluoric acid may be necessary. After finally fuming to near dryness, digest and
dissolve with water and transfer to a volumetric flask of a suitable size to give a
final concentration of 1–10 ppm as the element. Before diluting to volume, add
enough perchloric acid to make the sample solution 0.25% (v/v) in perchloric acid.

INSTRUMENT AND OPERATING CONDITIONS. Use a spectrophotometer having a
variable slit width adjustment that is capable of adequately resolving the lines of
the alkali elements (see listing below) as well as the spectra of any potential spectral
interferent in the sample. A Beckman DU fitted with a hydrogen–oxygen flame
attachment, and preferably having a spectral energy recording capability, is suitable. A photomultiplier detector, although not essential, is highly desirable. Set
the wavelength and slit to correspond with the following specifications for the
alkali being determined:

Element	Photo-tube used	Analytical line, nm	Slit width, mm	Concentration range, ppm
lithium	red	671	0.3	0–20
sodium	blue	589	0.1	5–25
sodium	blue	589	0.2	0–8
potassium	red	767	0.1	5–25
potassium	red	767	0.3	0–15
rubidium	red	795	0.3	0–20
cesium	red	852	0.3	0–20

Use the following settings:

load resistor	10,000 Ω
sensitivity selector switch	at 1
sensitivity knob	maximum
hydrogen pressure	10 psig
oxygen pressure	25 psig
hydrogen flow	5 ft³/hr
oxygen flow	10 ft³/hr

MEASUREMENT. Transfer portions of the standard and sample solutions to 5-ml beakers, and successively read the radiation intensity of the low standard S_1, the sample S_μ, and the high standard S_2. Repeat using fresh aliquots in the order, S_μ, S_1, S_μ, S_2, S_μ, S_1, and so on, until 6 sets of readings have been taken.

Prepare an analytical curve for each alkali for each hydrogen–oxygen burner by obtaining the radiation intensities of standards prepared to contain 2, 4, 6, 8, 10, 15 ppm of the alkali. Take 4–6 readings at each concentration and average the intensity and plot versus the corresponding concentration to obtain the analytical response calibration curve. Use this curve to make rough concentration estimates on unknowns and to maintain reasonably constant instrument and flame conditions. Compute by an interpolation method described in Reference 94.

Emission Spectroscopy

Emission spectroscopy has been employed for many years for both qualitative and quantitative chemical analysis of glass and similar silicate-base materials, such as slags, ores, rocks, soils, and ceramics. Early work on the analysis of glass has been documented by Cooper (108), by Hegemann and Zoellner (109), by Ward and Hartley (110), and by Lieberman (111). One of the principal applications of optical emission spectroscopy to glass and glass–ceramic materials is to provide a preliminary compositional survey prior to more extensive chemical analysis by other techniques. Quantitative analyses are useful when trace and minor concentrations of selected elements must be determined in large numbers of samples of similar matrix or when many elements must be determined at trace levels on a limited amount of sample. While specific references to emission spectrographic analysis of glass are scarce, the analysis of related nonmetallic and siliceous materials have been developed to a point where they approach standard procedures. For example, procedures for the analysis of silica brick and glass sand (112), silica refractories (113), slags (114,115), and ceramics (116,117) are included in ASTM Methods for Emission Spectrochemical Analysis (118). In addition to the ASTM methods, detailed discussions of various approaches of analysis can be found under EMISSION SPECTROSCOPY, Vol. 1, pp. 702–745. An emission spectrographic method using photographic detection which is applicable to glass is described in the CERAMICS article, Vol. 9, pp. 217–219. Table 9 lists typical instrumental conditions and photographic parameters for analysis of glass and glass–ceramics.

A spectrochemical pellet-spark technique for nonmetallic specimens, pioneered by Tingle and Matocha (119), and employing a multichannel photoelectric spectrometer can be adapted for the quantitative analysis of glasses. Two hundred mg of powdered sample (-200 mesh) is mixed with 1.8 g of anhydrous lithium tetraborate ($Li_2B_4O_7$) containing cobalt for an internal standard in a plastic vial for 60 sec in a suitable mixer-mill. The sample-flux mixture is transferred to a graphite crucible and placed in a preheated furnace at 950°C for 20 min. The fluxed material resulting from the fusion is ground to a fine powder and a portion is mixed with graphite in a 1:2 sample–graphite ratio. An appropriate amount of the fluxed sample–graphite mixture is pressed into a 0.5 in. diameter pellet with a standard briquetting press. A pressure of about 44,000 psi for 10 sec duration is recommended. Using the 0.5 in. diameter pellet as the lower electrode and a counter electrode of a shape similar to C-5 of ASTM designation (120), the electrodes are sparked and the response recorded on a multichannel photoelectric spectrometer under the following conditions, using a Jarrell-Ash Mark IV 3.4 m Ebert mount convertible spectrograph– spectrometer:

grating	15,000 lines/in.
primary slit	50 μm wide, 10 mm high
secondary slits	10–75 μm
excitation source	ac spark discharge
discharge current	6.0 A
discharge breaks	4/half cycle
inductance	40 μH
capacitance	0.0025 μF
resistance	residual
spark gap	3 mm
preburn	10 sec
exposure time	about 20 sec

Exposure time is controlled by a preselected integrated intensity value set for the internal standard channel.

The excitation of the sample is repeated four times with intervening resurfacing of the pellet with 400 grit silicon carbide abrasive paper. The location of the spectrometer photomultiplier tubes at particular analytical lines for the elements to be determined is dependent on the sample matrix, element concentration levels and spectral line interferences. Calibration curves are obtained by plotting response for standards versus known elemental composition. The concentration for elements in the sample is then established from individual calibration curves prepared from standards of similar matrix.

X-Ray Emission Spectroscopy

X-ray emission spectroscopy can be applied advantageously for both qualitative and quantitative analysis of glass and glass–ceramics. The technique is discussed in Vol. 3, pp. 796–817.

Table 9. Typical Instrumental Conditions and Photographic Parameters for Emission Spectrographic Analysis of Glass and Glass–Ceramics

Parameter	Spectrographic conditions	
	all elements	trace alkalies
spectral region, Å	2500–4700	4500–8000
grating, lines/in.	15,000	10,000
dispersion, Å/mm	5.5	7.6
slit width, μm	10	10 μm
slit height, mm	4	4 mm
total filter	none	yellow glass, cut-off below 4500 Å
emulsion	Kodak SA-1	Kodak 1-N
electrical discharge	dc arc	dc arc
current, A	10	10
preburn	none	none
exposure, to completion, min	ca 3	ca 3
atmosphere	30% O_2, 70% Ar	30% O_2, 70% Ar
	Photographic processing	
developer	Kodak D-19 for 3 min at 20°C	
stop batch	3:97 acetic acid for 15 sec	
fixer	Kodak Rapid Fix with hardener, 3 min at 20°C	
wash	running water for 5–10 min	
dry	blower and heater for 5 min	

Specimen Preparation. In general, the selection of suitable samples for x-ray emission analysis of glasses and glass–ceramics does not present any real problems, since these materials are inherently homogeneous and are either amorphous or of very small grain size. Where possible, a flat, freshly ground and polished surface of the material should be obtained. For quantitative analysis, loose or compressed powders should be avoided unless strict control of particle size and porosity can be assured, since small differences in the degree of compaction between samples and standards may give rise to quite different x-ray intensities. When flat solid specimens are not available, discs prepared by pressing 1:1–3:1 mixtures of powdered boric acid and ground glass are satisfactory. Pressures of about 50,000 psi produce fairly firm and uniform briquets.

All fresh glass surfaces are highly reactive and may adsorb water, carbon dioxide, sulfur compounds, and other atmospheric contaminants that can potentially affect analytical results. It is often good practice to remelt any sample initially ground to achieve homogeneity, provided volatilization of alkalies and halogens present no analytical problem. The use of flux–fusion techniques reviewed by Stephenson (284) may be helpful. The flux–sample ratio may be varied within reasonable limits. A mixture of 0.3 g of sample and 2.7 g of flux provides an optimum formula for most glasses. The fused glass buttons are smooth finished to 100, 200, 400, or 600 grit by wet grinding on silicon carbide paper or diamond-embedded grinding discs. In addition, it is recommended that all glass and glass–ceramic surfaces, including the flux–fusion buttons, be polished a few minutes prior to actual measurement on a ceric oxide or alumina polishing cloth, followed by a thorough distilled water wash and complete drying.

Qualitative Analysis. The main value of qualitative x-ray emission analysis of glass and glass–ceramics lies in its ability to quickly identify all elements present of atomic number 13 (aluminum) or greater. Contaminants may be readily found and similar samples compared to determine any compositional variations. The technique is one of the simplest nondestructive methods of analysis presently available. Typical instrument parameters recommended for complete qualitative analysis of most glass and glass–ceramic materials are listed below:

Lithium fluoride analyzing crystal scan

x-ray spectrometer	GE-XRD-6VS
x-ray tube	W, full power
counter tube	scintillation
scan speed	$2°$ 2θ/min (10–90°)
chart speed	0.5 in./min
rate meter	logarithmic or 5000 cps full scale
collimator	coarse

Ethylenediamine d-tartrate (EDDT) analyzing crystal scan

x-ray spectrometer	GE-XRD-6VS
x-ray tube	Cr, full power
counter tube	flow proportional
scan speed	$2°$ 2θ/min (30–145°)
chart speed	0.5 in./min
rate meter	logarithmic or 5000 cps full scale
collimator	coarse

Quantitative Analysis. The use of x-ray emission methods for quantitative elemental analysis of glass and glass–ceramic materials is well established (121–123). This is due in part to the widespread availability of vacuum spectrometers capable of determining all elements of atomic number 13 or greater on a routine basis, and the elements magnesium, sodium, and fluorine under ideal conditions, as fast or faster than many other techniques. Automation of x-ray spectrometers by several manufacturers has increased the accuracy, sensitivity, and speed of x-ray analyses tremendously.

Spark Source Spectrometry

Impurities in the ppm range can be determined by the spark source mass spectrometer analysis of glass and glass–ceramics (124,125); typical results are given in Table 10 (231). The technique can provide analytical information not readily available by other means. Examples of the analysis of glass (126), glass surfaces (127), and grain boundaries of polycrystalline insulator materials (128) suggest some of the useful applications.

The radio frequency spark excitation of insulating materials can be accomplished in several ways; by using a conducting counter electrode in conjunction with an insulator specimen electrode, by increasing the conductivity of the insulator specimen, by means of a conducting film or wrapping the sample with gold wire, and by using a pressed powdered mixture of a conducting material, such as carbon, silver, or gold, and the insulator sample. For comparative or semiquantitative analyses, excitation with a conducting probe electrode against the insulator material is usually satisfactory. Quantitative impurity analysis of insulators is possible using homogeneous pressed powder mixtures (282).

Table 10. Representative Impurity Analysis of Fused Silica Glass[a]

Element	ppma[b]	Element	ppma[b]
Al	<0.65	Ag	<0.17
Ti	<0.80	B	0.5
V	0.29	F	0.3
Cr	<0.92	Na	<2.03
Mn	0.09	Mg	<2.9
Fe	<2.2[c]	P	0.35
Ni	0.2	Cl	30
Cu	0.2	K	<16[d]

[a] Corning Glass code 7940.

[b] ppma, parts per million atomic.

[c] Fe determination uncertain due to Si^{2+} interference.

[d] Na and K determinations usually high due to thermal ionization.

Selective operating parameters for spark source mass spectrometer analysis of glass and glass–ceramics are tabulated below:

spark voltage	20 kV
pulse duration	200 μsec
repetition rate	300 cps
vacuum conditions	
analyzer pressure	<2 × 10^{-8} torr
source pressure	<2 × 10^{-8} torr
pressure while sparking with	
cryosorption pump	<2 × 10^{-7} torr
detector	2 × 10 in Ilford QII photographic plate
developing conditions	
developing	Ilford ID-13 modified at 20°C for 2 min
fixing	Eastman Rapid Fixer, 3 min
washing	running tap water, 3 min distilled water final rinse

Electroanalytical Methods

Electroanalytical techniques that have been particularly helpful in the analysis of glass and glass–ceramics include polarography, coulometric titrimetry, and controlled potential coulometry. Their range of application includes micro and trace analysis, highly accurate assay methods for major constituents, and redox state determinations.

Polarography. The principles, methodology, and scope of applicability of this technique are discussed in POLAROGRAPHY AND VOLTAMMETRY, Vol. 3, pp. 161–199. For versatility, selectivity, and speed of analysis, polarography is unsurpassed by the other major electroanalytical techniques. Even in its conventional dc form, this approach enabled Williams et al. to develop selective methods for the determination of zinc, cadmium, and lead present in the same glass sample (129), and a specific method for antimony (130). Zlotowska (131) has also determined lead and zinc in glass, and Marachevskii and Kalinin (132) have reported the polarographic measurement of microgram amounts of arsenic and antimony in silicate materials after a distillation separation of the halides. Square wave polarography was applied by Noshiro and Sugisaki, who reported the determination of antimony (133) and also the simultaneous determination of tin and zinc (134). Another capability of polarography was illustrated by Bien and Goldberg (135), who applied the technique to the determination of the valence states of iron in refractory silicate minerals, after a special decomposition by fusion with sodium metafluoborate in a nitrogen atmosphere. Presently, application of polarography to silicate analysis has slackened, due largely to the competition of other techniques such as controlled potential coulometry, atomic absorption spectrometry, and complexometry. There are, however, some interesting and relatively new approaches toward which one may look for renewal of interest and further applications. Improvements in instrumentation such as are typified by the cathode ray tube single-sweep polarograph (136), and especially the differential single-sweep polarograph (137), have done much to increase the speed, selectivity, and sensitivity of the basic technique. In addition, Raaen (138), who developed a Teflon dropping mercury electrode, and Bond and O'Donnell (139), who applied a rapid scan technique, both demonstrated the feasibility of polarography in hydrofluoric acid media. This would appear to offer considerable stimulus to glass analysts who normally expend considerable time preparatory to an analysis removing hydrofluoric acid from the sample by prolonged acid-fuming.

Coulometry. This technique and its applications are described in detail in COULOMETRY AND COULOMETRIC TITRATIONS, Vol. 1, pp. 489–506.

Coulometric Titrations. Especially advantageous in that no standardized titrants need be prepared, this highly accurate method is adaptable to a majority of the redox, precipitation, chelometric, and acidimetric titrations that customarily have been run volumetrically. Although the coulometric titration technique lends itself quite well to analysis both in the parts per million and major percentage ranges, and the instrumentation requirement is remarkably inexpensive, this approach has not been widely developed for glass analysis. This is in part related to the fairly restrictive requirements for the supporting electrolyte anion and the precursor reagent, coupled with the multielemental makeup of glass, and hence the possibility of deleterious side reactions. For example, use of sulfuric acid, a preferred electrolyte, is precluded for barium- or lead-containing glasses.

Coulometric methods have been described for determination of total and trivalent arsenic (59) and total and trivalent antimony (60) in glass. The methods are applicable at the fractional weight percent level, and all four species can be determined in the presence of each other. Of demonstrated applicability to fairly complex commercial glasses, the methods are valuable for verifying the volatilization losses of these somewhat volatile oxides after melting, and for establishing the redox states of these elements in the final glass, which is of significance to fining efficiency studies. A rapid coulometric technique for the determination of silica in glass and refractory materials has been reported by Su et al. (140). The method is based on an expeditious borate–carbonate decomposition, acid dissolution, and coulometric back titration of excess 8-quinolinol with bromine after precipitation of the silicomolybdate-8-quinolinol complex. In contrast to the conventional gravimetric procedure, the method is quite tolerant of high levels of fluoride and boron, and quite rapid. Including sample decomposition, the time required for an analysis is 3 hr.

Controlled Potential Coulometry. Although not quite so sensitive and versatile as polarography, controlled potential coulometry is considerably more selective and flexible than coulometric titrimetry. New instrumentation based on an all solid-state modular design (141) claims a coulometric accuracy and precision of ±0.1 relative percent. This kind of accuracy coupled with the wide dynamic concentration range of application, 0.1–100%, makes the technique the glass analyst's optimal choice for highly accurate determination of major to minor amounts of lead, zinc, cadmium, bismuth, tin, and uranium. The applicability and selectivity of the method has been demonstrated by Segatto (142) who reported techniques for determining lead, cadmium, and zinc in glass and in the presence of each other; by Wise and Williams (143) who determined tin in glass; and by Su and Campbell (144) who determined bismuth and lead in glass in the presence of each other.

DETERMINATION OF PROPERTIES

Spectrophotometry

The useful spectral transmittance range of most glasses is from near 300 nm in the ultraviolet to about 5.0 μm in the infrared. This is illustrated in Figure 7. The curve labeled "Plate" is for a commercial plate glass, and is typical for alkali–lime-silica glass types. Code 1723 is an aluminosilicate glass; the curve for this glass is similar to that for Code 7740 borosilicate glass used in laboratory glassware. Code 7940 is pure fused silica glass. Code 7905 is a high-silica glass used for infrared transmitting missile domes. The curve for Code 0160 is typical for the alkali–lead–silica glasses. The curve labeled EX is for an experimental glass with a longer wavelength infrared cut-off.

The infrared absorption bands in the 2–5 μm region are caused chiefly by water and boric oxide in the glasses (145). The transmission limit near 5 μm is due to absorption in the first overtone region of the fundamental vibration absorption of the oxide glass structure, which occurs at longer infrared wavelengths, near 9 μm.

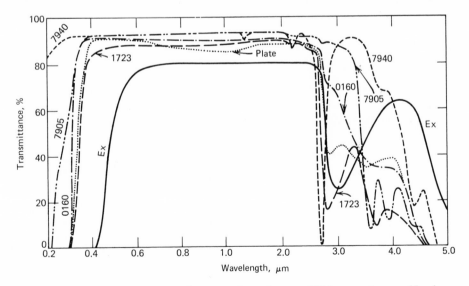

Fig. 7. Spectral transmittance curves for some clear glasses. Thickness: 2 mm. Numbers are Corning Glass Works code numbers.

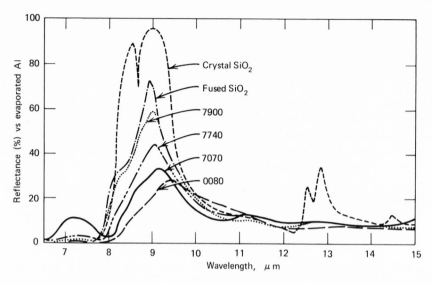

Fig. 8. Infrared reflectance of silicate glasses and quartz. Numbers are Corning Glass Works code numbers.

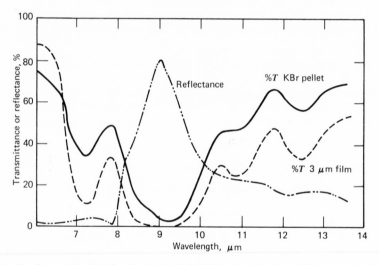

Fig. 9. Fundamental vibration bands in Code 7740 glass by three different techniques.

The long wavelength infrared absorption spectra of glasses are useful for identification and analysis of structure (146), and for qualitative and quantitative determinations of some structural units. Several methods are used. These are: (1) reflectance (147–148); (2) transmittance of thin blown films (149–152); (3) transmittance of powders in liquid mulls (153); and (4) transmittance of powders in pressed alkali halide discs (153–156). Figure 8 shows the reflectance curves for four silicate glasses, fused silica, and quartz, illustrating in particular the effect of the 9 μm Si—O fundamental absorption ("restrahlen") region. Figure 9 depicts this same absorption region as observed by three different techniques in the same glass. The 7.2 μm band is due to B—O linkages.

The presence of small quantities of various oxides, particularly of the transition elements, results in selective absorption in or near the visible region, thus imparting a variety of colors to glasses that are normally clear. These may occur as unwanted impurities, or as controlled additions, of the order 0.1–2.0%, in the production of

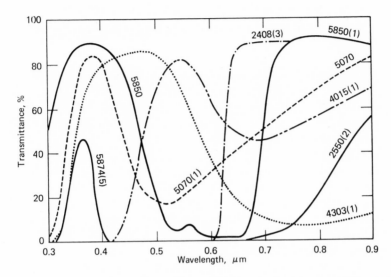

Fig. 10. Spectral transmittance of some colored glasses. Numbers in parentheses are thickness in mm. Four digit numbers are Corning Glass Works code numbers.

filter and signal glasses (157,158). Figure 10 illustrates some of the transmission spectra obtainable in the visible and near-visible regions, using various thicknesses of glasses used for color filter manufacture (159). Table 11 lists the colorants in these glasses.

Table 11. Coloring Materials in Glasses Used for Figure 10

Corning glass code	Colorant	Color
5850	CoO	blue
4303	CuO	blue green
5070	MnO_2	purple
4015	Cr_2O_3–CuO	yellow green
5874	NiO–Co_3O_4	black (UV)
2550	Cr_2O_3–Mn_2O_3	black (IR)
2408	$CdSe$	red

Several absorption spectrometry procedures used in analysis of glass are based on the following relationship, derived from basic considerations outlined in various literature sources (153,160). Ignoring second-order effects due to interreflections, the transmittance T_λ through a plate of glass at wavelength λ is given by

$$T_\lambda = K_\lambda 10^{-(\beta_1+\beta_2)_\lambda t} \tag{1}$$

where t = thickness, or pathlength through the glass

β_1 = peak absorption coefficient for the species to be determined, at analytical wavelength λ

β_2 = absorption coefficient for background absorption due to competing absorber(s)

K_λ contains surface reflectance losses, plus scattering losses by refraction in a geometrically poor sample (such as a tubing or bulb section, or an uneven plate)

Note that in the expression $A = abc$, cited in the ASTM methods (161), A is the absorbance, a is the absorptivity (formerly extinction coefficient) of the desired unknown, and c is the concentration. The absorption coefficient, β, used here is equivalent to $(a) \times (c)$. That is, β is proportional to, and is therefore a measure of, the concentration of the unknown absorber.

Water in Glass by "Beta OH" Method. Hydroxyl (OH) groups in glass cause absorption of infrared energy at wavelengths between 2.7 and 3.0 μm (145). Figure 11 shows the OH absorption region for several glasses. Scholze and co-workers (162,163) made a thorough study of water in glass and established relationships between water content and absorption coefficients for a variety of glass types that permit determination of the concentration, c. In commercial glasses the range of water content observed is 0–0.1 wt %.

In practice, hydroxyl ion ("water") concentration in glasses of the same type can be compared satisfactorily by determination of the absorption coefficient, β_1,

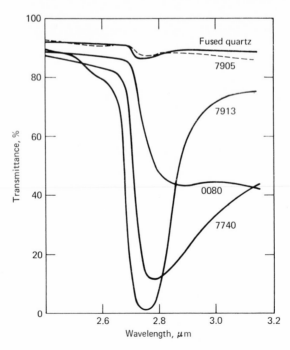

Fig. 11. Hydroxyl absorption bands in several glasses. Thickness: approximately 2 mm. Numbers are Corning Glass Works code numbers.

in Equation 1 (sometimes called "Beta-OH" or "Beta-Water"), which is proportional to c. From Equation 1,

$$\beta_1, \text{ or } \beta_{OH} = -\frac{1}{t} \log_{10} \frac{T_\lambda}{K_\lambda} - \beta_2 \tag{2}$$

The factors K and β_2 remain to be evaluated.

A nearby wavelength, outside the OH absorption band, is selected such that the reflection and refraction losses represented by K and the background absorption represented by β_2 are assumed to be the same as at the analytical wavelength, λ. At this nearby reference wavelength, λ_0, β_{OH} is zero, so the reference transmittance is as follows:

$$T_0 = K \ 10^{-\beta_2 t} \tag{3}$$

Combining equations 1 and 3,

$$\frac{T_0}{T_\lambda} = 10^{\beta_{OH} t} \tag{4}$$

from which

$$\beta_{OH} = \frac{1}{t} \log_{10} \frac{T_0}{T_\lambda} \tag{5}$$

The reference wavelength, λ_0, is usually taken to be 2.6 μm, which is seen in Figure 11 to be well displaced from the peak absorption wavelengths for most glasses.

Procedure

SAMPLING. The optimum sample is a plane parallel polished plate, but the method can also be used for a section of a blown bulb or tube, or a whole tube viewed through both walls. For the latter, as well as for imperfect flat plates, determine by visual observation that the area of the specimen to be viewed is of optimum optical quality available from the sample submitted, ie, minimum wedge, striations, inclusions. Measure thickness (in mm) at the area viewed. Measure both walls in the case of tubing.

MEASUREMENT AND COMPUTATION. Measure transmittance curve over the approximate wavelength range 2.5–3.0 μm. Divide the reference transmittance T_0 at 2.6 μm by the transmittance T_λ at the peak of the absorption band and find $\log_{10} T_0/T_\lambda$.

$$\beta_{OH}, \text{ in mm}^{-1} = \frac{\log_{10} (T_0/T_\lambda)}{t}$$

where t = total thickness

If the instrument has an absorbance scale, or can use absorbance recording chart, the procedure can be somewhat simplified. In Equation 1 the exponent $(\beta_1 + \beta_2)_\lambda t$ is the absorbance, A_λ (161). Thus,

$$A_\lambda = \beta_1 \ t + \beta_2 \ t$$

or

$$A_\lambda = A_{OH} + A_0$$

Then

$$A_{OH} = \beta_{OH} t = A_\lambda - A_0 \tag{6}$$

Thus, read the absorbance at the peak of the absorption band (A_λ), and the absorbance at 2.6 μm (A_0), and calculate β_{OH} from Equation 6:

$$\beta_{OH} = \frac{A_\lambda - A_0}{t}$$

Oxidation State by "Beta Ratio" Method. Douglas and co-workers have reported absorption spectra for such polyvalent ions as chromium (164,165), cerium (166), and manganese (167), as well as iron (168,169), in select glass compositions. Paul and Douglas have also shown the mutual interaction of different redox pairs in glass (170). The melting conditions and glass composition, of course, affect the oxidation of the glass which is evident from the redox state of the ions present.

Iron oxide is present in nearly every commercial glass, either as a planned additive or as an impurity carried in the raw materials. The reduced state of iron oxide, FeO, produces a well-defined, but broad, absorption band centered at 1.1 μm in the near infrared. The oxidized state, Fe_2O_3, has an absorption band centered near 260 nm in the ultraviolet. Thus, at a fixed total iron content, a measure of the absorption ratio between the two states provides a measure of the redox balance in the glass.

In Equation 1, the factor K for a polished plane parallel plate in which scattering losses are assumed small is measured by the surface reflectance losses:

$$K = (1 - r)^2 \tag{7}$$

where r is the surface reflectivity which can be determined by the refractive index n of the glass by

$$r = \left(\frac{n - 1}{n + 1}\right)^2 \tag{8}$$

For this procedure n is taken to be 1.50, which is closely approximated by most glasses. Thus $r = 0.04$, and $K = 0.922$. With this simplification, and eliminating consideration of background absorption, we have from Equation 1,

$$\beta_\lambda t = \log_{10} \frac{T_\lambda}{0.922} \tag{9}$$

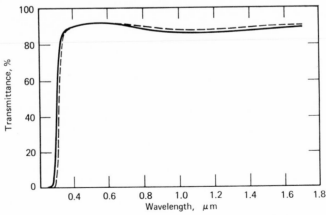

Fig. 12. Spectral transmittance of Code 7740 glass. Thickness: 7 mm. Solid curve is reduced glass; dashed curve, oxidized glass.

For a fixed thickness, t, it will be noticed that the quantity βt is proportional to the concentration of the absorbing species. It is convenient for frequent use to assemble a table of βt versus T based on Equation 9 (158a), but naturally, this is not necessary.

Figure 12 shows a portion of the transmittance curve for one type of borosilicate glass for which this redox procedure has been used. The solid line is for a typical glass sample. The dotted line represents the approximate shape taken by the transmittance curve as this glass becomes more oxidized. The 1.1 μm FeO absorption decreases. In the ultraviolet the cut-off for most ordinary glasses is near 300 nm, largely controlled by the major constituents of the glass. Thus one does not have access to the center of the oxidized iron absorption band near 260 mn. Increased absorption in this region is evidenced by a shift of the cut-off to longer wavelengths. Thus the ultraviolet absorption can be monitored at some analytical wavelength, chosen rather arbitrarily, in the cut-off region. For the Code 7740 glass illustrated this is 313 nm. The following procedure is applicable to Code 7740 glass; for other glasses different wavelengths have to be used.

Procedure

SAMPLING. Prepare a ground and polished plane parallel specimen of the glass at a thickness near 1.0 cm.

MEASUREMENT AND COMPUTATION. With a suitable manual or recording spectrophotometer, measure $\%$ transmittance, T_{313}, at 313 nm. With the same, or another instrument, measure the $\%$ transmittance, $T_{1.1}$ at 1.1 μm. Divide both T_{313} and $T_{1.1}$ by 0.922 and find logarithms of the quotients:

$$\beta t_{313} = \log_{10} \frac{T_{313}}{0.922}$$

$$\beta t_{1.1} = \log_{10} \frac{T_{1.1}}{0.922}$$

Calculate the Beta Ratio, the measurement of redox state:

$$\text{Beta Ratio} = \frac{\beta t_{313}}{\beta t_{1.1}}$$

X-Ray Diffraction

X-ray diffraction patterns of crystalline phases in glasses and glass–ceramics can be readily obtained by standard diffractometer–electron detection techniques or by photographic procedures, for example, with the Debye-Scherrer powder camera. Although x-ray diffraction is commonly thought to apply only to crystalline materials, useful structural information may also be gathered from noncrystalline bodies such as glass. The major distinction between the two types of material is that in crystalline matter long range order gives rise to Bragg x-ray scattering, while in glass short range order produces rather diffuse patterns. A comparison of x-ray diffraction patterns from a crystalline glass–ceramic and a noncrystalline glass is shown in Vol. 9, p. 221. The discussion of x-ray diffraction in the CERAMICS article, Vol. 9, pp. 219–222, applies to glass and glass–ceramics. In addition to the topics covered there, the following information is pertinent.

The x-ray diffraction work of Warren (171) and others have supported the general concept of short-range order in glass structure postulated by Zachariasen (172).

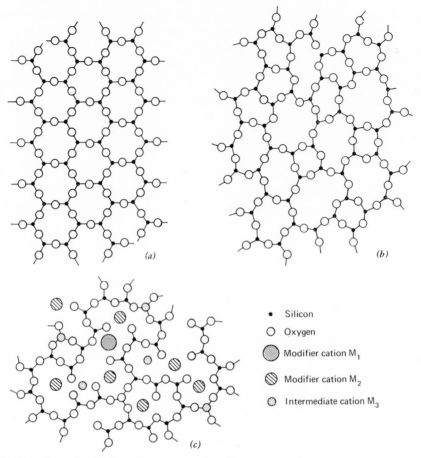

Fig. 13. Two-dimensional schematic representation of: *a*, a crystalline structure; *b*, a simple glass; and *c*, a multi-component glass.

Based on these views, two-dimensional representations of a crystalline structure, a simple glass, and a multicomponent glass (172a) are pictured in Figure 13.

All glasses are unstable with respect to one or more crystalline phases. Accidental or uncontrolled formation of crystals is called devitrification. Opacification of glass, usually controllable to some extent by suitable heat treatment, is the result of either liquid–liquid or solid–liquid phase separation. Phase separation also provides the basis of colloidal colors in glass and of photosensitive glasses. The formation of glass–ceramic materials depends on the use of a nucleating agent and heat treatments to provide controlled heterogeneous nucleation and crystal growth throughout the matrix. Table 12 lists the major crystalline phases, properties and uses of a number of crystallized glasses and glass–ceramics. Figures 14 and 15 illustrate portions of diffraction patterns from commercial opal and photosensitive glasses and from several glass–ceramics, respectively.

Quantitative x-ray diffraction analysis of the crystalline phases in a material can be carried out using either direct or internal standard methods. Williams et al. (173) have utilized the internal standard method to determine the concentration of β-spodumene–silica solid solution in lithia–alumina–titania–silica glass–ceramics.

Table 12. Crystal Phases, Properties, and Uses of Some Commercial Glass–Ceramics and Solid–Liquid Phase-Separated Glasses

Commercial identification	Major crystal phases[a]	Properties and use
Corning Code 9608 glass–ceramic	β-spodumene ss	low expansion, cooking ware
Corning Code 9606 glass–ceramic	cordierite and cristobalite	medium expansion, radomes for missiles
Corning Code 0303 glazed glass–ceramic	$Na_2O . Al_2O_3 . 2SiO_2$ and $BaO . Al_2O_3 . 2SiO_2$	high strength, tableware
Corning Code 6720 opal glass	calcium fluoride	opacity, tableware
Cornong Code 8603 glass	lithium metasilicate	acid leachable, printing plates
Corning Code 7580 solder glass	lead zinc borate and α-lead borate	thermal setting, solder glass
Owens-Illinois Cervit	β-quartz ss	zero expansion, telescope mirror blank
Narumi Neoceram	β-spodumene ss	low expansion, cooking ware

[a] ss = solid solution.

The results of this work are summarized in Table 13 (173) which shows selected integrated diffraction peak-intensity ratios of β-spodumene and the internal reference in both the crystalline standards and four glass–ceramics as well as the analyzed concentration of β-spodumene in the glass–ceramic materials. Ohlberg and Strickler

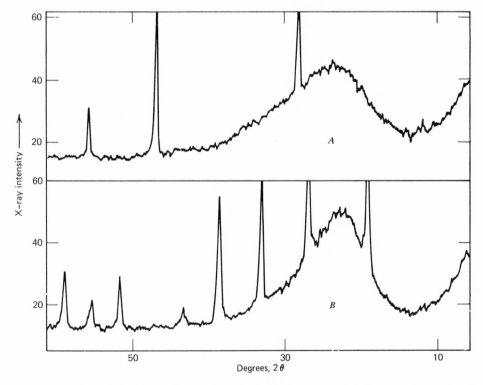

Fig. 14. X-ray diffraction patterns of solid–liquid phase-separated glasses. *A*, portion of a diffractometer trace of Corning Code 6720 opal glass. *B*, portion of a diffractometer trace of Corning Code 8603 glass.

(174) have suggested that the intensity of the noncrystalline scattering halo can be used as an indication of the amorphous content of devitrified glasses and the crystalline concentration estimated by difference.

As glass–ceramics are usually crystallized from glasses of complex composition, the possibility of solid solution is ever present. Variations in the degree and nature of atomic substitutions in glass–ceramic crystalline phases may be determined by comparing x-ray diffraction line positions and intensities with compounds of known purity and stoichiometry. Skinner and Evans (175) first showed that β-spodumene, $LiAlSi_2O_6$, is isostructural with keatite and forms a series of solid solutions with silica, where the unit cell decreases with increasing silica content. Finlayson and

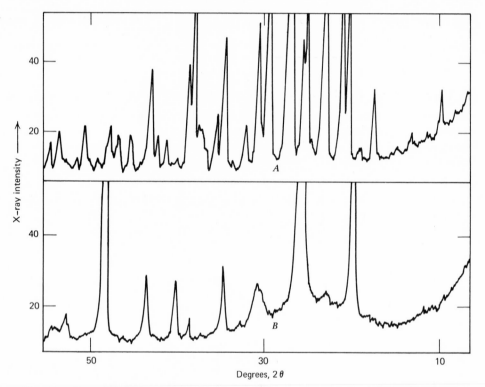

Fig. 15. X-ray diffraction patterns of glass–ceramics: *A*, portion of a diffractometer trace of Corning Code 0303 glazed glass-ceramic; *B*, portion of a diffractometer trace of an Owens-Illinois glass-ceramic.

Williams (176) have reported that β-spodumene–silica solid solution is present in lithia–alumina–titania–silica glass–ceramics and have determined the approximate silica content of the solid solution in a specific glass–ceramic composition as illustrated in Table 14 (176). A comprehensive report on the characterization of the microcrystalline phases in glass ceramics has been released by Muchow et al. (283).

The determination of structural changes as a function of temperature can be ascertained with high and low temperature attachments for various x-ray diffractometers (177,178). High-temperature x-ray diffraction techniques are applicable for studying thermal expansion, reaction kinetics, and phase transformations in glass–ceramic systems. The important effect of silica solid solution on the high-temperature

Table 13. Measured Integrated Diffraction Peak–Intensity Ratios and Calculated β-Spodumene Concentrations

Material	Diffraction peak ratios, spodumene/NaCl		
	d_{201}/d_{220}	d_{102}/d_{220}	d_{111}/d_{220}
25% crystalline standard	0.342	0.212	0.124
50% crystalline standard	0.666	0.430	0.249
75% crystalline standard	1.02	0.624	0.334
100% crystalline standard	1.36	0.815	0.464
glass–ceramic 1	1.02	0.560	0.308
glass–ceramic 2	1.20	0.695	0.394
glass–ceramic 3	0.876	0.528	0.299
glass–ceramic 4	0.838	0.493	0.278
1:1:8 solid-state material	1.36	0.832	0.466
	β-spodumene, wt %		
glass–ceramic 1	74.5	67.5	66.0
glass–ceramic 2	89.0	83.5	84.5
glass–ceramic 3	65.0	64.0	64.0
glass–ceramic 4	62.5	59.5	59.5
1:1:8 solid-state material	101.0	100.0	100.0

Table 14. Comparison of Interplanar Spacings from β-Spodumene ss and a Glass–Ceramic

hkl	$Li_2O \cdot Al_2O_3 \cdot nSiO_2$				Glass–ceramic
	$n = 4$	$n = 5$	$n = 6$	$n = 7$	
(404)	1.448_0	1.446_5			
(502)	1.426_0	1.425_2	1.419_4	1.415_3	1.419_4
(512)	1.400_3	1.400_3	1.394_4	1.391_5	1.394_3
(521)	1.378_9	1.377_7	1.372_5	1.369_4	1.373_2
(503)	1.346_4	1.345_3	1.338_9	1.335_6	1.340_1
(226)	1.318_7	1.316_6	1.307_9	1.303_4	1.311_0

thermal expansion of β-spodumene structures which are present in some low expansion commercial glass–ceramics is demonstrated in Figure 16 (285).

In certain instances x-ray film techniques may be more useful than the diffractometer. The Debye-Scherrer camera is well adapted for the analysis of small samples. The powdered specimen is placed in a small glass capillary in the middle of a cylindrical camera, the x-ray beam intersecting the capillary at right angles. The intersection of the cones of reflection with a strip of 35-mm film placed adjacent to the inside surface of the camera produces a series of curved diffraction lines of increasing radius. The analysis of semimicro volumes, such as crystalline inclusions in glass, is usually accomplished by removing the inclusion (179); however, an analysis can sometimes be greatly facilitated by direct examination using a microcamera. Such a device consists of a fine bore collimator to reduce the size of the x-ray beam and a circular or flat plate film cassette (177,180). In situ identification of polycrystalline inclusions as small as 50 μm in diameter can be made with a suitable microcamera. A thin section about 50–100 μm thick containing the crystalline defect is prepared and carefully aligned between the end of the beam collimator and the film cassette to obtain the diffraction pattern for the characterization. Rotation of the specimen minimizes orientation effects.

For high resolution diffraction, a Guinier camera is very useful (181,182). A monochromator used in conjunction with this device will eliminate all undesirable x-ray wavelengths except K_{α_1}. Closely spaced diffraction lines often found in glass–ceramics can be readily resolved using a Guinier camera mounted on a fine focus or microfocus x-ray generator.

Small angle x-ray scattering and radial distribution analysis are two x-ray techniques which may be used in the investigation of noncrystalline glasses. Small angle scattering (183,184) involves the measurement of the scattered intensity in the vicinity of the direct beam. The scattering is due to electron density differences between the matrix and dispersed phase in nonhomogeneous glasses. Both crystalline (185,186) and liquid–liquid phase-separated (187,188) inhomogeneities in glasses have been studied. In contrast to wide angle diffraction, a small angle experiment does not give rise to Bragg reflections; but instead, a monotonic curve of intensity as a function of scattering angle. Small angle x-ray scattering is independent of the internal structure of the glass and depends instead on the size, shape, and orientation of the randomly dispersed heterogeneities.

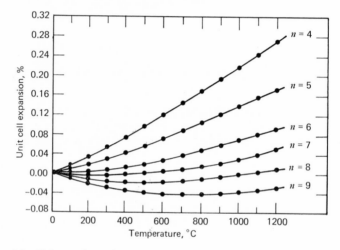

Fig. 16. Volume thermal expansion in $Li_2O.Al_2O_3.nSiO_2$ as determined by x-ray diffraction.

To understand the internal structure of a homogeneous glass it is desirable to know the statistical distribution of interatomic distances and angles in the material. These may be estimated by studying the diffuse maxima caused by the interaction of x rays (or neutrons) with the noncrystalline solid. The observed x-ray intensity must be corrected for Compton scattering and mathematically treated to obtain the radial distribution function. Warren et al. (189) have studied single component glasses, silica, and boric oxide, and have published radial distribution curves for these vitreous materials. Using improved experimental techniques (190), Mozzi and Warren (191) have completed a more recent study of vitreous silica and reported Si—O—Si bond angles ranging from 120 to 180° with a maximum at 144° and a Si—O distance close to 1.62 Å. One of the major limitations of noncrystalline x-ray scattering and radial distribution analysis is that data interpretation becomes difficult in multicomponent systems.

Although the mathematical analysis of the diffuse x-ray scattering to obtain atomic angles and distances is a complex problem, simplified practical uses of the major maximum can be made. The vitreous nature of materials may of course be readily detected by the absence of Bragg reflections. The use of the noncrystalline halo for quantitative analysis by Ohlberg has already been mentioned (p. 467). Nash (192) has outlined a rapid semiquantitative x-ray diffraction method for the analysis of silica in naturally occurring silicates where both crystalline as well as glassy material may be analyzed. Crystalline materials are first reduced to the vitreous state by fusion and quenching. The determination is based on the inverse relation of the two theta (2θ) position of the glass diffraction maximum with the silica content. An attempt to generalize this method of analysis to all glasses was not successful, as the presence of glass network formers other than silica, such as alumina and boric oxide, introduced considerable error in the location of the glassy halo maximum with relation to the silica content (193). Ion exchange treatment of glass (194) disrupts the surface structure, and changes in the diffuse scattering maxima can be observed as a result of the process. The position of the maximum at about 20 degrees 2θ may be used to determine the relative levels of ion exchange.

Microscopy

The optical quality and optical constants of glass, surface topography, fracture morphology, and break sources in glass and glass–ceramics, nucleation and phase separation in glass and glass–ceramics, and the variable microstructural features in glass–ceramics, all can be investigated advantageously by various microscopy techniques. Electron microscopy is discussed in Vol. 1, pp. 649–685, and optical microscopy in Vol. 2, pp. 561–600. The application of microscopy methods to glass and glass–ceramics is covered in the CERAMICS article, Vol. 9, on pp. 222–228. Additional methods and techniques are discussed below.

The use of various optical techniques to examine glass surfaces has been recorded by Holland (195). Löffler has combined chemical etching with interference microscopy to study cord or striae in glass (196). A summary of methods, including various optical techniques, for the assessment of the heterogeneity of glass has been published (197). Pruden et al. (198) have reported procedures for the examination of glass and other insulator materials by scanning electron microscopy. Doherty and Leombruno (199), Carrier (200), and Williams et al. (173) have shown that electron microscopy can be used to determine the crystalline content in glass–ceramics. The nature of glass surfaces after weathering and various modes of cleaning has been determined by Brosset and Hagstedt (201), Tichane (202), and Tichane and Carrier (203). Optimum conditions for three-dimensional and stereo observations in glass and glass–ceramic systems by means of scanning electron microscopy have been delineated by Korda et al. (204). Various transmission electron microscopy techniques have been used extensively to examine the microstructure of glass and glass–ceramics (205–208), phase separation in glasses (209–215), and nucleation, phase separation, and crystallization in glass and glass–ceramic systems (216–222).

Specimen Preparation for Microscopic Examination. The scope of microscopic examination of glass and glass–ceramics is extremely broad, ranging from the exploration of gross surface and optical defects at magnifications of 3× to 100× by optical microscopy to transmission electron microscope studies of nucleation, phase separation, and crystal growth of particles 15–1000 Å in size. Universal methods for sample preparation such as outlined by Insley and Frèchette (223), and Chamot and Mason (224), and Thornton (225) and Kay (226) are employed for optical, scanning, and transmission electron microscopy observations, respectively. Special preparative modifications are often required depending on the particular nature of the problem or the material being investigated.

Chemical etching to bring about phase relief is an important and often necessary step in the preparation of many samples for microscopic examination. In general,

Table 15. Some Etchants for Glass and Glass–Ceramics

Etchant	Conditions and applications
0.03–0.1% HF aqueous solution	time variable: 5 sec to 5 min; room temperature; phase relief in glass and glass–ceramics; glaze–ceramic interfaces; titania opacified enamels
0.1–3.0% HF aqueous solution	time variable: 10 sec to 10 min; room temperature; phase relief in glass and glass–ceramics; surface flaws and defects in glass; glass frit seal interfaces; opal and photochromic glasses; grain boundaries
5–48% HF aqueous solution	time variable: 10 sec to 5 min; room temperature; phase relief in glass–ceramics; more refractory phases
0.2–5% HNO_3 aqueous solution	time variable: 5 sec to 1 min; room temperature; phase relief, defects, and seal interfaces of high lead glasses; lead titanate glass–ceramics
1% EDTA + 5% NaOH aqueous solution	time variable: 10 to 30 min; temperature: about 95°C, phase relief or surface variation in vitreous silica, photosensitive glasses, and glass–ceramics
water	time variable: min to hr; room temperature to 100°C; phase separation alkali borosilicate glasses; phase relief and quantitative phase analysis of glass–ceramics; soluble phase, borosiliceous vitreous; insoluble phases, β-spodumene, rutile, etc
NH-5 Hypo Fixer (Heico, Inc., Stroudsburg, Pa.)	time variable: 1–5 min; room temperature; silver halide crystals in photochromic glass
5% NaOH aqueous solution	time variable: 1–15 min; room temperature to 95°C; phase relief in glass–ceramics
5% H_2SO_4 + 5% HCl aqueous solution	time variable: 1–5 min; room temperature; phase relief in non-silicate glass–ceramics
0.3% Super Soilax aqueous solution (Economics Lab, Inc., St. Paul, Minn.)	time variable: min to hr; temperature: about 95°C; phase separation in borosilicate glasses; surface quality, brush mark, cord, striae in glasses; chemical durability test for glasses and glass–ceramics
0.1 N HF aqueous solution (stopped with H_3BO_3)	time variable: min to hr; room temperature; phase relief and quantitative phase analysis of glass–ceramics; soluble phases, alumino and borosiliceous vitreous; insoluble phases, β-spodumene, rutile, aluminum titanate, etc
0.27 N HF aqueous solution	time variable: min to hr; room temperature; phase relief and quantitative phase analysis of glass–ceramics; soluble phases, siliceous vitreous, β-spodumene; insoluble phases, α-alumina, baddeleyite, mullite, rutile, etc
0.27 N HF + 0.30 N HCl aqueous solution	time variable: min to hr; room temperature; phase relief and quantitative phase analysis of glass–ceramics; soluble phase, baria siliceous vitreous; insoluble phase, mullite
1.27 N NaOH + 0.9 N glycerol + 0.001 N Na_2EDTA aqueous solution	time variable: min to hr; room temperature; phase relief and quantitative phase analysis of glass–ceramics; soluble phases, siliceous vitreous, lithium metasilicate; insoluble phases; rutile, tin oxide, etc

glass and glass–ceramic materials are silicate-based materials, and hydrofluoric acid is a key constituent in most etch solutions. Table 15 lists a number of etchants recommended for glass and glass–ceramics.

The examination of gross defects such as seeds, stones, cord or striae, and break sources in glass is usually carried out by means of optical microscopy on as-formed or as-fractured surfaces. Stones, ie, crystalline inclusions in glass, are often identified by petrographic procedures. Weathered surfaces of glass may be examined directly to ascertain extent of attack.

Chips of glass obtained by crushing a sample with a mortar and pestle can be used to determine the refractive index with an optical microscope. A few particles of glass are immersed in liquids of varying refractive index until a match results (227). Glass chips can also provide miniature thin sections for examination by optical and transmission electron microscopy. For direct transmission electron microscopy observation the crushed powder is sprinkled on a 400-mesh electron microscope grid, covered with a second grid, and the resulting sandwich placed in an electron microscope grid holder. The edges of the chips are examined to find a section thin enough for direct observation by transmission of the electron beam. Not all glasses or glass–ceramics fracture to form chips with edges thin enough for electron transmission ($\sim$0.1 μm). At best the wedges formed are of variable thickness, and uniform observations are often difficult. However, the time saved in using this method for direct electron transmission examinations make the technique an attractive one.

Thin sections ranging from 5 to 100 μm thick are often used for optical microscopy examination. The optimum thickness is determined by the complexity and size of the defects or grains to be examined. A thin slice of the sample about 0.5–1 mm, cut off with an alundum, silicon carbide, or diamond impregnated abrasive disc, is mounted on a glass slide with a glycol phthalate or vinyl acetate resin. Grinding of the specimen surface is carried out successively with number 80, 240, 400, and 600 grit silicon carbide abrasive. Final polishing is done on a lap charged with 1.0 and finally 0.05 μm alumina powder. The sample will now be reduced to a thickness of

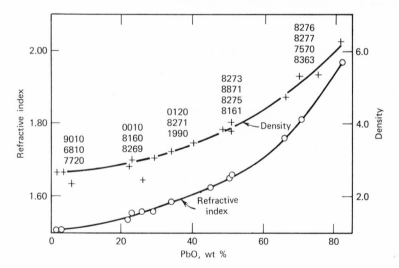

Fig. 17. Refractive index and density of some commercial lead-containing glasses. Four digit numbers refer to data points for Corning Glass Works glass codes.

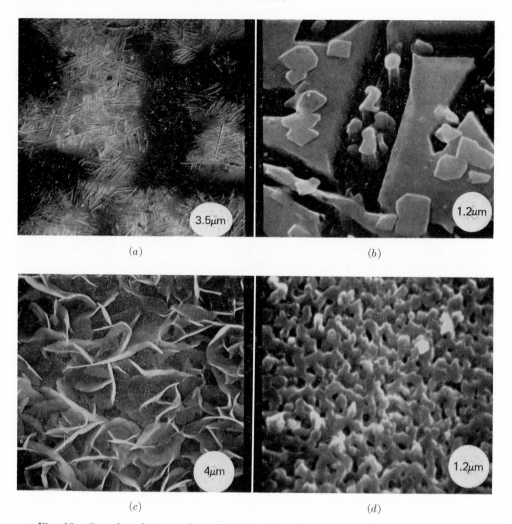

Fig. 18. Scanning electron micrographs showing microstructure of glass and glass–ceramic materials: *a*, Corning Glass Works Code 8603 glass; *b*, Corning Glass Works Code 8603 glass–ceramic; *c*, experimental glass–ceramic; *d*, experimental porous glass. All specimens etched in dilute hydrofluoric acid and coated with 200 Å aluminum.

approximately 0.3–0.5 mm and is carefully removed from the slide backing with acetone. The polished specimen is remounted, smooth side down, on a clean glass slide with glycol phthalate or vinyl acetate. Again the sample is ground and polished through a sequence as described above until a thin section of suitable thickness for optical microscopy examination is observed.

Glass and glass–ceramic specimens about 1000 Å thick are required for direct transmission electron microscope observations. Transmission of the electrons through the specimen is necessary when microstructural detail less than 30 Å is desired. Ultrathin sections for this work can be prepared by mechanical, chemical, and ion bombardment thinning techniques, or on occasion, edges of chips of glass can be used as described above. The use of a microtome for cutting ultra-thin slices of glass and glass–ceramics is not very satisfactory due to the brittle nature of these materials.

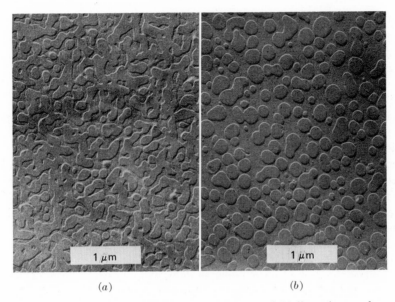

(a)   (b)

Fig. 19. Transmission electron micrographs of (a) continuous and (b) discontinuous phase separation in glass. Micrographs of replicas from etched specimens.

Selected Applications of Microscopy to Glasses and Glass–Ceramics. The refractive index of glass is an important optical constant which can be determined by optical microscopy. Various techniques can be employed (223,224) although immersion methods probably have widest application. Index of refraction is dependent on chemical composition and can be used to help identify or distinguish one glass from another. Lead, as well as certain other heavy elements, has a particularly strong effect on the refractive index of glass. This effect is apparent in Figure 17 which illustrates the dependence of refractive index and density with the lead content of some commercial glasses.

Scanning electron microscopy provides an excellent means to examine the microstructure of glass and glass–ceramics, usually brought in relief by etching; to delineate variations in chemical composition, for example, phase separation and ion-exchanged zones; and to investigate specimen topography where great depth of focus is an advantage, such as, fractured, porous, or friable surfaces. Figure 18 illustrates scanning electron micrographs of the microstructure of Code 8603 glass and glass–ceramic, of a glass–ceramic material, and of an experimental porous glass.

The structural features of glass and glass–ceramics are most clearly resolved by transmission electron microscopy. Micrographs of continuous and discontinuous phase separation in some experimental glasses are displayed in Figure 19.

Electron Microprobe Analysis

In recent years the application of the electron microprobe for glass analysis has been increasingly exploited. Electron microprobe techniques are described in Vol. 1, pp. 685–702. A review of the application of these techniques to glass and ceramic materials has been reported by Kane (228).

The electron microprobe has been utilized to chemically analyze defects, stones, inclusions, and cord in glass (229–236); to study ion diffraction in simple glass systems

(237–239); to investigate metal and refractory corrosion by molten glass (240,241); to scan ceramic to metal seals (242); to determine structural correlations in silicates with x-ray emission wavelength shifts (243); and to examine archaeological glass specimens (244,245).

Since glass and glass–ceramics are nonporous and reasonably uniform in chemical composition, specimen preparation is often routine. However, complications may arise when exposure of glass defects is required, in which case, cutting and polishing operations can prove to be a major task. Some criteria for satisfactory specimen preparation have been given by Yakowitz (246).

Glass and glass–ceramics are poor conductors of heat and electrons and a conductive coating should be applied to the polished specimen to prevent surface charge build-up and consequent distortion and deflection of the electron beam. Vacuum-evaporated copper, aluminum, or carbon films are usually employed to coat insulator specimens. Techniques are described in Reference 247.

The insulating properties of glass and glass–ceramics make electron microprobe analysis of these materials especially difficult if long electron beam dwell times are needed to collect the desired x-ray emission data. The kinetic energy of the electron beam is converted primarily into heat, and although the surface conductive coating may prevent the local build-up of electronic charge, the conductive layer is not adequate to remove the heat generated. Friskney and Haworth (248) have shown that temperatures exceeding 1000°C can be produced in a material of poor thermal conductivity by typical probe operating conditions: 30 kV electron beam accelerating voltage, 0.1×10^{-6} A beam current, and 0.5 μm beam diameter. It is clear that such conditions at the point of x-ray excitation can produce surface damage and volatilization and cause substantial analysis errors.

A number of investigators have noted anomalies in observed x-ray counts, particularly for the alkali elements, in various glass systems. Volatilization (249),

Table 16. Electron Microprobe Instrumental Conditions and Modes of Operation[a]

Instrument conditions	Electron beam parameters	
	crystal dispersion, proportional counters	energy dispersion, Si (Li) detector
accelerating voltage	10–20 kV	10–45 kV
beam current	$0.01–0.03 \times 10^{-6}$ A	$0.5–10 \times 10^{-9}$ A
spot size	1–10 μm	1–10 μm

Modes of operation	Beam time on specimen	
	crystal dispersion, proportional counters	energy dispersion, Si(Li) detector
qualitative analysis	30–90 min	1–5 min
quantitative analysis	20–60 sec/count	
specimen step profile	10–30 sec/step	
image	20–30/beam scan with raster-type scan	
isometric map	$10–100 \times 10^{-3}$ sec/beam step multiscaling with multichannel analyzer	$10–100 \times 10^{-3}$ sec/beam step multiscaling with multichannel analyzer

[a] Applied Research Laboratories EMX Electron Microprobe with Hawshaw lithium drifted silicon energy dispersion detector, Nuclear-Chicago 4096 channel multichannel analyzer, and Ortec matrix generator.

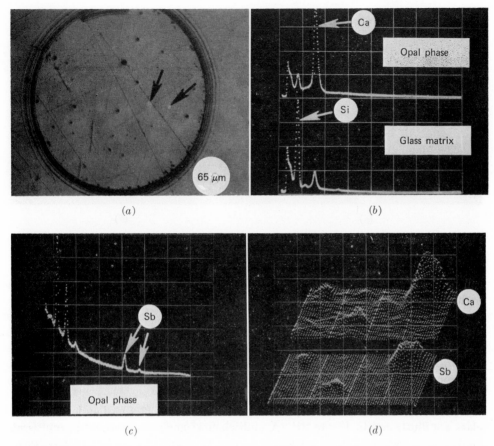

(a)   (b)

(c)   (d)

Fig. 20. Electron microprobe analysis of an opacifier phase in glass: (a) optical micrograph with arrows marking opal phase; (b) and (c) x-ray energy dispersion spectra of matrix glass and opal phase; (d) simultaneous isometric displays of calcium and antimony in sample area containing opal phase. Display area 15 × 30 μm.

surface damage and internal space charge (230), migration of alkali and oxygen evolution (250,251), surface charge and sodium diffusion (252), and composition-dependent ion migration (253) have been postulated as possible mechanisms to explain analytical results. Kane (228) suggests that the "mixed alkali" effect (254) may explain abnormal data obtained on ion-exchanged glasses.

The foregoing discussion indicates that electron microprobe analysis of glasses and glass–ceramics containing alkali elements requires skill and understanding. While quantitative analyses of glass can be carried out employing correction factors and a computer program reported by Colby (255), electron beam parameters such as spot size, current density, accelerating voltage, and beam dwell time must be closely monitored and kept within optimum limits to prevent surface damage and ion migration. Qualitative and comparative analyses in glass and glass–ceramic systems are very useful and relatively simple to accomplish. Typical instrumental conditions and modes of operation of an electron microprobe for analysis of glass specimens are given in Table 16. Comparison of electron beam parameters and dwell times required for the various methods of microprobe operation indicate that less specimen damage

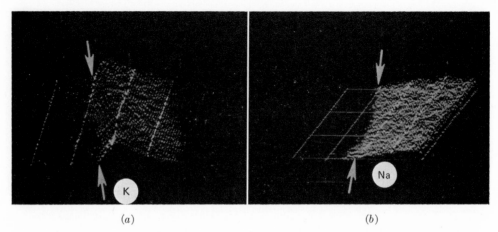

(a)   (b)

Fig. 21.   Electron microprobe isometric displays for (*a*) potassium and (*b*) sodium of a potassium-for-
sodium ion-exchanged glass.   Arrows delineate edge of specimen, glass to right.

can be expected when the energy dispersion silicon (lithium) detector (256) and the
multiscaling techniques are employed.

Figure 20 shows series of photographs concerning the identification of the opacifier
in an ancient glass.   The opacifier phase is marked by arrows in the optical micrograph.
X-ray energy dispersion spectra for the opacifier and the matrix glass suggest that
the opacifier contains calcium and antimony.   The presence of both calcium and
antimony in the opal phase is confirmed by the isometric concentration maps for
calcium and antimony.

Isometric concentration maps, as described by Kane (228), of an ion-exchanged
glass are illustrated in Figure 21.   A multichannel analyzer operated in multiscaler
mode and linked to a matrix generator is used to obtain the graphic representation.
The matrix generator moves the electron beam rapidly in discrete steps over the
sample with dwell times, during which the analyzer records counts, as low as ten
milliseconds.   The isometric displays are 64-by-64 step matrices showing the distribution of potassium and sodium at the surface of a potassium-for-sodium ion-exchanged
glass with the apparent height above the plane representing relative x-ray intensity.

Analysis of Gases in Glass

Analysis of Blisters.   Gaseous inclusions or bubbles in glass, usually called
blisters, seriously affect the optical characteristics of glass and, therefore, are of importance in glass quality considerations.   The gaseous components present can often
serve as a means of diagnosing the conditions governing the formation of the blisters,
and the value of knowing the composition of the gases present is self-evident.   The
mass spectrometer analysis of the gases in blisters in glass was pioneered by Todd
(257), and an improved sampling technique for the analysis has been reported by
Neerman and Bryan (258).

A schematic diagram of the blister sampling system employed by Todd (257)
is shown in Figure 22.   The system includes a capillary Pirani gage (No. 2) to measure
the pressure and a variable buret to measure the volume of the gas released when the
blister is broken open.   Condensation analysis of the released gases can be carried
out by means of the cold finger, CF.   The blister breaker arrangement consists of a

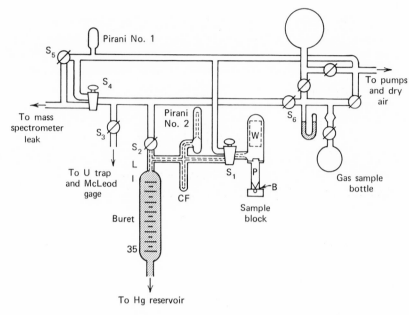

Fig. 22. Schematic diagram of blister sampling system.

steel plunger, P, with a tungsten carbide tip which fits closely inside a glass tube of 5 mm ID, having a 2-mm wall. The plunger has a slot along its length to reduce the impedance to gas flow, and a pin at the top to keep it in the open tube. The open end of the glass tube is polished flat. The plunger can be struck by the magnetically operated steel weight, W, which is a 5-cm length of 1-cm diameter rod and has a maximum travel of 2.5 cm. A piece of glass containing the blister, B, is ground and polished until part of the blister wall is quite thin. This thin wall is located under the tip of the plunger, and the sample block is sealed to the plunger casing with Apiezon W wax.

Gas chromatography has also been employed for the analysis of the gases in glass bubbles. Work reported by Bryan and Neerman (259), Schier and Bauer (260), Mairlot and Gilard (261), and Clarke and Cable (262) indicate that reliable gas analyses can be obtained by gas chromatography, but larger sample volumes are required as compared to the mass spectrometer method.

Outgassing of Glass. The gas evolved from glass at temperatures below the softening point is an important characteristic when glass is used as an envelope in vacuum or gas-filled devices. Outgassing of the glass envelope can lead to deterioration of the vacuum, contamination of the gas fill, and possibly harmful effects on the components in the device. The energy required for the outgassing process may be furnished in different ways, depending on the conditions under which the device is used. The principal gases evolved depend on the form of energy supplied: heat produces water; electron bombardment, oxygen; ultraviolet radiation, hydrogen; and thermal neutron bombardment of boron-containing glasses, helium (263–268). In addition to the major gases, all these processes produce some carbon oxides and water.

Outgassing experiments using a mass spectrometer as the analytical measurement tool can be carried out using a gas flow and sampling system (263) illustrated in Figure 23. In this schematic mass spectrometer flow apparatus, V represents the

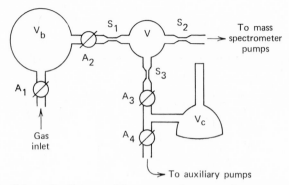

Fig. 23. Schematic diagram of flow system for outgassing measurements.

volume of the mass spectrometer source, V_b, a known volume used for calibration purposes, and V_c, the sample chamber. Depending on the experiment, V_c may be a specimen compartment for thermal treatment, a cathode ray tube in which the sample can be bombarded with electrons, a fused silica cell for ultraviolet irradiation, or a gas diffusion cell. S_1, S_2, and S_3 represent conductances of the tubing leading to the mass spectrometer source. The particulars for the calibration of the system are recorded by Todd, Lineweaver, and Kerr (266).

The thermal outgassing of glass is of broadest interest, since heat is the most common form of energy encountered in vacuum devices made from glass. Todd (264) has published details concerning an apparatus and method for determining the thermal outgassing characteristics of glass. The volume of water evolved from a unit surface of glass at constant temperature above 300°C is linear with respect to the square root of time. The intercept of the linear plot is a measure of the water residing at the surface. In general, the surface-held water is removed by baking at 300°C. The logarithm of the slope, which is a measure of the rate of evolution of water that has diffused to the surface from the interior, is a linear function of the reciprocal of the absolute temperature. The diffusion from the interior, involving only a thin layer of the bulk glass, can persist for a very long time. It is a reversible process dependent upon temperature and the partial pressure of water in contact with the glass. Methods have been developed for calculating the amount of water that will diffuse from certain glasses after a known bake-out (264). The fact that thermal outgassing at higher temperatures can be treated as diffusion from a semi-infinite body greatly simplifies the presentation of the data.

Permeation of Gases in Glass. The use of glass in ultrahigh vacuum systems where pressures in the order of 10^{-11}–10^{-12} torr are required, in closed systems which contain radioactive or other dangerous gases, and in gas storage devices such as might be utilized in outer space, has made the accurate determination of the permeation of gases through glass necessary. Early gas flow measurements were made by monitoring the low-pressure side of pressure gages, such as manometers, Pirani gages, McCleod gages, or ionization gages. More recently, mass spectrometers have been employed to measure the flow of gases for diffusion studies (269–275). The advantage of the mass spectrometer is that the gas to be studied can be monitored independently of any other gas in the system. This is particularly useful when, as in the case of diffusion in glasses, the gas flow rates to be measured are of the same order of magnitude as the outgassing rates, especially at high temperatures.

Bibliography

GENERAL REFERENCES

1. *ASTM C162-66, Standard Definitions of Terms Relating to Glass Products*, American Society of Testing and Materials, Philadelphia, 1969.
2. G. W. Morey, *The Properties of Glass*, 2nd ed., Reinhold Publishing Corp., New York, 1954.
3. C. J. Phillips, *Glass, The Miracle Maker*, 2nd ed., Pitman Publishing Co., New York, 1948.
4. C. J. Phillips, *Glass, Its Industrial Applications*, Reinhold Publishing Corp., New York, 1960.
5. W. Eitel, *Silicate Science, Glasses, Enamels, Slags*, Vol. 2, Academic Press, Inc., New York, 1965.
6. W. A. Weyl and E. C. Marboe, *The Constitution of Glasses, A Dynamic Interpretation*, Vols. 1 and 2, Interscience Publishers, a division of John Wiley & Sons, Inc., New York, 1967.
7. J. E. Stanworth, *Physical Properties of Glass*, Oxford University Press, London, 1953.
8. E. B. Shand, *Glass Engineering Handbook*, McGraw-Hill Book Co., Inc., New York, 1958.
9. W. A. Weyl, *Coloured Glasses*, Dawson's of Pall Mall, London, 1959.
10. M. B. Wolf, *Technical Glasses*, Sir Isaac Pitman and Sons, Ltd., London, 1961.
11. J. R. Hutchins, III and R. V. Harrington, "Glass," in A. Standen, ed., *Kirk-Othmer Encyclopedia of Chemical Technology*, Vol. 10, 2nd ed., Interscience Publishers, a division of John Wiley & Sons, Inc., New York, 1966, pp. 533–604.
12. P. W. McMillan, *Glass–Ceramics*, Academic Press, Inc., New York, 1964.

SPECIFIC REFERENCES

13. Ref. 11, p. 582.
14. Ref. 11, p. 580.
15. F. R. Bacon, *The Glass Industry* **49**, 438–446, 494–499, 519, 554–559 (1968).
16. H. Scholze, *The Glass Industry* **47**, 546–551, 622–628, 670–675 (1966).
17. D. E. Campbell and P. B. Adams, *Glass Technology* **10**, 29–31 (1969).
18. M. E. Nordberg, E. L. Mochel, H. M. Garfinkel, and J. S. Olcott, *J. Am. Ceram. Soc.* **47**, 37 (1964).
19. J. F. MacDowell, *Ind. Eng. Chem.* **50** (3) 38–45 (1966).
20. S. D. Stookey, *Ind. Eng. Chem.* **41**, 856 (1949).
21. W. H. Armistead and S. D. Stookey, *Science* **144**, 150 (1964).
22. G. P. Smith, *Preprint of Seventh International Congress on Glass, Brussels, Belgium, June 28–July 3, 1965*.
23. U.S. Pat. 2,106,744 (March, 1934), H. P. Hood and M. E. Nordberg.
24. U.S. Pat. 2,920,971 (Jan. 21, 1960), S. D. Stookey (to Corning Glass Works).
25. U.S. Pat. 2,933,857 (Apr. 26, 1960), S. D. Stookey (to Corning Glass Works).
26. *ASTM C338-57, Standard Method of Test Softening Point of Glass*, American Society of Testing and Materials, Philadelphia, 1969.
26a. *ASTM C336-64T, Tentative Method for Annealing Point and Strain Point of Glass*, American Society of Testing and Materials, Philadelphia, 1969.
27. W. F. Hillebrand, G. E. F. Lundell, H. A. Bright, and J. I. Hoffman, *Applied Inorganic Analysis*, 2nd ed., John Wiley & Sons, Inc., New York, 1953, pp. 813–814.
27a. W. Geilmann, *Glastechn. Ber.* **9**, 247–279 (1931).
28. *ASTM C 169-69, Chemical Analysis of Soda-Lime Glass*, American Society of Testing and Materials, Philadelphia, 1969.
29. H. Kramer, *Anal. Chem.* **27**, 144, 1024 (1955).
30. J. W. Tereshko, *Anal. Chem.* **35**, 157 (1963).
31. K. Kodama, *Methods of Quantitative Inorganic Analysis*, Interscience Publishers, a division of John Wiley & Sons, New York, 1963, p. 427.
32. H. H. Willard and E. W. Goodspeed, *Ind. Eng. Chem. Anal. Ed.* **8**, 414 (1936).
33. O. Samuelson, *Ion Exchange Separations In Analytical Chemistry*, John Wiley & Sons, Inc., New York, 1963, pp. 317–326.
34. F. W. E. Strehlow, C. J. Liebenberg, and F. Von S. Toerien, *Anal. Chim. Acta* **43**, 465 (1968).
35. J. H. Yoe and A. R. Armstrong, *Anal. Chem.* **19**, 100 (1947).
36. R. B. Hahn, "Zirconium and Hafnium," in I. M. Kolthoff and P. J. Elving, eds., *Treatise on Analytical Chemistry*, Part II, Vol. 5, Interscience Publishers, New York, pp. 95, 124.
37. D. F. Wood and J. T. Jones, *Analyst* **90**, 125 (1965).
38. J. A. Scherrer, *J. Res. Natl. Bur. Std.* **16**, 253 (1936).

39. R. E. VanAman, F. D. Hollibaugh, and J. H. Kanzelmeyer, *Anal. Chem.* **31**, 1783 (1959).

40. P. B. Adams and J. P. Williams, *J. Am. Ceram. Soc.* **41**, 377 (1958).

41. J. P. Williams, F. J. Farncomb, and T. S. Maglioca, *J. Am. Ceram. Soc.* **40**, 352 (1957).

42. P. Close, F. C. Raggon, and W. E. Smith, *J. Am. Ceram. Soc.* **33**, 345 (1950).

43. W. B. Huckabey, E. T. Welch, and A. V. Mettler, *Anal. Chem.* **19**, 154 (1947).

44. S. S. Yamamura and J. H. Sikes, *Anal. Chem.* **38**, 793 (1966).

45. E. B. Sandell, *Colorimetric Determination of Traces of Metals*, 3rd ed., Interscience Publishers, Inc., a division of John Wiley & Sons, Inc., New York, 1965, pp. 396, 397.

46. *Ibid.*, pp. 671, 672.

47. *Ibid.*, p. 430.

48. Ref. 45, p. 383.

49. J. Huré and R. Saint James-Schonberg, *Anal. Chim. Acta* **9**, 415 (1953).

50. L. A. Blatz, *Anal. Chem.* **33**, 249 (1961).

51. H. L. Smith and A. J. Cohen, *Phys. Chem. Glasses* **4**, 173 (1963).

52. Ref. 27, pp. 907–923.

53. P. Close, H. M. Shepherd, and C. H. Drummond, *J. Am. Ceram. Soc.* **41**, 455 (1958).

54. A. D. Wilson, *Analyst* **85**, 823 (1960).

55. P. Close, E. I. Harnyak, T. Baak, and J. F. Tillman, *Microchem. J.* **9**, 334 (1966).

56. P. Nath, A. Paul, and R. W. Douglas, *Phys. Chem. Glasses* **6**, 203 (1965).

57. A. Paul and R. W. Douglas, *Phys. Chem. Glasses* **6**, 212 (1965).

58. A. Paul and R. W. Douglas, *Phys. Chem. Glasses* **7**, 1 (1966).

59. W. M. Wise and J. P. Williams, *Anal. Chem.* **36**, 1 (1964).

60. W. M. Wise and J. P. Williams, *Anal. Chem.* **36**, 1863 (1964).

61. H. J. Cluley, *Analyst* **79**, 567 (1954).

62. R. Přibil, *Coll. Czech. Chem. Commun.* **19**, 58 (1954).

63. H. Flaschka, *Sprechsaal* **88**, 188 (1955).

64. M. Friedrich and M. Fáborský, *Sklář Keram* **6**, 114 (1956).

65. M. Holmberg, *Glastek. Tidskr.* **13**, 39 (1958).

66. J. Lange, *Silikat Tech.* **8**, 513 (1957).

67. H. J. Cluley, *Glass Tech.* **2**, 71 (1961).

68. R. Přibil and V. Veselý, *Talanta* **9**, 23 (1962).

69. Yao-sin Su, *Anal. Chem.* **37**, 1067 (1965).

70. R. Sales, *J. Soc. Glass Technol.* **43**, 37T (1959).

71. Report by Chemical Analysis Committee of the Society, *Glass Tech.* **4**, 109 (1963).

72. M. Malát, J. Pelikán, and V. Suk, *Chemist-Analyst* **45**, 61 (1956).

73. M. Malát and V. Múčka, *Chemist-Analyst* **50**, 110 (1961).

74. R. Přibil and V. Veselý, *Chemist-Analyst* **53**, 12 (1964).

75. R. Přibil and V. Veselý, *Chemist-Analyst* **53**, 43 (1964); **54**, 31 (1965).

76. H. Lundegårdh, *Quantitative Spectral-Analyse der Elemente*, Vols. 1 and 2, Gustav Fischer Verlagsbuchhandlung, Jena, 1929, 1954.

77. P. J. Elving and P. C. Chao, *Anal. Chem.* **21**, 507 (1949).

78. F. M. Biffen, *Anal. Chem.* **22**, 1014 (1950).

79. E. J. Broderick and P. G. Zack, *Anal. Chem.* **23**, 1455 (1951).

80. P. Close, W. E. Smith, and M. T. Watson, Jr., *Anal. Chem.* **25**, 1022 (1953).

81. P. Close and M. T. Watson, Jr., *J. Am. Ceram. Soc* **37**, 235 (1954).

82. J. P. Williams and P. B. Adams, *J. Am. Ceram. Soc.* **37**, 306 (1954).

83. *ASTM E-2 SM 10–13, Suggested Method for Spectrochemical Analysis of Glass for Alkali Elements by Flame Photometry*, American Society for Testing and Materials, Philadelphia, 1968.

84. J. P. Williams and P. B. Adams, *J. Am. Ceram. Soc.* **39**, 351 (1956).

85. *ASTM E-2 SM 10–17, Suggested Method for Spectrochemical Analysis of Glass for Alkaline Earth Elements by the Flame Photometer Technique*, American Society for Testing and Materials, Philadelphia, 1968.

86. N. Roy, *Anal. Chem.* **28**, 34 (1956).

87. J. A. Dean and J. C. Burger, Jr., *Anal. Chem.* **27**, 1052 (1955).

88. F. Hegemann, W. Hert, and W. Schmidt, *Glastech. Ber.* **31**, 81 (1958).

89. R. Ishida, *J. Chem. Soc. Japan, Pure Chem. Sect.* **76**, 60 (1955).

90. O. T. Menis, T. C. Rains, and J. A. Dean, *Anal. Chim. Acta* **19**, 179 (1958).

91. M. T. Kelley, D. J. Fisher, and H. C. Jones, *Anal. Chem.* **31**, 178 (1959).

92. I. Dobes, *Sklář. Keram.* **11**, 14 (1961).

93. W. Passmore and P. B. Adams, *At. Abs. News.* **4**, 237 (1965).

94. P. B. Adams and W. O. Passmore, *Anal. Chem.* **38**, 630 (1966).

95. *E-2 SM 10–24, Suggested Method for the Spectrochemical Analysis of Glasses and Ceramics for Magnesium and Zinc Using an Atomic Absorption Spectrometer*, American Society for Testing and Materials, Philadelphia, 1968.

96. A. H. Jones, *Anal. Chem.* **37**, 1761 (1965).

97. F. J. Langmyhr and P. E. Paus, *Anal. Chim. Acta* **43**, 397 (1968).

98. F. J. Langmyhr and P. E. Paus, *Anal. Chim. Acta* **43**, 508 (1968).

99. F. J. Langmyhr and P. E. Paus, *Anal. Chim. Acta* **47**, 371 (1969).

100. J. H. Medlin, N. H. Suhr, and J. B. Bodkin, *Atomic Absorption Newsletter* **8**, 25 (1969).

101. J. B. Willis, *Nature* **207**, 715 (1965).

102. P. B. Adams, "Flame and Atomic Absorption Spectrometry" in F. J. Welcher, ed., *Standard Methods of Chemical Analysis*, D. Van Nostrand Co., Inc., Princeton, N. J., 1966, pp. 1213–1228.

103. V. A. Fassel and D. W. Golightly, *Anal. Chem.* **39**, 466 (1967).

104. B. Bernas, *Anal. Chem.* **40**, 1682 (1968).

105. A. Katz, *Am. Mineralogist* **53**, 283 (1968).

106. S. M. Omang, *Anal. Chim. Acta* **46**, 225 (1969).

107. C. O. Ingamells, *Talanta* **11**, 665 (1964).

108. B. S. Cooper, *Trans. Soc. Glass Tech.* **20**, 252–257 (1934).

109. F. Hegemann and H. Zoellner, *Glas. Email. Keramo Tech.* **3**, 283, 316, 367, 415 (1952).

110. W. Ward and F. Hartley, *J. Soc. Glass Tech.*, **40**, 37N–46N (1956).

111. A. M. Leiberman, *Anal. Chem.* **29**, 899 (1957).

112. *ASTM E-2 SM 10–10, Suggested Method for Spectrochemical Analysis of Silica Brick and Glass Sand by the Powder–D-C Arc Technique*, American Society for Testing and Materials, Philadelphia, 1968.

113. *ASTM E-2 SM 10–1, Suggested Method for Spectrochemical Analysis of Silica Refractories by the Powder–Intermittent Arc Technique*, American Society for Testing and Materials, Philadelphia, 1968.

114. *ASTM E-2 SM 11–6, Suggested Method for Spectrochemical Analysis of Slags by the Powder–D-C Arc Technique*, American Society for Testing and Materials, Philadelphia, 1968.

115. *ASTM E-2 SM 11–12, Suggested Method for Spectrochemical Analysis of Blast Furnace and Steel Making Slags by the Fusion Spark Technique*, American Society for Testing and Materials, Philadelphia, 1968.

116. *ASTM E-2 SM 10–9, Suggested Method for the Spectrochemical Analysis of Ceramics and Other Nonmetallic Materials by the Powder–D-C Arc Technique*, American Society for Testing and Materials, Philadelphia, 1968.

117. *ASTM E-2 SM 10-14, Suggested Method for Spectrochemical Analysis of Alumina Ceramic Materials by the Powder–D-C Arc Technique*, American Society for Testing and Materials, Philadelphia, 1968.

118. *Methods for Emission Spectrochemical Analysis*, 5th ed., American Society for Testing and Materials, Philadelphia, 1968.

119. W. H. Tingle and C. K. Matocha, *Anal. Chem.* **30**, 494 (1958).

120. *ASTM E-130-66, Recommended Practice for Designation of Shapes and Sizes of Graphite Electrodes*, American Society for Testing and Materials, Philadelphia, 1968.

121. S. H. Lanning, "The Application of X-rays to the Analysis of Container Glass," in W. M. Mueller, ed., *Advances in X-ray Analysis*, Vol. 5, Plenum Press, New York, 1962, pp. 457–463.

122. R. J. Ryder and E. C. Taylow, *Norelco Reporter* **15**, 96 (1968).

123. "X-ray Emission Analysis of Glass with Low-Z Kit," *Lab Application Report No. 8*, General Electric Co., X-ray Department, Milwaukee, Wisc., 1966.

124. E. A. James and J. L. Williams, "The Analysis of Non-Conducting Solids by the Mass Spectrometer," in J. D. Waldron, ed., *Advances in Mass Spectrometry*, Vol. 1, Pergamon Press, Ltd., New York, 1959.

125. R. Brown and W. A. Wolstenholme "Analysis of Insulating Powders by Spark Source Mass Spectrometer," *Paper 75, ASTM Committee E-14, San Francisco, Calif., May 19–24, 1963.*

126. M. Desjardins, "Techniques in Spark Source Mass Spectrometry," in E. Kendrick, ed., *Advances in Mass Spectrometry*, Vol. 4, Institute of Petroleum, London, 1968.

127. M. Desjardins and J. P. Williams, *J. Am. Ceram. Soc.* **51**, 296 (1968).

128. S. S. C. Tong and J. P. Williams, *J. Am. Ceram. Soc.* **53**, 58 (1970).

129. J. P. Williams and T. A. Schwenkler, *J. Am. Ceram. Soc.* **38**, 119 (1955).

130. J. P. Williams and T. A. Schwenkler, *J. Am. Ceram. Soc.* **38**, 367 (1955).

131. Zofia Zlotawska, *Szklo Ceram.* **12**, 3 (1961); *Chem. Abstr.* **56**, 11247e (1962).

132. Yu. V. Marachevskii and A. I. Kalinin, *Zavodskaya Lab.* **27**, 274 (1961); *Chem. Abstr.* **56**, 1985g (1962).

133. M. Noshiro and M. Sugisaki, *Bunseki Kagaku* **15**, 356 (1966); *Chem. Abstr.* **65**, 10298c (1966).

134. M. Noshiro and M. Sugisaki, *Bunseki Kagaku* **15**, 498 (1966); *Chem. Abstr.* **65**, 16635g (1966).

135. G. S. Bien and E. D. Goldberg, *Anal. Chem.* **28**, 97 (1956).

136. H. M. Davis and J. E. Seaborn, *Electron. Eng.* **25**, 314 (1953).

137. H. M. Davis and J. E. Seaborn, "A Differential Cathode-Ray Polarograph," in I. S. Longmuir, ed., *Advances in Polarography*, (*Proceedings of the 2nd International Congress held at Cambridge, 1959*), Vol. 1, Pergamon Press, 1960, pp. 239–250.

138. H. P. Raaen, *Anal. Chem.* **37**, 1355 (1965).

139. A. M. Bond and T. A. O'Donnell, *Anal. Chem.* **41**, 1801 (1969).

140. Y. S. Su, D. E. Campbell, and J. P. Williams, *Anal. Chim. Acta* **32**, 559 (1965).

141. J. E. Harrar and E. Behm, *Anal. Chem.* **39**, 1230 (1967).

142. P. R. Segatto, *J. Am. Ceram. Soc.* **45**, 102 (1962).

143. W. M. Wise and J. P. Williams, *Anal. Chem.* **37**, 1292 (1965).

144. Y. S. Su and D. E. Campbell, *Anal. Chim. Acta* **47**, 261 (1969).

145. Anna J. Harrison, *J. Am. Ceram. Soc.* **30**, 362 (1947).

146. R. V. Adams, *Phys. Chem. Glasses* **2**, 101 (1961).

147. I. Simon and H. O. McMahon, *J. Am. Ceram. Soc.* **36**, 160 (1953).

148. P. E. Jellyman and J. P. Proctor, *J. Soc. Glass Tech.* **39**, 173 (1955).

149. H. Moore and P. W. McMillan, *J. Soc. Glass Tech.* **40**, 97 (1956).

150. N. F. Borrelli, B. D. McSwain, and G. J. Su, *Phys. Chem. Glasses* **4**, 11 (1963).

151. B. J. Blain and R. W. Douglas, *Phys. Chem Glasses* **6**, 233 (1965).

152. D. Crozier and R. N. Douglas, *Phys. Chem. Glasses* **6**, 240 (1965).

153. *ASTM E-168, Recommended Practices for General Techniques of Infrared Quantitative Analysis*, American Society of Testing and Materials, Philadelphia, 1969.

154. W. M. Tuddenham and J. P. Lyon, *Anal. Chem.* **32**, 1630 (1960).

155. E. R. Lippincott, A. V. Volkenburg, C. E. Weir, and E. N. Bunting, *J. Res. Natl. Bur. Stds.* **61**, 61 (1958).

156. G. J. Su, N. F. Borrelli, and A. Miller, *Phys. Chem. Glasses* **3**, 167 (1962).

157. C. W. Sill, *Anal. Chem.* **33**, 1984 (1961).

158. H. P. Gage, *J. Opt. Soc. Am.* **27**, 159 (1937).

158a. *Ibid.*, p. 161.

159. "Glass Color Filters," *Catalog Publication CF-2*, Corning Glass Works, 1965.

160. R. P. Bauman, *Absorption Spectroscopy*, John Wiley & Sons, Inc., New York, 1962, pp. 364–433.

161. *ASTM E-131, Tentative Definitions of Terms and Symbols Relating to Molecular Spectroscopy*, American Society of Testing and Materials, Philadelphia, 1969.

162. H. Scholze, *Glass Industry* **47**, 546, 622, 670 (1966).

163. H. Scholze, et al., *Glastechn. Ber.* **32**, 81–88, 142–152, 278–281, 314–320, 381–386, 421–426 (1959).

164. P. Nath and R. W. Douglas, *Phys. Chem. Glasses* **6**, 197 (1965).

165. P. Nath, A. Paul, and R. W. Douglas, *Phys. Chem. Glasses* **6**, 203 (1965).

166. A. Paul and R. W. Douglas, *Phys. Chem. Glasses* **6**, 212 (1965).

167. K. Bingham and S. Parke, *Phys. Chem. Glasses* **6**, 227 (1965).

168. A. Paul and R. W. Douglas, *Phys. Chem. Glasses* **6**, 207 (1965).

169. F. N. Steele and R. W. Douglas, *Phys. Chem. Glasses* **6**, 246 (1965).

170. A. Paul and R. W. Douglas, *Phys. Chem. Glasses* **7**, 1 (1966).

171. B. E. Warren, *J. Appl. Phys.* **13**, 602 (1942).

172. W. H. Zachariasen, *J. Am. Chem. Soc.* **54**, 3841 (1932).

172a. Ref. 11, p. 537.

173. J. P. Williams, G. B. Carrier, H. J. Holland, and F. J. Farncomb, *J. Mater. Sci.* **2**, 513 (1967).

174. S. M. Ohlberg and D. W. Strikler, *J. Am. Ceram. Soc.* **45**, 170 (1962).

175. B. J. Skinner and H. T. Evans, *Am. J. Sci.* **258A**, 312 (1960).

176. K. M. Finlayson and J. P. Williams, *J. Am. Ceram. Soc.* **50**, 488 (1967).

177. R. Reuben, "X-ray Diffraction Analysis," in G. W. Ewing, ed., *Topics in Chemical Instrumentation, J. Chem. Ed.* **1967**, A7, A99, A187, A289, A399, A499.

178. R. K. Schott and E. Ruh, *J. Am. Ceram. Soc.* **46**, 513 (1963).

179. H. P. Rooksby, *Analyst* **77**, 759 (1952).

180. H. P. Rooksby, *Analyst* **73**, 326 (1948).

181. H. E. Hofman and H. Jagodzinski, *Z. Metallkunde* **45**, 601 (1955).

182. R. W. M. D'Eye and E. Wait, *X-ray Powder Photography*, Academic Press, Inc., New York, 1960.

183. H. Brumberger, ed., *Small Angle X-ray Scattering*, Gordon and Beach, New York, 1967.

184. A. Guinier and G. Fournet, *Small Angle Scattering of X-Rays*, John Wiley & Sons, Inc., New York, 1955.

185. G. F. Neilson, "Small Angle X-ray Scattering Study of Nucleation and Devitrification in a Glass–Ceramic," *24th Pittsburgh Diffraction Conference, Pittsburgh, Pa., Nov. 9–11, 1966.*

186. D. L. Weinberg, *J. Appl. Phys.* **33**, 1012 (1962).

187. D. A. Goganov and E. A. Porai-Koshits, *Soviet Physics-Doklady* **10**, 1177 (1964).

188. J. Zarzyki and F. Naudin, *Phys. Chem. Glasses* **8**, 11 (1967).

189. B. E. Warren, H. Krutter, and O. Morningstar, *J. Am. Ceram. Soc.* **19**, 202 (1936).

190. B. E. Warren and G. Mavel, *Rev. Sci. Instr.* **36**, 196 (1965).

191. R. L. Mozzi and B. E. Warren, *J. Appl. Cryst.* **2**, 164 (1969).

192. D. B. Nash, "New Technique of Quantitative SiO_2 Determination of Silicate Materials by X-ray Diffraction Analysis of Glass," *Jet Propulsion Lab Technical Report No. 32-515, 1963.*

193. H. J. Holland, Private Communication, Corning Glass Works, 1970.

194. H. M. Garfinkel, *J. Phys. Chem.* **72**, 4175 (1968).

195. L. Holland, *The Properties of Glass Surfaces*, John Wiley & Sons, Inc., New York, 1964, pp. 74–193.

196. V. J. Löffler, *Glastechn. Ber.* **27**, 381–392 (1954); **30**, 457–463 (1957); **37**, 548–553 (1964).

197. Physical Properties Committee of the Society of Glass Technology, "The Assessment of Heterogeneity in Glass," *Glass Technol.* **2**, 192–198 (1961).

198. L. H. Pruden, E. J. Korda, and J. P. Williams, *Am. Ceram. Soc. Bull.* **46**, 750–755 (1967).

199. P. E. Doherty and R. R. Leombruno, *J. Am. Ceram. Soc.* **47**, 368–370 (1964).

200. G. B. Carrier, *J. Am. Ceram. Soc.* **47**, 365–367 (1964).

201. C. Brosset and M. Hagstedt, *Phys. Chem. Glasses* **2**, 141–144 (1961).

202. R. M. Tichane, *Am. Ceram. Soc. Bull.* **42**, 441–443 (1963).

203. R. M. Tichane and G. B. Carrier, *J. Am. Ceram. Soc.* **44**, 606–610 (1961).

204. E. J. Korda, L. H. Pruden, and J. P. Williams, *J. Am. Ceram. Soc.* **52**, 46–51 (1969).

205. P. W. McMillan, *Glass–Ceramics*, Academic Press, Inc., Ltd., London, 1964, pp. 65–67, 102–107.

206. W. Vogel, *Structur and Kristallisation der Gläser*, VEB Deutscher Verlag für Grundstoffindustrie, Leipzig, 1965.

207. E. A. Porai-Koshits, ed., *The Structure of Glass*, Vol. 6, Consultants Bureau, New York, 1966.

208. N. A. Toropov and E. A. Porai-Koshits, eds., *The Structure of Glass*, Vol. 5, Consultants Bureau, New York, 1965.

209. W. Haller, *J. Chem. Phys.* **42**, 686–693 (1965).

210. J. W. Cahn and R. J. Charles, *Phys. Chem. Glasses* **6**, 181–191 (1965).

211. P. F. James and P. W. McMillan, *Phil. Mag.* **18**, 863–868 (1968).

212. Y. Moriya, D. H. Warrington, and R. W. Douglas, *Phys. Chem. Glasses* **8**, 19 (1967).

213. G. B. Carrier, *J. Am. Ceram. Soc.* **50**, 686 (1967).

214. T. H. Elmer, M. E. Nordberg, G. B. Carrier, and E. J. Korda, *J. Am. Ceram. Soc.* **53**, 171 (1970).

215. T. P. Seward, III, D. R. Uhlmann, and D. Turnbull, *J. Am. Ceram. Soc.* **51**, 278–285 (1968).

216. J. P. Williams and G. B. Carrier, *Glass Technol.* **4**, 183–190 (1963).

217. P. E. Doherty, D. W. Lee, and R. S. Davis, *J. Am. Ceram. Soc.* **50**, 77–81 (1967).

218. T. P. Seward, III, D. R. Uhlmann, David Turnbull, and G. R. Pierce, *J. Am. Ceram. Soc.* **50**, 25–29 (1967).

219. G. H. Beall and D. A. Duke, *J. Matl. Sci.* **4**, 340–352 (1969).

220. D. A. Duke, J. F. MacDowell, and B. R. Karstetter, *J. Am. Ceram. Soc.* **50**, 67–74 (1967).

221. J. F. MacDowell and G. H. Beall, *J. Am. Ceram. Soc.* **52**, 17–25 (1969).

222. J. F. MacDowell, *Ind. Eng. Chem.* **58**, 39–45 (1966).

223. H. Insley and V. D. Frèchette, *Microscopy of Ceramics and Cements*, Academic Press, Inc., New York, 1955, pp. 37–55.

224. E. M. Chamot and C. W. Mason, *Handbook of Chemical Microscopy*, 3rd ed., Vol. 1, John Wiley & Sons, Inc., New York, 1958, pp. 135–174.

225. P. R. Thornton, *Scanning Electron Microscopy*, Chapman and Hall, Ltd., London, 1968, pp. 278–310.

226. D. H. Kay, ed., *Techniques for Microscopy*, 2nd ed., Blackwell Scientific Publications, Ltd., London, 1965, pp. 58–165, 213–253, 311–327.

227. H. Insley and V. D. Frèchette, *Microscopy of Ceramics and Cements*, Academic Press, Inc., New York, 1955, pp. 31–34.

228. W. T. Kane, "Ceramics and Glass Technology," in C. A. Anderson, ed., *Microprobe Analysis*, John Wiley & Sons, Inc., New York, 1971.

229. C. Löffler and J. Löffler, *Glastech. Ber.* **39**, 333 (1966).

230. R. V. Adams, H. Rawson, D. G. Fisher, and P. Worthington, *Glass Technol.* **7**, 98 (1966)

231. K. Wohlleben, H. Woelk, and K. Konopicky, *Glastech. Ber.* **39**, 329 (1966).

232. E. Plumat, "Genesis of Some Vitreous Defects During the Melting Process by the Optical Method and by the Electron Microprobe," *Annual Meeting of Symposium on Defects in Glass, International Commission on Glass, Tokyo and Kyoto, Japan, Sept. 12–17, 1966*.

233. S. N. Ruddlesden and A. C. Airey, *Trans. Brit. Ceram. Soc.* **12**, 599 (1966).

234. W. P. Whitney and E. Kennedy, "The Electron Microprobe: A Powerful Tool for the Analysis of Inhomogeneities in Glass," *Symposium on Inhomogeneity in Glass, Society of Glass Technology, Sheffield, England, April 8, 1965*.

235. O. Svensson, *Glasteknisk Tidskrift* **24**, 37 (1969).

236. J. P. Hazart and E. Weinryb, *Verres Refractaires* **22**, 145 (1968).

237. A. R. Cooper and A. K. Varshneya, *J. Am. Ceram. Soc.* **51**, 103 (1968).

238. M. P. Borom and J. A. Pask, *J. Am. Ceram. Soc.* **51**, 490 (1968).

239. S. N. Ruddlesdon and A. C. Airey, *Trans. Brit. Ceram. Soc.* **12**, 607 (1966).

240. R. C. Jewell, *Platinum Metals Rev.* **8**, 2 (1964).

241. J. P. Williams and W. P. Whitney, *Am. Ceram. Soc. Bull.* **47**, 195 (1968).

242. P. Lublin and L. Sama, *Am. Ceram. Soc. Bull.* **46**, 1083 (1967).

243. E. W. White and G. V. Gibbs, *Am. Min.* **52**, 985 (1967).

244. S. Moll and R. H. Brill, *Advances in Glass Technology*, Part 2, Plenum Press, New York, pp. 293–302, 1963.

245. W. T. Kane, "An Analysis of Ancient Glass with the Electron Microprobe," *Proceedings of the 13th Symposium of the American Scientific Glass Blowers Society, Detroit, Mich., June 12–14, 1968*.

246. H. Yakowitz, *ASTM STP 430, Evaluation of Specimen Preparation and the Use of Standards in Electron Microanalysis*, American Society for Testing and Materials, Philadelphia, Pa., 1968.

247. J. V. Smith, *J. Geol.* **73**, 830 (1965).

248. C. A. Friskney and C. W. Haworth, *J. Appl. Phys.* **38**, 3796 (1967).

249. P. H. Ribbe and J. V. Smith, *J. Geol.* **74**, 217 (1966).

250. A. K. Varshneya, A. R. Cooper, and M. Cable, *J. Appl. Phys.* **37**, 2199 (1966).

251. J. L. Lineweaver, *J. Appl. Phys.* **34**, 1786 (1963).

252. M. P. Borom and R. E. Hanneman, *J. Appl. Phys.* **38**, 2406 (1967).

253. L. F. Vassamillet and V. E. Caldwell, *J. Appl. Phys.* **40**, 1637 (1969).

254. R. M. Hakim and D. R. Uhlmann, *Phys. Chem. Glasses* **8**, 174 (1967).

255. J. W. Colby, "Quantitative Microprobe Analysis of Thin Insulating Films," in J. B. Newkirk, G. R. Mallet, and H. G. Pfeiffer, eds., *Advances in X-ray Analysis*, Plenum Press, New York. 1968, pp. 287–305.

256. R. Fitzgerald, K. Keil, and K. F. J. Heinrich, *Science* **159**, 528 (1968).

257. B. Johnson Todd, *Trans. Soc. Glass Tech.* **40**, 32 (1956).

258. J. C. Neerman and F. R. Bryan, *Anal. Chem.* **31**, 532 (1959).

259. F. R. Bryan and J. C. Neerman, *Anal. Chem.* **34**, 278 (1962).

260. K. H. Schier and W. Bauer, *Silikat Tech.* **14**, 119 (1963).

261. H. Mairlst and P. Gilard, *Glass Tech.* **8**, 123 (1967).

262. A. R. Clarke and M. Cable, *Glass Tech.* **8**, 82 (1967).

263. B. J. Todd, V. O. Altemose, and J. L. Lineweaver, "Outgassing of Glass," *Glass in Electronics Symposium, Sheffield, England, January 1966 (Sponsored by the Society of Glass Technology)*.

264. B. J. Todd, *J. Appl. Phys.* **26**, 1328 (1955).

265. B. J. Todd, *J. Appl. Phys.* **27**, 1209 (1956).

266. B. J. Todd, J. L. Lineweaver, and J. T. Kerr, *J. Appl. Phys.* **31**, 51 (1960).

267. J. L. Lineweaver, *J. Appl. Phys.* **34,** 1786 (1963).

268. V. O. Altemose, *J. Am. Ceram. Soc.* **49,** 446 (1966).

269. F. J. Norton, *J. Am. Ceram. Soc.* **36,** 90 (1953).

270. V. O. Altemose, *J. Appl. Phys.* **32,** 1309 (1961).

271. R. C. Frank, D. E. Swets, and D. L. Frey, *J. Appl. Phys.* **29,** 892 (1958).

272. D. E. Swets, R. W. Lee, and R. C. Frank, *J. Chem. Phys.* **34,** 17 (1961).

273. D. E. Swets, R. W. Lee, and R. C. Frank, *J. Chem. Phys.* **36,** 1062 (1962).

274. R. W. Lee, *J. Chem. Phys.* **38,** 448 (1963).

275. V. O. Altemose, "Permeation of Gases in Glass," *Proceedings of 67th National Meeting American Institute of Chemical Engineers, Symposium on Glass and Related Materials, Atlanta, Ga., Feb. 15–17, 1970.*

276. P. B. Adams and J. P. Williams, *Chemist-Analyst* **49,** 48 (1959).

277. G. E. F. Lundell, J. I. Hoffman, and H. A. Bright, *Chemical Analysis of Iron and Steel,* John Wiley & Sons, Inc., New York, 1931, p. 244, Fig. 46.

278. C. N. Reilley and R. W. Schmid, *Anal. Chem.* **30,** 947 (1958).

279. C. N. Reilley, R. W. Schmid, and D. W. Lamson, *Anal. Chem.* **30,** 953 (1958).

280. R. W. Schmid, *Chemist-Analyst* **51,** 56 (1962).

281. S. S. C. Tong, Unpublished data, Corning Glass Works, Corning, N.Y., 1969.

282. E. B. Owens, "The Mass Spectrometer Analysis of Powdered Samples," in W. L. Mead, ed., *Advances in Mass Spectrometry,* Vol. 3, Institute of Petroleum, London, 1966.

283. G. M. Muchow, H. Shultz, C.-T. Li, and S. Ray, "Characterization of the Microcrystalline Phases in Glass–Ceramic Materials," *Final Report to the Office of Naval Research, Contract N 00014-67-C-0539,* Owens-Illinois, Toledo, Ohio, April 14, 1970.

284. D. A. Stephenson, *Anal. Chem.* **41,** 966 (1969).

285. W. Ostertag, G. R. Fischer, and J. P. Williams, *J. Am. Ceram. Soc.* **51,** 651 (1968).

ACKNOWLEDGEMENT: The authors are indebted to a number of their associates for assistance; in particular, the contributions of P. B. Adams, D. A. Aikens, V. O. Altemose, G. B. Carrier, E. C. Goodrich, H. J. Holland, W. T. Kane, E. J. Korda, C. J. Parker, W. O. Passmore, G. D. Schucker, J. S. Sterlace, D. A. Stephenson, Y.-S. Su, K. F. Sugarwara, and S. S. C. Tong are gratefully acknowledged.

J. P. WILLIAMS
D. E. CAMPBELL
Corning Glass Works

GLUES OF ANIMAL ORIGIN

Animal glues are essentially natural high-polymer proteins. These organic colloids are derived from collagen which is the protein constituent of animal hides, connective tissue, and bones. There are two principal types of animal glues, hide and bone, differing in the type of raw materials used. In both cases, animal glue is obtained by hydrolysis of the collagen in the raw material.

Animal glues find application in a wide range of industrial uses. They are used in woodworking for such applications as assembly, edge gluing, and laminating. In the paper industry, they are used as sizing materials and as binders in paper coating, and also for paper creping. Animal glues find wide use during paper manufacture for the retention and recovery of paper fibers and pigments.

The coated abrasive industry uses animal glues in the manufacture of abrasive paper and cloth (see COATED ABRASIVES, Vol. 10, pp. 263–283). Closely allied with the coated abrasives is the use of animal glue in preparation of compounds for coating wheels, discs, belts, etc.

Animal glues are widely used in the manufacture of gummed papers and tapes and in paper and paperboard converting.

Animal glues and glue-based compounded products are used in paper containers—set up and folding boxes, spiral and convolute tube winding, and laminating. Applications in bookbinding, magazine and catalogue production, and allied fields include binding, casemaking, padding, looseleaf binders, and various luggage and case covering applications.

Animal glues are employed as warp sizing, throwing, and dye-leveling agents in the textile industry. They are used in the match industry for match-head compositions. Other uses include paper gaskets, cork compositions, rubber compounding, compositions for printing, coating and graining rollers, mining, ore refining, and metal plating.

Properties

Animal glue is a protein derived from collagen. Collagen and animal glue are closely related as to chemical composition and properties. Animal glues are described as hydrolyzed collagen with the following formula (1):

$$C_{102}H_{149}O_{38}N_{31} + H_2O \longrightarrow C_{102}H_{151}O_{39}N_{31}$$
$$\text{collagen} \qquad\qquad\qquad \text{animal glue protein}$$

The approximate chemical composition of glue protein is as follows: carbon, 51.3%; hydrogen, 6.4%; oxygen, 24.1%; nitrogen, 18.2%.

Glue molecules consist of amino acids connected through polypeptide linkages to form long-chain polymers of varying molecular weights. In hot aqueous solution the glue molecules take up random configurations of essentially linear form. A wide range of molecular weights, varying from 20,000 to 250,000 have been reported. Acidic and basic sites on the amino acid side chains and terminal groups affect the interactions among the protein molecules and water, and are believed to be responsible for the gelation and rheological properties of animal glues.

Because of the presence of both acidic and basic functional groups in the protein molecule, the molecules are amphoteric and can bear either a positive or negative charge. Animal glues can act either as acids or bases depending upon the pH in water solution. In acidic solution, the protein molecules have an overall positive charge and function as cations, in alkaline solution the molecules are negatively charged and behave as anions. The point where the net charge on the protein is zero is known as the isoelectric point (IEP). The isoelectric point of animal glues usually lies in the pH range of 4.5–5.6. Glues in solution at pH values lower than their IEP have cationic characteristics while they have anionic characteristics at pH values above their IEP. Many properties of glue solutions, such as viscosity, solubility, gel strength, and optical clarity, pass through a maximum or minimum at this point (2–6).

Commercial animal glues are dry, hard, odorless materials available in granular or pulverized form which vary in color from light amber to brown. They may be stored indefinitely in the dry form.

The density of dry animal glue is approximately 1.27 g/ml. A moisture content range of 10–14% is considered normal for the commercially dried product. Inorganic ash content, consisting mainly of calcium salts, may vary from 2% to 6%. Hide glues are generally neutral in water solution with a usual pH range of 6.5–7.5, and bone glues are slightly acidic with values in the pH range of 5.5–6.5.

Animal glues are soluble only in water. They are insoluble in oils, greases, alcohols, and other organic solvents. When placed in cold water, the glue particles absorb water and swell to form a spongy gel. When heated the particles dissolve to form a solution. When the solution is cooled the glue forms an elastic gel. This property is thermally reversible, and upon application of heat the gel liquifies. The gelling or melting point of an animal glue solution will vary from below room temperature to over 120°F, depending upon glue grade, concentration, and the presence of modifiers.

Viscosity in solution and the gel-forming characteristic when cooled are important properties of animal glues, especially in adhesive and sizing or coating applications. These properties vary with the degree of hydrolysis of the collagen precursor and have a marked bearing on working properties. Animal glues are graded as to viscosity (fluidity) and gel strength (stiffness of gel formation) under standard conditions and are available in a wide range of viscosities and gel strengths.

Animal glues are compatible with and may be modified by such water soluble materials as glycerin, sorbitol, glycols, sugars, syrups, and sulfonated oils to act as plasticizers and modify the working properties of the glue. A degree of moisture resistance and increase in the solution melting point of animal glues may be imparted by the proper use of such materials as aldehyde donors and metal salts.

Since they possess amphoteric properties, animal glues are highly effective with suitable modification as colloidal flocculants or suspending agents.

Methods of Manufacture

Both major types of animal glues are prepared by the hydrolysis of collagen and differ mainly in the type of raw material used and the manufacturing processes employed.

Hide glues are prepared by initially washing the raw material with water, followed by curing in a calcium hydroxide (lime) solution which conditions the collagen for subsequent glue extraction by hydrolysis. The cured stock is then washed, treated with dilute mineral acid, such as sulfuric, sulfurous, or hydrochloric, for pH adjustment, followed by a water rinse. The stock is then transferred to extraction kettles or tanks and is heated with water to extract the glue. Several hot water extractions are made until the glue is completely removed from the stock.

Dilute glue solutions are filtered, concentrated by vacuum evaporation and dried. The dry product is ground to the desired particle size.

Bone glues are made from the collagen occurring in animal bones. Green bone glues are prepared from fresh bones and extracted bone glues from bones which have been degreased prior to processing for glue.

Both types of bone glues are initially conditioned by cleansing with water and/or dilute acid solutions. The glue is extracted in pressure tanks with a series of steam and hot water applications. The dilute glue solutions are filtered or centrifuged to remove suspended particles and free grease, followed by vacuum evaporation, drying, and grinding.

Animal glues contain preservatives added during manufacture to provide adequate protection under conditions of normal usage and may contain foam control agents, depending upon the end use.

Commercial Grades and Specifications

Animal glues are graded according to standard methods developed and adopted by the National Association of Glue Manufacturers (NAGM). Grades are based on gel strength and viscosity values.

It is common to market animal glue under brand names or grade designations identified by the midpoint gram values shown in Table 1 or by National Association of Glue Manufacturers' grade number.

Table 2 lists the typical properties of hide and bone types of glues.

Viscosity of animal glue solutions vary over a wide range, depending upon grade, concentration, and temperature. Table 3 lists typical viscosity values at 140°F for a range of dry glue grades at various concentrations.

Table 1. Gel Strengths and Viscosities of Commercial Animal Glues

NAGM[a] grade	Gel strength, g		Viscosity, mP, min
	range	midpoint	
4	70–94	82	42
5	95–121	108	52
6	122–149	135	57
7	150–177	164	62
8	178–206	192	72
9	207–236	222	82
10	237–266	255	92
11	267–298	283	101
12	299–330	315	111
13	331–362	347	121
14	363–394	379	131
15	395–427	411	145
16	428–460	444	157
17	461–494	477	175
18	495–529	512	191

[a] National Association of Glue Manufacturers.

Table 2. Typical Properties of the Two Glue Types

	Hide glue	Bone glue
gel strength, g	50–512	50–220
viscosity, mP	30–200	25–90
pH	6.5–7.5	5.5–6.5
moisture, wt %	10.0–14.0	8.0–11.0
ash, wt %	2.0–6.0	2.0–4.0
grease, wt %	0.3–1.0	0.3–4.0

Table 3. Viscosity of Dry Glues at 140°F, mP

Glue concentration, %	High test	Medium high test	Medium test	Low test
5	3.0	2.4	2.0	1.6
10	8.8	5.6	3.6	2.6
12½	15.5	10.2	6.3	3.2
15	28.0	17.2	8.4	5.0
20	79.2	46.0	22.4	10.0
25	196	112	49.6	19.6
30	524	264	108	37.6
35	1360	612	224	72.0
40	3216	1320	476	133
50	16320	7240	2400	566

Methods of Analysis

SAMPLING

Samples of glues should preferably be taken with a "thief" sampler, a pointed double tube, having an inside diameter of $1\frac{1}{16}$ in. and slotted with openings at least $1 \times 3\frac{1}{2}$ in. The length of the sampler should be sufficient to reach diagonally across the largest dimension of the container.

Procedure

Take a sample with clean dry scoop from several inches below the surface of the glue or preferably with a "thief" sampler of sufficient length to reach diagonally across the container. Draw an amount proportional to 1 lb/100 lb of glue. Follow the "square root method" as listed below (7):

Total number of containers	*Number of containers to be sampled*
1–3	all
4–9	3
10–16	4
17–25	5
26–36	6
37–49	7
50–64	8
65–81	9
82–100	10

Blend or mix samples thoroughly and reduce to 2 lb or more by riffling or quartering. Place the final sample in an air-tight container.

IDENTIFICATION

The biuret test is commonly used for confirming the presence of animal glue in the absence of other proteins.

Procedure

To 10 ml of glue solution in a test tube, add 1 ml of 5% copper sulfate solution and several drops of 1% sodium hydroxide solution. Mix by inverting. If protein is present, a characteristic purple color develops.

PHYSICAL MEASUREMENTS

Viscosity

The viscosity of animal glues is generally determined from a 12.5% solution, by timing the flow of 100 ml of solution at 60°C through a calibrated pipet. The apparatus is available from the Scientific Glass Apparatus Co., Bloomfield, N.J. The technique of measurement is described in detail in Vol. 10, pp. 269–271.

If the viscosity of glue solutions of different concentrations is to be determined, the Brookfield model LV or RV viscometer is used. The procedure for the measurement is detailed in Vol. 10, pp. 271–273; the procedure for the preparation of the glue solution is given below.

Procedure

Prepare a glue solution at the desired use concentration. Soak the glue for 1 hr in cold water, heat to the desired use temperature (usually in range of 120–150°F), mix until the glue is dissolved and the solution is homogeneous. Place the glue solution in a 500-ml high form beaker, cover to prevent loss of moisture, and place in water bath at the desired sample temperature. Allow any entrained air to escape from sample.

Gel Strength

The gel (or jelly) strength of a glue is determined with the Bloom gelometer. It is the measure of the rigidity of a gel formed by a 12.5% glue solution at 10°C under prescribed conditions (7). The Bloom unit is a measure of the force (weight in grams) required to depress a 0.5 in. diameter plunger 4 mm into the surface of the gelled sample.

For details on the Bloom gelometer, and the procedure, see Vol. 10, p. 273.

Isoelectric Point

The protein in animal glue is amphoteric and possesses a net positive or negative charge depending upon its isoelectric point and the pH of the glue solution. The isoelectric point is the pH of the solution at which the net charge on the protein is zero. The glue protein can assume either cationic or anionic properties depending upon the pH value of the glue solution. Glue is cationic at any pH below its isoelectric point and anionic at any pH above its isoelectric point.

To determine the isoelectric point, a solution of glue is treated with a mixed bed ion exchange resin to remove inorganic materials. The resultant pH of the deionized solution measured at 40°C is the isoelectric point of the glue.

Procedure

Weigh 5 g of glue into a 250-ml beaker and add 15 ml of cold water. Allow the glue to soak for 30 min and heat to 40°C. Mix until the glue is dissolved. Heat to 50°C, add 10 g of an ion exchange resin (Amberlite MB-1) and agitate with a magnetic stirrer for 15–20 min. Stop the agitation and allow the resin to settle. Decant the supernatant glue solution and determine pH electrometrically at 40°C. Return the glue solution to original beaker containing the resin, add 2 additional grams of ion exchange resin and stir for 10 min. Again decant the supernatant solution and confirm the pH of solution. The two pH readings should be identical. If the pH readings are different, continue adding 2-g increments of resin, followed by a 10-min agitation period until two successive pH readings are identical. Such a constant pH value is the isoelectric point of the glue sample.

Hydrogen Ion Concentration

The pH of animal glues is determined from a 12.5% solution at 40°C (104°F). For the measurement 15 g of glue is soaked for 1 hr with 105 ml of cold water then dissolved by placing the beaker in a water bath at 140°F. Alternately, the sample solution from the gel strength determination may be melted, thermostated at 40°C and used for the pH determination.

Foam Content

This test is used to differentiate between glues which are foamy and glues which are defoamed. The foam content is expressed as the height of foam obtained after a specified agitation of the glue solution (7).

Procedure

Weigh 10 g of glue into a test bottle, add 70 ml of cold water and allow the glue mixture to soak 1 hr. Heat the solution to 60°C in a water bath and stir until glue is dissolved. Agitate 15 sec using a high speed mixer. Allow the sample to stand at room temperature for 10 min, then measure the height of the foam layer in the bottle. Defoamed glues generally have less than ¼ in. of foam at the end of 10 min.

Odor and Keeping Qualities

The following procedure is used to assure that the glue is adequately preserved and free of objectionable odor for intended end use (7).

Procedure

Prepare a 12.5% glue solution as prescribed for pH determination. Place 50 ml or more solution in an uncovered container and keep it in an incubator at 37–38°C for 48 hr. At the end of the incubation period the glue solution should have a bland odor free of any decomposition odor.

DETERMINATION OF OTHER CONSTITUENTS

Animal glues are routinely tested for moisture, ash, and fat content. The procedures for these determinations (7) are given below.

Procedures

MOISTURE. Weigh into a tared aluminum dish, 2 in. diameter $\times$ ⅞ in. high, approximately 10 g of the animal glue ground to pass a U.S. No. 8 standard sieve to an accuracy of ± 0.001 g. Place it in an atmospheric oven, with cover removed, at 105 ± 1°C for 17 ± 1 hr. Replace the cover and cool in a desiccator. Weigh and express the loss in weight as % moisture.

ASH. Weigh approximately 5 g of the glue with an accuracy of ± 0.001 g into a crucible which has been previously heated to approximately 550°C and then cooled and tared. Dry the sample in an oven at 105°C for at least 2 hr, then heat the crucible over a low flame to carbonize the glue and finally ignite at a dull red heat at approximately 550°C, until free of carbonaceous matter and to constant weight. If the residue contains fusible salts which retard the destruction of carbonaceous matter, cool the crucible, add 10–15 ml of water and filter through a fast, ashless filter paper. Wash the carbon residue on the filter paper with hot water to extract soluble salts. Place the filter paper in the crucible, dry and ignite to a carbon-free ash, then transfer the filtrate to the cooled crucible containing the ash, evaporate to dryness, and carefully heat to approximately 550°C until the crucible and contents reach constant weight. Cool in a desiccator and weigh. Express the residue as % ash.

FATS. Weigh approximately 10 g of glue with an accuracy of ± 0.005 g and place in a 300-ml Florence flask. Add 75 ml of water and soak for 20 min, then add 15 ml of concentrated hydrochloric acid and swirl to mix. Attach the flask to a reflux condenser, heat slowly until the glue is dissolved, then bring to boiling and reflux for 2 hr. Subsequently allow the flask to cool slightly; then pour a few ml of carbon tetrachloride down the condenser. Reflux the solvent and wash all traces of fat from the condenser. Remove the condenser from the flask and cool the latter to room temperature. Add 40 ml of carbon tetrachloride to the flask washing down the sides during the addition. Transfer the contents of the flask to a 500-ml separatory funnel. Rinse out the flask with 5 ml of carbon tetrachloride and add to the separatory funnel. Shake the funnel vigorously for 2 min, then allow the contents of the funnel to separate. Discharge the lower layer into a 100-ml tared beaker, filtering through a Whatman No. 4 filter paper. Add 40 ml of carbon tetrachloride to the solution in the separatory funnel and shake again for 2 min. Allow the contents to separate as before and filter into the same tared beaker. Wash the residue in the filter paper with a few ml of carbon tetrachloride.

Evaporate the solvent from the beaker and place the beaker in an oven at 105°C for 1 hr. Remove the beaker containing the fat residue from the oven, cool in a desiccator, then weigh. Express the residue as % fat.

Bibliography

1. F. Hofmeister, Z. *Physiol. Chem.* **2**, 299 (1878).
2. J. E. Eastoe, *Biochem. J.* **61**, 589–602 (1955).
3. R. E. Neuman, *Arch. Biochem.* **24**, 289–298 (1949).
4. J. Pouradier, *Sci. Ind. Phot.* **19**, 81–91 (1948).
5. A. G. Ward, *J. Phot. Sci.* **3**, 60–67 (1955).
6. A. Veis, *The Macromolecular Chemistry of Gelatin*, Academic Press, New York, 1964.
7. *Standard Methods for the Sampling and Testing of Animal Glues*, National Association of Glue Manufacturers, New York, 1962.

C. L. Pearson
Peter Cooper Corporation

GLUTAMIC ACID.   See Carboxylic acids, amino, Vol. 8, pp. 410–556.

GLYCEROL

Properties... 495
Occurrence and methods of manufacture...................... 498
Commercial grades and specifications....................... 501
Methods of analysis.. 501
Bibliography... 531

Glycerol, 1,2,3-propanetriol, was first discovered by the Swedish chemist Scheele in 1729. Chevreuil, in 1823, received a patent covering the manufacture of glycerol. The empirical formula was established in 1839, although the structure was not deduced until 1883 by Berthelot and Luce. The importance of glycerol experienced a significant increase when, in 1866, Nobel transformed the unstable trinitroglycerol into dynamite (see Explosives, Vol. 12, p. 405). Because of this and other uses, the consumption of glycerol has increased from 20 million lb in 1872 to over 500 million lb in 1968 (1).

In common practice, the term glycerol refers only to the pure compound. Purified commercial products normally containing more than 95% but less than 100% of glycerol are referred to as glycerins. Although the spelling "glycerine" is in widespread use, it is considered incorrect because the ending "ine" applies to a base.

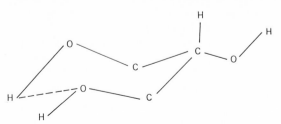

Fig. 1. Conformational structure of glycerol.

The principal uses of glycerol have been in alkyd resins, cellophane, drugs and toilet goods, tobaccos, monoglycerides, food products, explosives, and urethan foams. To a lesser extent, glycerol is utilized in adhesives, cements, ceramics and enamels, cork products, leathers, lubricants, photographic products, and textiles. For more information on the various applications of glycerol, the general references (1–3) should be consulted.

Properties

Glycerol is a clear, viscous, hygroscopic liquid. Its conformational structure has been reported (4), and is shown in Figure 1. The physical and thermodynamic properties of glycerol are listed in Table 1 (1,2).

Table 1. Properties of Glycerol

melting point, °C	18.17
boiling point, °C	290.00
density, 25°C, g/ml	1.2617
vapor pressure, torr	
50°C	0.0025
100°C	0.195
refractive index, n_D^{20}	1.47399
viscosity, absolute, cP	
20°C	1410
100°C	14.8
surface tension, 20°C, dyn/cm	63.4
specific heat, 26°C, 99.94% glycerol, cal/g	0.5795
heat of vaporization, 55°C, cal/mole	21,060
heat of solution, infinite dilution, cal/mole	1381
heat of formation, 15°C, kcal/g-mole	159.8
thermal conductivity, cal/(sec)(cm²)(°C/cm)	0.00068
flash point, °C	177
fire point, °C	204

Table 2. Miscibility of Organic Solvents With Glycerol[a]

acetone	I	ethyl cinnamate	I
isoamyl acetate	I	ethyl ether	I
n-amyl cyanide	I	ethyl phenylacetate	I
anisaldehyde	I	3-heptanol	I
benzene	I	n-heptyl acetate	I
benzyl ether	I	n-hexyl ether	I
chloroform	I	triethylenetetramine	M
cinnamaldehyde	I	α-methylbenzylamine	M
o-cresol	M	α-methylbenzyldiethanolamine	M
di-n-amylamine	S	α-methylbenzyldimethylamine	I
di-n-butylamine	S	α-methylbenzylethanolamine	M
diisobutyl ketone	I	2-methyl-5-ethylpyridine	M
diethyl acetic acid	I	methyl isopropyl ketone	I
2,6,8-trimethyl 4-nonanone	I	4-methyl-n-valeric acid	I
diethylenetriamine	M	o-phenetidine	I
diethylformamide	M	2-phenylethylamine	M
di(2-ethylhexyl)amine	I	isopropanolamine	M
diisopropylamine	M	pyridine	M
di-n-propyl aniline	I	salicylaldehyde	I
ethanol	M	tetradecanol	I
ethyl chloracetate	I	tri-n-butyl phosphate	I

[a] M = Miscible.   I = Immiscible.   S = Partially miscible.

Table 3. Solubility of Various Compounds in Glycerol

Substance	Glycerol concentration, wt %	Temperature, °C	Solubility, parts per 100 parts of solvent
alum	[a]	15	40
ammonium carbonate	[a]	15	20
	99.04	20	19.8
	87.27	20	13.7
ammonium chloride	[a]	15	20.06
anisic aldehyde	[a]	15	0.1
arsenic acid	[a]	15	20
arsenious acid	[a]	15	20
atropine	[a]	15	3
atropine sulfate	99.04	20	45.2
	87.27	20	45.8
barium chloride	[a]	15	9.73
benzoic acid	98.5		2
	95.1	23	2.01
	90	23	1.74
	86.5		1.18
	75	23	1.02
	50	23	0.60
benzyl acetate	[a]	15	0.1
boric acid	98.5	20	24.80
	86.5	20	13.79
brucine	[a]	15	2.25
calcium hydroxide	35	25	1.3
calcium hypophosphite	99.04	20	2.5
	87.27	20	3.2
calcium oleate	45	15	1.18
calcium sulfate	[a]	15	5.17
calcium sulfide	[a]	15	5
cinchonine	[a]	15	0.30
cinchonine sulfate	[a]	15	6.70
cinnamic aldehyde	[a]	15	0.1
codeine hydrochloride	99.04	20	11.1
	87.27	20	4.7
copper acetate	[a]	15	10
copper sulfate	[a]	15	30
ethyl acetate	99.04	20	1.9
	87.27	20	1.8
ethyl ether	99.04	20	0.65
	87.27	20	0.38
eugenol	[a]	15	0.1
ferrous sulfate	[a]	15	25
guaiacol	99.04	20	13.1
	87.27	20	9.05
guaiacol carbonate	99.04	20	0.043
	87.27	20	0.039
iodine	[a]	15	2
iodoform	95	15	0.12
iron and potassium tartrate	[a]	15	8
iron lactate	[a]	15	16
iron oleate	45	15	0.71
lead acetate	[a]	15	10
	98.5		143
	86.5		129.3

Table 3 (*continued*)

Substance	Glycerol concentration, wt %	Temperature, °C	Solubility, parts per 100 parts of solvent
lead sulfate	a	15	30.3
magnesium oleate	45	15	0.94
mercuric chloride	a	15	8
mercurous chloride	a	15	7.5
mercurous cyanide	a	15	27
morphine	a	15	0.45
morphine acetate	a	15	20
morphine hydrochloride	a	15	20
novocaine	99.04	20	11.2
	87.27	20	7.8
oxalic acid	a	15	15.1
pentaerythritol	100	100	9.3
phenacetin	99.04	20	0.47
	87.27	20	0.3
phenol	99.04	20	276.4
	87.27	20	361.8
phenylethyl alcohol	a	15	1.5
phosphorus	a	15	ca 0.25
potassium arsenate	a	15	50.13
potassium bromide	a	15	25
	98.5		17.15
	86.5		20.59
potassium chlorate	a	15	3.54
	98.5		1.03
	86.5		1.32
potassium chloride	a	15	3.72
potassium cyanide	a	15	31.84
potassium iodate	a	15	1.9
potassium iodide	a	15	39.72
	98.5		50.70
	86.5		58.27
quinine	a	15	0.47
quinine sulfate	98.5		1.32
	86.5		0.72
quinine tannate	a	15	0.25
	99.04	20	2.8
	87.27	20	2.45
salicin	a	15	12.5
salicylic acid	98.5		1.63
	86.4		0.985
santonin	a	15	6
sodium arsenate	a	15	50
	87.27	20	44
sodium biborate	98.5		111.15
	86.5		89.36
sodium bicarbonate	a	15	8.06
sodium tetraborate (borax)	a	15	60
sodium carbonate (crystals)	a	15	98.3
sodium chlorate	a	15	20
sodium hypophosphite	99.04	20	32.7
	87.27	20	42.2
sodium pyrophosphate	87.27	20	9.6

(*continued*)

Table 3 (*continued*)

Substance	Glycerol concentration, wt %	Temperature, °C	Solubility, parts per 100 parts of solvent
sodium sulfate.12H₂O	100	25	8.1
stearic acid	99.04	20	0.089
	87.27	20	0.066
strychnine	[a]	15	0.25
strychnine nitrate	[a]	15	4
strychnine sulfate	[a]	15	22.5
sulfur	[a]	15	ca 0.1
tannic acid	[a]	15	48.8
tannin	[a]	15	48.83
tartar emetic	[a]	15	5.5
theobromine	99.04	20	0.028
	87.27	20	0.017
urea	[a]	15	50
zinc chloride	[a]	15	49.87
zinc iodide	[a]	15	39.78
zinc sulfate	[a]	15	35.18
zinc valerate	99.04	20	0.336
	87.27	20	0.382

[a] Glycerol concentration not specified, probably 95–100%.

Glycerol is completely miscible with water and most of the lower aliphatic alcohols and glycols. Many inorganic salts are also soluble in glycerol. Table 2 gives the miscibility of organic solvents with glycerol. Table 3 lists some specific solubility data (5).

Glycerol forms a number of binary azeotropes with organic compounds. These are listed in Table 4 (2). Specifications for glycerol are found in Table 5.

The chemical reactions of glycerol are characteristic of the general reactions of alcohols. Acetals, esters, ethers, halides, amines, aldehydes, and unsaturates can be formed. Glycerates are formed by the replacement of the hydroxyl hydrogen by metal ions. Complexes result when metals such as Al, Fe, Cr, Ti, Pb, or Sn are used.

The most widely employed reactions are the esterifications. The formation of alkyl resins from glycerol and phthalic and maleic acids is quite important commercially. Other reactions include the formation of polyurethans from aromatic isocyanates and the trinitrate from nitric acid.

Oxidation yields a variety of products depending upon the severity of conditions. Mild oxidants attack only one hydroxy group, yielding glyceraldehyde or "glycerose," a mixture of glyceraldehyde and dihydroxyacetone. Nitric acid oxidizes glycerol to glyceric acid, $CH_2(OH)CH(OH)COOH$. Strong oxidants, such as periodate, destroy the carbon chain, forming formaldehyde and formic acid.

Alkyl and aromatic substitution at the nonfunctional hydrogen atoms can also be accomplished. Dehydration results in the formation of the unsaturated compound acrolein, $CH_2{=}CHCHO$.

Glycerol is not considered toxic; it is used as a food and is easily digestible. In 1959, it was reported as generally recognized as safe (GRAS) by the FDA.

Occurrence and Methods of Manufacture

Glycerol seldom occurs in the free state, but is commonly found as triglyceride esters in animal and vegetable fats and oils. The relevant fatty acids are often stearic,

Table 4. Binary Azeotropes of Glycerol (bp, 290.5°C)

| Component B | | Azeotrope | |
name	bp, °C	bp, at 760 torr, °C	glycerol, wt %
p-dibromobenzene	220.25	217.1	10
m-chloronitrobenzene	235.5	232.2	10
o-chloronitrobenzene	246.0	242.1	15?
p-chloronitrobenzene	239.1	235.6	13
triethylene glycol	288.7	285.1	37
m-nitrotoluene	230.8	228.8	13
o-nitrotoluene	221.75	220.7	8
p-nitrotoluene	238.9	235.6	17
m-dimethoxybenzene	214.7	212.5	7
methyl salicylate	222.35	221.4	7.5
indene	182.6	182.4	2
ethyl salicylate	233.7	230.5	10.3
phenyl propyl ether	190.5	190.0	<8
1-bromonaphthalene	281.0	272.5	
1-chloronaphthalene	262.7	256.0	17
naphthalene	218.05	215.2	10
isosafrole	252.0	243.8	~16
safrol	235.9	231.3	14.5
methyl phthalate	283.2	271.5	31
anethol	235.7	230.8	14
estragol	215.6	213.5	7.5
ethyl α-toluate	228.75	228.6	7
eugenol	254.5	251.3	14
isoeugenol	268.8	263.5	25
propyl benzoate	230.85	228.8	8
butylbenzene	183.1	<182.9	
carvone	231.0	230.85	3
d-limonene	177.8	177.7	~1
terpinolene	184.6	184.2	
thymene	179.7	179.6	1
1-methylnaphthalene	244.9	237.25	~18
2-methylnaphthalene	241.15	233.7	16.5
1-allyl-3,4-dimethoxybenzene	255.0	248.3	18
butyl benzoate	249.8	243	17
1,2-dimethoxy-4-propenylbenzene	270.5	258.4	25
ethyl β-phenyl propionate	248.1	242.0	15
isobutyl benzoate	241.9	~237.4	14
isobornyl methyl ether	192.4	192.0	7.5
terpineol methyl ether	216.2	214.0	8
acenaphthene	277.9	259.1	29
biphenyl	254.9	246.1	25
phenyl ether	259.3	247.9	22
isoamyl benzoate	262.05	251.6	22
isoamyl salicylate	279	267	
1,3,5-triethylbenzene	215.5	212.9	8
bornyl acetate	227.7	226.0	10
bornyl ethyl ether	204.9	203.5	~5
phenyl benzoate	315	279	~55
diphenylmethane	265.6	250.8	27
benzyl phenyl ether	286.5	264.5	30
benzyl benzoate	324	282.5	
1,2-diphenylethane	284	261.3	32
benzyl ether	297.0	269.5	36

Table 5. Specifications for Glycerol

	USP	ACS reagent grade	ASTM D 1257-55
assay	95	95	98.7
acid value, max			0.3 mg KOH/g sample
chloride, % max	0.001	0.0005	
fatty acid esters, % max		0.05 as butyric	
heavy metals, % max	0.0005	0.0002	
neutrality		to pass test	
residue after ignition, % max	0.01	0.005	0.1
silver-reducing substances		to pass test	
specific gravity, min, 25/25°C	1.249		1.2587
substances darkened by sulfuric acid	to pass test	to pass test	
sulfate, % max	0.002	0.001	
acrolein, glucose, and ammonia	to pass test		
arsenic, % max	0.0002		
physical appearance			clear and free of suspended matter
color	to pass test	to pass test	to pass test
odor			slight, characteristic

oleic, palmitic, and lauric. A triglyceride is usually formed from different fatty acids. Glycerol also occurs in plant and animal cells as lipids, such as lecithin and cephalin. The lipids have a phosphate acid residue in place of one of the fatty acids.

For many years, the only source of glycerin was from the glycerides in fats and oils. As a result of price fluctuations, periodic shortages, and the desire of the petrochemical industry for new markets, a synthetic method for glycerin production was developed. Synthetic glycerin is now a major source, accounting for 60% of the market in 1965.

Natural glycerin (from glycerides) is obtained principally in two manners: (*1*) The fats are saponified by caustic and salt, yielding an upper layer of soap and a lower layer of glycerin, water, salt, and caustic termed spent lye. (*2*) The fatty acid esters are hydrolyzed under pressure, forming the free fatty acids and "sweet water" which contains glycerin, some inorganic salts, organic matter, and water.

Synthetic glycerols all have propylene as a common starting material. The first commercial process, begun in 1948, followed the discovery that chlorination of propylene yielded allyl chloride, $ClCH_2CH=CH_2$. Allyl chloride can be converted to glycerol by two routes. In the first route, allyl chloride reacts with aqueous chlorine, forming a mixture of glycerol dichlorohydrin. Dehydrochlorination and hydrolysis give glycerol. Alternately, allyl chloride can be hydrolyzed to allyl alcohol, which is chlorohydrinated to yield monochlorohydrins. Hydrolysis again gives glycerol.

The second synthetic route is chlorine-free. Propylene is oxidized in high yield to acrolein which on epoxidation forms glycidaldehyde. Reduction and hydrolysis yield glycerol.

Other commercial syntheses involve the production of allyl alcohol by the catalytic rearrangement of propylene oxide, followed by the appropriate reactions or the simultaneous hydrogenation and hydrogenolysis of refined sugar, forming glycerol and other polyols.

Commercial Grades and Specifications

Crude glycerin is marketed in two grades, soap–lye crude, obtained from the caustic saponification process, after concentration to about 80%, and saponification crude glycerin, obtained from the hydrolysis procedure and concentrated to about 88–91%.

Refined glycerin is marketed in several grades, depending upon the intended use. High-specific-gravity glycerin for use in alkyd production must have a specific gravity of 1.2587, 25/25°C, as set by the ASTM (6). Dynamite grade glycerin must conform to the same specific gravity requirement, but can have more yellow coloration.

The ACS (7), USP (8), and ASTM (6) specifications for glycerol are given in Table 5.

Methods of Analysis

SEPARATION AND IDENTIFICATION

The preferred methods for the separation of glycerol from other substances are paper, thin-layer, liquid column, and gas chromatography. In addition, azeotropic distillation and solvent extraction methods are available. Identification can be made by physical methods such as freezing point, boiling point, specific gravity, or refractive index. Identification can also be confirmed by dehydrating glycerol to acrolein and reacting the acrolein with 2,7-dihydroxynaphthalene, forming a reddish yellow coloration with green fluorescence (9).

Chromatography

Paper Chromatography. Smullin, Hartman, and Stetgler (10) have reported a lengthy paper chromatographic separation of glycerol and other polyols. The separation was accomplished using ascending or descending elution on Whatman No. 1 filter paper. Propylene glycol, ethylene glycol, glycerol, erthyritol, and sorbitol were successfully separated after 16 hr ascending elution using water-saturated n-butanol as a developing solution. After separation, glycerol can be extracted from the paper with water for quantitative determination. Oxidation by periodic acid to formaldehyde and formic acid followed by reaction of the formaldehyde with chromotropic acid provided a colorimetric determination of glycerol. For solutions of 15–100% glycerol, an average recovery of 101.0% with average deviation of 0.3% was obtained.

Patterson (11) has reported similar results for the identification of glycerol in tobacco. By the descending technique, the chromatograms could be developed in 3–4 hr.

Thin-Layer Chromatography. Faster separation has been accomplished using thin-layer chromatography. Wright's procedure (12) efficiently separates the humectants sorbitol, glycerol, ethylene, propylene, butylene glycols, and some sugars found in tobacco. A description of the procedure follows.

Procedure

Prepare a thin layer plate, 20 × 20 cm on flat glass composed of a mixture of 40 g of silica gel in 100 ml of water spread in a 250 μm layer. Dry for 1 hr in the air and activate for 1 hr at 100°C.

Apply a 4 μl aqueous sample to the thin layer, keeping the diameter below 3 mm by touching and drying. For development, the spots are eluted with acetone for 45 min using conventional ascending techniques. After drying in air for a few minutes, spray the plate with 1% lead tetraacetate solution in dry benzene. The compounds appear as white spots on a brown background. Heating at 110°C for a few minutes will darken the background slightly, allowing the detection of as little as 1 μg of glycerol. The R_f values for the polyols and sugars are given in Table 6 (12).

Table 6. R_f Values for Polyols on Silica Gel

Compound	R_f
sucrose	0.01
sorbitol	0.05
fructose	0.09
glucose	0.15
glycerol	0.30
ethanediol	0.49
propane-1,2-diol	0.61
butane-2,3-diol	0.68

Liquid Column Chromatography. Glycerol has been separated from sugars by Sporek and Williams (13), using a column of alumina supported on cellulose. Eluting with a solvent of acetone containing 5% v/v of water and 0.05% v/v of acetic acid, approximately 95% of the glycerol was recovered from the column. Sodium sulfite and sodium acetate added to the sample solution assisted in the retention of the sugars by the adsorbent. The eluted glycerol was determined by sodium periodate oxidation and titration of the formic acid. Analysis of a sample containing a known amount of glycerol provided a correction factor for glycerol retained by the column.

A combined activated charcoal–alumina column was used by Patterson (11) to separate glycerol from sugars and tobacco materials. Using a 50 cm long × 2.5 cm ID column packed with 30 g of activated charcoal and 5 g of cellulose, glycerol was eluted with 2:1 v/v ethyl ether–ethanol solvent. The first 100 ml of the eluate is discarded and the glycerol appears in the following 500 ml. Complete recovery of added glycerol was observed.

Several column separations utilizing ion exchange resins have been shown to be feasible. Sargent and Reiman (14) have demonstrated the separation of glycerol from diethylene glycol, ethylene glycol, DL-1,2-propylene glycol and *meso*- and DL-2,3-butylene glycol. On a 20 cm long × 1.7 cm ID column of anion exchanger Dowex 1-X8, 200–300 mesh in the borax form, the polyols were eluted using 0.02 M aqueous borax solution. Elution of glycerol required approximately 400 min at the recommended flow rate of 0.5 ml/min. Samuelson and Stromberg (15) have reported a similar separation using a mixed solvent and cation exchange resin. The separation of glycerol from a mixture of polyols, carbonyls, and sugars is shown in Figure 2. A 1310 cm long × 2.6 cm ID column packed with Dowex 50W-8X 14–17 μm resin in the lithium form was employed.   The eluant was 85 wt % ethanol at 75°C flowing at 3 ml/ (cm²) (min).

Gas Chromatography.   Gas chromatography is quite useful for the separation and identification of glycerol and similar polyols.   Separations are performed using the free polyol or one of the more volatile derivatives.

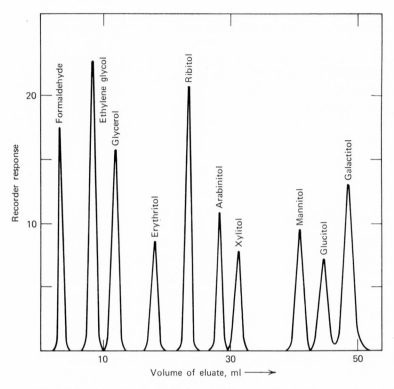

Fig. 2. Separation of glycerol and other polyols at 75°C on a cation exchange resin, using 85 wt % ethanol as the solvent.

Freidman and Raab (16) proposed a gas chromatographic separation of the tobacco humectants, propylene glycol, diethylene glycol, and glycerol as the free alcohols.   The polyol samples, extracted from tobacco, were dissolved in methanol and analyzed under the following conditions:

column	6 ft × ¼ in. OD packed
column packing	5 wt % Carbowax 1500 poly(ethylene glycol) on Haloport F
column temperature	programmed at 9°C/min from 50°C up to 200°C and held there isothermally until the end of the analysis

Under these conditions, the retention times of propylene glycol, diethylene glycol, and glycerol were 12.5, 18, and 24 min, respectively.

Cardini, Quercia, and Calo (17) reported a gas chromatographic procedure for the analysis of glycerol complying with the specifications of the *Italia Pharmacopeia*

VII.   The sample in ethanol solution was analyzed under the following chromatographic conditions:

column	1.8 m × 2.5 mm ID packed
column packing	15 wt % Carbowax on Chromosorb W pre-coated with 5% potassium hydroxide
temperature of	
injection port	300°C
column	200°C
carrier gas and flow rate	nitrogen, 33 ml/min
detector	flame ionization

The separation of a large number of diols and glycerol has been demonstrated by Vaver, Ishakov, and Bergel'son (18). The compounds were chromatographed as free alcohols in methanolic solution, under the following chromatographic conditions:

column	1.45 m × 3 mm ID packed
column packing	10 wt % diethyleneglycol succinate (LAC-3R-728) on silanized Chromosorb W 60/80 mesh
temperature of	
injection port	190°C
column	isothermal at 80°C for 3 min, then programmed at 4°C/min to 185°C
carrier gas and flow rate	argon, 60 ml/min

The elution temperatures obtained are listed in Table 7.

Table 7. Elution Temperatures for Polyols

Polyol	Elution temperature, °C
ethylene glycol	106
1,2-propanediol	102
1,3-propanediol	123
1,2-butanediol	111
2,3-butanediol	100
1,3-butanediol	118
1,4-butanediol	140
1,5-pentanediol	152
1,6-hexanediol	162
glycerol	183

Cross and Jones (19) have separated glycerol in cosmetics by a rapid gas chromatographic method. The glycerol was extracted from the sample into water and then prepared by the following procedure.

Procedure

Place accurately weighed samples containing 20–60 mg of glycerol in 125-ml separatory funnels. Add water to give a total volume of about 20 ml, make slightly acidic by the addition of hydrochloric acid, then add 10 ml of ethanol and 20–25 ml of chloroform. After mixing thoroughly, let the layers separate and drain off the lower layer. Extract the aqueous layer with a second portion of 20 ml of chloroform. Wash the combined organic extract with 10 ml of water and combine the aqueous portions. Add 10 ml of 2-methoxyethanol to the aqueous portions and evaporate to 10 ml. Transfer to a conical centrifuge tube and evaporate to 1 ml but do not evaporate to dryness. Add an additional 3–5 ml of 2-methoxyethanol and repeat the evaporation. Add an accurately measured volume of triethylene glycol standard in 2-methoxyethanol such that it approximates the glycerol concentration and inject 5 μl samples into the gas chromatograph.

The preceding analysis was carried out under the following conditions:

column	8 ft $\times$ $\frac{1}{4}$ in. OD packed
column packing	5 wt % sucrose acetate isobutyrate (SAIB) on Chromosorb G 60/80 mesh
temperature of	
injection port	320°C
column	200°C
detector	320°C
detector	thermal conductivity

Hartman analyzed glycerol and diglycerol as the acetate derivatives (20) under the following conditions:

column	8 ft $\times$ $\frac{1}{4}$ in. OD packed
column packing	0.25 wt % silicone high-vacuum grease or SE-30 silicone gum rubber on 0.177 mm diameter glass beads
column temperature	207°C
detector	argon ionization

The relative retention times (methyl stearate = 1.000) were as follows:

	Liquid phase	
	high-vacuum grease	*SE-30*
glycerol triacetate	0.081	0.067
diglycerol tetraacetate	0.516	0.468

Horrocks and Cornwell (21) have demonstrated the gas chromatographic separation and determination of glycerol and fatty acids in glycerides following quantitative acylation with acetic anhydride. Puschmann and Miller (22) have studied the determination of humectants in tobacco products by esterification to the acetates and gas chromatography.

Analysis as the Trimethylsilyl Ethers. The conversion of glycerol to the trimethylsilyl ether has provided a volatile derivative for several gas chromatographic separations. Smith and Carlson (23) reported the trimethysilyl (TMS) etherification of glycerol, diglycerol, and several sugars. Etherification was accomplished by a sealed tube reaction of the polyols in pyridine with trimethylchlorosilane at 100–150°C for

10–15 hr.   The TMS derivative is extracted from the resulting pyridine–pyridine hydrochloride with benzene and chromatographed under the following conditions:

column	1 m × 4 mm ID packed
column packing	10 wt % SE-30 silicone gum rubber or
	Apiezon M on Celite 545 60/100 mesh
column temperature	180°C
carrier gas and flow rate	helium, 75 ml/min
detector	thermal conductivity

Under these conditions, glycerol trimethylsilyl ether eluted as a single sharp peak with a retention time of about 2 min.   Free glycerol at the same conditions would appear as a greatly broadened peak.

The silylation procedure was simplified by the technique of Dutton, et al. (24). Glycerol, similar polyhydric alcohols, and some sugars, all from the periodate oxidation of polysaccharides, were effectively separated as the TMS ethers.   The etherification was accomplished by the reaction of the polyols in pyridine with a large excess of trimethylsilyl chloride and hexamethyldisilazane.   After 5 min, the samples were analyzed under the following conditions:

column	8 ft × ¼ in. OD packed
column packing	2 wt % SF-96 methyl silicone oil on Diatoport S,
	60/100 mesh
temperature of	
injection port	270°C
column	isothermal at 130°C for 6 min, then programmed
	at 3°C/min up to 220°C
detector	295°C
carrier gas	helium, 88 ml/min
detector	thermal conductivity

Figure 3 shows the chromatogram obtained.

The separation of a simple group of polyols corresponding to dentifrice humectants has been demonstrated by Blum and Koehler (25).   The procedure effectively separates glycerol, sorbitol, and propylene glycol as the TMS ethers.   The etherification is carried out in 3 ml of pyridine to which was added 1.0 ml of an internal standard containing 250 mg of erythritol in 50 ml of pyridine.   After mixing, 1.2 ml of hexamethyldisilazane and 0.4 ml of trimethylchlorosilane are added with stirring, which is continued for 30 min, at which time the sample is ready for injection.   The ethers are chromatographed under the following conditions:

column	6 ft × 3 mm ID packed
column packing	6 wt % SE-30 silicone gum rubber on silanized
	Chromosorb W
column temperature	programmed at 6°C/min from 75°C up to
	225°C

The approximate elution temperatures were as follows: propylene glycol, 105°C; glycerol, 130°C; erythritol, 160°C; and sorbitol, 195°C.   Using a flame ionization detector, no correction factor was necessary to convert relative peak areas to relative weights.

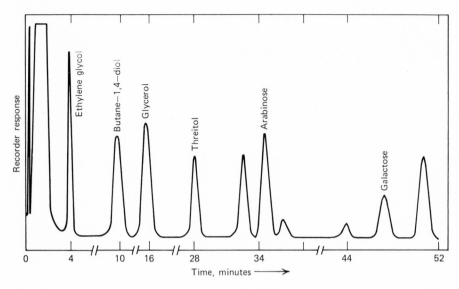

Fig. 3. Chromatogram of polyhydric alcohols as the TMS ethers from the periodate oxidation of arabinogalactan.

Azeotropic Distillation

The quantitative separation and determination of the mixture of water, ethylene glycol, and glycerol may be accomplished by azeotropic distillation. The procedure of Rosenberger and Showmaker (26) utilizes benzene, tetrachloroethylene, and *d*-limonene as entrainers. Benzene entrains only water and none of the polyols. Consequently, the water recovered in the benzene azeotropic distillation directly represents the water content. Tetrachloroethylene forms azeotropes with water and ethylene glycol, but not glycerol. All compounds form azeotropes with *d*-limonene.

Procedure

Carefully introduce 10 ml of the sample into a 250-ml round-bottom flask and add several glass boiling beads and 100–150 ml of the entrainer. Assemble the condenser and receiver and heat to a steady reflux, using a rheostat-controlled heating mantle. Reflux each sample until the collected volume of the entrained liquid remains constant. Rinse the condenser with small portions of the solvent to wash any droplets into the receiver and read the volume of the distillate directly. The total time required ranges from 9 to 16 hr.

Separation by Extraction

A procedure for the separation of glycerol from fats and oils has been described by Pohle and Mehlenbacher (27). The water-insoluble fats and oils are dissolved in chloroform. Upon equilibration with water, glycerol passes into the aqueous phase and can be determined by any conventional method.

Procedure

Dissolve the sample in 50 ml of chloroform with heating if necessary. Add 25 ml of water, stopper the flask, and shake vigorously for 1 min. Remove the aqueous layer and repeat the extraction three more times with 25, 25, and 20 ml of water, respectively. The combined aqueous extracts will contain the glycerol.

DETERMINATION OF GLYCEROL

Many of the procedures discussed under Separation and identification are applicable for the quantitative analysis of glycerol. A discussion of other methods follows. These methods can be used for the assay of pure glycerol as well as for the determination of glycerol in natural substances or commercial preparations.

In cases where the only impurity is water, the amount of glycerol present in the mixtures can also be established by refractive index or specific gravity measurements (see p. 530).

Acetylation

Acetylation of glycerol, referred to as the acetin method, was the basis of a glycerol analysis for a long time (3).

Procedure

Mix a sample of about 1 g of glycerol with not more than an equal weight of water, 2 g of anhydrous sodium sulfate, and 7.5 ml of acetic anhydride, and boil gently under reflux for 1 hr to convert the glycerol into triacetin. After cooling, dissolve the mixture in carbon dioxide-free water, not exceeding 80°C, and filter. Add a few drops of phenolphthalein solution to the filtrate and washings of the filter, and neutralize, carefully avoiding local excesses of alkali, which would hydrolyze the triacetin. After neutralization, add a measured quantity, sufficient to give an excess over that necessary to hydrolyze the triacetin, of standard N sodium or potassium hydroxide solution and boil gently for 15 min. Cool and back-titrate the excess of alkali with standard N acid. Carry out a blank determination and deduct the alkali consumed from that consumed in the glycerol test.

The acetin procedure is no longer in common use for analysis of crude and refined glycerols, having been superseded by the periodate methods (see p. 513).

Colorimetric and Fluorimetric Methods

An adaptation of the dichromate oxidation of glycerol to a colorimetric analysis has been reported by Sargent and Rieman (28). Polyols such as glycerol and ethylene glycol, in the range of 1–250 μg/ml, are oxidized by potassium dichromate in 50% sulfuric acid. The absorption of the resulting chromous ion is measured at 610 nm using 10-cm cells and correlated to the amount of polyol present.

Glycerol in μg levels can be determined fluorometrically (29). The reaction employed as the basis for the analysis involves the condensation of an α,β-unsaturated aldehyde with anthrone, ie, the formation of acrolein by glycerol dehydration and completion by cyclization, as shown in the following equations:

$$CH_2(OH)CH(OH)CH_2OH \xrightarrow{-2H_2O} CH_2{=}CHCHO$$
$$\text{acrolein}$$

anthrone   + $CH_2{=}CHCHO$ →   intermediate $\xrightarrow[\text{from H}_2\text{SO}_4]{+O}$ benzanthrone   + H_2O

Maximum fluorescence of the product benzanthrone was attained after heating the reaction solution at 120°C for 15–20 min. After that time, the fluorescence intensity decreased. The procedure can be used to determine glycerol in the 10–75 μg range with an accuracy of $\pm 5 \mu$g.

Procedure

Prepare a 0.1% w/v solution of anthrone in 85% sulfuric acid. Transfer 1-ml portions of the anthrone solution into a series of stoppered 15-ml test tubes, each containing 1 ml of glycerol standard in 85% sulfuric acid in known amounts between 0 and 100 μg. Allow to cool, add 5 ml of 95% sulfuric acid, and mix thoroughly. Measure the fluorescence intensity at 575 nm and prepare a calibration curve of intensity versus glycerol concentration. The wavelength of excitation is between 350 and 500 nm.

Dissolve an appropriate amount of the sample in 85% sulfuric acid, add 1 ml of the anthrone solution to 1 ml of the sample solution, heat, dilute as before, and measure the intensity of the fluorescence. Determine the amount of glycerol by reference to the calibration curve.

Organic materials carbonized by hot concentrated sulfuric acid will interfere and a prior separation is necessary. Liquid samples may be evaporated to dryness and the mass extracted with acetone, which is subsequently removed by evaporation. For oil and fat-containing materials, the acetone residue is taken up in chloroform or light petroleum, and glycerol extracted from the solution with water.

If darkening still occurs in the cyclization reaction, the benzanthrone product may be removed by extracting three times with 6 ml of benzene, removing the benzene, and redissolution of the solid in 10 ml of concentrated sulfuric acid prior to measuring the fluorescence intensity. Specific interferences encountered using the benzene extraction were gelatin, which quenched the fluorescence, formaldehyde, which formed a fluorescent product, ethylene glycol, which formed a fluorescent product at a higher temperature, acetone, in 1-mg quantities, and tartaric acid. The sugars dextrose, fructose, sucrose, and sorbitol only interfered significantly when present in 100-fold amounts. Eisenbrand and Rausch (30) have developed a fluorometric glycerol analysis based upon the Skraup synthesis. Upon irradiation of 0.5–1.0 mg/ml glycerol and aniline with ultraviolet light of 313 nm, conversion to quinoline occurs. The ultraviolet fluorescence of the resulting quinoline in 0.1 N sulfuric acid is measured at 313 nm. The results are reported to be in agreement with those obtained by the periodate methods (pp. 513–520).

Copper Complexation Method

The formation of a glycerol–copper(II) complex, though known for a long time, has been difficult to apply to a glycerol assay. The basic problem of hydrolysis of the 1:1 complex was overcome by McAloren and Reynolds (31) by the use of an alcoholic medium. Copper(II) chloride is added in small portions to a basic ethanolic solution of the glycerol. Copper in excess of that required for complexation immediately precipitates as the hydroxide and is removed by filtration. The glycerol analysis can now be completed by either an iodometric or colorimetric procedure. In the iodometric procedure (31), the complexed copper is liberated and allowed to react with iodide, and the resulting iodine is titrated with standard sodium thiosulfate solution. The colorimetric procedure (32) is based upon measurement of the absorption of light by the blue glycerol–copper(II) complex. A description of the two procedures follows.

Procedures

VOLUMETRIC METHOD. Place a 10-ml aliquot of the sample solution, adjusted to have a glycerol content within the range of 50–400 mg in a 250-ml stoppered flask, and add 10 ml of 7.5 M sodium hydroxide solution and 60 ml of ethanol. Add successively small volumes of M copper(II) chloride, stopper and shake the flask for 1 min after each addition. Continue until a slight permanent precipitate of copper(II) hydroxide remains. Add 50 ml of ethanol, stopper the flask, and shake for 1 min. Add more copper(II) solution if necessary.

Filter under light suction through a Büchner funnel fitted with a Whatman GFA glass-fiber filter disc. Collect the filtrate in a 500-ml conical flask, rinse the flask, and wash the residue with three 5-ml portions of a 0.75 M ethanolic sodium hydroxide solution containing not more than 10% of water. Add the washings to the filtrate. Dilute the filtrate and washings with 50 ml of water and make acidic to litmus paper by adding 1:9 sulfuric acid. Add 3 g of solid potassium iodide, and titrate the liberated iodine with 0.1 N sodium thiosulfate solution, using starch as indicator, with the addition of 2 g of ammonium thiocyanate near the end point.

Carry out a blank determination exactly as described above, but without the addition of glycerol. Filter without delay. Apply any necessary blank correction to the volume of standard thiosulfate solution required for sample titration.

PHOTOMETRIC METHOD. Place a 5-ml aliquot of the sample solution, adjusted to have a glycerol content in the range of 0.5–40 mg, in a 250-ml stoppered flask. Proceed with the formation and filtration of the complex as described above. Transfer the filtrate to a 100-ml volumetric flask. Rinse out the conical flask and wash the residue with three 5-ml portions of 0.75 M ethanolic sodium hydroxide solution containing not more than 10% water. Use the washing to complete the quantitative transfer of the original filtrate from the collection flask to the volumetric flask. Dilute to volume with ethanol. Measure the absorption at 635 nm.

Carry out a blank determination exactly as described above, but without the addition of glycerol. Filter without delay.

Determine the glycerol concentration by reference to the calibration curve after correction has been made for the reagent blank.

To obtain the calibration curve, prepare a series of standard solutions by dilution of a pure glycerol solution to give concentrations within the range of 0.05–4.0 mg/ml. Treat 10-ml aliquots of these solutions exactly as described for sample analysis. Plot the absorbance at the 635 nm against glycerol concentration.

Polyhydroxic compounds that form copper complexes cause some interference. Ethylene glycol in the volumetric procedure gave a 35% recovery of copper. In the colorimetric procedure, propylene glycol and ethylene glycol form copper complexes with less than one fourth the extinction of the glycerol complex. Trimethylene glycol, sucrose, lactose, mannitol, and tartaric acid caused negligible interference. Ammonium salts and sulfurous acid interfere.

Electrochemical Method

The chemical oxidation of aliphatic alcohols using perchloratocerate in perchloric acid can be monitored amperometrically (33). The titration procedure has been applied to ethylene glycol, glycerol, mannitol, methanol, and ethanol.

The same titration has also been monitored by constant current potentiometry (34). Aqueous samples, containing 0.5–5 mg of glycerol, can be titrated with perchloratocerate, with errors ranging from 0.2% for the large samples to 2.0% for the smaller samples.

Pyrolitic graphite electrodes, $4 \times \frac{1}{4} \times \frac{1}{4}$ in, with highest conductivity along the rod axis, are used for the method. Constant current is best provided by a 90 V battery with a 900,000 Ω resistor in series. The potential difference between the electrodes can be measured by a digital voltmeter or a pH meter with a 0–1400 mV scale.

The titration is performed in 150-ml beakers placed in a water bath or on an aluminum block heat reservoir with magnetic stirring. The titrant is a 0.1 M perchlorato-cerate solution, which is prepared from ammonium cerate, with sufficient perchloric acid to be 2 M for perchloric acid.

The electrodes, polarized by a 100 μA constant current, are immersed in a stirred solution of 2 M perchloric acid at 80°C. The glycerol solution is then added, and the solution titrated until the electrode potential changes from above 1.6 V to 0.3 V. The equivalence point is defined as the volume at which a one drop increment of titrant causes the potential to remain at or below 0.3 V for 30 sec. A blank solution without glycerol is also titrated. Easily oxidized organic compounds interfere with the determination.

Enzymatic Method

The determination of glycerol in biological samples constitutes a difficult assay. The presence of other oxidizable organic materials in the sample precludes the use of most oxidative methods. Enzymatic procedures, because of their specificity, have been developed to overcome this difficulty.

The assay of Wieland (35) is based upon the reduction of nicotinamide adenosine dinucleotide (NAD) to NADH by measuring the change in absorbance at 340 nm, using glycerol kinase and 1-glycerol 1-phosphate dehydrogenase. The procedure requires about 30 min for color development.

Hagen (36) has developed a similar method utilizing glycerol dehydrogenase. Glucose, lactate, malate, β-hydroxybutyrate, succinate, glutarate, α-glycerolphosphate, and α-oxoglutarate did not interfere. Some reduction of NAD was observed with large amounts of ethanol and with glyceraldehyde-3-phosphate. The reaction mixture contained 50 mmol of glycine buffer, pH 9.5, 5 mmol of NAD, and neutralized, protein-free plasma containing 2–10 μmol of glycerol in a total volume of 1.0 ml. After 30 min, the absorbance at 340 nm is measured and compared to a series of glycerol standards. It is necessary to correct for an enzyme blank and for material contained in the plasma absorbing at 340 nm.

The enzymatic procedure of Garland and Randle (37) is based upon the oxidation of reduced NAD and proceeds to completion in 3–5 min. The coupled enzyme reactions are as follows (ATP = adenosine triphosphate; ADP = adenosine diphosphate):

  1. Glycerol + ATP → L-glycerol 1-phosphate + ADP (glycerol kinase)
  2. ADP + phospho-enol-pyruvate → ATP + pyruvate (pyruvate kinase)
  3. Pyruvate + NADH → lactate + NAD (lactate dehydrogenase)

Procedure

Prepare a 75 mmol solution of the disodium salt of ATP, and a 3 mmol solution of NADH. Prepare a 0.1 M magnesium sulfate buffer solution (pH 7.6) containing 6 mmol of magnesium sulfate, 2 mmol of potassium chloride, and 7 mmol of the phospho-enol-pyruvate tricyclohexylammonium salt. Prepare an assay solution containing 0.25 ml of the ATP solution, 500 μg of pyruvate kinase, 200 μg of lactate dehydrogenase, 10 ml of the pH 7.6 buffer solution, and sufficient NADH to give an absorbance of 0.8 at 340 nm in 2-cm cells against a water blank. Store all these solutions at $-15°C$.

For the determination, add 2 ml of the sample solution containing 0.01–0.1 μmol of glycerol to 1 ml of the assay solution and observe the change in absorbance due to the presence of pyruvate of ADP in the sample. Add 10 μg of glycerol kinase and again observe the resulting change in the absorbance.

Calculate the glycerol concentration with help of a calibration curve prepared by analyzing solutions with known glycerol concentrations.

This procedure has been used by Drawert and Kupler (38) for the determination of unesterified glycerol in wines and grape musts by measuring the absorbance at 360 or 366 nm.

Several workers have adapted the enzymative procedure with automatic equipment for measuring reaction rates. Frings and Pardue (39) have developed an automated method that reduces the analysis time to 10–100 sec.

Oxidation Methods

The majority of glycerin assay methods used today incorporate the oxidation of glycerol to formaldehyde and formic acid or occasionally to carbon dioxide. A variety of oxidants have been suggested, including cerate, dichromate, tetravalent-lead, manganate, permanganate, periodate, and quinquevalent vanadium. Presently, the sodium periodate procedure is accepted as standard by the American Oil Chemists' Society, IUPAC, and the British Standards Institute (2).

Cerate Oxidation Method. The cerate oxidation of glycerol, as introduced by Smith and Duke (40), was designed to replace the time-consuming dichromate procedure. The oxidation, performed in perchloric acid, gives formic acid as the sole product. Excess cerate is determined by titration with standard oxalate, using nitroferroin as the indicator. The procedure for the determination of glycerol in fats and fatty oils is given below. The method may be modified for other sample types.

Procedure

REAGENTS. Prepare an ammonium perchloratocerate solution by dissolving 55 g of ammonium hexanitratocerate, $(NH_4)_2Ce(NO_3)_6$, in 340 ml of 72% perchloric acid and adding water slowly with stirring until the volume attains 1 liter. Standardize against 0.1 N sodium oxalate solution using nitroferroin indicator. Store in the dark and restandardize after two weeks.

Prepare a sodium oxalate solution by dissolving 13.412 g of NBS reference sodium oxalate in 1 liter of 0.1 M perchloric acid.

Prepare a lead solution by dissolving 100 g of lead acetate in 750 ml of water. Add 100 g of lead oxide, heat to reflux temperature for 1 hr and filter while hot.

SAMPLE PREPARATION. Warm the sample of fat or fatty oil until the temperature reaches about 80°C, allow the water to separate out, and decant. Weigh 10 g of the sample into a 250-ml Erlenmeyer flask, and add 100 ml of a 0.5 M ethanolic potassium hydroxide solution and several boiling chips. Heat the solution to reflux for $1\frac{1}{2}$ hr then transfer to a 500-ml beaker rinsing with hot water, dilute to 250 ml, and evaporate again to 50 ml.

Add 100 ml of 1:5 perchloric acid and heat on the steam bath until the fatty acids separate. Filter off the fatty acid and potassium perchlorate and wash thoroughly with cold water. Add the lead solution in small portions to precipitate any protein present. If no precipitation occurs upon the first addition, no more

precipitant need be added. Avoid a large excess of reagent by stepwise precipitation. Filter the solution, concentrate if necessary, transfer to a 500-ml volumetric
flask, and dilute to volume. Carry a blank through the entire procedure.

For soap–lye crudes, weigh sufficient sample to contain about 1 g of glycerol,
using a 400-ml beaker. Dilute the sample to 250 ml and test for protein with the
lead acetate solution. Filter the protein precipitate if necessary, transfer to a 500-
ml volumetric flask, and dilute to volume.

DETERMINATION. Transfer 10.0 ml aliquots of the sample solution to 400-ml
beakers. Pipet a volume of cerate solution known to be in excess of that required
for oxidation, and dilute to 100 ml with 4 M perchloric acid. Warm to 50°C and
hold at this temperature for 15 min, but do not exceed 60°C. Cool and titrate the
excess cerate with standard sodium oxalate solution, using 2 drops of 0.025 M nitroferroin indicator.

Sulfuric acid may be substituted for perchloric acid if desired; however, the
temperature must be increased to 90–100°C and maintained there for 90 min for
complete oxidation.

$$\text{Glycerol, wt \%} = \frac{(92)(V)(AN_a - BN_b)}{(80)(w)(C)}$$

where V = volume of sample solution, in ml
$\quad\quad\ A$ = volume of standard cerate solution used for the titration, in ml
$\quad\quad\ N_a$ = normality of the standard cerate solution
$\quad\quad\ B$ = volume of standard oxalate solution used for the titration, in ml
$\quad\quad\ N_b$ = normality of the standard oxalate solution
$\quad\quad\ C$ = volume of aliquot taken for analysis, in ml
$\quad\quad\ w$ = sample weight, in g

Sharma and Mehrotra (41) observed that both glycol and glycerol in the presence
of chromium catalysts were stoichiometrically oxidized to carbon dioxide by ceric
sulfate. By determining the volume of ceric sulfate consumed first in the oxidation to
formic acid and then in the oxidation to carbon dioxide, the amount of glycol and glycerol could be determined by simultaneous equation. The procedure and calculations
were not specified.

A method of catalyzing the cerate oxidation of glycerol to formic acid using
silver(I) and manganese(II) was reported by Guilbault and McCurdy (42). Carrying
out the oxidation at 90°C in perchloric acid, only 3–5 min were required. Excess
cerate was determined by back titration with ferrous ammonium sulfate. The procedure was applied to glycerol, erythritol, pentaerythritol, and chelates of 8-quinolinol.

Periodate Oxidation Methods. Oxidation of glycerol by the periodates,
periodic acid, and sodium periodate has replaced the oxidants such as dichromate and
cerate. The periodate methods are nearly free of many of the disadvantages of the
dichromate and cerate methods. The reaction of periodate with glycerol produces
iodate, formaldehyde, formic acid, and water according to the following equation:

$$C_3H_8O_3 + 2\ HIO_4 \rightarrow 2\ HIO_3 + 2\ HCHO + HCOOH + H_2O$$

Polyols with three or more adjacent hydroxy groups yield formic acid as one of the
oxidation products and may interfere with the assay. The common impurities, however, either do not react with periodate, as in the case of trimethylene glycol, or produce
only formaldehyde, as with ethylene glycol.

Periodic acid was first studied as an oxidant, due partially to a lack of quality
sodium metaperiodate. The procedure reported by the Glycerin Analysis Committee

of the American Oil Chemists' Society in 1946 (43), following oxidation by periodic acid, was based upon titration of the formic acid produced with standard base. Alternate procedures, based upon the amount of periodate and iodate, have subsequently been developed for the determination of glycerol and monoglycerides in small concentrations.

OXIDATION WITH PERIODIC ACID. Methods for the determination of glycerol through oxidation with periodic acid differ mainly by the method of end titration.

Alkali Titration. The procedure was tested (43) on a series of samples including distilled glycerol from salt crudes, commercial trimethylene glycol containing about 1% glycerol, and crude polyglycerol. Analysis of the distilled samples was without difficulty. However, the trimethylene glycol and polyglycerol assays required judicious choice of sample size. The results of all samples agreed within about 0.4% of the actual content.

Procedure

Prepare a solution of periodic acid by dissolving 20 g of periodic acid in 1 liter of water and filtering if not clear. Store in a dark bottle. Pepare a 0.1250 N sodium hydroxide solution and standardize against potassium acid phthalate using phenolphthalein indicator. It is necessary to know the approximate glycerol concentration because the amount of excess periodic acid is critical. Guides to the choice of sample size may be found in Reference 43. If the glycerol content is 30–100%, weigh the sample into a 2-liter volumetric flask, dilute to volume with water, and pipet a 50-ml aliquot into a 600-ml beaker for analysis. For samples with 10–30% glycerol concentration, use a 500-ml volumetric flask and continue as before. For glycerol concentrations below 10%, weigh the sample directly and dilute with 50 ml of water.

Add 1 drop of methyl red indicator to the beaker, acidify with 0.2 N sulfuric acid, and neutralize with 0.05 N sodium hydroxide solution to the yellow color of the indicator. Add 50 ml of periodic acid solution with a pipet, mix, cover the beaker with a watch glass, and allow to stand for 1 hr at room temperature. Prepare a blank simultaneously containing 50 ml of water instead of the sample.

After diluting to 250 ml, stir and titrate with 0.1250 N sodium hydroxide solution, using a pH meter to determine the end point. Titrate the sample to pH 6.2 and the blank to pH 5.4. When the sample fraction being titrated contains more than 0.1 g of sodium chloride, a correction for the end point pH must be made.

When approaching the end point, add the base in 0.1 ml increments up to and beyond the equivalence point. Record the volume of titrant and pH when within 0.2 ml of the end point.

$$V_x = V_1 + (V_2 - V_1)\frac{\mathrm{pH}_x - \mathrm{pH}_1}{\mathrm{pH}_2 - \mathrm{pH}_1}$$

where V_x = volume of sodium hydroxide solution added up to the end point, in ml
pH_x = pH corresponding to V_x after salt correction
V_1 = volume of sodium hydroxide solution added before the end point, in ml
pH_1 = pH corresponding to V_1
V_2 = volume of sodium hydroxide solution added after the end point, in ml
pH_2 = pH corresponding to V_2

$$\text{Glycerol, wt \%} = \frac{(V_x - V_\mathrm{b})(N)(92.094)(100)}{(w)(1000)}$$

where V_x = volume of sodium hydroxide solution used in sample titration, in ml

V_b = volume of sodium hydroxide solution used for blank titration, in ml

N = normality of sodium hydroxide solution

w = sample weight, in g

Iodometric Titration. This procedure, also known as the Pohle and Mehlenbacher method (27), for the determination of glycerol and monoglycerides is based upon the amount of iodate produced from the reduction of periodic acid. After separating the glycerol and monoglycerides and subsequent reaction with periodic acid, the excess periodate is reduced to iodate and iodine, and the iodate from the polyol oxidation is reduced to iodine according to the following equations:

$$H_5IO_6 + 2\ HI \rightarrow HIO_3 + I_2 + 3\ H_2O$$
$$HIO_3 + 5\ HI \rightarrow 3\ I_2 + 3\ H_2O$$

The iodine produced in this series of reactions is determined by titration with standard thiosulfate solution and compared to the iodine produced in the absence of glycerol. The difference represents the amount of periodate which has been reduced to iodate by the glycerol.

Procedure

REAGENTS. *Periodic Acid Solution.* Dissolve 5.4 g of periodic acid in 100 ml of water and add 1900 ml of glacial acetic acid. Store in dark bottle.

Potassium Dichromate Solution. Dissolve 4.9035 g of potassium dichromate in water and dilute to 1 liter in a volumetric flask. The solution is 0.1 N.

Starch Solution. Add 1 liter of boiled water with rapid stirring to a uniform paste of 10 g of starch in cold water. Cool, add 1.24 g/liter of salicylic acid as a preservative if desired, and keep in a refrigerator for storage.

Sodium Thiosulfate Solution. Dissolve 24.8 g of sodium thiosulfate in water and dilute to 1 liter. Standardize the solution against the dichromate solution in the following way. Pipet 25 ml of the dichromate solution into a 400-ml beaker, add 5 ml of concentrated hydrochloric acid and 10 ml of a potassium iodide solution with a concentration of 1.5 g/100 ml. Mix and allow to stand for 5 min, then add 100 ml of water and titrate with the sodium thiosulfate solution under continuous stirring until the yellow color almost disappears. Then add 1–2 ml of starch solution and continue the titration until the blue color disappears.

SAMPLE PREPARATION. Samples in the flake form may be mixed without melting and a portion taken for testing. Solids not in a flake form are melted at a temperature not more than 10°C above melting point, mixed thoroughly, and a portion taken for analysis. If the sample is semisolid or liquid, liquify by heating to not more than 10°C above the melting point, mix thoroughly, and take a sample for analysis.

DETERMINATION OF MONOGLYCERIDE. Weigh duplicate samples of monoglyceride into 100-ml stoppered volumetric flasks, using the following as guide:

% monoglyceride	Approximate sample size, g
100	0.3
75	0.4
50	0.6
40	0.7
30	1.0
20	1.5
10	3.0
5	6.0
3 or less	10.0

Add 50 ml of chloroform and dissolve the sample with shaking. Warm if necessary to effect solution. Add 25 ml of water, stopper tightly, and shake vigorously for 30–60 sec. When the layers have separated, transfer the aqueous layer by siphon into a glass-stoppered 100-ml volumetric flask. Repeat the extraction, using in sequence 25, 25, and 20 ml of water. Add chloroform to the flask until the chloroform layer reaches the mark on the neck of the flask and transfer as much of the remaining aqueous phase as possible. Save the aqueous extracts for glycerol determination.

Pipet 50-ml volumes of periodic acid solution into each of three 500-ml beakers. Pipet 50 ml of the chloroform sample solution into the first 500-ml beaker, shake gently to mix, cover with a watch glass, and allow to stand for at least 30 min, but not more than 90 min. Add 50 ml of chloroform to the second beaker and 50 ml of water to the third beaker as solvent blanks for the chloroform.

Add 20 ml of the 1.5% potassium iodide solution, mix, and wait at least 1 but not more than 5 min. Add 100 ml of water and titrate with the sodium thiosulfate solution using mechanical stirring. After the disappearance of the brown color from the aqueous layer, add 2 ml of starch solution, and continue titrating until the disappearance of the brown color of the iodine from the chloroform layer and the disappearance of the blue color from the aqueous layer. Vigorous agitation is essential. Carry the blanks through the same procedure. When the titration of the sample is less than 0.8 of the blank, an insufficient excess of periodic acid was used. Repeat the analysis using smaller portions of the chloroform solution.

$$\text{Monoglyceride, wt \%} = \frac{(B - A)(N)(MW)(100)}{(w)(2)(1000)}$$

where A = volume of sodium thiosulfate solution used for sample titration, in ml
B = volume of sodium thiosulfate solution used for blank titration, in ml
N = normality of sodium thiosulfate solution
MW = g-mol wt of the monoglyceride (for glyceryl monostearate, MW = 358.54)
w = sample weight, in g

DETERMINATION OF FREE GLYCEROL. Add water to the combined aqueous extract until the volume is 100 ml. Analyze as prescribed for monoglyceride, starting with the addition of 50 ml of periodic acid to a 500-ml beaker.

$$\text{Glycerol, wt \%} = \frac{(B - A)(N)(MW)(100)}{(w)(4)(1000)}$$

where MW = g-mol wt of glycerol (= 92.09)

Sodium Arsenite Method. Kruty, Segur, and Miner (44) have proposed a modification of the above procedure. In their method, excess periodate is reduced by iodide in a neutral or slightly acidic medium, thereby avoiding the reduction of iodate to iodine. Consequently, the iodine produced is equivalent to the excess periodate and is titrated with standard arsenite solution. An additional modification avoided the necessity of physical separation of the solutions of glycerol and monoglyceride. Firstly, the sum of glycerols is determined in a methanol–chloroform solution of the sample. A second titration allows the determination of free glycerol without actual separation. Water is added to the chloroform solution to extract the glycerol. Periodic acid in water is added, resulting in oxidation of the glycerol in the aqueous phase, but without oxidation of the glyceride in the chloroform phase. Excess periodate is determined as before, except that the titration is now biphasic. The precision for glycerol determination is better than that obtained using the former procedure, whereas in the monoglyceride analysis, it is slightly poorer.

Procedure

REAGENTS. *Methanolic Periodic Acid Solution.* Dissolve 12.0 g of periodic acid in water and dilute to 100 ml. Dilute 5 ml of this solution to 100 ml with absolute methanol. The aqueous stock solution is stable, but the methanolic solution should not be kept for more than 5 days.

Aqueous Periodic Acid Solution. Dissolve 3.0 g of periodic acid in 500 ml of water and store in a glass-stoppered dark bottle.

Sodium Bicarbonate–Potassium Iodide Solution. Dissolve 75 g of potassium iodide and 50 g of sodium bicarbonate in 1 liter of solution and store in a dark bottle.

Starch Solution. See p. 515.

Sodium Arsenite Solution. Weigh 2.4728 g of primary standard arsenious oxide, moisten with water, and add 7.5 g of sodium hydroxide and 100 ml of water. Swirl until the arsenious oxide has dissolved and dilute to 250 ml with water. Saturate the solution with carbon dioxide converting all of the sodium hydroxide to sodium bicarbonate. This will require approximately 1 hr and is judged complete when the addition of 1 drop of phenolphthalein produces a faint pink or no color. Dilute to volume.

SAMPLE PREPARATION. Follow the procedure on p. 515. Weigh duplicate samples into 100-ml glass-stoppered volumetric flasks, add 40 ml of 1:95 v/v dimethylformamide–chloroform solution and swirl until the sample dissolves. Dilute to volume with dimethylformamide–chloroform solution. Pipet two 25-ml aliquots into 500-ml flasks for the glycerol plus monoglyceride and the glycerol assay. Prepare four blanks containing 25 ml of the dimethylformamide–chloroform solution.

GLYCEROL + MONOGLYCERIDE ASSAY. Pipet 25 ml of methanolic periodic acid solution into the sample beaker and into two of the blank beakers. Add a boiling chip to the sample beaker and heat on a hot plate until boiling commences. Do not heat the blanks. Remove the beaker from the hot plate and, after 30 min, add 200 ml of water to the sample and blanks. Allow to stand between 5 and 45 min; the blanks may be titrated immediately. Add 40 ml of the sodium bicarbonate–potassium iodide solution, wait for 1 min, and begin titrating with the standard sodium arsenite solution using mechanical agitation. As the end point is approached, add 2–3 ml of the starch indicator solution and continue titrating to the disappearance of the blue starch–iodine color.

FREE GLYCEROL ASSAY. Add 100 ml of water to the dimethylformamide–chloroform solution of the sample and to the remaining two blanks. Swirl the sample several times to extract the glycerol. Pipet 25 ml of the aqueous periodic acid solution into the sample and the blanks. Wait for 30 min with occasional stirring. Proceed as in the above determination, starting with the addition of 40 ml of the sodium bicarbonate–potassium iodide solution.

CALCULATIONS.

$$\text{Glycerol, wt \%} = \frac{(B_1 - A_1)(N)(MW_1)(100)}{(w)(4)(1000)}$$

$$\text{Monoglyceride, wt \%} = \frac{[(B_2 - A_2) - (B_1 - A_1)](N)(MW_2)(100)}{(w)(2)(1000)}$$

where A_1 = volume of sodium arsenite solution used for the titration of glycerol, in ml

A_2 = volume of sodium arsenite solution used for the titration of glycerol plus monoglyceride, in ml

B_1 = volume of sodium arsenite solution used for the titration of water blank, in ml

B_2 = volume of sodium arsenite solution used for the titration of methanol blank, in ml

N = normality of sodium arsenite solution

MW_1 = g-mol wt of glycerol (= 92.09)

MW_2 = g-mol wt of the monoglyceride (for glyceryl monostearate = 358.54)

w = sample weight in 25-ml aliquot, in g

OXIDATION WITH SODIUM PERIODATE.   In most of the officially accepted procedures, oxidation with sodium periodate has replaced periodic acid oxidation because of the advantages of higher reproducibility, utilization of a larger sample, and larger titration volume.   The Glycerine Analysis Committee of the American Oil Chemists' Society in 1950 recommended the withdrawal of the periodic acid procedure (45) and acceptance with a tentative status of the sodium periodate method.   The procedure, although still based upon a formic acid titration, provided for the elimination of excess periodate by the addition of ethylene glycol.   The titration is carried to specified pH values for the blank and sample by the use of a pH meter.

Erskine, et al. (46), proposed a minor modification to the method of the American Oil Chemists' Society (45).   After international testing of the proposed method and modifications, a uniform standard procedure evolved (47).   The AOCS Method Ea 6-51 as amended in 1959 (48) is essentially the same as the methods of the International Oil and Fats Commission, a division of the IUPAC, the Deutsche Gesellschaft für Fettwissenschaft, and Method BS.2621–5, 1964 of the British Standards Institute (2).

Procedure

REAGENTS.   *Sodium Hydroxide Solution.*   Prepare a solution about 0.1250 N and accurately standardize against potassium acid phthalate using phenolphthalein indicator.

Bromothymol Blue Indicator Solution.   Dissolve 0.1 g of dry bromothymol blue in 16 ml of 0.01 N sodium hydroxide solution by grinding in a mortar, then transfer to a 100-ml volumetric flask, and dilute to volume.

Starch Indicator Solution.   Prepare as directed earlier.

Ethylene Glycol–Water.   Mix 1 vol of ethylene glycol, bp 195–197°C, with 1 vol of water.

Standard Buffer Solution.   Dissolve 10.21 g of dried potassium acid phthalate in water and dilute to 1 liter.

Sodium Periodate Solution.   Dissolve 60 g of sodium periodate, $NaIO_4$, in water containing 120 ml of 0.1 N sulfuric acid, with a total volume of 1 liter.   Do not heat to dissolve the sodium periodate.   If the solution is not clear, filter through a sintered glass filter and store in a dark glass-stoppered bottle.   The acidity may change with time, so a blank must be run each day that analysis is made.   If the sodium periodate does not dissolve, it is not reagent quality.

Pipet 10 ml of the sodium periodate solution into a 250-ml volumetric flask, dilute to volume with water, and mix thoroughly.   Dissolve 0.5–0.6 g of pure glycerol in 50 ml of water and add 50 ml of the diluted sodium periodate solution with a pipet. Prepare a blank using 50 ml of water. Allow to stand for 30 min, then add 5 ml of concentrated hydrochloric acid, 10 ml of a 15% potassium iodide solution, and rotate to mix. After 5 min, add 100 ml of water. Titrate with standardized 0.1 N sodium thiosulfate solution, shaking continuously until the yellow color has almost disappeared. Add 1–2 ml of the starch indicator solution and continue titration, adding the thiosulfate slowly until the blue color has just disappeared. The sodium periodate solution is satisfactory when the volume of the thiosulfate solution used for the titration of the glycerol-containing solution divided by the volume of the thiosulfate solution used for the blank titration is between 0.750 and 0.765.

SAMPLE PREPARATION. Samples containing separated salt, sediment, or suspended matter must be warmed and thoroughly mixed to ensure uniform distribution. Some sediment tends to cling to the bottom of the container and the inherent viscosity of glycerol retards rapid dispersion.

DETERMINATION. Perform all weighings of the sample accurately and rapidly. This is conveniently done by discharging the sample from a weighing pipet into a 600-ml beaker when the sample contains more than 20% glycerol. When the sample contains less than 20% glycerol, it may be weighed directly into a tared dish and then washed into the 600-ml beaker with water. When the sample volume is less than 50 ml, dilute to 50 ml with water. For the most accurate results, the sample analyzed must contain between 0.32 and 0.50 g of glycerol. Approximate weights of samples to be taken for analyses are given in Table 8. When the glycerol content is unknown, make a single preliminary test using the amount specified for 100% glycerol. From the results, determine the proper sample weight.

Table 8. Weight of Sample to be Taken for the Determination of the Glycerol Content

% glycerol in the product to be analyzed	Sample weight, g
100 or less	0.40–0.53
90 or less	0.45–0.55
80 or less	0.50–0.60
70 or less	0.55–0.75
60 or less	0.65–0.85
50 or less	0.80–1.00
40 or less	0.90–1.30
30 or less	1.20–1.80
20 or less	1.80–2.60
10 or less	4.00–5.00
5 or less	7.0–11.0
2.5 or less	16.0–20.0
1.0 or less	40.0
0.5 or less	80.0

Add 5 to 6 drops of bromothymol blue indicator to the sample in the 600-ml beaker and acidify with 0.2 N sulfuric acid to a definite green or greenish yellow color. Neutralize with 0.05 N sodium hydroxide solution to the indicator end point, a blue color free of green. Add the base dropwise when approaching the rapid green-to-blue transition. When the color of the solution interferes with the color change of the indicator use a pH meter and adjust to pH 8.1 ± 0.1.

Prepare a blank containing 50 ml of water but no glycerol and analyze simultaneously with the sample in an identical manner, using the indicator to adjust the pH before adding the sodium periodate solution.

Add 50 ml of the sodium periodate solution with a pipet, swirl gently to mix, cover with a watch glass, and allow to stand for 30 min in the dark or away from strong light. If the room temperature exceeds 35°C, both the reagent and sample solution must be cooled to 35°C or less before mixing, and must be maintained below this temperature until titration.

At the end of this period, add 10 ml of the 1:1 ethylene glycol–water mixture and allow to stand 20 min.

Dilute to approximately 300 ml and titrate with the 0.125 N sodium hydroxide solution, using a pH meter to determine the end point at pH 6.5 ± 0.1 for the blank and 8.1 ± 0.1 for the sample. When approaching the end point, add the alkali a drop at a time. The volume of the alkali used for blank titration must not exceed 4.5 ml.

$$\text{Glycerol, wt \%} = \frac{(A - B)(N)(MW)(100)}{(w)(1000)}$$

where A = volume of sodium hydroxide solution used for sample titration, in ml
B = volume of sodium hydroxide solution used for blank titration, in ml
N = normality of sodium hydroxide solution
MW = g-mol wt of glycerol (= 92.09)
w = sample weight, in g

If the sample contains an appreciable amount of buffering material, the pH must be adjusted with a pH meter to the end point to which the sample will be subsequently titrated. In some instances, buffering action may be sufficiently great to prevent good accuracy.

Cork stoppers must not be used to close any flask used in this determination.

The presence of a sufficient excess of sodium periodate in a given test can be confirmed as follows: Test the sample using $\frac{3}{4}$ of the sample weight used in the original test. If analysis of the smaller size sample agrees with that of the larger sample, there is a sufficient excess of sodium periodate in both cases. If the analysis of the smaller sample shows a higher glycerol content greater than the experimental error, there was not a sufficient excess of sodium periodate for the larger sample. When the glycerol content is unknown, weigh the amount specified for 100% glycerol, and from the results of this test, select the proper size sample, taking into account the fact that the results will tend to be high because the sample weighed is smaller than that required for an accurate analysis.

If the crude glycerol being analyzed contains more than 0.1% carbonate, expressed in terms of Na_2O, add 0.2 N H_2SO_4 until the pH is 3.0 or less, heat to boiling, and cool to room temperature. Then neutralize with 0.05 N sodium hydroxide as before, using bromothymol blue indicator, and continue the analysis.

Crutchfield and Sloviter (51) have adapted the sodium periodate oxidation to the determination of glycerol in blood–glycerol mixtures. Naturally occurring glucose interferes with the determination but can be reduced by heating the sample in aqueous alkali. By titration before and after treatment of the glucose with base, a moderately precise value of glycerol is obtained, and a less precise value of glucose is obtained.

The glycerol content of pharmaceutical preparations, such as suppositories and ointments, has been determined using potassium periodate oxidation by Ludwicki and Sobiczewska (49). After extraction of glycerol by water and periodate oxidation, the resulting formic acid is titrated with standard 0.01 N sodium hydroxide solution.

Oxidation With Vanadium. West and Skoog (50) have shown that quinquivalent vanadium stoichiometrically oxidizes glycerol to formic acid, utilizing eight equivalents of vanadium. A procedure for the analysis of dilute glycerol solutions uses an excess of vanadium and back-titration of the excess with ferrous ammonium sulfate with N-phenylanthranilic acid as a visual indicator. Secondary oxidation of the formic acid by excess vanadium occurs in strong acid media, but this can be avoided by careful control of acidity. Oxidation is performed at 100°C for 1 hr in sulfuric acid solution containing approximately 25 ml of sulfuric acid in 125 ml of solution. The results compared favorably with those obtained by cerate or dichromate oxidation in the sample size range of 17–31 mg of glycerol. Low results occur when the glycerol content is greater than 31 mg; high results occur when glycerol is less than 17 mg.

DETERMINATION OF IMPURITIES

Due to its mostly natural origin, a large number of impurities may be present in glycerol. Methods for their determination are outlined below.

Ash and Residue

There are a number of definitions and specifications related to these basic terms. The official AOCS method Ea 2-38 (51) prescribes a method to determine % ash by charring in a muffle furnace at 500–550°C. The ACS specification defines residue after ignition at 800°C, whereas the USP test prescribes burning in an open shallow porcelain dish, moistening the residue with sulfuric acid, and igniting to constant weight. The ASTM sulfate test (52) is equivalent to the ACS procedure. AOCS method Ea 3-58 (53) specifies separately total residue and organic residue at 175°C.

The residue from the ash determination, according to AOCS method Ea 2-38, is used to determine total alkalinity (p. 523).

The pertinent procedures are given below.

Procedures

ASH (AOCS METHOD Ea 2-38). Weigh a 2–5 g sample into a tared platinum dish which has been ignited and cooled in a desiccator. Warm carefully over the low flame of an Argand burner to drive off the water. If spattering occurs, cover the sample with a cone-shaped piece of filter paper. Drive off the volatile material, ignite the fumes, and allow burning to continue without the application of heat. Char in a muffle furnace controlled at a temperature between 500 and 550°C, never exceeding a dull red heat. When the sample is sufficiently charred, lixiviate with 15 ml of hot water and filter through ashless filter paper. Wash the dish twice with 10-ml portions of water. Return the filter paper and residue to the platinum dish and ignite at a dull red heat until all the carbonaceous matter is consumed. Return the filtrate and washings to the cooled dish and evaporate to dryness on a hot water bath. Dry to constant weight either over an Argand burner, in an air oven at 130°C, or in a muffle furnace below a dull, red heat. Cool to room temperature in a desiccator and weigh. Express residue as % ash.

RESIDUE ON IGNITION. *ACS Method.* Heat 20 g of glycerol sample in a tared open dish, ignite the vapors, and when the glycerol has been entirely consumed, ignite at 800°C for 15 min.

USP Method. Heat 50 g of sample in an open shallow 100-ml porcelain dish until it ignites, and allow it to burn without further application of heat in a draft-free location. Cool, moisten the residue with 0.5 ml of sulfuric acid, and ignite to constant weight.

TOTAL AND ORGANIC RESIDUE (AOCS METHOD Ea 3-58) (53). To prevent the loss of organic acids, adjust the alkalinity to a predetermined value in the following way.   Weigh 10 g of sample into a 100-ml volumetric flask and dilute with a few ml of water.   From the acidity or alkalinity determined separately (see pp. 523–525) calculate the volume of N hydrochloric acid or sodium carbonate solution which has to be added to the sample in the following way:

In case of acidic solution:

$$\text{Sodium carbonate solution, ml} = \frac{\% \text{ acidity as } Na_2O}{0.31} + 0.65$$

In case of basic solution:

(a) if less than 0.2% Na_2O

$$\text{Sodium carbonate solution, ml} = \frac{0.20 - \% Na_2O}{0.31}$$

(b) if more than 0.2% Na_2O

$$\text{Hydrochloric acid, ml} = \frac{\% Na_2O - 0.20}{0.31}$$

In the last two equations, % Na_2O is equal to the sum of % free caustic alkalinity and % carbonate alkalinity.

After the addition of the calculated volume of hydrochloric acid or sodium carbonate solution, dilute to volume with water and transfer a 10-ml aliquot into a weighed glass dish.   After heating for 4 hr at 175°C in a forced draft oven, remove from the oven, cool to room temperature in a desiccator, and weigh.

Dissolve the residue in water and transfer to a 400-ml beaker with about 50 ml of water.   Pipet 50 ml of periodic acid solution (p. 515) into the beaker containing the sample.   Determine the remaining glycerol using the AOCS method Ca 14-56 (54) or by the equivalent method of Pohle and Mehlenbacher.

For the calculation of % total residue, use one of the following equations:

1. If the sample is acidic:

$$\% \text{ residue} = 100[(A - 0.0022B) - 0.0034]$$

2. If the sample is alkaline, less than 0.2% Na_2O:

$$\% \text{ residue} = 100(A - 0.0053C)$$

3. If the sample is alkaline, greater than 0.2% Na_2O:

(a) Carbonate is less than 0.2% Na_2O, the remainder being caustic:

$$\% \text{ residue} = 100(A - 0.00018D)$$

(b) All alkalinity is due to carbonate:

$$\% \text{ residue} = 100(A - 0.0005D)$$

(c) Carbonate alkalinity is greater than 0.2% Na_2O, and caustic alkalinity is present:

$$\% \text{ residue} = 100[A - (0.0058E + 0.0016)F]$$

where A = weight of residue minus weight of remaining glycerol, G, both in g

B = volume of sodium carbonate added to the acidic sample, not including the term 0.65, in ml

C = volume of sodium carbonate added to the alkaline sample when alkalinity is less than 0.2% Na_2O, in ml

D = volume of hydrochloric acid added to alkaline sample, in ml

E = % of caustic alkalinity as Na_2O

F = % carbonate alkalinity as Na_2O minus 0.20

G = weight of glycerol in residue, in g

For the calculation of *nonvolatile organic residue at 175°C* subtract % ash from % total residue.

Acidity and Alkalinity

The ACS specifications (7) only require testing for neutrality; a 10% solution of the glycerol sample should not affect the color of either red or blue litmus paper in 1 min. The ASTM specifications (52) require the determination of the acid value of the sample.

Procedure

To 150 ml of water in a 250-ml Erlenmeyer flask, add 1.0 ml of a 1% phenolphthalein indicator solution, and neutralize the water to a faint pink color with 0.1 N potassium hydroxide solution. Transfer 50 ml of the neutralized water to another 250-ml Erlenmeyer flask into which has been previously weighed a 50 ± 0.1 g sample of glycerol; the remaining 100 ml of the neutralized water serves as the blank. Titrate the sample solution with 0.1 N potassium hydroxide solution to the phenolphthalein end point color of the blank.

$$\text{Acid value} = \frac{(V)(N)(56.1)}{w}$$

where V = volume of potassium hydroxide solution used for titration, in ml

N = normality of the potassium hydroxide solution

w = sample weight, in g

The official AOCS method Ea 2-38 (51) distinguishes between free or caustic alkalinity (sodium hydroxide), carbonate alkalinity (sodium carbonate or bicarbonate), and alkalinity combined with or equivalent to organic acids or esters.

The acidity of glycerin is expressed in terms of the sodium oxide, Na_2O, equivalent to the amount of free acids present. Organic acids may be in the free form or esterified with the glycerol. In the latter form they cannot be determined by direct titration.

Procedures

TOTAL ALKALINITY. Carry out ashing of a 2–5 g sample as discussed on p. 521. Dissolve the ash in about 25 ml of hot water. Cool to room temperature, add 2 or 3 drops of methyl orange indicator solution, and titrate to a faintly acidic end point with 0.25 N sulfuric acid. Save this solution for sodium chloride determination if necessary (see p. 525).

$$\% \text{ total alkalinity} = \frac{(V)(N)(3.1)}{w}$$

where V = volume of sulfuric acid used for titration, in ml

N = normality of sulfuric acid

w = sample weight, in g

FREE CAUSTIC ALKALINITY OR FREE ACIDITY. For a preliminary test, dissolve about 10 g of sample in 100 ml of water and add 1 ml of phenolphthalein indicator solution. Observe the color to determine whether the solution is acidic or alkaline.

If the solution is *alkaline*, weigh a 20-g sample into a 100-ml volumetric flask, add 50 ml of freshly boiled and cooled water and an excess, usually not more than 25 ml, of neutral 10% barium chloride solution. Dilute to volume and allow to stand until the precipitate settles.

Pipet 50 ml of the supernatant liquid into a 250-ml Erlenmeyer flask, add 1 ml of phenolphthalein indicator solution, and titrate to the disappearance of the pink color with 0.25 N hydrochloric acid. The end point must not be exceeded as back titration is not permissable.

If the original sample is *acidic*, weigh 10 g of the sample into a 250-ml Erlenmeyer flask, add 50 ml of freshly boiled and cooled water, 1 ml of phenolphthalein indicator solution, and titrate to the first pink tinge with 0.25 N sodium hydroxide solution.

$$\% \text{ free caustic alkalinity} = \frac{(V_1)(N_1)(3.1)}{(w)(0.5)}$$

$$\% \text{ free acidity} = \frac{(V_2)(N_2)(3.1)}{w}$$

where V_1 = volume of hydrochloric acid used for titration, in ml
N_1 = normality of hydrochloric acid solution
V_2 = volume of sodium hydroxide solution used for titration, in ml
N_2 = normality of sodium hydroxide solution
w = sample weight, in g

ALKALINITY COMBINED WITH/OR EQUIVALENT TO ORGANIC ACIDS AND ESTERS. If the sample is *alkaline*, weigh 10 g of the sample into a standard taper 250-ml Erlenmeyer flask and add 50 ml of water and sufficient 0.25 N sulfuric acid to exactly neutralize the total alkalinity as previously determined. Attach a reflux condenser and boil gently for 15–20 min. Wash the interior condenser tube with freshly boiled water, add 1 ml of phenolphthalein indicator solution, and titrate to the first pink color with 0.25 N sodium hydroxide solution.

$$\% \text{ alkalinity plus organic acids} = \frac{(V)(N)(3.1)}{w}$$

where V = volume of sodium hydroxide solution used for titration, in ml
N = normality of sodium hydroxide solution
w = sample weight, in g

If the sample is *acidic*, determine the alkaline equivalent to organic acids and esters as follows. Weigh a 10-g sample into a standard taper 250-ml Erlenmeyer flask, and add 50 ml of freshly boiled water and 20.0 ml of 0.25 N sodium hydroxide solution. Attach a reflux condenser and boil gently for 30 min. Prepare a blank using 50 ml of water and 20.0 ml of sodium hydroxide. Wash down the interior tube of the condenser with freshly boiled water, cool sufficiently to handle, add 1 ml of phenolphthalein indicator solution, and immediately titrate the blank and sample to the disappearance of the pink color with 0.25 N hydrochloric acid. The end point must not be exceeded as back titration is not permissible.

$$\% \text{ alkalinity equivalent to organic acids and esters} = \frac{(B - A)(N)(3.1)}{w}$$

where A = volume of hydrochloric acid used for sample titration, in ml

B = volume of hydrochloric acid used for blank titration, in ml

N = normality of hydrochloric acid

w = sample weight, in g

CARBONATE ALKALINITY. If the sample is alkaline, calculate carbonate alkalinity as follows:

$$\% \text{ carbonate alkalinity} = A - (B + C)$$

where A = % total alkalinity

B = % alkalinity plus organic acids

C = % free caustic alkalinity

Chloride

In the AOCS procedure, the amount of sodium chloride which may be present is determined from the titrated solution of total alkalinity determination. The ACS specifications (7) require a comparison of the turbidity of a sample solution with that of a standard chloride solution.

Procedures

AOCS METHOD. Wash the titrated solution saved from the total alkalinity determination from the platinum dish into a 100-ml volumetric flask with water and dilute to volume. Pipet a 50-ml aliquot into a 250 ml-Erlenmeyer flask, add a few drops of phenolphthalein indicator solution, and adjust to neutrality with 0.25 N sodium hydroxide solution and sulfuric acid, leaving the solution slightly acidic. Add 1 ml of a 10 wt % potassium chromate solution and titrate to the first permanent reddish tinge with 0.1 N silver nitrate solution.

$$\text{Sodium chloride, wt } \% = \frac{(V)(N)(58.45)(100)}{(0.5)(w)(1000)}$$

where V = volume of silver nitrate solution, in ml

N = normality of silver nitrate solution

w = sample weight, in g

ACS METHOD. Dissolve 2 g of sample in 20 ml of water. Add 1 ml of concentrated nitric acid and 1 ml of a silver nitrate solution containing 17 mg of $AgNO_3$. The turbidity should not exceed that produced by 0.01 mg of chloride ion in an equal volume of solution containing the same reagents.

Sulfate

Sulfate requirements are specified by the ACS (7) and USP (8).

Procedures

ACS TEST. Dilute a 8-ml (10-g) sample with 25 ml of water, add 1 ml of 0.1 N hydrochloric acid and 2 ml of a 12% w/v solution of barium chloride dihydrate. Any turbidity should not exceed that produced by 0.01 mg of sulfate in an equal volume of solution containing the same quantities of reagents as used in the test, the comparison being made after the sample and the standard have stood for 20 min.

USP TEST. Take a 10-g sample and dilute with water to 40 ml. Make the solution acidic to litmus paper with hydrochloric acid. Add 1 ml of 24:76 hydrochloric acid, 3 ml of the barium chloride solution, dilute to 50 ml, and mix well. Any turbidity should not exceed that produced by 0.2 ml of 0.02 N sulfuric acid in an equal volume of solution containing the same quantity of reagents as used in the test, the comparison being made after the sample and the standard have stood for 10 min.

Arsenic and Heavy Metals

According to USP, arsenic present in the sample is transformed to arsine, AsH_3, by the reaction of $HAsO_2^-$ with zinc and sulfuric acid. The gaseous arsine reacts with mercuric bromide test paper, forming an arsenide of mercury and producing a detectable brown stain. For details see Vol. 6, pp. 246–250.

Heavy metals are compared by comparing a sample solution treated with hydrogen sulfide and a standard lead solution treated in the same matter. For details, see Vol. 8, p. 363.

Water

Water is frequently the major impurity in glycerins, especially crude glycerins. Normally, water is determined by the Karl Fischer titration following the method Ea 8-58 of the American Oil Chemists' Society (55).

Procedure

REAGENTS. *Methanolic Iodine.* Dissolve 60 g of reagent grade iodine in 1000 ml of methanol, protecting the solution from moisture.

Pyridine–Methanol–Sulfur Dioxide Solution. Add 900 ml of anhydrous pyridine and 900 ml of anhydrous methanol to a 3-liter Erlenmeyer flask, stopper, and cool at about 4°C. On a balance, add 180 g of sulfur dioxide at a fairly rapid rate through a tube beneath the surface of the solution. If the solution becomes hot, interrupt the addition of sulfur dioxide, close the flask with a stopper fitted with a drying tube, and cool the flask. When the addition is completed, stopper the flask with a drying tube attached.

Standardization of Reagent. Dispense 25 ml of the pyridine–methanol–sulfur dioxide reagent solution into a flask and attach to the delivery tube of a buret filled with the methanolic iodine solution. Titrate until the first appearance of a red color that persists after 10 sec.

Add 1 drop of water from a weighed weighing bottle to the solution, observing the weight of water transferred. Titrate as before to the persistence of red color. Calculate a water factor, F, for the iodine methanol solution as follows:

$$F = \text{g of water/ml of titrant}$$

Use the average of two determinations that agree within 0.0001. If the factors do not agree within this value, repeat the calibration.

DETERMINATION. Measure from a buret 25 ml of the pyridine–methanol–sulfur dioxide solution into a flask. Attach the flask to the stopper on the delivery tube of a buret filled with the methanolic iodine solution. With stirring, preferably mechanical, titrate to the first appearance of red color that persists after 10 sec of stirring.

Remove the flask from the buret and weigh into the flask a sample of such size that 10–40 ml of titrant will be required. Use a 10-g sample for 0–1.5% moisture, a 5-g sample for 1.5–3% moisture, and a 2-g sample of 3–8% moisture.

Titrate the sample slowly with stirring, adding small increments near the end point. Titrate to the first appearance of a red color, which persists for 5 min when the flask is stoppered immediately after reading the end point.

$$\% \text{ moisture} = \frac{(V)(F)(100)}{w}$$

where V = volume of reagent required for sample titration, in ml

F = water factor, g of water equivalent to 1 ml of reagent

w = sample weight, in g

Alternately, the near infrared method of Chapman and Nancy (56) may be employed. A combination band absorption of water occurs at 1.93 μm and is separated from the glycerol band absorbing at 2.1 μm. The spectra are measured in a glass cell, 1.0 mm path length, against a reference solution of glycerol containing a trace of water. The procedure involves determination of the absorbance at 1.92 μm and establishment of % water from a calibration curve. Within the range of 1–20% water in glycerol, a standard deviation of ±0.06% was reported. Crude, discolored glycerols generally gave high results.

Organic Impurities

Total Organic Impurities. The total organic impurities present in glycerol are known as "matter(organic)non-glycerol" and abbreviated as MONG. This is calculated by subtracting from 100 the sum of the % glycerol, % water, and % ash (57). MONG gives an indication of organic impurities that includes materials that are volatile at 160°C. This is intended to supersede the nonvolatile organic residue which does not account for important impurities volatile at 160°C.

Propane-1,3-diol. Murray and Williams (58) have devised a simple gas chromatographic procedure for the determination of propane-1,3-diol (trimethylene glycol) in glycerol. An accuracy of ±10% on samples containing 0.2–2.5% propane-1,3-diol was obtained using ethylene glycol as an internal standard. The following conditions were recommended:

column	28 cm × 2 mm ID glass, packed
column packing	25 wt % Reoplex 400 polyester on Embacel kieselguhr 60/100 mesh
temperature of	
injection port	175°C
column	150°C
carrier gas and flow rate	nitrogen, 10 ml/min
detector	flame ionization

Fatty Acid Esters. According to the ACS specifications (7), a limit test must be performed. The specified difference between the volumes of acid used for the titration of the blank and sample must be 2.3 ml or less; this corresponds to 0.05% esters expressed as butyric acid esters.

Procedure

To a 50-g sample in a 250-ml Erlenmeyer flask add 50 ml of hot freshly boiled water. Add 10.0 ml of 0.1 N sodium hydroxide solution, cover with a loosely fitting pear-shaped bulb, and digest on a steam bath for 45 min. Cool and titrate excess alkali with 0.1 N hydrochloric acid, using 0.15 ml of bromothymol, blue indicator solution, and titrating to the bluish-green end point. Analyze a blank solution in the same manner.

Miscellaneous Tests

Acrolein, Glucose, and Ammonia. The USP (8) test involves the addition of 6.25 g of glycerol to 5 ml of 0.65 wt/vol % potassium hydroxide solution and heating the solution at 60°C for 5 min. The solution should neither turn yellow nor emit an odor of ammonia.

Silver Reducing Substances. The ACS specification prescribes a limit test.

Table 9. Relationship Between Specific Gravity and Glycerol Concentration of Glycerol–Water Mixtures

Glycerol, wt %	Apparent specific gravity				True specific gravity			
	15/15°C	15.5/15.5°C	20/20°C	25/25°C	15/15°C	15.5/15.5°C	20/20°C	25/25°C
100	1.26557	1.26532	1.26362	1.26201	1.26526	1.26501	1.26331	1.26170
99	1.26300	1.26275	1.26105	1.25945	1.26270	1.26245	1.26075	1.25910
98	1.26045	1.26020	1.25845	1.25685	1.26010	1.25985	1.25815	1.25655
97	1.25785	1.25760	1.25585	1.25425	1.25755	1.25730	1.25555	1.25395
96	1.25525	1.25500	1.25330	1.25165	1.25495	1.25470	1.25300	1.25140
95	1.25270	1.25245	1.25075	1.24910	1.25240	1.25215	1.25045	1.24880
94	1.25005	1.24980	1.24810	1.24645	1.24975	1.24950	1.24780	1.24615
93	1.24740	1.24715	1.24545	1.24380	1.24710	1.24685	1.24515	1.24350
92	1.24475	1.24450	1.24280	1.24115	1.24445	1.24420	1.24250	1.24085
91	1.24210	1.24185	1.24020	1.23850	1.24185	1.24155	1.23985	1.23825
90	1.23950	1.23920	1.23755	1.23585	1.23920	1.23895	1.23725	1.23500
89	1.23680	1.23655	1.23490	1.23320	1.23655	1.23625	1.23460	1.23295
88	1.23415	1.23390	1.23220	1.23055	1.23390	1.23360	1.23195	1.23025
87	1.23150	1.23120	1.22955	1.22790	1.23125	1.23095	1.22930	1.22760
86	1.22885	1.22855	1.22690	1.22520	1.22860	1.22830	1.22660	1.22495
85	1.22620	1.22590	1.22420	1.22255	1.22595	1.22565	1.22395	1.22230
84	1.22355	1.22325	1.22155	1.21990	1.22330	1.22300	1.22130	1.21965
83	1.22090	1.22055	1.21890	1.21720	1.22060	1.22030	1.21865	1.21695
82	1.21820	1.21790	1.21620	1.21455	1.21795	1.21765	1.21595	1.21430
81	1.21555	1.21525	1.21355	1.21190	1.21530	1.21500	1.21330	1.21165
80	1.21290	1.21260	1.21090	1.20925	1.21265	1.21235	1.21065	1.20900
79	1.21015	1.20985	1.20815	1.20655				
78	1.20740	1.20710	1.20540	1.20380				
77	1.20465	1.20440	1.20270	1.20110				
76	1.20190	1.20165	1.19995	1.19840				
75	1.19915	1.19890	1.19720	1.19565	1.19890	1.19865	1.19700	1.19540
74	1.19640	1.19615	1.19450	1.19295				
73	1.19365	1.19340	1.19175	1.19025				
72	1.19090	1.19070	1.18900	1.18755				
71	1.18815	1.18795	1.18630	1.18480				
70	1.18540	1.18520	1.18355	1.18210	1.18515	1.18495	1.18330	1.18185
69	1.18260	1.18240	1.18080	1.17935				
68	1.17985	1.17965	1.17805	1.17660				
67	1.17705	1.17685	1.17530	1.17385				
66	1.17430	1.17410	1.17255	1.17110				
65	1.17155	1.17130	1.16980	1.16835	1.17135	1.17110	1.16960	1.16815
64	1.16875	1.16855	1.16705	1.16560				
63	1.16600	1.16575	1.16430	1.16285				
62	1.16320	1.16300	1.16155	1.16010				
61	1.16045	1.16020	1.15875	1.15735				
60	1.15770	1.15745	1.15605	1.15460	1.15750	1.15725	1.15585	1.15445
59	1.15490	1.15465	1.15325	1.15185				
58	1.15210	1.15190	1.15050	1.14915				
57	1.14935	1.14910	1.14775	1.14640				
56	1.14655	1.14635	1.14500	1.14365				
55	1.14375	1.14355	1.14220	1.14090	1.14360	1.14340	1.14205	1.14075
54	1.14100	1.14080	1.13945	1.13815				
53	1.13820	1.13800	1.13670	1.13540				
52	1.13540	1.13525	1.13395	1.13265				
51	1.13265	1.13245	1.13120	1.12995				

Table 9 (*continued*)

Glycerol, wt %	Apparent specific gravity				True specific gravity			
	15/15°C	15.5/15.5°C	20/20°C	25/25°C	15/15°C	15.5/15.5°C	20/20°C	25/25°C
50	1.12985	1.12970	1.12845	1.12720	1.12970	1.12955	1.12830	1.12705
49	1.12710	1.12695	1.12570	1.12450				
48	1.12440	1.12425	1.12300	1.12185				
47	1.12165	1.12150	1.12030	1.11915				
46	1.11890	1.11880	1.11760	1.11650				
45	1.11620	1.11605	1.11490	1.11380	1.11605	1.11595	1.11475	1.11365
44	1.11345	1.11335	1.11220	1.11115				
43	1.11075	1.11060	1.10950	1.10845				
42	1.10800	1.10790	1.10680	1.10575				
41	1.10525	1.10515	1.10410	1.10310				
40	1.10255	1.10245	1.10135	1.10040	1.10240	1.10235	1.10125	1.10030
39	1.09985	1.09975	1.09870	1.09775				
38	1.09715	1.09705	1.09605	1.09510				
37	1.09445	1.09435	1.09335	1.09245				
36	1.09175	1.09165	1.09070	1.08980				
35	1.08905	1.08895	1.08805	1.08715	1.08895	1.08885	1.08790	1.08705
34	1.08635	1.08625	1.08535	1.08455				
33	1.08365	1.08355	1.08270	1.08190				
32	1.08100	1.08085	1.08005	1.07925				
31	1.07830	1.07815	1.07735	1.07660				
30	1.07560	1.07545	1.07470	1.07395	1.07550	1.07535	1.07460	1.07385
29	1.07295	1.07285	1.07210	1.07135				
28	1.07035	1.07025	1.06950	1.06880				
27	1.06770	1.06760	1.06690	1.06625				
26	1.06510	1.06500	1.06435	1.06370				
25	1.06250	1.06240	1.06175	1.06115	1.06240	1.06230	1.06165	1.06110
24	1.05985	1.05980	1.05915	1.05860				
23	1.05725	1.05715	1.05655	1.05605				
22	1.05460	1.05455	1.05400	1.05350				
21	1.05200	1.05195	1.05140	1.05095				
20	1.04935	1.04935	1.04880	1.04840	1.04930	1.04925	1.04875	1.04830
19	1.04685	1.04680	1.04630	1.04590				
18	1.04435	1.04430	1.04380	1.04345				
17	1.04180	1.04180	1.04135	1.04100				
16	1.03930	1.03925	1.03885	1.03850				
15	1.03675	1.03675	1.03635	1.03605	1.03670	1.03670	1.03630	1.03600
14	1.03425	1.03420	1.03390	1.03360				
13	1.03175	1.03170	1.03140	1.03110				
12	1.02920	1.02920	1.02890	1.02865				
11	1.02670	1.02665	1.02640	1.02620				
10	1.02415	1.02415	1.02395	1.02370	1.02415	1.02410	1.02390	1.02370
9	1.02175	1.02175	1.02155	1.02135				
8	1.01935	1.01930	1.01915	1.01900				
7	1.01690	1.01690	1.01675	1.01660				
6	1.01450	1.01450	1.01435	1.01425				
5	1.01210	1.01205	1.01195	1.01185	1.01205	1.01205	1.01195	1.01185
4	1.00965	1.00965	1.00955	1.00950				
3	1.00725	1.00725	1.00720	1.00710				
2	1.00485	1.00485	1.00480	1.00475				
1	1.00240	1.00240	1.00240	1.00235				

Procedure

Dilute 5 ml (6 g) of sample with 2.5 ml of water, add 2.5 ml of a 10% ammonium hydroxide solution, and heat to 60°C. Add 0.5 ml of a silver nitrate solution with a concentration of 17 mg/ml and allow to stand at 60°C for 5 min, protected from light. Any color should not exceed that produced by 2.5 ml of a standard solution containing 0.02 mg of lead, mixed with 2.5 ml of 10% ammonium hydroxide solution and 5 ml of saturated hydrogen sulfide solution.

Substances Darkened by Sulfuric Acid. Both the ACS and USP methods are limit tests. The USP refers to this group as readily carbonizable substances.

Procedures

ACS METHOD. *Ferric Chloride Color Solution.* In a 1-liter volumetric flask, dissolve 45.0 g of ferric chloride hexahydrate in a mixture of 25 ml of concentrated hydrochloric acid and excess of water. Dilute to volume with water.

Cobaltous Chloride Color Solution. In a 1-liter volumetric flask dissolve 59.5 g of cobaltous chloride hexahydrate in the same hydrochloric acid–water mixture as specified above.

Shake 5 ml (6.25 g) of glycerol with 5 ml of 94.5–95.5% sulfuric acid in a glass-stoppered 25-ml cylinder for 1 min and allow the liquid to stand 1 hr. The liquid should not be darker than a standard prepared by mixing 0.4 ml of the cobaltous chloride solution, 3.0 ml of the ferric chloride solution, and 6.6 ml of water.

USP METHOD. Rinse a glass-stoppered 25-ml cylinder with 94.5–95.5% sulfuric acid and allow to drain for 10 min. Add 6.25 g of glycerol and 5 ml of sulfuric acid, shake vigorously for 1 min and allow to stand for 1 hr. The mixture should not be darker than a standard prepared by mixing 0.3 ml of cobaltous chloride solution, 1.2 ml of ferric chloride solution, and 3.5 ml of water.

PHYSICAL MEASUREMENTS

Refractive Index

Refractive index measurement can be used for the determination of the glycerol content of glycerol–water mixtures. Hoyt (59) published extensive tables to convert refractive index to % glycerol. However, the results are less accurate than those obtained from specific gravity measurements.

Specific Gravity

The assay of glycerol solutions containing only water can be done conveniently by the measurement of apparent specific gravity. Procedures for this measurement are given in AOCS method Ea 7–50 (60), by ASTM (6), and USP (8); all three methods are very similar. For details see DENSITY AND SPECIFIC GRAVITY, Vol. 1, pp. 546–560.

Tables for the conversion of the measured apparent specific gravity to glycerol concentration at various temperatures have been published by Bosart and Snoddy (61); these are reproduced here in Table 9.

Color

According to the specifications of ACS (7) and USP (8), the color is observed by viewing the sample downwards in 50-ml Nessler tubes against a white surface. In the USP test, the color should not be darker than the standard prepared by diluting 0.4 ml of a ferric chloride solution (45 g of $FeCl_3.6H_2O$ dissolved in 1 liter of 1:40 hydrochloric acid) to 50 ml in a matching Nessler tube. The ACS method uses as the standard 0.3 ml of the ferric chloride solution diluted to 50 ml. The ASTM comparison (62) is made against Gardner-1933 standards (see Color designation and specification, Vol. 1, pp. 315–351). According to AOCS method Ea 9-65 (63), comparison is made in 100-ml tall-form Nessler APHA tubes against permanent APHA color discs.

Bibliography

General References

1. J. Kern, "Glycerol," in A. Standen, ed., *Kirk-Othmer Encyclopedia of Chemical Technology*, Vol. 10, 2nd ed., Interscience Publishers, a division of John Wiley & Sons, Inc., New York, 1963, pp. 619–631.
2. A. A. Newman, *Glycerol*, Chemical Rubber Company Press, Cleveland, Ohio, 1968.
3. C. S. Miner, N. N. Dalton, *Glycerol*, Reinhold Publishing Corp., New York, 1963.

Specific References

4. Cetina and Mateos, *Bol. Inst. Quim. Univ. Nov. Autom. Mex.* **49**, 17 (1965); *Chem. Abstr.* **63**, 17856g (1965).
5. *Physical Properties of Glycerine and Its Solutions*, Glycerine Producers' Association.
6. *ASTM D 1257-55, High Gravity Glycerine*, American Society for Testing and Materials, Philadelphia, Pa., 1970.
7. *Reagent Chemicals*, 4th ed., American Chemical Society, Washington, D. C., 1968; pp. 269–270.
8. *U. S. Pharmacopeia*, 17th Rev., Mack Printing Co., Easton, Pa., 1965, pp. 270–271.
9. K. Furst, *Mikrochim. Acta* **34**, 25 (1948).
10. C. F. Smullin, L. Hartman, and R. S. Stetgler, *J. Am. Oil Chem. Soc.* **35**, 179 (1958).
11. S. J. Patterson, *Analyst*, **88**, 387 (1963).
12. J. Wright, *Chem. Ind.* (*London*) **27**, 1125 (1963).
13. K. Sporek and A. F. Williams, *Analyst* **79**, 63 (1954).
14. R. Sargent and W. Rieman, III, *Anal. Chim. Acta* **16**, 144 (1957).
15. O. Samuelson and H. Stromberg, *Acta Chem. Scand.* **22**, 1252 (1968).
16. R. L. Friedman and W. J. Raab, *Anal. Chem.* **35**, 67 (1963).
17. C. Cardini, V. Quercia and A. Calo, *Boll. Chim. Farm.* **106**, 459 (1967); *Chem. Abstr.* **67**, 111495t (1967).
18. V. A. Vaver, A. N. Ushakov and L. D. Bergel'son, *Bull. Acad. Sci. USSR, Div. Chem. Sci.* **2**, 388 (1968).
19. F. C. Cross and J. H. Jones, *J. Assoc. Official Anal. Chemists* **50**, 1287 (1967).
20. L. Hartman, *J. Chromatog.* **16**, 223 (1964).
21. L. A. Horrocks and D. G. Cornwell, *J. Lipid Res.* **3**, 165 (1962).
22. H. Puschmann and J. E. Miller, *Z. Lebensm. Unter. Forsch.* **114**, 297 (1961); *Chem. Abstr.* **55**, 14831e (1961).
23. B. Smith and O. Carlson, *Acta Chem. Scand.* **17**, 455 (1963).
24. G. G. S. Dutton, K. B. Gibney, G. D. Jensen and P. E. Reid, *J. Chromatog.* **36**, 152 (1968).
25. J. Blum and W. R. Keohler, *J. Gas Chromatog.* **6**, 120 (1968).
26. H. M. Rosenberger and C. J. Showmaker, *Anal. Chem.* **29**, 100 (1957).
27. W. D. Pohle and V. C. Mehlenbacher, *J. Am. Oil Chem. Soc.* **27**, 54 (1950).
28. R. Sargent and W. Rieman, III, *Anal. Chim. Acta* **14**, 381 (1956).
29. F. A. Lyne, J. A. Radley, and M. B. Taylor, *Analyst* (*London*) **93**, 186 (1968).
30. J. Eisenbrand and M. Raisch, *Z. Anal. Chem.* **177**, 1 (1960).
31. J. T. McAloren and G. F. Reynolds, *Anal. Chim. Acta* **32**, 170 (1965).
32. J. T. McAloren and G. F. Reynolds, *Anal. Chim. Acta* **32**, 227 (1965).
33. E. Michalski and M. Stapor, *Lodz. Tow. Nauk. Wydz III, Acta Chim.* **11**, 25 (1966); *Chem. Abstr.* **66**, 72271z (1967).
34. J. R. Sand and C. O. Huber, *Talanta* **14**, 1309 (1967).
35. O. Weiland, *Biochem. Z.* **329**, 313 (1957).
36. J. H. Hagen, *Biochem. J.* **82**, 23 (1962).
37. P. B. Garland and P. J. Randle, *Nature* **196**, 987 (1962).

38. F. Drawert and G. Kupler, *Z. Lebensm. Untersuch. Forsch.* **123,** 211 (1963); *Chem. Abstr.* **60,** 6178e (1964).
39. C. S. Frings and H. L. Pardue, *Anal. Chim. Acta* **34,** 225 (1966).
40. G. F. Smith, *Cerate Oxidimetry,* The G. Fredrick Smith Chemical Co., Columbus, Ohio, 1942, pp. 97–99.
41. N. N. Sharma and R. C. Mehrotra, *Anal. Chim. Acta* **13,** 419 (1955).
42. G. G. Guilbault and W. H. McCurdy, Jr., *Anal. Chem.* **33,** 580 (1961).
43. W. D. Pohle, et al., *J. Am. Oil Chem. Soc.* **24,** 18 (1946).
44. M. Kruty, J. B. Segua and C. S. Miner, *J. Am. Oil Chem. Soc.* **31,** 466 (1954).
45. *J. Am. Oil Chem. Soc.* **27,** 412 (1950).
46. J. W. B. Erskine, C. R. N. Strauts, G. Walley, and W. Lazarus, *Analyst* **78,** 630 (1953).
47. W. D. Pohle, *J. Am. Oil Chem. Soc.* **34,** 591 (1957).
48. *Official and Tentative Methods,* 3rd ed., American Oil Chemists' Society, Chicago, Ill., 1964, Ea 6-51.
49. H. Ludwicki, M., Sobiczewska, *Farm. Polsk.* **19,** 228 (1963); *Chem. Abstr.* **60,** 370g (1964).
50. D. M. West and D. A. Skoog, *Anal. Chem.* **31,** 586 (1959).
51. Ref. 48, method Ea 2–38.
52. *ASTM D1258-55, Sampling and Testing High Gravity Glycerine,* American Society for Testing Materials, Philadelphia, Pa., 1970.
53. Ref. 48, method Ea 3–58.
54. Ref. 48, method Ca 14–56, D, 9, and 10.
55. Ref. 48, method Ea 8–58.
56. D. Chapman and J. F. Nacey, *Analyst* **83,** 377 (1958).
57. L. V. Cocks, *Analyst* **85,** 686 (1960).
58. W. J. Murray and A. F. Williams, *Analyst* **86,** 849 (1961).
59. L. F. Hoyt, *Ind. Eng. Chem.* **26,** 329 (1934).
60. Ref. 48, Ea 7–50.
61. L. W. Bosart and A. O. Snoddy, *Ind. Eng. Chem.* **19,** 506 (1927).
62. *ASTM D 891-51, Specific Gravity of Aromatic Hydrocarbons,* American Society for Testing Materials, Philadelphia, Pa., 1970.
63. Ref. 48, Ea 9–65.

JOHN E. GOING
University of Wisconsin

GLYCEROL NITRATES.   See EXPLOSIVES, Vol. 12, pp. 405–471.

GLYCINE.   See CARBOXYLIC ACIDS, AMINO, Vol. 8, pp. 410–556.

GLYCOLS AND POLYHYDRIC ALCOHOLS

Glycols. 533
    Properties. 534
    Methods of manufacture and applications. 538
    Commercial grades and specifications. 549
Polyglycols. 549
    Properties. 549
    Methods of manufacture and applications. 553
    Commercial grades and specifications. 560
Polyhydric alcohols. 560
    Properties. 560
    Methods of manufacture and applications. 561
    Commercial grades and specifications. 565
Determination of glycols and polyhydric alcohols. 567
    Separation and identification. 567
    Assay methods. 584
    Determination in mixtures. 595
    Determination in small amounts. 598
    Determination of impurities. 600
    Determination of properties. 601
Bibliography. 602

Glycols, also commonly called diols, are dihydric alcohols having an aliphatic carbon chain of the general formula $C_nH_{2n}(OH)_2$. Alcohols containing three or more hydroxyl groups are referred to as *polyhydric alcohols*.

This article deals with the analysis of those glycols and polyhydric alcohols which are of commercial importance. Polymeric derivatives of ethylene glycol with the general formula $HO(CH_2CH_2O)_nCH_2CH_2OH$ and of propylene glycol with the general formula $HO(C_3H_6O)_nC_3H_6OH$ are frequently referred to as *polyglycols* and are discussed separately in this article.

It is beyond the scope of the present article to discuss in detail all aspects of the chemical technology of glycols and polyhydric alcohols. For those readers desiring more detail, the bibliography should be consulted.

GLYCOLS

Glycols are characterized by two hydroxyl groups which contribute to their water solubility and hygroscopicity and also provide reactive sites. The effect of the hydroxyl groups on the properties of the molecule is dependent on the position of the hydroxyl groups, the length of the hydrocarbon chain, and the presence of branched chains. In general, the simple glycols have properties intermediate between the monohydric alcohols and the trihydric alcohol, glycerol. The names and formulas for the various glycols are summarized in Table 1.

Although glycols have been known for some 100 years, their commercial importance dates from 1925. The U.S. production of ethylene glycol, the simplest and most important glycol rose from 2 million lb in 1925 to an estimated 2.04×10^9 lb in 1968. Increased production of other glycols and glycol derivatives in recent years has established their position as an important class of industrial chemicals. The U.S. production of propylene glycol in 1968 was 352.9 million lb.

Table 1. Nomenclature of the Glycols

IUPAC name	Common name	Formula
1,2-ethanediol	ethylene glycol	$HOCH_2CH_2OH$

1,2-propanediol	propylene glycol	CH_3CHCH_2OH
		    |
		    OH

1,3-propanediol	trimethylene glycol	$HOCH_2CH_2CH_2OH$

1,3-butanediol	1,3-butylene glycol,
	β-butylene glycol,
	α-methyltrimethylene glycol
		$CH_3CHCH_2CH_2OH$
		    |
		    OH

1,4-butanediol	tetramethylene glycol, 1,4-butylene glycol	$HOCH_2CH_2CH_2CH_2OH$

2,3-butanediol	2,3-butylene glycol,
	sym-dimethylene glycol
		$CH_3CH—CHCH_3$
		   | |
		   OH OH

1,5-pentanediol	pentamethylene glycol	$HOCH_2CH_2CH_2CH_2CH_2OH$

2,5-hexanediol	2,5-hexylene glycol	$CH_3CHCH_2CH_2CHCH_3$
		    | |
		    OH OH

1,6-hexanediol	hexamethylene glycol	$HOCH_2CH_2CH_2CH_2CH_2CH_2OH$

2,2-dimethyl-1,3-propanediol	neopentyl glycol	CH_3
		       |
		$HOCH_2CCH_2OH$
		       |
		       CH_3

2-methyl-2-ethyl-1,3-propanediol	2,2-dimethylol butane	CH_3
		       |
		$HOCH_2CCH_2OH$
		       |
		       CH_2CH_3

2-methyl-2,4-pentanediol	hexylene glycol	CH_3
		          |
		$CH_3CHCH_2CCH_3$
		    | |
		    OH OH

2,2,4-trimethyl-1,3-pentanediol	trimethylpentanediol	CH_3 CH_3
		   | |
		$CH_3CHCH—CCH_2OH$
		     | |
		     OH CH_3

2-ethyl-1,3-hexanediol	ethohexadiol	$CH_3CH_2CH_2CH—CHCH_2OH$
		        | |
		       OH CH_2CH_3

Properties

With the exception of the oral toxicity of some, glycols as a class are not very toxic. They do not vaporize readily at normal temperature and therefore are not a breathing hazard. Even though they are not skin irritants, in applications where glycols or glycol-containing products are applied directly on the skin, they should not be used until they have been proved safe for the intended purpose. With the exception of propylene glycol, glycols should not be used internally. Serious injury or death, for instance, can result from swallowing two fluid ounces of ethylene glycol. Comprehensive discussions of the physiological aspects and toxicology of glycols and polyglycols have been published (1,2). Additional information and references to the physiological activity of many specific compounds can be found in the literature listed in the bibliography.

The simple glycols are stable, odorless, colorless liquids when pure. They have higher boiling points than water and most freeze below 0°C. The lower glycols are extremely hygroscopic and show a selective solvent action for certain dyes, synthetic resins, essential oils, and natural gums and resins.

The physical and thermodynamic properties of the glycols are summarized in Table 2.

Ethylene glycol, propylene glycol, and the simple glycols through those derived from C_7 hydrocarbons are generally miscible with water at 20°C. As the molecular weight increases, the solubility in water decreases. The water solubility of the glycols is shown in Table 3. Glycols are also soluble in many organic solvents.

The solubilities of various substances in ethylene and propylene glycols and of flavoring materials in propylene glycol are shown in Tables 4 and 5.

Table 6 lists the binary azeotropes of glycols with a number of solvents. Additional information on azeotropes of glycols can be found in the literature (3).

The lower glycols are extremely hygroscopic, a property which explains their widespread use as humectants, softeners, plasticizers, and gas desiccants. The relative humectant value is a property closely related to hygroscopicity and is defined

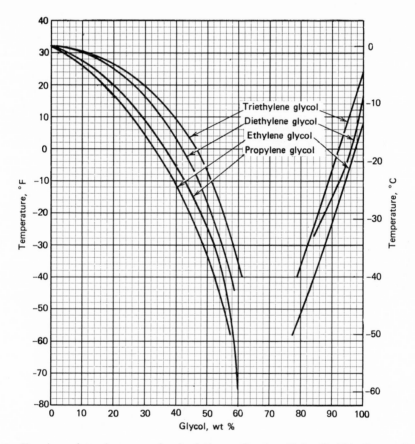

Fig. 1. Freezing points of aqueous glycol solutions. Courtesy Union Carbide Corporation (6).

Table 2. Physical and Thermodynamic Properties of Glycols

	Ethylene glycol	Propylene glycol	Trimethylene glycol	1,3-Butanediol	1,4-Butanediol	2,3-Butanediol[b]	1,5-Pentanediol	2,5-Hexanediol
molecular weight	62.07	76.09	76.09	90.12	90.12	90.12	104.15	118.17
boiling point, 760 torr, °C	197.6	187.4	210 211	207.5	228	182	242.5	220.8
dielectric constant, 20°C	38.66	32.0		28.8(25°C)				
dipole moment, esu	2.20×10^{-18}							
electrical conductivity at 25°C, Ω^{-1} cm^{-1}	1.07×10^{-6}							
flash point, open cup, °F	240	225		250		185	265°C	220°C
freezing point, °C	−12.7	−60[a]		−77		10	−15.6	−50[a]
heat of fusion at mp, cal/g	44.7				20.1			
heat of vaporization at 760 torr, cal/g	191	170		155				
refractive index, n_D^{20}	1.4316	1.4326	1.4398	1.4412	1.4446	1.4377	1.4489	1.4474
specific gravity (apparent), 20/20°C	1.1155	1.0381	1.0554	1.006	1.0154(25/4)	1.0093	0.9921	0.9617
surface tension, 20°C dyn/cm	48.4			37.8(25°C)			43.2	
vapor pressure at 20°C, torr	0.06	<0.1		0.06			<0.01	
viscosity at 20°C, cP	20.93	56.0		65(25°C)	71.5(25°C)	121(25°C)	128	

Table 2 (*continued*)

	1,6-Hexane-diol	2,2-Dimethyl-1,3-propane-diol	2-Methyl-2-ethyl-1,3-propanediol	2-Methyl-2,4-pentane-diol	2,2,4-Trimethyl-1,3-pentanetriol	2-Ethyl-1,3-hexane-diol
molecular weight	118.17	104.15	118.18	118.18	146.22	146.23
boiling point, 760 torr, °C	243		225.8	197	235	243.2
flash point, open cup, °F	265°C	305		215		265
freezing point, °C	42[c]	128[c]	40.3[c]	−50[a]	46.0[c]	−40[a]
heat of vaporization at 760 torr, cal/g			89	107		94
refractive index, n_D^{20}			1.4433(50°C)	1.4275		1.4511
specific gravity (apparent), 20/20°C	0.958(45/15.6)		0.9598(50°20)	0.9233	0.928(55/15)	0.9422
vapor pressure at 20°C, torr			<0.01	<0.1		
viscosity at 20°C, cP			66.4(50°C)	35		320

[a] Sets to glass below this temperature.

[b] Properties of a commercial product containing 85% of the meso and 15% of the dextro–levo isomers. Physical properties of the individual isomers can be found in Reference 7.

[c] Melting point.

as the limiting concentration of water that will be absorbed in contact with air of a specified temperature and relative humidity. It may also be described as the composition of an aqueous solution that will remain in equilibrium with air of a given temperature and relative humidity. The relative humectant value may be used to determine the amount of glycol needed to condition a given quantity of a product which requires a humectant. The relative humectant values for ethylene glycol and propylene glycol are shown in Table 7.

Table 3. Solubility of Glycols

	Solubility, at 20°C, wt %	
	glycol in water	water in glycol
C_2–C_4 glycols	complete	complete
C_5 glycols		
2,4-pentanediol	87.9 (solid)	complete (supercooled liquid)
1,5-pentanediol	complete	complete
C_6 glycols		
2,5-hexanediol	complete	complete
1,6-hexanediol	very soluble	very soluble
2-methyl-2-ethyl-1,3-propanediol	complete at 50°C	complete at 50°C
2-methyl-2,4-pentanediol	complete	complete
2-methyl-1,3-pentanediol	10	250 ml in 100 ml
C_7 glycols		
2,2-diethyl-1,3-propanediol	25	
C_8 glycols		
2-ethyl-1,3-hexanediol	4.2	12

When glycols are used for the dehydration of gases, the dew point, or temperature at which the water vapor will condense from the gas, is a measure of the amount of water-vapor present in the gas. Gases may be dried by bringing them in contact with glycol–water solutions, the dew point being depressed as water vapor is removed. Water-vapor dew points for gases in equilibrium with glycol–water solutions over a large temperature range have been published (4–6), and may be used to calculate dew point depression of gases at equilibrium with the glycol solution at atmospheric pressure.

Freezing point curves for aqueous ethylene glycol and aqueous propylene glycol are shown in Figure 1.

Methods of Manufacture and Applications

Ethylene Glycol (1,2-Ethanediol). Ethylene glycol is the most important of the glycols. It was first prepared by Wurtz in 1859 by saponification of ethylene glycol diacetate with potassium hydroxide. A year later he also succeeded in preparing ethylene glycol by hydration of ethylene oxide, a basic process which is the major source of ethylene glycol produced today.

Ethylene oxide is produced either by catalytic oxidation of ethylene or by reaction of ethylene and hypochlorous acid to yield ethylene chlorohydrin which is then converted to ethylene oxide by reaction with alkali. In the former method, a 1:10 ethylene–air mixture is passed over a silver oxide catalyst at essentially atmospheric pressure and a temperature of 270–290°C. Usually a small amount of anticatalyst, such as ethylene dichloride, is added to the ethylene feed to suppress formation of carbon dioxide. When a contact time of about 1 sec is employed, 60–70% of the ethylene is converted to ethylene oxide. The reaction products are passed through

Table 4. Solubilities of Various Materials in Ethylene Glycol and Propylene Glycol[a]

	Solubility, at 25°C, g/100 ml of glycol	
	ethylene glycol	propylene glycol
acetone	completely soluble	soluble
benzene	6.0	23.8
benzyl alcohol		25
carbon tetrachloride	6.6	30.5
chlorobenzene	6.0	29.0
dibutyl phthalate	0.5	8.8
dichloroethyl ether	11.8	144
o-dichlorobenzene	4.7	24.1
diethanolamine	completely soluble	completely soluble
ethyl ether	8.9	completely soluble
ethylene glycol stearate	slightly soluble	very slightly soluble
heptane	very slightly soluble	soluble
methanol	completely soluble	soluble
methyl orange	1.8	0.6
methyl salicylate		24.7
monoethanolamine	completely soluble	completely soluble
phenol	completely soluble	completely soluble
tetrachloroethylene		11.7
toluene	3.1	14.0
urea	44.0	26.0
castor oil	insoluble	0.8
coconut oil	insoluble	insoluble
cottonseed oil	insoluble	insoluble
hydrous wool fat	slightly soluble	slightly soluble
lard oil	insoluble	insoluble
linseed oil	insoluble	slightly soluble
olive oil	insoluble	insoluble
paraffin oil	insoluble	insoluble
pine oil	infinitely soluble	infinitely soluble
soya bean oil	very slightly soluble	insoluble
sperm oil	very slightly soluble	insoluble
tall oil	1.1	9.9
tung oil	insoluble	insoluble
turkey red oil	3.3	3.7
animal glue (dry)	very slightly soluble	very slightly soluble
cellulose acetate	insoluble	insoluble
dextrin	slightly soluble	slightly soluble
dextrin (10% aqueous solution)	soluble	infinitely soluble
gum damar	slightly soluble	slightly soluble
kauri gum	slightly soluble	
nitrocellulose	insoluble	insoluble
rosin	slightly soluble	slightly soluble
rubber	insoluble	insoluble
shellac	very slightly soluble	very slightly soluble

[a] Reproduced in part from *Glycols, Brochure F-41515*, Union Carbide Corp., 1968.

Table 5. Solubility of Flavoring Materials in Aqueous Propylene Glycol Solutions[a]

	Solubility at 25°C, wt % of solute in final mixture				
Glycol, vol % →	100	80	60	40	20
amyl acetate	∞	∞	∞	1.48	1.34
benzaldehyde	∞	18.97	4.62	1.80	0.82
cassia oil	∞	3.13	0.85	0.69	0.21
citral	∞	0.35	0.17	0.10	0.04
clove oil	∞	1.19	0.26	0.24	0.12
ethyl acetate	∞	∞	∞	11.65	8.09
ethyl formate	∞	∞	∞		17.45
ethyl vanillin	14.20	10.80	5.20	1.84	0.79
eucalyptol	19.90	4.75	1.73	0.35	0.25
isoamyl formate	∞	5.22	4.51	1.68	1.53
lemon oil	0.81	0.52	0.32	0.13	0.03
methyl anthranilate	∞	∞	∞		
nutmeg oil	1.53	0.34	0.17	0.14	0.11
orange oil	0.26	0.13	0.08	0.06	0.03
phenyl ethyl alcohol	∞	∞	∞	18.95	3.11
sassafras oil	2.02	1.21	0.20	0.12	0.08
vanillin	20.20	20.10	12.60	5.85	2.09

[a] Reproduced in part from *Glycols, Brochure F-4763H*, Union Carbide Corp., 1964.

a scrubber where the ethylene oxide is absorbed under pressure and hydrated to ethylene glycol. The reactions are as follows:

$$CH_2{=}CH_2 \ + \ \tfrac{1}{2} \ O_2 \ \xrightarrow[\Delta]{AgO} \ CH_2{-}CH_2 \ + \ (CO_2 + H_2O)$$

$$CH_2{-}CH_2 \ + \ H_2O \ \longrightarrow \ HOCH_2CH_2OH$$

In the ethylene chlorohydrin process, ethylene is charged in a hydrated lime solution at 200 atm pressure and 20°C. Chlorine is then mixed with the solution where it reacts with the lime to form calcium oxychloride, which immediately decomposes to form hypochlorous acid and calcium chloride. The hypochlorous acid reacts with the ethylene in solution to give ethylene chlorohydrin. The ethylene chlorohydrin–calcium chloride solution is treated with the theoretical amount of sodium bicarbonate solution at 70–80°C to yield ethylene glycol which is separated from the salts by distillation at reduced pressure.

Because the high-boiling glycol is difficult to separate from the salts, indirect hydrolysis is often preferred. In the indirect hydrolysis, the ethylene chlorohydrin is heated with lime or sodium hydroxide to yield ethylene oxide which is easily distilled from the salts and then hydrated with slightly acidified water under high temperature and pressure. The reactions for the formation of ethylene chlorohydrin and the direct hydrolysis are shown below. The major by-products are ethylene dichloride and dichlorodiethyl ether.

$$CaO + Cl_2 \rightarrow CaClOCl$$

$$CaClOCl + Cl_2 + H_2O \rightarrow CaCl_2 + 2 \, HOCl$$

$$CH_2{=}CH_2 + HOCl \rightarrow CH_2OHCH_2Cl$$

$$CH_2OHCH_2Cl + NaHCO_3 + H_2O \rightarrow HOCH_2CH_2OH + CO_2 + H_2O + NaCl$$

Table 6. Some Binary Azeotropes of Glycols

Component		Boiling point of azeotrope, at 760 torr, °C	Composition of azeotrope, wt %	
A	B		A	B
ethylene glycol	butyl carbitol	196.2	72.5	27.5
ethylene glycol	butyl ether	139.5	6.4	93.6
ethylene glycol	diethyl carbitol	178.0	26.1	73.9
ethylene glycol	phenyl ether	192.3	64.5	35.5
ethylene glycol	ethoxy diglycol	192	45.5	54.5
ethylene glycol	methyl carbitol	192	30	70
ethylene glycol	toluene	110.1	2.3	97.7
ethylene glycol	o-xylene	135.7	6.9	93.1
ethylene glycol	aniline	145[a]	16.8	83.2
ethylene glycol	benzyl alcohol	193.1	56	44
ethylene glycol	o-cresol	189.5	26	74
ethylene glycol	N,N-dimethylaniline	120[b]	21.8	78.2
ethylene glycol	naphthalene	183.6	46	54
ethylene glycol	hexyl ether	112.8	35.6	64.4
propylene glycol	toluene	110.5	1.5	98.5
propylene glycol	o-xylene	135.8	10	90
propylene glycol	dodecane	175	67	33
propylene glycol	tetradecane	179	76	24
propylene glycol	aniline	179.5	43	57
1-2,3-butanediol	meso-2,3-butanediol diacetate	177.6	60.5	39.5
pinacol	pentachloroethane	158.8	16	84
pinacol	o-cresol	191.5	8	92
pinacol	p-methylanisole	168.7	44	56
pinacol	phenetole	165.2	33	67
pinacol	methylheptenone	171.7	40	60
pinacol	2-octanone	171.5	35	65
pinacol	mesitylene	160.2	35	65
pinacol	propylbenzene	156.3	28	72
pinacol	cymene	167.7	50	50
pinacol	camphene	155.5	28	72
pinacol	isoamyl ether	167.2	40	60
2-ethyl-1,3-hexanediol	bis(2-ethylhexyl) ether	123	40	60

[a] 257.9 torr.

[b] 115 torr.

Smaller quantities of ethylene glycol are also obtained commercially by reaction of formaldehyde, carbon monoxide, and water to produce glycolic acid. The glycolic acid is esterified, purified by distillation, and hydrogenated at 200°C and 30 atm pressure, in the presence of a chromite catalyst to yield ethylene glycol. The reactions are as follows:

$$CH_2O + CO + H_2O \rightarrow CH_2OHCOOH$$

$$CH_2OHCOOH + ROH \rightarrow CH_2OHCOOR + H_2O$$

$$CH_2OHCOOR + 2 H_2 \rightarrow HOCH_2CH_2OH + ROH$$

Applications. Low volatility, low molecular weight, and low solvent action on automobile finishes account for ethylene glycol's major use as a base for all-winter antifreeze formulations (see Vol. 6, pp. 1–23). The same properties contribute to its use in deicing solutions for automobile windshields and in special deicing fluids for aircraft.

Ethylene glycol is also used as a high-temperature coolant for internal combustion stationary engines, snow melting systems, industrial heat transfer fluids, and in refrigeration systems where corrosion by brine is a problem.

Most applications of ethylene glycol for antifreeze or coolant use require the addition of special inhibitors. The chemical composition of the inhibitors varies according to the corrosion or oxidation protection desired and the metallurgy of the system being used. The following compounds have been employed satisfactorily as inhibitors: ethanolamine, triethanolamine, fatty acid salts, phosphate and borate salts, glycol and glycerol monoricinoleates, guanidine carbonate, 1,4-piperazinedi-ethanol, polymethylpyridine, benzopyridines, and borax and mercaptobenzothiazole.

Table 7.   Relative Humectant Values of Ethylene Glycol and Propylene Glycol[a]

Temperature of air, °F	Glycol	Relative humidities[b]								
		10%	20%	30%	40%	50%	60%	70%	80%	90%
20	ethylene	97.5	93.4	89.3	85.7	82	78	72	63	48
	propylene	96.8	91.4	90.0	84.6	77	73	68	55	40
40	ethylene	97.3	93.2	89.1	85.4	82	76	69	60	42
	propylene	97.0	92.3	90.2	85.2	78	74	68	55	40
60	ethylene	97.1	93.0	88.9	85.0	81	75	66	57	37
	propylene	97.1	92.9	90.4	85.8	80	74	68	55	40
80	ethylene	96.8	92.8	88.6	84.7	80	73	64	55	36
	propylene	97.1	93.5	90.5	86.3	81	75	68	55	40
100	ethylene	96.6	92.7	88.4	84.3	79	72	63	53	35
	propylene	97.2	93.9	90.6	86.6	82	75	68	55	40
120	ethylene	96.4	92.5	88.2	84.0	78	71	62	51	34
	propylene	97.2	94.3	90.7	86.7	83	76	68	55	40

[a] Reprinted in part from *Glycols—Properties and Uses*, Dow Chemical Co., Midland, Mich., 1961.

[b] Values are given as the wt % of glycol in water solutions required to maintain equilibrium in contact with air of various temperatures and humidities.

Ethylene glycol is used in brake fluids (see Vol. 7, pp. 423–440) and hydraulic fluids and in the manufacture of low-freezing dynamite (see EXPLOSIVES, Vol. 12, pp. 405–471). It is an important humectant for materials such as textile fibers, paper, leather, and abrasives. Large volumes of ethylene glycol are used in the manufacture of alkyd resins and polyester fibers, and in solvent systems for paints and varnishes.

Special high-purity ethylene glycol, iron- and chloride-free, is used as a solvent and suspending medium for ammonium perborate, the conductor in practically all electrolytic capacitors.

For details on the properties, manufacture, and applications of ethylene glycol, References 4–6,8–14 should be consulted.

Propylene Glycol (1,2-Propanediol).   Propylene glycol was first prepared by Wurtz in 1859 by hydrolysis of the diacetate. It became commercially available in 1931 when it was produced by hydrolysis of propylene oxide derived from propylene chlorohydrin:

$$CH_3CH\!-\!CH_2 \ + \ H_2O \ \longrightarrow \ CH_3CHCH_2$$

At present, propylene glycol is still produced commercially from propylene oxide in a manner similar to that described for the production of ethylene glycol from ethylene oxide.

Propylene glycol is a component in some all-winter antifreeze formulations and in deicing solutions for automobile windshields and aircraft surfaces. Due to its low oral toxicity, it is the preferred antifreeze in refrigeration systems in breweries, dairies, food and ice cream plants, and packing houses where the coolant may accidentally come into contact with food.

Propylene glycol is used extensively in the food, cosmetic and pharmaceutical industries. The humectant properties of the glycol extend shelf life of products where moisture retention is important. In addition, it is also effective as a retardant for mold and fungi growth. The use of propylene glycol in cosmetic and pharmaceutical formulations is related to its special properties as a solvent, humectant, emulsifier, softening agent, emollient, and preservative. It is an excellent solvent or vehicle for many medications and is nontoxic when used in prescribed amounts.

Propylene glycol is used extensively as an intermediate in the production of polyester resins, and in the synthesis of plasticizers for cellulose nitrate, polyvinyl chloride, and polyvinyl acetate.

For details on the properties, manufacture, and applications of propylene glycol, References 4–6,9,10,13–16 should be consulted.

Trimethylene Glycol (1,3-Propanediol). This substance was first described as occurring in certain glycerols as long ago as 1895. It is of minor commercial importance and is usually recovered in commercial glycerol plants only when there is sufficient demand. It has also been prepared synthetically by heating γ,γ-dihydroxydipropyl ether with hydrobromic acid followed by hydrolysis of the reaction product with sodium hydroxide.

Trimethylene glycol is used as an ingredient in some antifreeze formulations, and as an intermediate in the manufacture of alkyd resins. For details, see References 13, 17, and 18.

1,3-Butanediol (1,3-Butylene Glycol). 1,3-Butanediol was first prepared by Kekulé in 1872 as a by-product of the reduction of acetaldehyde with sodium amalgam. It has been produced on a small scale in the past by several routes including condensation of propylene with formaldehyde, hydrolysis of 2-methyloxetane, and hydrogenation of 4-hydroxy-2-butanone.

The present major source of commercial 1,3-butanediol is catalytic hydrogenation of acetaldol which in turn is prepared by condensation of acetaldehyde in alkaline solution. Hydrogenation can be effected with copper, platinum oxide, or Raney nickel. Pressures of about 700 psi and temperatures of 65–120°C are usually employed.

Low-boiling impurities which include ethanol, water, *n*-butanol, and sometimes 2,4-dimethyl-1,3-dioxane are stripped off under reduced pressure from the hydrogenation product. Redistillation at low pressure gives pure 1,3-butanediol. The reactions are as follows:

$$2\ CH_3-\!\!\overset{\overset{\textstyle O}{\|}}{C}H \longrightarrow CH_3\overset{\overset{\textstyle H}{\underset{}{|}}}{\underset{\textstyle O}{}}CHCH_2\overset{\overset{\textstyle O}{\|}}{C}H$$

$$CH_3\overset{\overset{\textstyle H}{|}}{\underset{\textstyle O}{}}CHCH_2\overset{\overset{\textstyle O}{\|}}{C}H \quad\xrightarrow[\Delta,\ \text{pressure}]{H_2,\,(Ni)}\quad CH_3\overset{\overset{\textstyle H}{|}}{\underset{\textstyle O}{}}CHCH_2CH_2OH$$

1,3-Butanediol is used in the preparation of chemical intermediates, pharmaceuticals, and dyestuffs. Because of its somewhat hindered configuration at carbon three, derivatives of 1,3-butanediol tend to be more stable than those of comparable glycols, which can lead to important and useful differences in the properties of end products. For example, borate esters of 1,3-butanediol exhibit unusual bacteriostatic activity. 1,3-Butanediol is also used in the synthesis of polyester plasticizers and in the manufacture of saturated polyesters for polyurethan coatings. 1,3-Butanediol is of very low toxicity and is an excellent solvent, emollient, and lubricant. It is used as a component in some hand cleansers, lotions, and other cosmetic preparations.

For details on the properties, manufacture, and applications of 1,3-butanediol, References 13,14,19–21 should be consulted.

1,4-Butanediol (Tetramethylene Glycol). This substance was first synthesized by Dekkers in 1890 by hydrolysis of *N*,*N*′-dinitro-1,4-butanediamine with dilute sulfuric acid. Numerous other syntheses have since been described in the literature.

1,4-Butanediol is obtained commercially by hydrogenation of 2-butyne-1,4-diol, which in turn is prepared by the reaction of acetylene and formaldehyde. The hydrogenation of butynediol is usually carried out in a 30–40% solution at 200–300 atm using a nickel–copper–manganese catalyst supported on silica. Because the reaction is highly exothermic, a large excess of hydrogen is circulated through the reactors as a cooling medium. 1-Butanol is topped off the product, and the remaining liquid is distilled to remove water and other components.

1,4-Butanediol is used as a chemical intermediate in the production of numerous products including synthetic fibers and artificial leather, plasticizers, softening agents, binding agents, plastics and synthetic rubber, casting and laminating resins, and various pharmaceuticals. Its physical properties suggest uses as a lubricant, size component, softener, moistener, and solvent. For further details see References 13,22–24.

2,3-Butanediol. 2,3-Butanediol is produced by fermentation of materials such as sugars, potatoes, molasses, wheat or enzyme mash, corn mash, or cornstarch. The products of fermentation depend upon the species of bacteria used and may also include carbon dioxide, hydrogen, formic acid, glycerol, ethanol, and lactic acid. The species of bacteria employed for the fermentation also determines the relative proportion of the optical isomers of 2,3-butanediol which are produced. The diol is recovered from the fermentation liquor by distillation, solvent extraction, steam stripping, or dialysis. 2,3-Butanediol can also be produced by hydration of the corresponding oxide.

2,3-Butanediol is employed as a solvent for certain dyes and as a humectant and coupling agent. For further details see References 13 and 25.

1,5-Pentanediol.   1,5-Pentanediol is commercially synthesized from the reaction of acrolein and vinyl ethyl ether.   An intermediate pyran (2-ethoxy-3,4-dihydro-1,2-pyran) is formed which is subsequently hydrolyzed to glutaraldehyde and hydrogenated to yield the glycol.   Water is removed from the crude product by a flash distillation and purified 1,5-pentanediol is obtained by a final high-vacuum distillation.

Ester and polyester derivatives of 1,5-pentanediol are important intermediates for alkyd and polyurethan resins, foams, fibers, adhesives, and molding compounds. It is also used as a solvent and humectant in inks, and as a plasticizer for casein and cellulose products.   For details on the properties, manufacture, and applications of the substance, References 4,6,10,13, and 26 should be consulted.

2,5-Hexanediol.   2,5-Hexanediol is prepared by reduction of acetonylacetone with sodium amalgam.   Potential applications of 2,5-hexanediol are similar to those of other simple glycols.   It is a solvent for various dyestuffs, gums, and resins and an intermediate for polyester resins.   It has been recommended as an anti-icing additive for engine fuels.   The silicon esters are used as hydraulic fluids and lubricants.   For details on the substance, see References 13 and 27.

1,6-Hexanediol.   1,6-Hexanediol is prepared from hexamethylene dibromide or diacetate by the classical Wurtz method.   It can also be prepared by reduction of esters of adipic acid.

1,6-Hexanediol is particularly useful in the plastics industry as an intermediate in the production of polyesters, polyester amides, and polyurethans.   Other areas of potential application include the fatty acid esters which have been proposed for use in lubricants for gas turbine oils and the hexane-1,6-diol ester of methane sulfonic acid which can be used as a hardener for gelatin in silver halide gelatin photographic emulsions.   Other hexanediol polyesters are reported to be effective stabilizers and plasticizers for polyvinyl chloride.   1,6-Hexanediol is also used in certain pharmaceutical and cosmetic formulations.

For details on the properties, manufacture, and applications of 1,6-hexanediol, References 13,28–30 should be consulted.

2,2-Dimethyl-1,3-Propanediol (Neopentyl Glycol).   The first preparation of neopentyl glycol was described in the literature by Apel and Tollens in 1894.   It is now produced commercially by a crossed Cannizzaro reaction of isobutyraldehyde with 2 moles of formaldehyde.

2,2-Dimethyl-1,3-propanediol finds considerable applications as a chemical intermediate, particularly in the production of unsaturated polyesters with improved thermal, hydrolytic, and ultraviolet stability.   The manufacture of polyurethan foams and elastomers are other applications for hydroxy-terminated polyesters derived from neopentyl glycol.   Other uses include the manufacture of polyester thickening agents for synthetic lubricants, and alkyd resins which show excellent resistance to thermal discoloration.

References 11,31–32 discuss in detail the substance, its manufacture, and applications.

2-Methyl-2,4-Pentanediol (Hexylene Glycol).   This substance was first prepared in 1901 by Zelinsky and Zelikow, who reduced diacetone alcohol with sodium amalgam under a carbon dioxide atmosphere, and by Franke who reduced an aqueous solution of the same compound with aluminum amalgam.

2-Methyl-2,4-pentanediol is at present commercially produced by liquid phase hydrogenation of diacetone alcohol.   Conventional hydrogenation catalysts are employed.

Table 8. Specifications of Technical Grades of Glycols

	Ethylene glycol	Propylene glycol	Trimethylene glycol	1,3-Butanediol	1,4-Butanediol	2,3-Butanediol
purity, wt %, min				99.0	97.0	
distillation range, 760 torr, °C				200–215		174–186
ibp	193 min	185 min	212.3			
95%	200 max					
dp	201.5 max	189 max	215.5			
ash, wt %, max	0.005[a]	0.005				
water, wt %, max	0.2	0.2	0.5	0.5	0.4	0.5
water solubility at 25°C	miscible in all proportions					
acidity, as acetic acid, wt %, max	0.005	0.003		0.005		0.01
carbonyl content, wt %, max						
ester content, wt %, max						
specific gravity, 20/20°C	1.1151–1.1156	1.0375–1.0390		1.004–1.006		1.006–1.010
iron, ppm, max		0.5				
chloride, ppm, max		1				
diethylene glycol, wt %, max	0.5					
appearance	free of suspended matter	free of suspended matter			clear liquid	
color, Pt–Co, max	10	10	5	10	20 (APHA)	20
odor	mild					

Table 8 (*continued*)

	1,5-Pentanediol	2,5-Hexanediol	1,6-Hexanediol	2,2-Dimethyl-1,3-propanediol	2-Methyl-2,4-pentanediol	2,2,4-Trimethyl-1,3-pentanediol	2-Ethyl-1,3-hexanediol
purity, wt %, min	96.0		98.5			96.0^f	97.0
freezing point, °C, min			41.0				
melting point range, °C			120.0–130.0				
start						46.0 min	
finish						50.0–55.0	
distillation range, 760 torr, °C		103–105 (bp)					
ibp	238 min				196 min	215 min	241 min
95%	250 max						
dp	258 max				199 max	235 max	249 max
ash, wt % max							
water, wt % max	0.2	0.5	0.05	1.00	0.1		0.1
acidity, as acetic acid, wt % max	0.01		0.02	0.05	0.005	0.10^g	0.01
carbonyl content, wt %, max	0.5^b						
ester content, wt %, max	1.5^c			1.50^d			
aldehyde content, wt %, max				0.70^e			
refractive index, n_D^{25}							1.4465–1.4515
specific gravity, 20/20°C	0.990–0.994				0.921–0.924		0.939–0.942
iron, ppm, max			1				
appearance	free of suspended matter				free from haze or turbidity		
color, Pt–Co, max	30		10 (molten)		15	50 (molten)	15
odor					mild		mild

^{a} g/100 ml, max.
^{b} As glutaraldehyde.
^{c} As valerolactone.
^{d} As neopentyl hydroxypivalate.
^{e} As hydroxypivaldehyde.
^{f} Assay.
^{g} As isobutyric acid.

Hexylene glycol finds application in many industries as a blending and coupling agent for immiscible oil–liquid systems such as liquid detergent formulations, dry-cleaning soaps, and emulsions. As a penetrating and wetting agent it is used to speed the rate of penetration of textile soaps, printing and duplicating inks, and paper coatings.

Hexylene glycol is frequently included in latex paint formulations where it improves the leveling properties and scrub resistance of the paint and permits a higher pigment volume concentration. It is a component of certain inks and hydraulic brake fluids. Other uses for hexylene glycol are as an anticracking agent and gloss improver for photographic prints, a solvent and antiblowing agent for pentachlorophenol, and as a mercerizing assistant which insures even and rapid penetration of caustic solution into textile fibers.

For further details see References 4,6,10,13,14,33, and 34.

2,2,4-Trimethyl-1,3-Pentanediol. This substance is commercially produced by hydrogenation of the aldehyde dimer resulting from the aldol condensation of isobutyraldehyde. It is used in diverse applications in the automotive, textile, pharmaceutical, plastics, and petroleum fields. Unsaturated polyesters derived from trimethylpentanediol are characterized by low exotherm, low shrinkage during cure, low specific gravity, good electrical properties, and improved chemical and hydrolytic stability, and show excellent potential in the reinforced plastics field. Mixtures of trimethylpentanediol and diethylene glycol are used as a vehicle component in some moisture-set printing inks and as a solvent for low-cost limed rosins. Derivatives of trimethylpentanediol are used in the synthetic lubricant field. For details see References 11,31, and 35.

2-Ethyl-1,3-Hexanediol. 2-Ethyl-1,3-hexanediol is produced commercially by the hydrogenation of butyraldol. The substance is an effective repellent for mosquitos, flies, chiggers, and certain other biting insects. Due to its limited water solubility and low volatility, it retains its efficiency for several hours in spite of perspiration. It is used as an efficient blending and coupling agent for immiscible oil–water systems such as hair dressings and shampoos. 2-Ethyl-1,3-hexanediol is used as a film coalescing aid in some latex paint formulations and as a solvent in

Table 9.   Specifications for USP Propylene Glycol

purity, wt %, min	99
specific gravity	
20/20°C	1.0376–1.0389
25/25°C	1.0351–1.0364
distillation range, 760 torr, ibp–dp, °C	186–189
acidity as acetic acid, wt %, max	0.003
chlorides, max, ppm	1
sulfates	none
heavy metals (as Pb), ppm, max	5
arsenic (as As_2O_3), ppm, max	1
solubility, 25°C	miscible in all proportions with water, chloroform, and acetone
water, wt %, max	0.2
ash, sulfated, ppm, max	0.005
APHA color, max	10
odor	practically odorless
taste	slight, characteristic
suspended matter	substantially free

some specialty inks. Borates, vanadates, arsenites, antimonites, molybdates, and titanates derived from 2-ethyl-1,3-hexanediol are used as antioxidants and corrosion inhibitors in some lubricants.

For details on the properties, manufacture, and applications of 2-ethyl-1,3-hexanediol, References 4,6,10,13, and 36 should be consulted.

Commercial Grades and Specifications

The glycols are commercially available in technical grades, typical specifications for which are shown in Table 8. Propylene glycol is also available in a USP grade for food, pharmaceutical, and cosmetic applications. Specifications for USP grade propylene glycol are shown in Table 9.

POLYGLYCOLS

Condensation polymers of ethylene glycol having the general formula $HO(CH_2CH_2O)_nCH_2CH_2OH$ and of propylene glycol with the general formula $HO(C_3H_6O)_nC_3H_6OH$ are commonly referred to as polyglycols. The lower members have properties closely akin to those of the simple glycols. Higher members are commercially available as mixtures within specified molecular weight ranges. Polyglycols discussed in this section are diethylene glycol, triethylene glycol, polyethylene glycols, dipropylene glycol, and polypropylene glycols. Mixed polyethylene–polypropylene glycols are also briefly covered.

Properties

The physical and thermodynamic properties of diethylene glycol, triethylene glycol, and dipropylene glycol are shown in Table 10. Properties of typical com-

Table 10. Physical and Thermodynamic Properties of the Lower Polyglycols

	Diethylene glycol, $HOCH_2CH_2(OCH_2CH_2)OH$	Triethylene glycol, $HOCH_2CH_2(OCH_2CH_2)_2OH$	Dipropylene glycol, $HO(C_3H_6O)C_3H_6OH$
molecular weight	106.12	150.17	134.18
boiling point, 760 torr, °C	245.8	288	232.8
flash point, open cup, °F	290	330	280
freezing point, °C	−7.8	−4.3	−60[a]
heat of vaporization at 1 atm, Btu/lb	233	175	172
refractive index, n_D^{20}	1.4474	1.4561	1.4407
specific gravity, apparent, 20/20°	1.1184	1.1255	1.0232
surface tension at 25°C, dyn/cm	48.5	45(20°C)	32
vapor pressure, 20°C, torr	<0.01	<0.01	<0.01
viscosity, 20°C, cP	36	49	107

[a] Sets to glass below this temperature.

Table 11. Physical Properties of Typical Commercially Available Polyethylene Glycols (37)

Polyethylene glycols	Average mol wt	Freezing range, °C	d_{20}^{20}	Flash point (Cleveland open cup), °F	Viscosity at 210°F, Saybolt units	Solubility, water at 20°C, g/100 g	Comparative hygroscopicity (glycerol = 100)	pH of 5% aqueous solution at 25°C	Refractive index, n_D^{20}
Liquid									
200	190–210	supercools	1.125	340	38–42	complete	70	4.5–7.0	1.459
300	285–315	−15–+8	1.125	385	42–48	complete	60	4.5–7.0	1.463
400	380–420	4–10	1.128	435	45–55	complete	55	4.5–7.0	1.465
600	570–630	20–25	1.127	475	56–66	complete	40	4.5–7.0	
Solid									
1000	950–1050	38–41	1.101	510	85–100	70 (approx)	35	4.5–7.0	
1500[a]	500–600	38–41	1.151[c]	430	70–90	73	35	4.5–7.0	
1540	1300–1600	43–46	1.15	510	120–150	70	30	4.5–7.0	
4000	3000–3700	53–56	1.204[c]	515	350–400	62	1	4.5–7.0	
6000	6000–7500	60–63[b]		520	3200–4200	50 (approx)	1	4.5–7.0	

[a] Mixture of approximately equal parts by weight of polyethylene glycol 300 and polyethylene glycol 1540.
[b] Melting point range.
[c] Density, g/ml.

mercial polyethylene glycols and polypropylene glycols are shown in Tables 11 and 12. Freezing point curves for diethylene and triethylene glycol are shown in Figure 1.

In general, as the molecular weight of the polyglycol increases, the water solubility, compatibility with organic liquids, and hygroscopicity decrease, whereas the flash point, pour point, and viscosity increase.

Table 12. Physical Properties of Some Typical Commercial Polypropylene Glycols (38)

Compound	Average mol wt	Freezing range, °C	d_{20}^{20}	Water solubility at 20°C, g/100 g solution	Viscosity at 99°C, cSt	Flash point (Cleveland open cup), °F
polypropylene glycol 150	140–160		1.02	complete		250
polypropylene glycol 400	400		1.007_{25}^{25}	complete^a	4.48	390
polypropylene glycol 425	400–450	-60^b	1.0103	complete	4.2	420
polypropylene glycol 750	750		1.004_{25}^{25}	15.25^a	7.62	>440
polypropylene glycol 1025	975–1075	-50^b	1.0072	1.5	10.94	450
polypropylene glycol 1200	1200		1.003_{25}^{25}	1.96^a	12.70	>440
polypropylene glycol 2000	2000		1.003_{25}^{25}	<0.1^a	22.90	>440
polypropylene glycol 2025	1950–2100	-45^b	1.0055	0.15	23.9	450

^{a} At 25°C.
^{b} Sets to a glass below this temperature.

The high molecular weight polyglycols are stable materials of low volatility. Polyethylene glycols up to an average molecular weight of about 700 are liquids at room temperature. Polyethylene glycols with average molecular weights above 700 are solids at room temperature with the melting point increasing regularly with molecular weight until an upper limit of about 65°C is reached at a molecular weight of approximately 7000–8000. All the polypropylene glycols, other than isotactic high polymers of propylene oxide, are liquids at room temperature. Polypropylene glycols are less water soluble, less hygroscopic, and more compatible with organic materials than polyethylene glycols of comparable molecular weight.

Commercial polypropylene glycols differ chemically from polyethylene glycols in that they contain methyl substitution and the hydroxyl groups are mainly secondary. The secondary:primary ratio is approximately 13:1.

Mixed polyethylene–polypropylene glycols, where the oxide units are of random distribution, are bland liquids ranging from free-flowing to very viscous. They are available in both water soluble and insoluble forms. Generally, the products which contain at least 40 wt % of ethylene oxide units are water soluble at room temperature.

The mixed polyethylene–polypropylene glycols are also available as block copolymers where the oxide units are added to the growing molecule as blocks of oxypropylene units or oxyethylene units. The block copolymers, marketed under the trade name Pluronic by BASF Wyandotte Corp., contain hydrophilic polyoxyethylene groups at both ends of the hydrophobic polyoxypropylene base. Controlled variation in the size of the groups determines the properties of the final product. The physical form

Table 13. Solubilities of Various Materials in Diethylene Glycol, Triethylene Glycol, and Dipropylene Glycol[a]

	Solubility, g/100 ml of glycol at 25°C		
	diethylene glycol	triethylene glycol	dipropylene glycol
acetone	completely soluble	completely soluble	miscible
benzene	45.5	completely soluble	miscible
carbon tetrachloride	35.5	40.6	miscible
chlorobenzene	112.0	soluble	
dibutyl phthalate	11.8	19.8	miscible
dichloroethyl ether	soluble	soluble	miscible
o-dichlorobenzene	93.6	soluble	miscible
diethanolamine	soluble	soluble	miscible
ethyl ether	19.5	20.4	miscible
ethylene glycol stearate	very slightly soluble	very slightly soluble	
heptane	slightly soluble	very slightly soluble	
methanol	completely soluble	completely soluble	miscible
methyl orange	4.2		
monoethanolamine	soluble	soluble	miscible
phenol	soluble	soluble	miscible
tetrachloroethylene	12.0	17.7	miscible
toluene	20.7	33.0	miscible
urea	24.0	31.0	
castor oil	0.1	0.3	
coconut oil	insoluble	insoluble	
cottonseed oil	insoluble	insoluble	
hydrous wool fat	slightly soluble	slightly soluble	
lard oil	insoluble	insoluble	
linseed oil	insoluble	insoluble	
olive oil	insoluble	insoluble	
paraffin oil	insoluble	insoluble	
pine oil	soluble	soluble	
soya bean oil	insoluble	insoluble	
sperm oil	insoluble	insoluble	
tall oil	3.1	10.1	
tung oil	insoluble	insoluble	
turkey red oil	6.3	12.3	miscible
animal glue (dry)	very slightly soluble	very slightly soluble	
cellulose acetate		soluble	
dextrin	slightly soluble	soluble	
dextrin (10% aqueous solution)	soluble	insoluble	
gum damar	slightly soluble	slightly soluble	
kauri gum	slightly soluble	slightly soluble	
cellulose nitrate	soluble	soluble	
rosin	<2.0	5.0	
rubber			
shellac	very slightly soluble	very slightly soluble	

[a] Reprinted in part from *Glycols, Brochure F4763H*, Union Carbide Corp., 1964.

varies from mobile liquids to flaked solids and from materials which are almost water insoluble to those which have no cloud point—even at the boiling point of water.

Diethylene glycol, triethylene glycol, and dipropylene glycol are miscible with water in all proportions. They are also soluble in numerous organic solvents. In addition, many water insoluble materials can be brought into a clear aqueous solution by means of the coupling action of the mutually soluble glycol. Due to the larger number of carbon atoms, dipropylene glycol has more extensive solvent power for certain organic materials such as hydrocarbons and oils. The solubility of various materials in diethylene glycol, triethylene glycol, and dipropylene glycol are shown in Table 13.

The solubility of several polyethylene glycols of widely varying molecular weight in water and common organic solvents is shown in Table 14.

Table 14. Approximate Solubilities of Polyethylene Glycols 400, 1500, and 4000 in Common Solvents, g/100 g solution[a] (39)

Solvents	Polyethylene glycol 400		Polyethylene glycol 1500		Polyethylene glycol 4000	
	20°C	50°C	20°C	50°C	20°C	50°C
water	M	M	69	97	60	84
methanol	M	M	48	96	35	M
ethanol (200 proof)	M	M	<1	M	<1	M
acetone	M	M	20	M	<1	99
dichloroethyl ether	M	M	44	M	25	85
trichloroethylene	M	M	50	90	30	80
2-ethoxyethanol	M	M	<1	M	<1	88
2-(n-butoxy)ethanol	M	M	<1	M	<1	52
monoethyl ether of diethylene glycol	M	M	2	M	<1	63
mono(n-butyl) ether of di- ethylene glycol	M	M	<1	M	<1	64
ethyl acetate	M	M	15	M	<1	93
dimethyl phthalate	M	M	30	90	13	74
dibutyl phthalate	M	M	<1	M	<1	55
ethyl ether	insoluble	I	insoluble	I	insoluble	I
isopropyl ether	insoluble	insoluble	insoluble	insoluble	insoluble	insoluble
toluene	M	M	13	M	<1	M
heptane	insoluble	insoluble	0.50	0.01	<0.01	<0.01

[a] M = completely miscible. I = insoluble at boiling point.

Low molecular weight polypropylene glycols are completely miscible with water at ambient temperatures. Above an average molecular weight of 500, the water solubility decreases rapidly. The water solubility of various polypropylene glycols was listed in Table 12. Polypropylene glycols are generally soluble in nonpolar solvents.

Mixed polyethylene–polypropylene glycols are available in both water soluble and water insoluble forms.

Selected binary azeotropes of diethylene glycol, triethylene glycol, and dipropylene glycol are shown in Table 15. Additional information concerning azeotropes of these glycols can be found in the literature (3).

Methods of Manufacture and Applications

Diethylene Glycol. Diethylene glycol, the simplest member of the polyglycol family, was independently discovered by Lourenco and by Wurtz in 1859 and has been of commercial significance since 1928. Diethylene glycol is commercially obtained as a co-product in the manufacture of ethylene glycol from ethylene oxide and

Table 15. Azeotropes of Lower Polyglycols

| Component A | | Component B | | Azeotrope | |
name	bp, °C	name	bp, °C	bp, at 760 torr, °C	wt % A
diethylene glycol	245.5	p-dibromobenzene	220.25	212.85	13
		m-chloronitrobenzene	235.5	228.2	32
		o-chloronitrobenzene	246.0	233.5	41
		p-chloronitrobenzene	239.1	229.5	34
		nitrobenzene	210.75	210.0	10
		o-nitrophenol	217.2	216.0	10.5
		pyrocatechol	245.9	259.5	46
		o-bromoanisole	217.7	211.0	25
		m-nitrotoluene	230.8	224.2	25
		o-nitrotoluene	221.75	218.2	17.5
		p-nitrotoluene	238.9	228.75	35
		2-[2-(2-methoxyethoxy)ethoxy]-ethanol	245.25	245.0	22
		anisaldehyde	249.5	<244	
		methyl salicylate	222.95	220.55	16
		p-bromophenetole	234.2	222.0	32
		2-phenoxyethanol	245.2	<244.5	
		o-phenetidine	232.5	<225.0	<18
		p-phenetidine	249.9	<232.0	>52
		ethyl fumarate	217.85	217.1	10
		ethyl maleate	223.3	222.65	10.0
		quinoline	237.3	233.6	29
		benzyl acetate	215.0	214.85	7
		ethyl benzoate	212.5	211.65	10
		ethyl salicylate	233.8	225.15	30
		1-bromonaphthalene	281.2	240.8	59.5
		1-chloronaphthalene	262.7	234.1	47
		naphthalene	218.0	212.6	22.0
		quinaldine	246.5	<241.0	
		isosafrol	252.0	233.5	46
		methyl cinnamate	261.9	240.0	63
		safrole	235.9	225.5	33
		methyl phthalate	283.7	245.4	96.3
		anethole	235.7	210.0	20
		ethyl-α-toluate	228.75	224.0	20
		propyl benzoate	230.85	222.7	26
		carvacrol	237.85	236.0	27
		thymol	232.9	232.25	13
		α-terpineol	218.85	217.45	13.5
		1-methylnaphthalene	244.6	227.0	45
		2-methylnaphthalene	241.15	225.45	39
		ethyl cinnamate	272.0	244.5	85?
		1-allyl-3,4-dimethoxybenzene	254.7	235.0	47
		butyl benzoate	249.0	232.2	43
		1,2-dimethoxy-4-propenylbenzene	270.5	238.8	60
		isobutyl benzoate	241.9	228.65	37
		methyl thymyl ether	216.5	210.5	19
		isobornyl methyl ether	192.4	<191.0	<9
		methyl α-terpineol ether	216.2	210.5	20
		acenaphthene	277.9	239.6	62
		biphenyl	256.1	232.65	48

Table 15 (*continued*)

Component A		Component B		Azeotrope	
name	bp, °C	name	bp, °C	bp, at 760 torr, °C	wt % A
diethylene glycol	245.5	phenyl ether	259.0	234.4	49.5
		isoamyl benzoate	262.0	236.55	52.5
		1,3,5-triethylbenzene	215.5	210.0	22
		bornyl acetate	227.6	223.0	18
		fluorene	295.0	243.0	80
		diphenylmethane	265.4	236.0	52
		benzyl phenyl ether	286.5	241.5	80
		1,2-diphenylethane	284.5	241.0	66
		benzyl ether	297	<243.8	>87
triethylene glycol	288.7	1-bromonaphthalene	281.2	273.4	33
		1-chloronaphthalene	262.7	261.5	5
		methyl phthalate	283.2	277.0	33
		ethyl cinnamate	272.0	<271.5	>7
		acenaphthene	277.9	271.5	35
		biphenyl	256.1	255.3	10
		phenyl ether	259.0	258.7	3
		ethyl phthalate	298.5	<285.5	>58
		isoamyl benzoate	262.0	261.4	14
		isoamyl salicylate	277.5	269.0	30
		phenyl benzoate	315	286.0	80
		diphenylmethane	265.4	263.0	20
		benzyl phenyl ether	286.5	280.0	40
		stilbene	306.5	284.5	60
		1,2-diphenylmethane	284.5	275.5	42
dipropylene glycol	229.2	*o*-bromoanisole	217.7	212.0	30
		o-nitrotoluene	221.75	216.9	>21
		methyl salicylate	222.95	213.0	35
		p-bromophenetole	234.2	221.0	45
		quinoline	237.3	<228.0	<72
		ethyl salicylate	233.8	218.2	55
		isosafrole	252.0	225.5	60
		safrole	235.9	222.0	50
		anisole	235.7	221.5	48
		1-allyl-3,4-dimethoxybenzene	254.7	226.5	65
		methyl thymyl ether	216.5	211.0	30
		methyl α-terpineol ether	216.2	<211.5	>24
		phenyl ether	259.0	<228.0	<77

water as described on p. 538. The proportion of diethylene glycol produced can be controlled by the molar ratio of ethylene oxide and water in the reaction mixture. Larger amounts of polyglycols are produced when the ethylene oxide–water ratio is increased. Diethylene glycol can also be produced by the direct reaction of ethylene glycol with ethylene oxide. The U.S. output of diethylene glycol in 1968 was 225.8 million lb.

Diethylene glycol is used as a hygroscopic agent, plasticizer, lubricating agent, and solvent for cellulose nitrate and various resins, gums, dyes, and oils. Because of its low volatility and unusual hygroscopicity, it is effective for softening and controlling the moisture content of tobacco, cork, glue, casein, paper, and synthetic sponges.

Diethylene glycol is a conditioning agent and lubricant for cotton, rayon, and wool fibers.

Mixtures of diethylene glycol and water exhibit selective solvent properties for the separation of aromatic hydrocarbons from mixtures containing paraffinic hydrocarbons. A special extraction grade of diethylene glycol is available for this application.

Diethylene glycol is used for gas dehydration and as a coupling agent. The added solubility imparted by the ether group in the molecule has resulted in its use as a coupler for oils used in metal cutting, agricultural sprays, and polishes. It is also a component of some automotive brake fluids and antifreezes. Diethylene glycol is an important intermediate in the production of various polyester resins and urethan foams.

Derivatives of diethylene glycol are also of commercial importance. The monoether derivatives are used as solvents, coupling agents, and diluents in hydraulic fluids. The esters of diethylene glycol are used as solvents and plasticizers.

For details on the properties, manufacture, and applications of diethylene glycol, References 4–6,9–11,13,14, and 40 should be consulted.

Triethylene Glycol. This substance was first obtained by Lourenco and Wurtz as a co-product in their diethylene glycol synthesis. It also is obtained commercially as a co-product in the manufacture of ethylene glycol, high ratios of ethylene oxide–water favoring a higher yield of triethylene glycol. It has been commercially available since 1928. The U.S. production in 1968 was 73.1 million lb.

Triethylene glycol is used in many of the same applications as diethylene glycol. Because triethylene glycol has a higher boiling point, it may be used in preference to diethylene glycol when a less volatile compound is required.

Triethylene glycol is used in air-dehumidification systems to remove water vapor without cooling the air. It is also used in air-sanitation systems to aid in the control of the bacteria and virus content of the air.

Ester derivatives of triethylene glycol find use in plasticizers. Fatty acid derivatives are used as emulsifiers, demulsifiers, and lubricants.

References 4,5,9,10,13 and 41 give detailed information on the properties, manufacture, and application of triethylene glycol.

Dipropylene Glycol. Dipropylene glycol is commercially obtained as a co-product in the manufacture of propylene glycol from propylene oxide and water (see p. 542). The formation is analogous to that of diethylene glycol. Three structural isomers of dipropylene glycol are possible; their structures are shown below. Commercial dipropylene glycol contains about 53% of the primary–secondary isomer, 43% of the disecondary isomer, and 4% of the diprimary isomer.

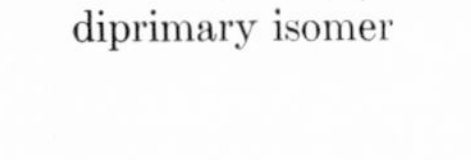

$$HOCH_2CHOCHCH_2OH \qquad\qquad CH_3CHCH_2OCH_2CHCH_3$$
$$| \quad | \qquad\qquad\qquad\qquad\qquad | \qquad\qquad |$$
$$CH_3 \;\; CH_3 \qquad\qquad\qquad\qquad\quad OH \qquad\quad OH$$
diprimary isomer disecondary isomer

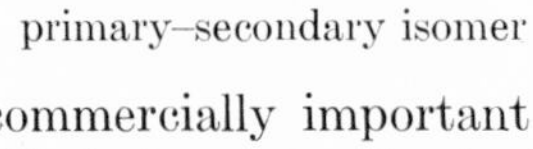

$$CH_3CHCH_2OCHCH_2OH$$
$$| \qquad\qquad |$$
$$OH \qquad\quad CH_3$$
primary–secondary isomer

Dipropylene glycol is a commercially important material and its uses overlap those of ethylene glycol and diethylene glycol. It is useful in applications where a glycol of lower volatility and hygroscopicity is desirable. In this respect, it is superior to most of the lower glycols as a high-boiling, odorless coupling agent or mutual solvent for normally immiscible liquid systems. It is a component of some hydraulic fluids, textile lubricants, and printing ink formulations.

Ester derivatives of dipropylene glycol find application as plasticizers and resins for coating paper and cloth. Ether derivatives are used as solvents and coupling agents. Polyesters formed by reaction with dibasic acids are useful in the production of urethan foams.

For further information on dipropylene glycol, References 4–6,9,10,13, and 42 should be consulted.

Polyethylene Glycols. Ethylene glycols having the general formula $HO(CH_2CH_2O)_nH$ and average molecular weights above 200 are usually classified as polyethylene glycols. They were first prepared by Lourenco in 1859 by heating a mixture of ethylene glycol and ethylene dibromide in a sealed tube at 115–120°C. Wurtz, at about the same time, prepared polyethylene glycol fractions by reacting ethylene oxide with ethylene glycol or water.

Polyethylene glycols are commercially prepared by adding ethylene oxide to either water, ethylene glycol, or diethylene glycol containing a small amount of sodium hydroxide catalyst. The ethylene oxide is added at a rate which maintains the liquid content at 120–135°C, the total pressure of the system at this temperature being approximately 60 psig. The reaction is exothermic and it is necessary to employ a heat exchanger to maintain this temperature and pressure. When reaction is complete, the contents are neutralized and filtered. The molar ratio of ethylene oxide to initiator controls the average molecular weight of the product.

Polyethylene glycols are characterized by good lubricity, heat stability, and inertness to many chemical agents. They do not hydrolyze or deteriorate and have an extremely low toxicity. As such, they find application in many areas of industry, especially the pharmaceutical and textile industries. They are of special interest in cosmetics, ointments, and medications where blandness, water solubility, and lubricity are desired. They are frequent components of protective hand creams, astringent creams, hair conditioners, and shaving creams. Water solubility of the polyethylene glycols permits them to release medication to the skin more quickly than do water-in-oil emulsion bases. Water solubility is also an advantage in that it permits easy removal of the formulation after it has served its purpose.

Polyethylene glycols are used extensively in "lost-wax" metal casting processes. Polyethylene glycols are added to the spinning bath in the manufacture of rayon as fiber-forming aids which impart additional strength to the fiber. They are used as plasticizers and dispersants for casein and gelatin compositions, glues, zein, cork, and special printing inks.

Ester derivatives of polyethylene glycols are used as nonionic surfactants in the textile, petroleum, pharmaceutical, and food industries. The esters are also employed as emulsifiers for insecticidal and herbicidal preparations, as lubricants in spinning and weaving operations, and in the formulation of ointments, creams, lotions, and suspensions used in the pharmaceutical and cosmetic industries.

For details on the properties, manufacture, and applications of polyethylene glycols, see References 4,6,9,10,13,43–49.

Polypropylene Glycols. Polypropylene glycols, $HO(C_3H_6O)_nH$, are produced in a manner similar to that described for polyethylene glycols by addition of propylene oxide to water, propylene glycol, or dipropylene glycol in the presence of a caustic catalyst. As mentioned earlier, polypropylene glycols also contain methyl substitution and the hydroxyl groups are mainly secondary. The secondary–primary ratio is approximately 13:1.

Polypropylene glycols are used as high quality, heavy-duty lubricants. Under most conditions of use, they are noncorrosive to metals and have little swelling or solvent effect on most natural and synthetic rubbers and on other materials used for gasketing, packing, and sealing.

Because of their excellent lubricating and solvent properties and high flash points, they are used in formulating high quality hydraulic brake fluids. They are of interest as coupling agents in the manufacture of textiles, papers, leathers, adhesives, and cosmetics.

Polypropylene glycols are useful as intermediates in the preparation of emulsifiers, alkyd resins, and lubricants. The monoesters are nonionic surface active agents useful in numerous applications.

Further details on polypropylene glycols can be found in References 4,6,9,10,13, 48,50–53.

Mixed Polyethylene–Polypropylene Glycols. Mixed polyethylene–polypropylene glycols, $HO(CH_2CH_2O)_x(C_3H_6O)_yH$, are produced in a manner similar to that described for polyethylene glycols and polypropylene glycols. Ethylene oxide and propylene oxide are used. The oxide units in the mixed polyglycols may have

Table 16. Specifications for Technical Grade Diethylene Glycol, Triethylene Glycol, and Dipropylene Glycol

Specification	Diethylene glycol	Triethylene glycol	Dipropylene glycol
acidity, as acetic acid, wt %, max	0.005	0.01	0.01
ash, wt %, max	0.005	0.01	0.005
distillation range at 760 torr			
ibp, min, °C	242	278	228
dp, max, °C	250	300	236
color, Pt–Co, max	15	25	10
odor and suspended matter	free from suspended matter	mild odor, free from suspended matter	mild odor, free from suspended matter
water, wt %, max	0.20	0.10	0.10
specific gravity, 20/20°C	1.1170–1.1200	1.124–1.126	1.020–1.025
iron, ppm, max			0.5
chlorides, ppm, max			1

random distribution or they may be added to the growing molecule as blocks of pure oxyethylene units or oxypropylene units. The latter block copolymers differ markedly in their properties from the random copolymers.

The random mixed polyethylene–polypropylene glycols are used extensively as functional fluids, that is, fluids principally valuable for their physical properties in mechanical work rather than their chemical properties. As such, they are employed as hydraulic fluids, metal coating and preservative fluids, heat-transfer fluids, and lubricants. They are useful as thickeners for hydrolube water–glycol fire-resistant hydraulic fluids used in the die-casting industry and in guided missile launching systems. The mixed polyglycols and their many ether derivatives also find application in the cosmetic industry due to their lubricity and low order of toxicity.

Table 17. Specifications for Technical Grade Polyethylene Glycols[a]

Poly-ethylene glycol	Average mol wt	pH, at 25°C, 5% aqueous solution	Water solubility, 25% aqueous solution	Color, Pt–Co, max	Clarity of 100% material	Ash, wt %, max	Suspended matter	Freezing point, °C	Viscosity at 210°F, cSt
200	190–210	4.5–7.0	free from haze or turbidity	18	clear, after 1 hr at 15°C	0.05	substantially free		
300	285–315	4.5–7.0	free from haze or turbidity	18	clear, after 1 hr at 15°C	0.01	substantially free		
400	380–420	4.5–7.0	free from haze or turbidity	18	clear, after 1 hr at 20°C	0.01	substantially free		special requirement: total ethylene and diethylene glycol 0.15% by wt, max
600	570–630	4.5–7.0	free from haze or turbidity	18	clear, after 1 hr at 35°C	0.01	substantially free		
1000	950–1050	4.5–7.0	free from haze or turbidity	18[c]	melt shall be clear	0.03	melt substantially free	36.5–39.5	
1500		4.5–7.0	free from haze or turbidity	18[c]	melt shall be clear	0.03	melt substantially free	38.0–41.0	13–18
1540		4.5–7.0	free from haze or turbidity	18[c]	melt shall be clear	0.03	melt substantially free	43.0–46.0	25–32
4000		4.5–7.0	[b]	25[c]		0.03	melt substantially free from dirt and lint	53.0–56.0	75–85
6000		4.5–7.0	[b]	50[c]		0.03	melt substantially free from dirt and lint	melting range 60.0–63.0	700–900

[a] Reprinted in part from *Carbowax Polyethylene Glycols, Brochure F-4772*, Union Carbide Corp., 1965.
[b] A 25% aqueous solution shall transmit at least 95% of the light transmitted by the same solution after filtering.
[c] 25% aqueous solution.

Block polyethylene–polypropylene glycols find extensive use as surfactants, defoamers, emulsifiers, and dispersants. They are widely employed in the formulation of various paints, detergents, cosmetics, and pharmaceuticals.

For detailed information on the properties, manufacture, and applications of these substances, see References 9,13,54–57.

Commercial Grades and Specifications

Diethylene glycol is available in a technical grade and a special grade for production of polyester resins. Typical specifications for the technical product are shown in Table 16.

Triethylene glycol is available in a technical grade and in a special high-purity grade for use in cellophane and paper that may come into contact with food. Typical specifications for the technical grade are shown in Table 16.

Dipropylene glycol is available in a technical grade, typical specifications for which are shown in Table 16.

Polyethylene glycols are available in technical grades. In addition, several molecular weight ranges are available in NF and USP grades. Typical specifications for the commercial products are shown in Table 17.

Polypropylene glycols are commercially available in molecular weights covering the approximate range 400–4000. Specifications for these materials generally include a water content of 0.15% maximum, an ash content of 0.01% maximum, and a maximum APHA color of 35.

POLYHYDRIC ALCOHOLS

Alcohols with three or more hydroxyl groups are referred to as polyhydric alcohols. The generic name "glycerols" is often applied to trihydric alcohols after glycerol, the simplest and most important member. An important class of polyhydric alcohols having the general formula $CH_2OH(CHOH)_nCH_2OH$ can be obtained by reduction of the corresponding sugars and are hence called sugar alcohols.

The polyhydric alcohols discussed in this article are summarized in Table 18. The table also includes the simplest trihydric alcohol, glycerol, which is discussed elsewhere (pp. 494–532).

Properties

The physical and thermodynamic properties of the polyhydric alcohols other than glycerol are summarized in Table 19. The properties of glycerol are listed on pp. 495–499.

Solubility. Glycerol has solvent properties similar to water and the lower alcohols. It is miscible in all proportions with water, simple alcohols, glycols, and phenols. Its miscibility with acetone, ethyl acetate, dioxane, and aniline is limited and it is practically immiscible with hydrocarbons and higher alcohols. For details see pp. 495–498.

1,2,4-Butanetriol and 1,2,6-hexanetriol are completely miscible with water and ethanol.

Trimethylolethane is soluble in water and the lower aliphatic alcohols. It is slightly soluble in ketones, esters, and ethers, and insoluble in aliphatic and aromatic hydrocarbons.

Trimethylolpropane is soluble in water, acetone, and alcohols. It is insoluble in aliphatic and aromatic hydrocarbons.

Table 18. Nomenclature of Polyhydric Alcohols

IUPAC name	Common name	Formula
1,2,3-propanetriol	glycerol, glycerin	$$\underset{\displaystyle \text{OH}}{\text{CH}_2}{-}\underset{\displaystyle \text{OH}}{\text{CH}}{-}\underset{\displaystyle \text{OH}}{\text{CH}_2}$$
2-hydroxymethyl-2-methyl-1,3-propanediol	trimethylolethane, pentaglycerol	$$\begin{array}{c}\text{CH}_2\text{OH}\\ \mid \\ \text{CH}_3\text{CCH}_2\text{OH}\\ \mid \\ \text{CH}_2\text{OH}\end{array}$$
2-hydroxymethyl-2-ethyl-1,3-propanediol	trimethylolpropane, hexaglycerol	$$\begin{array}{c}\text{CH}_2\text{OH}\\ \mid \\ \text{CH}_3\text{CH}_2\text{CCH}_2\text{OH}\\ \mid \\ \text{CH}_2\text{OH}\end{array}$$
1,2,4-butanetriol	1,2,4-trihydroxybutane	$$\underset{\displaystyle \text{OH}}{\text{CH}_2}\text{CH}_2\underset{\displaystyle \text{OH}}{\text{CH}}{-}\underset{\displaystyle \text{OH}}{\text{CH}_2}$$
1,2,6-hexanetriol	1,2,6-trihydroxyhexane	$$\underset{\displaystyle \text{OH}}{\text{CH}_2}\text{CH}_2\text{CH}_2\text{CH}_2\underset{\displaystyle \text{OH}}{\text{CH}}{-}\underset{\displaystyle \text{OH}}{\text{CH}_2}$$
2,2-bis(hydroxymethyl)-1,3-propanediol	pentaerythritol	$$\begin{array}{c}\text{CH}_2\text{OH}\\ \mid \\ \text{HOCH}_2\text{CCH}_2\text{OH}\\ \mid \\ \text{CH}_2\text{OH}\end{array}$$
	dipentaerythritol	$$\begin{array}{c}\text{CH}_2\text{OH}\quad\quad\text{CH}_2\text{OH}\\ \mid \quad\quad\quad\quad \mid \\ \text{HOCH}_2\text{CCH}_2\text{OCH}_2\text{CCH}_2\text{OH}\\ \mid \quad\quad\quad\quad \mid \\ \text{CH}_2\text{OH}\quad\quad\text{CH}_2\text{OH}\end{array}$$
	tripentaerythritol	$$\begin{array}{c}\text{CH}_2\text{OH}\quad\text{CH}_2\text{OH}\quad\text{CH}_2\text{OH}\\ \mid \quad\quad\quad \mid \quad\quad\quad \mid \\ \text{HOCH}_2\text{CCH}_2\text{OCH}_2\text{CCH}_2\text{OCH}_2\text{CCH}_2\text{OH}\\ \mid \quad\quad\quad \mid \quad\quad\quad \mid \\ \text{CH}_2\text{OH}\quad\text{CH}_2\text{OH}\quad\text{CH}_2\text{OH}\end{array}$$

Pentaerythritol is moderately soluble in cold water, and freely soluble in hot water. It has limited solubility in alcohols and other organic solvents. The solubility of pentaerythritol in selected organic solvents is shown in Table 20 (58).

Dipentaerythritol is less soluble than pentaerythritol in water and organic solvents, whereas the solubility of tripentaerythritol in the same solvents is even lower.

Methods of Manufacture and Applications

Glycerol (1,2,3-Propanetriol). Glycerol is present as the triglyceride in all animal and vegetable fats and oils, although it is rarely found in the free state in these materials. The triglyceride ester is usually present as the derivative of fatty acids such as stearic, oleic, palmitic, and lauric. Glycerol also occurs naturally as the triglyceride in animal and vegetable matter in the form of lipids such as lecithin and cephalin. Prior to 1949, glycerol was almost entirely a by-product of soap manufacture. In 1948, synthetic glycerol became commercially available and by 1965, it accounted for some 60% of the market. For more information on glycerol, see pp. 500–501.

Trimethylolethane. 2-Hydroxymethyl-2-methyl-1,3-propanediol is prepared by condensation of formaldehyde with propionaldehyde in the presence of an alkaline

Table 19. Physical and Thermodynamic Properties of Polyhydric Alcohols

	Trimethylol-ethane	Trimethylol-propane	1,2,4-Butane-triol	1,2,6-Hexane-triol	Penta-erythritol	Dipenta-erythritol	Tripenta-erythritol
molecular weight	120.15	134.18	106.12	134.18	136.15	254.29	372.42
boiling point, °C					276^f		
5 torr		160	119^b	178			
50 torr		210					
760 torr	283	295	312				
fire point, open cup, °F		380					
flash point, open cup, °F		355		193°C			
heat of combustion, kcal/mole		864			660	1848	3070
heat of fusion, cal/g		43.83					
heat of formation, kcal/mole					226.6		
heat of sublimation, kcal/mole					31.4		
heat of vaporization, kcal/mole					22		
melting point, °C	200.5–202	58.8			261–262	221–222.5	248–250
freezing point, °C			supercools	-20^d			
specific gravity		1.0889^a	1.018^c	1.1043^e	1.395^c	1.365^g	1.30^g
refractive index, n_D^{20}			1.4688	1.58	1.548		
viscosity, cP			1227(25°C)	2584(20°C)			

^{a} 70/4°C.
^{b} 0.17 torr.
^{c} 25/4°C.
^{d} Sets to glass below this temperature.
^{e} 20/4°C.
^{f} 30 torr.
^{g} Density, g/ml.

condensation catalyst such as sodium hydroxide or lime. The product is recovered from the reaction mixture by extraction with an organic solvent and crystallization from the solvent extract.

Trimethylolethane is used in the production of alkyd resins which have excellent hardness, gloss, and durability. Synthetic drying oils prepared by esterification of trimethylolethane with drying-oil fatty acids are used in varnishes and other surface coating compositions. Other ester derivatives are used for plasticizers, emulsifiers, and lubricants.

For details see References 59–61.

Table 20.   Solubility of Pentaerythritol

Solvent	Temperature, °C	Solubility, g/100 g solvent	Temperature, °C	Solubility, g/100 g solvent
water	25	7.23	97	77.2
methanol (100%)	25	0.75	50	2.1
methanol (65%)	25	3.0	50	8.1
ethanol (100%)	25	0.33	50	1.0
ethanol (65%)	25	3.1	50	8.0
n-butylamine	25	16	78	16
dimethyl sulfoxide	25	4.5	90	30
ethanolamine	25	16.5	100	44.5
ethylene glycol	25	1.0	100	12.9
formamide	25	1.7	100	21.3
glycerol	25	0.8	100	10.3
pyridine	25	1.1	100	5.7
tetrafurfuryl alcohol	25	0.2	100	3.7
acetone	56	<1.0		
amyl acetate	100	<1.0		
benzene	80	<1.0		
carbon tetrachloride	78	<1.0		
diethyl ether	68	<1.0		
dioxane	100	<1.0		
furfural	100	<1.0		
nitrobenzene	100	<1.0		
petroleum ether	71	<1.0		

Trimethylolpropane.   2-Hydroxymethyl-2-ethyl-1,3-propanediol is prepared by the alkaline condensation of formaldehyde with butyraldehyde. The product is separated from the reaction mixture by vacuum distillation.

The principal use of trimethylolpropane is for the synthesis of polyurethan foams, prepared by reacting trimethylolpropane and dibasic acids with aromatic diisocyanates. Esters of trimethylolpropane are used as synthetic drying oils, lubricants, and plasticizers. Other uses include the synthesis of surfactants, textile treating agents, and heat stabilizers for polyvinyl chloride resins.

For more information on the properties, manufacture, and applications of trimethylolpropane, References 14,59,60,62 and 63 may be consulted.

1,2,4-Butanetriol.   This compound is prepared by hydrogenation of 1,4-dihydroxy-2-butanone in the presence of a molybdenum sulfide catalyst. The 1,4-dihydroxy-2-butanone is in turn obtained by catalyzed hydration of 1,4-butynediol.

1,2,4-Butanetriol finds application as a solvent, humectant, and an intermediate in the production of explosives and pharmaceuticals. For further details see References 59,60, and 64.

1,2,6-Hexanetriol. This substance is prepared by hydrolyzing acrolein dimer and hydrogenating the resulting 2-hydroxyadipaldehyde:

$$2\ CH_2{=}CHCH{=}O \xrightarrow{\Delta} \text{acrolein dimer} \xrightarrow[H_2O]{H^+} CHOCHOH(CH_2)_3CHO \xrightarrow{2H_2}$$

acrolein

2-hydroxyadipalde-
hyde

$$CH_2OHCHOH(CH_2)_3CH_2OH$$
1, 2, 6-hexanetriol

1,2,6-Hexanetriol is used as a plasticizer for polyamide resins and as a humectant for cellophane and tobacco. It is an excellent anticurl agent for dextrin adhesives, being superior to glycerol in this respect. Polyester and polyether derivatives of the triol are used in the production of polyurethan foams and elastomers. 1,2,6-Hexanetriol also finds application as a medicament carrier and base in water-soluble ointments and lotions.

Further details on the properties, manufacture, and applications of 1,2,6-hexanetriol can be found in References 4,10,59, and 60.

Pentaerythritol. 2,2-Bis-(hydroxymethyl)-1,3-propanediol was described by Tollens in 1882 as a by-product of the reaction between impure formaldehyde and barium hydroxide. Subsequent investigation showed that the pentaerythritol was the reaction product of formaldehyde and acetaldehyde, the acetaldehyde being an impurity in the formaldehyde.

Pentaerythritol is prepared commercially by reacting formaldehyde and acetaldehyde with an alkaline condensing agent. The reaction involves an aldol condensation of formaldehyde and acetaldehyde to form pentaerythrose, followed by a crossed Canizzaro reaction between the pentaerythrose and formaldehyde to form pentaerythritol:

$$CH_3CHO + 3\ HCHO \xrightarrow{MOH} HOCH_2\overset{\displaystyle CH_2OH}{\underset{\displaystyle CH_2OH}{C}}CHO \xrightarrow[HCHO]{MOH} HOCH_2\overset{\displaystyle CH_2OH}{\underset{\displaystyle CH_2OH}{C}}CH_2OH + HCOOM$$

Sodium hydroxide and calcium hydroxide are the usual condensation catalysts. The reaction product is treated with sodium carbonate to precipitate calcium, filtered and concentrated by heating under vacuum. The solution is then cooled to precipitate pentaerythritol. Polypentaerythritols, principally dipentaerythritol, are the main by-products. The technical product which contains 10–15% of di- and higher pentaerythritol can be purified by recrystallization from water to isolate the pentaerythritol crystals.

The major use of pentaerythritol, accounting for some 90% of domestic production, is as an intermediate for the synthesis of alkyd resins and rosin esters. Pentaerythritol contributes improved hardness, gloss, color stability, and water resistance to the resins. The rosin esters are used in a variety of end products, including paints, varnishes, lacquers, printing inks, floor coverings, and adhesives. Synthetic drying oils derived from drying-oil or semidrying oil fatty acids are used in formulating paints, enamels, varnishes, putties, caulking compounds, and linoleum cements.

Esters derived from pentaerythritol and fatty acids containing up to twelve carbon atoms are used as lubricants and as plasticizers for polyvinyl chloride resin. The esters prepared from long-chain fatty acids are used as waxes and surface active agents.

Polyspiroacetal resins derived from the reaction between pentaerythritol and polyfunctional aldehydes such as acrolein, crotonaldehyde, and glutaraldehyde find application as electrical insulators, crosslinking agents and surface coating materials.

Pentaerythritol is used in fire-retardant surface coatings and as a heat stabilizer for polyvinyl chloride resins.

For further details on the properties, manufacture, and applications of penta-erythritol References 14,59–60,65–68 should be consulted.

Dipentaerythritol. This compound is obtained as a by-product of the reaction of formaldehyde and acetaldehyde to form pentaerythritol. Dipentaerythritol, present to the extent of 10–15% in technical grade pentaerythritol, is separated from the latter by procedures based on differences in solubility in water or alcohols.

Dipentaerythritol is used in the preparation of drying oils, resin esters, and alkyd resins. Fatty acid esters of the hexahydric alcohol are used as waxes, lubricants for aircraft engines, and plasticizers for polyvinyl chloride resins. Dipentaerythritol is also used in the preparation of intumescent fire-retardant compositions. For further information see References 59–60, and 66.

Tripentaerythritol. This compound is also a by-product of the reaction between formaldehyde and acetaldehyde to form pentaerythritol. It is separated from the technical pentaerythritol product by fractional crystallization and is purified by recrystallization from solution containing formic, sulfuric, or hydrochloric acids.

Tripentaerythritol is used in the preparation of fire-retardant surface coatings. It is also used in rosin esters and modified phenolic resins where it gives high viscosity and good hardness. For further information see References 59,66,68–69.

Commercial Grades and Specifications

For commercial grades of glycerol and their specifications see pp. 500–501.

Trimethylolethane is commercially available in a technical and refined grade. Specifications for trimethylolethane are shown in Table 21.

Table 21. Specifications for Trimethylolethane

Specification	Technical	Pure
ash, wt %, max[a]	0.01	0.01
color, APHA modified, max[b]	200	100
hydroxyl content, wt %, min	40.5	41.75
water, wt %, max	0.5	0.3
water insolubles, ppm, max		50

[a] Total calcium and magnesium calculated as calcium formate.
[b] APHA color of 50% solution in phthalic anhydride at 200°C.

Trimethylpropane is commercially available in a technical grade, specifications of which are shown in Table 22.

Table 22. Specifications for Trimethylolpropane

acidity, as formic acid, wt %, max	0.002
color of 10% aqueous solution, Pt–Co, max	5
freezing point, °C, min	58.0
hydroxyl content, wt %, min	37.5
phthalic color, Gardner, max	1
water, wt %, max	0.05

1,2,4-Butanediol is available in a technical grade with the following tentative specifications:

purity	95% min
water	0.4% max
appearance	straw yellow
odor	practically none

1,2,6-Hexanetriol is available in a technical grade, specifications for which are shown in Table 23.

Table 23. Specifications for 1,2,6-Hexanetriol

carbonyl content, wt %, max[a]	0.1
color, Pt–Co, max	100
n_D^{25}	1.4745–1.4770
pH of 30% solution in H_2O at 25°C	4.5–7.5
purity, wt %, min	98.5
specific gravity, 20/20°C	1.104–1.110
water, wt %, max	0.1

[a] As hydroxyadipaldehyde.

Pentaerythritol is commercially available in technical, purified, and nitration grades. The technical product, which accounts for some 80% of the pentaerythritol sold in the U.S. contains 85–90% pentaerythritol and 10–15% di- and higher polypentaerythritols.   The purified monopentaerythritol contains 98–99% pentaerythritol, while the nitration grade is a special highly purified material for use in the preparation of pentaerytnritol tetranitrate explosive. Specifications for the technical and purified monopentaerythritol grades are shown in Table 24.

Table 24. Specifications of Pentaerythritol, Dipentaerythritol, and Tripentaerythritol

	Pentaerythritol		Dipenta-erythritol	Tripenta-erythritol
	technical	purified		
ash, wt %, max[a]	0.01	0.01	0.07	0.4
monopentaerythritol, wt %	87.0–89.0	98.0 min	3.0 max	1.0 max
dipentaerythritol, wt %	11.0–13.0	2.0 max	97.0 min	
hydroxyl content, wt %	46.5–48.5	49.0 min	38.0 min	34.0–36.0
water, wt %, max	0.5	0.5	0.75	1.0
water insolubles, ppm, max	50	50	100	
color, APHA modified[b], max	125	100	175	

[a] Total calcium and magnesium calculated as calcium formate.

[b] APHA color of 50% solution in phthalic anhydride, at 200°C.

Dipentaerythritol is available in a technical grade which may contain appreciable amounts of pentaerythritol and tripentaerythritol. Specifications offered by one manufacturer are shown in Table 24.

Tripentaerythritol is available in a technical grade which may contain appreciable amounts of pentaerythritol and dipentaerythritol. Specifications offered by one manufacturer are shown in Table 24.

DETERMINATION OF GLYCOLS AND POLYHYDRIC ALCOHOLS

In this section of the article, methods used for the identification, separation, and analysis of glycols and polyhydric alcohols are detailed. In general, methods for the analysis of these substances closely parallel those of monohydric alcohols; therefore, consult also the article on ALCOHOLS (Vol. 4, pp. 495–586) for additional information on analytical procedures which might be applicable to the compound(s) in question. Information related to the analysis of glycerol is given on pp. 501–521 of this volume; many of these methods can be adopted for the analysis of other polyhydric alcohols.

Separation and Identification

Derivatives for Identification

Derivatives most commonly used for the separation and identification of glycols include the diesters of benzoic, *p*-nitrobenzoic, and 3,5-dinitrobenzoic acids, diesters of *N*-substituted carbamic acids, and bis(triphenylmethyl) ethers. While numerous identifying derivatives of glycerol have been reported, including the corresponding triesters of the above, relatively little information is available in the literature on other polyhydric alcohols.

A summary of the derivatives most frequently employed for the separation and identification of the more common glycols and polyhydric alcohols is shown in Table 25. References to the preparation of many of the derivatives are given by Huntress and Mullikin (70). Melting points of alcohol derivatives, including glycols and polyhydric alcohols, have been summarized in tabular form by Frankel and Patai (71). Additional information on glycol derivatives is presented by Hillenbrand (72), while Segur (73) has discussed the preparation of glycerol derivatives.

General procedures for the preparation of various monohydric alcohol derivatives are discussed in Vol. 4, pp. 516–521, and should be applicable, with necessary adjustment of reagent quantity, to glycols and polyhydric alcohols. Modifications of these and other procedures which have been employed for preparing solid derivatives of glycols are listed below.

Benzoates and p-Nitrobenzoates. The procedure for the preparation of the derivatives of glycols according to Hillenbrand (72) and McElvain (74) is given below.

Procedure

Prepare the diester derivative by mixing 0.5 ml of the glycol with 2 equivalents of the corresponding acid chloride and 5 ml of pyridine. Heat under reflux for 1 hr, then cool and add 20 ml of 5% aqueous sodium bicarbonate solution. Cool in an ice bath until the precipitate solidifies, then filter. Recrystallize the precipitate by solution in a minimum volume of hot ethanol, than add warm water dropwise until the solution just becomes turbid. Cool and collect the crystals by filtration.

The following procedures for preparation of glycerol derivatives should be applicable to other polyhydric alcohols (73).

Table 25. Derivatives of Glycols and Polyhydric Alcohols

Glycol or polyhydric alcohol	Derivative	mp of derivative, °C
1,2-ethanediol	dibenzoate	73
	di(p-nitrobenzoate)	140; 141
	di(3,5-dinitrobenzoate)	169
	bis(phenylurethan)	157; 156
	bis(α-naphthylurethan)	176
	bis(p-nitrophenylurethan)	135.5
	bis(triphenylmethyl ether)	187–188
(d,l) 1,2-propanediol	di(phenylurethan)	153; 143–144
	distearate	72.3
	monostearate	59.5
	di(triphenylmethyl ether)	176.5–176.7
1,3-propanediol	dibenzoate	57; 59
	di(p-nitrobenzoate)	119
	di(3,5-dinitrobenzoate)	178
	bis(phenylurethan)	137
	bis(α-naphthylurethan)	164
(d,l) 1,3-butanediol	di(phenylurethan)	122–123
	di(α-naphthylurethan)	184
1,4-butanediol	dibenzoate	81–82
	di(p-nitrobenzoate)	175
	bis(phenylurethan)	180; 183–183.5
	bis(α-naphthylurethan)	199
2,3-butanediol	dibenzoate(meso)	75.5–76.2
	dibenzoate (d,l)	53–54
	bis(phenylurethan)(meso)	201
1,5-pentanediol	di(p-nitrobenzoate)	104–105
	bis(phenylurethan)	174–175
	bis(α-naphthylurethan)	147
diethylene glycol	di(3,5-dinitrobenzoate)	149
	bis(triphenylmethyl ether)	157.5–158
triethylene glycol	bis(triphenylmethyl ether)	142–142.5
1,2,3-propanetriol	tribenzoate	71–72; 75–76
	tri(p-nitrobenzoate)	188–189
	tri(3,5-dinitrobenzoate)	190–192
	tri(phenylurethan)	180; 180–182
	tri(p-nitrophenylurethan)	216
	tri(α-naphthylurethan)	191–192
pentaerythritol	tetraacetate	84
	tetrabenzoate	99–101

Procedures

TRIBENZOATE. Add 1 drop of glycerol, 0.4 ml of benzoyl chloride, and 5.0 ml of 10% sodium hydroxide solution to a test tube and mix. Cool and shake until a solid separates. Filter and wash with 20 ml of water followed by 10 ml of 20% acetic acid. Recrystallize the precipitate from 15 ml of hot 1:2 ethanol.

TRI(p-NITROBENZOATE). Place 2.0 g of p-nitrobenzoyl chloride and 0.35 g of anhydrous glycerol in a test tube. Add 5 ml of pyridine and swirl to mix. Considerable heat is evolved and a clear solution results. Maintain the solution near the boiling point for 5 min, then pour the hot solution into 50 ml of ice water in a small beaker. Stir and allow to stand overnight. Break up the solid lumps, filter, and wash with 5% sodium carbonate solution followed by water. Transfer the moist cake to a small Erlenmeyer flask and reflux with about 30 ml of acetic acid until solution is complete. On slow cooling to room temperature, the pure derivative crystallizes almost quantitatively.

Phenylurethans and α-Naphthylurethans. The diurethan derivatives are prepared by reaction of the glycol with 2 equivalents of phenyl or α-naphthyl isocyanate. The procedure is given below (72,74). When working with phenylisocyanate care is necessary as the reagent is a lachrymator.

Procedure

Mix up to 0.5 g of the glycol with a 10% excess of the isocyanate in a small test tube. If no reaction is apparent, heat on a steam bath for 10 min, taking care to protect the mixture from moisture. Extract the reaction mixture with 5 ml of hot petroleum ether (bp 100–120°C) to dissolve the urethan. Filter the hot petroleum ether extract if any insoluble matter is present and allow to cool to crystallize the derivative. Recrystallize from ethanol.

The following procedure for the preparation of the triphenylurethan derivative of glycerol is also applicable to other polyhydric alcohols (73). It is important that reactants and solvents be anhydrous and that rigid precautions are taken to exclude moisture from the system. Phenylisocyanate reacts readily with water to form carbanilide, a white solid (mp 238–239°C) which is insoluble in all common organic solvents. If water is present in the sample, carbanilide will precipitate when the mixture is taken up with chloroform. In this case, the solution can be filtered and further treatment carried out on the clear filtrate. Moisture contamination during reflux, however, may cause a precipitate of carbanilide to be mistaken for one of the phenylurethans sought.

Procedure

Place 0.5 g of anhydrous glycerol and 2.5 g of phenyl isocyanate in a small Erlenmeyer flask. Carefully warm while swirling until the reaction starts as indicated by the evolution of heat and the formation of a small amount of white fumes. Cool and add 50 ml of chloroform. Reflux the syrupy reaction mixture under a cold finger condenser. A white precipitate will form within 15 min to several hours. Continue refluxing until sufficient solid has accumulated, then filter the hot solution and wash with boiling chloroform. If the solution is allowed to cool before filtration, a mixture of partially reacted glycerol phenylurethans will crystallize with a melting point anywhere from 100 to 170°C. The product may be recrystallized from a large volume of chloroform with almost quantitative recovery.

Bis(triphenylmethyl) Ethers. The bis(triphenylmethyl) ethers were recommended by Seikel and Huntress (75) as solid derivatives for the identification of glycols. They crystallize readily and no special purification or dehydration of the reagents is required. The procedure described below was used by Seikel and Huntress for preparing derivatives of ethylene glycol, diethylene glycol, and triethylene glycol. A similar procedure was employed by Green and Green (76) for preparing the diether derivative of propylene glycol.

Procedure

Mix 0.10 ml of ethylene glycol, 0.25 ml of diethylene glycol, or 0.25 ml of tri-ethylene glycol with exactly 2 equivalents of triphenylmethyl (trityl) chloride and 1–2 ml of pyridine. Heat on a steam bath in a test tube protected from moisture with a calcium chloride guard tube for 15 min in the case of ethylene glycol or tri-ethylene glycol or for 1 hr in the case of diethylene glycol. Cool and collect the crude solid. Recrystallize from acetone using 15–30 ml for 1 g of precipitate evaporating the solution to one half volume before cooling.

Qualitative Tests

Numerous qualitative tests are available to detect the presence of glycols and polyhydric alcohols or establish the identity of a specific compound in various mixtures. Although these qualitative tests in general are frequently subject to interference from other functional groups, they are nevertheless of value when history of the sample in question is known. In addition to the following described tests, also consult Vol. 4, pp. 521–523 for additional information concerning qualitative tests for hydroxyl compounds. See also the reviews of Hillenbrand (72) and Segur (73).

Gauthier (77) employed bromine water or potassium permanganate to oxidize ethylene glycol and propylene glycol to glycolic aldehyde and acetol, respectively. The reaction product reduces Fehling's solution, ammoniacal silver nitrate, or Nessler's reagent, produces characteristic colors with various phenols in sulfuric acid, and reacts with phenylhydrazine acetate to form characteristic precipitates. In the case of propylene glycol a positive iodoform test is obtained.

Procedure

OXIDATION. Oxidize 0.1 ml of the glycol by adding 10 ml of 0.6% bromine water and heating on a steam bath for 20 min. Alternatively place 2–3 drops of the glycol in a test tube, add 3 ml of water and 0.1 ml of concentrated sulfuric acid. Boil and add 5 drops of a 2% potassium permanganate solution. Shake, and if necessary, add several drops of saturated oxalic acid solution to clear any turbidity which has not disappeared after 1 min.

TEST WITH FEHLING'S AND NESSLER'S REAGENT, AND AMMONIACAL SILVER NITRATE SOLUTION. In case of glycols, the above reaction mixture gives positive test with all three reagents.

TEST WITH PHENOL REAGENTS. Add 0.1 ml of a 5% ethanolic phenol reagent solution and 2 ml of concentrated sulfuric acid to 0.4 ml of the above reaction product. The following characteristic colors are obtained for ethylene and propylene glycols.

	Color	
Phenol reagent	*ethylene glycol*	*propylene glycol*
thymol	bordeaux red	blood red
codeine	blue-green	violet
resorcinol	currant red	cherry red
guaiacol		wine red—increases on warming
β-naphthol	green, fluorescent	

TEST WITH PHENYLHYDRAZINE ACETATE SOLUTION. Add an equal volume of phenylhydrazine acetate solution to a portion of the reaction product. After heating the solution for several minutes, ethylene glycol forms on cooling a crystalline deposit of long, sharp, yellow needles mixed with clear yellow plates of irregular shape with notched edges. In the case of propylene glycol, yellow crystals which appear to be irregular spheres under a microscope form almost immediately without heating.

TEST WITH POTASSIUM TRIIODIDE. Make a portion of the above reaction product alkaline and add a potassium triiodide solution. In case of glycols, a heavy precipitate of iodoform occurs.

1,2-Glycols and glycerol are oxidized by periodates to aldehydes which can be detected colorimetrically. The following procedure, adapted by Hillenbrand (78) from the quantitative method of Desnuelle and Nandet (79), can be used to distinguish between ethylene glycol, propylene glycol, and glycerol.

$$\text{ethylene glycol} \xrightarrow{\text{HIO}_4} \text{formaldehyde}$$

$$\text{propylene glycol} \xrightarrow{\text{HIO}_4} \text{formaldehyde} + \text{acetaldehyde}$$

$$\text{glycerol} \xrightarrow{\text{HIO}_4} \text{formaldehyde} + \text{formic acid}$$

Procedure

Mix 2.5 ml of 6.6% sodium periodate solution with 5 ml of a 4% aqueous solution of the sample in a glass-stoppered test tube. Allow to stand for 20 min, then cool to 0°C and precipitate the excess sodium periodate by addition of 0.5 ml of saturated potassium nitrate. Immerse the tube in an ice bath and allow the precipitate to settle for 10 min. Test separate portions of the clear supernatant liquid for formic acid, formaldehyde, and acetaldehyde:

(a) Determine if formic acid is present by titrating an aliquot of the supernatant liquid with dilute base using methyl red as indicator.

(b) Add 2 ml of 1% aqueous phenylhydrazine hydrochloride solution and 1 ml of 2% potassium ferricyanide solution, both freshly prepared, to an aliquot of the supernatant liquid. Cool in an ice bath and add 5 ml of cold concentrated hydrochloric acid. A red color indicates the presence of formaldehyde.

(c) Add 1 ml of saturated piperazine hydrate solution and 0.5 ml of 4% sodium nitroprusside solution to another portion of the supernant liquid. A blue color develops if acetaldehyde is present.

Oxidation with periodate was also employed by Orchin (80) for the identification of glycerol and other polyhydric compounds with three or more hydroxyl groups on vicinal carbons, eg, hexatols and sugars, in the presence of ethylene glycol, propylene glycol, and diethylene glycol. The sample is made very slightly alkaline to methyl red indicator and a solution of dilute neutralized periodic acid reagent is added. Glycerol, if present, is oxidized to formaldehyde and formic acid and the indicator immediately turns red. Glycols do not produce formic acid. The test solution can be qualitatively checked for formaldehyde with phloroglucinol and for acetaldehyde by the iodoform reaction. If glycerol is absent but formaldehyde is found, the presence of ethylene glycol or propylene glycol is indicated. A positive test for acetaldehyde indicates the presence of propylene glycol. If formaldehyde is found but negative tests are obtained for both formic acid and acetaldehyde, ethylene glycol is present. Diethylene glycol is not oxidized by periodic acid. A similar procedure, based upon oxidation with periodate and identification of formic acid by the color reaction with methyl red indicator, was used by Allen et al. (81) to distinguish between glycerol and ethylene glycol solutions.

The reaction of simple alcohols and glycols with guaiacol and other phenolic reagents in the presence of concentrated sulfuric acid to give characteristic colors was used by Bogs (82) to detect and differentiate ethylene glycol, triethylene glycol, propylene glycol, and glycerol. The reactions of a wide range of alcohols, glycols, and glycol ethers with color-forming reagents in sulfuric acid medium were studied by Counts (83). The same investigator, examining the reaction between pure ethylene glycol and guaiacol in the presence of sulfuric acid, was unable to obtain the intense purple color previously reported, and attributed positive tests to impure material containing oxidation products (84).

Middleton (85) has described a qualitative test for ethylene glycol based upon its oxidation to oxalic acid with nitric acid. Oxalic acid is identified by its character-istic reaction with potassium permanganate. The test is sensitive to 0.1 g of ethylene glycol and will detect 0.3 g of the glycol in the presence of 0.7 g of glycerol.

Glycerol and polyhydric alcohols give characteristic colors when heated with catechol in the presence of concentrated sulfuric acid. No color is formed by ethylene glycol, diethylene glycol, or ethanol. Triethylene glycol and propylene glycol yield only a faint pink color. Interference is encountered from trimethylene glycol and aldehydes which also yield colored products with the reagent in the presence of sul-furic acid. The reaction, described by Hovey and Hodges (86), may be used to distinguish glycols from polyhydric alcohols.

Procedure

Place 3 ml of the solution to be tested in a test tube. Add 3 ml of freshly prepared 10% aqueous catechol solution and swirl to mix. Add 6 ml of concentrated sulfuric acid and heat the solution gently at 140–145°C for 30 sec. Observe the color formed:

Polyhydric alcohol	Color
glycerol	red-orange
pentaerythritol	dark purple-red
erythritol	faint pink
mannitol	red-orange

Interfering substances yield the following colors:

Substance	Color
trimethylene glycol	dark brown
formaldehyde	purple turning brown
acetaldehyde	purplish red
benzaldehyde	red-orange

A rapid procedure for the detection of vicinal glycols in alkyd resins was described by Jordan (87). After saponification and extraction, the glycols are separated by an azeotropic reflux distillation from toluene–water and concentrated in a Dean and Stark receiver trap. The solution is tested for vicinal glycols by addition of periodic acid followed by silver nitrate. The formation of a white precipitate, silver iodate, indicates the presence of vicinal glycols.

Polyglycols. Numerous qualitative tests have been developed for the identifica-tion of the polyoxyethylene group due to its important and wide use as a hydrophilic linkage in many surface active agents. Most of the earlier procedures are based on precipitation of the polyoxyethylene compound as the oxonium salt by a large anion such as BI_4^- (88), cobaltothiocyanate (89), phosphomolybdate (90–92), silicotungstate (90), or phosphotungstate (93), and can usually be made quantitative either by measuring the amount of precipitate or by dissolving the precipitate and determining the metal content colorimetrically. As the stoichiometry may differ considerably with molecular weight and the commercial polyethylene glycols and derivatives are available as mixtures within specified molecular weight ranges, calibration with the proper polyglycol is required when these methods are used quantitatively. The above tests are of limited use in that cationic surfactants are also precipitated by the large anions. A review of methods applicable to polyoxyethylene and polyoxypropylene type compounds is covered in Rosen and Goldsmith's monograph (94).

Rosen (95) described a qualitative test for the detection of polyoxyethylene or polyoxypropylene groups based on thermal decomposition in the presence of phosphoric acid to yield acetaldehyde or propionaldehyde and its polymers, respectively. The former gives a blue color when reacted with sodium nitroprusside and diethanolamine while the latter produces orange colors. The reactions are as follows:

$$(OCH_2-CH_2)_x \xrightarrow[\Delta]{H^+} n\,CH_3CHO + (OCH_2-CH_2)_{x-n}$$

polyoxyethylene   acetaldehyde

$$\underset{\underset{CH_3}{|}}{(OCH-CH_2)}_x \xrightarrow[\Delta]{H^+} n\,CH_3CH_2CHO + (CH_3CH_2CHO)_m + \underset{\underset{CH_3}{|}}{(OCH-CH_2)}_{x-(n+m)}$$

polyoxypropylene   propionaldehyde

Table 26. Reaction of Compounds Containing the Polyoxyethylene or Polyoxypropylene Group to the Rosen Test

Product	Source	Structure	Color produced
ethylene glycol	Union Carbide Co.	$H(OCH_2CH_2)_xOH$ $(x = 1)$	purple
diethylene glycol	Union Carbide Co.	$H(OCH_2CH_2)_xOH$ $(x = 1)$	blue
polyethylene glycol 400	Union Carbide Co.	$H(OCH_2CH_2)_xOH$ $(x \cong 9)$	blue
Carbowax 4000	Union Carbide Co.	$H(OCH_2CH_2)_xOH$ $(x \cong 90)$	blue
propylene glycol	Union Carbide Co.	$H(OCHCH_2)_xOH$ $(x = 1)$ $\quad\ \ \ \overset{\textstyle|}{CH_3}$	pale yellow
dipropylene glycol	Dow Chemical Co.	$H(OCHCH_2)_xOH$ $(x = 2)$ $\quad\ \ \ \overset{\textstyle|}{CH_3}$	orange
Polyglycol P-400	Dow Chemical Co.	$H(OCHCH_2)_xOH$ $(x \cong 7)$ $\quad\ \ \ \overset{\textstyle|}{CH_3}$	orange
Polyglycol P-750	Dow Chemical Co.	$H(OCHCH_2)_xOH$ $(x \cong 13)$ $\quad\ \ \ \overset{\textstyle|}{CH_3}$	orange
Dowanol 50-B	Dow Chemical Co.	$CH_3(OCHCH_2)_2OH$ $\quad\ \ \ \overset{\textstyle|}{CH_3}$	orange
Pluronic F68	Wyandotte Corp.	propylene oxide–ethylene oxide polymer	orange, then brown
Pluronic L62	Wyandotte Corp.	propylene oxide–ethylene oxide polymer	orange, then brown
Tergitol XC	Union Carbide Co.	alkyl ether of propylene oxide–ethylene oxide polymer	orange, then brown

Procedure

Place about 200 mg of anhydrous surfactant and 1–1.5 ml of 85% phosphoric acid in a 5–6-in. test tube and swirl to mix. Place a small plug of cotton in the mouth of the test tube to prevent condensed water from falling back into the hot reaction mixture during pyrolysis. Attach a glass delivery tube with a 60° angle bend by means of a one-hole stopper. Clamp the tube at an angle of 30° so that the outlet of the delivery tube is vertical. Add 1 ml of water, 1 drop of diethanolamine, and 2 drops of sodium nitroprusside solution prepared by dissolving 20 g of sodium nitroprusside dihydrate in 50 ml of water and diluted with 450 ml of methanol to a 4-in. test tube. Position the tube so that the end of the delivery tube is beneath the surface of the solution.

Heat the mixture of phosphoric acid and surfactant with a small flame until the mixture turns dark brown. If foaming is excessive, discontinue heating momentarily to allow the foam to subside, then heat the test tube strongly just above the level of the foam, gradually moving the flame downward until the liquid mixture is again heated by the flame. Continue heating until a blue or orange color appears in the distillate solution. A blue color indicates the presence of the polyoxyethylene group whereas an orange color is due to the presence of the polyoxypropylene group. An orange color which quickly turns dark brown indicates the presence of both groups. If no color appears within 5 min, the test is negative.

Every type of surfactant tested, including anionics, cationics, and nonionics, which contain either the polyoxyethylene or the polyoxypropylene group, or both, gave a positive reaction to the test. Surfactants containing only the polyoxyethylene group produce a blue color; those containing only the polyoxypropylene group produce an orange color; those containing both the polyoxyethylene group and the polyoxypropylene group produce an orange color which quickly turns dark brown. No interference was encountered from other groups which may also be present including the ester, alkylaryl, sulfide, sulfonate, sulfate, amino, amido, and phosphate groups. The only compounds which give positive results in the absence of the polyoxyethylene or polyoxypropylene group are glycerides which, under the test conditions, decompose to acrolein, which also gives a blue color with sodium nitroprusside and diethanolamine. A partial list of the compounds screened by the procedure is given in Table 26.

Rosen's procedure was modified for quantitative work by Williams and Graham (96) who pyrolyzed the polyoxyethylene- or polyoxypropylene-containing surface active agents in the presence of phosphoric acid and determined the resulting aldehydes by measuring the color of the complexes formed with sodium nitroprusside and diethanolamine.

A spectrophotometric method for the detection and quantitative determination of polyoxyethylene surface active agents was described by Gatewood and Graham (97). The anhydrous sample is heated with an acidic solution of carbonyl-free, methanolic 2,4-dinitrophenylhydrazine. After cooling, 10% ethanolic potassium hydroxide solution is added. A characteristic purple color with an absorption maximum at 560 nm is obtained. With careful control, the intensity of the color developed is proportional to the concentration of polyoxyethylene compound present and can be used as a quantitative micro method. Ethylene glycol itself gives a negative reaction, but other glycols of both the ethylene and propylene series react.

Other surfactants which do not contain an ethylene oxide or propylene oxide unit do not react. The reaction apparently depends on the presence of a free hydroxyl group, as diester derivatives were found to give a negative result.

Chromatography

The chromatographic procedures discussed in this section may be used for the separation and identification as well as for the quantitative determination of glycols and polyhydric alcohols in mixtures.

Gas Chromatography. Gas chromatography has been applied widely for the analysis of various classes of glycols and polyhydric alcohols.

Glycols. The important gas chromatographic methods developed to date are summarized in Table 27. Most of the methods are described in detail in the references cited. These should be consulted when developing methods suitable for the separation of various combinations of compounds.

The conversion of glycols and polyhydric alcohols to stable lower-boiling derivatives for gas chromatography has been reported. According to Smith and Carlsson (98), polyhydric alcohols are easily converted quantitatively to trimethylsilyl ethers which are more stable than the parent compounds. Puschmann and Miller (99) used the acetate esters of diethylene glycol, 1,2-propylene glycol, 1,3-butylene glycol, and glycerol. These were prepared by reaction with acetic anhydride at 120°C.

Polyethylene Glycols. The direct analysis of polyethylene glycols by gas chromatography has not been feasible due to their low volatility.

Calzolari et al. (100) used gas chromatography to determine the distribution of the degree of polymerization in polyethylene glycols with molecular weights up to 1000. Three commercial polyethylene glycols with average molecular weights of 300, 400, and 600 were converted to dimethyl, diphenyl, and disilyl ethers, a sulfur derivative, and a higher-boiling chloro derivative. These lower-boiling derivatives were then chromatographed successfully using 5% silicone gum rubber on Chromosorb W and a flame ionization detector. Temperature programming was used from 100 to 350°C at a rate of 7 or 8°/min. Satisfactory molecular weight fractionation was obtained. The dimethyl derivatives were the most volatile but the bis-trimethylsilyl compounds were best suited for chromatography under the conditions used. The factors determining suitability are maximum volatility and thermal stability, minimum energy of adsorption on the support and simplicity of synthesis. For the series studied, the order of volatility of the derivatives for the same value of n was as follows: dimethyl > bistrimethylsilyl > dichloro > diphenyl > bisthiophenoxy and the order of elution varied linearly with n. Using the more volatile derivatives, compounds with molecular weights up to 900 can be fractionated.

Withers (101) separated polyethylene glycols with molecular weights up to 500 as trimethylsilyl ethers on a 3 ft × 1/8 in. column packed with 3.3% phenylmethyl silicone oil on 110–120 mesh Anakron ABS. Temperature programming was used from 100 to 300°C at a rate of 10°/min. The method was used on a routine basis and no deterioration of the column occurred in 18 months.

Polyhydric Alcohols. Methods are available for the determination of impurities in glycerol and pentaerythritol. In most cases, conversion to lower-boiling derivatives is used. Smith et al. (102) converted mono-, di- and triglycerol to trimethylsilyl ethers by refluxing with trimethylchlorosilane in pyridine or heating in a sealed tube at 150°C for 15 hr with 0.5 ml of hexamethyldisilane and 0.5 ml of trimethyl-

Table 27. Gas Chromatographic Conditions for the Analysis of Glycols

Compounds separated	Column	Column temperature	Other conditions[a]	Reference
up to 2% monoethylene glycol and triethylene glycol in diethylene glycol; up to 8% diethylene glycol in monoethylene glycol	2 m × ¼ in. OD, 20% Apiezon L on Chromosorb	200°C	helium at 210 ml/min; TCD	(103)
0–3% ethylene and propylene glycol in mixtures	2 m × ¼ in. OD, 5% tetrahydroxyethylenediamine on Chromosorb W	200°C	helium at 300 ml/min; TCD	(104)
5 ppm to 0.15% diethylene glycol in triethylene glycol	1 m × ¼ in. OD, 5% Igepal CO-880[b] on Fluopak 20/80 mesh	200°C	helium at 40 ml/min	(105)
ethylene, diethylene, pentamethylene, octylene, triethylene, tetramethylene, and 1,3-butanediols	4 ft × ¼ in. OD, 2% Versamid 900 polyamide resin on silanized Chromosorb W, 60/80 mesh	programmed from 100 to 250°C at 9°C/min	FID	(106)
ethylene glycol, propylene glycol, 2,3-butanediol, 2,4-pentanediol, 1,3-propanediol, 2,5-hexanediol, 1,3-butenediol, 2-butene-1,4-diol, diethylene glycol, 1,5-pentanediol, glycerol, 1,6-hexanediol, triethylene glycol in order of separation	4 ft × ¼ in. OD, 10% polyphenyl ether and 2% Carbowax on Fluopak 80	programmed from 75 to 200°C at 15°C/min	helium at 60 ml/min; TCD	(107)
propylene glycol, diethylene glycol, and glycerol in tobacco	6 ft × ¼ in. OD, 5% Carbowax 1500 on Haloport F	programmed from 50 to 200°C at 9°C/min	helium at 70 ml/min; TCD	(108)
ppm ethylene and propylene glycol in water	2 m × ¼ in. OD, 10% poly-*m*-phenyl ether on Haloport F, 60/80 mesh	110°C	helium at 28–30 ml/min with the addition of steam at 50–55 ml/min; FID	(109)
ppm diethylene glycol in water		150°C		
0.1–1% mono- and 4–5% diethylene glycol in triethylene glycol by vacuum gas chromatography	0.6 m × 3 cm OD, 25% polyethylene glycol adipate on INZ-600, 0.25–0.50 mm grain size	175°C	inlet pressure = 371 torr; outlet pressure = 63 torr; BID	(110)
dipropylene glycol isomers	11 ft × ¼ in. OD, 5% Carbowax 20M on Fluopak 80	175°C	helium at 80 ml/min; TCD	(111)
5–10% methanol, 0.5% diethylene glycol in ethylene glycol	4 ft × ¼ in. OD, 5% Carbowax on Haloport F	190°C	FID	(112)

Compounds	Column	Temperature	Carrier gas; detector	Ref.
ethylene, diethylene, and triethylene glycols; propylene, dipropylene, and tripropylene glycols; tetraethylene glycol	4 ft × ¼ in. OD, 7% polyethylene glycol (MW = 2000) on Haloport F	programmed from 150 to 225°C at 5.6°C/min or isothermal at 170°C (ethylene, di- and triethylene glycols), 190°C (propylene glycols), and at 200°C (tetraethylene glycol)	helium at 75 ml/min; TCD	(113)
propane-1,2-diol, ethane-1,2-diol, butane-1,3-diol, propane-1,3-diol, 2,2-dimethyl-propane-1,3-diol, butane-1,4-diol, pentane-1,5-diol, hexane-1,6-diol	25 ft × 3/16 in. OD, 15% diethylene glycol adipate crosslinked with pentaerythritol (LAC-2R-446) on silanized Celite, 60–80 mesh	175°C	hydrogen at 40 ml/min; TCD	(114)
small amounts of ethanediol in glycol ethers	4 ft × 4 mm OD, Porapak S 100/120 mesh	200°C	argon at 50 ml/min; AID	(115)
monoethylene glycol dinitrate, diethylene glycol dinitrate, triethylene glycol dinitrate, 1,2-dinitropropanediol, 1,5-dinitropentanediol	35–50 cm × ¼ in. OD, 10% ethylene glycol succinate on acid-washed Celite C-22 40/60 mesh	145–150°C	helium at 250 ml/min; TCD	(116)
1,2-tetradecanediol and 1,2-hexadecanediol	6 ft × ⅛ in. OD, 7% Zonyl E-7 on Chromosorb W, 80/100 mesh	195°C	helium at 50 ml/min; FID	(117)
	3 ft × ⅛ in. OD, 2% Versamid 900 polyamide resin on silanized Chromosorb W, 80/100 mesh	195°C		
	3 ft × ⅛ in. OD, 2% OV-17 methyl phenyl silicone oil on Anakrom Q 60/70 mesh	160°C		
1.8 ppm 2,3-butanediol in 1,2-propanediol; 22 ppm of 2,3-butanediol, 1,2-propanediol, 1,3-butanediol, 1,2-ethanediol, 1,3-propanediol, 1,4-butanediol; 20 ppm ethanediol in 1,2-propanediol	2–10 ft × ¼ in. OD, 0.6% water on silanized Chromosorb W, 80/100 mesh	91–94°C	nitrogen at 37–51 ml/min with the addition of steam at 34–46 ml/min; FID	(118)
100 ppm diethylene glycol in monoethylene glycol, and in triethylene glycol	polyethylene adipate on Celite		FID	(119)
high-boiling glycols and glycerol	hexakis(2-cyanoethyl) hexane liquid phase	240°C		(120)

[a] TCD = thermal conductivity detector. FID = flame ionization detector. BID = β-ray ionization detector. AID = argon ionization detector.
[b] Nonylphenoxypoly(ethyleneoxy)ethanol.

Table 28. Gas Chromatographic Conditions for the Analysis of Polyhydric Alcohols

Compounds separated	Column	Column temperature	Other conditions[a]	Reference
0.1% or more propane-1,3-diol in glycerol	62 cm × 2 mm ID; 25% Reoplex polyester on Celite 60/80 mesh	120°C	argon at 40–50 ml/min; AID	(121)
0.26–2.5% propane-1,3-diol in glycerol, dilute aqueous solutions	28 cm × 2 mm ID; 25% Reoplex polyester on Embacel kieselguhr 60/100 mesh	150°C	nitrogen at 10 ml/min; FID	(122)
glycerol and diglycerol as tetraacetates	240 cm × 6.5 mm ID, 0.25% SE-30 methyl silicone gum rubber on 0.177 mm dia glass beads	207°C	AID	(123)
2–25% di- and tripentaerythritol in monopentaerythritol as esters; pentaerythritol cyclic monoformal diacetate and bispentaerythritol monoformal hexaacetate are also separated	4 ft × 3/16 in. OD, 15% SE-30 methyl silicone gum rubber on Chromosorb W 30/60 mesh	programmed from 220 to 320°C at 5°C/min	helium at 140 ml/min; TCD	(124)
mono-, di-, tri-, tetra- and pentaerythritol other components detected: pentaerythritol dicyclic diformal, pentaerythritol cyclic monoformal and pentaerythritol components tentatively detected: bis(pentaerythritol)monoformal, pentaerythritol–dipentaerythritol monoformal, tris(pentaerythritol) diformal and bis(dipentaerythritol) monoformal; all compounds converted to trimethylsilyl ethers	4 ft × 3/16 in. OD, 17% SE-30 methyl silicone gum rubber on Gas-Chrom Z, 60/80 mesh	programmed from 125 to 326°C at 13°C/min	helium at 100 ml/min; TCD	(125)

[a] Detectors:
TCD = thermal conductivity detector.
FID = flame ionization detector.
AID = argon ionization detector.

Table 29. Gas Chromatographic Conditions for the Analysis of Glycols, Polyglycols, and Polyhydric Alcohols in Synthetic Resins

Compounds separated	Column	Column temperature	Other conditions[a]	Reference
propylene glycol, ethylene glycol, diethylene glycol, glycerol, trimethylolethane, trimethylolpropane, pentaerythritol liberated by aminolysis with butylamine and determined as acetates by treatment with acetic anhydride	4 ft × ¼ in. OD, 10% Carbowax 20M on Chromosorb W 60/80 mesh	programmed from 50 to 225°C at 7.9°C/min	helium at 60 ml/min; TCD	(126)
neopentyl glycol, 1,4-butanediol dipropylene glycol, triethylene glycol liberated by aminolysis with benzylamine and determined as acetates	4 ft × ¼ in. OD, 10% Carbowax 20M on Chromosorb W 60/80 mesh	programmed from 50 to 225°C at 7.9°C/min	helium at 60 ml/min; TCD	(127)
propylene glycol, ethylene glycol 1,3-butylene glycol, neopentyl glycol, dipropylene glycol, dimethylene glycol, and triethylene glycol isolated by precipitation of resin followed by methanolysis and determination as free glycols	12 ft × ¼ in. OD, 33% SF-96 methyl silicone oil on Fluopak 80	programmed from 110 to 180°C at 8°C/min	helium at 50 ml/min; TCD	(128)
500 ppm–3% diethylene glycol in polyethylene terephthalate after pressure hydrolysis at 230°C	10 ft × ⅛ in. OD, 10% Carbowax 20M on silanized Chromosorb W 80/100 mesh	180°C	helium at 50 ml/min FID for 500 ppm–0.5%, and TCD for concentrations above 0.5% FID	(129)
ethylene glycol, 1,2-propylene glycol, 2,3-, 1,3- and 1,4-butylene glycols, cyclohexanediol, diethylene glycol, and glycerol (I); glycerol, trimethylolethane, trimethylolpropane, triethylene glycol, erythritol, and pentaerythritol (II), after transesterification to acetates with acetic acid and sulfuric acid	4 ft × ¼ in. OD, 5% polyethylene glycol on Embacel	group I: 100°C group II: 140°C		

[a] TCD = thermal conductivity detector.
FID = flame ionization detector.

Table 30. Liquid Column Chromatography of Glycols and Polyhydric Alcohols

Compounds separated	Column	Solvent systems	Notes	Reference
ethylene glycol, propylene glycol, 1,2-, and 2,3-butylene glycol	Celite or chromatographic grade silicic acid	1:4 n-butanol–chloroform, 1:1 n-butanol–chloroform, and n-butanol	glycols in fractions determined by periodate oxidation and subsequent titration	(130)
ethylene glycol, diethylene glycol, 1,2-propylene glycol, the meso and dl isomers of 2,3-butylene glycol, and glycerol	76.5 cm × 4.3 mm ID, Dowex I-X8, 200/300 mesh (borate form)	0.925 M sodium metaborate or 0.02 M borax solution		(131)
polyoxyethylene glycol (MW = 1000) in a mixture of three nonionic surfactants	silica gel	1:2 methanol–chloroform	glycerol may also be separated	(132)
polyglycols (chain length up to 20 moles of EtO per mole of higher alcohol) in methoxylated higher alcohols	Hyflo Super-Cel; stationary phase = octanol	1:2:7 acetic acid–acetone–water	polyglycols separated from the fractions by precipitation with phosphomolybdic acid and barium chloride	(133)
ethylene glycol, propylene glycol, erythritol, and glycerol	Dowex 50	butanol–pyridine–water		(134)

Table 31. Paper Chromatography of Glycols and Polyalcohols

Compounds separated	Remarks	Reference
ethylene glycol, diethylene glycol, triethylene glycol, 1,2-propylene glycol, 1,3-propanediol, 2,3-butylene glycol, 1,3-butanediol, 1,4-butanediol, 1,2,4-butanetriol	R_f values in various solvent systems are given	(135)
ethylene glycol, propylene glycols, butylene glycols, hexanediols, and polyethylene glycols through C_{10} as 3,5-dinitrobenzoyl esters	R_f values are given for 20 developing solutions	(136)
ethylene glycol, glycerol, pentaerythritol	identification with vanadium quinolate in acetic acid–xylene mixtures	(137)
ethylene glycol, propylene glycol, glycerol	10:3:3, butanol–pyridine–water	(138)
compounds of type $ROC_2H_4(OC_2H_4)$-OC_2H_4OH esterified with 3,5-dinitrobenzoic acid	formamide or dimethylformamide stationary phases; hexane, cyclohexane, benzene, chloroform, and their mixtures as mobile phases	(139)
polyoxyethylene glycol in nonionic surfactants	ascending paper chromatography, semiquantitative spot area method, estimation to nearest 1%	(140)
glycerol, pentaerythritol, diethylene glycol, propylene glycol, trimethylolethane, trimethylolpropane, and neopentyl glycol	chloroform–alcohol stationary phase; 8:2:1 isoamyl alcohol–ethanol–water mobile phases; detection with ammoniacal silver nitrate	(141)
polyols in polyesters after hydrolysis	10:10:1, acetone–benzene–water, 1:1 butyl acetate–water, or 1:1 butyl alcohol–water as eluting solution	(142)
ethylene glycol, diethylene glycol, triethylene glycol	water–saturated butanol developing solution; no derivatives required	(143)
glycerol in mixtures containing ethylene glycol, propylene glycol, erythritol, 1,2,4-butanetriol	sec-butanol saturated with water or n-butanol saturated with water as developing solvents; silver nitrate detection reagent	(144)
separation and determination of diglycerols, 3,3′-oxydipropanediol and 2,3′-oxydipropanediol in glycerol	1-butanol saturated with water as developing solvent; sodium periodate and benzidine used for detection	(145)

chlorosilane. The products were chromatographed either isothermally or with temperature programming.

Table 28 summarizes the gas chromatographic methods reported in the literature for the analysis of polyhydric alcohols.

Glycols and Polyhydric Alcohols in Resins. Methods for the identification and determination of glycols and polyhydric alcohols in synthetic resins involve the liberation or isolation of these compounds from the resin by chemical treatment followed by gas chromatography. Table 29 summarizes the most important procedures and the gas chromatographic conditions recommended.

Liquid Column Chromatography. Although the methods described in the section on gas chromatography can be applied to most mixtures of glycols and polyhydric alcohols available commercially, liquid column chromatography can also be used for some of these separations. Table 30 summarizes some of the most important applications published.

Table 32. Thin-Layer Chromatography of Glycols and Polyhydric Alcohols

Compounds separated	Adsorbent	Developing solvent	Note	Reference
ethylene glycol, propylene glycol, glycerol, and 2,3-dimethyl-1-hexyne-3,4-diol	silica gel	1:9 methanol–chloroform	ammoniacal silver nitrate developing reagent	(146)
1,2-propanediol, 1,3-, 1,4-, and 2,3-butanediol, 1,5-pentanediol, and 2-methyl-2,4-pentanediol	alumina (0.2 mm layer)	99:1 ethyl ether–ethanol, or 3:1 or 4:1 hexane–acetone		(147)
glycerol and 2-methyl-1,2,3-pentanetriol	paste of cellulose paper, gypsum, and water	a number of systems		(148)
0.1% ethylene glycol or glycerol in propylene glycol	aluminum oxide (0.5 mm layer)	77:17:6 chloroform–toluene–acetic acid	development with periodate and rosaniline as the detecting agent	(149)
17 polyhydric alcohols from ethylene glycol to pentaerythritol	alumina, silica gel, and kieselguhr impregnated with polyamine	chloroform–toluene–formic acid, butanol–ammonium hydroxide, and chloroform		(150)
polyethylene glycols ranging from 200 to 6000 ethylene units	silica gel G	3:25:12 chloroform–methanol–water		(151)

Paper and Thin-Layer Chromatography. Pertinent paper chromatographic methods that might be applicable to particular problems are summarized in Table 31. Table 32 lists a number of thin-layer chromatographic systems used successfully for the separation and determination of a number of glycols and polyhydric alcohols.

Spectroscopy

Infrared Spectroscopy. Polyhydric alcohols in unsaturated polyesters have been identified by infrared spectroscopy (152). A solution of precipitated polyester in acetone or benzene is saponified with 0.5 N methanolic potassium hydroxide. The insoluble dipotassium salts are removed and the water solution is acidified and extracted with ethyl ether. The water extract is made slightly alkaline and then evaporated and dried. This polyhydric alcohol fraction is then analyzed by infrared. The identification of a single unknown polyhydric alcohol simply involves careful comparison with standard spectra. Mixtures of two or more polyhydric alcohols that do not interact can be analyzed. Fourteen combinations of common, commercial polyhydric alcohols in different ratios and combinations were examined. After identification the proportions of the polyhydric alcohols present can be roughly estimated by comparison with solutions of similar composition.

Turi and Giuli (153) differentiated between polyethylene and polypropylene glycols by pyrolysis of a sample at 350°C and treatment of the pyrolyzate with 2,4-dinitrophenylhydrazine. After separation of the derivatives by paper chromatography, the phenylhydrazones were identified by infrared analysis.

Nuclear Magnetic Resonance Spectroscopy. Nuclear magnetic resonance spectroscopy has been applied to a limited extent for the identification of glycols. Goodlett (154) showed that esterification of hydroxy compounds produced downfield shifts of hydrogen peaks in alpha position to hydroxy groups. These shifted peaks are valuable aids in structure determination. Trichloroacetyl isocyanate is the most desirable esterification reagent, reacting rapidly with the hydroxyl groups. This was illustrated by the effect on the NMR spectrum of 2,2-dimethyl-5-phenyl-1,3-pentanediol. The procedure can be used to determine the relative reactivities of different types of hydroxyl groups and should be applicable to other glycols.

Sawyer and Brannan (155) studied the NMR spectra of ethylene glycol, glycerol, and erythritol using tetramethylammonium chloride as an internal reference. These polyalcohols have the simplest spectra to interpret because of their symmetry. The major peak for this group of compounds occurs between 0.45 and 0.55 ppm and is due to the protons in the CH_2OH and CHOH groups.

NMR has also been used for end-group analysis and number-average molecular weight determination of some polyalkylene glycols (156). The methylene and methine groups attached to the hydroxyl can be differentiated from those attached to the ether oxygen in polyalkylene glycols using the technique described.

Moniz and Poranski (157) reported the analysis of mixed pentaerythritol, dipentaerythritol, and trimethylolpropane as esters. An absolute accuracy of 5 mole % for each ester type was obtained. The method was used for a group of commercial esters and several aircraft lubricants. Other studies reported in the literature deal with the structure of dihydroxypentanes (158), the spin-lattice and spin-spin relaxation times of 1,3-butanediol, 2-methyl-2,4-pentanediol, glycerol, and 1,2,6-hexanetriol (159), and hydrogen bonding in six diols (160).

Assay Methods

The assay of technical grade glycols and polyhydric alcohols can be accomplished by a number of methods. In case of mixtures where the impurity is essentially only water, the glycol content may be determined from specific gravity or refractive index measurements. Assay is also possible by determining the hydroxyl content of the sample. Besides these, a number of chemical methods are also in use. Among the instrumental methods, gas chromatography is well suited for assay, and infrared spectroscopy can be used for hydroxyl-group determination.

Glycols

Assay by Density and Refractive Index. MacBeth and Thompson (161) used density data at 35°C and refractive index data at 25°C to determine the concentration of propylene glycol in aqueous solution over the entire composition range. The smoothed data are shown in Table 33.

Table 33. Determination of Propylene Glycol in Aqueous Solutions from Density and Refractive Index Data

Propylene glycol, wt %	Refractive index, n_D, at 25.00°C	Absolute density, at 35.00°C, g/ml
0 (pure water)	1.3325	0.99406
10.00	1.3432	1.00089
20.00	1.3544	1.00852
30.00	1.3658	1.01615
40.00	1.3770	1.02295
50.00	1.3878	1.02818
60.00	1.3980	1.03154
70.00	1.4075	1.03299
80.00	1.4162	1.03240
90.00	1.4241	1.02982
100.00	1.4316	1.02510

The refractive index data can be used to determine propylene glycol over the entire composition range within about ±0.1%. Although a maximum appears in the density–composition curve, it may be used to determine glycol contents below 50 within ± 0.04%.

Chiao and Thompson (162) have developed density and refractive index data for aqueous solutions of triethylene glycol, dipropylene glycol, and hexylene glycol.

Table 34. Properties of Pure Compounds

	Specific gravity, 20/20°C		Density, at 25°C, g/ml	Refractive index, n_D		
				at 20°C		at 25°C
	A[a]	B[b]	A[a]	A[a]	B[b]	A[a]
triethylene glycol	1.1254	1.1254	1.1195	1.4558	1.4559	1.4541
dipropylene glycol	1.0232	1.0252	1.0165	1.4407	1.4440	1.4389
hexylene glycol	0.9240	0.9234	0.9181	1.4275	1.4263	1.4257

[a] A = Ref. 162.

[b] B = earlier data.

Table 35. Experimental Density and Refractive Index Data for Triethylene Glycol

Glycol, wt %	Absolute density, at 25°C, g/ml	Refractive index, n_D	
		at 20°C	at 25°C
0 (pure water)		1.3330	1.3325
10.05	1.0117	1.3450	1.3444
20.02	1.0272	1.3573	1.3565
29.68	1.0426	1.3699	1.3689
40.10	1.0592	1.3835	1.3824
49.69	1.0740	1.3965	1.3952
59.97	1.0883	1.4102	1.4086
69.85	1.1000	1.4225	1.4208
79.76	1.1091	1.4343	1.4327
90.00	1.1155	1.4453	1.4437
purified[a]	1.1195	1.4558	1.4541

[a] Containing 0.02% of water.

Table 36. Experimental Density and Refractive Index Data for Dipropylene Glycol

Glycol, wt %	Absolute density at 25°C, g/ml	Refractive index, n_D	
		at 20°C	at 25°C
0 (pure water)		1.3330	1.3325
10.00	1.0046	1.3452	1.3446
20.00	1.0131	1.3578	1.3569
29.97	1.0215	1.3709	1.3698
39.99	1.0288	1.3836	1.3822
49.69	1.0337	1.3958	1.3940
60.07	1.0359	1.4071	1.4054
69.94	1.0354	1.4171	1.4154
79.76	1.0323	1.4261	1.4244
89.47	1.0273	1.4339	1.4322
purified[a]	1.0165	1.4407	1.4389

[a] Containing 0.03% of water.

Table 37. Experimental Density and Refractive Index Data for Hexylene Glycol

Glycol, wt %	Absolute density at 25°C, g/ml	Refractive index, n_D	
		at 20°C	at 25°C
0 (pure water)		1.3330	1.3325
9.98	0.9967	1.3457	1.3450
19.95	0.9972	1.3588	1.3580
30.00	0.9962	1.3717	1.3705
40.01	0.9918	1.3833	1.3819
49.92	0.9851	1.3936	1.3921
60.04	0.9764	1.4032	1.4014
69.89	0.9662	1.4117	1.4099
80.02	0.9538	1.4190	1.4172
89.89	0.9390	1.4247	1.4228
purified[a]	0.9181	1.4275	1.4257

[a] Containing 0.04% of water.

The pertinent information is given in Tables 34–37. Because of the points of inflection in two of the density–composition curves, the usefulness of the density data for analytical purposes varies considerably with composition. Using refractive index, analyses accurate to within ±0.1 wt % are obtained for all three glycols except for hexylene glycol for which the value is ±0.4% above 95%.

Esterification Methods. All the esterification methods described under ALCOHOLS (Vol. 4, pp. 529–538) are also applicable to glycols. Since the publication of that article, the phthalic anhydride and pyromellitic dianhydride (PMDA) methods have been thoroughly studied and the procedures modified to give the best precision and accuracy (163,164). These two procedures are described in detail. The reaction times of four glycols and pentaerythritol at 98°C with phthalic anhydride are listed in Table 38 (165).

Table 38. Reaction Times for Glycols and Polyalcohols with Phthalic Anhydride

Compound	Minimum reaction time at 98°C, minutes
diethylene glycol	15
dipropylene glycol	150
2-ethyl-1,3-hexanediol	180
1,5-pentanediol	30
pentaerythritol	15

Procedures

PHTHALIC ANHYDRIDE METHOD. Carry out the following qualitative test for the pyridine to be used in the procedure. Dissolve 7 g of phthalic anhydride in 50 ml of pyridine in a glass-stoppered flask. Heat at 50–60°C for 30 min and allow to stand in the dark at room temperature for 24 hr. Measure the color of the solution: it should be less than 200 on the Pt–Co scale. If the reagent is marginal, purify it by distillation from phthalic anhydride in a packed column at a reflux ratio of 5:1. When the head temperature reaches 114°C, collect the distillate between 114 and 116°C for preparation of the phthalation reagent.

Prepare the phthalation reagent by dissolving 130 ± 3 g of phthalic anhydride in 800 ml of pyridine with vigorous shaking. Store in a brown bottle and let stand overnight before use. Discard the solution when its color exceeds 200 Pt–Co scale.

Pipet 25 ml of phthalation reagent into enough pressure bottles (350 ml) for blanks and sample determinations in duplicate. Use a uniform drainage time for all aliquots. Determine the sample weight as follows:

$$\text{Sample weight, g} = \frac{(702)(0.98)}{\text{approximate hydroxyl number}}$$

Adhere closely to the calculated weight since it is near the maximum permitted by the method. The weight should not exceed 10 g. If the sample contains an appreciable amount of water, calculate the sample weight as follows:

$$\text{Sample weight, g} = \frac{(0.213)(0.98)}{0.0094R + \left[(0.01S)\left(\frac{(N)(17.01)}{M}\right)\right]}$$

where R = water in sample, in wt %

S = purity of sample, in wt %

M = g-mol wt of compound

N = number of OH groups in the molecule

Transfer the calculated weights of sample to the bottles containing reagent, stopper and swirl to dissolve the samples. If necessary, warm the bottle on a steam bath for several minutes. Enclose each bottle in a fabric bag and place them in a steam bath at $98 \pm 2°C$ for 2 hr. The water in the bath should be above the liquid level in the bottles. Remove the bottles from the bath and cool to room temperature. Release any pressure build-up and remove the bag. The solution should be yellow if enough reagent is present. Rinse any solution on the stopper into the bottle and wash the sides of the bottle with 50 ml of water. Add 5–6 drops of a 1% (wt/vol) phenolphthalein solution in pyridine and titrate immediately with 0.5 N sodium hydroxide solution to the first pink end point that persists for 15 sec. If the volume of the 0.5 N sodium hydroxide solution used for sample titration is less than 75% of that required for the blank, the sample was too large; in this case, repeat the analysis with a smaller sample.

Calculate the hydroxyl content either as hydroxyl number or wt % hydroxyl-containing compound as follows:

$$\text{Hydroxyl number} = \frac{(A - B)(N)(56.1)}{w}$$

$$\text{Hydroxyl-containing compound, wt \%} = \frac{(A - B)(N)(M)(100)}{(w)(n)(1000)}$$

where A = volume of sodium hydroxide solution used for blank titration, in ml
  B = volume of sodium hydroxide solution used for sample titration, in ml
  N = normality of the sodium hydroxide solution at the temperature of analysis
  n = number of hydroxyl groups in the molecule of the compound
  M = g-mol wt of the hydroxyl-containing compound
  w = sample weight, in g

If the sample contains free acid or base, apply a correction as follows. Add 5–6 drops of the phenolphthalein indicator solution to 25 ml of pyridine and 50 ml of water in a flask. Titrate with 0.5 N sodium hydroxide solution to the first pink end point that persists for 15 sec. To this neutralized solution, add an accurately weighed sample of about the same weight used for the hydroxyl determination. Titrate to the original end point using either 0.5 N sodium hydroxide or 0.5 N hydrochloric acid. Use the volume of titrant to calculate the acid number or alkaline number as follows:

$$\text{Acid number or alkaline number} = \frac{(V)(N)(56.1)}{w}$$

where V = volume of acid or base used in the titration, in ml
  N = normality of the acid or base
  w = sample weight, in g

To apply the correction, add the acid number to the hydroxyl number or subtract the alkaline number from the hydroxyl number. Report wt % hydroxyl-containing compound to the nearest 0.1 unit. Report the hydroxyl number to the nearest 0.1 unit if the value is below 100 and to the nearest 1 unit if the value is above 100. Results of duplicate determinations may be averaged if they agree within 1.2 relative %.

PYROMELLITIC DIANHYDRIDE METHOD. Check the purity of pyromellitic dianhydride (PMDA) to be used for the determination; it should be at least 90%. The practical grade available from Du Pont or Eastman Kodak Co., Eastman Organic Chemicals is suitable. Consult References 163 and 164 for a method of assay. If the PMDA gives an anhydride content lower than 90% due to water pick-up, dry it at 170°C for 48 hr.

Prepare the 0.5 M esterification reagent by dissolving a weight of practical grade PMDA containing 109 g of PMDA in 525 ml of dimethyl sulfoxide and adding 425 ml of pyridine. If the solution is not clear, filter through a sintered glass filter. Do not use filter paper.

Pipet 50 ml of esterification reagent into a sufficient number of 300-ml glass-stoppered Erlenmeyer flasks for blank and sample determinations in duplicate, using a uniform drainage time. Determine the sample weight as follows:

$$\text{Sample weight, in g} = \frac{(841)(0.98)}{\text{approximate hydroxyl number}}$$

Adhere closely to the calculated weight, since it is close to the optimum required by the method. The weight should not exceed 10 g. If the hydroxyl content is low, or the sample is limited, use a 0.1 M PMDA solution for esterification, 0.2 N sodium hydroxide solution for titration and increase the reaction time by 50%.

Transfer the calculated weights of sample to the flasks containing the reagent. Wet the stoppers with pyridine, insert loosely in the flasks and swirl until the samples dissolve completely. Place the flasks on a steam bath for 20 min. Some compounds may require a shorter or longer time; determine the optimum time for each compound. Add 20 ml of water and heat on the steam bath for 2 min. Cool to room temperature, remove the stopper and rinse it down into the flask with a little water. Add 0.5–1 ml of 1% (wt/vol) phenolphthalein solution in pyridine and titrate with N sodium hydroxide solution to the first pink end point that persists for 15 sec. If the volume of titrant used for the sample is less than 85% of that required for the blank, the sample was too large; in this case, repeat the analysis with a smaller sample. In no case should the sample titration be less than 70% of that required for the blank.

Calculate the hydroxyl content either as hydroxyl number or wt % hydroxyl-containing compound using the formulas given in the phthalation method. Correct for any free acid or base that may be present.

Report the wt % hydroxyl-containing compound to the nearest 0.1 unit. Report the hydroxyl number to the nearest 0.1 unit if the value is below 100 and to the nearest 1 unit if the value is above 100. Results of duplicate determinations may be averaged if they agree within 0.9 relative %.

In an interlaboratory study, in 1966, the following precision figures were obtained using dodecanol, pentanol, and 1,6-hexanediol:

Phthalic Anhydride Method: The coefficient of variation of results, each the average of duplicates, has been estimated to be 0.35 relative % at 28 degrees of freedom. Two such values should be considered suspect if they differ by more than 1.0 relative %. The coefficient of variation of results, each the average of duplicates, obtained by analysts in different laboratories has been estimated to be 1.36 relative % at 6 degrees of freedom. Two values should be considered suspect if they differ by more than 4.7 relative %.

PMDA Method: The coefficient of variation of results, each the average of duplicates, obtained by the same analyst on different days has been estimated to be 0.57 relative % at 20 degrees of freedom. Two such values should be considered suspect if they differ by more than 1.7 relative %. The coefficient of variation of results, each the average of duplicates, obtained by analysts in different laboratories, has been estimated to be 1.48 relative % at 6 degrees of freedom. Two such values should be considered suspect if they vary by more than 5.2 relative %.

Gas Chromatographic Methods. ASTM E 202-67T prescribes a gas chromatographic assay for ethylene and propylene glycols (13). The basic recommended conditions are as follows:

column	4 ft $\times$ ¼ in. OD, packed
column packing	7 wt % Carbowax 20M on Haloport F or other tetrafluoroethylene polymer
temperature of injection port	215°C or, if tetraethylene glycol is also present, 235°C
detector	270°C
carrier gas and flow rate	helium, 75 ml/min
detector	thermal conductivity

The selection of column temperature depends on the composition of the sample. If the sample consists of ethylene, diethylene, and triethylene glycols, the suggested column temperature is 170°C while if the sample also contains tetraethylene glycol and only a small amount of ethylene glycol a temperature of 200°C is recommended. For propylene glycol samples, the suggested column temperature is 190°C. In all three cases, the analysis can also be carried out under programmed temperature conditions; in this case, programming between 150 and 225°C at 5.6°C/min is recommended.

Table 39. Approximate Retention Times of Ethylene Glycols

	Retention time, min		
	isothermal operation		programmed temperature operation
Compound	170°C	200°C	
air + water	0.3	0.3	0.4
ethylene glycol	1.3	0.8	2.2
diethylene glycol	4.2	2.3	7.0
triethylene glycol	14.0	5.8	11.9
tetraethylene glycol		16.3	19.3

Table 40. Approximate Retention Times of Propylene Glycols

	Retention time, min	
Compound	isothermal operation at 190°C	programmed temperature operation
air + water	0.3	0.5
propylene glycol	1.3	4.0
dipropylene glycol,	3.3	8.1
three partially resolved	3.9	9.3
isomers	4.8	10.3
tripropylene glycol[a]	7.9	12.4

[a] Several isomers are usually indicated by the shape of the peak, but they are not sufficiently resolved to list separate retention times.

Tables 39 and 40 list the approximate retention times obtained under the specified conditions.

For the quantitative evaluation of the chromatograms, calibration factors are to be determined by analyzing standards prepared from the "hearts cuts" from the distillation of each of the glycols, and these factors are used in converting the peak area % values to concentration in wt %. Table 41 lists the expected repeatability and reproducibility data according to the ASTM method.

Table 41. Repeatability and Reproducibility Data for the Gas Chromatographic Analysis of Glycols, expressed as wt % absolute[a]

	Ethylene glycols		Propylene glycols	
	major component[b]	minor component[c]	major component[b]	minor component[c]
repeatability[d]				
isothermal operation	0.15	0.080	0.15	0.14
programmed temperature operation	0.21	0.10	0.10	0.074
reproducibility[e]				
isothermal operation	0.45	0.23	0.24	0.20
programmed temperature operation	0.35	0.18	0.22	0.17

[a] At 95% confidence level.
[b] Concentration range: 97–100 wt %.
[c] Concentration range: less than 1 wt %.
[d] Duplicate analyses by a single analyst on different days.
[e] Results obtained by analysts in different laboratories.

Infrared Spectroscopic Methods.   Infrared spectroscopy has been used to determine the hydroxyl concentration in polyethylene and polypropylene glycols. Burns and Muraca (166) found that the hydroxyl stretching vibration of fourteen different polypropylene glycols followed the Beer-Lambert law with a coefficient of variation of 2.2%. The effective molar absorptivity of the hydroxyl was 6.74 (g)/(mM) (mm) at a slit width of 0.012 mm. Mamiya (167) determined the hydroxyl content of polyglycols by titration of toluene solutions containing zinc powder with acetyl chloride in toluene. The acetylation was quantitative in the presence of zinc, the end point being detected by the absorption at 1.45 μm which is associated with the first overtone of the hydroxyl group vibration. A correction was made for water by Karl Fischer titration. Kyriacou (168) used a direct titration with standard acetyl chloride in the presence of zinc. Absorbance measurements were made at 2.87–2.88 μm and a titration curve plotted. Hendrickson (169) used the reaction with triphenylchloromethane to determine the primary alcohol groups in polyglycols. The reaction was monitored by the disappearance of the hydroxyl band at 3280 cm^{-1}. The reaction rate of triphenylchloromethane with primary alcohols is 25 to 100 times faster than the rate for secondary alcohols. Anderson and Zardi (170) adapted modified Zeisel reactions for the analysis of 1,2-diols.

Vicinal 1,2-Glycols

The esterification methods described previously can be used for assay of 1,2-glycols containing the group —CH—CH—. However, procedures using cleavage
$$\begin{array}{cc} | & | \\ \text{OH} & \text{OH} \end{array}$$

with periodate are more specific for this type of compound and are based on the Malaprade reaction:

$$\underset{\underset{|}{\text{OH}}}{} \underset{\underset{|}{\text{OH}}}{}$$

$$\text{R—CH—CH—R}' + \text{IO}_4^- \rightarrow \text{RCH}{=}\text{O} + \text{R}'\text{CH}{=}\text{O} + \text{IO}_3^- + \text{H}_2\text{O}$$

Ethylene glycol gives two moles of formaldehyde whereas propylene glycol gives one mole of formaldehyde and one mole of acetaldehyde. Three types of methods are available, an acid–base method, an oxidation–reduction method using periodic acid and a colorimetric method in which the formaldehyde formed as a cleavage product is determined. This last method is ideal for trace amounts of 1,2-glycols and will be described later (p. 598). The bromination method described under ALCOHOLS (Vol. 4, p. 542) is also applicable to 1,2-glycols and certain 1,3-glycols. The reaction times for a few glycols are shown in Table 42 (165).

Table 42.   Reaction Times for Certain Diols, Hydrogen Bromide Method

Compound	Minimum reaction time, at 25°C, hr
2,7-dimethyl-2,7-octanediol	1
ethylene glycol	4
propylene glycol	4
2-ethyl-1,3-hexanediol	2

Acid–Base Method.   The acid–base method utilizes the fact that sodium meta-periodate undergoes the following equilibrium reaction in water:

$$\text{NaIO}_4 + 2\,\text{H}_2\text{O} \rightleftharpoons \text{NaH}_4\text{IO}_6$$

The paraperiodate formed by hydration is acidic and can be titrated with standard sodium hydroxide. When a vicinal glycol is cleaved with this reagent, the iodate formed is neutral so that the decrease in acidity is a measure of the amount of 1,2-glycol present. The method of Dal Nogare and Oemler (171) described below uses low temperature for the titration to sharpen the inflection point. Good accuracy is obtained. Acidic or basic compounds interfere but can be corrected for. Weak bases, such as amines, cannot be present. Vicinal compounds other than glycols which cleave may interfere. Such compounds contain the following groups:

$$\underset{\text{—C—C—}}{\overset{\overset{\displaystyle\text{O}\ \ \text{O}}{\|\ \ \ \|}}{}}, \quad \underset{\text{—C—C—}}{\overset{\overset{\displaystyle\text{O}\ \ \text{OH}}{\|\ \ \ |}}{}}, \quad \underset{\text{—C—C—}}{\overset{\overset{\displaystyle\text{H}_2\text{N}\ \ \text{OH}}{|\ \ \ \ |}}{}}$$

Procedure

Pipet 50 ml of 0.1 M sodium metaperiodate, NaIO$_4$, into two 250-ml Erlenmeyer flasks. Use one of the solutions as a blank. Weigh about 3.5 meq of the 1,2-glycol sample into the other flask. Allow the flasks to stand for 20 min and then add enough crushed ice to reduce the temperature to 1°C and maintain this temperature during the titration. Add 2 ml of a mixed indicator solution containing 0.4 g of thymolphthalein and 0.2 g of 1-naphtholbenzein in 100 ml of 9:1 ethanol–water and titrate to a grayish-blue color with 0.1 N sodium hydroxide solution, matching the color of the sample and blank solutions.

$$\text{Vicinal hydroxyl, meq/g} = \frac{(B - A)N}{w}$$

where A = volume of sodium hydroxide solution used for sample titration, in ml
B = volume of sodium hydroxide solution used for blank titration, in ml
N = normality of sodium hydroxide solution
w = sample weight, in g

Oxidation–Reduction Methods. Reddaway (172) described a periodate oxidation method for alcohol-soluble vicinal glycols using arsenite–iodine titration in a nonaqueous ethyl acetate–ethanol medium containing triethylamine and acetic acid. A triethylammonium periodate reagent containing periodic acid is used as the titrant. The method is rapid and specific and gave standard deviations well below 0.5% with butyl alcohol and cyclohexane-1,2-diol.

Redox methods for 1,2-glycols are not affected by the presence of acids and bases. The modified method described below (171) can be used for most 1,2-glycols. Amines do not interfere as the amino group in the sulfate form is more resistant to periodate oxidation than the free amine. Although it is less accurate than the acid–base procedure there are fewer interferences.

Procedure

Prepare 0.1 M periodic acid reagent by dissolving 22.8 g of periodic acid, $HIO_4.2 H_2O$, in 400 ml of 0.5 N sulfuric acid and dilute to 1 liter with water.

Prepare 0.1 N sodium arsenite by dissolving 4.0 g of sodium hydroxide and 5.0 g of arsenious oxide, As_2O_3, in a minimum of water. Add 10 g of sodium bicarbonate and dilute to 1 liter with water.

Weigh not more than 2 meq of vicinal glycol into one of two 250-ml Erlenmeyer flasks containing 50 ml of water and mix. Reserve the other as a blank. Pipet 15 ml of the periodic acid reagent into each flask and allow them to stand at room temperature for 30 min. Add 30 ml of saturated sodium bicarbonate solution and pipet 50 ml of the 0.1 N sodium arsenite solution into each flask. Allow to stand for 10 min, then add 1 ml of 15% potassium iodide solution, 2 ml of 1% starch indicator solution and 10–12 g of sodium bicarbonate. Titrate with standard 0.1 N iodine to the first appearance of a blue color. If the difference in titer for the blank and sample exceeds 20 ml, repeat the analysis with a smaller sample.

Polyhydric Alcohols

Some of the methods developed for glycols can also be used for the analysis of polyalcohols. For example, the amount of glycerol in a glycerol–water mixture can be assayed by specific gravity measurement (see GLYCEROL, p. 530), and the phthalic anhydride esterification method (p. 586) can also be applied to the assay of pentaerythritol. Similarly, assay methods developed for glycerol (see pp. 508–521) may also be adapted for the analysis of other polyalcohols.

Assay of Pentaerythritol. ASTM Method D 2195-66 (173) describes two methods for the assay of pentaerythritol: either determination as the dibenzal or through the hydroxyl content. These procedures are given below in detail. Pentaerythritol can also be assayed by gas chromatography.

Procedures

DIBENZAL METHOD. Prepare a methanolic benzaldehyde reagent by adding 20 ml of benzaldehyde of 98% minimum purity to 100 ml of methanol. Prepare the reagent fresh for each series of determinations.

Weigh approximately a 0.5 g portion of a ground sample into a small glass-stoppered weighing bottle, dry for 3 hr at 105°C, then weigh accurately, transfer the sample to a 125-ml Erlenmeyer flask, and reweigh the bottle to obtain the sample weight by difference. Add 5.0 ml of water to the sample, insert a stopper loosely, and heat to incipient boiling on a hot plate with swirling until the sample is dissolved. Add to the hot solution, preferably under a hood, 15 ml of the methanolic benzaldehyde reagent and 12 ml of concentrated hydrochloric acid. Insert the stopper loosely and allow the flask to stand for 15 min at room temperature. Swirl the flask occasionally to prevent the precipitate from adhering to the bottom of the flask. After 15 min place the flask in an ice bath at 0–2°C for 1 hr or more. Also place 25 ml of 1:1 methanol–water in the ice bath for later use.

Remove the flask from the ice bath and immediately filter the reaction mixture with suction through a weighed fritted glass crucible. Complete the transfer of the precipitate with the 25 ml of ice-cold 1:1 methanol–water wash solution. After the transfer is complete wash the precipitate with a total of 100 ml of 1:1 methanol–water at 20–25°C in several portions as follows. Disconnect the vacuum line, pour 10 ml of the methanol–water wash solution into the crucible, and stir the precipitate to form a homogeneous slurry, then connect again the vacuum line and draw the wash solution through the crucible. Repeat this washing operation six times, and with the remaining 30 ml of the wash solution, rinse the interior walls of the crucible and the stirring rod. Aspirate thoroughly the precipitate and dry at 105°C for 2 hr.

$$\text{Pentaerythritol, wt \%} = \frac{(W + 0.0269)(0.4359)(100)}{w}$$

where W = weight of precipitate, in g
      w = sample weight, in g
   0.0269 = solubility correction factor
   0.4359 = (g-mol wt of pentaerythritol)/(g-mol wt of the dibenzal)

HYDROXYL CONTENT. Prepare the acetylation reagent by mixing 105 ml of acetic anhydride with 1 liter of pyridine containing 0.30–0.45 wt % of water. Prepare the reagent freshly every day.

Weigh approximately a 0.30–0.33 g portion of the ground sample into a small glass-stoppered weighing bottle, dry for 3 hr at 105°C, then weigh accurately, transfer the sample to a 250-ml Erlenmeyer flask with ground joint, and reweigh the bottle to obtain the sample weight by difference. Pipet 25 ml of the acetylation reagent into the flask using a uniform drainage time for all aliquots. Connect the flask to a reflux condenser, sealing the joint with 1–2 drops of pyridine and place on a hot plate; if necessary, swirl the flask to dissolve the sample. Heat at reflux for 30 min, then cool the flask somewhat and rinse the condenser with 25 ml of water. Remove the condenser and rinse the joint with water, collecting the rinsings in the flask.

Cool the flask in an ice bath so that the contents are below 20°C, add 0.5–1.0 ml of a phenolphthalein indicator solution containing 1 g of phenolphthalein in 100 ml of 1:1 pyridine–water and titrate slowly with 0.5 N sodium hydroxide solution to the first permanent faint pink end point. Swirl or magnetically stir the solution during titration and swirl vigorously as the end point is approached. Simultaneously carry out a blank determination with the same amounts of reagents involved. If the volume of sodium hydroxide solution required for sample titration is less than 80% of that required for the blank, repeat the analysis using a smaller sample.

$$\text{Hydroxyl, wt \%} = \frac{(B - A)(N)(17.01)(100)}{(w)(1000)}$$

where A = volume of sodium hydroxide solution required for sample titration, in ml

B = volume of sodium hydroxide solution required for blank titration, in ml

N = normality of sodium hydroxide solution

w = sample weight, in g

The ASTM method specifies the following maximum repeatibility values: 0.8% absolute for the determination of the hydroxyl content, and 1.2% absolute for the determination by the benzal method. The reproducibility values as specified are 1.2 and 3.3% absolute, respectively.

Assay by Gas Chromatography. The benzal method is specific for monopentaerythritol if only the dimer is present as impurity whereas the hydroxyl determination is naturally not specific for any particular pentaerythritol. On the other hand, assay by gas chromatography also permits the determination of the impurities representing homologs of pentaerythritol and also the assay of technical di-, tri- or tetrapentaerythritols.

Suchanec (125) successfully analyzed commercial samples as their trimethylsilyl ethers, using mannitol as internal standard, under the following conditions:

column	4 ft × ³⁄₁₆ in. OD packed
column packing	17 wt % SE-30 silicone gum rubber on GasChrom Z 60/80 mesh
temperature of	
injection port	325°C
column	programmed at 10–13°C/min from 125 to 326°C and held there until the end of the analysis
detector	325°C
carrier gas and flow rate	helium, 100 ml/min
detector	thermal conductivity

The separated and identified components were in order of their elution: pentaerythritol cyclic monoformal, monopentaerythritol, mannitol (internal standard), dipentaerythritol, dipentaerythritol hemiacetal, tripentaerythritol, trispentaerythritol diformal, tetrapentaerythritol, and bisdipentaerythritol monoformal. The procedure for the formation of the trimethylsilyl ethers is given below.

Procedure

Weigh a 200-mg sample (100 mg if large amounts of polypentaerythritols are expected) and 50 mg of mannitol into a 50-ml Erlenmeyer flask, add 7 ml of dry pyridine and 1 ml of hexamethyldisilazane, place the flask on a hot plate in a hood, and heat just under boiling for 10 min with intermittent gentle swirling. Cool the flask to at least 50°C; if the solution is not clear add a few ml of pyridine, reheat, then cool. Add 2 ml of distilled trimethylchlorosilane, and swirl the flask for 2–3 min. Warm the reaction mixture to 70–80°C, then immediately remove from the hot plate, swirl for 1 min, and cool to room temperature during which the white precipitate of ammonium chloride and pyridinium chloride will settle at the bottom of the flask. Introduce an aliquot of the supernatant into the gas chromatograph for analysis.

Determination in Mixtures

Ethylene glycol and glycerol have been determined by reaction with lead tetra-acetate in dilute acetic acid in the presence of alkali metal acetate (174). The excess tetraacetate was determined by potentiometric titration with standard hydroquinone. Plsko (175) used solutions of sodium tungstate to form complexes with ethylene glycol and glycerol. The resultant rise in pH was the basis of the titrimetric method developed. Maros and Schulek (176) oxidized ethylene glycol and glycerol with periodic acid to formaldehyde. The bisulfite addition compound of the aldehyde was decomposed with potassium cyanide and the sulfurous acid determined iodometrically.

Benson and Fletcher (177) developed a kinetic method of analysis for the determination of two-component mixtures of ethanediol, propane-1,2-diol, and butane-2,3-diol based on the difference in reaction rates of these compounds with lead tetraacetate. After the determination of the rate constants, the concentrations of the two components in a mixture can be determined from data obtained at two temperatures provided there is sufficient difference in the temperature dependence of the two reaction rates.

Hanna and Siggia (178) determined the primary and secondary hydroxyl group content of commercial polypropylene glycols such as Niax and the Wyandotte Pluronics by using the difference in reaction rates with phenylisocyanate. The primary hydroxyl groups react much more rapidly, so that the primary hydroxyl reaction is complete at a time when only a fraction of the secondary hydroxyl has reacted. The first slope is the combination of the two reactions and the second represents the specific rate constant of the secondary hydroxyl reaction. By separating the contribution of the slowed reaction from the first slope, the amount of primary hydroxyl can be determined. Since the above method is somewhat cumbersome with respect to time of analysis and calculation, Willeboordse and Meeker (179) used a simplified pseudo first-order reaction rate approach to determine the primary hydroxyl content of polyglycols. A considerable saving in time resulted. A calibration curve is set up and the effective fractional lifetime in the urethan reaction is determined.

Levins and Ikeda (180) used a simple, direct potentiometric titration to determine polyethylene glycols and their derivatives. Sodium tetraphenylboron was the titrant in the presence of barium ions. Polyethylene glycols with molecular weights between 600 and 4000 react stoichiometrically to form complex precipitates containing 2 moles of tetraphenylboron and 10.4 ± 0.2 moles of ethylene oxide for a mole of barium. The approximate molecular weight of an unknown polyethylene glycol can be obtained from the infrared spectrum of the precipitate. Maros et al. (181) precipitated polyglycols with barium tetraphenylboron and determined the excess barium by EDTA titration using methyl thymol blue as an indicator.

Siggia et al. (182) determined the oxyalkylene groups in ethylene, propylene, and polypropylene glycol by reaction with hydriodic acid. One mole of 1,2-diiodoalkane was formed for each oxyalkylene group. The diodo compounds are unstable and give off a mole of iodine which is determined with standard thiosulfite solution. In a similar procedure, Cheng (183) converted oxyethylene groups to ethyl iodide by treatment with hydriodic acid at low temperature. All the ethyl iodide is collected in silver nitrate and determined by Volhard titration.

Methods for the determination of glycerol are discussed in detail in a separate article (pp. 508–521). Many of them may also be adapted for the analysis of other polyalcohols.

Naturally, the gas chromatographic methods discussed earlier for separation and identification (p. 575) and assay (p. 589) can also be used for the analysis of mixtures.

Polarography. Francis (184) determined diethylene glycol or dipropylene glycol in monoglycols by oxidizing the monoglycols with periodic acid and removing the products by distillation. The excess periodic acid was reduced to iodic acid and the diglycols oxidized with potassium dichromate. The excess dichromate was determined polarographically. Takiura et al. (185) worked out the conditions for the microdetermination of glycols using the known method of glycol splitting with periodic acid. The excess periodic acid was determined polarographically.

Badinand et al. (186) showed that the addition of 1–10 mg/liter of polyethylene glycol to a solution of 0.005 M nickel sulfate in 0.001 M KCl produced a reduction in the height of the maximum in the wave between -0.8 V and -1.5 V. The concentration of polyethylene glycol required to reduce the maximum by half was determined. This value was characteristic of the molecular weight of the polyglycol. The same effect is obtained with 0.005 M copper sulfate in 0.1 M potassium chloride solution. These methods are nonspecific, since the same effect can be obtained with many surface active agents.

Determination in Resins. ASTM D 1615 describes a method to determine glycerol, ethylene glycol, and pentaerythritol in alkyd resins and resin solutions. In the procedure, the primary hydroxyl groups of ethylene glycol and glycerol are oxidized by periodic acid to formaldehyde while the secondary hydroxyl group of glycerol is oxidized to formic acid. In two subsequent steps, the amounts of formic acid and formaldehyde are determined by acidimetric and iodometric titrations, respectively, and calculated to glycerol and ethylene glycol by algebraic equations. Pentaerythritol does not react with periodic acid and thus has to be determined separately as the benzal.

The determination has to be preceded by an alkaline saponification of the resin and separation of the fatty acids and alcohols by extraction.

The procedures are given below in detail (187). They cannot be applied to urea, melamine, or phenolic resins. If other polyhydric alcohols are present that can be oxidized by periodic acid to formaldehyde or formic acid or both, they will interfere with the determination.

Procedures

EXTRACTION OF FATTY ACIDS. Weigh, by difference, a few grams of resin sample and transfer it into a 500-ml Erlenmeyer flask. Add 150 ml of benzene, warming slightly on a steam bath, if necessary, to effect solution. Add 60 ml of an ethanolic potassium hydroxide solution containing 66 g of potassium hydroxide in 1 liter of absolute ethanol, and attach to a reflux condenser. Place the flask on a water bath, warm the bath to 40°C and hold it there for 1 hr, then gradually raise the temperature until the alcoholic solution boils gently; reflux for 90 min.

Remove the flask from the bath, wash down the inside of the condenser with a few ml of 1:3 absolute ethanol–benzene wash solution, remove the condenser, cap the flask with a soda-lime guard tube, and cool by means of running water or ice bath. When cool, filter immediately, and as rapidly as possible, through a tared fritted-glass crucible using the ethanol–benzene wash solution for transferring the precipitate and washing the reaction flask. Wash the precipitate with successive portions of the wash solution until a few ml of washings collected in a second suction flask are no longer alkaline to phenolphthalein. Normally about 75 ml of wash solution are sufficient. Do not allow air to contact the crystals as they are hygroscopic. Finally, pour 25 ml of ethyl ether into the crucible and draw through the precipitate by suction.

Transfer the combined filtrate and washings to a 400-ml beaker with the aid of 25 ml of water from a wash bottle, and concentrate on a steam bath to a volume of approximately 25 ml under a blanket of nitrogen. Transfer the concentrate to a 500-ml separatory funnel with the aid of water from a wash bottle, dilute with water to approximately 300 ml, and add 10 ml of ethanol.

Extract the unsaponifiable and volatile thinners with at least three 50-ml portions of ethyl ether until a colorless ether extract is obtained. Combine the ether extracts in the first separatory funnel and use two other funnels for the successive extractions. Finally, wash the combined ether extracts with three 15-ml portions of water and add the water washings to the main water phase. Discard the combined ether extracts.

Acidify the aqueous phase to approximately pH 2 by slowly adding hydrochloric acid and cooling the funnel under running tap water. When the mixture has cooled to room temperature, extract the fatty acids with at least three 25-ml portions of ethyl ether until a colorless ether extract is obtained. Combine the ether extracts in the first separatory funnel and use two other funnels for the successive extractions. Wash the combined ether extracts with successive 10-ml portions of water until free of mineral acid when tested with an indicator paper. If desired, use the combined ether extracts for the determination of total fatty acids.

DETERMINATION OF ALCOHOLS. Transfer the aqueous phase to a 400-ml beaker and evaporate to about 60 ml on a hot plate keeping the beaker covered with a watch glass during boiling. Cool to room temperature, filter through a rapid paper into a 100-ml volumetric flask, and dilute to volume.

Glycerol and Ethylene Glycol. Pipet a 20-ml aliquot into a 1-liter Erlenmeyer flask with a glass stopper. Add 2 drops of methyl purple indicator (available from the Fleisher Chemical Co., Washington, D.C.) and neutralize with 0.1 N sodium hydroxide solution. Add, by pipet 50 ml of a periodic solution containing 11 g of periodic acid in 1 liter prepared fresh daily, stopper, and swirl to mix thoroughly. Simultaneously prepare two blanks containing 20 ml of water. Allow to stand 50–70 min at room temperature. To each solution, add 100 ml of water and 3 drops of methyl purple indicator, and titrate with 0.1 N sodium hydroxide solution to neutrality. Immediately after the titration add 150 ml of water, 30 ml of a potassium iodide solution with a KI concentration of 0.2 g/ml, and 25 ml of 1:5 sulfuric acid. Titrate with 0.2 N sodium thiosulfate solution to a faint iodine color, then add 10 ml of a starch indicator solution (5 g of starch/liter of water) and titrate to the disappearance of the blue color.

If the amount of periodic acid consumed is more than 20% of that added, the determination should be repeated by taking a smaller sample aliquot.

$$\text{Glycerol, wt \%} = \frac{(A - B)(N_1)(92.09)(100)}{(w)(1000)}$$

$$T = \frac{(D - C)(N_2)(23.015)(100)}{(w)(1000)}$$

$$\text{Ethylene glycol, wt \%} = 1.348 \, (T - \text{wt \% glycerol})$$

where A = volume of sodium hydroxide solution required for sample titration, in ml

B = volume of sodium hydroxide solution required for blank titration, in ml

C = volume of sodium thiosulfate solution required for sample titration, in ml

D = volume of sodium thiosulfate solution required for blank titration, in ml

N_1 = normality of the sodium hydroxide solution

N_2 = normality of the sodium thiosulfate solution

w = sample weight in aliquot, in g

T = % of glycerol and ethylene glycol as % glycerol

In practice, samples containing no ethylene glycol yield ethylene glycol values of up to 1%.

Pentaerythritol. Transfer an aliquot containing 0.15–0.55 g of pentaerythritol to a 100-ml beaker and evaporate on a steam bath to approximately 5 ml. To the hot solution add 15 ml of the methanolic benzaldehyde reagent and 12 ml of concentrated hydrochloric acid and continue the determination as described on pp. 592–594.

Kirby et al. (188) decomposed terephthalate polyesters by quantitative saponification with alcoholic potassium hydroxide. The ethylene glycol was oxidized to formaldehyde with sodium metaperiodate. After removal of the volatile formaldehyde and ethanol, diethylene glycol was determined by oxidation with potassium dichromate. As little as 1 mg of diethylene glycol could be detected in 1 g of polyester. Since α-glycols in epoxy resins cannot be determined by an aqueous periodate method due to their insolubility, Stenmark (189) used chlorofrom as a solvent and a quaternary ammonium periodate as the titrant. His method gives accurate results with pure glycols and is sensitive to small amounts of glycols in epoxy resins.

Determination in Small Amounts

The methods covered in this section are not necessarily trace methods. Methods for the determination of small amounts of glycerol are covered in the article on GLYCEROL (pp. 508–521).

Glycols

Many dihydroxy compounds and 1,2-glycols react quantitatively with the 3,5-dinitrobenzoyl chloride reagent used in the colorimetric procedure described under ALCOHOLS (Vol. 4, p. 547). However, the esters are not extractable from the aqueous solution and cannot be determined.

A trace colorimetric procedure for the determination of most 1,2-glycols is based on the cleavage of the compounds to formaldehyde which is then determined colorimetrically with chromotropic acid (190). As little as 1 ppm of 1,2-glycols can be determined in 10 g of water-soluble material with this method. The method is not applicable to 1,2-glycols with the following structure: R—CH—CH—R where

$$\underset{\text{HO} \quad \text{OH}}{\text{R—CH—CH—R}}$$

R represents alkyl groups. Formaldehyde and other vicinal compounds that form formaldehyde on cleavage will interfere. Large concentrations of organic compounds such as aldehydes and unsaturates which are susceptible to discoloration in hot, concentrated sulfuric acid will also interfere.

Procedure

Add 2 ml of 0.1 N sodium periodate solution to two 100-ml glass-stoppered graduated cylinders, reserving one for a blank. Transfer a weight of 1,2-glycol not exceeding 0.7 mg of formaldehyde to the other cylinder, dilute to 20 ml with water and allow the reaction to proceed for 1 hr. Pipet 2 ml of 5.5% sodium sulfite solution, prepared fresh weekly, into each cylinder. Dilute to 100 ml with water, stopper, and mix.

Transfer 10-ml aliquots of each solution to 100-ml glass-stoppered graduated cylinders. Add 0.05 ± 0.01 g of sodium chromotropate and dissolve. Dilute to 50 ml with concentrated sulfuric acid and let the temperature rise. Sparge the solution vigorously with nitrogen for 10 min using a glass tube immersed in the acid solution. Allow the contents to cool to room temperature. Measure the absorbance of the sample against the blank at 570 nm using 1-cm cells. Determine the amount of 1,2-glycol from a calibration curve prepared from the glycol being determined.

Adelberg (191) determined 1,2-glycols in mixtures by separating them by paper chromatography and using 2,4-dinitrophenylhydrazine as the colorimetric reagent for the carbonyl compounds formed from the glycols by periodate oxidation. A similar procedure was described by Liebman and Ortiz (192). The phenylhydrazone of the carbonyl acid was extracted with chloroform. Dixon and Lipkin (193) used a shorter procedure by following the consumption of periodate by vicinal glycols spectrophotometrically, using the ultraviolet absorption band of metaperiodate at 223 nm. Only 10^{-8}–10^{-6} mole of sample is required and the rate of oxidation can be readily followed.

Baumel (194) determined 1,2-propylene glycol in antifreeze mixtures also containing polyglycols. The vicinal glycol was oxidized with periodic acid and the aldehydes distilled. Acetaldehyde was determined by absorbance measurements at 277 nm. Jones and Riddick (195) converted propylene glycol to a violet ninhydrin complex by dehydration and rearrangement to a mixture of allyl alcohol and propionaldehyde with sulfuric acid. The complex absorbed at 595 nm and Beer's law was obeyed in the range of 5–50 μg. The reaction is specific for propylene glycol and its polymers in glycol mixtures.

Shagov (196) determined 1,4-butylene glycol by measuring the UV absorbance of the dinitrite derivative in the presence of ethylene glycol, glycerol, and small amounts of 2,3-butylene glycol. The method is applicable to aqueous solutions.

Traces of triethylene glycol vapor in air have been determined by Kaye (197). By sampling 30 liters, concentrations as low as 2 μg/liter can be analyzed using 1-naphthol in sulfuric acid as the color reagent.

Whitman et al. (198) used oxidation with potassium dichromate as the basis of a titrimetric method for the determination of 1% or less of diethylene or triethylene glycol in aqueous solutions. By control of acidity and reduction time, the oxidation was stopped after consumption of 16 and 20.5 equivalents of dichromate per mole of diethylene or triethylene glycol, respectively. Results were reproducible and recoveries were of the order of 99.5%.

Polyglycols

Han (199) adapted the 3,5-dinitrobenzoyl chloride method for the microanalysis of hydroxyl groups in polyethylene glycols and nonionic surfactants of the polyethylene oxide type. The excess acid chloride was removed by liquid column chromatography and the dinitrobenzoates were then determined colorimetrically. The relative accuracy was 4.5% for 100 μg of hydroxyl. Products containing less than ten ethylene oxide units per molecule do not react satisfactorily.

Free polyglycols in cation-active ethylene oxide condensates can be determined after isolating them in dilute aqueous solutions with ion exchange resins (200). The amount and average molecular weight of the polyglycols are then obtained by colorimetric analysis and a total dichromate oxidation.

Crummett (201) investigated the application of Schmulyakovskii's nitrite spectrophotometric method for primary and secondary alcohols to the determination of the primary hydroxyl content of polypropylene glycols. Direct application of the method was not possible due to the instability of the nitrosation products. However, by modifying the procedure so that air was excluded, introducing a filtration step and correcting for background absorbance, the method worked satisfactorily for polypropylene glycols. Alcohols or glycols present will interfere. Ketones give high results but are not usually present.

Burger (88) precipitated surface active polyethylene glycols with a mixture of $KBiI_4$ and barium chloride in dilute acetic acid. The fluffy orange-red precipitates were centrifuged in capillary tubes and the level measured to give the concentration of the polyglycol in the 0.1–10 ppm range. The method has to be modified for compounds with only two to ten ethylene oxide groups (202).

Determination of Impurities

Impurity specifications most frequently encountered include those for acidity, odor, pH, ash, suspended matter, and water. These are determined by procedures similar to those employed for alcohols (see Vol. 4, p. 543). Other impurities occasionally determined by conventional procedures include chloride, arsenic, iron, heavy metals, and sulfate.

Small amounts of ethylene glycol in polyester-grade diethylene glycol are determined titrimetrically by periodate oxidation (pp. 571–572). Traces of diethylene glycol in ethylene glycol are determined by gas chromatographic procedures, several of which were outlined in Table 27. The carbonyl content can be determined colorimetrically with 2,4-dinitrophenylhydrazine or by the titrimetric hydroxylamine hydrochloride procedure. Detailed descriptions of test procedures used for determining specification impurities can be found in many of the brochures and literature available from the suppliers (4–5,26,32,35,43,61). Standard test methods for ethylene and propylene glycols (113,203), polypropylene glycols (204), pentaerythritol (173), and glycerol (205–210) include procedures for the determination of certain impurities.

A method for the determination of water in glycol–water or glycerol–water solutions was described by Jordan and Hatch (211). The procedure is essentially a reflux distillation and salting-out process using 1-butanol as the reflux medium. This solvent forms an azeotrope with water, but not with glycols or glycerol, and is capable of breaking the hydrates which are formed in aqueous glycol solutions. The method was especially applicable to permanent-type antifreeze solutions, with no interference from inhibitors or inorganic impurities. The determination of 0.05–0.2% of benzotriazole in inhibited glycol products and antifreeze mixtures was described by Harrison and Woodroffe (212). Benzotriazole is precipitated as the silver complex and weighed.

Determination of Properties

The properties of glycols, polyglycols, and polyhydric alcohols may be determined by the usual methods which are discussed in the General Techniques section of this Encyclopedia, Vol. 1–3. For the lower members, color, distillation range, and specific gravity are the most important for specification purposes.

Color. Color is determined using suitable platinum–cobalt standards according to the method described in the American Public Health Association's standards and in ASTM standards (213). For directions, see ACRYLIC AND METHACRYLIC ACIDS AND ESTERS, Vol. 4, pp. 181–218. To test pentaerythritol, the ASTM method utilizes a modified Pt–Co color test based on formation of the phthalate ester (173).

Procedure

Prepare a Pt–Co stock solution in the following way. Dissolve 1.245 g of potassium hexachloroplatinate, K_2PtCl_6, and 1.000 g of cobaltous chloride hexahydrate, $CoCl_2.6 H_2O$, in water, add 25 ml of concentrated hydrochloric acid and dilute to 250 ml with water. The color standard number of this stock solution is 2000.

Weigh 20.0 g of phthalic anhydride (solidification point, min: 131°C; melt color Pt–Co scale, max: 15) into a clear, dry 22×175 mm test tube. Clamp the tube in a 225 ± 1°C oil bath with the lip of the tube 20 ± 5 mm above the level of the bath liquid and wait until the crystals have melted, then add 20.0 g of the sample in small portions while stirring with a stirring rod. Set a timer for 45 min. When the crystals have dissolved, remove the stirring rod and immediately cap the tube lightly with aluminum foil.

After the end of the 45 min, remove the test tube from the bath. If appreciable phthalic anhydride crystals have collected on the inside of the test tube, rerun the esterification. If only a few crystals are present, pour a portion of the melted ester into a waste receptacle to clear the lip and side of the test tube of any crystals which may interfere with the photometric measurement.

Preheat the cuvet or optical cell at 100°C and carefully pour the melted ester into it. If air has been entrained, heat the melt at 100–150°C so that bubbles may rise clean of the optical light path. Only perfectly clear melted esters can be used for the measurement.

While still warm, measure the absorbance or transmittance of the ester at 450 nm and read the Pt–Co color from a previously prepared calibration curve obtained by carrying out the same measurement with Pt–Co standards representing the color standard number range between 200 and 2000 obtained by diluting the required volumes of the Pt–Co stock solution to 20 ml with water:

Color standard number	Stock solution, ml	Color standard number	Stock solution, ml
200	2	1200	12
400	4	1400	14
600	6	1800	18
1000	10	2000	20

Distillation Range. The ASTM method (214) for the distillation range of volatile organic liquids is used. See DISTILLATION, Vol. 1, p. 624. The distillations are performed at 760 torr or corrected by algebraically adding the correction for deviation of barometric pressure from the normal as follows:

$$\text{Correction} = K \ (760\text{-}P)$$

where K = rate of change of boiling point with pressure in °C/torr (see Table 43).

P = barometric pressure, in torr

Table 43. Change of Boiling Point with Pressure

Compound	Value of K at bp, °C/torr
1,2-ethanediol	0.045
1,2-propanediol	0.044
1,5-pentanediol	0.050
2-methyl-2,4-pentanediol	0.043
2-ethyl-1,3-hexanediol	0.049
diethylene glycol	0.050
triethylene glycol	0.054
tetraethylene glycol	0.060
dipropylene glycol	0.049
tripropylene glycol	0.055

Specific Gravity. Specific gravity is determined at 20°C with either a hydrometer or a 60-ml glass pycnometer calibrated to give the apparent specific gravity at 20/20°C and capable of being read to the nearest 0.0005 unit. The constant temperature bath must be regulated to 20 ± 0.05°C.

Bibliography

1. G. O. Curme, Jr. and F. Johnston, eds., *Glycols, ACS Monograph Series No. 114*, Reinhold Publishing Corp., New York, 1953, pp. 300–327.
2. V. K. Rowe, "Glycols," in F. A. Patty, ed., *Industrial Hygiene and Toxicology*, Vol. 2, 2nd rev. ed., Interscience Publishers, a division of John Wiley & Sons, Inc., New York, 1963, pp. 1497–1536.
3. L. H. Horsley, E. C. Britton, and H. S. Nutting, *Azeotropic Data*, No. 6 of *Advances in Chemistry Series*, American Chemical Society, Washington, D.C., 1952; L. H. Horsley and W. S. Tamplin, *Azeotropic Data-II*, No. 35 of *Advances in Chemistry Series*, American Chemical Society, Washington, D.C., 1962.
4. *Glycols, Brochures F-4763G, F-4763H*, Union Carbide Chemical Co., New York, 1964.
5. *Glycols–Properties and Uses*, Dow Chemical Co., Midland, Mich., 1961.
6. *Glycols, Brochure F-41515*, Union Carbide Chemical Co., New York, 1968.
7. Ref. 1, p. 289.
8. W. L. Faith, D. B. Keyes, and R. L. Clark, *Industrial Chemicals*, 3rd ed., John Wiley & Sons, Inc., New York, 1965, pp. 372–385.
9. P. H. Miller, "Ethylene Glycol, Propylene Glycol, and Their Derivatives," in A. Standen, ed., *Kirk-Othmer Encyclopedia of Chemical Technology*, Vol. 10, 2nd ed., Interscience Publishers, a division of John Wiley & Sons Inc., New York, 1966, pp. 638–660.
10. *Physical Properties of Synthetic Organic Chemicals, Booklet F-61365*, Union Carbide Chemical Co., New York, 1965.
11. *Glycols, Brochure N-136*, Eastman Kodak Co., Rochester, N. Y., 1968.
12. Ref. 1, pp. 7–73.
13. J. A. Monick, *Alcohols—Their Chemistry, Properties and Manufacture*, Reinhold Publishing Co., New York, 1968, Chap. 4.
14. *Product Index, 1968–1969*, Celanese Chemical Co., New York.
15. *Propylene Glycol USP*, Dow Chemical Co., Midland, Mich., 1964.
16. Ref. 1, pp. 203–249.
17. *Trimethylene Glycol, Technical Data Sheets*, Aceto Chemical Co., Inc., Flushing, New York, 1965.
18. Ref. 1, pp. 206–207.
19. F. S. Wagner, Jr., "1,3-Butylene Glycol," in A. Standen, ed., *Kirk-Othmer Encyclopedia of Chemical Technology*, Vol. 10, 2nd ed., Interscience Publishers, a division of John Wiley & Sons, Inc., New York, 1966, pp. 660–667.

20. *1,3-Butanediol, Product Bulletin S-26-7*, Celanese Chemical Co., New York, 1962.

21. Ref. 1, pp. 287–288.

22. M. Freifeld and E. V. Hort, "1,4-Butylene Glycol and γ-Butyrolacetone," in A. Standen, ed., *Kirk-Othmer Encyclopedia of Chemical Technology*, Vol. 10, 2nd ed., Interscience Publishers, a division of John Wiley & Sons Inc., New York, 1966, pp. 667–676.

23. *1,4-Butanediol, Brochure IM-1-64*, General Aniline and Film Corp., New York.

24. Ref. 1, pp. 291–293.

25. Ref. 1, pp. 288–291.

26. *1,5-Pentanediol, Technical Information Sheets F-40,006A* (1957) and *1-6Q5-1* (1965), Union Carbide Chemical Co., New York.

27. *2,5-Hexanediol*, Aceto Chemical Co., Inc., Flushing, New York, 1965.

28. *1,6-Hexanediol*, Provisional Leaflet, Badische Anilin and Soda Fabrik A.G., 1963.

29. *1,6-Hexanediol, Specification Sheet S-163-1*, Celanese Chemical Co., 1966.

30. *1,6-Hexanediol, Brochure S-76-1*, Celanese Chemical Co., 1966.

31. H. C. Twiggs and J. E. Hutchins, "Other Glycols," in A. Standen, ed., *Kirk-Othmer Encyclopedia of Chemical Technology*, Vol. 10, 2nd ed., Interscience Publishers, a division of John Wiley & Sons, Inc., New York, 1966, pp. 676–680.

32. *Neopentyl Glycol, Specification Sheet No. 3818-3*, Texas Eastman Co., Longview, Texas, 1966.

33. Ref. 1, pp. 284–286.

34. *ASTM D 2636-67, Specifications for Hexylene Glycol*, American Society for Testing and Materials, Philadelphia, Pa., 1970.

35. *2,2,4-Trimethyl-1,3-Pentanediol, Specification Sheet No. 3843-3*, Texas Eastman Co., Longview, Texas, 1967.

36. Ref. 1, pp. 286–287.

37. Ref. 9, p. 652.

38. Ref. 9, p. 656.

39. Ref. 9, p. 653.

40. Ref. 1, pp. 153–170.

41. Ref. 1, pp. 170–176.

42. Ref. 1, pp. 274–276.

43. *Polyethylene Glycols*, Allied Chemical Corp., New York.

44. *Polyethylene Glycols*, Jefferson Chemical Co., Inc., Houston, Texas, 1961.

45. *Carbowax Polyethylene Glycols, Brochure F-4772F*, Union Carbide Chemical Co., New York, 1965.

46. *Polyethylene Glycols*, Dow Chemical Co., Midland, Mich., 1962.

47. *Polyethylene Glycols for Pharmaceuticals and Cosmetics, Brochure F-7658B*, Union Carbide Chemical Co., New York, 1959.

48. *Choosing the Right Polyglycol*, Dow Chemical Co., Midland, Mich., 1962.

49. Ref. 1, pp. 176–193.

50. *Polypropylene Glycols*, Dow Chemical Co., Midland, Mich., 1960.

51. *Polypropylene Glycols*, Jefferson Chemical Co., Houston, Texas, 1961.

52. Ref. 1, pp. 277–280.

53. *Potential Uses for Polypropylene Glycols, Brochure 125-430-68*, Dow Chemical Co., 1968.

54. Ref. 1, pp. 280–281.

55. *Pluronics*, Wyandotte Chemical Corp., 1957.

56. *Physical Properties of Pluronic Polyols, Brochure 0-82R*, BASF, Wyandotte Corp. Wyandotte, Mich.

57. *The Pluronic Grid*, 6th ed., Wyandotte Chemicals Corp.

58. Ref. 9, p. 589.

59. E. Berlow, "Other Polyhydric Alcohols," in A. Standen, ed., *Kirk-Othmer Encyclopedia of Chemical Technology*, Vol. 1, 2nd ed., Interscience Publishers, a division of John Wiley & Sons, Inc., New York, pp. 588–598.

60. Ref. 13, Chap. 5.

61. *Trojan Quality Polyols*, Trojan Powder Co., Allentown, Pa.

62. *Trimethylolpropane, Product Manual S-52-2*, Celanese Chemical Co., New York, 1962.

63. *Trimethylolpropane in Alkyd Coating Resins, Brochure S-43-5*, Celanese Chemical Co., 1961.

64. *1,2,4-Butanetriol, Technical Data Sheet CDD-6010*, General Aniline and Film Corp., New York. 1962.

65. *Pentaerythritol, Product Bulletin S-58-2*, Celanese Chemical Co., New York, 1964.

66. *Pentaerythritols*, Trojan Powder Co., Allentown, Pa.

67. Ref. 8, pp. 572–576.

68. *Pentaerythritol and Tripentaerythritol*, Delaware Chemicals, Inc.

69. *Tripentaerythritol, Data Sheet No. 97*, Heyden Newport Chemical Corp.

70. E. H. Huntress and S. P. Mulliken, *Identification of Pure Organic Compounds—Order I*, John Wiley & Sons, Inc., New York, 1941.

71. M. Frankel and S. Patai, *Tables for Identification of Organic Compounds*, 2nd ed., The Chemical Rubber Co., Cleveland, Ohio, 1964.

72. Ref. 1, Chap. 16.

73. J. B. Segur in C. S. Miner and N. N. Dalton, eds., *Glycerol, ACS Monograph Series No. 117*, Reinhold Publishing Corp., New York, 1953, Chap. 6.

74. S. M. McElvain, *The Characterization of Organic Compounds*, The Macmillan Co., New York, 1946.

75. M. K. Seikel and E. H. Huntress, *J. Am. Chem. Soc.* **63**, 593–595 (1941).

76. N. Green and M. W. Green, *J. Am. Chem. Soc.* **66**, 1610–1611 (1944).

77. B. Gauthier, *Ann. Pharm. France* **2**, 29–33 (1944).

78. Ref. 72, pp. 329–330.

79. P. Desnuelle and N. Nandet, *Bull. Soc. Chim. France*, [5] **12**, 871–874 (1945).

80. M. Orchin, *J. Ass. Offic. Agr. Chem.* **26**, 99–101 (1943).

81. N. Allen, H. Y. Charbonnier, and R. M. Coleman, *Ind. Eng. Chem. Anal. Ed.* **12**, 384–387 (1940).

82. H. V. Bogs, *Pharm. Zentralh. Dent.* **106** (1), 7–8 (1967).

83. J. B. Counts (Aberdeen Proving Ground, Aberdeen, Md.) *AD 618879, Avail. CFSTI* (1965) (Eng.) *U.S. Govt. Res. Develop. Dept.* **40** (18), 59 (1965).

84. J. B. Counts, *Anal. Chem.* **37**, 926 (1965).

85. A. W. Middleton, *Analyst* **59**, 522–524 (1934).

86. A. G. Hovey and T. S. Hodgins, *Ind. Eng. Chem. Anal. Ed.* **9**, 509–511 (1937).

87. C. B. Jordan, *Anal. Chem.* **26**, 1657–1658 (1954).

88. K. Burger, *Z. Anal. Chem.* **196**, 251–259 (1963).

89. E. G. Brown and T. J. Hayes, *Analyst* **80**, 755–767 (1955).

90. C. B. Shaffer and F. Critchfield, *Anal. Chem.* **19**, 32–34 (1947).

91. J. Oliver and C. Preston, *Nature*, **164**, 242–243 (1949).

92. D. G. Stevenson, *Analyst* **79**, 504–507 (1954).

93. H. Etienne, *Parfum., Cosmet. Savons* **137**, 33–37 (1957).

94. M. J. Rosen and H. A. Goldsmith, "*Systematic Analysis of Surface Active Agents*," in Vol. 12 of *Chemical Analysis*, Interscience Publishers, Inc., New York (1960).

95. M. J. Rosen, *Anal. Chem.* **27**, 787–790 (1955).

96. J. L. Williams and H. D. Graham, *Anal. Chem.* **36**, 1345–1349 (1964).

97. L. Gatewood, Jr. and H. D. Graham, *Anal. Chem.* **33**, 1393–1396 (1961).

98. B. Smith and O. Carlssor., *Acta Chem. Scand.* **17**, 455–460 (1963).

99. H. Puschmann and J. E. Miller, *Z. Lebensm. Untersuch. Forsch.* **114**, 297–301 (1961).

100. C. Calzolari, B. Stancher, and L. Favretto, *J. Chromatog.* **38**, 7–17 (1968).

101. M. K. Withers, *J. Gas Chromatog.* **6**, 242–244 (1968).

102. B. Smith and L. Tullberg, *Acta Chem. Scand.* **19** (3), 605–611 (1965); *Chem. Abstr.* **63**, 6315f (1965).

103. L. Ginsburg, *Anal. Chem.* **31**, 1822–1824 (1959).

104. H. G. Nadeau and D. M. Oaks, *Anal. Chem.* **32**, 1760–1762 (1960).

105. S. Spencer and H. G. Nadeau, *Anal. Chem.* **33**, 1626–1627 (1961).

106. S. Spencer and L. Mikkelsen, *Facts and Methods* (F & M Scientific Corp., Avondale, Pa.) **3**, 3 (1962).

107. I. Ghanayem and W. B. Swann, *Anal. Chem.* **34**, 1847–1848 (1962).

108. R. L. Friedman and W. J. Raab, *Anal. Chem.* **35**, 67–69 (1963).

109. A. Davis, A. Roaldi, and L. E. Tufts, *J. Gas. Chromatog.* **2**, 306–308 (1964).

110. P. F. Komissarov, L. V. Kondakova, and D. A. Vyakhirev, *Gazov. Khromatogr.* **1**, 99–107 (1964); *Chem. Abstr.* **67**, 60736n (1967).

111. F. C. Gross, *J. Assoc. Offic. Agri. Chem.* **48**, 647 (1965).

112. J. D. Forlini, *J. Chromatog. Sci.* **7**, 319–320 (1969).

113. *ASTM E 202-67, Analysis of Ethylene Glycols and Propylene Glycols*, American Society for Testing and Materials, Philadelphia, Pa., 1970.

114. I. L. Weatherall, *J. Chromatog.* **26**, 251–253 (1967).

115. J. F. Palframan and E. A. Walker, *Analyst* **92**, 535 (1967).

116. E. Camera and D. Prarisani, *Anal. Chem.* **36**, 2108–2109 (1964).

117. A. J. Markovitz and M. J. Klug, *J. Chromatog.* **36**, 342–343 (1968).

118. L. H. Phifer and K. H. Plummer, Jr., *Anal. Chem.* **38**, 1652–1656 (1966).

119. E. M. Perepletchikova and A. Lazaris, *Zh. Anal. Khim.* **21** (10), 1280–1281 (1966); *Chem. Abstr.* **66**, 25937m (1966).

120. H. P. Angelé, *Monatsber. Deutsch. Akad. Wiss.* **4**, 761 (1962).

121. J. Clifford, *Analyst* **85**, 475–478 (1960).

122. W. J. Murray and A. F. Williams, *Analyst* **86**, 849–853 (1961).

123. L. Hartman, *J. Chromatog.* **16**, 223–225 (1964).

124. D. S. Wiersma, R. E. Hoyle, and H. Rempis, *Anal. Chem.* **34**, 1533–1536 (1965).

125. R. R. Suchanec, *Anal. Chem.* **37**, 1361–1366 (1965).

126. G. C. Esposito and M. H. Swann, *Anal. Chem.* **33**, 1854–1858 (1961).

127. G. C. Esposito and M. H. Swann, *Anal. Chem.* **34**, 1173 (1962).

128. D. F. Percival, *Anal. Chem.* **35**, 236–238 (1963).

129. L. H. Ponder, *Anal. Chem.* **40**, 229–231 (1968).

130. S. Dal Nogare, *Anal. Chem.* **25**, 1874–1877 (1953).

131. R. Sargent and W. Rieman III, *Anal. Chim. Acta* **16**, 144–148 (1957).

132. M. J. Rosen, *Anal. Chem.* **35**, 2074–2077 (1963).

133. J. Pollerberg and E. Heinerth, *Vorträge Originalfassung Intern. Kongr. Grenzflächenaktive Stoffe, 3, Cologne, Germany* **3**, 89–91 (1960); *Chem. Abstr.* **57**, 13908c (1962).

134. R. T. Clark, *Anal. Chem.* **30**, 1676–1678 (1958).

135. K. C. Bergner and H. Sperlich, *Z. Lebensm. Untersuch. Forsch.* **97**, 253–263 (1953); *Chem. Abstr.* **48**, 2273g (1954).

136. J. Gasparic and J. Borecky, *J. Chromatog.* **5**, 466–499 (1961).

137. S. Maruta and F. Jwama, *Nippon Kagaku Zasshi* **80**, 1131–1133 (1959); *Chem. Abstr.* **55**, 4255a (1961).

138. W. E. Moore, M. J. Effland, D. B. Johnson, M. N. Daugherty, and E. G. Schwerdtfegen, *Appl. Microbiol.* **8**, 169–173 (1960).

139. J. Borecky and J. Gasparic, *Mikrochim. Acta* **1961**, 96–104.

140. M. E. Ginn, C. L. Church Jr., and J. C. Harris, *Anal. Chem.* **33**, 143–145 (1961).

141. A. April, *Ingr. Chimiste* **43**, 209–219 (1961).

142. P. Fijolka and W. Radowitz, *Plaste Kaut.* **12**, 207–209 (1965).

143. H. H. Brownell, *J. Chromatog.* **19**, 556–563 (1965).

144. C. F. Smullin, L. Hartmann, and R. S. Stetzler, *J. Am. Oil Chem. Soc.* **35**, 179–182 (1958).

145. H. Siegel, A. B. Bullock, and G. B. Carter, *Anal. Chem.* **36**, 502–505 (1964).

146. L. D. Bergelson, E. V. Dyatlovitskaya, and V. V. Voronkova, *Dokl. Akad. Nauk. SSSR* **141**, 84–86 (1961); *Chem. Abstr.* **57**, 8005d (1962).

147. J. Kucera, *Collect. Czech. Chem. Commun.* **28**, 1341–1344 (1963).

148. E. V. Dyatlovitskaya, V. V. Voronkova and L. D. Bergelson, *Dokl. Akad. Nauk. SSSR* **145**, 325–327 (1962); *Chem. Abstr.* **57**, 15780c (1957).

149. H. B. S. Conacher and D. I. Rees, *Analyst* **91**, 55–56 (1966).

150. E. Knappe, D. Peteri, and I. Rohdewald, *Z. Anal. Chem.* **199**, 270–276 (1964).

151. K. Thoma, M. Rombach, and E. Ullmann, *Sci. Pharm.* **32**, 216–224 (1964).

152. J. F. Shay, S. Skilling, and R. W. Stafford, *Anal. Chem.* **26**, 652–656 (1954).

153. C. J. Turi and G. DeGiuli, *Rend. Ist. Super. Sanita* **23**, 140–145 (1960); *Chem. Abstr.* **54**, 23374c (1960).

154. V. W. Goodlett, *Anal. Chem.* **37**, 431–432 (1965).

155. D. T. Sawyer and J. R. Brannan, *Anal. Chem.* **38**, 192–198 (1966).

156. T. F. Page, Jr. and W. E. Bressler, *Anal. Chem.* **36**, 1981–1985 (1964).

157. W. B. Moniz and C. F. Poranski, Jr., *AD 621566, Avail CFSTI* (1965). *U.S. Govt. Res. Develop. Rept.* **40**, 56 (1965).

158. P. E. McMahon and W. C. Tincher, *J. Mol. Spectroscy.* **15**, 180–198 (1965).

159. A. G. Favret and R. Meister, *J. Chem. Phys.* **41**, 1011 (1964).

160. T. Yonezawa, H. Saito, S. Matsuoka, and K. Fukui, *Bull. Chem. Soc. Japan* **38**, 1431–1435 (1965).

161. G. MacBeth and A. R. Thompson, *Anal. Chem.* **23**, 618–619 (1951).

162. T. Chiao and A. R. Thompson, *Anal. Chem.* **25,** 1678–1681 (1957).

163. *ASTM E-326-67, Test for Hydroxyl Groups by Phthalic Anhydride Esterification,* American Society for Testing and Materials, Philadelphia, Pa., 1970.

164. *ASTM E-335-67, Test for Hydroxyl Groups by Pyromellitic Anhydride Esterification,* American Society for Testing and Materials, Philadelphia, Pa., 1970.

165. F. E. Critchfield, *Organic Functional Group Analysis, International Series of Monographs on Analytical Chemistry,* Vol. 8, Macmillan Co., New York, 1963, pp. 81–92.

166. E. A. Burns and R. F. Muraca, *Anal. Chem.* **31,** 397–399 (1959).

167. M. Mamiya, *Bunseki Kagaku* **11,** 739–743 (1962).

168. D. Kyriacon, *Anal. Chem.* **33,** 153–154 (1961).

169. J. G. Hendrickson, *Anal. Chem.* **36,** 126–128 (1964).

170. D. M. W. Anderson and S. S. H. Zaidi, *Talanta* **10,** 691–692 (1963).

171. S. Dal Nogare and A. N. Oemler, *Anal. Chem.* **24,** 902–904 (1952).

172. B. J. B. Reddaway, *Analyst* **82,** 506–511 (1957).

173. *ASTM D 2195-66, Methods for Testing Pentaerythritol,* American Society for Testing and Materials, Philadelphia, Pa., 1970.

174. A. Berka, V. Dvorak and J. Zyka, *Mikrochim. Acta* **1962,** 541–559.

175. E. Plsko, *Chem. Zvesti* **12,** 312–315 (1958).

176. L. Maros and E. Schulek, *Acta Chim. Acad. Sci. Hung.* **20,** 358–364 (1959).

177. D. Benson and N. Fletcher, *Talanta* **13,** 1207–1209 (1966).

178. J. G. Hanna and S. Siggia, *J. Polymer Sci.* **56,** 297–304 (1962).

179. F. Willeboordse and R. L. Meeker, *Anal. Chem.* **38,** 854–858 (1966).

180. R. J. Levins and R. M. Ikeda, *Anal. Chem.* **37,** 671–674 (1965).

181. L. Maros, I. Perl, and M. Szakács-Pintér, *Ann. Univ. Sci. Budapest Rolando Eötvös Nominatae, Sect. Chim.* **7,** 37–44 (1965); *Chem. Abstr.* **65,** 8008h (1966).

182. G. Siggia, A. C. Starke, Jr., J. J. Garis, Jr., and C. R. Stahl, *Anal. Chem.* **30,** 115–116 (1958).

183. F. W. Cheng, *Microchem. J.* **9,** 270–281 (1965).

184. C. V. Francis, *Anal. Chem.* **21,** 1238–1239 (1949).

185. K. Takiura and K. Koizumi, *Yakugaku Zasshi* **78,** 961–964 (1958); *Chem. Abstr.* **53,** 983i (1959).

186. A. Badinand and A. Boucherle, *Cong. Soc. Pharm. Fr. 9e* **1957,** 147–155; *Chem. Abstr.* **53,** 17747i (1958).

187. *ASTM D 1615-60, Methods of Test for Glycerol, Ethylene Glycol and Pentaerythritol in Alkyd Resins,* American Society for Testing and Materials, Philadelphia, Pa., 1970.

188. J. R. Kirby, A. J. Baldwin, and R. H. Heidner, *Anal. Chem.* **37,** 1306–1309 (1965).

189. G. A. Stenmark, *Anal. Chem.* **30,** 381–383 (1958).

190. J. C. Speck, Jr. and A. A. Forist, *Anal. Chem.* **26,** 1942–1944 (1954).

191. E. A. Adelberg, *Anal. Chem.* **25,** 1553–1554 (1953).

192. K. C. Leibman and E. Ortiz, *Anal. Chem.* **40,** 251–252 (1968).

193. J. S. Dixon and D. Lipkin, *Anal. Chem.* **26,** 1092–1093 (1954).

194. I. M. Baumel, *Anal. Chem.* **26,** 930–931 (1954).

195. L. R. Jones and J. A. Riddick, *Anal. Chem.* **29,** 1214–1216 (1957).

196. V. S. Shagov, *Zh. Analit. Khim.* **21,** 122–125 (1966).

197. S. Kaye, *Anal. Chem.* **22,** 661–663 (1950).

198. C. L. Whitman, G. W. Roecker, and C. F. McNerney, *Anal. Chem.* **33,** 781–782 (1961).

199. K. W. Han, *Analyst* **92,** 316–318 (1967).

200. J. V. Kilheffer, Jr. and E. Jungermann, *Anal. Chem.* **32,** 1178–1180 (1960).

201. W. B. Crummett, *Anal. Chem.* **34,** 1147–1150 (1962).

202. K. Burger, *Z. Anal. Chem.* **199,** 434–438 (1964).

203. *Pharmacopeia of the United States of America,* 18th rev. ed. (USP XVIII), United States Pharmacopeial Convention, Inc., Mack Publishing Co., Easton, Pa., 1970, p. 558.

204. *Ibid.,* pp. 514–515.

205. *ASTM D 1258-55, Methods of Sampling and Testing High-Gravity Glycerin,* American Society for Testing and Materials, Philadelphia, Pa., 1970.

206. *ASTM D 1257-55 (1961), Specifications for High-Gravity Glycerin,* American Society for Testing and Materials, Philadelphia, Pa., 1970.

207. "Sampling and Analysis of Glycerin," *Official and Tentative Methods of the American Oil Chemists Society,* 2nd ed., Sect. E, American Oil Chemists Society, Chicago, Ill.

208. Ref. 203, p. 285.

209. *Reagent Chemicals, ACS Specifications*, 4th ed., American Chemical Society, Washington, D.C., 1968, p. 269.
210. *Federal Standard Stock Catalog O-G-491*, Sect. 4, Part 5, 1931.
211. C. B. Jordan and V. O. Hatch, *Anal. Chem.* **22**, 177–179 (1950).
212. S. Harrison and G. L. Woodroffe, *Analyst* **90**, 44–49 (1965).
213. *ASTM D 1209-62, Test for Color of Clear Liquids*, American Society for Testing and Materials, Philadelphia, Pa., 1970.
214. *ASTM D 1078-63, Test for Distillation Range of Volatile Organic Liquids*, American Society for Testing and Materials, Philadelphia, Pa., 1970.

C. C. BUDKE
D. K. BANERJEE
U.S. Industrial Chemicals Company
Division of National Distillers & Chemical Corp.